PreK–2 Standards
NUMBER AND OPERATIONS
In prekindergarten through grade 2 all students should—

Understand numbers, ways of representing numbers, relationships among numbers, and number systems and should—
- Count with understanding and recognize "how many" in sets of objects;
- Use multiple models to develop initial understandings of place value and the base-ten number system;
- Develop understanding of the relative position and magnitude of whole numbers and of ordinal and cardinal numbers and their connections;
- Develop a sense of whole numbers and represent and use them in flexible ways, including relating, composing, and decomposing numbers;
- Connect number words and numerals to the quantities they represent, using various physical models and representations;
- Understand and represent commonly used fractions, such as $\frac{1}{4}$, $\frac{1}{3}$, and $\frac{1}{2}$

Understand meanings of operations and how they relate to one another and should—
- Understand various meanings of addition and subtraction of whole numbers and the relationship between the two operations;
- Understand the effects of adding and subtracting whole numbers;
- Understand situations that entail multiplication and division, such as equal groupings of objects and sharing equally

Compute fluently and make reasonable estimates and should—
- Develop and use strategies for whole-number computations, with a focus on addition and subtraction;
- Develop fluency with basic number combinations for addition and subtraction;
- Use a variety of methods and tools to compute, including objects, mental computation, estimation, paper and pencil, and calculators

ALGEBRA
In prekindergarten through grade 2 all students should—

Understand patterns, relations, and functions and should—
- Sort, classify, and order objects by size, number, and other properties;
- Recognize, describe, and extend patterns such as sequences of sounds and shapes or simple numeric patterns and translate from one representation to another;
- Analyze how both repeating and growing patterns are generated

Represent and analyze mathematical situations and structures using algebraic symbols and should—
- Illustrate general principles and properties of operations, such as commutativity, using specific numbers;
- Use concrete, pictorial, and verbal representations to develop an understanding of invented and conventional symbolic notations

Use mathematical models to represent and understand quantitative relationships and should—
- Model situations that involve the addition and subtraction of whole numbers, using objects, pictures, and symbols

Analyze change in various contexts and should—
- Describe qualitative change, such as a student's growing taller;
- Describe quantitative change, such as a student's growing two inches in one year

PreK–2 Standards
GEOMETRY
In prekindergarten through grade 2 all students should—

Analyze characteristics and properties of two- and three-dimensional geometric shapes and develop mathematical arguments about geometric relationships and should—
- Recognize, name, build, draw, compare, and sort two- and three-dimensional shapes;
- Describe attributes and parts of two- and three-dimensional shapes;
- Investigate and predict the results of putting together and taking apart two- and three-dimensional shapes

Specify locations and describe spatial relationships using coordinate geometry and other representational systems and should—
- Describe, name, and interpret relative positions in space and apply ideas about relative position;
- Describe, name, and interpret direction and distance in navigating space and apply ideas about direction and distance;
- Find and name locations with simple relationships such as "near to" and in coordinate systems such as maps

Apply transformations and use symmetry to analyze mathematical situations and should—
- Recognize and apply slides, flips, and turns;
- Recognize and create shapes that have symmetry

Use visualization, spatial reasoning, and geometric modeling to solve problems and should—
- Create mental images of geometric shapes using spatial memory and spatial visualization;
- Recognize and represent shapes from different perspectives;
- Relate ideas in geometry to ideas in number and measurement;
- Recognize geometric shapes and structures in the environment and specify their location

MEASUREMENT
In prekindergarten through grade 2 all students should—

Understand measurable attributes of objects and the units, systems, and processes of measurement and should—
- Recognize the attributes of length, volume, weight, area, and time;
- Compare and order objects according to these attributes;
- Understand how to measure using the nonstandard and standard units;
- Select an appropriate unit and tool for the attribute being measured

Apply appropriate techniques, tools, and formulas to determine measurements and should—
- Measure with multiple copies of units of the same size, such as paper clips laid end to end;
- Use repetition of a single unit to measure something larger than the unit, for instance, measuring the length of a room with a single meterstick;
- Use tools to measure;
- Develop common referents for measures to make comparisons and estimates

PreK–2 Standards
DATA ANALYSIS AND PROBABILITY
In prekindergarten through grade 2 all students should—

Formulate questions that can be addressed with data and collect, organize, and display relevant data to answer them and should—
- Pose questions and gather data about themselves and their surroundings;
- Sort and classify objects according to their attributes and organize data about their objects;
- Represent data using concrete objects, pictures, and graphs

Select and use appropriate statistical methods to analyze data and should—
- Describe parts of the data and the set of data as a whole to determine what the data show

Develop and evaluate inferences and predictions that are based on data and should—
- Discuss events related to student's experiences as likely or unlikely

Grades 3–5
NUMBER AND OPERATIONS
In grades 3–5 all students should—

Understand numbers, ways of representing numbers, relationships among numbers, and number systems and should—
- Understand the place-value structure of the base-ten number system and be able to represent and compare whole numbers and decimals;
- Recognize equivalent representations for the same number and generate them by decomposing and composing numbers;
- Develop understanding of fractions as parts of unit wholes, as parts of a collection, as locations on number lines, and as divisions of whole numbers;
- Use models, benchmarks, and equivalent forms to judge the size of fractions;
- Recognize and generate equivalent forms of commonly used fractions, decimals, and percents;
- Explore numbers less than 0 by extending the number line and through familiar applications;
- Describe classes of numbers according to characteristics such as the nature of their factors

Understand meanings of operations and how they relate to one another and should—
- Understand various meanings of multiplication and division;
- Understand the effects of multiplying and dividing whole numbers;
- Identify and use relationships between operations, such as division and the inverse of multiplication, to solve problems;
- Understand and use properties of operations, such as the distributivity of multiplication over addition

Compute fluently and make reasonable estimates and should—
- Develop fluency with basic number combinations for multiplication and division and use these combinations to mentally compute related problems, such as 30×50;
- Develop fluency in adding, subtracting, multiplying, and dividing whole numbers;
- Develop and use strategies to estimate the results of whole-number computations and to judge the reasonableness of such results

Grades 3–5
NUMBER AND OPERATIONS (continued)
In grades 3–5 all students should—

- Develop and use strategies to estimate computations involving fractions and decimals in situations relevant to students;
- Use visual models, benchmarks, and equivalent forms to add and subtract commonly used fractions and decimals;
- Select appropriate methods and tools for computing with whole numbers from among mental computation, estimation, calculators, and paper and pencil according to the context and nature of the computation and use the selected method or tool

ALGEBRA
In grades 3–5 all students should—

Understand patterns, relations, and functions and should—
- Describe, extend, and make generalizations about geometric and numeric patterns;
- Represent and analyze patterns and functions, using words, tables, and graphs

Represent and analyze mathematical situations and structures using algebraic symbols and should—
- Identify such properties as commutativity, associativity, and distributivity and use them to compute with whole numbers;
- Represent the idea of a variable as an unknown quantity using a letter or a symbol;
- Express mathematical relationships using equations

Use mathematical models to represent and understand quantitative relationships and should—
- Model problem situations with objects and use representations such as graphs, tables, and equations to draw conclusions

Analyze change in various contexts and should—
- Investigate how a change in one variable relates to a change in a second variable;
- Identify and describe situations with constant or varying rates of change and compare them

GEOMETRY
In grades 3–5 all students should—

Analyze characteristics and properties of two- and three-dimensional geometric shapes and develop mathematical arguments about geometric relationships and should—
- Identify, compare, and analyze attributes of two- and three-dimensional shapes and develop vocabulary to describe the attributes;
- Classify two- and three-dimensional shapes according to their properties and develop definitions of classes of shapes such as triangles and pyramids;
- Investigate, describe, and reason about the results of subdividing, combining, and transforming shapes;
- Explore congruence and similarity;
- Make and test conjectures about geometric properties and relationships and develop logical arguments to justify conclusions

Specify locations and describe spatial relationships using coordinate geometry and other representational systems and should—
- Describe location and movement using common language and geometric vocabulary;
- Make and use coordinate systems to specify locations and to describe paths;
- Find the distance between points along horizontal and vertical lines of a coordinate system

Instructor's Edition

A PROBLEM SOLVING APPROACH TO

Mathematics

for Elementary School Teachers

8TH EDITION

Rick Billstein
University of Montana

Shlomo Libeskind
University of Oregon

Johnny W. Lott
University of Montana

PEARSON

Addison
Wesley

Boston San Francisco New York
London Toronto Sydney Tokyo Singapore Madrid
Mexico City Munich Paris Cape Town Hong Kong Montreal

Publisher: Greg Tobin
Sponsoring Editor: Anne Kelly
Associate Project Editor: Joanne Ha
Editorial Assistant: Cecilia Stashwick
Senior Production Supervisor: Karen Wernholm
Production Coordination: Jenny Bagdigian
Marketing Manager: Becky Anderson
Marketing Coordinator: Julia Coen
Associate Producer: Sharon Smith
Software Development: Gail Light and John O'Brien
Senior Manufacturing Buyer: Evelyn Beaton
Senior Designer: Barbara T. Atkinson
Text and Cover Design: Andrea M. Toth
Composition: UG / GGS Information Services, Inc.
Illustrations: Tech-Graphics

The Geometer's Sketchpad and Dynamic Geometry are registered trademarks of Key Curriculum Press. Sketchpad is a trademark of Key Curriculum Press.

For permission to use copyrighted material, grateful acknowledgment is made to the copyright holders on page 937, which is hereby made part of this copyright page.

Library of Congress Cataloging-in-Publication Data

Billstein, Rick.
 A problem solving approach to mathematics for elementary school teachers / Rick Billstein, Shlomo Libeskind, Johnny W. Lott.—8th ed.
     p. cm.
 Includes bibliographical references and index.
 ISBN 0-321-15680-3 (student edition), ISBN 0-321-16194-7 (instructor edition)
 1. Mathematics—Study and teaching (Elementary)   2. Problem solving   I. Libeskind, Shlomo.   II. Lott, Johnny W., 1944–   III. Title.

QA135.6 .B55 2003
372.7—dc21

2002034364

1 2 3 4 5 6 7 8 9 10—DOW—06050403

To my mother Esther as she continues to fight all the hard knocks and challenges that life now gives her each day. There could be no better role model. —RWB

In memory of my parents Mendel and Genia Libeskind ז״ל. —SL

To my co-authors with whom work has been enjoyable and challenging; and to my family, Carolyn, Jon and Elizabeth. —JWL

–Preface–

The eighth edition of *A Problem Solving Approach to Mathematics for Elementary School Teachers* is designed to meet the education needs of prospective elementary teachers who will be the future's high-quality teachers.

Standards of the NCTM

We focus on the National Council of Teachers of Mathematics (NCTM) publication, *Principles and Standards of School Mathematics* (2000) (hereafter referred to as *Principles and Standards*). In this edition, we expand references to the *Principles and Standards* so that students will realize what will be expected of their students when they are teaching.

We also emphasize the need for the teaching of mathematics to include:
- Algebraic thinking;
- Mathematical reasoning;
- Updated data analysis and statistical thinking;
- Emphasis on the use of geometric utilities;
- Conjecturing, inventing, and problem solving; and
- Connecting mathematics, its ideas, and its applications.

Our goals remain:
- To present appropriate mathematics in an intellectually honest and mathematically correct manner.
- To use problem solving as an integral part of mathematics.
- To approach mathematics in a sequence that instills confidence AND challenges students.
- To provide opportunity for alternate forms of teaching and learning.
- To provide communication problems to develop writing skills and allow students to practice explanation.
- To encourage integration of technology tools.
- To provide core mathematics for prospective elementary teachers in a way that they are challenged to determine why mathematics is done as it is.
- To provide core mathematics that allows instructors to use methods integrated with content.

The eighth edition allows instructors a variety of approaches to teaching, encourages discussion and collaboration among students and with their instructors, and allows for the integration of projects into the curriculum. Most importantly, it promotes discovery and active learning for the students and the teacher.

Features Retained in the Eighth Edition:

We continue to incorporate various study aids and features that facilitate learning.

- **Historical Notes** add context and humanize the mathematics.
- **Brain Teasers** provide a different avenue for problem solving. They are solved in the Instructor's Resource Guide, and may be assigned or used by the teacher to challenge students.
- **Definitions** are either set off in text or presented as key terms in the margin for quick review.
- **Key Terms** are presented in the margins for quick review.
- *Updated* **student pages** are included to show how the mathematics is actually introduced to the K-8 student. The number of student pages has been expanded and students are now asked to complete many of the activities on the student pages so they can see what is expected of the elementary students.
- **Laboratory Activities** are integrated throughout the book to provide hands-on learning exercises. A separate activities book is also available.
- *New* **Now Try This** activities appear throughout each chapter, and are intended to help students become actively involved in their learning, to facilitate the development and improvement of their critical thinking and problem-solving skills, and to stimulate both in-class and out-of-class discussion.
- **Problem-solving strategies** are often highlighted in italics, and indicated by �.
- **Relevant quotes** from the *Principles and Standards* are incorporated throughout the text, and are marked by the standards icon ◆.
- **Questions from the Classroom** present questions posed by actual students in K-8 classrooms for instructors to build a course syllabus.
- **Chapter Outlines** at the end of each chapter help students review the chapter.
- **Chapter Reviews** at the end of each chapter allow students to test themselves.
- **Optional sections,** as well as problems based on these sections, are marked with an asterisk (*). **More difficult problems** are marked with a star (★). **Problems numbered in color** have answers at the back of the book.
- **Selected Bibliographies** have been updated and revised, and appear at the end of each chapter.
- **Cartoons** teach or emphasize important material, and add levity.
- **Communication Problems** require students to explain or justify their answers.
- **Full color** has been used for pedagogical reasons and to help students better visualize concepts. Figures are modern, attractive, and easy to follow. All of the pages taken from elementary mathematics texts are presented in full color.
- **Problem sets** contain six different types of problems: (1) ongoing assessment, (2) communication, (3) open-ended, (4) cooperative learning (5) technology, and (6) review. **Communication, Open-ended**, and **Cooperative Learning** problem sections are included as major *Principles and Standards'* processes.
- **Relevant and realistic problems** are more accessible and appealing to students of diverse backgrounds.
- **Technology Corners** include use of spreadsheets, both graphing and scientific calculators, The Geometer's Sketchpad, and computer activities.

Content Highlights

The eighth edition has new content added, and existing content re-organized in many chapters.

Chapter 1 An Introduction to Problem Solving

Chapter 1 emphasizes reasoning with different problem solving strategies. A section on algebraic thinking has been enhanced.

Chapter 2 Sets, Whole Numbers, and Functions

In Chapter 2, whole numbers and basic operations on whole numbers are introduced using set concepts. Sequences are revisited as functions and new examples and exercises are presented throughout.

Chapter 3 Numeration Systems and Whole Number Computation

Numeration systems and other number bases are introduced. Algorithms for addition, subtraction, multiplication and addition are explored, along with mental mathematics and estimation for whole-number computation. In this edition, more models for computation are added as well as more alternative algorithms. More work with multibase blocks is included.

Chapter 4 Integers and Number Theory

In Chapter 4 we introduce the system of integers and develop an understanding of basic number theory. Properties of integers are justified in a variety of ways and the coordinate system is expanded to include all integers. Information on large primes has been updated and in several historical notes, we discuss recent developments in number theory.

Chapter 5 Rational Numbers as Fractions

Chapter 5 includes the development of the set of rational numbers.

Chapter 6 Decimals, Percents, and Real Numbers

Chapter 6 provides a full treatment of decimals, percents, and real numbers. Computing interest is covered as an application of percents and decimals.

Chapter 7 Probability

Chapter 7 introduces how probabilities are determined and the role of experimental and theoretical probability. Geometric probabilities and simulations are explored, as are odds, conditional probability, expected value, and permutations and combinations.

Chapter 8 Data Analysis/Statistics: An Introduction

Chapter 8 includes an introduction to different types of graphs. There is a section on measures of central tendency and variation, as well as a section on abuses of statistics. The normal curve has been added to the book, and the language of data analysis conforms to the latest language recommended by educators.

Chapter 9 Introductory Geometry

Chapter 9 contains several new examples and problems with an expanded discussion of three-dimensional geometry.

Chapter 10   Constructions, Congruence, and Similarity

In Chapter 10 some of the material on coordinate geometry has been moved into a section on similarity to show how slope and equations of lines is developed. In addition, a brief section on trigonometry has been added to show how similarity is related to right triangle trigonometry.

Chapter 11   Concepts of Measurement

Linear measure along with areas, surface areas, the Pythagorean Theorem, volume, mass, and temperature are covered in Chapter 11. Both metric and customary units of measure are considered with metric being the primary system.

Chapter 12   Motion Geometry and Tessellations

Chapter 12 presents new material on semi-regular tessellations and three-dimensional geometry.

Appendices

Appendices in this edition include:

I. Using a Spreadsheet
II. Graphing Calculators
III. Using a Geometry Drawing Utility (based on The Geometer's Sketchpad)

Appendix III is completely revised and includes 11 new Geometer's Sketchpad (GSP 4.00) activities. These lab activities are designed to be used with the various geometry sections of the book. The appropriate sections are listed on each of the labs.

Calculator Usage

As stated in the *Principles and Standards*, coverage of calculators is necessary and timely. The use of the graphing calculator is presented, where relevant, in the Technology Corners. In addition, problems involving the use of both scientific/fraction and graphing calculators appear in the problem sets.

Supplements for the Student

Student's Solutions Manual
Louis Levy
ISBN 0-321-17019-9
This manual contains detailed worked-out solutions to all odd-numbered section exercises and to all Chapter Review exercises.

Activities Manual—Mathematics Activities for Elementary School Teachers: A Problem Solving Approach, Fifth Edition
Daniel Dolan, Jim Williamson, and Mari Muri
ISBN 0-321-17413-5
This revised edition features activities that can be used to develop, reinforce, and/or apply mathematical concepts. The activities for each concept are ordered by developmental level within each chapter.

Addison-Wesley Math Tutor Center
Free tutoring is available to students who purchase a new copy of the Eighth Edition. The Addison-Wesley Math Tutor Center is staffed by qualified math and statistics instructors who provide students with tutoring on examples and odd-numbered exercises from the textbook. Tutoring is available via toll-free telephone, fax, email, or the Internet, and White Board technology allows tutors and students to actually see the problems worked while they "talk" in real time over the Internet during tutoring sessions. An access code is required. For more information, go to *www.aw.com/tutorcenter*.

Digital Video Tutor
ISBN 0-321-17412-7
The Digital Video Tutor provides our videos on CD-ROM, making it easy and convenient for students to watch video segments from a computer at home or on campus. This complete video set is ideal for distance learning or extra instruction.

Supplements for the Instructor

Instructor's Edition
ISBN 0-321-16194-7
This version of the text includes sequential answers to all text exercises in a special section at the back to the book.

Instructor's Solutions Manual
Louis Levy
ISBN 0-321-17018-0
This manual contains detailed solutions to all exercises.

Instructor's Resource Guide
Joan Henn, Eastern Illinois University
ISBN 0-321-17021-0
This fully comprehensive guide contains two forms of chapter assessments with answers for each test; suggested answers to Questions from the Classroom and Now Try This Activities; answers to the Laboratory Activities and Technology Corners; and solutions to the Preliminary Problems and Brain Teasers.

A Problem Solving Approach to Mathematics for Elementary School Teachers
Videotapes
A complete set of updated videotapes is correlated to each important topic and is available to departments. Basic concepts from the text are reinforced in these videotapes. Contact your Addison-Wesley Sales Consultant.

Instructor's Guide to *Mathematics Activities for Elementary School Teachers: A Problem Solving Approach, Fifth Edition*
Daniel Dolan, Jim Williamson, and Mari Muri
ISBN 0-321-17017-2
Contains answers for all activities, as well as additional teaching suggestions for some activities.

TestGen with QuizMaster
ISBN 0-321-17022-9
TestGen enables instructors to build, edit, print, and administer tests using a computerized bank of questions developed to cover all the objectives of the text. TestGen is algorithmically based so that multiple yet equal versions of the same question or test can be generated at the click of a button. Instructors can also modify test bank questions or add new questions by using the built-in question editor, which allows users to create graphs, import graphics, insert math notation, and insert variable numbers or text. Tests can be printed or administered on-line via the Web or other network. Many questions in TestGen can be expressed in a short-answer or multiple-choice form, giving instructors greater flexibility in their test preparation. TestGen comes packaged with QuizMaster, which allows students to take tests on a local area network. The software is available on a dual-platform Windows/Macintosh CD-ROM.

MathXL is designed for use in a lecture, lab, or an online course. It will save you time and help your students succeed in their math courses.

With MathXL, students can:

- Prepare for exams by taking practice tests, or tests that you have created and assigned.
- Receive personalized study plans based on test results, listing the sections they will need to practice.
- Link to tutorial exercises that correlate to the end-of-section exercises in their textbook for all the practice and instruction they will need.
- Complete all homework online, to be scored and tracked in an online class grade-book.

With MathXL, you can:

- Assign homework and tests provided by Addison-Wesley or create your own tests using the online test bank or TestGen-EQ.
- Store and manage all of your tests from one location.
- Track the work of the entire class in your online grade-book.

An access code is required. For more information go to *www.mathxl.com*.

MyMathLab is a complete online course available with the eighth edition of *A Problem Solving Approach to Mathematics for Elementary School Teachers* and is perfect for a lecture-based, self-paced, or online course. This site offers instructors and students a wide variety of resources from dynamic multimedia—video clips, practice exercises, and more—to course management tools. With MyMathLab, instructors can customize their course and help students increase their comprehension and succeed in their courses!

- MyMathLab has a powerful system for creating and assigning tests and homework, as well as a grade-book for tracking all student performance.
- The entire textbook is available online and is supplemented by multimedia content, such as new Power Point presentations and updated videos. The videos are correlated to each section in the text, and are used to help explain concepts.
- MyMathLab features all of the printed instructor supplements online, such as the Instructor's Solutions Manual, Instructor's Guide to the Activities Manual, and the Instructor's Resource Guide. In addition, a sample of the Student's Solutions Manual is available.

- With MyMathLab, students can work with tutorial exercises tied directly to those in their textbook.
- MyMathLab allows students to do practice work and to complete instructor-assigned tests and homework assignments online. Based on these results, MyMathLab automatically builds an individual study plan that students can use to improve their skills.
- MyMathLab includes links to some of the most useful online resources available, from sources like NCTM and Sketchpad. Students can access these manipulatives and activities online, correlated to the chapter and section that they are studying, to explore and expand their understanding of key concepts.
- All of the material previously found at *www.aw.com/billstein* is also available through MyMathLab.

MyMathLab requires a student access code. For more information about MyMathLab, contact your Addison-Wesley sales representative or go to *www.mymathlab.com*.

−Acknowledgments−

For past editions of this book, many noted and illustrious mathematics educators and mathematicians have served as reviewers. To honor the work of the past as well as to honor the reviewers of this edition, we list all but place asterisks by this edition's reviewers.

Leon J. Ablon
G.L. Alexanderson
Haldon Anderson
Bernadette Antkoviak
*Richard Avery
Sue H. Baker
Jane Barnard
Joann Becker
Cindy Bernlohr
James Bierden
*Jackie Blagg
Jim Boone
Sue Boren
Barbara Britton
Beverly R. Broomell
Jane Buerger
Maurice Burke
David Bush
Laura Cameron
Louis J. Chatterley
Phyllis Chinn
Donald J. Dessart
Ronald Dettmers
Jackie Dewar
Amy Edwards
*Lauri Edwards
Margaret Ehringer
Albert Filano
Marjorie Fitting
Michael Flom
Martha Gady
*Dwight Galster
Sandy Geiger
Glenadine Gibb
Don Gilmore

*Diane Ginsbach
Elizabeth Gray
Jerrold Grossman
Alice Guckin
*Joan Henn
Boyd Henry
Alan Hoffer
E. John Hornsby, Jr.
Judith E. Jacobs
Donald James
Jerry Johnson
Wilburn C. Jones
Robert Kalin
Sarah Kennedy
Steven D. Kerr
Leland Knauf
Margret F. Kothmann
Kathryn E. Lenz
Hester Lewellen
Ralph A. Liguori
Don Loftsgaarden
Sharon Louvier
Stanley Lukawecki
*Judith Merlau
Barbara Moses
*Cynthia Naples
Charles Nelson
Glenn Nelson
Kathy Nickell
Dale Oliver
*Mark Oursland
Linda Padilla
Dennis Parker
Clyde Paul
Keith Peck

Barbara Pence
Glen L. Pfeifer
*Debra Pharo
Jack Porter
Edward Rathnell
Jennifer Rutherford
Helen R. Santiz
*Sherry Scarborough
Jane Schielack
Barbara Shabell
M. Geralda Shaefer
Nancy Shell
Wade H. Sherard
Gwen Shufelt
*Julie Sliva
Ron Smit
Joe K. Smith
William Sparks
Virginia Strawderman
Mary M. Sullivan
Viji Sundar
Sharon Taylor
C. Ralph Verno
Hubert Voltz
John Wagner
*Edward Wallace
Virginia Warfield
Lettie Watford
Mark F. Weiner
Grayson Wheatley
*Jim Williamson
Ken Yoder
Jerry L. Young
*Deborah Zopf

–Brief Contents–

Solution to the cover puzzle follows the index.

–Contents–

Integers and Number Theory 186

Rational Numbers and Fractions 265

Decimals, Percents, and Real Numbers 318

Probability 373

Data Analysis/Statistics: An Introduction 439

Introductory Geometry   496

Constructions, Congruence, and Similarity   559

Concepts of Measurement   644

Solution to the cover puzzle follows the index.
*indicates optional section

–1–
An Introduction to Problem Solving

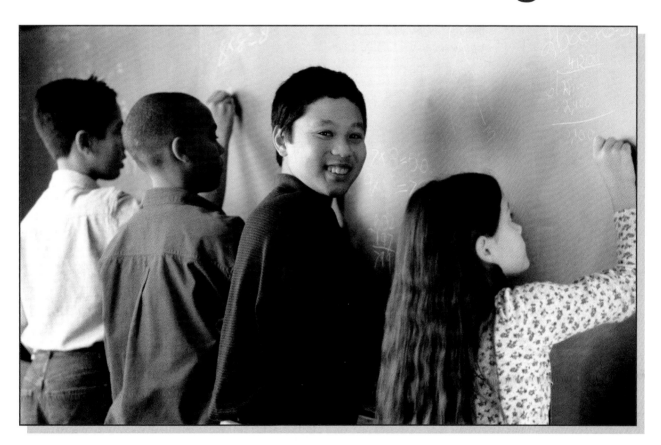

A student posed the following problem to his classmates:
I am thinking of a number multiplied times itself. The result of that multiplication is a number that has an odd tens digit. What is the ones digit?
Find the ones digit and argue that your answer is correct.

P roblem solving has long been recognized as one of the hallmarks of mathematics. The greatest goal of learning mathematics is to have people become good problem solvers. We do not mean doing exercises that are routine practice for skill building. What does *problem solving* mean? George Polya (1887–1985), one of the great mathematicians and teachers of the twentieth century, pointed out that "Solving a problem means finding a way out of difficulty, a way around an obstacle, attaining an aim which was not immediately attainable." (Polya 1981, p. ix)

In *Principles and Standards of School Mathematics* (NCTM 2000), we find the following:

Problem solving means engaging in a task for which the solution method is not known in advance. In order to find a solution, students must draw on their knowledge, and through this process, they will often develop new mathematical understandings. Solving problems is not only a goal of learning mathematics but also a major means of doing so. Students should have frequent opportunities to formulate, grapple with, and solve complex problems that require a significant amount of effort and should then be encouraged to reflect on their thinking. (p. 52)

Further, we find that

Instructional programs from prekindergarten through grade 12 should enable all students to

- *build new mathematical knowledge through problem solving;*
- *solve problems that arise in mathematics and in other contexts;*
- *apply and adapt a variety of appropriate strategies to solve problems;*
- *monitor and reflect on the process of mathematical problem solving.* (p. 52)

Exercises, or practice problems, serve a purpose in learning mathematics, but problem solving must be a focus of school mathematics. Your mathematical experience often determines whether situations are *problems* or *exercises*. In the "Fox Trot" cartoon, the word problems appear to be a challenge to Paige, but not to Jason. For him, they are exercises.

FOXTROT © Bill Amend. Reprinted with permission of UNIVERSAL PRESS SYNDICATE. All rights reserved.

In this text, you will have many opportunities to solve problems. Each chapter opens with a problem that can be solved by using the concepts developed in the chapter.

A hint for the solution to the problem is given at the end of each chapter. Throughout the text, there are numerous problems solved using a four-step process and others solved using other formats.

Working with other students to solve problems can enhance your problem-solving ability and communication skills. We encourage *cooperative learning* and encourage students to work in groups whenever possible. To encourage group work and help identify when cooperative learning could be useful, we identify activities that involve tasks where it might be helpful to have several people gathering data, or the problems might be such that group discussions could lead to strategies for solving the problem.

Students in a group or individually may use strategies explained in the remaining sections of this chapter. One problem-solving strategy, *looking for a pattern*, is used so often that it is the focus of the next section.

Throughout the book, we remind you of definitions of mathematical terms. However, you do not come to this section or the book with a *tabula rasa*, or blank slate. You have mathematical experience from school and from daily life. We ask you to build on what you know, to correct any misconceptions you have, to challenge yourself to learn as we try to challenge you. Most of all, we ask you to think about why you do what you do in mathematics. Having you understand and question mathematics will help make you a better learner and consequently a better teacher.

 ## Explorations with Patterns

Mathematics has been described as the study of patterns. Patterns are everywhere—in wallpaper, tiles, traffic, and even television schedules. Police investigators study case files to find the modus operandi, or pattern of operation, when a series of crimes is committed. Scientists look for patterns in order to isolate variables so that they can reach valid conclusions in their research. In the *Principles and Standards*, we find the following,

 . . . students should investigate numerical and geometric patterns and express them mathematically in words or in symbols. They should analyze the structure of the pattern and how it grows or changes, organize this information systematically, and use their analysis to develop generalizations about the mathematical relationships in the pattern. (p. 159)

Patterns can be surprising. Consider Example 1-1.

EXAMPLE 1-1

a. Describe any patterns seen in the following:

$$1 + 0 \cdot 9 = 1$$
$$2 + 1 \cdot 9 = 11$$
$$3 + 12 \cdot 9 = 111$$
$$4 + 123 \cdot 9 = 1111$$
$$5 + 1234 \cdot 9 = 11111$$

b. Do the above patterns continue? Why or why not?

Solution   **a.** There are several patterns in the example. The following descriptions are intuitive at this stage. The numbers on the far left are **natural numbers**; that is, numbers from the set 1, 2, 3, 4, 5, ... The pattern starts with 1 and

natural numbers

continues to the next greater natural number in each successive line. The numbers "in the middle" are products of two numbers, the second of which is 9. The first number in the first product is 0; after that the first number is formed using natural numbers and including one more in each successive line. The resulting numbers on the right are formed using 1s and including an additional 1 in each successive line.

b. The pattern in the complete equation appears to continue for a number of cases, but it does not continue in general; for example,

$$13 + 123456789101112 \cdot 9 = 1,111,111,101,910,021.$$

This pattern breaks down when the pattern of digits in the number being multiplied by 9 contains previously used digits.

As seen in Example 1-1, determining a pattern on the basis of a few cases is not reliable. For all patterns found, we should explain why we think they either do or do not continue.

Patterns do not always have to be numerical, as shown in Now Try This 1-1.

NOW TRY THIS 1-1

> **a.** Find three more terms to continue a pattern:
>   o, Δ, Δ, o, Δ, Δ, o ____, ____, ____
> **b.** Describe the pattern found in words.

Inductive and Deductive Reasoning

Scientists make observations and propose general laws based on these observations and patterns seen. Statisticians use patterns when they form conclusions based on collected data. This process, **inductive reasoning**, is the method of making generalizations based on observations and patterns. While inductive reasoning may lead to new discoveries, its weakness is that conclusions are drawn only from the collected evidence. If not all cases have been checked, the possibility exists that another case will prove the conclusion false. Inductive reasoning may lead to a **conjecture**, a statement thought to be true but not yet proved true or false. For example, considering only that $0^2 = 0$ and that $1^2 = 1$, a conjecture might be that *every number squared is equal to itself*. When we find an example that contradicts the conjecture, we provide a **counterexample** and prove the conjecture false in general. To show that the above conjecture is false, it is enough to exhibit only one counterexample; for example, $2^2 = 4$. Sometimes finding a counterexample is difficult, but the lack of a counterexample does not automatically make a conjecture true.

The following discussion illustrates the danger of making a conjecture based on a few cases. In Figure 1-1, we choose points on a circle and connect them to form distinct, nonoverlapping regions. In this figure, 2 points determine 2 regions, 3 points determine 4 regions, and 4 points determine 8 regions. What is the maximum number of regions that would be determined by 10 points?

inductive reasoning

conjecture

counterexample

FIGURE 1-1

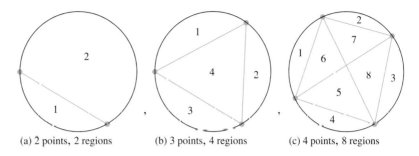

(a) 2 points, 2 regions   (b) 3 points, 4 regions   (c) 4 points, 8 regions

The data from Figure 1-1 are recorded in Table 1-1. It appears that each time we increase the number of points by 1, we double the number of regions. If this were true, then for 5 points we would have 2 times the number of regions with 4 points, or $2 \cdot 8 = 16$, and so on. If we base our conjecture on this pattern, we believe that for 10 points, we would have 512 regions. (Why?)

Table 1-1

Number of Points	2	3	4	5	6	...	10
Maximum Number of Regions	2	4	8				?

FIGURE 1-2

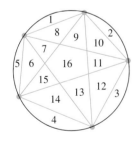

An initial check for this conjecture is to see whether we obtain 16 regions for 5 points. We obtain a figure similar to that in Figure 1-2, and our guess of 16 regions is confirmed. For 6 points, the pattern predicts that the number of regions will be 32. Choose the points so that they are neither symmetrically arranged nor equally spaced and count the regions carefully. You should obtain 31 regions and not 32 regions as predicted. No matter how the points are located on the circle, the guess of 32 regions is not correct. The counterexample tells us that the doubling pattern is not correct; note that it does not tell us whether or not there are 512 regions with 10 points, but only that the pattern is not what we conjectured.

A natural-looking pattern 2, 4, 8, 16, . . . is suggested in this example, but the pattern does not continue, as shown when actual pictures are drawn. If we look at only the first four terms of the sequence 2, 4, 8, 16 without context, the doubling pattern is logical. In the context of counting the number of regions of a circle, however, the pattern is incorrect.

Arithmetic Sequences

sequence   A **sequence** is an ordered arrangement of numbers, figures, or objects. A sequence has items or terms identified as *1st, 2nd, 3rd,* and so on. Often, sequences can be classified by their properties. For example, what property do the following first three sequences have that the fourth does not?

a. 1, 2, 3, 4, 5, 6, . . .
b. 0, 5, 10, 15, 20, 25, . . .
c. 2, 6, 10, 14, 18, 22, . . .
d. 1, 11, 111, 1111, 11111, 111111, . . .

In each of the first three sequences, each term—starting from the second—is obtained from the preceding one by adding a fixed number. In other words, the difference between consecutive numbers in the sequences is always the same. In part (d), the difference between the first two terms is $11 - 1$, or 10; the second difference is $111 - 11$, or 100; the third difference is $1111 - 111$, or 1000; and so on. Sequences such as the first three are arithmetic sequences. An **arithmetic sequence** is one in which each successive term is obtained from the previous term by the addition or subtraction of a fixed number, the **difference**. The difference in part (c) is 4 because 4 is the fixed number that is added each time to obtain the next number.

arithmetic sequence

difference

Arithmetic sequences can be generated from objects, as shown in Example 1-2.

EXAMPLE 1-2

Find a pattern in the number of matchsticks required to continue the pattern shown in Figure 1-3.

FIGURE 1-3

Solution   Assume the matchsticks are arranged so that each figure has one more square on the right than the preceding figure. Note that the addition of a square to an arrangement requires the addition of three matchsticks each time. Thus, the numerical pattern obtained is 4, 7, 10, 13, 16, 19, . . . , an arithmetic sequence with a difference of 3.

REMARK   An informal description of an arithmetic sequence is one that can be described as an "add d" pattern where d is the common difference.

In the language of children, the pattern in Example 1-2 is "add 3," meaning that 3 must be added to any term after the first to find the next. This is an example of a **recursive pattern**. In a recursive pattern, after one or more consecutive terms are given to start, each successive term of the sequence is obtained from the previous term(s). For example, 3, 6, 9, . . . is another "add 3" sequence starting with 3, while 1, 2, 3, 5, 8, 13, . . . is a recursive pattern in which the next term (from the third on) is obtained from adding the two previous terms.

recursive pattern

A recursive pattern is typically used in a spreadsheet, as seen in Table 1-2 where column A tracks the order of the terms; the headers for the columns are A, B, etc. The first entry in the B column (in the B1 cell) is 4; and to find the term in the B2 cell, we use the number in the B1 cell and add 3. Once the B2 cell entry is found, the pattern is continued using the *Fill Down* command. In spreadsheet language, the formula = B1 + 3 finds any term after the first by adding 3 to the previous term. The formula is based on a recursive pattern, is a **recursive formula**. [For more explicit directions on using a spreadsheet, see Appendix I.]

recursive formula

Table 1-2

	A	B
1	1	4
2	2	7
3	3	10
4	4	13
5	5	16
6	6	19
7	7	22
8	8	25
9	9	28
10		
11		
12		
13		

If you want to find the number of matchsticks in the 100th figure in Example 1-2 then the spreadsheet may be used or we can find a different type of general rule for finding the number of matchsticks when given the number of the term. The problem-solving strategy of *making a table* is again helpful here.

The spreadsheet in Table 1-2 gives an easy way to form a table. Column A gives the numbers of the terms and column B gives the terms of the sequence. If one is building such a table without a spreadsheet, it might look like Table 1-3. An *ellipsis*, denoted by three dots, indicates that the sequence continues in the same manner.

Table 1-3

Number of Term	Term
1	4
2	$7 = 4 + 3 = 4 + 1 \cdot 3$
3	$10 = (4 + 3) + 3 = 4 + 2 \cdot 3$
4	$13 = (4 + 2 \cdot 3) + 3 = 4 + 3 \cdot 3$
.	.
.	.
.	.
n	$4 + (n - 1)3$

nth term   **REMARK**   The **nth term** of the sequence is $4 + (n - 1)3$, which could be written as $3n + 1$.

We have already seen that the common difference of the sequence in Table 1-3 is 3. A natural sequence of numbers with this common difference is found in the elementary grades by "skip-counting." For example, if a child skip-counts by 3, we would hear the child saying, "3, 6, 9, 12, 15, . . ." Suppose we append the sequence of skip-count terms listed in a third column of Table 1-2, as seen in Table 1-4.

Table 1-4

Number of Term	Term	Skip-Count Term
1	4	3
2	7	6
3	10	9
4	13	12
5	16	15
6	19	18
7	22	21
8	25	24
9	28	27
.	.	.
.	.	.
.	.	.
n	$3n + 1$	$3n$

To find the nth term of the original sequence, the skip-count terms are helpful. The skip-count terms are just the multiples of 3 with the first being $1 \cdot 3$, the second being $2 \cdot 3$, the third being $3 \cdot 3$, and so on. Thus the nth term in the skip-count column is $3n$. Note that the terms in the middle column are 1 more than the corresponding terms in the skip-count column. Thus, a general pattern for the numbers in the middle column is $3n + 1$. With this pattern, the 100th term is $3 \cdot 100 + 1$, or 301.

Still a different approach to finding the number of matchsticks in the 100th term of Figure 1-3 might be as follows: If the matchstick figure has 100 squares, we could find the total number of matchsticks by adding the number of horizontal and vertical sticks. There are $2 \cdot 100$ placed horizontally. (Why?) Notice that in the first figure, there are 2 matchsticks placed vertically; in the second, 3; and in the third, 4. In the one hundredth figure, there should be $100 + 1$ vertical matchsticks. Altogether there will be $2 \cdot 100 + (100 + 1)$, or 301 matchsticks in the one hundredth figure. Similarly, in the nth figure, there would be $2n$ horizontal and $(n + 1)$ vertical matchsticks for a total of $3n + 1$. This discussion is summarized in Table 1-5.

Table 1-5

Number of Term	Number of Matchsticks Horizontally	Number of Matchsticks Vertically	Total
1	2	2	4
2	4	3	7
3	6	4	10
4	8	5	13
.	.	.	.
.	.	.	.
.	.	.	.
100	200	101	301
.	.	.	.
.	.	.	.
.	.	.	.
n	$2n$	$n + 1$	$2n + (n + 1) =$ $3n + 1$

If we were given the value of the term, we could use the formula for the nth term in Table 1-5 to *work backward* to find the number of the term. For example, given the term 1798, we know that $3n + 1 = 1798$. Therefore $3n = 1797$ and $n = 599$. Consequently, the 599th term is 1798. We could obtain the same answer by solving $4 + (n - 1) \cdot 3 = 1798$ for n.

In the matchstick problem, we found the nth term of a sequence. If the nth term of a sequence is given, we can find any term of the sequence, as shown in Example 1-3.

E X A M P L E
1-3

Find the first four terms of a sequence whose nth term is given by the following and determine whether the sequence is arithmetic.

a. $4n + 3$ **b.** $n^2 - 1$

Solution   **a.** To find the first term, substitute $n = 1$ in the formula $4n + 3$ in order to obtain $4 \cdot 1 + 3$, or 7. Similarly, substituting $n = 2, 3, 4$, we obtain, respectively, $4 \cdot 2 + 3$, or 11; $4 \cdot 3 + 3$, or 15; and $4 \cdot 4 + 3$, or 19. Hence, the first four terms of the sequence are 7, 11, 15, and 19; this sequence is arithmetic with a difference of 4.

   b. Substituting $n = 1, 2, 3, 4$ in the formula $n^2 - 1$, we obtain, respectively, $1^2 - 1$, or 0; $2^2 - 1$, or 3; $3^2 - 1$, or 8; and $4^2 - 1$, or 15. Thus the first four terms of the sequence are 0, 3, 8, and 15. This sequence is not arithmetic, having no common difference.

NOW TRY THIS 1-2

In an arithmetic sequence with the 2nd term 11 and the 5th term 23, find the 100th term.

To generalize our work with arithmetic sequences, suppose the first term in an arithmetic sequence is a and the difference is d. The strategy of *making a table* can be used to investigate the general term for the sequence $a, a + d, a + 2d, a + 3d, \ldots$, as shown in Table 1-6. *The nth term of any sequence with first term a and difference d is given by $a + (n - 1)d$.* For example, in the arithmetic sequence 5, 9, 13, 17, 21, 25, $\ldots$, the first term is 5 and the difference is 4. Thus the nth term is given by $a + (n - 1)d = 5 + (n - 1)4$. Simplifying algebraically, we obtain $5 + (n - 1)4 = 5 + 4n - 4 = 4n + 1$.

Table 1-6

Number of Term	Term
1	a
2	$a + d$
3	$a + 2d$
4	$a + 3d$
5	$a + 4d$
.	.
.	.
.	.
n	$a + (n - 1)d$

The diagrams in Figure 1-4 show the molecular structure of alkanes, a class of hydrocarbons. C represents a carbon atom and H a hydrogen atom. A connecting segment shows a chemical bond. (Remark: CH_4 stands for C_1H_4.)

FIGURE 1-4

```
     H              H  H            H  H  H
     |              |  |            |  |  |
  H - C - H  ,  H - C- C - H  ,  H- C- C- C - H
     |              |  |            |  |  |
     H              H  H            H  H  H
```

methane (CH_4)   ethane (C_2H_6)   propane (C_3H_8)

a. Hectane is an alkane with 100 carbon atoms. How many hydrogen atoms does it have?

b. Write a general rule for alkanes C_nH_m showing the relationship between m and n.

Solution   **a.** To determine the relationship between the number of carbon and hydrogen atoms, we study the drawing of the alkanes and disregard the extreme left and right hydrogen atoms in each. We can see that for every carbon atom, there are two hydrogen atoms. Therefore there are twice as many hydrogen atoms as carbon atoms plus the two hydrogen atoms at the extremes. For example, when there are 3 carbon atoms, there are $(2 \cdot 3) + 2$, or 8, hydrogen atoms. This notion is summarized in Table 1-7. If we extend the table for 4 carbon atoms, we get $(2 \cdot 4) + 2$, or 10, hydrogen atoms. For 100 carbon atoms, there are $(2 \cdot 100) + 2$, or 202, hydrogen atoms.

Table 1-7

No. of Carbon Atoms	No. of Hydrogen Atoms
1	4
2	6
3	8
.	.
.	.
.	.
100	?
.	.
.	.
.	.
n	m

b. In general, for n carbon atoms there would be n hydrogen atoms attached above, n attached below, and 2 attached on the sides. Hence, the total number of hydrogen atoms would be $2n + 2$. Because the number of hydrogen atoms was designated by m, it follows that $m = 2n + 2$.

EXAMPLE
1-5

A theater is set up in such a way that there are 20 seats in the first row and 4 additional seats in each consecutive row. The last row has 144 seats. How many rows are there in the theater?

Solution   Because there are 4 additional seats in each consecutive row, the number of seats in the rows form an arithmetic sequence. The first term of the sequence is 20 and the difference, d, is 4. The last term in the sequence is 144. A computerized spreadsheet could easily be used to count the number of terms in the sequence, 20, 24, 28, . . . , 144. However, without technology, we count the terms as follows: In an arithmetic sequence, the nth term is $a + (n - 1)d$, where a is the first term, d is the difference, and n is the number of the term. In this case, $a = 20$ and $d = 4$. Therefore

$$a + (n - 1)d = 20 + (n - 1)4.$$

We now want to find the number of the term, n, when the nth term, $20 + (n - 1)4$, is equal to 144. Therefore

$$20 + (n - 1)4 = 144$$
$$(n - 1)4 = 124$$
$$n - 1 = 31$$
$$n = 32.$$

This tells us that when $n = 32$, the value of the term is 144. This implies that there are 32 rows in the theater. Instead of using a formula, we could have made a table and looked for a pattern.

Geometric Sequences

geometric sequence

ratio

A child has 2 biological parents, 4 grandparents, 8 great grandparents, 16 great-great grandparents, and so on. The number of ancestors form the **geometric sequence** 2, 4, 8, 16, 32, ... Each successive term of a geometric sequence is obtained from its predecessor by multiplying by a fixed number, the **ratio**. In this example, both the 1st term and the ratio are 2. (The ratio is 2 because each person has two parents.) To find the nth term, examine the pattern in Table 1-8.

Table 1-8

Number of Term	Term
1	$2 = 2^1$
2	$4 = 2 \cdot 2 = 2^2$
3	$8 = (2 \cdot 2) \cdot 2 = 2^3$
4	$16 = (2 \cdot 2 \cdot 2) \cdot 2 = 2^4$
5	$32 = (2 \cdot 2 \cdot 2 \cdot 2) \cdot 2 = 2^5$
.	.
.	.
.	.

The pattern of the terms in Table 1-8 can be generalized as follows.

> **Definition**
>
> $$\overbrace{a^n = a \cdot a \cdot a \cdot \ldots \cdot a}^{n \text{ terms}}$$
>
> If n is a natural number, then $a^n = a \cdot a \cdot a \cdot \ldots \cdot a$.

exponent

Table 1-9

Number of Term	Term
1	a
2	ar
3	ar^2
4	ar^3
5	ar^4
.	.
.	.
.	.
n	ar^{n-1}

When the given term is written as a power of 2, the number of the term is the **exponent**. Following this pattern, the 10th term is 2^{10}, or 1024, the 100th term is 2^{100}, and the nth term is 2^n. Thus the number of ancestors in the nth previous generation is 2^n.

Finding the nth Term for a Geometric Sequence

It is possible to find the nth term of any geometric sequence when given the first term and the ratio. If the first term is a and the ratio is r, then the terms are as listed in Table 1-9.

Notice that the second term is ar, the third term is ar^2, the fourth term is ar^3. The power of r in each term is 1 less than the number of the term. This pattern continues since we multiply by r to get the next term. Thus, the nth term is ar^{n-1}. For $n = 1$, we have $ar^{1-1} = ar^0$. Because the 1st term is a, then $ar^0 = a$. When $a \neq 0$, for all numbers $r \neq 0$ then $r^0 = 1$, as discussed in Chapter 6. For the geometric sequence 3, 12, 48, 192, . . . , the first term is 3 and the ratio is 4, and so the nth term is given by $ar^{n-1} = 3 \cdot 4^{n-1}$.

NOW TRY THIS 1-3

> **a.** Two bacteria are in a dish. The number of bacteria triples every hour. Following this pattern, find the number of bacteria in the dish after 10 hours and after n hours.
>
> **b.** Suppose that instead of increasing geometrically as in part (a), the number of bacteria increases arithmetically by 3 each hour. Compare the growth after 10 hours and after n hours. Comment on the difference in growth of a geometric sequence versus an arithmetic sequence.

Other Sequences

figurate numbers

Figurate numbers provide examples of sequences that are neither arithmetic nor geometric. Such numbers can be represented by dots arranged in the shape of certain geometric figures. The number 1 is the beginning of most patterns involving figurate numbers. The array in Figure 1-5 represents the first four terms of the sequence of **triangular numbers**.

triangular numbers

FIGURE 1-5

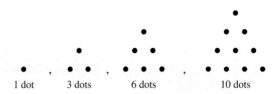

1 dot   ,   3 dots   ,   6 dots   ,   10 dots

The triangular numbers can be written numerically as 1, 3, 6, 10, 15, . . . The sequence 1, 3, 6, 10, 15, . . . is not an arithmetic sequence because there is no common difference, as Figure 1-6 shows.

FIGURE 1-6

$$\begin{array}{ccccccc} 1 & & 3 & & 6 & & 10 & & 15 \\ & \vee & & \vee & & \vee & & \vee \\ & 2 & & 3 & & 4 & & 5 \end{array}$$

(First difference)

However, the sequence of differences 2, 3, 4, 5, . . . is an arithmetic sequence with difference 1, as Figure 1-7 shows.

FIGURE 1-7

$$\begin{array}{ccccccccccccc} 1 & & 3 & & 6 & & 10 & & 15 & & 21 & & 28 \\ & \vee & & \vee & & \vee & & \vee & & \vee & & \vee \\ & 2 & & 3 & & 4 & & 5 & & 6 & & 7 \\ & & \vee & & \vee & & \vee & & \vee & & \vee \\ & & 1 & & 1 & & 1 & & 1 & & 1 \end{array}$$

(First difference)

(Second difference)

The next successive terms for the original sequence are shown in color in Figure 1-7.

Table 1-10 suggests a pattern for finding the next terms and the nth term for the triangular numbers. The second term is obtained from the first term by adding 2; the third term is obtained from the second term by adding 3; and so on. In general, because the nth triangular number has n dots in the nth row, it is equal to the sum of the dots in the previous triangular number (the $(n - 1)$st one) plus the n dots in the nth row. Following this pattern, the 10th term is $1 + 2 + 3 + 4 + 5 + 6 + 7 + 8 + 9 + 10$, or 55, and the nth term is $1 + 2 + 3 + 4 + 5 + \ldots + (n - 1) + n$.

Table 1-10

Number of Term	Term
1	1
2	$3 = 1 + 2$
3	$6 = 1 + 2 + 3$
4	$10 = 1 + 2 + 3 + 4$
5	$15 = 1 + 2 + 3 + 4 + 5$
.	.
.	.
.	.
10	$55 = 1 + 2 + 3 + 4 + 5 + 6 + 7 + 8 + 9 + 10$

Next consider the first four *square numbers* in Figure 1-8. These square numbers, 1, 4, 9, 16, . . . , can be written as 1^2, 2^2, 3^2, 4^2, and so on. The number of dots in the 10th array is 10^2; the number of dots in the 100th array is 100^2; and the number of dots in the nth array is n^2. The sequence of square numbers is neither arithmetic nor geometric.

FIGURE 1-8

| 1 dot | 4 dots | 9 dots | 16 dots |

E X A M P L E
1-6

Assuming that the pattern discovered continues, find the seventh term in each of the following sequences:

a. 5, 6, 14, 29, 51, 80, . . .   **b.** 2, 3, 9, 23, 48, 87, . . .

Solution   a. Following is the sequence of first differences:

$$5 \quad 6 \quad 14 \quad 29 \quad 51 \quad 80$$

(First difference)   1   8   15   22   29

To discover a pattern for the original sequence, we try to find a pattern for the sequence of differences 1, 8, 15, 22, 29, ... This sequence is an arithmetic sequence with fixed difference 7:

$$5 \quad 6 \quad 14 \quad 29 \quad 51 \quad 80$$

(First difference)   1   8   15   22   29

(Second difference)   7   7   7   7

Thus the 6th term in the first difference row is $29 + 7$, or 36, and the 7th term in the original sequence is $80 + 36$, or 116. What number follows 116?

b. Because the second difference is not a fixed number, we go on to the third difference:

$$2 \quad 3 \quad 9 \quad 23 \quad 48 \quad 87$$

(First difference)   1   6   14   25   39

(Second difference)   5   8   11   14

(Third difference)   3   3   3

The third difference is a fixed number; therefore the second difference is an arithmetic sequence. The 5th term in the second-difference sequence is $14 + 3$, or 17; the 6th term in the first-difference sequence is $39 + 17$, or 56; and the 7th term in the original sequence is $87 + 56$, or 143.

When asked to find a pattern for a given sequence, first look for some easily recognizable pattern and determine whether the sequence is arithmetic or geometric. If a pattern is unclear, taking successive differences may help. *It is possible that none of the methods described reveal a pattern.*

BRAIN
T E A S E R

Female bees are born from fertilized eggs, and male bees are born from unfertilized eggs. This means that a male bee has only a mother, while a female bee has a mother and a father. If the ancestry of a male bee is traced 10 generations back, how many bees are there in all 10 generations?

O N G O I N G   A S S E S S M E N T   1 - 1

1. For each of the following sequences of figures, determine a possible pattern and draw the next figure according to that pattern:

a.

b.

c.

d.

e.

f.

2. In each of the following, list terms that continue a possible pattern. Which of the sequences are arithmetic, which are geometric, and which are neither?
   a. 1, 3, 5, 7, 9
   b. 0, 50, 100, 150, 200
   c. 3, 6, 12, 24, 48
   d. 10, 100, 1000, 10,000, 100,000
   e. 9, 13, 17, 21, 25, 29
   f. 1, 8, 27, 64, 125

3. Find the 100th term and the nth term for each of the sequences in problem 2 above.

4. Use a traditional clock face to determine the next three terms in the following sequence:

$$1, 6, 11, 4, 9, \ldots$$

5. Observe the following pattern:

$$1 + 3 = 2^2,$$
$$1 + 3 + 5 = 3^2,$$
$$1 + 3 + 5 + 7 = 4^2$$

a. State a generalization based on this pattern.
b. Based on the generalization in (a), find

$$1 + 3 + 5 + 7 + \ldots + 35.$$

6. Following is a pattern of circular shapes:

If this pattern is continued until there are 10 black circles in a row, how many open circles and how many black circles are needed?

7. The following geometric arrays suggest a sequence of numbers:

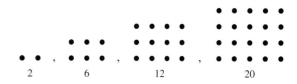

a. Find the next three terms.
b. Find the 100th term.
c. Find the nth term.

8. In the following pattern, one hexagon takes 6 toothpicks to build, two hexagons take 11 toothpicks to build, and so on. How many toothpicks would it take to build (a) 10 hexagons? (b) n hexagons?

9. The first windmill takes 5 matchstick squares to build, the second takes 9 to build, and the third takes 13 to build, as shown. How many matchstick squares will it take to build (a) the 10th windmill? (b) the nth windmill?

10. Each of the following figures is made of small triangles like the first one in the sequence. (The second figure is made of 4 small triangles.) Make a conjecture concerning the number of small triangles needed to make **(a)** the 100th figure and **(b)** the *n*th figure.

11. In the following sequence, the figures are made of cubes that are glued together. If the exposed surface needs to be painted, how many squares will be painted in **(a)** the 10th figure? **(b)** the *n*th figure?

12. The school population for a certain school was predicted to increase by 50 students per year for the next 10 years. If the current enrollment is 700 students, what will the enrollment be after 10 years?

13. A tank contains 15,360 L of water. At the end of each day, half of the water is removed and not replaced. How much water is left in the tank after 10 days?

14. Joe's annual income has been increasing each year by the same amount. The first year his income was $24,000, and the ninth year his income was $31,680. In which year was his income $45,120?

15. The first difference of a sequence is 2, 4, 6, 8, ... Find the first six terms of the original sequence in each of the following cases:
    a. The first term of the original sequence is 3.
    b. The sum of the first two terms of the original sequence is 10.
    c. The fifth term of the original sequence is 35.

16. List the next three terms to continue a pattern in each of the following. (Finding differences may be helpful.)
    a. 5, 6, 14, 32, 64, 115, 191
    b. 0, 2, 6, 12, 20, 30, 42

17. How many terms are there in each of the following sequences?
    a. 51, 52, 53, 54, . . . , 151   **b.** $1, 2, 2^2, 2^3, . . . , 2^{60}$
    c. 10, 20, 30, 40, . . . , 2000   **d.** 9, 13, 17, 21, 25, . . . , 353
    e. 1, 2, 4, 8, 16, 32, . . . , 1024

18. Find the first five terms of the sequence whose *n*th term is as follows:
    a. $n^2 + 2$
    b. $5n - 1$
    c. $10^n - 1$
    d. $3n + 2$

19. The number of petals on many flowers generates the following sequence:

$$1, 1, 2, 3, 5, 8, 13, 21, . . . ,$$

which is a *Fibonacci sequence*. This sequence is named after the great Italian mathematician Leonardo Fibonacci, who lived in the twelfth and thirteenth centuries.
    a. Write the first 12 terms of the sequence.
    b. Notice that the sum of the first three terms in the sequence is one less than the fifth term of the sequence. Does a similar relationship hold for the sum of the first four terms, five terms, and six terms?
    c. Guess the sum of the first 10 terms of the sequence.
    d. Make a conjecture concerning the sum of the first *n* terms of the sequence.

20. The Fibonacci sequence defined in problem 19 can start with arbitrary first and second terms. If the 1st term is 2 and the 2nd is 4, then the sequence is 2, 4, 6, 10, 16, 26, 42, ... Answer the questions in problem 19(a) and (c) for this sequence.

21. Consider the following sequences:
    300, 500, 700, 900, 1100, 1300, . . .
    2, 4, 8, 16, 32, 64, . . .
    Find the number of the term in which the geometric sequence becomes greater than the arithmetic sequence.

22. Cut a piece of paper into 5 pieces. Take any one of the pieces and cut it into 5 pieces, and so on.
    a. What number of pieces can be obtained in this way?
    b. What is the number of pieces obtained in the *n*th cut?

23. The sequence 32, *a, b, c,* 512 is a geometric sequence. Find *a, b, c*.

24. Each box in the following row had a number written in it such that the sum of any three numbers in succession in the row was 15. Many of the numbers were erased. Determine the missing number for each square.

6						4		

Communication

25. Explain how to show that each of these statements is false:
    a. All rectangles have diagonals that are perpendicular.
    b. The sum of two even numbers is always divisible by 4.

26. Elsa met 3 university students from Montana, and they all wore cowboy boots. Elsa generalized that all Montana university students wear cowboy boots. How could you show that her generalization is false?

27. Give two examples of how inductive reasoning might be used in everyday life. Is a conclusion based on inductive reasoning certain?

28. **a.** If a fixed number is added to each term of an arithmetic sequence, is the resulting sequence an arithmetic sequence? Justify the answer.
    b. If each term of an arithmetic sequence is multiplied by a fixed number, will the resulting sequence always be an arithmetic sequence? Justify the answer.
    c. If the corresponding terms of two arithmetic sequences are added, is the resulting sequence arithmetic?

Open-Ended

29. Patterns can be used to count the number of dots on the Chinese checkerboard; two patterns are shown below. Determine several other patterns to count the dots.

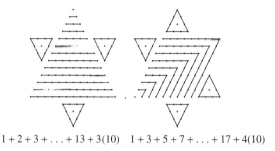

$1 + 2 + 3 + \ldots + 13 + 3(10)$ $1 + 3 + 5 + 7 + \ldots + 17 + 4(10)$

30. Make up a pattern involving figurate numbers and find a formula for the 100th term. Describe the pattern and how to find the 100th term.

Cooperative Learning

31. Each person in the group follows this set of directions:
    Pick a number.
    Multiply by 3.
    Add 6.
    Divide by 3.
    Subtract your original number.

a. Compare your answers and make a generalization based on your results.
b. What type of reasoning did you use in making your generalization?
c. In your group, make up a number puzzle where the answer is always 17 and write an explanation of why your puzzle works.
d. Write another number puzzle; try it with another group.

32. If the pattern below continued indefinitely, the resulting figure would be called the *Sierpinski triangle*, or *Sierpinski gasket*.

In a group, determine each of the following. Discuss different counting strategies.
a. How many black triangles would be in the fifth figure?
b. How many white triangles would be in the fifth figure?
c. If the pattern is continued for n figures, how many black triangles will there be?
d. If the pattern is continued for n figures, how many white triangles will there be?

Mathematics and Problem Solving

George Polya (1887–1985) described the experience of problem solving in his book, *How to Solve It* (p. v):

A great discovery solves a great problem, but there is a grain of discovery in the solution of any problem. Your problem may be modest; but if it challenges your curiosity and brings into play your inventive facilities, and if you solve it by your own means, you may experience the tension and enjoy the triumph of discovery.

To solve a problem, we must first understand both the task and the given information. Next, it is helpful to determine a strategy to accomplish the task. Once we arrive at a solution, we should determine whether the solution makes sense and is reasonable. This process of problem solving can be described using a four-step process similar to the one developed by George Polya.

Four-Step Problem-Solving Process

1. **Understanding the problem**
   a. Can you state the problem in your own words?
   b. What are you trying to find or do?
   c. What are the unknowns?

    d. What information do you obtain from the problem?

    e. What information, if any, is missing or not needed?

2. Devising a plan

The following list of strategies, although not exhaustive, is very useful:

    a. Look for a pattern.

    b. Examine related problems and determine if the same technique applied to them can be applied here.

    c. Examine a simpler or special case of the problem to gain insight into the solution of the original problem.

    d. Make a table.

    e. Make a diagram.

    f. Write an equation.

    g. Use guess and check.

    h. Work backward.

    i. Identify a subgoal.

    j. Use indirect reasoning.

    k. Use direct reasoning.

3. Carrying out the plan

    a. Implement the strategy or strategies in step 2 and perform any necessary actions or computations.

    b. Check each step of the plan as you proceed. This may be intuitive checking or a formal proof of each step.

    c. Keep an accurate record of your work.

4. Looking back

    a. Check the results in the original problem. (In some cases, this will require a proof.)

    b. Interpret the solution in terms of the original problem. Does your answer make sense? Is it reasonable? Does it answer the question that was asked?

    c. Determine whether there is another method of finding the solution.

    d. If possible, determine other related or more general problems for which the techniques will work.

Avoiding Mind Sets

If problems are approached in only one way, a mind set may be formed. For example, consider the following. Spell the word "spot" three times out loud. "S-P-O-T! S-P-O-T! S-P-O-T!" Now answer the question, "What do we do when we come to a green light?" Write an answer. If we answered "Stop," we may be guilty of having formed a mind set. We do not stop at a *green* light.

    Consider the following problem: "A shepherd had 36 sheep. All but 10 died. How many lived?"

    Did you answer "10"? If you did, you are catching on and are ready to try some problems. If you did not answer "10," then you did not understand the question. *Understanding the problem* is the first step in the four-step problem-solving process. Using the four-step process does not guarantee a solution to a problem, but it does provide a systematic means of attacking problems.

Strategies for Problem Solving

To aid in problem solving, *Principles and Standards* provides the following guidance.

Instead of teaching problem solving separately, teachers should embed problems in the mathematics-content curriculum. When teachers integrate problem solving into the context of mathematical situations, students recognize the usefulness of strategies. Teachers should choose specific problems because they are likely to prompt particular strategies and allow for the development of certain mathematical ideas. (p. 119)

Strategies are tools that might be used to discover or construct the means to achieve a goal. For each strategy described next, an example is given that can be solved with that strategy. Often, problems can be solved in more than one way. You may devise a different strategy to solve the sample problems. There is no one best strategy to use.

HISTORICAL N O T E

Carl Gauss (1777–1855) is regarded as the greatest mathematician of the nineteenth century and one of the greatest mathematicians of all time. Born to humble parents in Brunswick, Germany, he was an infant prodigy who, it is said, at age 3 corrected an arithmetic error in his father's bookkeeping. Gauss claimed that he could figure before he could talk.

Gauss made contributions in the areas of astronomy, geodesy, and electricity. After Gauss's death, the King of Hanover ordered a commemorative medal prepared in his honor. On the medal was an inscription referring to Gauss as the "Prince of Mathematics," a title that stayed with his name.

Strategy: Look for a Pattern

The strategy of looking for a pattern was examined in the previous section, where we concentrated on sequences of numbers. We continue that investigation here.

PROBLEM SOLVING   Gauss's Problem

When the German mathematician Carl Gauss was a child, his teacher required the students to find the sum of the first 100 natural numbers. The teacher expected this problem to keep the class occupied for some time. Gauss gave the answer almost immediately. Can you?

Understanding the Problem   The natural numbers are 1, 2, 3, 4, ... Thus the problem is to find the sum $1 + 2 + 3 + 4 + \ldots + 100$.

Devising a Plan   One strategy is to *look for a pattern*. If we consider $1 + 100$, $2 + 99$, $3 + 98, \ldots, 50 + 51$, it is evident that there are 50 pairs of numbers, each with a sum of 101, as shown in Figure 1-9.

FIGURE 1-9

Carrying Out the Plan   There are 50 pairs, each with the sum 101. Thus the total can be found by multiplying $50 \cdot 101$, or 5050.

Looking Back   The method is mathematically correct because addition can be performed in any order, and multiplication is repeated addition.

The method used computes the required addition as a multi-step problem. First the 100 numbers are considered as 50 pairs, each of which has the same sum. Now we have the following:

$$1 + 2 + 3 + 4 + \ldots + 97 + 98 + 99 + 100$$

becomes

$$\underbrace{101 + 101 + 101 + \ldots + 101}_{\text{50 terms}}$$

Adding the terms in the last expression can be achieved by multiplying 50 times 101, so the method is correct.

A more general problem is to find the sum of the first n natural numbers, $1 + 2 + 3 + 4 + 5 + 6 + \ldots + n$, where n is any natural number. We use the same plan as before and notice the relationship in Figure 1-10. If n is an even natural number, there are $n/2$ pairs of numbers. The sum of each pair is $n + 1$. Therefore the sum $1 + 2 + 3 + \ldots + n$ is given by $\left(\dfrac{n}{2}\right)(n + 1)$, or $\dfrac{n(n + 1)}{2}$ for n even.

FIGURE 1-10

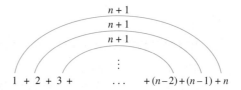

A different strategy for finding the sum $1 + 2 + 3 + \ldots + n$ involves *making a diagram* and thinking of the sum geometrically as a stack of blocks. To find the sum, consider the stack in Figure 1-11(a) and a stack of the same size placed differently, as in Figure 1-11(b). The total number of blocks in the stack in Figure 1-11(b) is $n(n + 1)$, which is twice the desired sum. Thus the desired sum is $n(n + 1)/2$.

FIGURE 1-11

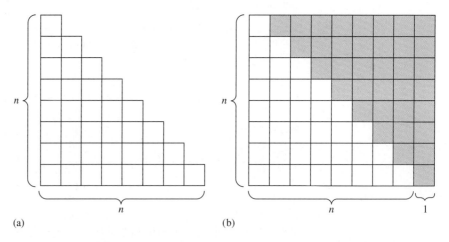

(a)   (b)

[Note: This problem is connected to the problems in the previous section that involved triangular numbers.]

Strategy: Make a Table

A table can be used to summarize data or to help us see a pattern. It can also help us to consider all possible cases in a given problem.

PROBLEM SOLVING   <u>**Sums of Even Natural Numbers**</u>

Find the sum of the even natural numbers less than or equal to 100. Devise a strategy for finding that sum and generalize the result.

Understanding the Problem   We begin to find the sum of the even natural numbers $2 + 4 + 6 + 8 + \ldots + 100$ by searching for a pattern used in this sum. Recognizing that

$$2 = 1 + 1$$
$$4 = 2 + 2$$
$$6 = 3 + 3$$
$$\cdot$$
$$\cdot$$
$$\cdot$$
$$100 = 50 + 50$$

a plan can be devised *using simpler related problems.*

Devising a Plan   Recognizing that the sum can be *separated into two simpler parts* related to Gauss's original problem helps us devise a plan. Consider the following:

$$2 + 4 + 6 + 8 \ldots + 100 = (1 + 1) + (2 + 2) + (3 + 3) + \ldots + (50 + 50)$$
$$= (1 + 2 + 3 + \ldots + 50) + (1 + 2 + 3 + \ldots + 50)$$

Thus we can use Gauss's method to find the sum of the first 50 natural numbers and then double that.

Carrying Out the Plan   We carry out the plans as follows:

$$2 + 4 + 6 + 8 + \ldots + 100 = (1 + 1) + (2 + 2) + (3 + 3) + \ldots + (50 + 50)$$
$$= (1 + 2 + 3 + \ldots + 50) + (1 + 2 + 3 + \ldots + 50)$$
$$= 2 \cdot [50(50 + 1)/2]$$
$$= 2550$$

Thus, the sum is 2550.

Looking Back   A different way to consider this problem is to realize that there are 25 pairs of even numbers, each of whose sum is seen in Figure 1-12 as 102.

FIGURE 1-12

$$2 + 4 + 6 + 8 + \ldots + 94 + 96 + 98 + 100$$

Thus the sum is $25 \cdot 102$, or 2550.

NOW TRY THIS 1-4

Jean wants to build a rectangular picture frame that encloses an area of 120 cm² (square centimeters). She wants the length and width to be natural numbers, {1, 2, 3, 4, . . . }. What dimensions give the least perimeter?

Strategy: Examine a Simpler Case

One strategy for solving a complex problem is to *examine a simpler case* of the problem and then consider other parts of the complex problem. An example is shown on the student page on page 23.

NOW TRY THIS 1-5

Nikki is setting up tables for a noon luncheon in the gym. She has 25 small square tables that hold one person to a side. She plans to put 25 of these tables in a row to make one long rectangular table that is only one table wide. (a) If 60 people will be attending the lunch, will she have enough space to seat them all using this plan? (b) If she placed all 25 tables in the form of a big square, how many people could she seat?

Strategy: Identify a Subgoal

As we attempt to devise a plan for solving some problems, it may become apparent that the problem could be solved if the solution to a somewhat easier or more familiar related problem could be found. In such a case, finding the solution to the easier problem may become a subgoal of the primary goal of solving the original problem. The following Magic Square problem shows an example of this.

PROBLEM SOLVING **A Magic Square**

FIGURE 1-13

Arrange the numbers 1 through 9 into a square subdivided into nine smaller squares like the one shown in Figure 1-13 so that the sum of every row, column, and main diagonal is the same. (The result is a *magic square*.)

Understanding the Problem We need to put each of the nine numbers 1, 2, 3, . . . , 9 in the small squares, a different number in each square, so that the sum of the numbers in each row, in each column, and in each of the two diagonals is the same.

Devising a Plan If we knew the fixed sum of the numbers in each row, column, and diagonal, we would have a better idea of which numbers can appear together in a single row, column, or diagonal. Thus our *subgoal* is to find that fixed sum. The sum of the nine numbers, $1 + 2 + 3 + \ldots + 9$, equals 3 times the sum in one row. Consequently, the fixed sum is obtained by dividing $1 + 2 + 3 + \ldots + 9$ by 3. Using the process developed by Gauss, we have $(1 + 2 + 3 + \ldots + 9) \div 3 = \dfrac{9 \cdot 10}{2} \div 3$, or $45 \div 3 = 15$, so the sum in each row, column, and diagonal must be 15. Next, we need to decide what numbers could occupy the various squares. The number in the center space will appear in 4 sums,

Sample School Book Page:
SOLVING A SIMPLER PROBLEM

**Chapter 6
Lesson
5**

Problem Solving

**Analyze Strategies:
Solve a Simpler Problem**

Windsor,
Ontario
Canada

Learn

You Will Learn

how solving a simpler problem can help you solve more difficult problems

Marc has had his own greeting card company since he was 6 years old.

Suppose Marc and 7 of his artist co-workers have a meeting. As they arrive, each one hands a sample of his or her work to each of the other artists.

How many greeting cards will be passed around?

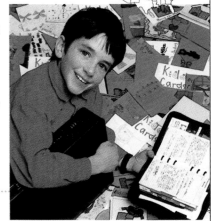

Marc lives in Windsor, Ontario, in Canada.

Work Together

▶ **Understand**   What information do you have?

What are you trying to find?

▶ **Plan**   How will you find out the number of cards?   Solve a simpler problem similar to this one.

▶ **Solve**   Solve the simpler problem.

Start with 2 artists.
2 cards would be passed.

Continue with 3 artists.
6 cards would be passed.

Use a table to organize the data.

Find a pattern and complete the table.

Artists	2	3	4	5	6	7	8
Cards	2	6	12	20	30	42	56
Pattern	2×1	3×2	4×3	5×4	6×5	7×6	8×7

What is the answer?   There will be 56 greeting cards passed around.

▶ **Look Back**   What other strategy could you have used?

Source: Scott Foresman-Addison Wesley, Grade 5, 2002 (p. 278).

each adding to 15 (two diagonals, the second row, and the second column). Each number in the corners will appear in three sums of 15. (Do you see why?) If we write 15 as a sum of three different numbers 1 through 9 in all possible ways, we could then count how many sums contain each of the numbers 1 through 9. The numbers that appear in at least four sums are candidates for placement in the center square, whereas the numbers that appear in at least three sums are candidates for the corner squares. Thus our new *subgoal* is to write 15 in as many ways as possible as a sum of three different numbers from the set $\{1, 2, 3, \ldots, 9\}$.

Carrying Out the Plan The sums of 15 can be written systematically as follows:

$$9 + 5 + 1$$
$$9 + 4 + 2$$
$$8 + 6 + 1$$
$$8 + 5 + 2$$
$$8 + 4 + 3$$
$$7 + 6 + 2$$
$$7 + 5 + 3$$
$$6 + 5 + 4$$

Notice that the order in each sum is not important. (Do you see why?) Hence, $1 + 5 + 9$ and $5 + 1 + 9$, for example, are counted as the same. Notice that 1 appears in only two sums, 2 in three sums, 3 in two sums, and so on. Table 1-11 summarizes this pattern.

Table 1-11

Number	1	2	3	4	5	6	7	8	9
Number of Sums Containing the Number	2	3	2	3	4	3	2	3	2

The only number that appears in four sums is 5; hence, 5 must be in the center of the square. (Why?) Because 2, 4, 6, and 8 appear three times each, they must go in the corners. Suppose we choose 2 for the upper left corner. Then 8 must be in the lower right corner. (Why?) This is shown in Figure 1-14(a). Now we could place 6 in the lower left corner or upper right corner. If we choose the upper right corner, we obtain the result in Figure 1-14(b). The magic square can now be completed, as shown in Figure 1-14(c).

FIGURE 1-14

(a)   (b)   (c)

Looking Back We have seen that 5 was the only number among the given numbers that could appear in the center. However, we had various choices for a corner, and hence it seems that the magic square we found is not the only one possible. Can you find all the others?

Another way to see that 5 could be in the center square is to consider the sums $1 + 9$, $2 + 8$, $3 + 7$, $4 + 6$, as shown in Figure 1-15. We could add 5 to each to obtain 15.

FIGURE 1-15

NOW TRY THIS 1-6

Five friends decided to give a party and split the costs equally. Al spent $4.75 on invitations, Betty spent $12 for drinks and $5.25 on vegetables, Carl spent $24 for pizza, Dani spent $6 on paper plates and napkins, and Ellen spent $13 on decorations. Determine who owes money to whom and how the money can be paid.

Strategy: Examine a Related Problem

Sometimes a problem is similar to a previously encountered problem. If so, it is often possible to apply a similar approach to solve the new problem. Such is the case in the next problem.

PROBLEM SOLVING **Matchstick Patterns**

Ryan is building matchstick square sequences, as shown in Figure 1-16. He used 67 matchsticks to form the last figure in his sequence. How many matchsticks will he use for the entire project?

FIGURE 1-16

Understanding the Problem From experience with patterns, we can recognize the sequence generated by the matchsticks as 4, 7, 10, 13, . . . , 67. The last number is 67 because Ryan used 67 matchsticks to form the last figure in the sequence. This is an arithmetic sequence with difference 3. Find the sum of the numbers in this sequence.

Devising a Plan A *related problem* is Gauss's problem of finding the sum $1 + 2 + 3 + 4 + \ldots + 100$. In that problem, we paired 1 with 100, 2 with 99, 3 with 98, and so on, and observed that there were 50 pairs of numbers, each with a sum of 101. A similar approach in the present problem yields a sum of 71 for each pair. To find the total, we need to know the number of pairs in Figure 1-17.

FIGURE 1-17

To find the number of pairs, we need the number of terms in the sequence. Thus we have identified a *subgoal*, which is to find the number of terms in the sequence. From the discussion after Example 1-2, we see the nth term of this sequence is $4 + (n - 1)3$. To find the number of the term corresponding to 67, we solve the equation $4 + (n - 1)3 = 67$ and obtain $n = 22$. Thus there are 22 terms in the given sequence.

Carrying Out the Plan Because the number of terms is 22, we have 11 pairs of matchstick figures, each of whose sum is 71 matchsticks. Therefore the total is $11 \cdot 71$, or 781 matchsticks.

Looking Back Using the outlined procedure, we should be able to find the sum of any arithmetic sequence in which we know the first two terms and the last term.

Strategy: Write an Equation

A problem-solving strategy commonly used in algebraic thinking consists of *writing an equation*. An example that might combine using a table and writing an equation for solution is seen on the student page on page 27. What equation is involved?

Strategy: Draw a Diagram

It has often been said that a picture is worth a thousand words. This is particularly true in problem solving. In geometry, drawing a picture often provides the insight necessary to solve a problem. The following problem is a nongeometric problem that can be solved by drawing a diagram or could be done using a piece of paper.

PROBLEM SOLVING **Paper-Measuring Problem**

Miguel has a single sheet of 8 1/2-by-11-in. paper. He needs to measure exactly 6 in. Can he do it using the sheet of paper?

Understanding the Problem The problem is to use only an 8 1/2-by-11-in. paper to measure something of exactly 6 in. There are the two edge lengths with which to work.

Devising a Plan A natural thing to ask is, what combinations of lengths can be made from the two given lengths? We could fold to halve the lengths, but this would lead to such fractional lengths as 4 1/4 in., 2 1/8 in., 5 1/2 in., and so on, that appear unhelpful. Another idea is to consider other folds that could be used to combine 8 1/2 in. and 11 in. to get 6 in. For example, consider how to obtain 6 from 8 1/2 and 11.

$$11 - 8\ 1/2 = 2\ 1/2$$
$$8\ 1/2 - 2\ 1/2 = 6$$

Sample School Book Page:
EXAMINING A SIMPLER CASE

2.1 Trading Land

In this problem, you will explore whether a trade like the one offered by U.S. Malls Incorporated will always be fair, sometimes be fair, or never be fair. You will look at a simple trade situation to see if you can discover a pattern that will help you make predictions about more complex situations.

Problem 2.1

Suppose you own a square piece of land with sides n meters long. You trade your land for a rectangular lot. The length of your new lot is 2 meters longer than the side length of your original lot, and the width of your new lot is 2 meters shorter than the side length of the original lot.

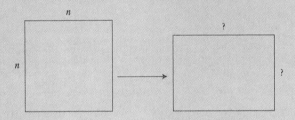

A. Copy and complete the table below.

Original square		New rectangle			Difference in areas (m²)
Side length (m)	Area (m²)	Length (m)	Width (m)	Area (m²)	
3	9	5	1	5	4
4					
5					
6					
7					

B. For each side length in the table, tell how the area of your new lot compares with the area of the original lot. For which side lengths, if any, is this a fair trade?

C. The side length of the original square lot was n meters. For each column in the table, write an expression for the values in the column in terms of n. For example, the expression for the area of the original square is n^2.

20 **Frogs, Fleas, and Painted Cubes**

Source: Connected Mathematics: Frogs, Fleas, and Painted Cubes, 2002 (p. 20).

If we could fold the paper to obtain 2 1/2 in. from the two given lengths and then "subtract" the 2 1/2 from 8 1/2, then we could obtain the desired result of 6. One strategy to investigate how to obtain 2 1/2 in. from the 11 in. and 8 1/2 in. lengths is to *draw a diagram*.

Carrying Out the Plan   By folding the paper as shown by the arrows in Figure 1-18, we can obtain a length of 6 in.

FIGURE 1-18

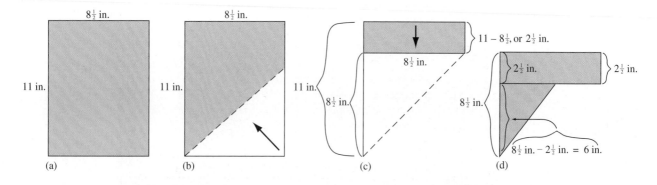

With the fold in Figure 1-18(b), we obtain a length of 11 − 8 1/2, or 2 1/2 in. With the fold in Figure 1-18(c), we obtain 8 1/2 − 2 1/2, or 6 in.

Looking Back   Though there are other ways to solve this problem, drawing a diagram showing the folds of the paper combines notions of geometry and gives a way to fold a square from a rectangle. An entirely different way to solve the problem is possible if we have more than one sheet of paper. That problem is left to the reader.

NOW TRY THIS 1-7

> An elevator stopped at the middle floor of a building. It then moved up 4 floors and stopped. It then moved down 6 floors, and then moved up 10 floors and stopped. The elevator was now 3 floors from the top floor. How many floors does the building have?

Strategy: Guess and Check

In the strategy of *guess and check*, we first guess at a solution using as reasonable a guess as possible. Then we check to see whether the guess is correct. If not, the next step is to learn as much as possible about the solution based on the guess before making the next guess. This strategy can be regarded as a form of trial and error, where the information about the error helps us choose what trial to make next.

 The guess-and-check strategy is often used when a student does not know how to solve the problem more efficiently or if the student does not yet have the tools to solve the problem in a faster way. The guess-and-check strategy is demonstrated on the student page on page 29. Is the answer reasonable?

Sample School Book Page:
GUESS AND CHECK

Chapter 3 Lesson 16

Problem Solving
Analyze Strategies: Guess and Check

You Will Learn
how to solve problems using the Guess and Check strategy

Learn •

A mountain bike rider pumped the brakes twice to stop at a stop sign 34 ft away. After each pump, the bike traveled the same distance. The bike stopped 12 ft beyond the stop sign. How far did the bike travel after each pump of the brakes?

Work Together

▶ **Understand**   What do you know?

What do you need to find out?

▶ **Plan**   How will you find out?   Use the Guess and Check strategy.

▶ **Solve**   Write a number sentence.

2 brake pumps   34 ft to the stop sign
$n + n = 34 + 12$ ← 12 ft past the stop sign
$n + n = 46$

Guess	Check
25	$n + n = 46$
	$25 + 25 = 50$ Too great!
23	$23 + 23 = 46$ Correct guess!

Reading Tip
Pictures can help you understand a problem.

Make a guess, then check.

Make a second guess. Check the guess. Write the answer.

The bike traveled 23 ft after each pump.

▶ **Look Back**   Is your answer reasonable? Explain.

Talk About It

When can you use the Guess and Check strategy?

Source: Scott Foresman-Addison Wesley, Grade 5, 2002 (p. 156).

Strategy: Work Backward

In some problems, it is easier to start with the result and to work backward. This is demonstrated on the following student page on page 31.

Strategy: Use Indirect Reasoning

To show that a statement is true, it is sometimes easier to show that it is impossible for the statement to be false. This can be done by showing that if the statement were false, something contradictory or impossible would follow. This approach is useful when it is difficult to start a direct argument and when negating the given statement gives us something tangible with which to work. An example follows.

PROBLEM SOLVING   <u>**Checkerboard Problem**</u>

In Figure 1-19, we are given a checkerboard with the two squares on opposite corners removed and a set of dominoes such that each domino can cover 2 adjacent squares on the board. Can the dominoes be arranged in such a way that all the remaining squares on the board can be covered with no dominoes hanging off the board? If not, why not?

FIGURE 1-19

Understanding the Problem   Two red spaces on opposite corners were removed from the checkerboard in Figure 1-19. We are asked whether it is possible to cover the remaining 62 squares with dominoes the size of 2 squares.

Devising a Plan   If we try to cover the board in Figure 1-19 with dominoes, we will find that the dominoes do not fit and some squares will remain uncovered. To show that there is no way to cover the board with dominoes, we use *indirect reasoning*. If the remaining 62 squares could be covered with dominoes, it would take 31 dominoes to accomplish the task. We want to show that this implies something impossible.

Carrying Out the Plan   Each domino must cover 1 black and 1 red square. Hence, 31 dominoes would cover 31 red and 31 black squares. This is impossible, however, because the board in Figure 1-19 has 30 red and 32 black squares. Consequently, our assumption that the board in Figure 1-19 can be covered with dominoes is wrong.

Looking Back   The counting of black and red squares implies that if we remove any number of squares from a checkerboard so that the number of remaining red squares differs from the number of remaining black squares, the board cannot be covered with dominoes.

Sample School Book Page:
WORK BACKWARD

Chapter 7
Lesson 14

Problem Solving
Analyze Strategies: **Work Backward**

You Will Learn
how working backward can help you solve problems

Did You Know?
Bananas, apples, grapes, and oranges, in that order, are the most favorite fruit in the United States.

Learn

Florida mangoes were donated for a Teacher Appreciation lunch. Two mangoes were too ripe to use. Three groups of four students cut up the remaining fruit. Each student cut up five mangoes. How many mangoes were donated?

Work Together

▶ **Understand**
What do you know?
What do you need to find?

▶ **Plan**
Try working backward.   Find how many mangoes were cut up. Add the number of mangoes that were not used.

▶ **Solve**
How many mangoes were cut up?   students × mangoes × groups:
$4 \times 5 \times 3 = 60$

How many mangoes were donated?   cut-up + 2 unused:
$60 + 2 = 62$ 62 mangoes were donated.

▶ **Look Back**
How can you check your answer?

Talk About It

How did working backward help you solve the problem?

Source: Scott Foresman-Addison Wesley, Grade 4, 2002 (p. 332).

(Do you see why?) We could also investigate what happens when two squares of the same color are removed from an 8-by-7 board and other-sized boards. Also, is it always possible to cover the remaining board if two squares of opposite colors are removed? ▨

Strategy: Use Direct Reasoning

PROBLEM SOLVING   **Checker Games**

Each of two people won three games of checkers. Is it possible that only five games were played?

■ **Solution**   We know that each person won 3 games. *Reasoning directly* we see that if the people each won three games and they played each other, then there would have had to be six games played. Thus they could not each play each other in all games and have three wins each. Could they in fact each win three games while playing only five total games and not have played each other? The answer is no and the situation is impossible. ▨

O N G O I N G   A S S E S S M E N T   1 - 2

1. Use the approach in Gauss's Problem to find the following sums (do not use formulas):
   a. $1 + 2 + 3 + 4 + \ldots + 99$
   b. $1 + 2 + 3 + 4 + \ldots + n$ where n is odd
   c. $1 + 3 + 5 + 7 + \ldots + 1001$
2. How many cuts does it take to divide a segment into
   a. 5 equal-sized pieces?
   b. 6 equal-sized pieces?
   c. n equal-sized pieces?
3. How many ways can you make change for a $50 bill using $5, $10, and $20 bills?
4. Cookies are sold singly or in packages of 2 or 6. How many ways can you buy a dozen cookies?
5. The sign says you are leaving Missoula, Butte is 120 miles away, and Bozeman is 200 miles away. There is a rest stop halfway between Butte and Bozeman. How far is the rest stop from Missoula?
6. Alababa, Bubba, Cory, and Dandy are in a horse race. Bubba is the slowest, Cory is faster than Alababa but slower than Dandy. Name the finishing order of the horses.
7. Frankie and Johnny began reading a novel on the same day. Frankie reads 8 pages a day and Johnny reads 5 pages a day. If Frankie is on page 72, what page is Johnny on?
8. How many squares are in the following figure?

9. What is the largest sum of money—all in coins and no silver dollars—that you could have in your pocket without being able to give change for a dollar, a half-dollar, a quarter, a dime, or a nickel?
10. If 0.2 oz of catsup is used on each of 22 billion hamburgers, how many 16-oz bottles of catsup are needed?
11. a. Place the digits 1, 2, 4, 5, and 7 in the following boxes so that in (i) the greatest product is obtained and in (ii) the greatest quotient is obtained:

    (i)   (ii)

    b. Use the same digits as in (a) to obtain (i) the least product and (ii) the least quotient.
12. How many terms are there in the following sequence? 1, 8, 15, 22, . . . , 113
13. Suppose you could spend $10 every minute, night and day. How much could you spend in a year? (Assume there are 365 days in a year.)
14. Refer to the following pattern and answer questions (a) through (c):

$$1 = 2^1 - 1$$
$$1 + 2 = 2^2 - 1$$
$$1 + 2 + 2^2 = 2^3 - 1$$
$$1 + 2 + 2^2 + 2^3 = 2^4 - 1$$
$$1 + 2 + 2^2 + 2^3 + 2^4 = 2^5 - 1$$

   a. Write a simpler expression for
   $$1 + 2 + 2^2 + 2^3 + 2^4 + 2^5.$$
   Justify your answer.

b. Write a simpler expression for the sum in the *n*th row in the pattern.

c. Use a spreadsheet or a calculator to check your answer in (b) for *n* = 15.

15. How many four-digit numbers have the same digits as 1993?

16. A compass and a ruler together cost $4. The compass costs 90¢ more than the ruler. How much does the compass cost?

17. Two houses on the same street are separated by a large, empty field. The first house is numbered 29, and the other is numbered 211. An architect is designing 13 new houses to be built between the two existing houses.

a. What should the numbers of the new houses be if along with the existing houses, the numbers need to form an arithmetic sequence?

b. What is the difference of this sequence?

18. Same-sized cubes are glued together to form a staircase-like sequence of solids as shown:

All of the unglued faces of the cubes need to be painted. How many squares will need to be painted in (a) the 100th solid? **(b)** the *n*th solid?

19. Marc goes to the store with exactly $1.00 in change. He has at least one of each coin less than a half-dollar coin, but he does not have a half-dollar coin.

a. What is the least number of coins he could have?

b. What is the greatest number of coins he could have?

20. A farmer needs to fence a rectangular piece of land. She wants the length of the field to be 80 ft longer than the width. If she has 1080 ft of fencing material, what should the length and the width of the field be?

21. Find a 3-by-3 magic square using the numbers 3, 5, 7, 9, 11, 13, 15, 17, and 19.

22. Find the following sums:

a. $1 + 6 + 11 + 16 + 21 + \ldots + 1001$

b. $3 + 7 + 11 + 15 + 19 + \ldots + 403$

23. Eight marbles look alike, but one is slightly heavier than the others. Using a balance scale, explain how you can determine the heavier one in exactly

a. 3 weighings   **b.** 2 weighings

24. a. Find the sum of all the numbers in the following array.

1	2	3	4	5	6	...	100
2	4	6	8	10	12	...	200
3	6	9	12	15	18	...	300
.							
.							
100	200	300	400	500	600	...	100 · 100

b. Generalize part (a) to a similar array in which each row has *n* numbers and there are *n* rows.

25. Use the strategy of *indirect reasoning* to justify each of the following:

a. If the product of two positive numbers is greater than 82, then at least one of the numbers is greater than 9.

b. If the product of two positive numbers is greater than 81, then at least one of the numbers is greater than 9.

26. a. Using the existing lines on the checkerboard shown below, how many squares are there?

b. If the number of rows and columns of the checkerboard is doubled, is the number of squares doubled? Justify your answer.

Communication

27. A different version of the story of Gauss's computing $1 + 2 + 3 + \ldots + 100$ reports that he simply listed the numbers in the following way to discover the sum and divided by 2:

$$
\begin{array}{r}
1 + \quad 2 + \quad 3 + \quad 4 + \quad 5 + \ldots + \quad 98 + \quad 99 + 100 \\
100 + \quad 99 + \quad 98 + \quad 97 + \quad 96 + \ldots + \quad 3 + \quad 2 + \quad 1 \\
\hline
101 + 101 + 101 + 101 + 101 + \ldots + 101 + 101 + 101
\end{array}
$$

Does this method give the same answer? Discuss the advantages of this method over the one described in the text.

28. Explain why it is impossible to have a 3-by-3 magic square with numbers 1, 3, 4, 5, 6, 7, 8, 9, and 10.

Open-Ended

29. How many breaths do you take in a year?

30. Choose a problem-solving strategy and make up a problem that would use this strategy. Write the solution using Polya's four-step approach.

31. Explain when you might use the *guess-and-check* strategy.

Cooperative Learning

32. The distance around the world is approximately 40,000 km. Approximately how many people of average size in your group would it take to stretch around the world if they were holding hands?

33. Work in pairs on the following version of a game called NIM. A nongraphing calculator is needed for each pair.

a. Player 1 presses [1] and [+] or [2] and [+]. Player 2 does the same. The players take turns until the target number of 21 is reached. The first player to make the display read 21 is the winner. Determine a strategy for deciding who always wins.

b. Try a game of NIM using the digits 1, 2, 3, and 4, with a target number of 104. The first player to reach 104 wins. What is the winning strategy?

c. Try a game of NIM using the digits 3, 5, and 7, with a target number of 73. The first player to exceed 73 loses. What is the winning strategy?

d. Now play Reverse NIM with the keys $\boxed{1}$ and $\boxed{2}$. Instead of $\boxed{+}$, use $\boxed{-}$. Put 21 on the display. Let the target number be 0. Determine a strategy for winning Reverse NIM.

e. Try Reverse NIM using the digits 1, 2, and 3 and starting with 24 on the display. The target number is 0. What is the winning strategy?

f. Try Reverse NIM using the digits 3, 5, and 7 and starting with 73 on the display. The first player to display a negative number loses. What is the winning strategy?

Review Problems

34. List three terms to complete possible patterns:
   a. 3, 6, 9, 12, 15, 18, ___, ___, ___
   b. 1, 2, 3, 2, 9, 2, 27, 2, 81, 2, ___, ___, ___

35. Find the nth term for the sequence 22, 32, 42, 52, ...

36. How many terms are in the sequence 3, 7, 11, 15, 19, . . . , 83?

37. Find the sums of the terms in the sequence in problem 35.

38. Examine the following:

$$2 \cdot 9 = 18. \qquad 5 \cdot 9 = 45.$$
$$3 \cdot 9 = 27. \qquad 6 \cdot 9 = 54.$$
$$4 \cdot 9 = 36.$$

   a. What patterns do you see? Check to see if your patterns work for $7 \cdot 9$, $8 \cdot 9$, $9 \cdot 9$, and $10 \cdot 9$.
   b. Explain how the patterns you noticed might be helpful in remembering the basic multiplication table for 9s.

BRAIN
T E A S E R

Ten women are fishing all in a row in a boat. One seat in the center of the boat is empty. The 5 women in the front of the boat want to change seats with the 5 women in the back of the boat. A person can move from her seat to the next empty seat or she can step over one person without capsizing the boat. What is the minimum number of moves needed for the 5 women in front to change places with the 5 in back?

LABORATORY
A C T I V I T Y

Place a half-dollar, quarter, and nickel in position *A* as shown in Figure 1-20. Try to move these coins, one at a time, to position *C*. At no time may a larger coin be placed on a smaller coin. Coins may be placed in position *B*. How many moves does it take to get them to position *C*? Now add a penny to the pile and see how many moves it takes. This is a simple case of the famous Tower of Hanoi problem, in which ancient Brahman priests were required to move a pile of 64 disks of decreasing size, after which the world would end. How long would it take at a rate of one move per second?

FIGURE 1-20

1-3   Algebraic Thinking

One of the strategies of the previous section is *write an equation*. This strategy is part of the bigger picture of algebraic thinking. In the *Principles and Standards*, we find the following:

Instructional programs from prekindergarten through grade 12 should enable all students to

- *understand patterns, relations, and functions;*
- *represent and analyze mathematical situations and structures using algebraic symbols;*
- *use mathematical models to represent and understand quantitative relationships;*
- *analyze change in various contexts.* (p. 37)

Because algebraic thinking is so important in mathematics at all levels, from the early grades on, we chose to include a separate section on it. Because patterns were included in the previous section, we concentrate on other features of algebraic thinking in this section.

For PreK–2, we find that *Principles and Standards* recommends that students be able to

 - *use concrete, pictorial, and verbal representations to develop an understanding of invented and conventional symbolic notations.*
- *model situations that involve the addition and subtraction of whole numbers, using objects, pictures, and symbols.* (p. 90)

For grades 3–5, we find the following:

 - *represent and analyze patterns and functions, using words, tables, and graphs.*
- *represent the idea of a variable as an unknown quantity using a letter or a symbol;*
- *express mathematical relationships using equations;*
- *investigate how a change in one variable relates to a change in a second variable;*
- *identify and describe situations with constant or varying rates of change and compare them.* (p. 158)

For grades 6–8, we have:

 - *identify functions as linear or nonlinear and contrast their properties from tables, graphs, or equations;*
- *develop an initial conceptual understanding of different uses of variables;*
- *explore relationships between symbolic expressions and graphs of lines, paying particular attention to the meaning of intercept and slope;*
- *use symbolic algebra to represent situations and to solve problems, especially those that involve linear relationships;*
- *recognize and generate equivalent forms for simple algebraic expressions and solve linear equations.* (p. 222)

Developing Algebraic Thinking Skills

variable   One of the big ideas of algebraic thinking is the notion of **variable**, a word listed in the *Standards* recommendations. Understanding the concept of a variable is fundamental to mathematics in general. However, "variable" can mean many things in mathematics. It can stand for a missing element or an unknown, as in the following:

I can add some number to 3 to obtain 5.

In this situation, many possible numbers could be placed in the sentence, but there is exactly one number that makes the sentence true. Here the unknown is 2.

In a different situation, a variable can represent more than one thing. For example, for a certain group of children, we could say that their heights vary with their ages. If h represents height and a represents age, then both h and a can have different values for different children in the group. Here a variable represents a changing quantity.

To apply algebra in solving problems, we frequently need to translate given information into a symbolic expression involving variables designated by letters or words. In all such examples, we may name the variables as we choose.

E X A M P L E
1-7

In each of the following, translate the given information into a symbolic expression involving quantities designated by letters:

a. One weekend, a store sold twice as many CDs as DVDs and 25 fewer tapes than CDs. If the store sold d DVDs, how many tapes and CDs did it sell?

b. French fries have about 12 calories apiece. A hamburger has about 600 calories. Akiva is on a diet of 2000 calories per day. If he ate f french fries and one hamburger, how many more calories can he consume that day?

c. First-class postage in early 2002 was 34¢ for the first ounce and 23¢ for each additional ounce. At this rate, what was the cost of mailing a letter that weighs z oz?

Solution   **a.** Because d DVDs were sold, twice as many CDs as DVDs implies $2d$ CDs. Thus 25 fewer tapes than CDs implies $2d - 25$ tapes.

b. First, find how many calories Akiva consumed eating f french fries and one hamburger. Then, to find how many more calories he can consume, subtract this expression from 2000.

1 french fry	12 calories
f french fries	$12f$ calories

Therefore the number of calories in f french fries and one hamburger is

$$600 + 12f.$$

The number of calories left for the day is $2000 - (600 + 12f)$, or $2000 - 600 - 12f$, or $1400 - 12f$.

c. If a letter weighs z ounces, the first ounce costs 34¢ and the remaining $(z - 1)$ oz cost 23¢ each. The cost of the $(z - 1)$ oz therefore is $23(z - 1)$ cents. We have the following:

Cost of mailing a z-ounce letter = cost of first ounce + cost of next $(z - 1)$ oz

$$= 34 + 23(z - 1)$$
$$= 34 + 23z - 23$$
$$= 11 + 23z \text{ cents}$$

HISTORICAL NOTE

The word *algebra* comes from the Arabic book *Al-jabr wa'l muqabalah* written by Mohammed al-Khowârizmî (ca. 825). Algebra was introduced in Europe in the thirteenth and fourteenth centuries by Leonardo of Pisa (also called Fibonacci). Algebra was occasionally referred to as *Ars Magna*, or "the great art." Both Diophantus (ca. A.D. 250) and François Viète (1540–1603) have been called "fathers of algebra." Little is known about Diophantus, a Greek, except that he is supposed to have lived to be 84 years old and that he wrote *Arithmetica*, a treatise originally in thirteen books. Viète was a French lawyer who devoted his leisure time to mathematics. Not liking the word *algebra*, he referred to the subject as "the analytic art."

Algebraic thinking is frequently needed to understand how simple number tricks work, as seen in Example 1-8.

EXAMPLE
1-8

A teacher instructed her class as follows:

Take any number and add 15 to it. Now multiply that sum by 4. Next subtract 8 and divide the difference by 4. Now subtract 12 from the quotient and tell me the answer, I will tell you the original number.

Analyze the instructions to see how the teacher was able to determine the original number.

Solution   Translate the information into an algebraic form.

Instructions	Discussion	Symbols
Take any number.	Since any number is used, we need a variable to represent the number. Let n be that variable	n
Add 15 to it.	We are told to add 15 to "it." "It" refers to the variable n.	$n + 15$
Multiply that sum by 4.	We are told to multiply "that sum" by 4. "That sum" is $n + 15$.	$4(n + 15)$
Subtract 8.	We are told to subtract 8 from the product.	$4(n + 15) - 8$
Divide the difference by 4.	The difference is $4(n + 15) - 8$. Divide it by 4.	$\dfrac{4(n + 15) - 8}{4}$
Subtract 12 from the quotient and tell me the answer.	We are told to subtract 12 from the quotient.	$\dfrac{4(n + 15) - 8}{4} - 12$

Translating what the teacher told the class to do results in the algebraic expression $\dfrac{4(n + 15) - 8}{4} - 12$. We are also told that we have to tell the teacher the answer obtained and then she produces the original number. Let's use the strategy of *working backward* to see if we can tell what happens. Suppose we tell the teacher that our final result is r. Think about how r was obtained. Just before we told the teacher "r," we had subtracted 12. To reverse that operation, we could add 12 to obtain $r + 12$. Prior to that we had divided by 4. To reverse that, we could multiply by 4 to obtain $4r + 48$. To get that result, we had subtracted 8, so that now we add 8 to obtain $4r + 56$. Just previous to that we had multiplied by 4 so that now we divide $4r + 56$ by 4 to obtain $r + 14$. The first operation had been to add 15 so now we subtract 15 from $r + 14$ to get $r - 1$. Thus the teacher knows when we tell her that our final result is r, is 1 more than the number with which we started, or the number with which we started, n, is the result minus 1.

This can be shown as follows:

$$\frac{4(n+15)-8}{4} - 12 = \frac{4n+60-8-4\cdot 12}{4}$$

$$= \frac{4n+4}{4}$$

$$= \frac{4(n+1)}{4}$$

$$= n+1.$$

EXAMPLE
1-9

Find an algebraic expression to represent the number of white tiles in Figure 1-21. Write this in terms of the number of dark tiles on a side of the largest dark tile square in the *n*th term of the pattern.

FIGURE 1-21

Solution The dark tiles have sides with increasing lengths 1, 2, 3, and so on. In the *n*th term, the length of a side of the dark tiles would be *n*. What are ways to count the number of white tiles?

One way to think about the number of white tiles is to recognize that the number of white tiles on a side is 2 more than *n*, or $n + 2$. The number of white tiles could be 4 times $(n + 2)$, less any overlapping counting. In this case, each corner tile would be duplicated so that there are 4, white tiles overcounted giving us $4(n + 2) - 4$, or $4n + 4$ white tiles.

There are many other ways to count the tiles. Describe two other ways of determining the number of white tiles in the *n*th term.

Algebraic thinking can occur in different ways. One example that uses pictures is seen below.

EXAMPLE
1-10

At a local farmer's market, the price tags in Figure 1-22 were seen. What is the cost of each object?

FIGURE 1-22

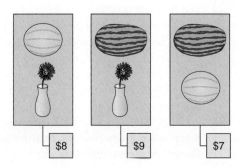

Solution   Approaches to this problem may vary. For example, if the objects in the two tags on the left are put together, the total cost would be $8 + $9, or $17. That cost would be for two vases and one each of the canteloupe and watermelon, as in Figure 1-23.

FIGURE 1-23

Now if the canteloupe and watermelon are taken away from that total, then according to the cost of those two objects from the right tag, the cost should be reduced to $10 for two vases. That means each of the two vases costs $5. This in turn tells us that the canteloupe costs $8 − $5, or $3, and the watermelon costs $9 − $5, or $4.

The solutions of Example 1-10 could involve the strategy of *writing an equation*. But first we need a basic knowledge of solving equations.

Properties of Equations

To solve equations, we need several properties of equality. Children discover many of these by using a balance scale. For example, consider two weights of amounts a and b on the balances, as in Figure 1-24(a). If the balance is level, then $a = b$. When we add an equal amount of weight c to both sides, the balance is still level, as in Figure 1-24(b).

FIGURE 1-24

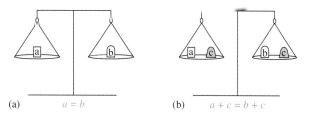

(a) $a = b$ (b) $a + c = b + c$

This demonstrates that *if $a = b$, then $a + c = b + c$, which is the Addition Property of Equality*.

Similarly, if the scale is balanced with amounts a and b, as in Figure 1-25(a), and we put additional a's on one side and an equal number of b's on the other side, the scale remains level, as in Figure 1–25(b).

FIGURE 1-25

(a) $a = b$ (b) $5a = 5b$

Figure 1-25 suggests that *if c is any real number and a = b, then ac = bc, which is the Multiplication Property of Equality*. These properties are summarized next.

> ## Properties

The Addition Property of Equality For any numbers *a, b,* and *c,* if $a = b$, then $a + c = b + c$.
The Multiplication Property of Equality For any numbers *a, b,* and *c,* if $a = b$, then $ac = bc$.

The properties imply that we may add the same number to both sides of an equation or multiply both sides of the equation by the same number without affecting the equality. A new statement results from reversing the order of the *if* and *then* parts of the addition property of equality. The new statement is the *converse* of the original statement. In the case of the addition property, the converse is a true statement. The converse of the multiplication property of equality is also true when $c \neq 0$. These properties are summarized next.

> ## Cancellation Properties of Equality

1. For any numbers *a, b,* and *c,* if $a + c = b + c$, then $a = b$.
2. For any numbers *a, b,* and *c,* with $c \neq 0$, if $ac = bc$, then $a = b$.

substitution property

Equality is not affected if we substitute a number for its equal. This property is referred to as the **substitution property**. Examples of substitution follow:

1. If $a + b = c + d$ and $d = 5$, then $a + b = c + 5$.
2. If $a + b = c + d$, if $b = e$, and if $d = f$, then $a + e = c + f$.

Solving Equations

Part of algebraic thinking involves operations on numbers and other elements represented by symbols. Finding solutions to equations is one part of algebra.

To solve equations, we may use the properties of equality developed earlier. A balance scale can be used to demonstrate solving equations. Consider $3x - 14 = 1$. Put the equal expressions on the opposite pans of the balance scale. Since the expressions are equal, the pans should be level, as in Figure 1-26.

FIGURE 1-26

To solve for x, we use the properties of equality to manipulate the expressions on the scale so that after each step, the scale remains level and, at the final step, only an x remains on one side of the scale. The number on the other side of the scale represents the solution to the original equation. To find x in the equation of Figure 1-26, consider the scales pictured in successive steps in Figure 1-27. In Figure 1-27, each successive scale represents an equation that is equivalent to the original equation; that is, each has the same solution as the original. The last scale shows $x = 5$. To check that 5 is the correct solution, we substitute 5 for x in the original equation. Because $3 \cdot 5 - 14 = 1$ is a true statement, 5 is the solution to the original equation.

FIGURE 1-27

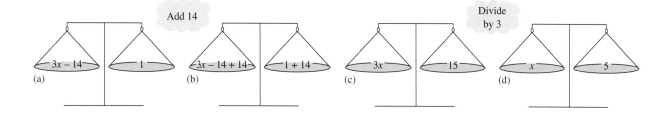

EXAMPLE 1-11

Solve each of the following for x:

a. $x + 4 = {}^-6$.
b. ${}^-x - 5 = 8$.

Solution   The solutions that follow show all the steps in the process:

a.
$$x + 4 = {}^-6.$$
$$(x + 4) + {}^-4 = {}^-6 + {}^-4.$$
$$x + (4 + {}^-4) = {}^-6 + {}^-4.$$
$$x + 0 = {}^-10.$$
$$x = {}^-10.$$

b.
$${}^-x - 5 = 8.$$
$$({}^-x + {}^-5) + 5 = 8 + 5.$$
$${}^-x + ({}^-5 + 5) = 13.$$
$${}^-x + 0 = 13.$$
$${}^-x = 13.$$
$$({}^-x)({}^-1) = 13({}^-1).$$
$$x = {}^-13.$$

Mary Fairfax Somerville (1780–1872) was born in Scotland of upper-class parents. Her introduction to algebra came at about age 13 while reading a ladies' fashion magazine that contained some puzzles. Although not allowed to study mathematics formally, at age 27, widowed, and with two children, she bought and studied a set of mathematics books. In her autobiography, she wrote, "I was sometimes annoyed when in the midst of a difficult problem someone would enter and say, 'I have come to spend a few hours with you.'" Shortly before her death, she wrote, "I am now in my ninety-second year, . . . , I am extremely deaf, and my memory of ordinary events, and especially of the names of people, is failing, but not for mathematical and scientific subjects. I am still able to read books on the higher algebra for four or five hours in the morning and even to solve the problems. Sometimes I find them difficult, but my old obstinacy remains, for if I do not succeed today, I attack them again tomorrow."

Application Problems

The simple model in Figure 1-28 demonstrates a method for solving application problems. Formulate the problem as a mathematical problem, solve the mathematical problem, and then interpret the solution in terms of the original problem.

FIGURE 1-28

At the third-grade level, an example of this model appears in Figure 1-29.

FIGURE 1-29

We can apply Polya's four-step problem-solving process to solving word problems in which the use of algebraic thinking is appropriate.

In Understanding the Problem, we identify what is given and what is to be found. In Devising a Plan, we assign letters to the unknown quantities and translate the information in the problem into a model involving equations. In Carrying Out the Plan, we solve the equations or inequalities. In Looking Back, we interpret and check the solution in terms of the original problem.

In the following problems, we demonstrate Polya's four-step problem-solving process.

PROBLEM SOLVING   Overdue Books

Bruno has five books overdue at the library. The fine for overdue books is 10¢ a day per book. He remembers that he checked out an astronomy book a week earlier than four novels. If his total fine was $8.70, how long was each book overdue?

Understanding the Problem   Bruno has five books overdue. He checked out an astronomy book seven days earlier than the four novels, so the astronomy book is overdue seven days more than the novels. The fine per day for each book is 10¢, and the total fine was $8.70. We need to find out how many days each book is overdue.

Devising a Plan   Let d be the number of days that each of the four novels is overdue. The astronomy book is overdue seven days longer, that is, $d + 7$ days. To *write an equation* for d, we express the total fine in two ways. The total fine is $8.70. This fine in cents equals the fine for the astronomy book plus the fine for the four novels.

Fine for each of the novels = fine per day times the number of overdue days.

$$10 \quad \cdot \quad d$$

Fine for the four novels = 1 day's fine for 4 novels times number of overdue days.

$$4 \cdot 10 \quad \cdot \quad d$$
$$= (4 \cdot 10)d$$
$$= 40d.$$

Fine for the astronomy book = fine per day times the number of overdue days.

$$10 \quad \cdot \quad (d + 7)$$
$$= 10 \cdot (d + 7)$$

Because each of the above expressions is in cents, we need to write the total fine of $8.70 as 870¢ to produce the following:

Fine for the 4 novels + fine for the astronomy book = total fine.

$$40d \quad + \quad 10(d + 7) \quad = 870.$$

Carrying Out the Plan   Solve the equation for d.

$$40d + 10(d + 7) = 870.$$
$$40d + 10d + 70 = 870.$$
$$50d = 870 - 70.$$
$$50d = 800.$$
$$d = 16.$$

Thus each of the 4 novels was 16 days overdue, and the astronomy book was overdue $d + 7$, or 23, days.

Looking Back   To check the answer, follow the original information. Each of the four novels was 16 days overdue, and the astronomy book was 23 days overdue. Because the fine was 10¢ per day per book, the fine for each of the novels was $16 \cdot 10$¢, or 160¢. Hence, the fine for all four novels was $4 \cdot 160$¢, or 640¢. The fine for the astronomy book was $23 \cdot 10$¢, or 230¢. Consequently, the total fine was 640¢ + 230¢, or 870¢, which agrees with the given information of $8.70 as the total fine.

PROBLEM SOLVING   **Newspaper Delivery**

In a small town, three children deliver all the newspapers. Abby delivers three times as many papers as Bob, and Connie delivers 13 more than Abby. If the three children delivered a total of 496 papers, how many papers does each deliver?

Understanding the Problem   The problem asks for the number of papers that each child delivers. It gives information that compares the number of papers that each child delivers as well as the total number of papers delivered in the town.

Devising a Plan   Let a, b, and c be the number of papers delivered by Abby, Bob, and Connie, respectively. We translate the given information into *equations* as follows:

Abby delivers three times as many papers as Bob: $a = 3b$.

Connie delivers 13 more papers than Abby: $c = a + 13$.

Total delivery is 496: $a + b + c = 496$.

To reduce the number of variables, substitute $3b$ for a in the second and third equations:

$$c = a + 13 \qquad \text{becomes} \qquad c = 3b + 13.$$
$$a + b + c = 496 \qquad \text{becomes} \qquad 3b + b + c = 496.$$

Next, make an equation in one variable, b, by substituting $3b + 13$ for c in the equation $3b + b + c = 496$, solve for b, and then find a and c.

Carrying Out the Plan

$$3b + b + 3b + 13 = 496.$$
$$7b + 13 = 496.$$
$$7b = 483.$$
$$b = 69.$$

Thus $a = 3b = 3 \cdot 69 = 207$. Also, $c = a + 13 = 207 + 13 = 220$. So, Abby delivers 207 papers, Bob delivers 69 papers, and Connie delivers 220 papers.

Looking Back   To check the answers, follow the original information, using $a = 207$, $b = 69$, and $c = 220$. The information in the first sentence, "Abby delivers three times as many papers as Bob" checks, since $207 = 3 \cdot 69$. The second sentence, "Connie delivers 13 more papers than Abby" is true because $220 = 207 + 13$. The information on the total delivery checks, since $207 + 69 + 220 = 496$.

O N G O I N G   A S S E S S M E N T   1 - 3

1. In the following, write an expression in terms of the given variable that represents the indicated quantity. For example, the distance d traveled at a constant speed of 60 mph during t hours could be written as $d = 60t$.
   a. The cost of having a plumber spend h hours at your house if the plumber charges $20 for coming to the house and $25 per hour for labor
   b. The amount of money in cents in a jar containing d dimes and some nickels and quarters, if there are 3 times as many nickels as dimes and twice as many quarters as nickels

   c. The sum of three consecutive integers if the least integer is x
   d. The amount of bacteria after n minutes if the initial amount of bacteria is q and the amount of bacteria doubles every minute. (*Hint:* The answer should contain q as well as n.)
   e. The temperature after t hours if the initial temperature is 40°F and each hour it drops by 3°F
   f. Pawel's total salary after 3 yr if the first year his salary was s dollars, the second year it was $5000 higher, and the third year it was twice as much as the second year

g. The sum of three consecutive odd natural numbers if the least is x

h. The sum of three consecutive natural numbers if the middle is m

2. Pluto, once thought to be the farthest planet from the sun in our solar system, was also the smallest. The following table gives the weight P on Pluto for a given weight E on Earth measured in the same units.

Weight on Earth (E)	1	2	3	4	5	10	100
Weight on Pluto (P)	0.04	0.08	0.12	0.16	0.2	0.4	4

Based on the information given in the table, answer each of the following:
   a. Find an equation for P in terms of E.
   b. Express E in terms of P.
   c. What is Debbie's weight on Pluto if her weight on Earth is 135 lb?
   d. Find the weight on Earth of an object that weighs 100 lb on Pluto.

3. If 1 U.S. dollar is worth 1.35 Swiss francs and 1 Swiss franc is worth 1.22 Dutch gilders, find a formula that will give a U.S. tourist the amount of Dutch gilders g for U.S. dollars d.

4. Joel is designing squares made of matchsticks. The following are 1×1, 2×2, and 3×3 such squares. How many matchsticks will he need for
   a. a 10×10 square?
   b. an $n \times n$ square?

5. The formula for converting degrees Celsius (C) to degrees Fahrenheit (F) is $F = \left(\dfrac{9}{5}\right)C + 32$. Samantha reads that the temperature is $32°C$ in Spain. What is the Fahrenheit temperature?

6. To convert a temperature on the Celsius (C) scale to the Kelvin (K) scale, you need to add 273.15 to the Celsius temperature.
   a. Write a formula for K in terms of C.
   b. Write a formula for converting from the Kelvin scale to the Celsius scale.

7. Write an equation relating the variables described in each of the following situations:
   a. The pay P for t hours if you are paid $8 an hour
   b. The pay P for t hours if you are paid $15 for the first hour and $10 for each additional hour

   c. The total pay P for a visit and t hours of gardening if you are paid $20 for the visit and $10 for each hour of gardening
   d. The total cost C of membership in a health club that charges a $300 initiation fee and $4 for each of n days attended
   e. The cost C of renting a midsized car for 1 day of driving m miles if the rent is $30 per day plus 35¢ per mile.

8. Solve each of the following:
   a. $3 - x = -15$
   b. $-x - 3 = 15$

9. A teacher instructed her class as follows: *Take any number, multiply it by 3, add 49, and divide the result by 7. Subtract 7 from the quotient, divide the new result by 3, and tell me your answer. I will tell you the original number.* To determine each student's original number, the teacher multiplied each answer by 7. Explain how the teacher was able to tell each student's original number.

10. David has three times as much money as Rick. Together, they have $400. How much does each have?

11. Model the solution of the following equation with a scale: $2x + 3 = 7$.

12. Draw pictures as in Example 1-10 to find a solution to the following:
    • Two silk butterflies and a silk rose cost $18.
    • One silk butterfly and a silk rose cost $11.
    What is the cost of each?

13. For a certain event, 812 tickets were sold for a total of $1912. If students paid $2 per ticket and nonstudents paid $3 per ticket, how many student tickets were sold?

14. A man left an estate of $64,000 to three children. The eldest child received three times as much as the youngest. The middle child received $14,000 more than the youngest. How much did each child receive?

Communication

15. Students were asked to write an algebraic expression for the sum of three consecutive natural numbers. One student wrote $x + (x + 1) + (x + 2) = 3x + 3$. Another wrote $(x - 1) + x + (x + 1) = 3x$. Explain who is correct and why.

16. **a.** Find the sum of the following five expressions:
    $x - 2, x - 1, x, x + 1, x + 2$
    b. Based on your answer to part (a), state a generalization.

Open-Ended

17. In Example 1-8, a teacher instructed her class to take any number and perform a series of computations using that number. The teacher was able to tell each student's original number by subtracting 1 from the student's answer.

Create similar instructions for students so that the teacher needs to do only the following to obtain the student's original number:

a. Add 1 to the answer.
b. Multiply the answer by 2.
c. Multiply the answer times itself.

Cooperative Learning

18. Examine several elementary school textbooks for grades 1 through 4 and report on which algebraic concepts are introduced in each and how they are introduced.

Review Problems

19. List the terms to continue a possible pattern in the following sequences:
   a. 7, 14, 21, 28, . . .
   b. 4, 1, 8, 1, 12, . . .
20. Find the *n*th term for the following arithmetic sequence: 12, 32, 52, 72, . . .
21. Find how many terms are in the following arithmetic sequence:
   6, 10, 14, 18, . . . , 86
22. In how many ways can you make change for $0.21?

*Logic: An Introduction

statement

Logic is a tool used in mathematical thinking and problem solving. It is essential for reasoning. In logic, a **statement** *is a sentence that is either true or false, but not both.* The following expressions are not statements because their truth values cannot be determined without more information.

1. She has blue eyes.
2. $x + 7 = 18$.
3. $2y + 7 > 1$.
4. $2 + 3$

5. How are you?
6. Look out!
7. Carter was the best president.

Expressions (**1**), (**2**), and (**3**) become statements if, for (**1**), "she" is identified, and for (**2**) and (**3**), values are assigned to *x* and *y*, respectively. However, an expression involving he or she or *x* or *y* may already be a statement. For example, "If he is over 210 cm tall, then he is over 2 m tall," and "$2(x + y) = 2x + 2y$" are both statements because they are true no matter who he is or what the numerical values of *x* and *y* are.

negation

From a given statement, it is possible to create a new statement by forming a **negation**. The negation of a statement is *a statement with the opposite truth value of the given statement.* If a statement is true, its negation is false, and if a statement is false, its negation is true. Consider the statement "It is snowing now." The negation of this statement may be stated simply as "It is not snowing now."

E X A M P L E
1-12

Negate each of the following statements:

a. $2 + 3 = 5$
b. A hexagon has 6 sides.

Solution   **a.** $2 + 3 \neq 5$
   b. A hexagon does not have 6 sides.

Sentences like "The shirt is blue" and "The shirt is green" are statements if put in context. However, they are not negations of each other. A statement and its negation must have opposite truth values. If the shirt is actually red, then both of the statements are false and, hence, cannot be negations of each other. However, the statements "The shirt is blue" and "The shirt is not blue" are negations of each other because they have opposite truth values no matter what color the shirt really is.

quantifiers   Some statements involve **quantifiers** and are more complicated to negate. Quantifiers include words such as *all, some, every,* and *there exists.*

- The quantifiers *all, every,* and *no* refer to each and every element in a set.
- The quantifiers *some* and *there exists at least one* refer to one or more, or possibly all, of the elements in a set.
- *All, every,* and *each* have the same mathematical meaning. Similarly, *some* and *there exists at least one* all have the same meaning.

Consider the following statement involving the existential quantifier *some* and known to be true. "Some professors at Paxson University have blue eyes." This means that at least one professor at Paxson University has blue eyes. It does not rule out the possibilities that all the Paxson professors have blue eyes or that some of the Paxson professors do not have blue eyes. Because the negation of a true statement is false, neither "Some professors at Paxson University do not have blue eyes" nor "All professors at Paxson have blue eyes" are negations of the original statement. One possible negation of the original statement is "No professors at Paxson University have blue eyes."

To discover if one statement is a negation of another, we use arguments similar to the preceding one to determine if they have opposite truth values in all possible cases.

General forms of quantified statements with their negations follow:

Statement	**Negation**
Some *a* are *b*.	No *a* is *b*.
Some *a* are not *b*.	All *a* are *b*.
All *a* are *b*.	Some *a* are not *b*.
No *a* is *b*.	Some *a* are *b*.

EXAMPLE 1-13

Negate each of the following regardless of its truth value.

a. All students like hamburgers.
b. Some people like mathematics.
c. There exists a counting number x such that $3x = 6$.
d. For all counting numbers, $3x = 3x$.

Solution
a. Some students do not like hamburgers.
b. No people like mathematics.
c. For all counting numbers x, $3x \neq 6$.
d. There exists a counting number x such that $3x \neq 3x$.

Table 1-11

Statement p	Negation $\sim p$
T	F
F	T

truth table   There is a symbolic system defined to help in the study of logic. If p represents a statement, the negation of the statement p is denoted by $\sim p$ and is read "not p." **Truth tables** are often used to show all possible true-false patterns for statements. Table 1-11 summarizes the truth tables for p and $\sim p$.

Compound Statements

compound statement

From two given statements, it is possible to create a new, **compound statement** by using a connective such as *and*. For example, "It is snowing" and "The ski run is open" together with *and* give "It is snowing and the ski run is open." Other compound statements can be obtained by using the connective *or*. For example, "It is snowing or the ski run is open."

The symbols $\wedge$ and $\vee$ are used to represent the connectives *and* and *or*, respectively. For example, if p represents "It is snowing" and q represents "The ski run is open," then "It is snowing and the ski run is open" is denoted by $p \wedge q$. Similarly, "It is snowing or the ski run is open" is denoted by $p \vee q$.

The truth value of any compound statement, such as $p \wedge q$, is defined using the truth value of each of the simple statements. Because each of the statements p and q may be either true or false, there are four distinct possibilities for the truth value of $p \wedge q$, as shown in Table 1-12. The compound statement $p \wedge q$ is the **conjunction** of p and q and is defined to be true if, and only if, both p and q are true. Otherwise, it is false.

conjunction

disjunction

The compound statement $p \vee q$—that is, p *or* q—is a **disjunction**. In everyday language, *or* is not always interpreted in the same way. In logic, we use an *inclusive or*. The statement "I will go to a movie or I will read a book" means I will either go to a movie, or read a book, or do both. Hence, in logic, p or q, symbolized $p \vee q$, is defined to be false if both p and q are false and true in all other cases. This is summarized in Table 1-13.

Table 1-12

p	q	Conjunction $p \wedge q$
T	T	T
T	F	F
F	T	F
F	F	F

Table 1-13

p	q	Disjunction $p \vee q$
T	T	T
T	F	T
F	T	T
F	F	F

EXAMPLE 1-14

Classify each of the following as true or false.

$$p: 2 + 3 = 5. \qquad q: 2 \cdot 3 = 6. \qquad r: 5 + 3 = 9.$$

a. $p \wedge q$
b. $q \vee r$

Solution   **a.** p is true and q is true, so $p \wedge q$ is true.

b. q is true and r is false, so $q \vee r$ is true.

Truth tables are used not only to summarize the truth values of compound statements; they also are used to determine if two statements are logically equivalent. Two statements

logically equivalent

are **logically equivalent** if, and only if, they have the same truth values. If p and q are logically equivalent, we write $p \equiv q$.

Conditionals and Biconditionals

conditionals ◆ implications

hypothesis ◆ conclusion

Statements expressed in the form "if p, then q" are called **conditionals**, or **implications**, and are denoted by $p \rightarrow q$. Such statements also can be read "p implies q." The "if" part of a conditional is the **hypothesis** of the implication and the "then" part is the **conclusion**.

Many types of statements can be put in "if-then" form. An example follows:

Statement: All equilateral triangles have acute angles.

If-then form: If a triangle is equilateral, then it has acute angles.

An implication may also be thought of as a promise. Suppose Betty makes the promise, "If I get a raise, then I will take you to dinner." If Betty keeps her promise, the implication is true; if Betty breaks her promise, the implication is false. Consider the following four possibilities:

	p	q
(1)	T	T Betty gets the raise; she takes you to dinner.
(2)	T	F Betty gets the raise; she does not take you to dinner.
(3)	F	T Betty does not get the raise; she takes you to dinner.
(4)	F	F Betty does not get the raise; she does not take you to dinner.

The only case in which Betty breaks her promise is when she gets her raise and fails to take you to dinner, case (2). If she does not get the raise, she can either take you to dinner or not without breaking her promise. The definition of implication is summarized in Table 1-14. Observe that the only case for which the implication is false is when p is true and q is false.

An implication can be worded in several equivalent ways, as follows:

1. If the sun shines, then the swimming pool is open. (If p, then q.)
2. If the sun shines, the swimming pool is open. (If p, q.)
3. The swimming pool is open if the sun shines. (q if p.)
4. The sun is shining implies the swimming pool is open. (p implies q.)
5. The sun is shining only if the pool is open. (p only if q.)
6. The sun's shining is a sufficient condition for the swimming pool to be open. (p is a sufficient condition for q.)
7. The swimming pool's being open is a necessary condition for the sun to be shining. (q is a necessary condition for p.)

Any implication $p \rightarrow q$ has three related implication statements, as follows:

Statement:	If p, then q.	$p \rightarrow q$
Converse:	If q, then p.	$q \rightarrow p$
Inverse:	If not p, then not q.	$\sim p \rightarrow \sim q$
Contrapositive:	If not q, then not p.	$\sim q \rightarrow \sim p$

Table 1-14

p	q	Implication $p \rightarrow q$
T	T	T
T	F	F
F	T	T
F	F	T

EXAMPLE 1-15

Write the converse, the inverse, and the contrapositive for the following statement:
If I am in San Francisco, then I am in California.

Solution

Converse:	If I am in California, then I am in San Francisco.
Inverse:	If I am not in San Francisco, then I am not in California.
Contrapositive:	If I am not in California, then I am not in San Francisco.

Example 1-15 can be used to show that if an implication is true, its converse and inverse are not necessarily true. However, the contrapositive is true. Let's check these observations on the following: *If a number is a natural number, the number is not 0.* We check the truth of the converse, inverse, and contrapositive.

Inverse: *If a number is not a natural number, then it is 0.* This is false, since ⁻6 is not a natural number but it also is not 0.

Converse: *If a number is not 0, then it is a natural number.* This is false, since ⁻6 is not 0 but neither is it a natural number.

Contrapositive: *If a number is 0, then it is not a natural number.* This is true.

The contrapositive of the last statement is the original statement. Hence the above discussion suggests that if $p \rightarrow q$ is true, its contrapositive $\sim q \rightarrow \sim p$ is also true and if the contrapositive is true, the original statement must be true. It follows that a statement and its contrapositive cannot have opposite truth values. We summarize this in the following property.

> ## Property
>
> **Equivalence of a statement and its contrapositive** The implication $p \rightarrow q$ and its contrapositive $\sim q \rightarrow \sim p$ are logically equivalent.

REMARK The fact that a statement and its contrapositive are logically equivalent can also be established by showing that they have the same truth tables.

Connecting a statement and its converse with the connective *and* gives $(p \rightarrow q) \wedge (q \rightarrow p)$. This compound statement can be written as $p \leftrightarrow q$ and usually is read **if and only if** ◆ **biconditional** "*p* **if and only if** *q*." The statement "*p* if and only if *q*" is a **biconditional**. When is a biconditional statement true?

Valid Reasoning

valid reasoning In problem solving, the reasoning is said to be **valid** if the conclusion follows unavoidably from true hypotheses. Note that if the hypotheses are false, then regardless of the truth value of the conclusion, the truth of the conditional statement forming the argument is true, and the argument is valid. Thus, in all arguments in this section we assume the hypotheses are true. Consider the following example:

Hypotheses: All roses are red.
                        This flower is a rose.

Conclusion: Therefore this flower is red.

Euler diagram The statement "All roses are red" can be written as the implication "If a flower is a rose, then it is red" and pictured with the **Euler diagram** in Figure 1-30.

FIGURE 1-30

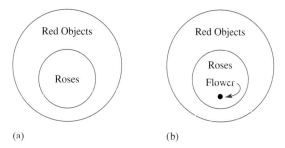

(a) (b)

The information "This flower is a rose" implies that this flower must belong to the circle containing roses, as pictured in Figure 1-30(b). This flower also must belong to the circle containing red objects. Thus the reasoning is valid because it is impossible to draw a picture that satisfies the hypotheses and contradicts the conclusion.

Consider the following argument with true hypotheses:

Hypotheses:　　All elementary school teachers are mathematically literate.
　　　　　　　Some mathematically literate people are not children.

Conclusion:　　Therefore no elementary school teacher is a child.

Let E be the set of elementary school teachers, M be the set of mathematically literate people, and C be the set of children. Then the statement "All elementary school teachers are mathematically literate" can be pictured as in Figure 1-31(a). The statement "Some mathematically literate people are not children" can be pictured in several ways. Three of these are illustrated in Figure 1-31(b) through (d).

According to Figure 1-31(d), it is possible that some elementary school teachers are children, and yet the given statements are satisfied. Therefore the conclusion that "No elementary school teacher is a child" does not follow from the given hypotheses. Hence, the reasoning is not valid.

FIGURE 1-31

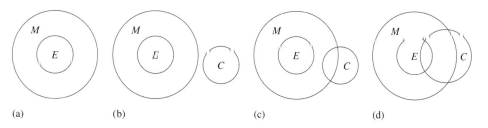

(a)　　　　　(b)　　　　　(c)　　　　　(d)

If only one picture can be drawn to satisfy the hypotheses of an argument and contradict the conclusion, the argument is not valid. However, to show that an argument is valid, *all* possible pictures must show that there are no contradictions. There must be no way to satisfy the hypotheses and contradict the conclusion if the argument is valid.

E X A M P L E
1–16

Determine if the following argument is valid:

Hypotheses: In Washington, D.C., all lobbyists wear suits.
                        No one in Washington, D.C., over 6 ft tall wears a suit.

Conclusion: Persons over 6 ft tall are not lobbyists in Washington, D.C.

Solution   If *L* represents the lobbyists in Washington, D.C., and *S* the people who wear suits, the first hypothesis is pictured as shown in Figure 1-32(a). If *W* represents the people in Washington, D.C., over 6 ft tall, the second hypothesis is pictured in Figure 1-32(b). Because people over 6 ft tall are outside the circle representing suit wearers and lobbyists are in the circle *S*, the conclusion is valid and no person over 6 ft tall is a lobbyist in Washington, D.C.

FIGURE 1-32

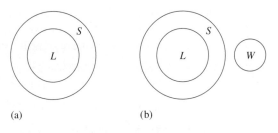

(a)   (b)

direct reasoning
law of detachment/
modus ponens

A different method for determining whether an argument is valid uses **direct reasoning** and a form of argument called the **law of detachment** (or *modus ponens*). For example, assume the following are true statements:

If the sun is shining, then we shall take a trip.

The sun is shining.

Using these two statements, we can conclude that we shall take a trip. In general, the law of detachment is stated as follows:

If the statement "if p, then q" is true, and p is true, then q must be true.

E X A M P L E
1–17

Determine whether the following argument is valid if the hypotheses are true:

Hypotheses: If you eat spinach, then you will be strong.
                        You eat spinach.

Conclusion: Therefore you will be strong.

Solution   Using the law of detachment, we see that the conclusion is valid.

indirect reasoning
modus tollens

A different type of reasoning, **indirect reasoning**, uses a form of argument called *modus tollens*. For example, consider the following true statements:

If a figure is a square, then it is a rectangle.

The figure is not a rectangle.

The conclusion is that the figure cannot be a square.
Modus tollens can be interpreted as follows:

> *If we have a conditional accepted as true, and we know the conclusion is false, then the hypothesis must be false.*

E X A M P L E
1-18

Determine conclusions for each of the following pairs of true statements:

a. If a person lives in Boston, then the person lives in Massachusetts. Jessica does not live in Massachusetts.
b. If $x = 3$, then $2x \neq 7$. We know that $2x = 7$.

Solution   **a.** Jessica does not live in Boston.
               b. $x \neq 3$.

chain rule   The final reasoning argument to be considered here involves the **chain rule**. Consider the following statements:

If I save, I will retire early.

If I retire early, I will play golf.

What is the conclusion? The conclusion is that if I save, I will play golf. In general, the chain rule can be stated as follows:

> *If "if p, then q" and "if q, then r" are true, then "if p, then r" is true.*

People often make invalid conclusions based on advertising or other information. Consider, for example, the true statement "Healthy people eat Super-Bran cereal." Are the following conclusions valid?

If a person eats Super-Bran cereal, then the person is healthy.

If a person is not healthy, the person does not eat Super-Bran cereal.

If the original statement is denoted by $p \rightarrow q$, where p is "a person is healthy" and q is "a person eats Super-Bran cereal," then the first conclusion is the converse of $p \rightarrow q$, that is, $q \rightarrow p$, and the second conclusion is the inverse of $p \rightarrow q$, that is, $\sim p \rightarrow \sim q$. Hence, neither is valid.

E X A M P L E
1-19

Determine conclusions for the following true statements:

a. If a triangle is equilateral, then it is isosceles. If a triangle is isosceles, it has at least two congruent sides.
b. If natural numbers are whole numbers, then natural numbers are integers. If numbers are integers, then the numbers are rational numbers. If numbers are rational numbers, then the numbers are real numbers.

Solution   **a.** If a triangle is equilateral, then it has at least two congruent sides.
               b. If a number is a whole number, then it is a real number.

O N G O I N G   A S S E S S M E N T   1 - 4

1. Determine which of the following are statements and then classify each statement as true or false:
   a. $2 + 4 = 8$.   b. Shut the window.
   c. Los Angeles is a state.   d. He is in town.
   e. What time is it?   f. $5x = 15$.
   g. $3 \cdot 2 = 6$.   h. $2x^2 > x$.
   i. This statement is false. j. Stay put!

2. Use quantifiers to make each of the following true, where x is a natural number:
   a. $x + 8 = 11$.
   b. $x + 0 = x$.
   c. $x^2 = 4$.
   d. $x + 1 = x + 2$.
   e. $x + 3 = 3 + x$.
   f. $3(x + 2) = 12$.
   g. $5x + 4x = 9x$.

3. Use quantifiers to make each equation in problem 2 false.

4. Write the negation of each of the following statements:
   a. This book has 500 pages.
   b. Six is less than 8.
   c. $3 \cdot 5 = 15$.
   d. Some people have blond hair.
   e. All dogs have 4 legs.
   f. Some cats do not have 9 lives.
   g. All squares are rectangles.
   h. Not all rectangles are squares.

5. Complete each of the following truth tables:
   a.

p	$\sim p$	$\sim(\sim p)$
T		
F		

   b.

p	$\sim p$	$p \vee \sim p$	$p \wedge \sim p$
T			
F			

   c. Based on part (a), is p logically equivalent to $\sim(\sim p)$?
   d. Based on part (b), is $p \vee \sim p$ logically equivalent to $p \wedge \sim p$?

6. If q stands for "This course is easy" and r stands for "Lazy students do not study," write each of the following in symbolic form:
   a. This course is easy, and lazy students do not study.
   b. Lazy students do not study, or this course is not easy.
   c. It is false that both this course is easy and lazy students do not study.
   d. This course is not easy.

7. If p is false and q is true, find the truth values for each of the following:
   a. $p \wedge q$ b. $p \vee q$ c. $\sim p$ d. $\sim q$
   e. $\sim(\sim p)$ f. $\sim p \vee q$ g. $p \wedge \sim q$ h. $\sim(p \vee q)$
   i. $\sim(\sim p \wedge q)$ j. $\sim q \wedge \sim p$

8. Find the truth value for each statement in problem 7 if p is false and q is false.

9. For each of the following, is the pair of statements logically equivalent?
   a. $\sim(p \vee q)$ and $\sim p \vee \sim q$ b. $\sim(p \vee q)$ and $\sim p \wedge \sim q$
   c. $\sim(p \wedge q)$ and $\sim p \wedge \sim q$ d. $\sim(p \wedge q)$ and $\sim p \vee \sim q$

10. Complete the following truth table:

p	q	$\sim p$	$\sim q$	$\sim p \vee \sim q$
T	T			
T	F			
F	T			
F	F			

11. Restate the following in a logically equivalent form:
    a. It is not true that today is Wednesday and the month is June.
    b. It is not true that yesterday I both ate breakfast and watched television.
    c. It is not raining, or it is not July.

12. Write each of the following in symbolic form if p is the statement "It is raining" and q is the statement "The grass is wet."
    a. If it is raining, then the grass is wet.
    b. If it is not raining, then the grass is wet.
    c. If it is raining, then the grass is not wet.
    d. The grass is wet if it is raining.
    e. The grass is not wet implies that it is not raining.
    f. The grass is wet if, and only if, it is raining.

13. For each of the following implications, state the converse, inverse, and contrapositive:
    a. If $x = 5$, then $2x = 10$.
    b. If you do not like this book, then you do not like mathematics.
    c. If you do not use Ultra Brush toothpaste, then you have cavities.
    d. If you are good at logic, then your grades are high.

14. Iris makes the true statement, "If it rains, then I am going to the movies." Does it follow logically that if it does not rain, then Iris does not go to the movies?

15. Consider the statement "If every digit of a number is 6, then the number is divisible by 3." Which of the following is logically equivalent to the statement?
    a. If every digit of a number is not 6, then the number is not divisible by 3.
    b. If a number is not divisible by 3, then some digit of the number is not 6.
    c. If a number is divisible by 3, then every digit of the number is 6.

16. Write a statement logically equivalent to the statement "If a number is a multiple of 8, then it is a multiple of 4."

17. Investigate the validity of each of the following arguments:
    a. All women are mortal.
       Hypatia was a woman.
       Therefore Hypatia was mortal.
    b. All squares are quadrilaterals.
       All quadrilaterals are polygons.
       Therefore all squares are polygons.
    c. All teachers are intelligent.
       Some teachers are rich.
       Therefore some intelligent people are rich.
    d. If a student is a freshman, then the student takes mathematics.
       Jane is a sophomore.
       Therefore Jane does not take mathematics.
18. For each of the following, form a conclusion that follows logically from the given statements:
    a. All college students are poor.
       Helen is a college student.
    b. Some freshmen like mathematics.
       All people who like mathematics are intelligent.
    c. If I study for the final, then I will pass the final.
       If I pass the final, then I will pass the course.
       If I pass the course, then I will look for a teaching job.
    d. Every equilateral triangle is isosceles.
       There exist triangles that are equilateral.
19. Write the following in if-then form:
    a. Every figure that is a square is a rectangle.
    b. All integers are rational numbers.
    c. Polygons with exactly 3 sides are triangles.
    d. It rains only if it is cloudy.
20. Write two logical equivalences discovered in problem 9(a) through (d). These equivalences are called DeMorgan's laws for *and* and *or*.

Communication

21. Translate each of the following statements into symbolic form. Give the meanings of the symbols that you use.
    a. If Mary's little lamb follows her to school, then its appearance there will break the rules and Mary will be sent home.
    b. If it is not the case that Jack is nimble and quick, then Jack will not make it over the candlestick.
    c. If the apple had not hit Isaac Newton on the head, then the laws of gravity would not have been discovered.

Open-Ended

22. Give two examples from mathematics for each of the following:
    a. A statement and its converse are true.
    b. A statement is true, but its converse is false.
    c. An "if and only if" true statement.
    d. An "if and only if" false statement.

Cooperative Learning

23. Each person in a group makes 5 statements similar to the ones in Examples 1-16 through 1-19 but concerning mathematical objects, each with a valid or invalid conclusion. The statements should be as varied as possible. Each group member exchanges his or her statements with another person—not revealing which are valid and which are not—and determines which of the other person's statements are valid and which are not. The two group members compare their answers and discuss any discrepancies.
24. Discuss the paradox arising from the following:
    a. This textbook is 1000 pages long.
    b. The author of this textbook is Dante.
    c. The statements (a), (b), and (c) are all false.

Hint for Solving the Preliminary Problem

The easiest way to find a solution is to build a table of perfect squares, or square numbers, and to look at the digits in the squares. This will not automatically find the correct answer, nor will it prove that the answer is what you find, but it is a good start for making a conjecture about the ones digit.

To argue that your conjecture is correct, consider all of the squares of the single digits and whether the tens digit is even or odd. Then consider all natural numbers with two or more digits and their squares. What digit determines the ones digit of the squares? How many cases do we really have to think about in proving this answer?

QUESTIONS FROM THE CLASSROOM

1. A student claims she checked that $n^{50} > 2^n$ (the symbol $>$ designates "greater than") for $n = 1, 2, 3, \ldots, 50$. Hence, she claims that $n^{50} > 2^n$ should be true for all values of n. How do you respond?

2. A student says she read that Thomas Robert Malthus (1766–1834), a renowned British economist and demographer, claimed that the increase of population will take place, if unchecked, in a geometric sequence, while the supply of food will increase in only an arithmetic sequence. This theory implies that population increases faster than food production. The student is wondering why. How do you respond?

3. A student claims that the sequence 6, 6, 6, 6, 6, ... never changes, so it is neither arithmetic nor geometric. How do you respond?

4. A student claims that two terms are enough to determine any sequence. For example, 3, 6, ... means the sequence would be 3, 6, 9, 12, 15, ... What is your response?

5. A student claims that algebra cannot be taught to students before grade 8. How do you respond?

6. A student says that if the hypothesis is false, an argument cannot be valid. How do you respond?

CHAPTER OUTLINE

I. Mathematical patterns
   A. Patterns are an important part of problem solving.
   B. Patterns are used in **inductive reasoning** to form conjectures. Inductive reasoning is the method of making generalizations based on observations and patterns. A **conjecture** is a statement that is thought to be true but that has not yet been proved to be true or false.
   C. A **sequence** is a group of terms in a definite order.
      1. **Arithmetic sequence:** Each successive term is obtained from the previous one by the addition of a fixed number called the **difference**. The nth term is given by $a + (n - 1)d$, where a is the first term and d is the difference.
      2. **Geometric sequence:** Each successive term is obtained from its predecessor by multiplying it by a fixed number called the **ratio**. The nth term is given by ar^{n-1}, where a is the first term and r is the ratio.
      3. $a^n = \underbrace{a \cdot a \cdot a \cdot a \cdot a \cdot \ldots \cdot a}_{n \text{ terms}}$, where $n \neq 0$.
      4. $a^0 = 1$, where a is a natural number.
      5. Finding differences for a sequence is one technique for finding the next terms.
II. Problem solving
   A. Problem solving can be guided by the following four-step process:
      1. Understanding the problem
      2. Devising a plan
      3. Carrying out the plan
      4. Looking back
   B. Important problem-solving strategies include the following:
      1. Look for a pattern.
      2. Make a table.

   3. Examine a simpler or special case of the problem to gain insight into the solution of the original problem.
   4. Identify a subgoal.
   5. Examine related problems and determine if the same technique can be applied.
   6. Work backward.
   7. Write an equation.
   8. Draw a diagram.
   9. Guess and check.
   10. Use indirect reasoning.
   11. Use direct reasoning.
   C. Beware of mind sets!
III. Properties of equality
   A. **Addition property:** For numbers a, b, and c, if $a = b$, then $a + c = b + c$.
   B. **Multiplication property:** For numbers a, b, and c, if $a = b$, then $ac = bc$.
   C. **Cancellation properties:** For numbers a, b, and c
      1. if $a + c = b + c$, then $a = b$.
      2. if $c \neq 0$, and $ac = bc$, then $a = b$.
   D. Equality is not affected if we substitute a number for its equal.
*IV. Logic
   A. A **statement** is a sentence that is either true or false but not both.
   B. The **negation** of a statement is a statement with the opposite truth value of the given statement. The negation of p is denoted by $\sim p$.
   C. The **compound statement** $p \wedge q$ is the **conjunction** of p and q and is defined to be true if, and only if, both p and q are true.
   D. The compound statement $p \vee q$ is the **disjunction** of p and q and is true if either p or q or both are true.
   E. Statements of the form "if p, then q" are **conditionals** or **implications** and are false only if p is true and q is false.

F. Given the conditional $p \rightarrow q$, the following can be found:
   1. **Converse:** $q \rightarrow p$
   2. **Inverse:** $\sim p \rightarrow \sim q$
   3. **Contrapositive:** $\sim q \rightarrow \sim p$

G. If $p \rightarrow q$ is true, the converse and the inverse are not necessarily true, but the contrapositive is true.

H. Two statements are **logically equivalent** if, and only if, they have the same truth value. An implication and its contrapositive are logically equivalent.

I. The statement "$p \rightarrow q$ and $q \rightarrow p$" is written $p \leftrightarrow q$, a **biconditional**, and referred to as "p if and only if q."

J. Laws to determine the validity of arguments include the **law of detachment, *modus tollens,*** and the **chain rule**.

CHAPTER REVIEW

1. List three more terms that complete a pattern in each of the following:
   a. 0, 1, 3, 6, 10, _____, _____, _____
   b. 52, 47, 42, 37, _____, _____, _____
   c. 6400, 3200, 1600, 800, _____, _____, _____
   d. 1, 2, 3, 5, 8, 13, _____, _____, _____
   e. 2, 5, 8, 11, 14, _____, _____, _____
   f. 1, 4, 16, 64, _____, _____, _____
   g. 0, 4, 8, 12, _____, _____, _____
   h. 1, 8, 27, 64, _____, _____, _____

2. Classify each sequence in problem 1 as arithmetic, geometric, or neither.

3. Find a possible nth term in each of the following:
   a. 5, 8, 11, 14, . . .
   b. 0, 7, 26, 63, . . .
   c. 3, 9, 27, 81, 243, . . .

4. Find the first five terms of the sequences whose nth term is given as follows:
   a. $3n - 2$ b. $n^2 + n$ c. $4n - 1$

5. Find the following sums:
   a. $2 + 4 + 6 + 8 + 10 + \ldots + 200$
   b. $51 + 52 + 53 + 54 + \ldots + 151$

6. a. Determine a possible pattern in the sequence 1, 12, 123, 1234, 12345, ...
   b. If the tenth term of the sequence in part (a) is supposed to have 10 digits, what is the tenth term? Explain your reasoning.

7. Complete the following magic square; that is, complete the square so that the sum in each row, column, and diagonal is the same.

16	3	2	13
	10		
9		7	12
4		14	

8. How many people can be seated at 12 square tables lined up end to end if each table individually holds four persons?

9. A shirt and a tie sell for $9.50. The shirt costs $5.50 more than the tie. What is the cost of the tie?

10. If fence posts are to be placed in a row 5 m apart, how many posts are needed for 100 m of fence?

11. A total of 129 players entered a single-elimination handball tournament. In the first round of play, the top-seeded player received a bye and the remaining 128 players played in 64 matches. Thus 65 players entered the second round of play. How many matches must be played to determine the tournament champion?

12. Given the six numbers 3, 5, 7, 9, 11, and 13, pick five of them that when multiplied together give 19,305.

13. If a complete turn of a car tire moves a car forward 6 ft, how many turns of the tire occur before the tire goes off its 50,000-mi warranty?

14. The members of Mrs. Grant's class are standing in a circle; they are evenly spaced and are numbered in order. The student with number 7 is standing directly across from the student with number 17. How many students are in the class?

15. A carpenter has three large boxes. Inside each large box are two medium-sized boxes. Inside each medium-sized box are five small boxes. How many boxes are there altogether?

16. How many triangles are there in the following figure? Explain your reasoning.

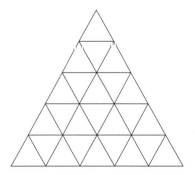

17. Mary left her home and averaged 16 km/hr riding her bicycle on an uphill trip to Larry's house. On the return trip over the same route, she averaged 20 km/hr. If it took 4 hr to make the return trip, how much cycling time did the entire trip take?

18. The perimeter of a rectangle is 68 ft. The length of the rectangle is 4 ft more than twice the width. Find the length and width of the rectangle. Explain your reasoning.

19. An ant farm can hold a total of 100,000 ants. If the farm held 1500 ants on the first day, 3000 ants on the second day, 6000 ants on the third day, and so on in this manner, in how many days will the farm be full?

20. Toma's team entered a mathematics contest where teams of students compete by answering questions that are worth either 3 points or 5 points. No partial credit was given. Toma's team scored 44 points on 12 questions. How many 5-point questions did the team answer correctly?

21. There are three baskets sitting next to each other on a high shelf so that you cannot see the contents of any basket. Under the first basket is a sign that says APPLES. Under the second basket is a sign that says ORANGES. And under the third basket is a sign that says APPLES AND ORANGES. Each basket is incorrectly labeled. One basket contains all apples, one all oranges, and one a combination of apples and oranges. Is it possible to reach up on the shelf and without looking into any of the baskets select one piece of fruit and on the basis of knowing what that piece of fruit is correctly label all three baskets? Explain your reasoning.

22. Solve the following for *x* if possible:
    a. $3x + 5 = 17$
    b. $4 - 2x = 0$
    c. $3(x + 1) = 3x$

*23. Which of the following are statements?
    a. The moon is inhabited.
    b. $3 + 5 = 8$
    c. $x + 7 = 15$
    d. Some women have Ph.D.s in mathematics.

*24. Negate each of the following:
    a. Some women smoke.
    b. $3 + 5 = 8$
    c. All heavy-metal rock is loud.
    d. Beethoven wrote only classical music.

*25. Write the converse, inverse, and contrapositive of the following: If we have a rock concert, someone will faint.

*26. Find valid conclusions for the following true hypotheses.
    a. All Americans love Mom and apple pie.
       Joe Czernyu is an American.
    b. Steel eventually rusts.
       The Statue of Liberty has a steel structure.
    c. Albertina passed Math 100 or Albertina dropped out.
       Albertina did not dropout.

*27. Write the following argument symbolically and then determine its validity:
    If you are fair-skinned, you will sunburn.
    If you sunburn, you will not go to the dance.
    If you do not go to the dance, your parents will want to know why you didn't go to the dance.
    Your parents do not want to know why you didn't go to the dance.
    Therefore you are not fair-skinned.

SELECTED BIBLIOGRAPHY

Bishop, J., A. Otto, and C. Lubinski. "Promoting Algebraic Reasoning Using Student Thinking." *Mathematics Teaching in the Middle School* 6 (May 2001): 508–514.

Bradley, E. "Is Algebra in the Cards?" *Mathematics Teaching in the Middle School* 2 (May 1997): 398–403.

Chappell, M., and M. Strutchens. "Creating Connections: Promoting Algebraic Thinking with Concrete Models." *Mathematics Teaching in the Middle School* 7 (September 2001): 20–25.

Curcio, F. "Exploring Patterns in Nonroutine Problems." *Mathematics Teaching in the Middle School* 2 (February 1997): 262–269.

Day, R., and G. Jones. "Building Bridges to Algebraic Thinking." *Mathematics Teaching in the Middle School* 2 (February 1997): 208–212.

Ferrini-Mundy, J., G. Lappan, and E. Phillips. "Experiences with Patterning." *Teaching Children Mathematics* 3 (February 1997): 262–268.

Fouche, K. "Algebra for Everyone: Start Early." *Mathematics Teaching in the Middle School* 2 (February 1997): 226–229.

Koirala, H., and P. Goodwin. "Teaching Algebra in the Middle Grades Using Mathmagic." *Mathematics Teaching in the Middle School* 5 (May 2000): 562–566.

Malloy, C. "Mathematics Projects Promote Students' Algebraic Thinking." *Mathematics Teaching in the Middle School* 2 (February 1997): 282–288.

Mikusa, M. G. "Problem Solving Is More Than Solving Problems." *Mathematics Teaching in the Middle School* 4 (November 1998): 20–25.

Norman, F. "Figurate Numbers in the Classroom." *Arithmetic Teacher* 38 (March 1991): 42–45.

Olson, J. "Guess the Weight!" *Teaching Children Mathematics* 5 (October 1998): 104.

———."Marbles." *Teaching Children Mathematics* 6 (January 2000): 306.

Olson, M. "Darts, Anyone?" *Teaching Children Mathematics* 5 (May 1999): 532.

———."Stair Skipping." *Teaching Children Mathematics* 6 (April 2000): 511.

———."Wrist Bands." *Teaching Children Mathematics* 5 (December 1998): 242.

Olson, M., and J. Olson. "Puzzling Prices." *Teaching Children Mathematics* 7 (April 2001): 474.

Ploger, D. "Spreadsheets, Patterns, and Algebraic Thinking." *Teaching Children Mathematics* 3 (February 1997): 330–334.

Polya, G. *How to Solve It.* Princeton, N.J.: Princeton University Press, 1957.

———. *Mathematical Discovery, Combined Edition.* New York: John Wiley & Sons, Inc., 1981.

Rubenstein, R. "Building Explicit and Recursive Forms of Patterns with the Function Game." *Mathematics Teaching in the Middle School* 7 (April 2002): 426–431.

Sakshaug, L. "Take Two: Fair or Unfair." *Teaching Children Mathematics* 5 (January 1999): 286.

———. "The Orange Game." *Teaching Children Mathematics* 5 (April 1999): 488.

———. "The Talking Club." *Teaching Children Mathematics* 6 (October 1999): 114.

Strutchens, M. "Multicultural Literature as a Context for Problem Solving: Children and Parents Learning Together." *Teaching Children Mathematics* 8 (April 2002): 448–454.

Swarthout, M. "Great Garlands." *Teaching Children Mathematics* 8 (December 2001): 217.

Thompson, A. "On Patterns, Conjectures, and Proof: Developing Students." *Arithmetic Teacher* 33 (September 1985): 20–23.

Thornton, S. "New Approaches to Algebra: Have We Missed the Point?" *Mathematics Teaching in the Middle School* 6 (March 2001): 388–392.

Usiskin, Z. "Doing Algebra in Grades K–4." *Teaching Children Mathematics* 3 (February 1997): 346–356.

van Reeuwijk, M., and M. Wijers. "Students' Construction of Formulas in Context." *Mathematics Teaching in the Middle School* 2 (February 1997): 230–236.

Verzoni, K. "Turning Students into Problem Solvers." *Mathematics Teaching in the Middle School* 3 (October 1997): 102–107.

–2–
Sets, Whole Numbers, and Functions

Mr. Gonzales' and Ms. Chan's seventh-grade classes in Paxson Middle School have 24 and 25 students, respectively. Linda, a student in Mr. Gonzales' class, claims that the number of school committees that could be formed to contain at least one student from each class is greater than the number of people in the world. Assuming that a committee can have up to 49 students, find the number of committees and determine if Linda is right.

Georg Cantor, in the years from 1871 through 1884, created *set theory*, a new area of mathematics. His theories had a profound effect on research and mathematics teaching.

HISTORICAL
N O T E

Georg Cantor, 1845–1918, was born in St. Petersburg, Russia. His family moved to Frankfurt when he was 11. Against his father's advice, Cantor pursued a career in mathematics and obtained his doctorate in Berlin at age 22. Most of his academic work was spent at the University of Halle. His hope of becoming a professor at the University of Berlin did not materialize because his work gained little recognition during his lifetime.

Cantor's work was praised as an "astonishing product of mathematical thought, one of the most beautiful realizations of human activity."

The languages of set theory and basic set operations clarify and unify many mathematical concepts and are useful for teachers in understanding the mathematics covered in elementary school. Sets and relations between sets form a basis to teach children the *concept* of whole numbers and the concept of "less than" as well as addition, subtraction, and multiplication of whole numbers. After introducing set notation, relations between sets, set operations and their properties, we will show how some of these concepts can be used to understand the concept of a whole number, operations on whole numbers, and the properties of these operations. We also use the concept of a set to define relations and functions.

Your knowledge of set theory should enable you to better understand the elementary school curriculum. The importance of such knowledge is emphasized by the NCTM's *Principles and Standards* in *The Teaching Principle Standard*:

Teachers need several different kinds of mathematical knowledge—knowledge about the whole domain; deep, flexible knowledge about curriculum goals and about the important ideas that are central to their grade level; knowledge about the challenges students are likely to encounter in learning these ideas; knowledge about how the ideas can be represented to teach them effectively; and knowledge about how students' understanding can be assessed. This knowledge helps teachers make curricular judgments, respond to students' questions, and look ahead to where concepts are leading and plan accordingly. (p. 17)

The concept of a function is a fundamental unifying concept in all of mathematics. The Algebra Standard lists "Understand Patterns, Relations, and Functions" in each grade level:

Algebraic concepts can evolve and continue to develop during prekindergarten through grade 2. They will be manifested through work classification, patterns and relations, operations with whole numbers, exploration of function, and step-by-step processes. (p. 91)

For grades 3–5 the *Standards* point out that

Students should investigate numerical and geometric patterns and express them mathematically in words or symbols. They should analyze the structure of the pattern and how it grows or changes, organize this information systematically, and use their analysis to develop generalizations about the mathematical relationship in the pattern. (p. 159)

For grades 6–8 the *Standards* point out that

 The study of patterns and relationships in the middle grades should focus on patterns that relate to linear functions, which arise when there is a constant rate of change. Students should solve problems in which they use tables, graphs, words, and symbolic expressions to represent and examine functions and patterns of change. (p. 223)

2-1 Describing Sets

sets
elements
members

A **set** is understood to be any collection of objects. However, in abstract mathematical logic and set theory, a *set* is an undefined term. Individual objects in a set are **elements,** or **members,** of the set. For example, each letter is an element of the set of letters in the English language.

We use braces to enclose the elements of a set and label the set with a capital letter for easy reference. The set of letters of the English alphabet can be written as

$$A = \{a, b, c, d, e, f, g, h, i, j, k, l, m, n, o, p, q, r, s, t, u, v, w, x, y, z\}.$$

The order in which the elements are written makes no difference, and *each element is listed only once.* For example, the set of letters in the word *book* could be written as $\{b, o, k\}$, $\{o, b, k\}$, or $\{k, o, b\}$.

We symbolize an element belonging to a set by using the symbol $\in$. For example, $b \in A$. If an element does not belong to a set, we use the symbol $\notin$. For example, the fact that A does not contain the Greek letter α (alpha) is written as $\alpha \notin A$.

REMARK   In mathematics, the same letter, one lowercase and the other uppercase cannot be freely interchanged. For example, in the earlier mentioned set A we have $b \in A$ but $B \notin A$.

---

well defined

For a given set to be useful in mathematics, it must be **well defined**; that is, if we are given a set and some particular object, then we must be able to tell whether the object does or does not belong to the set. For example, the set of all citizens of Pasadena, California, who ate rice on January 1, 2003, is well defined. We may not know if a particular resident of Pasadena ate rice or not, but that resident either belongs or does not belong to the set. On the other hand, the set of all tall people is not well defined because we do not know which people qualify as "tall."

natural numbers

We may use sets to define mathematical terms. For example, the set N of **natural numbers** is defined by the following:

$$N = \{1, 2, 3, 4, \ldots \}.$$

Notice in the above set the use of *ellipsis*—three dots that indicate that the sequence continues in the same manner indefinitely.

set-builder notation

Sometimes the individual elements of a set are not known or they are too numerous to list. In these cases, the elements may be indicated by using **set-builder notation**. For example, the set of decimals between 0 and 1 can be written as

$$D = \{x \mid x \text{ is a decimal between 0 and 1}\}.$$

This is read "*D* is the set of all elements *x* such that *x* is a decimal between 0 and 1." The vertical line is read "such that." It would be impossible to list all the elements of *D*. Hence the set-builder notation is indispensable here.

EXAMPLE 2-1

Write the following sets using set-builder notation:

a. $\{2, 4, 6, 8, 10, \dots\}$
b. $\{1, 3, 5, 7, \dots\}$

Solution
a. $\{x \mid x \text{ is an even natural number}\}$. Or because every even natural number can be written as 2 times some natural number, this set can be written as $\{x \mid x = 2n, \text{ and } n \in N\}$ or, in a somewhat simpler form, as $\{2n \mid n \in N\}$.
b. $\{x \mid x \text{ is an odd natural number}\}$. Or because every odd natural number can be written as some even number minus one, this set can be written as $\{x \mid x = 2n - 1, \text{ and } n \in N\}$ or $\{2n - 1 \mid n \in N\}$.

EXAMPLE 2-2

Each of the following sets is described in set-builder notation. Write each of the sets by listing its elements.

a. $A = \{2k + 1 \mid k = 3, 4, 5\}$
b. $B = \{a^2 + b^2 \mid a = 2 \text{ or } 3, \text{ and } b = 2, 3, \text{ or } 4\}$

Table 2-1

k	2k + 1
3	$2 \cdot 3 + 1 = 7$
4	$2 \cdot 4 + 1 = 9$
5	$2 \cdot 5 + 1 = 11$

Solution
a. We substitute $k = 3, 4, 5$ in $2k + 1$ and obtain the corresponding values shown in Table 2-1. Thus $A = \{7, 9, 11\}$.
b. Here $a = 2$ or 3 and $b = 2, 3,$ or 4. Table 2-2 shows all possible combinations of a and b and the corresponding values of $a^2 + b^2$. Thus $B = \{8, 13, 20, 18, 25\}$. Notice that 13 appears twice in the table but only once in the set. Why?

Table 2-2

a \ b	2	3	4
2	$2^2 + 2^2 = 8$	$2^2 + 3^2 = 13$	$2^2 + 4^2 = 20$
3	$3^2 + 2^2 = 13$	$3^2 + 3^2 = 18$	$3^2 + 4^2 = 25$

equal sets   Two sets are **equal** if, and only if, they contain exactly the same elements. The order in which the elements are listed does not matter. If *A* and *B* are equal, written $A = B$, then every element of *A* is an element of *B*, and every element of *B* is an element of *A*. If *A* does not equal *B*, we write $A \neq B$. Consider sets $D = \{1, 2, 3\}$, $E = \{2, 5, 1\}$, and $F = \{1, 2, 5\}$. Sets *D* and *E* are not equal; sets *E* and *F* are equal.

One-to-One Correspondence

one-to-one correspondence

Consider the set of people P = {Tomas, Dick, Mari} and the set of swimming lanes S = {1, 2, 3}. Suppose each person in P is to swim in a lane numbered 1, 2, or 3 so that no two people swim in the same lane. Such a person-lane pairing is a **one-to-one correspondence**. One way to exhibit a one-to-one correspondence is Tomas ↔ 1, Dick ↔ 2, and Mari ↔ 3, as shown in Figure 2-1.

FIGURE 2-1

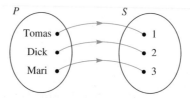

Other possible one-to-one correspondences exist between the sets P and S. There are several schemes for exhibiting them. For example, all six possible one-to-one correspondences between sets P and S can be listed as follows:

1. Tomas ↔ 1   **2.** Tomas ↔ 1   **3.** Tomas ↔ 2
   Dick ↔ 2   Dick ↔ 3   Dick ↔ 1
   Mari ↔ 3   Mari ↔ 2   Mari ↔ 3

4. Tomas ↔ 2   **5.** Tomas ↔ 3   **6.** Tomas ↔ 3
   Dick ↔ 3   Dick ↔ 1   Dick ↔ 2
   Mari ↔ 1   Mari ↔ 2   Mari ↔ 1

Notice that the diagram in (**1**) as well as Figure 2-1 represent a single one-to-one correspondence between the sets P and S. The correspondence Tomas ↔ 1 can also be a one-to-one correspondence but between two different sets, namely the sets {Tomas} and {1}.

> ### Definition of One-to-One Correspondence

If the elements of sets P and S can be paired so that for each element of P there is exactly one element of S and for each element of S there is exactly one element of P, then the two sets P and S are said to be in **one-to-one correspondence**.

NOW TRY THIS 2-1

Consider a set of four people {A, B, C, D} and a set of four swimming lanes {1, 2, 3, 4}.
   a. Exhibit all the one-to-one correspondences between the two sets.
   b. How many such one-to-one correspondences are there?
   c. Conjecture the number of one-to-one correspondences between two sets with five elements each and explain how you arrived at your conjecture.

Another method of demonstrating a one-to-one correspondence is to use a table, such as Table 2-3, where the lane numbers are listed across the top of the table and the possible pairings of swimmers to lanes are listed in the table.

Table 2-3

1	2	3
Tomas	Dick	Mari
Tomas	Mari	Dick
Dick	Tomas	Mari
Dick	Mari	Tomas
Mari	Tomas	Dick
Mari	Dick	Tomas

We can also use a tree diagram to list the possible one-to-one correspondences, as Figure 2-2 shows. To read the tree diagram and see the one-to-one correspondence, we follow each branch. The person occupying a specific lane in a correspondence is listed below the lane number. For example, the top branch gives the pairing (Tomas, 1), (Dick, 2), and (Mari, 3).

FIGURE 2-2

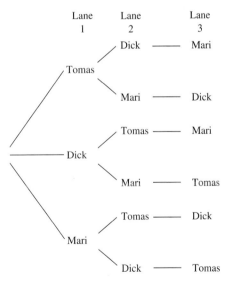

Observe in Figure 2-2 that, in assigning a swimmer to lane 1, we have a choice of three people: Tomas, Dick, or Mari. If we put Tomas in lane 1, then he cannot be in lane 2, and hence the second lane must be occupied by either Dick or Mari. In the same way, we see that if Dick is in lane 1, then there are two choices for lane 2: Tomas or Mari. Similarly, if Mari is in lane 1, then again there are two choices for the second lane: Tomas or Dick. Thus for each of the three ways we can fill the first lane, there are two subsequent ways to fill the second lane, and hence there are $2 + 2 + 2$, or $3 \cdot 2$, or 6 ways to arrange the swimmers in the first two lanes.

Notice that for each arrangement of the swimmers in the first two lanes, there remains only one possible swimmer to fill the third lane. That is, if Mari fills the first lane and Dick fills the second, then Tomas must be in the third. Thus the total number of arrangements for the three swimmers is equal to $3 \cdot 2$, or 6.

Similar reasoning can be used to find how many ice cream arrangements are possible on a two-scoop cone if ten flavors are offered. If we count chocolate and vanilla (chocolate on bottom and vanilla on top) different from vanilla and chocolate (vanilla on bottom and chocolate on top) and allow two scoops to be of the same flavor, we can proceed as follows. There are 10 choices for the first scoop and for each of these 10 choices there are 10 subsequent choices for the second scoop. Thus the total number of arrangements is $10 \cdot 10$, or 100.

The counting argument used to find the number of possible one-to-one correspondences between the set of swimmers and the set of lanes and the previous problem about ice cream scoop arrangements are examples of the Fundamental Counting Principle.

> ## Property

Fundamental Counting Principle If event M can occur in m ways and, after it has occurred, event N can occur in n ways, then event M followed by event N can occur in $m \cdot n$ ways.

NOW TRY THIS 2-2

Extend the Fundamental Counting Principle to any number of events.

Equivalent Sets

equivalent sets

Suppose a room contains 20 chairs and one student is sitting in each chair with no one standing. There is a one-to-one correspondence between the set of chairs and the set of students in the room. In this case, the set of chairs and the set of students are **equivalent sets**.

> ## Definition of Equivalent Sets

Two sets A and B are **equivalent**, written $A \sim B$, if and only if, there exists a one-to-one correspondence between the sets.

The term *equivalent* should not be confused with *equal*. The difference should be made clear by Example 2-3.

EXAMPLE
2-3

Let

$$A = \{p, q, r, s\}, \quad B = \{a, b, c\}, \quad C = \{x, y, z\}, \quad \text{and} \quad D = \{b, a, c\}.$$

Compare the sets, using the terms *equal* and *equivalent*.

Solution   Each set is both equivalent to and equal to itself.

Sets *A* and *B* are not equivalent ($A \nsim B$) and not equal ($A \neq B$).

Sets *A* and *C* are not equivalent ($A \nsim C$) and not equal ($A \neq C$).

Sets *A* and *D* are not equivalent ($A \nsim D$) and not equal ($A \neq D$).

Sets *B* and *C* are equivalent ($B \sim C$) but not equal ($B \neq C$).

Sets *B* and *D* are equivalent ($B \sim D$) and equal ($B = D$).

Sets *C* and *D* are equivalent ($C \sim D$) but not equal ($C \neq D$).

NOW TRY THIS 2-3

If two sets are equivalent, are they necessarily equal? Explain why or why not.

Cardinal Numbers

The concept of one-to-one correspondence can be used to introduce the notion of two sets having the same number of elements. Suppose a child knows how to count only to three. The child might still tell that there are as many fingers on the left hand as on the right hand by matching the fingers on one hand with the fingers on the other hand. Naturally placing the fingers so that the left thumb touches the right thumb, the left index finger touches the right index finger, and so on, exhibits a one-to-one correspondence between the fingers of the two hands. Similarly, without counting, children realize that if every student in a class sits in a chair and no chairs are empty, there are as many chairs as students.

One-to-one correspondence between sets is often used to introduce the concept of a number as follows. (In elementary school, the approach is similar but without the abstract notation.) The five sets $\{a, b\}$, $\{p, q\}$, $\{x, y\}$, $\{b, a\}$, and $\{*, \#\}$ are equivalent to one another and share the property of "twoness." These sets have the same cardinal number, namely, 2. The **cardinal number** of a set *X*, denoted $n(X)$, indicates the number of elements in the set *X*. If $D = \{a, b\}$, the cardinal number of *D* is 2, and we write $n(D) = 2$. If *A* is equivalent to *B*, then *A* and *B* have the same cardinal number; that is, $n(A) = n(B)$.

cardinal number

finite set   A set is a **finite set** if the cardinal number of the set is zero or a natural number. For example, the set of letters in the English alphabet is a finite set because it contains exactly 26 elements. Another way to think of this is that the set of letters in the English alphabet can be put into a one-to-one correspondence with the set $\{1, 2, 3, \ldots, 26\}$.

infinite set   The set of natural numbers *N* is an example of an **infinite set**, a set that is not finite.

The following "Peanuts" cartoon demonstrates how a lack of understanding of set theory concepts can lead to frustration.

NOW TRY THIS 2-4

Determine whether the set of natural numbers N is equivalent to the set of whole numbers $W = \{0, 1, 2, 3, 4, \ldots\}$.

More About Sets

empty set ◆ null set A set that contains no elements has cardinal number 0 and is an **empty**, or **null**, **set**. The empty set is designated by the symbol $\varnothing$ or { }. Three examples of sets with no elements are the following:

$$C = \{x \mid x \text{ was a state of the United States before A.D. 1200}\}$$
$$D = \{x \mid x \text{ is a natural number less than 1}\}$$
$$E = \{x \mid x \text{ is a natural number and } x^2 = 10\}$$

REMARK   The empty set is often incorrectly recorded as $\{\varnothing\}$. This set is not empty but contains one element. Likewise, $\{0\}$ does not represent the empty set. Why?

---

universal set ◆ universe   The **universal set**, or the **universe**, denoted U, is the set that contains all elements being considered in a given discussion. For this reason, you should know what the universal set is in any given problem. Suppose $U = \{x \mid x \text{ is a person living in California}\}$ and $F = \{x \mid x \text{ is a female living in California}\}$. The universal set and set F can be represented by a diagram, as in Figure 2-3(a). The universal set is usually indicated by a large rectangle, and particular sets are indicated by geometric figures inside the rectangle, as shown in **Venn diagram**   Figure 2-3(a). This figure is an example of a **Venn diagram**, named after the Englishman John Venn (1834–1923) who used such diagrams to illustrate ideas in logic. The set of elements in the universe that are not in F is the set of males living in California and is the **complement**   **complement** of F. It is represented by the shaded region in Figure 2-3(b).

FIGURE 2-3

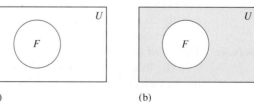

(a)   (b)

> ## Definition of Set Complement

The **complement** of a set F, written $\overline{F}$, is the set of all elements in the universal set U that are not in F; that is, $\overline{F} = \{x \mid x \in U \text{ and } x \notin F\}$.

E X A M P L E
2-4

a. If $U = \{a, b, c, d\}$ and $B = \{c, d\}$, find (i) $\overline{B}$; (ii) $\overline{U}$; (iii) $\overline{\varnothing}$.
b. If $U = \{x \mid x$ is an animal in the zoo$\}$ and $S = \{x \mid x$ is a snake in the zoo$\}$, describe $\overline{S}$.
c. If $U = N$, $E = \{2, 4, 6, 8, \ldots\}$, and $O = \{1, 3, 5, 7, \ldots\}$, find (i) $\overline{E}$; (ii) $\overline{O}$.

Solution   a. (i) $\overline{B} = \{a, b\}$; (ii) $\overline{U} = \varnothing$; (iii) $\overline{\varnothing} = U$
        b. Because the individual animals in the zoo are not known, $\overline{S}$ must be described using set-builder notation:

$$\overline{S} = \{x \mid x \text{ is a zoo animal that is not a snake}\}.$$

        c. (i) $\overline{E} = O$; (ii) $\overline{O} = E$

Subsets

Consider the sets $A = \{1, 2, 3, 4, 5, 6\}$ and $B = \{2, 4, 6\}$. All the elements of B are contained in A and we say that B is a **subset** of A. We write $B \subseteq A$. In general, we have the following definition.

subset

> ## Definition of Subset

B is a **subset** of A, written $B \subseteq A$, if and only if, every element of B is an element of A.

This definition allows B to be equal to A. The definition is written with the phrase "if and only if," which means "if B is a subset of A, then every element of B is an element of A, and if every element of B is an element of A, then B is a subset of A." If both $A \subseteq B$ and $B \subseteq A$, then $A = B$.

proper subset

If B is a subset of A and B is not equal to A, then B is a **proper subset** of A, written $B \subset A$. This means that every element of B is contained in A and there is at least one element of A that is not in B.

To indicate this, sometimes a Venn diagram like the one shown in Figure 2-4 is used.

FIGURE 2-4

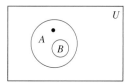

E X A M P L E
2-5

Given $A = \{1, 2, 3, 4, 5\}, B = \{1, 3\}, P = \{x \mid x = 2^n - 1, \text{ and } n \in N\}$:

a. Which sets are subsets of each other?
b. Which sets are proper subsets of each other?

Solution   a. Because $2^1 - 1 = 1, 2^2 - 1 = 3, 2^3 - 1 = 7, 2^4 - 1 = 15$, and $2^5 - 1 = 31$, $P = \{1, 3, 7, 15, 31, \ldots\}$. Thus $B \subseteq P$. Also $B \subseteq A, A \subseteq A, B \subseteq B$, and $P \subseteq P$.
b. $B \subset A$ and $B \subset P$

NOW TRY THIS 2-5

a.   Suppose $A \subset B$. Can we always conclude that $A \subseteq B$?
b.   If $A \subseteq B$, does it follow that $A \subset B$?

When a set A is not a subset of another set B, we write $A \nsubseteq B$. To show that $A \nsubseteq B$, we must find at least one element of A that is not in B. If $A = \{1, 3, 5\}$ and $B = \{1, 2, 3\}$, then A is not a subset of B because 5 is an element of A but not of B. Likewise, $B \nsubseteq A$ because 2 belongs to B but not to A.

Figures 2-4 and 2-5 show three relationships between two sets. In Figure 2-4, $B \subset A$. In Figure 2-5(a), A and B have no elements in common; in (b) A and B have at least one element in common.

FIGURE 2-5

(a)

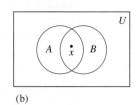
(b)

It is not obvious how the empty set fits the definition of a subset because no elements in the empty set are elements of another set. To investigate this problem, we use the strategies of *indirect reasoning* and *looking at a special case*.

For the set $\{1, 2\}$, either $\varnothing \subseteq \{1, 2\}$ or $\varnothing \nsubseteq \{1, 2\}$. Suppose $\varnothing \nsubseteq \{1, 2\}$. Then there must be some element in $\varnothing$ that is not in $\{1, 2\}$. Because the empty set has no elements, there cannot be an element in the empty set that is not in $\{1, 2\}$. Consequently, $\varnothing \nsubseteq \{1, 2\}$ is false. Therefore the only other possibility, $\varnothing \subseteq \{1, 2\}$, is true.

The same reasoning can be applied in the case of the empty set and any other set. In particular, note that the empty set is a subset of itself and a proper subset of any set other than itself.

Subsets and elements of sets are often confused. We say that $2 \in \{1, 2, 3\}$. But because 2 is not a set, we cannot substitute the symbol $\subseteq$ for $\in$. However, $\{2\} \subseteq \{1, 2, 3\}$ and $\{2\} \subset \{1, 2, 3\}$. Notice that the symbol $\in$ cannot be used between $\{2\}$ and $\{1, 2, 3\}$.

Inequalities: An Application of Set Concepts

The notion of a proper subset and the concept of one-to-one correspondence can be used to define the concept of "less than" among natural numbers. The set $\{a, b, c\}$ has fewer elements than the set $\{w, x, y, z\}$ because when we try to pair the elements of the two sets, as in

$$\{a, b, c\}$$
$$\uparrow \uparrow \uparrow$$
$$\downarrow \downarrow \downarrow$$
$$\{x, y, z, w\},$$

we see that there is an element of the second set that is not paired with an element of the first set. The set $\{a, b, c\}$ is equivalent to a proper subset of the set $\{x, y, z, w\}$.

less than
greater than
In general, if A and B are finite sets, A has fewer elements than B, if A is equivalent to a proper subset of B. We say then that $n(A)$ is **less than** $n(B)$ and write $n(A) < n(B)$. We say that a is **greater than** b, written $a > b$, if and only if $b < a$. Defining the concept of "less than or equal to" in a similar way is explored in the Ongoing Assessment.

We have just seen that if A and B are finite sets and $A \subset B$, then A has fewer elements than B and it is not possible to find a one-to-one correspondence between the sets. Consequently, A and B are not equivalent. However, when both sets are infinite and $A \subset B$, the sets could be equivalent. For example, consider the set N of counting numbers and the set E of even counting numbers. We have $E \subset N$, but it is still possible to find a one-to-one correspondence between the sets. To do so, we correspond each number in set N to a number in set E that is twice as large. That is, $n \in N$ corresponds to $2n \in E$, as shown below.

$$N = \{1, 2, 3, 4, \ 5, \ldots, n, \ldots\}.$$
$$\uparrow \uparrow \uparrow \uparrow \ \uparrow$$
$$\downarrow \downarrow \downarrow \downarrow \ \downarrow \qquad \searrow$$
$$E = \{2, 4, 6, 8, 10, \ldots, 2n, \ldots\}.$$

Notice that in the above correspondence, every element of N corresponds to a unique element in E and, conversely, every element of E corresponds to a unique element in N. For example, 11 in N corresponds to $2 \cdot 11$, or 22, in E. And 100 in E corresponds to $100 \div 2$, or 50, in N. Thus $N \sim E$; that is, N and E are equivalent.

PROBLEM SOLVING   **<u>Passing a Senate Measure</u>**

A committee of senators consists of Abel, Baro, Carni, and Davis. Suppose each member of the committee has one vote and a simple majority is needed to either pass or reject any measure. A measure that is neither passed nor rejected is considered to be blocked and will be voted on again. Determine the number of ways a measure could be passed or rejected and the number of ways a measure could be blocked.

Understanding the Problem   We are asked to determine how many ways the committee of four could pass or reject a proposal and how many ways the committee of four could block a proposal. To pass or reject a proposal requires a winning coalition; that is, a group of senators that can pass or reject the proposal, regardless of what the others do. To block a proposal, there must be a blocking coalition; that is, a group that can prevent any proposal from passing but that cannot reject the measure.

Devising a Plan   To solve the problem, we can *make a list* of subsets of the set of senators. Any subset of the set of senators with three or four members will form a winning coalition. Any subset of the set of senators with exactly two members will form a blocking coalition.

Carrying Out the Plan   We list all subsets of the set $S = \{$Abel, Baro, Carni, Davis$\}$ that have at least three elements and all subsets that have exactly two elements. For ease, we identify the members as follows: *A*—Abel, *B*—Baro, *C*—Carni, *D*—Davis. All the subsets are given next:

$\varnothing$	$\{A, B\}$	$\{A, B, C\}$	$\{A, B, C, D\}$
$\{A\}$	$\{A, C\}$	$\{A, B, D\}$	
$\{B\}$	$\{A, D\}$	$\{A, C, D\}$	
$\{C\}$	$\{B, C\}$	$\{B, C, D\}$	
$\{D\}$	$\{B, D\}$		
	$\{C, D\}$		

There are five subsets with at least three members that can form a winning coalition and pass or reject a measure and six subsets with exactly two members that can block a measure.

Looking Back   Other questions that might be considered include the following:

1. How many minimal winning coalitions are there? In other words, how many subsets are there of which no proper subset could pass a measure?
2. Devise a method to solve this problem without listing all subsets.
3. In "Carrying Out the Plan," 16 subsets of $\{A, B, C, D\}$ are listed. Use that result to systematically list all the subsets of a committee of five senators. Can you find the number of subsets of the five-member committee without actually counting the subsets? ▨

NOW TRY THIS 2-6

Suppose a committee of U.S. senators consists of five members.
a. Compare the number of winning coalitions having exactly four members with the number of senators on the committee. What is the reason for the result?
b. Compare the number of winning coalitions having exactly three members with the number of subsets of the committee having exactly two members. What is the reason for the result?

Number of Subsets of a Set

How many subsets can be made from a set containing n elements? To obtain a general formula, we use the strategy of *trying simpler cases* first.

1. If $P = \{a\}$, then P has two subsets, $\varnothing$ and $\{a\}$.
2. f $Q = \{a, b\}$, then Q has four subsets, $\varnothing$, $\{a\}$, $\{b\}$, and $\{a, b\}$.
3. If $R = \{a, b, c\}$, then R has eight subsets, $\varnothing$, $\{a\}$, $\{b\}$, $\{c\}$, $\{a, b\}$, $\{a, c\}$, $\{b, c\}$, and $\{a, b, c\}$.

Using the information from these cases, we *make a table and search for a pattern*, as in Table 2-4.

Table 2-4

Number of Elements	Number of Subsets
1	2, or 2^1
2	4, or 2^2
3	8, or 2^3
.	.
.	.
.	.

Table 2-4 suggests that for 4 elements, there are 2^4, or 16, subsets. Is this guess correct? If $E = \{a, b, c, d\}$, then all the subsets of $D = \{a, b, c\}$ are also subsets of E. Eight new subsets are also formed by adjoining the element d to each of the eight subsets of D. The eight new subsets are $\{d\}$, $\{a, d\}$, $\{b, d\}$, $\{c, d\}$, $\{a, b, d\}$, $\{a, c, d\}$, $\{b, c, d\}$, and $\{a, b, c, d\}$. Thus there are twice as many subsets of set E (with four elements) as there are of set D (with three elements). Consequently, there are $2 \cdot 8$, or 2^4, subsets of a set with four elements. In a similar way, there are $2 \cdot 2^4$, or 2^5, subsets of a set with five elements. Because including one more element in a finite set doubles the number of possible subsets of the new set, a set with 6 elements will have $2 \cdot 2^5$, or 2^6, subsets and so on. In each case, the number of elements and the power of 2 used to obtain the number of subsets are equal. *Therefore, if there are n elements in a set, 2^n subsets can be formed.* If we apply the above result to the empty set— that is when $n = 0$—then we have $2^0 = 1$ because the empty set has only one subset—itself.

ONGOING ASSESSMENT 2-1

1. Write the following sets by listing their members or using set-builder notation:
   a. The set of letters in the word *mathematics*
   b. The set of states in the continental United States
   c. The set of natural numbers greater than 20
   d. The set of states in the United States that border the Pacific Ocean

2. Rewrite the following using mathematical symbols:
   a. P is equal to the set whose elements are a, b, c, and d.
   b. The set consisting of the elements 1 and 2 is a proper subset of $\{1, 2, 3, 4\}$.
   c. The set consisting of the elements 0 and 1 is not a subset of $\{1, 2, 3, 4\}$.
   d. 0 is not an element of the empty set.
   e. The set whose only element is 0 is not equal to the empty set.

3. Which of the following pairs of sets can be placed in one-to-one correspondence?
   a. $\{1, 2, 3, 4, 5\}$ and $\{m, n, o, p, q\}$
   b. $\{m, a, t, h\}$ and $\{f, u, n\}$
   c. $\{a, b, c, d, e, f, \ldots, m\}$ and $\{1, 2, 3, 4, 5, 6, \ldots, 13\}$

   d. $\{x \mid x$ is a letter in the word *mathematics*$\}$ and $\{1, 2, 3, 4, \ldots, 11\}$
   e. $\{\bigcirc, \triangle\}$ and $\{2\}$

4. How many one-to-one correspondences are there between two sets with
   a. 5 elements each?
   b. 6 elements each?
   c. n elements each?

5. How many one-to-one correspondences are there between the sets $\{x, y, z, u, v\}$ and $\{1, 2, 3, 4, 5\}$ if in each correspondence
   a. x must correspond to 5?
   b. x must correspond to 5 and y to 1?
   c. x, y, and z must correspond to odd numbers?

6. Which of the following represent equal sets?
   $A = \{a, b, c, d\}$ $B = \{x, y, z, w\}$
   $C = \{c, d, a, b\}$ $D = \{x \mid 1 \leq x \leq 4, x \in N\}$
   $E = \varnothing$ $F = \{\varnothing\}$
   $G = \{0\}$ $H = \{\ \}$
   $I = \{x \mid x = 2n + 1, n \in W\}$, where $W = \{0, 1, 2, 3, \ldots\}$
   $J = \{x \mid x = 2n - 1, n \in N\}$

7. Find the cardinal number of each of the following sets:
   a. $\{101, 102, 103, \ldots, 1100\}$
   b. $\{1, 3, 5, \ldots, 1001\}$
   c. $\{1, 2, 4, 8, 16, \ldots, 1024\}$
   d. $\{x \mid x = k^2, k = 1, 2, 3, \ldots, 100\}$
   e. $\{\{1, 2\}, \{3, 4\}, \{5, 6\}\}$
   f. $\{i + j \mid i \in \{1, 2, 3\} \text{ and } j \in \{1, 2, 3\}\}$

8. If U is the set of all college students and A is the set of all college students with a straight-A average, describe $\overline{A}$.

9. Suppose B is a proper subset of C.
   a. If $n(C) = 8$, what is the maximum number of elements in B?
   b. What is the least possible number of elements in B?

10. Suppose C is a subset of D and D is a subset of C.
   a. If $n(C) = 5$, find $n(D)$.
   b. What other relationship exists between sets C and D?

11. Indicate which symbol, $\in$ or $\notin$, makes each of the following statements true:
   a. $0 \underline{\hspace{0.6cm}} \varnothing$
   b. $\{1\} \underline{\hspace{0.6cm}} \{1, 2\}$
   c. $\varnothing \underline{\hspace{0.6cm}} \varnothing$
   d. $\{1, 2\} \underline{\hspace{0.6cm}} \{1, 2\}$
   e. $1024 \underline{\hspace{0.6cm}} \{x \mid x = 2^n \text{ and } n \in N\}$
   f. $3002 \underline{\hspace{0.6cm}} \{x \mid x = 3n - 1 \text{ and } n \in N\}$

12. Indicate which symbol, $\subseteq$ or $\not\subseteq$, makes each part of problem 11 true.

13. Answer each of the following. If your answer is *no*, tell why.
   a. If $A = B$, can we always conclude that $A \subseteq B$?
   b. If $A \subseteq B$, can we always conclude that $A \subset B$?
   c. If $A \subset B$, can we always conclude that $A \subseteq B$?
   d. If $A \subseteq B$, can we always conclude that $A = B$?

14. Use the definition of *less than* to show each of the following:
   a. $2 < 4$ b. $3 < 100$ c. $0 < 3$

15. On a certain senate committee there are seven senators: Abel, Brooke, Cox, Dean, Eggers, Funk, and Gage. Three of these members are to be appointed to a subcommittee. How many possible subcommittees are there?

Communication

16. Which of the following sets are not well defined? Explain.
   a. The set of wealthy school teachers
   b. The set of great books
   c. The set of natural numbers greater than 100
   d. The set of subsets of $\{1, 2, 3, 4, 5, 6\}$
   e. The set $\{x \mid x \neq x \text{ and } x \in N\}$

17. Is $\varnothing$ a proper subset of every nonempty set? Explain your reasoning.

18. Define *less than or equal to* in a way similar to the definition of *less than*.

19. a. Give three examples of sets A and B and a universal set U such that $A \subset B$; find $\overline{A}$ and $\overline{B}$.
   b. Based on your observations, conjecture a relationship between $\overline{B}$ and $\overline{A}$.
   c. Justify your conjecture in (b) using a Venn diagram.

Open-Ended

20. a. Describe three sets of which you are a member.
   b. Describe three sets that have no members.

21. Find an infinite set A such that
   a. $\overline{A}$ is finite.   b. $\overline{A}$ is infinite.

22. Describe two sets from real-life situations such that it is clear from using one-to-one correspondence, and not from counting, that one set has fewer elements than the other.

Cooperative Learning

23. a. Use a calculator if necessary to estimate the time in years it would take a computer to list all the subsets of $\{1, 2, 3, \ldots, 64\}$. Assume the fastest computer can list one subset in approximately 1 microsecond (one millionth of a second).
   b. Estimate the time in years it would take the computer to exhibit all the one-to-one correspondences between the sets $\{1, 2, 3, \ldots, 64\}$ and $\{65, 66, 67, \ldots, 128\}$.

2-2   **Other Set Operations and Their Properties**

FIGURE 2-6

Finding the complement of a set is an operation that acts on only one set at a time. In this section, we consider operations that act on two sets at a time.

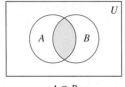

$A \cap B$

intersection

Set Intersection

Suppose that during the fall quarter, a college wants to mail a survey to all its students who are enrolled in both art and biology classes. To do this, the school officials must identify those students who are taking both classes. If A and B are the sets of students taking art courses and the set of students taking biology courses during the fall quarter, respectively, then the desired set of students includes those common to A and B, or the **intersection** of A and B. The intersection of sets A and B is the shaded region in Figure 2-6.

> ## Definition of Set Intersection

FIGURE 2-7

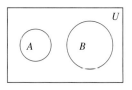

The **intersection** of two sets A and B, written $A \cap B$, is the set of all elements common to both A and B. $A \cap B = \{x \mid x \in A \text{ and } x \in B\}$.

The key word in the definition of *intersection* is *and*. In everyday language, as in mathematics, *and* implies that both conditions must be met. In the above example, the desired set is the set of those students enrolled in both art and biology.

disjoint sets   If sets such as A and B have no elements in common, they are **disjoint sets**. In other words, two sets A and B are disjoint if, and only if, $A \cap B = \varnothing$. For example, the set of males taking biology and the set of females taking biology are disjoint. The Venn diagram in Figure 2-7 implies that sets A and B are disjoint.

**E X A M P L E
2-6**

Find $A \cap B$ in each of the following:

a. $A = \{1, 2, 3, 4\}, B = \{3, 4, 5, 6\}$
b. $A = \{0, 2, 4, 6, \dots\}, B = \{1, 3, 5, 7, \dots\}$
c. $A = \{2, 4, 6, 8, \dots\}, B = \{1, 2, 3, 4, \dots\}$

Solution   **a.** $A \cap B = \{3, 4\}$
             b. $A \cap B = \varnothing$; therefore A and B are disjoint.
             c. $A \cap B = A$ because all the elements of A are also in B.

FIGURE 2-8

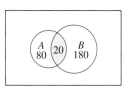

If A represents all students enrolled in art classes and B all students enrolled in biology classes, we may use a Venn diagram, taking into account that some students are enrolled in both subjects. If we know that 100 students are enrolled in art and 200 in biology and that 20 of these students are enrolled in both art and biology, then $100 - 20$, or 80, students are enrolled in art but not in biology and $200 - 20$, or 180, are enrolled in biology but not art. We can record this information as in Figure 2-8. Notice that the total number of students in set A is 100 and the total in set B is 200.

Set Union

If A is the set of students taking art courses during the fall quarter and B is the set of students taking biology courses during the fall quarter, then the set of students taking art or biology or both during the fall quarter is the **union** of sets A and B. The union of sets A and B is pictured in Figure 2-9.

union

FIGURE 2-9

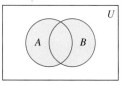

$A \cup B$

> ## Definition of Set Union

The **union** of two sets A and B, written $A \cup B$, is the set of all elements in A or in B, $A \cup B = \{x \mid x \in A \text{ or } x \in B\}$.

The key word in the definition of *union* is *or*. In mathematics, *or* usually means "one or the other or both." This is known as the *inclusive or*.

EXAMPLE 2-7

Find $A \cup B$ for each of the following:

a. $A = \{1, 2, 3, 4\}, B = \{3, 4, 5, 6\}$ **b.** $A = \{0, 2, 4, 6, \dots\}, B = \{1, 3, 5, 7, \dots\}$
c. $A = \{2, 4, 6, 8, \dots\}, B = \{1, 2, 3, 4, \dots\}$

Solution   **a.** $A \cup B = \{1, 2, 3, 4, 5, 6\}$
  b. $A \cup B = \{0, 1, 2, 3, 4, \dots\}$
  c. Because every element of A is already in B we have $A \cup B = B$.

NOW TRY THIS 2-7

Notice that in Figure 2-8, $n(A \cup B) = 80 + 20 + 180 = 280$, but $n(A) + n(B) = 100 + 200 = 300$; hence in general $n(A \cup B) \neq n(A) + n(B)$. Use the concept of intersection of sets to write a formula for $n(A \cup B)$.

Set Difference

If A is the set of students taking art classes during the fall quarter and B is the set of students taking biology classes, then the set of all students taking biology but not art is called the **complement of A relative to B**, or the **set difference** of B and A.

complement of A relative to B
◆ **set difference**

> ### Definition of Relative Complement

The **complement of A relative to B**, written $B - A$, is the set of all elements in B that are not in A; $B - A = \{x \mid x \in B \text{ and } x \notin A\}$.

A Venn diagram representing $B - A$ is shown in Figure 2-10(a). The shaded region represents all the elements that are in B but not in A. A Venn diagram for $B \cap \overline{A}$ is given in Figure 2-10(b). The shaded region represents all the elements that are in B and in $\overline{A}$.

FIGURE 2-10

$B - A$
(a)

$B \cap \overline{A}$
(b)

Notice that $B \cap \overline{A} = B - A$ because $B \cap \overline{A}$ is, by definition of intersection and complement, the set of all elements in B and not in A.

EXAMPLE 2-8

If $U = \{a, b, c, d, e, f, g\}$, $A = \{d, e, f\}$, $B = \{a, b, c, d, e, f\}$, and $C = \{a, b, c,\}$, find each of the following:

a. $A - B$
b. $B - A$
c. $B - C$
d. $C - B$

Solution a. $A - B = \varnothing$
b. $B - A = \{a, b, c\}$
c. $B - C = \{d, e, f\}$
d. $C - B = \varnothing$

Properties of Set Operations

commutative property of set union

commutative property of set intersection

Because the order of elements in a set is not important, $A \cup B$ is equal to $B \cup A$. This is the **commutative property of set union**. It does not matter in which order we write the sets when the union of two sets is involved. Similarly, $A \cap B = B \cap A$. This is the **commutative property of set intersection**.

NOW TRY THIS 2-8

Use Venn diagrams and other means to find whether grouping is important when the same operation is involved. For example, is it always true that $A \cap (B \cap C) = (A \cap B) \cap C$? Similar questions should be investigated involving union and set difference.

EXAMPLE 2-9

Is grouping important when two set operations are involved? For example, is it true that $A \cap (B \cup C) = (A \cap B) \cup C$?

Solution To investigate this, we let $A = \{a, b, c, d\}$, $B = \{c, d, e\}$, and $C = \{d, e, f, g\}$. Then

$$A \cap (B \cup C) = \{a, b, c, d\} \cap (\{c, d, e\} \cup \{d, e, f, g\})$$
$$= \{a, b, c, d\} \cap \{c, d, e, f, g\}$$
$$= \{c, d\}$$
$$(A \cap B) \cup C = (\{a, b, c, d\} \cap \{c, d, e\}) \cup \{d, e, f, g\}$$
$$= \{c, d\} \cup \{d, e, f, g\}$$
$$= \{c, d, e, f, g\}.$$

In this case, $A \cap (B \cup C) \neq (A \cap B) \cup C$. So we have found a counterexample, that is, an example illustrating that the general statement is not always true.

FIGURE 2-11

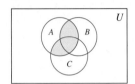

To discover an expression that is equal to $A \cap (B \cup C)$, consider the Venn diagram for $A \cap (B \cup C)$ shown by the shaded region in Figure 2-11. In the figure, $A \cap C$ and $A \cap B$ are subsets of the shaded region. The union of $A \cap C$ and $A \cap B$ is the entire shaded region. Thus $A \cap (B \cup C) = (A \cap B) \cup (A \cap C)$. This property is stated formally below.

> ## Property

Distributive property of set intersection over union   For all sets A, B, and C,
$$A \cap (B \cup C) = (A \cap B) \cup (A \cap C).$$

E X A M P L E
2-10

Use set notation to describe the shaded portions of the Venn diagrams in Figure 2-12.

FIGURE 2-12

(a)

(b)

(c)

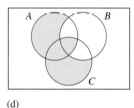

(d)

Solution   The solutions can be described in many different, but equivalent, forms. The following are possible answers:

a. $(A \cup B) - (A \cap B)$, $(A \cup B) \cap \overline{(A \cap B)}$, or $(A - B) \cup (B - A)$
b. $(A \cap B) \cup (B \cap C)$, or $B \cap (A \cup C)$
c. $(A - B) - C$, or $A - (B \cup C)$, or $(A - (A \cap B)) - (A \cap C)$
d. $((A \cup C) - B)) \cup (A \cap B \cap C)$, or $(A - (B \cup C)) \cup (C - (A \cup B)) \cup (A \cap C)$

NOW TRY THIS 2-9

If, on both sides of the equation in the distributive property of set intersection over union, the symbol $\cap$ is replaced by $\cup$ and the symbol $\cup$ is replaced by $\cap$, is the new property true? Explain why or why not.

Using Venn Diagrams as a Problem-Solving Tool

Venn diagrams can be used as a problem-solving tool for modeling information, as shown in the following examples.

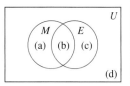

E X A M P L E
2-11

FIGURE 2-13

Suppose M is the set of all students taking mathematics and E is the set of all students taking English. Identify the students described by each region in Figure 2-13.

Solution

Region (a) contains all students taking mathematics but not English.

Region (b) contains all students taking both mathematics and English.

Region (c) contains all students taking English but not mathematics.

Region (d) contains all students taking neither mathematics nor English.

NOW TRY THIS 2-10

The following student page is another example of the use of Venn diagrams in modeling information. Answer questions 48 through 56 on the student page.

Sample School Book Page:
V E N N   D I A G R A M S

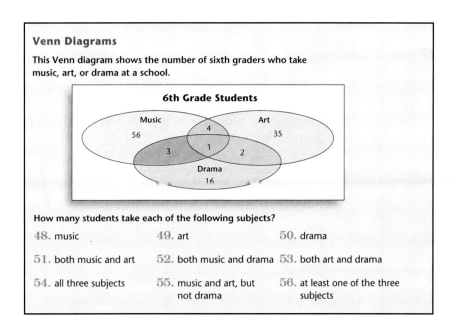

Venn Diagrams

This Venn diagram shows the number of sixth graders who take music, art, or drama at a school.

6th Grade Students

Music   56   4   Art   35

3   1   2

Drama   16

How many students take each of the following subjects?

48. music

49. art

50. drama

51. both music and art

52. both music and drama

53. both art and drama

54. all three subjects

55. music and art, but not drama

56. at least one of the three subjects

Source: McDougal Littell Middle Grades MATH Thematics, Book 1, 2002 (p. 169).

EXAMPLE
2-12

In a survey of 110 college freshmen that investigated their high school backgrounds, the following information was gathered:

> 25 took physics
> 45 took biology
> 48 took mathematics
> 10 took physics and mathematics
> 8 took biology and mathematics
> 6 took physics and biology
> 5 took all 3 subjects

a. How many students took biology but neither physics nor mathematics?
b. How many took physics, biology, or mathematics?
c. How many did not take any of the 3 subjects?

FIGURE 2-14

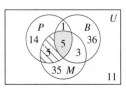

Solution   To solve this problem, we *build a model* using sets. Because there are three distinct subjects, we should use three circles. The maximum number of regions of a Venn diagram determined by three circles is eight. In Figure 2-14, *P* is the set of students taking physics, *B* is the set taking biology, and *M* is the set taking mathematics. The shaded region represents the five students who took all three subjects. The lined region represents the students who took physics and mathematics, but who did not take biology.

In part (a) we are asked for the number of students in the subset of *B* that has no element in common with either *P* or *M*. That is, $B - (P \cup M)$. In part (b) we are asked for the number of elements in $P \cup B \cup M$. Finally, in part (c) we are asked for the number of students in $\overline{P \cup B \cup M}$, or $U - (P \cup B \cup M)$. Our strategy is to find the number of students in each of the eight non-overlapping regions.

One mind set to beware of in this problem is thinking that the 25 who took physics, for example, took only physics. That is not necessarily the case. If those students had been taking only physics, then we should have been told so.

a. Because a total of 10 students took physics and mathematics and 5 of those also took biology, $10 - 5$, or 5, students took physics and math but not biology. Similarly, because 8 students took biology and mathematics and 5 took all 3 subjects, $8 - 5$, or 3, took biology and mathematics but not physics. Also $6 - 5$, or 1, student took physics and biology but not mathematics. To find the number of students who took biology but neither physics nor mathematics, we subtract from 45 (the total number that took biology) the number of those that are in the distinct regions that include biology and other subjects, that is, $1 + 5 + 3$, or 9. Because $45 - 9 = 36$, we know that 36 students took biology but neither physics nor mathematics.

b. To find the number of students in all the distinct regions in *P, M,* or *B*, we proceed as follows. The number of students who took physics but neither mathematics nor biology is $25 - (1 + 5 + 5)$, or 14. The number of students who took mathematics but neither physics nor biology is $48 - (5 + 5 + 3)$, or 35. Hence the number of students who took mathematics, physics, or biology is $35 + 14 + 36 + 3 + 5 + 5 + 1$, or 99.

c. Because the total number of students is 110, the number that did not take any of the three subjects is $110 - 99$, or 11.

Cartesian Products

Cartesian product   Another way to produce a set from two given sets is by forming the **Cartesian product**. This formation pairs the elements of one set with the elements of another set in a specific way. Suppose a person has three pairs of pants, $P = \{$blue, white, green$\}$, and two shirts, $S = \{$blue, red$\}$. According to the Fundamental Counting Principle, there are $3 \cdot 2$, or 6, possible different pant-and-shirt pairs, as shown in Figure 2-15.

FIGURE 2-15

The pairs of pants and shirts form a set of all possible pairs in which the first member of the pair is an element of set P and the second member is an element of set S. The set of all possible pairs is given in Figure 2-15. Because the first component in each pair represents pants and the second component in each pair represents shirts, the order in which the components are written is important. Thus (green, blue) represents green pants and a blue shirt, whereas (blue, green) represents blue pants and a green shirt. Therefore the two pairs represent different outfits. Because the order in each pair is important, the pairs are **ordered pairs**. The positions that the ordered pairs occupy within the set of outfits is immaterial. Only the order of the **components** within each pair is significant.

ordered pairs

components

equality for ordered pairs

The pant-and-shirt pairs suggest the following definition of **equality for ordered pairs**: $(x, y) = (m, n)$ *if, and only if, the first components are equal and the second components are equal.* A set consisting of ordered pairs such as the ones in the pants-and-shirt example is the Cartesian product of the set of pants and the set of shirts. A formal definition follows.

> ### Definition of Cartesian Product

For any sets A and B, the **Cartesian product** of A and B, written $A \times B$, is the set of all ordered pairs such that the first component of each pair is an element of A and the second component of each pair is an element of B.

$$A \times B = \{(x, y) \mid x \in A \text{ and } y \in B\}$$

REMARK $A \times B$ is commonly read as "*A* cross *B*."

EXAMPLE 2-13

If $A = \{a, b, c\}$ and $B = \{1, 2, 3\}$, find each of the following:

a. $A \times B$ **b.** $B \times A$ **c.** $A \times A$

Solution **a.** $A \times B = \{(a, 1), (a, 2), (a, 3), (b, 1), (b, 2), (b, 3), (c, 1), (c, 2), (c, 3)\}$
b. $B \times A = \{(1, a), (1, b), (1, c), (2, a), (2, b), (2, c), (3, a), (3, b), (3, c)\}$
c. $A \times A = \{(a, a), (a, b), (a, c), (b, a), (b, b), (b, c), (c, a), (c, b), (c, c)\}$

It is possible to form a Cartesian product involving the null set. Suppose $A = \{1, 2\}$. Because there are no elements in $\emptyset$, no ordered pairs (x, y) with $x \in A$ and $y \in \emptyset$ are possible, so $A \times \emptyset = \emptyset$. This is true for all sets A. Similarly, $\emptyset \times A = \emptyset$ for all sets A.

There is an analogy between the last equation and the multiplication fact that $0 \cdot a = 0$, where a is a natural number. In Section 2-4 we use the concept of Cartesian product to define multiplication of natural numbers.

ONGOING ASSESSMENT 2-2

1. If $N = \{1, 2, 3, 4, \dots\}$, $A = \{x \mid x = 2n - 1, n \in N\}$, $B = \{x \mid x = 2n, n \in N\}$, and $C = \{x \mid x = 2n + 1, n = 0,$ or $n \in N\}$, find the simplest possible expression for each of the following:
   a. $A \cup C$
   b. $A \cap C$
   c. $A \cup B$
   d. $A \cap B$

2. Use a Venn diagram or any other approach to decide whether the following pairs of sets are equal.
   a. $A \cap B$ and $B \cap A$
   b. $A \cup B$ and $B \cup A$
   c. $A \cup (B \cup C)$ and $(A \cup B) \cup C$
   d. $A \cup \emptyset$ and A
   e. $A \cup A$ and $A \cup \emptyset$
   f. $(A \cap A)$ and $(A \cap \emptyset)$

3. Tell whether each of the following is true or false for all sets A, B, or C. If false, give a counterexample.
   a. $A \cup \emptyset = A$
   b. $A - B = B - A$
   c. $A \cup A = A$
   d. $\overline{A \cap B} = \overline{A} \cap \overline{B}$
   e. $(A \cup B) \cup C = A \cup (B \cup C)$
   f. $(A \cup B) - A = B$
   g. $(A - B) \cup A = (A - B) \cup (B - A)$

4. If $B \subseteq A$, find a simpler expression for each of the following:
   a. $A \cap B$ b. $A \cup B$ c. $B - A$ d. $B \cap \overline{A}$

5. For each of the following, shade the portion of the Venn diagram that illustrates the set:
   a. $\overline{A \cup B}$
   b. $A \cap \overline{B}$
   c. $\overline{A \cap B}$
   d. $(A \cap B) \cup (A \cap C)$
   e. $\overline{A} \cap \overline{B}$
   f. $(A \cup B) \cap \overline{C}$
   g. $(A \cap B) \cup C$
   h. $(\overline{A} \cap B) \cup C$

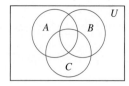

6. If S is a subset of universe U, find each of the following:
   a. $S \cup \overline{S}$ b. $\emptyset \cup S$ c. $\overline{U}$
   d. $\overline{\emptyset}$ e. $S \cap \overline{S}$ f. $\emptyset \cap S$

7. For each of the following conditions, find $A - B$:
   a. $A \cap B = \emptyset$ b. $B = U$
   c. $A = B$ d. $A \subseteq B$

8. a. Give two examples of sets A and B for which $A - B = \emptyset$. Show that in each example $A \subseteq B$.
   b. If for sets A and B we know that $A - B = \emptyset$, is it necessarily true that $A \subseteq B$? Justify your answer.

9. Use set notation to identify each of the following shaded regions:

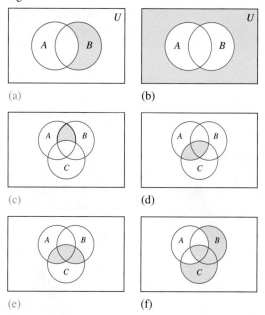

10. In the following, shade the portion of the diagram that represents the given sets:

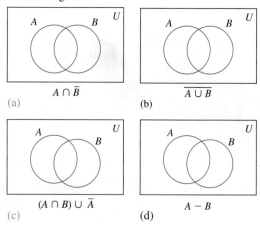

11. Use Venn diagrams to determine if each of the following is true:
    a. $A \cup (B \cap C) = (A \cup B) \cap C$
    b. $A \cap (B \cup C) = (A \cap B) \cup C$
    c. $A - (B - C) = (A - B) - C$

12. For each of the following pairs of sets, explain which is a subset of the other. If neither is a subset of the other, explain why.
    a. $A \cap B$ and $A \cap B \cap C$ b. $A \cup B$ and $A \cup B \cup C$
    c. $A \cup B$ and $(A \cup B) \cap C$ d. $A - B$ and $B - A$

13. a. If A has three elements and B has two elements, what is the greatest number of elements possible in (i) $A \cup B$? (ii) $A \cap B$? (iii) $B - A$? (iv) $A - B$?
    b. If A has n elements and B has m elements, what is the greatest number of elements possible in (i) $A \cup B$? (ii) $A \cap B$? (iii) $B - A$? (iv) $A - B$?

14. If $n(A) = 4$, $n(B) = 5$, and $n(C) = 6$, what is the greatest and least number of elements in
    a. $A \cup B \cup C$?   b. $A \cap B \cap C$?

15. The equation $\overline{A \cup B} = \overline{A} \cap \overline{B}$ and a similar equation for $\overline{A \cap B}$ are referred to as *DeMorgan's laws* in honor of the famous British mathematician who first discovered them.
    a. Use Venn diagrams to show that $\overline{A \cup B} = \overline{A} \cap \overline{B}$.
    b. Discover an equation similar to the one in part (a) involving $\overline{A \cap B}$, $\overline{A}$, and $\overline{B}$. Use Venn diagrams to show that the equation holds.
    c. Verify the equations in (a) and (b) for specific sets.

16. Given that the universe is the set of all humans, $B = \{x \mid x$ is a college basketball player$\}$, and $S = \{x \mid x$ is a college student more than 200 cm tall$\}$, describe each of the following in words:
    a. $\overline{B} \cap S$ b. $\overline{S}$ c. $B \cup \overline{S}$
    d. $B \cup S$ e. $\overline{B} \cap S$ f. $B \cap \overline{S}$

17. Suppose P is the set of all eighth-grade students at the Paxson School, with B the set of all students in the band and C the set of all students in the choir. Identify in words the students described by each region of the following figure:

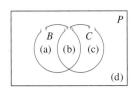

18. Of the eighth graders at the Paxson School, 7 played basketball, 9 played volleyball, 10 played soccer, 1 played basketball and volleyball only, 1 played basketball and soccer only, 2 played volleyball and soccer only, and 2 played volleyball, basketball, and soccer. How many played one or more of the three sports?

19. In a fraternity with 30 members, 18 take mathematics, 5 take both mathematics and biology, and 8 take neither mathematics nor biology. How many take biology but not mathematics?

20. Write the letters in the appropriate sections of the following Venn diagram using the following information:

    Set A contains the letters in the word *Iowa*.
    Set B contains the letters in the word *Hawaii*.
    Set C contains the letters in the word *Ohio*.

    The universal set U contains the letters in the word *Washington*.

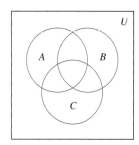

21. When three sets A, B, and C intersect as in problem 20, eight nonoverlapping regions are created. Describe each of the regions in words and using set notation.

22. In Paul's bicycle shop, 40 bicycles are inspected. If 20 needed new tires and 30 needed gear repairs, answer the following:
    a. What is the greatest number of bikes that could have needed both?
    b. What is the least number of bikes that could have needed both?
    c. What is the greatest number of bikes that could have needed neither?

23. A pollster interviewed 500 university seniors who owned credit cards. She reported that 240 owned Goldcard, 290 had Supercard, and 270 had Thriftcard. Of those seniors, the report said that 80 owned only a Goldcard and a Supercard, 70 owned only a Goldcard and a Thriftcard, 60 owned only a Supercard and a Thriftcard, and 50 owned all 3 cards. When the report was submitted for publication in the local campus newspaper, the editor refused to publish it, claiming the poll was not accurate. Was the editor right? Why or why not?

24. The Red Cross looks for three types of antigens in blood tests: A, B, and Rh. When the antigen A or B is present, it is listed, but if both these antigens are absent, the blood is type O. If the Rh antigen is present, the blood is positive; otherwise, it is negative. If a laboratory technician reports the following results after testing the blood samples of 100 people, how many were classified as O negative? Explain your reasoning.

Number of Samples	Antigen in Blood
40	A
18	B
82	Rh
5	A and B
31	A and Rh
11	B and Rh
4	A, B, and Rh

25. Classify the following as true or false. If false, give a counterexample. Assume that A and B are finite sets.
    a. If $n(A) = n(B)$, then $A = B$.
    b. If $A \sim B$, then $A \cup B$ is not equivalent to B.
    c. If $A - B = \emptyset$, then $A = B$.
    d. If $B - A = \emptyset$, then $B \subseteq A$.
    e. If $A \subset B$, then $n(A) < n(B)$.
    f. If $n(A) < n(B)$, then $A \subset B$.

26. Three announcers each tried to predict the winners of Sunday's professional football games. The only team not picked that is playing Sunday was the Giants. The choices for each person were as follows:

    Phyllis: Cowboys, Steelers, Vikings, Bills
    Paula: Steelers, Packers, Cowboys, Redskins
    Rashid: Redskins, Vikings, Jets, Cowboys

    If the only teams playing Sunday are those just mentioned, which teams will play which other teams?

27. Let $A = \{x, y\}$, $B = \{a, b, c\}$, and $C = \{0\}$. Find each of the following:
    a. $A \times B$
    b. $B \times A$
    c. $B \times \emptyset$
    d. $(A \cup B) \times C$
    e. $A \cup (B \times C)$

28. For each of the following, the Cartesian product $C \times D$ is given by the following sets. Find C and D.
    a. $\{(a, b), (a, c), (a, d), (a, e)\}$
    b. $\{(1, 1), (1, 2), (1, 3), (2, 1), (2, 2), (2, 3)\}$
    c. $\{(0, 1), (0, 0), (1, 1), (1, 0)\}$

29. Answer each of the following:
    a. If A has five elements and B has four elements, how many elements are in $A \times B$?
    b. If A has m elements and B has n elements, how many elements are in $A \times B$?
    c. If A has m elements, B has n elements, and C has p elements, how many elements are in $(A \times B) \times C$?

30. If there are six teams in the Alpha league and five teams in the Beta league and if each team from one league plays each team from the other league exactly once, how many games are played?

31. José has four pairs of slacks, five shirts, and three sweaters. From how many combinations can he choose if he chooses a pair of slacks, a shirt, and a sweater each day?

Communication

32. Answer each of the following and justify your answer:
    a. If $a \in A \cap B$, is it true that $a \in A \cup B$?
    b. If $a \in A \cup B$, is it true that $a \in A \cap B$?

33. The primary colors are red, blue, and yellow. If each is considered a set, write an explanation of what we would expect to get with the intersection of each of these sets from the regions pictured in the following figure:

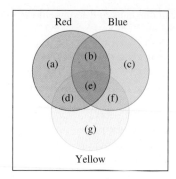

34. Is the operation of forming Cartesian products commutative? Explain why or why not.

Open-Ended

35. Make up and solve a story problem concerning specific sets A, B, and C for which $n(A \cup B \cup C)$ is known and it is required to find $n(A)$, $n(B)$, and $n(C)$.

36. Describe a real-life situation that can be represented by each of the following:
    a. $A \cap \overline{B}$
    b. $A \cap B \cap C$
    c. $A - (B \cup C)$

Cooperative Learning

37. Use set operations like union, intersection, complement, and set difference to describe the shaded region in the following figure in as many ways as possible. Compare your expressions with those of other groups to see which has the most. What is the total number of different expressions found by all the groups? Which expressions appeared in all the groups?

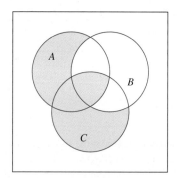

Review Problems

38. Find the number of elements in the following sets:
    a. $\{x \mid x$ is a letter in *commonsense*$\}$
    b. The set of letters appearing in the word *committee*

39. If $A = \{1, 2, 3, 4\}$ and $B = \{1, 2, 3, 4, 5\}$, answer the following questions:
    a. How many subsets of A do not contain the element 1?
    b. How many subsets of A contain the element 1?
    c. How many subsets of A contain either the element 1 or 2?
    d. How many subsets of A contain neither the element 1 nor 2?
    e. How many subsets of B contain the element 5 and how many do not?
    f. If all the subsets of A are known, how can all the subsets of B be listed systematically? How many subsets of B are there?

40. a. Which of the following sets are equal?
    b. Which sets are proper subsets of the other sets?

    $A = \{2, 4, 6, 8, 10, \ldots \}$
    $B = \{x \mid x = 2n + 2 \text{ and } n = 0, 1, 2, 3, 4, \ldots \}$
    $C = \{x \mid x = 4n \text{ and } n \in N\}$

41. Give examples from real life for each of the following:
    a. A one-to-one correspondence between two sets
    b. A correspondence between two sets that is not one-to-one

LABORATORY
A C T I V I T Y

A set of attribute blocks consists of 32 blocks. Each block is identified by its own shape, size, and color. The 4 shapes in a set are square, triangle, rhombus, and circle; the 4 colors are red, yellow, blue, and green; the 2 sizes are large and small. In addition to the blocks, each set contains a group of 20 cards. Ten of the cards specify one of the attributes of the blocks (for example, red, large, square). The other 10 cards are negation cards and specify the lack of an attribute (for example, not green, not circle). Many set-type problems can be studied with these blocks. For example, let A be the set of all green blocks and B be the set of all large blocks. Using the set of all blocks as the universal set, describe elements in each set listed below to determine which are equal:

1. $A \cup B; \overline{B \cup A}$
2. $\overline{A \cap B}; \overline{A} \cap \overline{B}$
3. $\overline{A \cap B}; \overline{A} \cup \overline{B}$
4. $A - B; A \cap \overline{B}$

2-3   Addition and Subtraction of Whole Numbers

In Section 2-1 we saw that the concept of one-to-one correspondence between sets can be used to introduce children to the concept of a number. The *Principles and Standards* in "Number and Operation" for grades Pre K–2 point out that on that level all students should:

- *understand meanings of operations and how they relate to one another*
- *understand various meanings of addition and subtraction of whole numbers and the relationship between the two operations;*
- *understand the effects of adding and subtracting whole numbers;*
- *understand situations that entail multiplication and division, such as equal groupings of objects and sharing equally.* (p. 78)

In addition the *Principles and Standards* point out that:

Counting is a foundation for students' early work with number. Young children are motivated to count everything from the treats they eat to the stairs they climb, and through their repeated experience with the counting process, they learn many fundamental number concepts. They can associate number words with small collections of objects and gradually learn to count and keep track of objects in larger groups. They can establish one-to-one correspondence by moving, touching, or pointing to objects as they say the number words. They should learn that counting objects in a different order does not alter the result, and they may notice that the next whole number in the counting sequence is one more than the number just named. Children should learn that the last number named represents the last object as well as the total number of objects in the collection. They often solve addition and subtraction problems by counting concrete objects, and many children invent problem-solving strategies based on counting strategies (Ginsburg, Klein, and Starkey 1998; Siegler 1996). (p. 79)

In the following "Peanuts" cartoon, it seems that Lucy's little brother has not yet learned to associate number words with a collection of objects.

whole numbers

When zero is joined with the set of natural numbers, $N = \{1, 2, 3, 4, 5, \dots \}$, we have the set of **whole numbers**, denoted $W = \{0, 1, 2, 3, 4, 5, \dots \}$. In this section, we provide a variety of models for teaching computational skills and allow students to revisit mathematics at a level they must know in order to be competent teachers.

Historians think that the word *zero* originated from the Hindu word *sūnya*, which means "void." Then *sūnya* was translated into the Arabic *sifr*, which when translated to Latin became *zephirum*, from which the word *zero* was derived.

Addition of Whole Numbers

Children encounter addition in preschool years by combining objects and wanting to know how many objects there are in the combined set. A set model is one way to represent addition of whole numbers.

Set Model

Suppose Jane has 4 blocks in one pile and 3 in another. If she combines the two groups of blocks, how many blocks are there in the combined group? Figure 2-16 shows the solution as it might appear in an elementary school text. The combined set of blocks is the union of the disjoint sets of 4 blocks and 3 blocks. After the sets have been combined, children count the blocks to determine that there are 7 blocks in all. Note the importance of the sets having no elements in common. If the sets have common elements, then an incorrect conclusion can be drawn.

FIGURE 2-16

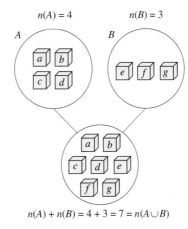

$$n(A) = 4 \qquad n(B) = 3$$

$$n(A) + n(B) = 4 + 3 = 7 = n(A \cup B)$$

Using these ideas we can use set terminology to define addition formally.

> ### Definition of Addition of Whole Numbers

Let A and B be two disjoint finite sets. If $n(A) = a$ and $n(B) = b$, then $a + b = n(A \cup B)$.

addends ◆ sum   The numbers a and b in $(a + b)$ are the **addends** and $(a + b)$ is the **sum**.

NOW TRY THIS 2-11

If the sets in the preceding definition of addition of whole numbers are not disjoint, explain why the definition is incorrect.

HISTORICAL NOTE

The symbol "+" first appeared in a 1417 manuscript and was a short way of writing the Latin word *et,* which means "and." However, Johann Widmann wrote a book in 1498 that made use of the + and − symbols for addition and subtraction. The word *minus* means "less" in Latin. First written as an *m,* it was later shortened to a horizontal bar.

Number-Line Model

For some problems, the set model for addition that we have developed is not the appropriate model. For example, consider the following questions:

1. Josh has 4 feet of red ribbon and 3 feet of white ribbon. How many feet of ribbon does he have altogether?
2. One day, Gail drank 4 ounces of orange juice in the morning and 3 ounces at lunch time. If she drank no other orange juice that day, how many ounces of orange juice did she drink for the entire day?

A *number line* can be used to model whole-number addition. Any line marked with two fundamental points, one representing 0 and the other representing 1, can be turned into a number line. The points representing 0 and 1 mark the ends of a *unit segment*. Other points can be marked and labeled, as shown in Figure 2-17. Any two consecutive points in Figure 2-17 mark the ends of a segment that has the same length as the unit segment on the number line.

FIGURE 2-17

Addition problems can be modeled using directed arrows on the number line. For example, the sum of $4 + 3$ is shown in Figure 2-17. Arrows representing the addends, 4 and 3, are combined into one arrow representing the sum. Figure 2-17 poses an inherent problem for students. If an arrow starting at 0 and ending at 3 represents 3, why should an arrow starting at 4 and ending at 7 represent 3?

In Section 2-1 we used the concept of a set and the concept of a one-to-one correspondence to define *greater-than* relations. A number line can also be used to describe **greater-than** and **less-than** relations on the set of whole numbers. For example, in Figure 2-17, notice that 4 is to the left of 7 on the number line. We say, "four is less than seven," and we write $4 < 7$. We can also say "seven is greater than four" and write $7 > 4$. Since 4 is to the left of 7, there is a natural number that can be added to 4 to get 7, namely, 3. Thus $4 < 7$ because $4 + 3 = 7$. We can generalize this discussion to form the following definition of *less than*.

greater than ◆ **less than**

> ### Definition of Less Than
>
> For any whole numbers a and b, a is **less than** b, written $a < b$, if and only if there exists a natural number k such that $a + k = b$.

greater than or equal to ◆
less than or equal to

Sometimes equality is combined with the inequalities, greater than and less than, to give the relations **greater than or equal to** and **less than or equal to**, denoted $\geq$ and $\leq$. Thus, $a \leq b$ means $a < b$ or $a = b$. The emphasis with respect to these symbols is on the *or*. Observe that "$3 < 5$ or $3 = 5$" is a true statement, so $3 \leq 5$ is true. Both $5 \geq 3$ and $3 \geq 3$ are true statements.

Whole-Number Addition Properties

Any time two whole numbers are added, we are guaranteed that a unique whole number will be obtained. This property is sometimes referred to as the *closure property of addition of whole numbers*. We say that "the set of whole numbers is closed under addition." Figure 2-18(a) shows two additions. Pictured above the number line is $3 + 5$ and below the number line is $5 + 3$. The sums are exactly the same. Figure 2-18(b) shows the same sums obtained with colored rods with the result being the same. Both illustrations in Figure 2-18 demonstrate the idea that two whole numbers can be added in either order. This property is true in general and is the *commutative property of addition of whole numbers*. We say that "addition of whole numbers is commutative."

FIGURE 2-18

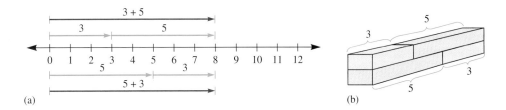

(a)　　　　　　　　　　　　　　　　　　　　　　　　(b)

> ## Property

Commutative property of addition of whole numbers　If a and b are any whole numbers, then $a + b = b + a$.

The commutative property of addition of whole numbers is not obvious to many young children. They may be able to find the sum $9 + 2$ and not be able to find the sum $2 + 9$. This is because one of the techniques used to teach addition is *counting on*. Using this technique, $9 + 2$ can be computed by starting at 9 and then counting on two more as "ten" and "eleven." To compute $2 + 9$, the *counting on* is more involved. Students need to understand that $2 + 9$ is another name for $9 + 2$.

Another property of addition is demonstrated when we select the order in which to add three or more numbers. For example, we could compute $24 + 8 + 2$ by grouping the 24 and the 8 together: $(24 + 8) + 2 = 32 + 2 = 34$. (The parentheses indicate that the first two numbers are grouped together.) We might also recognize that it is easy to add any number to 10 and compute it as $24 + (8 + 2) = 24 + 10 = 34$. This example illustrates the *associative property of addition of whole numbers*.

> ## Property

Associative property of addition of whole numbers　If a, b, and c are any whole numbers, then $(a + b) + c = a + (b + c)$.

When several numbers are being added, the parentheses are usually omitted, since the grouping does not alter the result.

Another property of addition of whole numbers operates when one addend is 0. In Figure 2-19; set *A* has 5 blocks and set *B* has 0 blocks. The union of sets *A* and *B* has only 5 blocks.

FIGURE 2-19

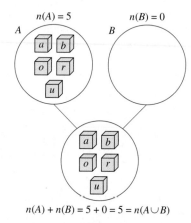

$$n(A) + n(B) = 5 + 0 = 5 = n(A \cup B)$$

This example illustrates the following property of whole numbers.

> **Property**

additive identity

Identity property of addition of whole numbers   There is a unique whole number 0, the **additive identity**, such that for any whole number a, $a + 0 = a = 0 + a$.

E X A M P L E 2-14

Which properties justify each of the following?

a. $5 + 7 = 7 + 5$ **b.** $1001 + 733$ is a whole number.
c. $(3 + 5) + 7 = (5 + 3) + 7$ **d.** $(8 + 5) + 2 = 2 + (8 + 5) = (2 + 8) + 5$
e. $(10 + 5) + (10 + 3) = (10 + 10) + (5 + 3)$

Solution   **a.** Commutative property of addition
  b. Closure property of addition
  c. Commutative property of addition
  d. Commutative and associative properties of addition
  f. Commutative and associative properties of addition combined

Mastering Basic Addition Facts

Certain mathematical facts are *basic addition facts*. Basic addition facts are those involving a single digit plus a single digit. In the following "Dennis The Menace" cartoon it seems that Dennis has not mastered the basic addition facts.

DENNIS THE MENACE

"MAKE UP YOUR MIND. FIRST YOU TELL ME 3 PLUS 3 IS SIX, AND NOW YOU SAY 4 PLUS 2 IS SIX!"

One method of learning the basic facts is to organize them according to different strategies, listed as follows:

1. *Counting On.* The strategy of counting on from the greater of the addends can be used any time we need to add whole numbers, but is inefficient. It is usually used when the other addend is 1, 2, or 3. For example, $5 + 3$ can be computed by starting at 5 and then counting on 6, 7, and 8. Likewise, $2 + 8$ would be computed by starting at 8 and then counting on 9 and 10.

2. *Doubles.* The next strategy involves the use of *doubles*. Doubles such as $4 + 4$ and $6 + 6$ receive special attention with students. After doubles are mastered, *doubles + 1* and *doubles + 2* can be learned easily. For example, if a student knows $6 + 6 = 12$, then $6 + 7$ is $(6 + 6) + 1$, or one more than the double of 6, or 13. Likewise, $7 + 9$ is $(7 + 7) + 2$ or two more than the double of 7, or 16.

3. *Making 10.* Another strategy is that of *making 10* and then adding any leftover. For example, we could think of $8 + 5$ as shown in Figure 2-20. Notice that we are really using the associative property of addition.

FIGURE 2-20

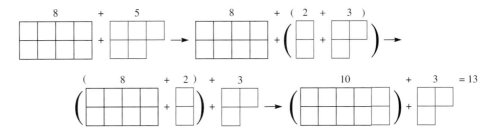

Many basic facts might be classified under more than one strategy. For example, we could find $9 + 8$ using *making 10* as $9 + (1 + 7) = (9 + 1) + 7 = 10 + 7 = 17$ or using a *double plus 1* as $(8 + 8) + 1$.

Subtraction of Whole Numbers

Subtraction of whole numbers can be modeled in several ways including the *set (take-away)* model, the *missing-addend* model, the *comparison* model, and the *number-line* model.

Take-Away Model

One way to think about subtraction is this: Instead of imagining a second set of objects as being joined to a first set (as in addition), consider the second set as being *taken away* from a first set. For example, suppose we have 8 blocks and take away 3 of them, as shown in Figure 2-21. We record this process as $8 - 3 = 5$.

FIGURE 2-21

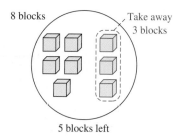

8 blocks

Take away 3 blocks

5 blocks left

NOW TRY THIS 2-12

Recall how addition of whole numbers was defined using the concept of union of two disjoint sets. Similarly, write a definition of subtraction of whole numbers using the concept of set difference.

Missing-Addend Model

A second model for subtraction, the *missing-addend* model relates subtraction and addition. Recall that in Figure 2-21, $8 - 3$ is pictured as 8 blocks "take away" 3 blocks. The number of blocks left is the number $8 - 3$, or 5. This can also be thought of as the number of blocks that could be added to 3 blocks in order to get 8 blocks, that is,

$$\boxed{8 - 3} + 3 = 8.$$

missing addend The number $8 - 3$, or 5, is the **missing addend** in the equation

$$\boxed{} + 3 = 8.$$

The missing-addend model gives elementary school students an opportunity to begin algebraic thinking. An unknown is a major part of the problem of trying to decide the difference of 8 minus 3.

Cashiers often use the missing-addend model. For example, if the bill for a movie is $8 and you pay $10, the cashier might calculate the change by saying "8 and 2 is 10." This idea can be generalized: for any whole numbers a and b, such that $a \geq b$, $a - b$ is the unique whole number such that $(a - b) + b = a$. That is, $a - b$ is the unique solution of the equation $\boxed{} + b = a$. The definition can be written more formally as follows:

> ### Definition of Subtraction of Whole Numbers

For any whole numbers a and b such that $a \geq b$, $a - b$ is the unique whole number c such that $a = b + c$.

Comparison Model

A third way to consider subtraction is by using a *comparison* model. Suppose Juan has 8 blocks and Susan has 3 blocks and we want to know how many more blocks Juan has than Susan. We can pair Susan's blocks with some of Juan's blocks, as shown in Figure 2-22, and determine that Juan has 5 more blocks than Susan. We also write this as $8 - 3 = 5$.

FIGURE 2-22

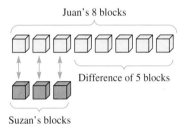

Number-Line Model

Subtraction can also be modeled on a number line, as suggested in Figure 2-23, where it is shown that $5 - 3 = 2$.

FIGURE 2-23

Properties of Subtraction

In an attempt to find $3 - 5$, we use the definition of subtraction: $3 - 5 = c$ if there is a solution to $c + 5 = 3$. Since there is no whole number c that satisfies the equation, $3 - 5$ is not meaningful in the set of whole numbers. In general, it can be shown that if $a < b$, then $a - b$ is not meaningful in the set of whole numbers.

NOW TRY THIS 2-13

How do the different ways of looking at subtraction on the following student page relate to the material in this section?

Sample School Book Page:
SUBTRACTION

Mixed Practice
Lessons 7–10

Concepts and Skills
Add or subtract.

① 7   14   ② 6   15   ③ 5   13
  +7 −7   +9 −9   +8 −8

④ 16   7   9   11   8   18   15
  −8   +6   +8   −6   +7   −9   −8

Problem Solving
Write a number sentence. Solve.

⑤ Malinda had 9 colors of paint. Joe gave her 8 more. How many colors did she have then?

_____ colors

⑥ Malinda had 17 colors of paint. She gave Joe 8. How many colors did she have left?

_____ colors

MIXED PRACTICE

Use the graph to answer the questions.

⑦ Which activity got the most votes?

_____

⑧ How many more votes did **Reading** get than **Painting**?

_____ more votes

Our Favorite Activities

Number of Votes: 6 5 4 3 2 1

Reading   Singing   Painting
Activities

Journal
⑨ Draw a picture to show these related facts: $5 + 6 = 11$ $11 − 6 = 5$

Notes for Home: Your child practiced adding and subtracting related facts, reading a graph, and solving problems. **Home Activity:** Ask your child to tell you a related subtraction fact for $6 + 8 = 14$. $(14 − 8 = 6$ or $14 − 6 = 8)$

Source: Scott Foresman–Addison Wesley Math, Grade 2, 2002 (p. 107).

ONGOING ASSESSMENT 2-3

1. Give an example to show why, in the definition of addition, sets A and B must be disjoint.

2. Explain whether the following given sets are closed under addition:
   a. $B = \{0\}$
   b. $T = \{0, 3, 6, 9, 12, \ldots\}$
   c. $N = \{1, 2, 3, 4, 5, \ldots\}$
   d. $V = \{3, 5, 7\}$
   e. $\{x \mid x \in W \text{ and } x > 10\}$

3. Draw a picture to illustrate the commutative property of addition.

4. Rewrite each of the following subtraction problems as an equivalent addition problem:
   a. $21 - 7 = x$
   b. $x - 119 = 213$
   c. $213 - x = 119$
   d. $213 - 119 = x$

5. Each of the following is an example of one of the properties for addition of whole numbers. Identify the property illustrated.
   a. $6 + 3 = 3 + 6$
   b. $(6 + 3) + 5 = 6 + (3 + 5)$
   c. $(6 + 3) + 5 = (3 + 6) + 5$

6. In the definition of *less than*, can the natural number k be replaced by the whole number k? Why or why not?

7. a. Recall how we have defined *less-than* and *greater-than* relations and give a similar definition using the concept of subtraction for each of the following:
   (i) $a < b$ (ii) $a > b$
   b. Use subtraction to define $a \geq b$.

8. Find the next three terms in each of the following arithmetic sequences:
   a. 8, 13, 18, 23, 28, _____, _____, _____
   b. 98, 91, 84, 77, 70, 63, _____, _____, _____

9. If A, B, and C each stand for a different single digit from 1 to 9, answer the following if
   $$A + B = C.$$
   a. What is the greatest digit that C could be? Why?
   b. What is the greatest digit that A could be? Why?
   c. What is the smallest digit that C could be? Why?
   d. If A, B, and C are even, what number(s) could C be? Why?
   e. If C is 5 more than A, what number(s) could B be? Why?
   f. If A is three times as great as B, then what number(s) could C be? Why?
   g. If A is odd and A is 5 more than B, what number(s) could C be? Why?

10. If A, B, C, and D each stand for a different single digit from 1 to 9, answer each of the following if

$$\begin{array}{r} A \\ + B \\ \hline CD \end{array}$$

   a. What is the value of C? Why?
   b. Can D be 1? Why?
   c. If D is 7, what values can A be?
   d. If A is 6 greater than B, then what is the value of D?

11. Assuming the same pattern continues, find the total of the terms in the 50th row in the following figure:

1	1st row
$1 - 1$	2nd row
$1 - 1 + 1$	3rd row
$1 - 1 + 1 - 1$	4th row
$1 - 1 + 1 - 1 + 1$	5th row

12. Make each of the following a magic square:

a.

	1	6
	5	7
4		2

b.

17	10	
		14
13	18	

13. a. Place whole numbers in the following four squares so that each pair has the sum shown. Note that one diagonal sum must be 20 and the other diagonal sum must be 7.

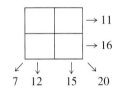

   b. Will examples similar to the one in part (a) always be possible with any numbers written for the sums as shown? Explain your answer.

14. a. A domino set contains all number pairs from double-zero to double-six, with each number pair occurring only once; that is, the following domino counts as two-four and four-two. How many dominoes are in the set?

   b. When considering the sum of all dots on a single domino in an ordinary set of dominoes, explain how the commutative property might be important.

15. Make a calculator count to 100 as follows (use a constant operation if available):
   a. By ones b. By twos c. By fives

16. a. At a volleyball game, the players stood in a row ordered by height. If Kent is shorter than Mischa, Sally is taller than Mischa, and Vera is taller than Sally, who is the tallest and who is the shortest?
   b. Write possible heights for the players in part (a).

17. Make a calculator count backward from 27 to 0 as follows (use a constant operation if possible):
 a. By ones   **b.** By threes   **c.** By nines

18. If a calculator is made to count by twos starting at 2, what is the thirteenth number in the sequence?

Communication

19. In Figure 2-17, arrows were used to represent numbers in completing an addition. Explain whether you think an arrow starting at 0 and ending at 3 represents the same number as an arrow starting at 4 and ending at 7. How would you explain this to students?

20. To make some additions easier Ben calculates as in the following example: $37 + 29 = (37 - 1) + (29 + 1) = 36 + 30 = 66$.
 a. Use letters to state the general principle that Ben uses.
 b. Use a concrete model to justify the principle in part (a).

21. To make subtraction easier Abby performs some subtractions as follows: $97 - 28 = (97 + 2) - (28 + 2) = 99 - 30 = 69$.
 a. Find $63 - 27$ using Abby's method.
 b. Use letters to state the general principle that Abby uses.
 c. Justify the general principle in part (b) in two ways, one of which could be suitable to fifth graders.

22. When subtraction and addition appear in an expression without parentheses, it is agreed that the operations are performed in order of their appearance from left to right. Taking this into account, answer the following:
 a. Use an appropriate model for subtraction to explain why

$$a - b - c = a - c - b,$$

 assuming that all expressions are meaningful.
 b. Use an appropriate model for subtraction to explain why

$$a - b - c = a - (b + c).$$

23. Explain whether it is important for elementary students to learn various properties of addition of whole numbers.

24. Explain whether it is important for elementary students to learn more than one model for performing the operations of addition and subtraction.

25. Do elementary students still have to learn their basic facts when the calculator is a part of the curriculum? Why or why not?

26. Explain how the following model can be used to illustrate each of the following addition and subtraction facts:
 a. $9 + 4 = 13$ **b.** $4 + 9 = 13$
 c. $4 = 13 - 9$ **d.** $9 = 13 - 4$

Open-Ended

27. Describe any model not in this text that you might use to teach addition to students.

28. Investigate whether your calculator has constant addition and subtraction features. Write an example to show how each feature works.

29. Suppose $A \subseteq B$. If $n(A) = a$ and $n(B) = b$, then $b - a$ could be defined as $n(B - A)$. Choose two sets A and B and illustrate this definition.

Cooperative Learning

30. Use groups of people to illustrate properties of addition.

31. Have each person in your group choose a different grade textbook and report on when and how subtraction of whole numbers is introduced. Compare with different ways subtraction is introduced in this section.

Review Problems

32. Determine whether the following sets are equivalent. Justify your answers.
 a. $\{2, 4, 6, 8, \ldots, 1000\}$ and $\{3, 6, 9, 12, 15, \ldots, 1500\}$
 b. $\{1, 4, 7, 10, 13, \ldots, 2998\}$ and $\{1, 2, 3, 4, \ldots, 1000\}$
 c. $\{0, 1, 2, 3, 4, \ldots\}$ and $\{1, 2, 3, 4, 5, \ldots\}$
 d. $S = \{x \mid x = 2n, n \in N\}$ and $W = \{x \mid x = 4n, n \in N\}$

33. Decide which of the following are always true. If true, justify the statement and if false, provide a counterexample.
 a. $A - (B \cup C) = (A - B) \cap (A - C)$
 b. If $A \cup B = B$, then $A \subseteq B$.
 c. If $A \cap B = \varnothing$, then $\overline{A} \cup \overline{B} = U$.
 d. If $A \not\subseteq B$ and $B \not\subseteq C$, then $A \not\subseteq C$.

34. a. How many one-to-one correspondences are possible between $A = \{a, b, c\}$ and $B = \{1, 2, 3\}$?
 b. How many elements are there in $A \times B$?

35. Classify each of the following as true or false. If true, justify the statement, and if false, provide a counterexample.
 a. If $A \cup B = A \cup C$, then $B = C$.
 b. If $A \cap B = A \cap C$, then $B = C$.
 c. If $A \cap B = \varnothing$ and $B \cap C = \varnothing$, then $A \cap C = \varnothing$.

36. A committee of senators has 6 members. A two-thirds vote is needed to carry any proposal. How many winning coalitions are there?

37. Oakridge has a population of 4800 and only one movie theater. One week the movie *Minority Report* was shown, and 3100 people went to see it. The following week, the movie *Gosford Park* was shown, and 2200 residents went to see it.
 a. What is the greatest number of townspeople that could have seen both movies? Justify your answer.
 b. What is the least number of people that could have seen both movies? Justify your answer.

38. If $U = \{a, b, c, d\}$, $A = \{a, b, c\}$, $B = \{b, c\}$, and $C = \{d\}$, find each of the following:
 a. $A \cup \overline{B}$ **b.** $\overline{A \cap B}$
 c. $A \cap \varnothing$ **d.** $B \cap C$
 e. $B - A$

BRAIN
T E A S E R

Use Figure 2-24 to design an *unmagic square*. That is, use each of the digits 1, 2, 3, 4, 5, 6, 7, 8, and 9 exactly once so that every column, row, and diagonal adds to a different sum.

FIGURE 2-24

Multiplication and Division of Whole Numbers

Multiplication of Whole Numbers

In this section, we use three models to discuss multiplication: the *repeated-addition* model, the *array* model, and the *Cartesian-product* model. We also investigate the distributive property of multiplication over addition.

The *Principles and Standards* lists the following expectations under "Number and Operations Standards" for grades 3–5

- *understand various meanings of multiplication and division;*
- *understand the effects of multiplying and dividing whole numbers;*
- *identify and use relationships between operations, such as division as the inverse of multiplication, to solve problems;*
- *understand and use properties of operations, such as the distributivity of multiplication over addition.* (p. 148)

Repeated-Addition Model

FIGURE 2-25

Suppose we have a classroom with 5 columns of 4 chairs each, as shown in Figure 2-25. How many chairs are there altogether? We can think of this as combining 5 sets of 4 objects into a single set.

The 5 columns of 4 suggest the following addition:

$$4 + 4 + 4 + 4 + 4 = 20$$

five 4s

We write $4 + 4 + 4 + 4 + 4$ as $5 \cdot 4$ and say "5 times 4" or "5 multiplied by 4." The advantage of the multiplication notation is evident when the number of addends is large. Thus if we have 25 columns of 4 chairs each, we can find the total number of chairs by adding 25 fours, or $25 \cdot 4$.

HISTORICAL
N O T E

William Oughtred (1575–1660), an English mathematician, placed emphasis on mathematical symbols. He first introduced the use of "St. Andrew's cross" ($\times$) as the symbol for multiplication. This symbol was not readily adopted because, as Gottfried Wilhelm von Leibnitz (1646–1716) objected, it was too easily confused with the letter *x*. Leibnitz adopted the use of the dot ($\cdot$) for multiplication, which then became commonly used after grade school.

The *repeated-addition* model can be illustrated in several ways, including the use of a number line and the use of arrays. For example, using colored rods of length 4, we could show that the combined length of five 4-rods has a combined length that can be found by joining the rods end-to-end, as in Figure 2-26(a). Figure 2-26(b) shows the process using arrows on a number line.

FIGURE 2-26

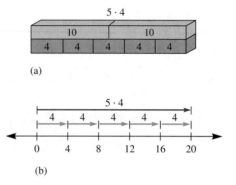

The Array and Area Models

Another representation of repeated addition that is useful in exploring multiplication of whole numbers is an *array*. In Figure 2-27(a), we cross sticks to create intersection points, thus forming an array of points. The number of points on a single vertical stick is 4 and there are 5 sticks, forming a total of $4 \cdot 5$ points in the array. In Figure 2-27(b), the array is shown as a 4-by-5 grid. The number of unit squares required to fill in the grid is 20. These models motivate the following definition of multiplication of whole numbers.

FIGURE 2-27

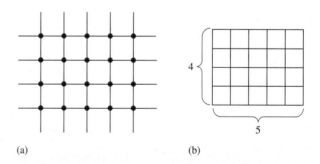

> ### Definition of Multiplication of Whole Numbers

For any whole numbers a and $n \neq 0$,

$$n \cdot a = \underbrace{a + a + a + \cdots + a}_{n \text{ terms}}.$$

If $n = 0$, then $0 \cdot a = 0$.

Cartesian-Product Model

The *Cartesian-product* model offers another way to discuss multiplication. Suppose you can order a soyburger on light or dark bread with one condiment: mustard, mayonnaise, or horseradish. To show the number of different soyburger orders that a waiter could write for the cook, we use a *tree diagram*. The ways of writing the order are listed in Figure 2-28 where the bread is chosen from the set $B = \{$light, dark$\}$ and the condiment is chosen from the set $C = \{$mustard, mayonnaise, horseradish$\}$.

FIGURE 2-28

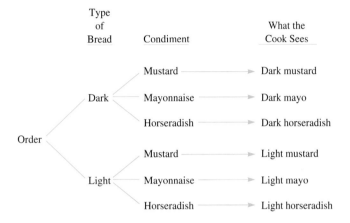

Each order can be written as an ordered pair, for example, (dark, mustard). The set of ordered pairs forms the Cartesian product $B \times C$. The Fundamental Counting Principle tells us that the number of ordered pairs in $B \times C$ is $2 \cdot 3$.

The preceding discussion demonstrates how multiplication of whole numbers can be defined in terms of Cartesian products. Thus an alternative definition of multiplication of whole numbers follows.

> ### Alternative Definition of Multiplication of Whole Numbers

For finite sets A and B, if $n(A) = a$ and $n(B) = b$, then $a \cdot b = n(A \times B)$.

---

product ◆ factors

REMARK In this definition, sets A and B do not have to be disjoint. The expression $a \cdot b$ is the **product** of a and b, and a and b are **factors**. Also, note that $A \times B$ indicates the Cartesian product, not multiplication. We multiply numbers, not sets.

NOW TRY THIS 2-13

How would you use the repeated-addition definition of multiplication to explain to a child unfamiliar with both the Fundamental Counting Principle and the concept of cross product, that the number of possible outfits consisting of a shirt and pants combination—given 6 shirts and 5 pairs of pants—is $6 \cdot 5$?

Properties of Whole-Number Multiplication

The set of whole numbers is *closed* under multiplication. That is, if we multiply any two whole numbers, the result is a whole number. This property is referred to as the *closure property of multiplication of whole numbers*. Multiplication on the set of whole numbers, like addition, has the commutative, associative, and identity properties.

> ### Properties of Multiplication of Whole Numbers
>
> **Closure property of multiplication of whole numbers**   For any whole numbers a and b, $a \cdot b$ is a unique whole number.
>
> **Commutative property of multiplication of whole numbers**   For any whole numbers a and b, $a \cdot b = b \cdot a$.
>
> **Associative property of multiplication of whole numbers**   For any whole numbers a, b, and c, $(a \cdot b) \cdot c = a \cdot (b \cdot c)$.
>
> **Identity property of multiplication of whole numbers**   There is a unique whole number 1 such that for any whole number a, $a \cdot 1 = a = 1 \cdot a$.
>
> **Zero multiplication property of whole numbers**   For any whole number a, $a \cdot 0 = 0 = 0 \cdot a$.

FIGURE 2-29

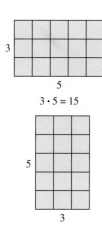

$3 \cdot 5 = 15$

$5 \cdot 3 = 15$

The *commutative property of multiplication of whole numbers* is illustrated easily by building a 3-by-5 grid and then turning it sideways, as shown in Figure 2-29. We see that the number of 1×1 squares present in either case is 15, that is, $3 \cdot 5 = 15 = 5 \cdot 3$. The commutative property can be verified by recalling that $n(A \times B) = n(B \times A)$.

The *associative property of multiplication of whole numbers* can be illustrated as follows. Suppose $a = 3$, $b = 5$, and $c = 4$. In Figure 2-30(a), we see a picture of $3 \cdot (5 \cdot 4)$ blocks. In Figure 2-30(b), we see the same blocks, this time arranged as $(3 \cdot 5) \cdot 4$. Because both sets of blocks in Figure 2-30(a) and (b) compress to the set shown in Figure 2-30(c), we see that $3 \cdot (5 \cdot 4) = (3 \cdot 5) \cdot 4$. The associative property is useful in computations such as the following:

$$3 \cdot 40 = 3 \cdot (4 \cdot 10) = (3 \cdot 4) \cdot 10 = 12 \cdot 10 = 120.$$

FIGURE 2-30

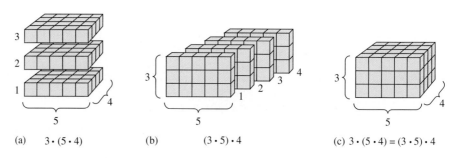

(a) $3 \cdot (5 \cdot 4)$ (b) $(3 \cdot 5) \cdot 4$ (c) $3 \cdot (5 \cdot 4) = (3 \cdot 5) \cdot 4$

In the accompanying student page, the associative property of multiplication is referred to as the *grouping property*. Notice the application of the property in problem 5 at the bottom of the page.

Sample School Book Page:
GROUPING PROPERTY

Chapter 5
Lesson
11

Multiplying 3 Factors

You Will Learn
how to multiply when you have three factors

Vocabulary
grouping property
when the grouping of factors is changed, the product remains the same

Learn

Ashley spends a lot of her free time dancing. She competes in Scottish Highland dance and has won many championships.

The Highland fling can have 6 steps. Each step takes up 8 bars of music. And each bar has 4 counts. How many counts are in the fling?

Ashley lives in Shelby Township, Michigan.

Find $6 \times 8 \times 4$.

Here are some ways you can find the product when there are 3 factors. The parentheses tell which factors to multiply first.

Did You Know?
There are about 3,000 official tartan plaids. A tartan plaid is a kind of woven cloth with different color patterns.

Example 1	**Example 2**	**Example 3**
Multiply these first.	Multiply these first.	Pick any two. Try these.
↓ ↓	↓ ↓	↓ ↓
$(6 \times 8) \times 4$	$6 \times (8 \times 4)$	$6 \times 8 \times 4$
$48 \times 4 = 192$	$6 \times 32 = 192$	$24 \times 8 = 192$

There are 192 counts in this Highland Fling.

The examples show the **grouping property.** Changing the grouping of the factors does not change the product.

Talk About It

In what way are $(3 \times 2) \times 7$ and $3 \times (2 \times 7)$ the same? Different?

Check

Find each product.

1. $4 \times 7 \times 5$ 2. $3 \times 2 \times 5$ 3. $4 \times 9 \times 8$ 4. $6 \times 7 \times 3$

5. **Reasoning** What is an easy way to multiply $4 \times 8 \times 25$? Explain.

Source: Scott Foresman–Addision Wesley Math, Grade 4, 2002 (p. 230).

The *multiplicative identity for whole numbers* is 1. For example, $3 \cdot 1 = 1 + 1 + 1 = 3$. In general, for any whole number a,

$$a \cdot 1 = \underbrace{1 + 1 + 1 + \cdots + 1}_{a \text{ terms}} = a.$$

Thus $a \cdot 1 = a$, which, along with the commutative property for multiplication, implies that $a \cdot 1 = a = 1 \cdot a$. Cartesian products can also be used to show that $a \cdot 1 = a = 1 \cdot a$.

Next, consider multiplication involving 0. For example $6 \cdot 0 = 0 + 0 + 0 + 0 + 0 + 0 = 0$. Thus we see that multiplying 0 by 6 yields a product of 0 and, by commutativity, $0 \cdot 6 = 0$. This is an example of the *zero multiplication property*. This property can also be verified by using the definition of multiplication in terms of Cartesian products.

The Distributive Property of Multiplication over Addition

The next property we investigate is the basis for understanding multiplication algorithms for whole numbers. The area of the large rectangle in Figure 2-31 equals the sum of the areas of the two smaller rectangles and hence $5 \cdot (3 + 4) = 5 \cdot 3 + 5 \cdot 4$.

FIGURE 2-31

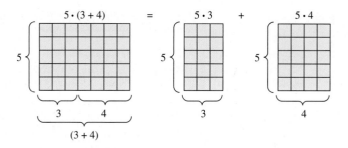

The properties of addition and multiplication also can be used to justify this result:

$$5 \cdot (3 + 4) = \underbrace{(3 + 4) + (3 + 4) + (3 + 4) + (3 + 4) + (3 + 4)}_{5 \text{ terms}}$$

Definition of multiplication

$$= (3 + 3 + 3 + 3 + 3) + (4 + 4 + 4 + 4 + 4)$$

Commutative and associative properties of addition

$$= 5 \cdot 3 + 5 \cdot 4 \qquad \text{Definition of multiplication}$$

This example illustrates the *distributive property of multiplication over addition* for whole numbers. Because in algebra it is customary to write $a \cdot b$ as ab, we state the distributive property of multiplication over addition as follows:

> **Property**

Distributive property of multiplication over addition for whole numbers   For any whole numbers a, b, and c,

$$a(b + c) = ab + ac.$$

REMARK   Because the commutative property of multiplication of whole numbers holds, the distributive property of multiplication over addition can be rewritten as $(b + c)a = ba + ca$.

The distributive property can be generalized to any finite number of terms. For example, $a(b + c + d) = ab + ac + ad$.

The distributive property can be written as

$$ab + ac = a(b + c).$$

This is commonly referred to as *factoring*.

Students find the distributive property of multiplication over addition useful when doing mental mathematics. For example, $13 \cdot 7 = (10 + 3) \cdot 7 = 10 \cdot 7 + 3 \cdot 7 = 70 + 21 = 91$. This property is used to combine like terms when we work with variables; for example, $3ab + 2ab = (3 + 2)ab = 5ab$.

**EXAMPLE
2-15**

FIGURE 2-32

a. Use an area model to show that $(x + y)(z + w) = xz + xw + yz + yw$.

b. Use the distributive property of multiplication over addition to justify the result in part (a).

Solution   **a.** Consider the rectangle in Figure 2-32 whose width is $x + y$ and whose length is $z + w$. The area of the entire rectangle is $(x + y)(z + w)$. If we divide the rectangle into smaller rectangles as shown, we notice that the sum of the areas of the four smaller rectangles is $xz + xw + yz + yw$. Because the area of the original rectangle equals the sum of the areas of the smaller rectangles, the result follows.

b. To apply the distributive property of multiplication over addition, we think about $x + y$ as one number and proceed as follows:

$$(x + y)(z + w) = (x + y)z + (x + y)w$$

$$ = xz + yz + xw + yw \qquad \text{The distributive property of multiplication over addition}$$

$$ = xz + xw + yz + yw \qquad \text{The commutative property of addition}$$

Order of Operations

Difficulties involving the order of arithmetic operations sometimes arise. For example, many students will treat $2 + 3 \cdot 6$ as $(2 + 3)6$, while others will treat it as $2 + (3 \cdot 6)$. In the first case, the value is 30; in the second case, the value is 20. To avoid confusion, mathematicians agree that when no parentheses are present, multiplications are performed *before* additions. Thus, $2 + 3 \cdot 6 = 2 + 18 = 20$. This order of operations is not built into calculators that display an incorrect answer of 30.

Division of Whole Numbers

We discuss division using three models: the *set (partition)* model, the *missing-factor* model, and the *repeated-subtraction* model.

Set (Partition) Model

Suppose we have 18 cookies and want to give an equal number of cookies to each of 3 friends: Bob, Dean, and Charlie. How many should each person receive? If we draw a picture, we can see that we can divide (or partition) the 18 cookies into 3 sets, with an equal number of cookies in each set. Figure 2-33 shows that each friend received 6 cookies.

FIGURE 2-33

The answer may be symbolized as $18 \div 3 = 6$. Thus $18 \div 3$ is the number of cookies in each of 3 disjoint sets whose union has 18 cookies. In this approach to division, we partition a set into a number of equivalent subsets.

Missing-Factor Model

Another strategy for dividing 18 cookies among 3 friends is to use the *missing-factor* model. If each friend receives c cookies, then the 3 friends receive $3c$, or 18, cookies. Hence, $3c = 18$. Since $3 \cdot 6 = 18$, then $c = 6$. We have answered the division computation by using multiplication. This leads us to the following definition of division of whole numbers.

> ### Definition of Division of Whole Numbers
>
> For any whole numbers a and b, with $b \neq 0$, $a \div b = c$ if, and only if, c is the unique whole number such that $b \cdot c = a$.

dividend ◆ divisor ◆ quotient

REMARK The number a is the **dividend**, b is the **divisor**, and c is the **quotient**. Note that $a \div b$ can also be written as $\frac{a}{b}$ or $b\overline{)a}$.

Repeated-Subtraction Model

Suppose we have 18 cookies and want to package them in cookie boxes that hold 6 cookies each. How many boxes are needed? We could reason that if one box is filled, then we would have $18 - 6$ (or 12) cookies left. If one more box is filled, then there are $12 - 6$

(or 6) cookies left. Finally, we could place the last 6 cookies in a third box. This discussion can be summarized by writing $18 - 6 - 6 - 6 = 0$. We have found by repeated subtraction that $18 \div 6 = 3$.

Calculators can be used to show that division of whole numbers can be thought of as repeated subtraction. For example, consider $135 \div 15$. If the calculator has a constant key, $\boxed{K}$, press $\boxed{1}\,\boxed{5}\,\boxed{-}\,\boxed{K}\,\boxed{1}\,\boxed{3}\,\boxed{5}\,\boxed{-}$ ... and then count how many times you must press the $\boxed{=}$ key in order to make the display read 0. Calculators with a different constant feature may require a different sequence of entries. For example, if the calculator has an automatic constant, we can press $\boxed{1}\,\boxed{3}\,\boxed{5}\,\boxed{-}\,\boxed{1}\,\boxed{5}\,\boxed{-}$ and then count the number of times we press the $\boxed{=}$ key to make the display read $\boxed{0}$.

The Division Algorithm

Just as subtraction of whole numbers is not always meaningful, division of whole numbers is not always meaningful. For example, to find $383 \div 57$ we look for a whole number c such that $57c = 383$.

Table 2-5 shows several products of whole numbers times 57. Since 383 is between 342 and 399, there is no whole number c such that $57c = 383$. Because no whole number c satisfies this equation, we see that $383 \div 57$ has no meaning in the set of whole numbers, and the set of whole numbers is not closed under division.

Table 2-5

$57 \cdot 1$	$57 \cdot 2$	$57 \cdot 3$	$57 \cdot 4$	$57 \cdot 5$	$57 \cdot 6$	$57 \cdot 7$
57	114	171	228	285	342	399

remainder

division algorithm

However, if 383 apples were to be divided among 57 students, each student would receive 6 apples and 41 apples would remain. The number 41 is the **remainder**. Thus 383 contains six 57s with a remainder of 41. Observe that the remainder is a whole number less than 57. The concept illustrated is the **division algorithm**.

Division Algorithm

Given any whole numbers a and b with $b \neq 0$, there exist unique whole numbers q (quotient) and r (remainder) such that

$$a = bq + r \quad \text{with} \quad 0 \leq r < b.$$

When a is "divided" by b and the remainder is 0 we say that a is *divisible* by b or that b is a *divisor* of a or that b *divides* a. By the *division algorithm*, a is divisible by b if $a = bq$ for a unique whole number q. Thus 63 is divisible by 9 because $63 = 9 \cdot 7$. Notice that 63 is also divisible by 7.

E X A M P L E
2-16

If 123 is divided by a number and the remainder is 13, what are the possible divisors?

Solution   If 123 is divided by b, then from the division algorithm we have

$$123 = bq + 13 \qquad \text{and} \qquad b > 13.$$

Using the definition of subtraction, we have $bq = 123 - 13$, and hence $110 = bq$. Now we are looking for two numbers whose product is 110, where one number is greater than 13. Table 2-6 shows the pairs of whole numbers whose product is 110.

Table 2-6

1	110
2	55
5	22
10	11

We see that 110, 55, and 22 are the only possible values for b because each is greater than 13.

Division by 0 and 1

The whole numbers 0 and 1 deserve special attention with respect to division of whole numbers. Before reading on, try to find the values of the following three expressions:

1. $3 \div 0$ **2.** $0 \div 3$ **3.** $0 \div 0$

Consider the following explanations:

1. By definition, $3 \div 0 = c$ if there is a unique number c such that $0 \cdot c = 3$. Since the zero property of multiplication states that $0 \cdot c = 0$ for any whole number c, there is no whole number c such that $0 \cdot c = 3$. Thus $3 \div 0$ is undefined because there is no answer to the equivalent multiplication problem.
2. By definition, $0 \div 3 = c$ if there exists a unique number such that $3 \cdot c = 0$. Because any number times 0 is 0, and in particular $3 \cdot 0 = 0$, then $c = 0$ and $0 \div 3 = 0$. Note that $c = 0$ is the only number that satisfies $3 \cdot c = 0$.
3. By definition, $0 \div 0 = c$ if there is a unique whole number c such that $0 \cdot c = 0$. Notice that for *any* c, $0 \cdot c = 0$. According to the definition of division, c must be unique. Since there is no *unique* number c such that $0 \cdot c = 0$, it follows that $0 \div 0$ is indeterminate, or undefined.

Division involving 0 may be summarized as follows. Let n be any nonzero whole number. Then

1. $n \div 0$ is undefined;
2. $0 \div n = 0$;
3. $0 \div 0$ is indeterminate, or undefined.

Recall that $n \cdot 1 = n$ for any whole number n. Thus, by the definition of division, $n \div 1 = n$. For example, $3 \div 1 = 3$, $1 \div 1 = 1$, and $0 \div 1 = 0$. A discussion similar to the above can be found on the student page that follows.

Sample School Book Page:
SPECIAL QUOTIENTS

 Chapter 4 Lesson 10

Special Quotients

You Will Learn
how to divide with 0 and 1

Learn

Look what happened to the calculator display when Jeremy tried to divide 2 by 0. Division rules with 0 and 1 can help you divide.

ERROR

Example 1
Division rules with 0.

$0 \div 2 = n$
Think: $2 \times 0 = 0$
Divide. $0 \div 2 = 0$
0 divided by any number (except 0) is 0.

$2 \div 0 = n$
Think: $0 \times \square = 2$
No numbers work.
You cannot divide by 0.

Here are rules to remember when you divide by 1.

Example 2
Division rules with 1.

$6 \div 1 = n$
Think: $1 \times 6 = 6$
Divide. $6 \div 1 = 6$
Any number divided by 1 is that number.

$6 \div 6 = n$
Think: $6 \times 1 = 6$
Divide. $6 \div 6 = 1$
Any number divided by itself (except 0) is 1.

Source: Scott Foresman–Addison Wesley Math, Grade 4, 2002 (p. 172).

O N G O I N G   A S S E S S M E N T   2 - 4

1. For each of the following, find, if possible, the whole numbers that make the equations true:
   a. $3 \cdot \square = 15$ b. $18 = 6 + 3 \cdot \square$
   c. $\square \cdot (5 + 6) = \square \cdot 5 + \square \cdot 6$

2. In terms of set theory, the product na could be thought of as the number of elements in the union of n sets with a elements in each. If this were the case, what must be true about the sets?

3. Determine if the following sets are closed under multiplication:
   a. $\{0, 1\}$
   b. $\{0\}$
   c. $\{2, 4, 6, 8, 10, \ldots\}$
   d. $\{1, 3, 5, 7, 9, \ldots\}$
   e. $\{1, 4, 7, 10, 13, \ldots\}$
   f. $\{0, 1, 2\}$

4. a. If 5 is removed from the set of whole numbers, is the set closed with respect to addition?
   b. If 5 is removed from the set of whole numbers, is the set closed with respect to multiplication?
   c. Answer the same questions as (a) and (b) if 6 is removed from the set of whole numbers.

5. Rename each of the following using the distributive property for multiplication over addition so that there are no parentheses in the final answer:
   a. $(a + b)(c + d)$
   b. $3(x + y + 5)$
   c. $\square(\Delta + \bigcirc)$
   d. $(x + y)(x + y + z)$
   e. $a(b + c) - ac$
   f. $x(y + 1) - x$

6. Place parentheses, if needed, to make each of the following equations true:
   a. $4 + 3 \cdot 2 = 14$ b. $9 \div 3 + 1 = 4$
   c. $5 + 4 + 9 \div 3 = 6$ d. $3 + 6 - 2 \div 1 = 7$

7. The generalized distributive property for three terms states that for any whole numbers a, b, c, and d, $a(b + c + d) = ab + ac + ad$. Justify this property using the distributive property for two terms.

8. Using the distributive property of multiplication over addition we can factor as in $x^2 + xy = x(x + y)$. Use the distributive property to factor each of the following.
   a. $xy + y^2$
   b. $47 \cdot 99 + 47$
   c. $xy + x$
   d. $(x + 1)y + (x + 1)$
   e. $a^2b + ab^2$

9. For each of the following, find whole numbers to make the statement true, if possible:
   a. $18 \div 3 = \square$
   b. $\square \div 76 = 0$
   c. $28 \div \square = 7$

10. Rewrite each of the following division problems as a multiplication problem:
    a. $40 \div 8 = 5$ b. $326 \div 2 = x$
    c. $48 \div x = 16$ d. $x \div 5 = 17$

11. Think of a number. Multiply it by 2. Add 2. Divide by 2. Subtract 1. How does the result compare with your original number? Will this work all the time? Explain your answer.

12. Show that, in general, each of the following is false if a, b, and c are whole numbers:
    a. $(a \div b) \div c = a \div (b \div c)$
    b. $a \div (b + c) = (a \div b) + (a \div c)$

13. Show that $(a + b)^2 = a^2 + 2ab + b^2$ using
    a. the distributive property of multiplication over addition.
    b. an area model.

14. Show that if $b > c$ then $a(b - c) = ab - ac$ using
    a. an area model suggested by the given figure (express the shaded area in two different ways).

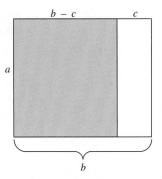

    b. the definition of subtraction in terms of addition and the distributive property of multiplication over addition.
    c. Name the property you have justified in parts (a) and (b).

15. Factor each of the following:
    a. $xy - y^2$
    b. $xy - y$
    c. $47 \cdot 101 - 47$
    d. $(x + 1)y - (x + 1)$
    e. $ab^2 - ba^2$

16. Suppose c is a divisor of a and of b. Show that $(a + b) \div c = (a \div c) + (b \div c)$ using
    a. a model.
    b. the definition of division in terms of multiplication and the distributive property of multiplication over addition.

17. Millie and Samantha began saving money at the same time. Millie plans to save \$3 a month, and Samantha plans to save \$5 a month. After how many months will Samantha have exactly \$10 more than Millie?

18. String art is formed by connecting evenly spaced nails on the vertical and horizontal axes by line segments. Connect the nail farthest from the origin on the vertical axis with the nail closest to the origin on the horizontal axis. Con-

tinue until all nails are connected, as shown in the figure that follows. How many intersection points are created with 10 nails on each axis?

3 nails per axis
3 intersections

19. There were 17 sandwiches for 7 people on a picnic. How many whole sandwiches were there for each person if they were divided equally? How many were left over?

20. a. Find all pairs of whole numbers whose product is 36.
   b. Plot the points found in (a) on a grid.
   c. Compare the pattern shape formed by the points to the graph of the pattern shape that could be found using all pairs of whole numbers whose sum is 36.

21. A new model of car is available in 4 exterior colors and 3 interior colors. Use a tree diagram and specific colors to show how many color schemes are possible for the car.

22. Students were divided into 8 teams with 9 on each team. Later the same students were divided into teams with 6 on each team. How many teams were there then?

 23. To find $7 \div 5$ on the calculator, press $\boxed{7}$ $\boxed{\div}$ $\boxed{5}$ $\boxed{=}$, which yields 1.4. To find the whole-number remainder, ignore the decimal portion of 1.4, multiply $5 \cdot 1$, and subtract this product from 7. The result is the remainder. Use a calculator to find the whole-number remainder for each of the following divisions:
   a. $28 \div 5$ **b.** $32 \div 10$
   c. $29 \div 3$ **d.** $41 \div 7$
   e. $49{,}382 \div 14$

24. Jonah has a large collection of marbles. He notices that if he borrows 5 marbles from a friend, he can arrange the marbles in rows of 13 each. What is the remainder when he divides his original number of marbles by 13?

25. Is it possible to find a whole number less than 100 that when divided by 10 leaves remainder 4 and when divided by 47 leaves remainder 17?

26. A number leaves remainder 6 when divided by 10. What is the remainder when the number is divided by 5? Justify your reasoning.

27. In the following problems, use only the designated number keys on the calculator. You may use any function keys.
   a. Use the keys $\boxed{1}$, $\boxed{9}$, and $\boxed{7}$ exactly once each in any order and use any operations available to write as many of the whole numbers as possible from 1 to 20. For example, $9 - 7 - 1 = 1$ and $1 \cdot 9 - 7 = 2$.
   b. Use the $\boxed{4}$ key as many times as desired with any operations to display 13.

c. Use the $\boxed{2}$ key three times with any operations to display 24.
   d. Use the $\boxed{1}$ key five times with any operations to display 100.

28. In each of the following, tell what computation must be done last:
   a. $5(16 - 7) \quad 18$ **b.** $54/(10 - 5 + 4)$
   c. $(14 - 3) + (24 \cdot 2)$ **d.** $21{,}045/345 + 8$

29. Is $x \div x$ always equal to 1? Explain your answer.

30. Is $x \cdot x$ ever equal to x? Explain your answer.

31. Describe all pairs of whole numbers whose sum and product are the same.

32. Write an algebraic expression for each of the following:
   a. Width of a rectangle whose area is A and length is l
   b. Feet, f, in yards
   c. Hours, h, in minutes
   d. Days, d, in weeks

33. Find infinitely many whole numbers that leave remainder 3 upon division by 5.

34. The operation $\odot$ is defined on the set $S = \{a, b, c\}$, as shown in the following table. For example, $a \odot b = b$ and $b \odot a = b$.

$\odot$	a	b	c
a	a	b	c
b	b	a	c
c	c	c	c

   a. Is S closed with respect to $\odot$?
   b. Is $\odot$ commutative on S?
   c. Is there an identity for $\odot$ on S? If yes, what is it?
   d. Is $\odot$ associative on S?

Communication

35. Suppose a student argued that $0 \div 0 = 0$ because "nothing divided by nothing" is "nothing." How would you help that person?

36. Sue claims the following is true by the distributive law, where a and b are whole numbers.

$$3(ab) = (3a)(3b).$$

How might you help her?

37. Can 0 be the identity for multiplication? Explain why or why not.

Open-Ended

38. Investigate whether your calculator has constant addition and subtraction features. Write an example to show how each feature works.

39. Describe a real-life situation that could be represented by the expression $5 + 8 \cdot 6$.

40. How would you explain to a child that an even number has the form $2q$ and an odd number has the form $2q + 1$ where q is a whole number?

Cooperative Learning

41. Multiplication facts that most children have memorized can be stated in the table that is partially filled:

×	1	2	3	4	5	6	7	8	9
1									
2									
3									
4			16						
5									
6									
7									
8									72
9									81

Fill out the table of multiplication facts. Find as many patterns as you can. List all the patterns that your group discovered and explain why some of those patterns occur in the table.

Review Problems

42. Give a set that is not closed under addition.

43. Are the whole numbers commutative under subtraction? If not, give a counterexample.

44. Illustrate $11 - 3$ using a number-line model.

45. Explain why if a, b, and c are whole numbers, and $c \neq 0$, then $a < b$ implies $ac < bc$.

LABORATORY
A C T I V I T Y

 Enter a number less than 20 on the calculator. If the number is even, divide it by 2; if it is odd, multiply it by 3 and add 1. Next, use the number on the display. Follow the given directions. Repeat the process.

1. Will the display eventually reach 1?

2. Which number less than 20 takes the most steps before reaching 1?

3. Do even or odd numbers reach 1 more quickly?

4. Investigate what happens with numbers greater than 20.

2-5 Functions

The *Principles and Standards* point out that the concept of a function is central in all of mathematics and in particular in algebra.

 By viewing algebra as a strand in the curriculum from prekindergarten on, teachers can help students build a solid foundation of understanding and experience as a preparation for more sophisticated work in algebra in the middle grades and high school. For example, systematic experience with patterns can build up to an understanding of the idea of function (Erick Smith forthcoming), and experience with numbers and their properties lays a foundation for later work with symbols and algebraic expressions. By learning that situations often can be described using mathematics, students can begin to form elementary notions of mathematical modeling. (p. 37)

Also the *Principles and Standards* point out that:

As they progress from preschool through high school, students should develop a repertoire of many types of functions. (p. 38)

The following is an example of a game called "guess my rule," often used to introduce the concept of a function.

When Tom said 2, Noah said 5. When Dick said 4, Noah said 7. When Mary said 10, Noah said 13. When Liz said 6, what did Noah say? What is Noah's rule?

The answer to the first question may be 9, and the rule could be, "Take the original number and add 3"; that is, for any number n, Noah's answer is $n + 3$.

EXAMPLE 2-17

Guess the teacher's rule for the following responses:

(a)

You	Teacher
1	3
0	0
4	12
10	30

(b)

You	Teacher
2	5
3	7
5	11
10	21

(c)

You	Teacher
2	0
4	0
7	1
21	1

Solution
a. The teacher's rule could be, "Multiply the given number n by 3," that is, $3n$.
b. The teacher's rule could be, "Double the original number n and add 1," that is, $2n + 1$.
c. The teacher's rule could be, "If the number n is even, answer 0; if the number is odd, answer 1." Another possible rule is "If the number is less than 5, answer 0; if greater than or equal to 5, answer 1."

HISTORICAL NOTE

The Babylonians (ca. 2000 B.C.) probably had a working idea of what a function was. To them, it was a table or a correspondence. René Descartes (1637), Gottfried Wilhelm von Leibnitz (1692), Johann Bernoulli (1718), Leonhard Euler (1750), Joseph Louis Lagrange (1800), and Jean Joseph Fourier (1822) were among the mathematicians contributing to the notion of a function. Leonhard Euler in 1734 first used the notation $f(x)$. In the late 1800s, Georg Cantor and others began to use the modern definition.

Another way to prepare students for the concept of a function is by using a "function machine." The following student page shows an example of a function machine. What goes in the machine is referred to as *input* and what comes out as *output*. Thus, on the student

Sample School Book Page:
ALGEBRA

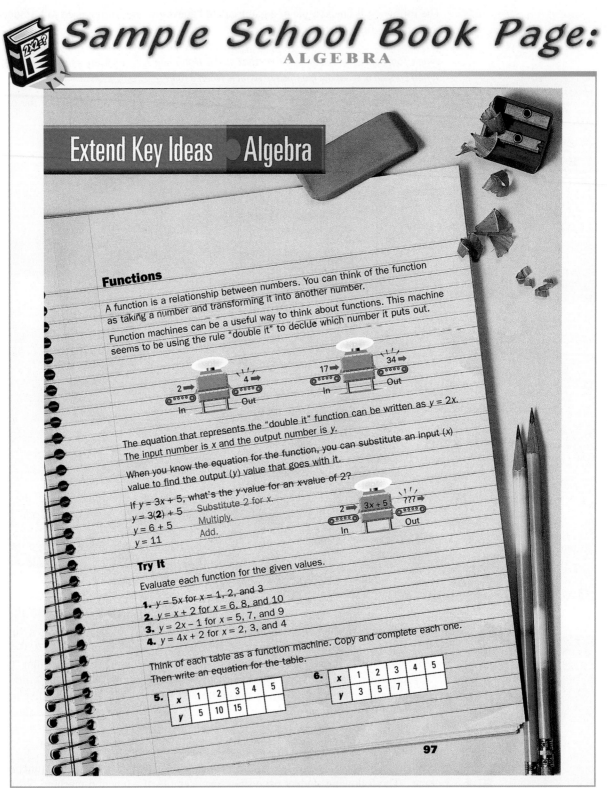

Extend Key Ideas ▶ Algebra

Functions

A function is a relationship between numbers. You can think of the function as taking a number and transforming it into another number.

Function machines can be a useful way to think about functions. This machine seems to be using the rule "double it" to decide which number it puts out.

The equation that represents the "double it" function can be written as $y = 2x$. The input number is x and the output number is y.

When you know the equation for the function, you can substitute an input (x) value to find the output (y) value that goes with it.

If $y = 3x + 5$, what's the y-value for an x-value of 2?

$y = 3(\textbf{2}) + 5$	Substitute 2 for x.
$y = 6 + 5$	Multiply.
$y = 11$	Add.

Try It

Evaluate each function for the given values.

1. $y = 5x$ for $x = 1, 2,$ and 3
2. $y = x + 2$ for $x = 6, 8,$ and 10
3. $y = 2x - 1$ for $x = 5, 7,$ and 9
4. $y = 4x + 2$ for $x = 2, 3,$ and 4

Think of each table as a function machine. Copy and complete each one. Then write an equation for the table.

5.

x	1	2	3	4	5
y	5	10	15		

6.

x	1	2	3	4	5
y	3	5	7		

97

Source: Scott Foresman–Addison Wesley Middle School Math Course 2, 2002 (p. 97).

page, if the input to the first function machine is 8, the output is 16. In later grades, a special notation for the output is used. For any input element *x*, the output is denoted $f(x)$, read "*f* of *x*." For the function machine pictured on the student page, when the input is 17, the output could be written $f(17)$. Because the output is 34, we have $f(17) = 34$. Because the machine works according to the rule "double it," $f(x) = 2x$ and $f(17) = 2 \cdot 17 = 34$. Do problems 1 through 6 on the student page.

E X A M P L E
2-18

Consider the function machine in Figure 2-34. What will happen if the numbers 0, 1, 3, and 6 are entered?

Solution   If the numbers output are denoted by $f(x)$, the corresponding values can be described using Table 2-7.

FIGURE 2-34

$f(4) = 7$

Table 2-7

x	f(x)
0	3
1	4
3	6
6	9

We can write an equation to depict the rule in Example 2-18 as follows. If the input is *x*, the output is *x* + 3; that is, $f(x) = x + 3$. The output values can be obtained by substituting the values 0, 1, 3, 4, and 6 for *x* in $f(x) = x + 3$, as shown:

$$f(0) = 0 + 3 = 3$$
$$f(1) = 1 + 3 = 4$$
$$f(3) = 3 + 3 = 6$$
$$f(4) = 4 + 3 = 7$$
$$f(6) = 6 + 3 = 9$$

In many applications, both the inputs and the outputs of a function machine are numbers. However, inputs and outputs can be any objects. For example, consider a particular candy machine that accepts only 25¢, 50¢, and 75¢ and outputs one of three types of candy. A function machine associates *exactly one output with each input*. If you enter some element *x* as input and obtain $f(x)$ as output, then every time you enter the same *x* as input, you will obtain the same $f(x)$ as output. The idea of a function machine associating exactly one output with each input according to some rule leads to the following definition.

> ### Definition of Function

A **function** from set *A* to set *B* is a correspondence from *A* to *B* in which each element of *A* is paired with one, and only one, element of *B*.

domain   The set *A* in the previous definition is the set of all allowable inputs and is the **domain** of the function. The set *B* is any set that includes all the possible outputs. The set of all out-

range   puts is the **range** of the function. Set *B* in the definition is any set that includes the range and can be the range itself. The distinction is made for convenience sake, since sometimes the range is not easy to find. For example, consider corresponding to each student at a university the student's Social Security number. This is a function from the set of all students to the set *W* of whole numbers. The range in this case is all the Social Security numbers of students who are enrolled at the university. The range is a proper subset of the set *W*. Normally *if no domain is given to describe a function, then the domain is assumed to contain all elements for which the rule is meaningful.*

A calculator is a function machine. Suppose a student enters $\boxed{9}$ $\boxed{\times}$ $\boxed{K}$ on the calculator that has a constant key, $\boxed{K}$. The student then presses $\boxed{0}$ and hands the calculator to another student. The other student is to determine the rule by entering various numbers followed by the $\boxed{=}$ key. Machines with an automatic constant feature can also be used.

Other buttons on a calculator are function buttons. For example, the $\boxed{\pi}$ button always displays an approximation for π, such as 3.1415927; the $\boxed{+/-}$ button either displays a negative sign in front of a number or removes an existing negative sign; and the $\boxed{x^2}$ and $\boxed{\sqrt{}}$ buttons square numbers and take the square root of numbers, respectively.

FIGURE 2-35

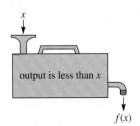

Are all input-output machines function machines? Consider the machine in Figure 2-35. For any natural-number input *x*, the machine outputs a number that is less than *x*. If, for example, you input the number 10, the machine may output 9, since 9 is less than 10. If you input 10 again, the machine may output 3, since 3 is less than 10. Such a machine is not a function machine because the same input may give different outputs.

E X A M P L E
2-19

Which, if any, of the parts of Figure 2-36 exhibits a function from *A* to *B*? If a correspondence is a function from *A* to *B*, find the range of the function.

FIGURE 2-36

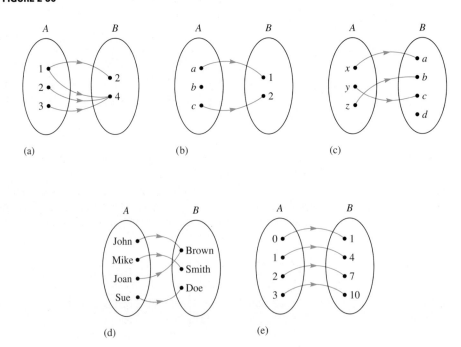

Solution **a.** Figure 2-36(a) does not define a function from *A* to *B*, since the element 1 is paired with both 2 and 4.

b Figure 2-36(b) does not define a function from *A* to *B*, since the element *b* is not paired with any element of *B*. (It is a function from a subset of *A* to *B*.)

c. Figure 2-36(c) does define a function from *A* to *B*, since there is one and only one arrow leaving each element of *A*. The fact that *d*, an element of *B*, is not paired with any element in the domain does not violate the definition. The range is {*a*, *b*, *c*} and does not include *d* because *d* is not an output of this function, as no element of *A* is paired with *d*.

d. Figure 2-36(d) illustrates a function, since there is only one arrow leaving each element in *A*. It does not matter that an element of set *B*, Brown, has two arrows pointing to it. The range is {Brown, Smith, Doe}.

e. Figure 2-36(e) illustrates a function whose range is {1, 4, 7, 10}.

Figure 2-36(e) also illustrates a one-to-one correspondence between *A* and *B*. In fact, any one-to-one correspondence between *A* and *B* defines a function from *A* to *B* as well as a function from *B* to *A*.

NOW TRY THIS 2-14

Determine which of the following are functions from the set of natural numbers to {0, 1}. Justify your reasoning.

a. For every natural-number input, the output is 0.

b. For every natural-number input, the output is 0 if the input is an even number and the output is 1 if the input is an odd number.

A function can be represented in a variety of ways. A useful way to describe a function is in a table. Consider the information in Table 2-8 relating the amount spent on advertising and the resulting sales in a given month for a small business. If *A* = {0, 1, 2, 3, 4} and *S* = {1, 3, 6, 8, 10}, the table describes a function from *A* to *S*.

The information in Table 2-8 can also be given using ordered pairs. When 0 is the input and 1 is the output, that is recorded as the ordered pair (0, 1). Similarly, the information in the second row is recorded as (1, 3) and the rest of the information as (2, 6), (3, 8), and (4, 10). The first component in the ordered pair is always an element in the domain and the second is the corresponding output.

Table 2-8

Amount of Advertising (In $1000s)	Amount of Sales (In $1000s)
0	1
1	3
2	6
3	8
4	10

E X A M P L E
2-20

Which of the following sets of ordered pairs represent functions? If a set represents a function, give its domain and range. If it does not, explain why.

a. $\{(1, 2), (1, 3), (2, 3), (3, 4)\}$
b. $\{(1, 2), (2, 3), (3, 4), (4, 5)\}$
c. $\{(1, 0), (2, 0), (3, 0), (4, 4)\}$
d. $\{(a, b) \mid a \in N, b = 2a\}$

Solution **a.** This is not a function because the input 1 has two different outputs.
b. This is a function with domain $\{1, 2, 3, 4\}$ and range $\{2, 3, 4, 5\}$.
c. This is a function with domain $\{1, 2, 3, 4\}$ and range $\{0, 4\}$. The output 0 appears more than once, but this does not contradict the definition of a function in that each input corresponds to only one output.
d. This is a function with domain N and range E, the set of all even natural numbers.

Perhaps one of the most widely recognized representations of a function is a graph. Graphs are visual representations of functions and appear in newspapers and books and on television. To graph the function in Table 2-8, consider the set of ordered pairs $\{(0, 1),$ $(1, 3), (2, 6), (4, 10)\}$ and correspond to each ordered pair a point on the grid in Figure 2-37. We use the horizontal scale for the inputs and the vertical scale for the outputs and mark the point corresponding to $(0, 1)$ by starting at 0 on the horizontal scale and going up 1 unit on the vertical scale. To mark the point that corresponds to $(1, 3)$, we start at 0 and move 1 unit horizontally and then 3 units vertically. Marking the point that corresponds to **graphing** an ordered pair is referred to as **graphing** the ordered pair. The set of all points that correspond to all the ordered pairs is the graph of the function.

FIGURE 2-37

In applications of mathematics it is often convenient to have different scales for vertical and horizontal axes. For example, consider the following partial student page. The points on the graphs on the student page have been connected. This implies that we could find the recommended maximum pulse rate at any age between 10 and 50.

Problem Solving and Applications

33. A table and graph in a doctor's office give recommended maximum pulse rates during exercise, according to age. Susana and Larry are 15 years old. What is their recommended pulse rate?

Age (years)	10	20	30	40	50
Rates (beats/min)	152	144	136	128	120

a. How can you use the table to answer the question?

b. How can you use the graph to answer the question?

c. What is the recommended pulse for a 15-year-old?

d. Which method would you use to find the recommended pulse rate for a person who is 32 years old? Explain.

Source: Scott Foresman–Addison-Wesley Math, Grade 6, 2002 (p. 496).

NOW TRY THIS 2-15

Answer the questions on the student page.

Explain why a telephone company would not set rates for telephone calls as depicted on the graph in Figure 2-38.

FIGURE 2-38

Telephone Call Costs

Solution   The graph does not depict a function. For example, a customer could be charged either $.50 or $.85 for a 2-minute call.

More on Applications of Functions

Functions have many real-life applications. For example, on direct-dial long-distance calls you pay only for the minutes you talk. Suppose with the Supercel phone company the weekday rate for a long-distance phone call from Madison, Wisconsin, to Urbana, Illinois, is 27¢ per minute. We have seen that one way to describe a function is by writing an equation. Based on the information in Table 2-9, the equation relating time to cost is

Table 2-9

Number of Minutes Talked	Total Cost in Cents
1	$1 \cdot 27 = 27$
2	$2 \cdot 27 = 54$
3	$3 \cdot 27 = 81$
4	$4 \cdot 27 = 108$
4	$5 \cdot 27 = 135$
.	.
.	.
.	.
t	$t \cdot 27$

$C = t \cdot 27$, where t is a natural number. This could also be written as $f(t) = 27t$, where $f(t)$ is the cost of the call in cents. If we restrict the time in minutes to the first 5 natural numbers, the function can be described as the set of ordered pairs {(1, 27), (2, 54), (3, 81), (4, 108), (5, 135)}. Figure 2-39(a) shows the graph of the function. The graph consists of 5 points that are not connected, since the phone company charges for any part of a minute t as if it were a full minute. The break in the vertical axis shown by ⌇ indicates that part of the vertical axis between 0 and 27 has been compressed and that the scale is not accurate between 0 and 27.

In graphing the function in Figure 2-39(a), we assumed the domain to be the set of natural numbers. Because the phone company charges for any part of a minute as if it were a full minute, the charge for any call that is 1 min long or less is 27¢. The charge for any call less than or equal to 2 min but longer than 1 min is 54¢. The cost is calculated similarly for calls between two consecutive minutes. The graph reflecting this information is shown in Figure 2-39(b). The filled dot at the right endpoint of each segment in the graph indicates that the point belongs to the graph, while the empty dot at the left endpoint of each segment indicates that the point does not belong to the graph. The domain of the function graphed in Figure 2-39(b) is the set of all positive numbers.

FIGURE 2-39

(a)

(b)

NOW TRY THIS 2-16

Find the cost of 4.5 min of phone conversation from Madison, Wisconsin, to Urbana, Illinois, from the graph in Figure 2-39(b). Next find the cost by substituting $t = 4.5$ into the formula $C = 27t$ developed above. What is the reason for the different answers?

Functions and their graphs are used frequently in the business world, as the following example illustrates.

E X A M P L E
2-22

In Figure 2-40 the blue graph shows the cost C in dollars of producing a given length of material (in meters). The red graph shows the revenue R in dollars from selling any number of meters of the material.

FIGURE 2-40

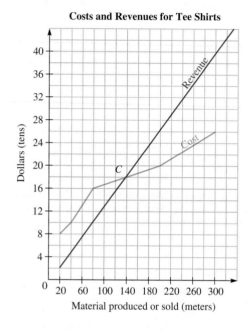

Based on the information in the graphs, find the following:

a. The cost of producing the first 300 meters of material
b. The revenue from the sale of the first 80 meters of material
c. The profit or loss if the first 80 meters of material are produced and sold
d. The break-even point, that is, the number of meters of material that must be produced and sold in order for the net profit to be $0

Solution   **a.** From the blue graph in Figure 2-40 we see that the cost corresponding to 300 meters is $260.
b. From the red graph, we see that the revenue from the sale of the first 80 meters of material is $100.
c. The cost of producing 80 meters of material is $160. Because the profit is the difference between the cost and the revenue, the loss in this case is $160 − $100, or $60.
d. The break-even point is at point C, where the graphs intersect. At that point, the cost and the revenue are the same. The number of meters of material corresponding to point C is 140.

Sequences as Functions

Arithmetic, geometric, and other sequences introduced in Chapter 1 can be thought of as functions whose inputs are natural numbers and whose outputs are the terms of a particular sequence. For example, the arithmetic sequence 2, 4, 6, 8, . . . whose nth term is $2n$ can be described as $f(n) = 2n$ where n is a natural number and $f(n)$ stands for the value of the nth term.

EXAMPLE 2-23

If $f(n)$ denotes the *n*th term of a sequence, find $f(n)$ terms of *n* for each of the following.

a. An arithmetic sequence whose first term is 3 and whose difference is 3
b. A geometric sequence whose first term is 3 and whose ratio is 3
c. The sequence: $1, 1 + 2, 1 + 2 + 3, 1 + 2 + 3 + 4, \ldots$

Solution
a. The first term is 3, the second term is $3 + 3$ or $2 \cdot 3$, the third is $2 \cdot 3 + 3$ or $3 \cdot 3$, and the fourth term is $3 \cdot 3 + 3$ or $4 \cdot 3$, the *n*th term is $n \cdot 3$ and hence $f(n) = n \cdot 3 = 3n$, where *n* is a natural number.
b. The first term is 3, the second $3 \cdot 3$ or 3^2, the third $3 \cdot 3^2$ or 3^3, and so on. Hence, the *n*th term is 3^n and therefore $f(n) = 3^n$, where *n* is a natural number.
c. The *n*th term is $1 + 2 + 3 + 4 + \ldots + n$. In Chapter 1 we have seen that this sum equals $\dfrac{n(n + 1)}{2}$ so the function is $f(n) = \dfrac{n(n + 1)}{2}$, where *n* is a natural number.

Operations on Functions

Consider the function machines in Figure 2-41. If 2 is entered in the top machine, then $f(2) = 2 + 4 = 6$. Six is then entered in the second machine and $g(6) = 2 \cdot 6 = 12$.

composition of two functions

The functions in Figure 2-41 illustrate the **composition of two functions**. In the composition of two functions, the range of the first function becomes the domain of the second function.

FIGURE 2-41

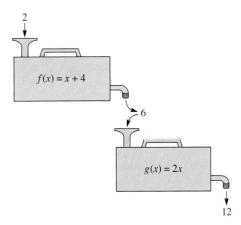

If the first function *f* is followed by a second function *g*, as in Figure 2-41, symbolize the composition of the functions as $g \circ f$. If we input 3 in the function machines of Figure 2-41 then the output is symbolized by $(g \circ f)(3)$. Because *f* acts first on 3, to compute $(g \circ f)(3)$ we find $f(3) = 3 + 4 = 7$ and then $g(7) = 2 \circ 7 = 14$. Hence, $(g \circ f)(3) = 14$ and $(g \circ f)(3) = g(f(3))$. Also note that $(g \circ f)(x) = g(f(x)) = 2 \cdot f(x) = 2(x + 4)$ and hence $g(f(3)) = 2(3 + 4) = 14$.

EXAMPLE
2-24

If $f(x) = 2x + 3$ and $g(x) = x - 3$, find the following:

a. $(f \circ g)(3)$ **b.** $(g \circ f)(3)$ **c.** $(f \circ g)(x)$ **d.** $(g \circ f)(x)$

Solution   **a.** $(f \circ g)(3) = f(0) = 2 \cdot 0 + 3 = 3$
b. $(g \circ f)(3) = g(9) = 9 - 3 = 6$
c. $(f \circ g)(x) = f(g(x)) = 2 \cdot g(x) + 3 = 2(x - 3) + 3 = 2x - 6 + 3 = 2x - 3$
d. $(g \circ f)(x) = g(f(x)) = f(x) - 3 = (2x + 3) - 3 = 2x$

REMARK   Example 2-24 shows that composition of functions is not commutative, since $(f \circ g)(3) \neq (g \circ f)(3)$.

We have seen that a function can be represented in a variety of ways: a table, a function machine, pictures of sets and arrows, a set of ordered pairs, and a graph. Pictures of sets with arrows and function machines are used mostly as pedagogical devices in learning the concept of a function. The most common representations are a table, an equation, and a graph. Depending on the situation, one representation may be more useful than another. For example, if the domain of a function is a large set, a table is not a convenient representation. An equation is a compact way to represent a function, but if one is given a graph of a function, it is not always possible to find an equation that represents the function. In later chapters, we learn how to graph certain kinds of equations. Graphing calculators are capable of graphing most functions given by equations with specified domains.

TECHNOLOGY
C O R N E R

A sketch of the function $y = 2x + 1$ for x between 0 and 5 is shown in Figure 2-42. Use a graphing calculator to sketch the graphs of $y = 2x + b$ for three choices of b. What do the graphs seem to have in common? Why?

FIGURE 2-42

ONGOING ASSESSMENT 2-5

1. The following sets of ordered pairs are functions. Give a rule that could describe each function.
   a. {(2, 4), (3, 6), (9, 18), (12, 24)}
   b. {(5, 3), (7, 5), (11, 9), (14, 12)}
   c. {(2, 8), (5, 11), (7, 13), (4, 10)}
   d. {(2, 5), (3, 10), (4, 17), (5, 26)}

2. Which of the following are functions from the set {1, 2, 3} to the set {a, b, c, d}? If the set of ordered pairs is not a function, explain why not.
   a. {(1, a), (2, b), (3, c), (1, d)}   b. {(1, c), (3, d)}
   c. {(1, a), (2, b), (3, a)}   d. {(1, a), (1, b), (1, c)}

3. a. Draw a diagram of a function with domain {1, 2, 3, 4, 5} and range {a, b}.
   b. How many possible functions are there in part (a)?

4. Suppose $f(x) = 2x + 1$ and the domain is {0, 1, 2, 3, 4}. Describe the function in the following ways:
   a. Draw an arrow diagram involving two sets.
   b. Use ordered pairs.   c. Make a table.
   d. Draw a graph to depict the function.

5. Determine which of the following are functions from $W = \{0, 1, 2, 3, \ldots\}$ or a subset of W, to W. If your answer is that it is not a function, explain why not.
   a. $f(x) = 2$ for all $x \in W$
   b. $f(x) = 0$ if $x \in \{0, 1, 2, 3\}$, and $f(x) = 3$ if $x \notin \{0, 1, 2, 3\}$
   c. $f(x) = x$
   d. $f(x) = 0$ for all $x \in W$ and $f(x) = 1$ if $x \in \{3, 4, 5, 6, \ldots\}$
   e. $f(x)$ is the sum of the digits in x for all $x \in W$.

6. a. Write a rule for computing the cost of mailing a first-class letter based on its weight.
   b. Find the cost of mailing a 3-oz letter.
   c. Show that the rule you found in part (a) is a function whose inputs are weights in ounces. Find the range of this function.
   d. Graph the function in part (c).

7. The dosage of a certain drug is related to the weight of a child as follows: 50 mg of the drug and an additional 15 mg for each 2 lb or fraction of 2 lb of body weight above 30 lb. Sketch the graph of the dosage as a function of the weight of a child for children who weigh between 20 and 40 lb.

8. According to wildlife experts, the rate at which crickets chirp is a function of the temperature; specifically, $C = T - 40$, where C is the number of chirps every 15 sec and T is the temperature in degrees Fahrenheit.
   a. How many chirps does the cricket make per second if the temperature is 70°F?
   b. What is the temperature if the cricket chirps 40 times in 1 min?

9. If taxi fares are $3.50 for the first half mile and $0.75 for each additional quarter mile, answer the following:
   a. What is the fare for a 2-mi trip?
   b. Write a rule for computing the fare for an n-mile trip by taxi.

10. For each of the following, guess what might be Latifah's rule. In each case, if n is your input and $L(n)$ is Latifah's answer, express $L(n)$ in terms of n.

    a.
You	Latifah
3	8
4	11
5	14
10	29

    b.
You	Latifah
0	1
3	10
5	26
8	65

    c.
You	Latifah
6	42
0	0
8	72
2	6

11. The following graph shows arithmetic achievement-test scores for students of a sixth-grade class. From the graph, estimate the following:
    a. The frequency of the score made most often
    b. The highest score obtained
    c. The number of boys who would have had to score 54 on the test in order to match the number of girls who scored 54

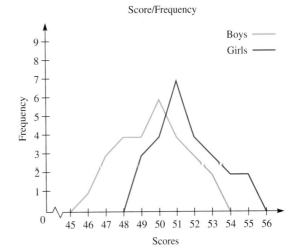

Score/Frequency

12. The *Principles and Standards* for grades 6–8 points out that "in their study of algebra, middle grades students should encounter questions that focus on quantities that change." (p. 229) It poses the following problem along with graphs.

    ChitChat charges $0.30 a minute for cellular phone calls. The cost per minute does not change, but the total cost changes as the telephone is used.

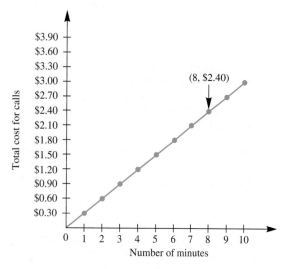

a. When the number of minutes is 6, what do the values of the corresponding point on each graph represent?

b. What kind of assumption about the charges needs to be made to allow the connection of the points on each graph? Explain.

c. If time in minutes is t and the total cost for calls is c, write c as a function of t for each graph.

13. In the *Principles and Standards* for grades 6–8, the "Algebra" section (p. 229) poses the following problem. Quick-Talk advertises monthly cellular phone service for $0.50 a minute for the first 60 minutes but only $0.10 a minute for each minute thereafter. Quick-Talk also charges for the exact amount of time used. Answer the following.

a. Graph two graphs similar to the ones in problem 12; one graph showing the cost per minute as a function of number of minutes, and the other showing the total cost for calls as a function of number of minutes up to 100 minutes.

b. If you connect the points in the second graph in part (a), what kind of assumption needs to be made about the way the telephone company charges phone calls?

c. Why does the total cost for calls consist of two line segments? Why is one part steeper than the other?

d. The function representing the total cost for calls as a function of number of minutes talked can be represented by two equations. Write these equations.

14. For each of the following sequences, find a possible function whose domain is the set of natural numbers and whose outputs are the terms of the sequence.

a. 3, 8, 13, 18, 23, . . .

b. 3, 9, 27, 81, 243, . . .

c. 2, 4, 6, 8, 10, . . .

15. Consider two function machines that are placed as shown. Find the final output for each of the following inputs:

   a. 5   **b.** 3   **c.** 10

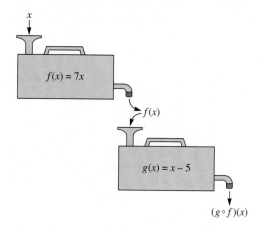

16. Let $t(n)$ represent the nth term of a sequence for $n \in N$. Answer the following:

a. If $t(n) = 4n - 3$, determine which of the following are values of the function.

   (i) 1   (ii) 385   (iii) 389   (iv) 392

b. If $t(n) = n^2$, determine which of the following are values of the function.

   (i) 1   (ii) 4   (iii) 9   (iv) 10   (v) 900

c. If $t(n) = n(n + 1)$, determine which are in the range of the function.

   (i) 2   (ii) 12   (iii) 2550   (iv) 2600

17. Consider a function machine that accepts inputs as ordered pairs. Suppose the components of the ordered pairs are natural numbers and the first component is the length of the rectangle and the second is its width. The following machine computes the perimeter (the distance around a figure) of the rectangle. Thus for a rectangle whose length, l, is 3 and whose width, w, is 2, the input is (3, 2) and the output is $2 \cdot 3 + 2 \cdot 2$, or 10. Answer each of the following:

a. For each of the following inputs, find the corresponding output: (1, 7), (2, 6), (6, 2), (5, 5).

b. Find the set of all the inputs for which the output is 20.

c. What is the domain and the range of the function?

(l, w)

$2l + 2w$

18. The following graph shows Mandy's height in centimeters measured every month starting 1 month after her fourteenth birthday. Answer the following:

a. What was the change in Mandy's height from the first to the second month after her birthday?

b. During which consecutive months was the change in Mandy's height the greatest?

c. What missing information would enable you to find Mandy's change in height one month after her birthday?

Mandy's Height after Age 14

19. The following graph shows the relationship between the number of cars on a certain road at different times between 5:00 A.M. and 9:00 A.M.

Traffic Patterns

a. What was the increase in the number of cars on the road between 6:30 A.M. and 7:00 A.M.?

b. During which half hour was the increase in the number of cars the greatest?

c. What was the increase in the number of cars between 8:00 A.M. and 8:30 A.M.?

d. During which half hour(s) did the number of cars decrease? By how much?

20. A health club charges a one-time initiation fee of $100 plus a membership fee of $40 per month.

a. Write an expression for the cost function $C(x)$ that gives the total cost for membership at the health club for x months.

b. Draw the graph of the function in (a).

c. The health club decided to give its members an option of a higher initiation fee but a lower monthly membership charge. If the initiation fee is $300 and the monthly membership fee is $30, use a different color and draw on the same set of axes the cost graph under this plan.

d. Determine from the graphs after how many months the second plan is less expensive for the member.

21. A ball is thrown straight up. We know its height H in feet after t seconds is given by the function $H(t) = 128t - 16t^2$.

a. Find $H(2)$, $H(6)$, $H(3)$, and $H(5)$. Why are some of the outputs equal?

b. Graph the function and from the graph find at what instant the ball is at its highest point. What is its height at that instant?

c. How long will it take the ball to hit the ground?

d. What is the domain of H?

e. What is the range of H?

22. A rectangular plot is to be bound on one side by a straight river and on the other sides by a fence. Suppose 900 yd of fence are available and the length of the side of the rectangle parallel to the river is denoted by x.

a. Find an expression for the area $A(x)$ in terms of x.

b. Graph $A(x)$.

c Use the graph in (b) or your calculator to estimate the length and width of the rectangle for which the area will be the largest.

River

x

23. For each of the following sequences of matchstick figures, let $S(n)$ be the function giving the total number of matchsticks in the nth figure.

a. For each of the following, find the total number of matchsticks in the 4th figure.

b. For each of the following, find as simple a formula as possible for $S(n)$ in terms of n.

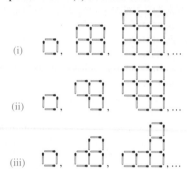

(i)

(ii)

(iii)

24. Assume the pattern continues for each of the following sequences of square tile figures. Let $S(n)$ be the function giving the total number of tiles in the nth figure. For each of the following find a formula for $S(n)$ in terms of n.

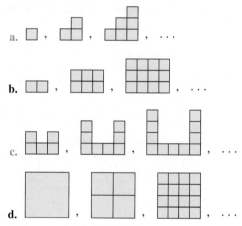

a.

b.

c.

d.

Each square is divided into four squares in the subsequent figure.

25. A function can be represented as a set of ordered pairs where the set of all the first components is the domain and the set of all the second components is the range. Is the converse also true? That is, is every set of ordered pairs a function whose domain is the set of first components and whose range is the second components? Justify your answer.

26. Suppose each point in the figure represents a child on a playground, the letters represent their names, and an arrow going from I to J means that I "is the sister of" J.

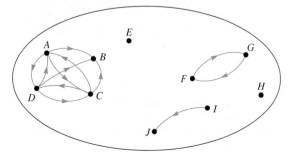

a. Based on the information in the figure, who are definitely girls and who are definitely boys?

b. Suppose we write "A is the sister of B" as an ordered pair (A, B). Based on the information in the diagram, write the set of all such ordered pairs.

c. Is the set of all ordered pairs in (b) a function with domain equal to the set of all first components of the ordered pairs and with the range equal to the set of all second components?

27. A generalization of the concept of a function is the concept of a *relation. Given two sets* A *and* B, *a relation from* A *to* B *is any set of ordered pairs in which the first components are from* A *and the second are from* B. Which of the following are functions and which are relations but not functions from the set of first components of the ordered pairs to the set of second components?

a. {(Montana, Helena), (Oregon, Salem), (Illinois, Springfield), (Arkansas, Little Rock)}

b. {(Pennsylvania, Philadelphia), (New York, New York), (New York, Niagara Falls), (Florida, Ft. Lauderdale)}

c. $\{(x, y) \mid x$ resides in Birmingham, Alabama, and x is the mother of y, where y is a U.S. resident$\}$

d. {(1, 1), (2, 4), (3, 9), (4, 16)}

e. $\{(x, y) \mid$ where x and y are natural numbers and $x + y$ is an even number$\}$

28. a. Is the rule "has as mother" a function whose domain is the set of all people?

b. Is the relation "has as brother" a function from the set of all boys to the set of all boys?

The following definitions are needed to answer problems 29 and 30.

A *relation on a set* X. This is a relation from X to X. A relation on X may have one or more of the following properties: *The reflexive property.* A relation on a set X is reflexive if, and only if, for all a in X, a is related to a, that is (a, a) is in the set of ordered pairs.

The symmetric property. A relation on a set X is symmetric if, and only if, for all elements a and b in X, whenever a is related to b, then b is also related to a; that is, if (a, b) is in the set of ordered pairs, so is (b, a).

The transitive property. A relation on a set X is transitive if, and only if, for all elements a, b, and c in X, whenever a is related to b and b is related to c, then a is related to c; that is, if (a, b) and (b, c) are in the set of ordered pairs, then (a, c) is also in the same set (a, b, and c do not have to be different).

An **equivalence relation** on a set X is any relation on X that satisfies the reflexive, symmetric, and transitive properties.

29. Tell whether each of the following is reflexive, symmetric, or transitive on the set of all people. Which are equivalence relations?

a. "Is a parent of"

b. "Is the same age as"

c. "Has the same last name as"

d. "Is the same height as"

e. "Is married to"

f. "Lives within 10 mi of"

g. "Is older than"

30. Tell whether each of the following is reflexive, symmetric, or transitive on the set of subsets of a nonempty set. Which are equivalence relations?

   a. "Is equal to"

   b. "Is a proper subset of"

   c. "Is not equal to"

   d. "Has the same cardinal number as"

Communication

31. Does the diagram define a function from *A* to *B*? Why or why not?

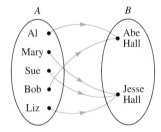

32. Is a one-to-one correspondence a function? Explain your answer and give an example.

33. Which of the following are functions from *A* to *B*? If your answer is "not a function," explain why not.

   a. *A* is the set of mathematics faculty at the university. *B* is the set of all mathematics classes. To each mathematics faculty member, we associate the class that person is teaching during a given term.

   b. *A* is the set of mathematics classes at the university. *B* is the set of mathematics faculty. To each mathematics class, we associate the teacher who is teaching the class.

   c. *A* is the set of all U.S. senators and *B* is the set of all Senate committees. We associate each senator to the committee of which the senator is chairperson.

34. When a boat is put in the water, its hull is partially above and partially below the water. The part below the water is the "draft" and the part above the water is the "freeboard." The following table shows the relationship between the draft and freeboard for a 50-cm-deep boat:

Draft	Freeboard
5	45
10	40
15	35
20	30
30	20

   a. Graph the freeboard as a function of the draft. Is it meaningful to connect the points graphed? Explain.

   b. If *d* stands for the draft in centimeters and $f(d)$ for the freeboard, write an equation expressing $f(d)$ in terms of *d*.

Open-Ended

35. Examine several newspapers and magazines and describe at least three examples of functions that appear. What is the domain and range of each function?

36. Give at least three examples of functions from *A* to *B* where neither *A* nor *B* is a set of numbers.

37. Draw a sequence of figures of matchsticks and describe the pattern in words. Find as simple an expression as possible for $S(n)$, the total number of matchsticks in the *n*th figure.

38. A function whose output is always the same regardless of the input is a *constant function*. Give several examples of constant functions from real life.

39. A function whose output is the same as its input is an *identity function*. Give several concrete examples of identity functions.

Cooperative Learning

40. Each person in a group picks a natural number and uses it as an input in the following function machine:

   a. Compare your answers. Based on the answers, make a conjecture about the range of the function.

   b. Based on your answer in (a), graph the function.

   c. Write the function in the simplest possible way using $f(x)$ notation.

   d. Justify your conjecture in (a).

   e. Make up similar function machines and try different inputs in your group.

   f. Devise a function machine in which the machine performs several operations, but the output is always the same as the input. Exchange your answer with someone in the group and check that the other person's function machine performs as required.

   g. Write the functions the group came up with in the simplest way using $f(x)$ notation and graph them.

41. In the following two-person (or two-group) activity, one person presents the graphs of several arithmetic and several geometric sequences. The second person is required to find what kind of sequence corresponds to each graph and the simplest possible expression for $T(n)$, the *n*th term of the sequence. Compare your expressions for $T(n)$ and make a conjecture on how to tell from the graph if a sequence is arithmetic.

Review Problems

42. Rewrite each of the following in equivalent form using only multiplication or addition operations.
   a. $109 - 11 = 98$.   b. $x - y = z$.
   c. $60 \div 4 = 15$.   d. $x \div 3 = y$.
   e. $(x - 3) \div 5 = 10$.

43. Is the number of elements in $A \cup B$ always equal to the sum of the number of elements in A and the number of elements in B? Why or why not?

44. Shade the portion of the Venn diagram that illustrates the set $(B - C) \cup (A \cap B)$.

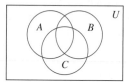

BRAIN TEASER

Only 10 rooms were vacant in the Village Hotel. Eleven men went into the hotel at the same time, each wanting a separate room. The clerk, settling the argument, said, "I'll tell you what I'll do. I'll put two men in Room 1 with the understanding that I will come back and get one of them a few minutes later." The men agreed to this. The clerk continued, "I will put the rest of you men in rooms as follows: the third man in Room 2, the fourth man in Room 3, the fifth man in Room 4, the sixth man in Room 5, the seventh man in Room 6, the eighth man in Room 7, the ninth man in Room 8, and the tenth man in Room 9." Then the clerk went back and got the extra man he had left in Room 1 and put him in Room 10. Everybody was happy. What is wrong with this plan?

Hint for Solving the Preliminary Problem

Find the number of nonempty subsets of each class and use the Fundamental Counting Principle. Compare the number of committees to the population of the world, which is about 6 billion—that is, 6,000,000,000.

QUESTIONS FROM THE CLASSROOM

1. A student argues that $\{\varnothing\}$ is the proper notation for the empty set. What is your response?

2. A student asks, "If $A = \{a, b, c\}$ and $B = \{b, c, d\}$, why isn't it true that $A \cup B = \{a, b, c, b, c, d\}$?" What is your response?

3. A student says that she can show that if $A \cap B = A \cap C$, then it is not necessarily true that $B = C$; but she thinks that whenever $A \cap B = A \cap C$ and $A \cup B = A \cup C$, then $B = C$. What is your response?

4. A student claims that a finite set of numbers is any set that has a greatest element. Do you agree?

5. A student claims that the complement bar can be broken over the operation of intersections; that is, $\overline{A \cap B} = \overline{A} \cap \overline{B}$. What is your response?

6. A student claims that $\overline{A} \cap \overline{B}$ includes all elements that are not in A. What is your response?

7. A student asks whether a formula and a function are the same. What is your response?

8. A student states that either $A \subseteq B$ or $B \subseteq A$. Is the student correct?

9. A student is asked to find all one-to-one correspondences between 2 given sets. He finds the Cartesian product of the sets and claims that his answer is correct because it includes all possible pairings between the elements of the sets. How do you respond?

10. A student argues that adding two sets A and B, or $A + B$, and taking the union of two sets, $A \cup B$, is the same thing. How do you respond?

11. A student asks "Does $2(3 \cdot 4)$ equal $(2 \cdot 3)(2 \cdot 4)$?" Is there a distributive property of multiplication over multiplication?

12. Since $39 + 41 = 40 + 40$, is it true that $39 \cdot 41 = 40 \cdot 40$?

13. The division algorithm, $a = bq + r$, holds for $a \geq b$; $a, b, q, r \in W, r < b$, and $b \neq 0$. Does the division algorithm hold when $a < b$?

14. Can we define $0 \div 0$ as 1? Why or why not?

15. **a.** A student claims that for all whole numbers $(a \cdot b) \div b = a$. How do you respond?

    b. The student in part (a) claims that $0 \div 0 = 0$. The student's reasoning is, "if $a = 0$ and $b = 0$ are substituted in the equation in part (a), the result is $0 \cdot 0 \div 0 = 0$. But because $0 \cdot 0 = 0$, it follows that $0 \div 0 = 0$." How do you respond?

16. A student asks if division on the set of whole numbers is distributive over subtraction. How do you respond?

17. A student says that 0 is the identity for subtraction. How do you respond?

18. A student claims that on the following number line, the arrow doesn't really represent 3 because the end of the arrow does not start at 0. How do you respond?

19. A student asks whether a function from A to B is related to the cross product $A \times B$. How do you respond?

20. A student claims that the following machine does not represent a function machine because it accepts two inputs at once rather than a single input. How do you respond?

21. A student wants to know whether there are functions whose inputs are ordered pairs and whose outputs are also ordered pairs. How do you respond?

22. A student asks, "If every sequence is a function, is it also true that every function is a sequence?" How do you respond?

CHAPTER OUTLINE

I. Set definitions and notation

   A. A **set** can be described as any collection of objects.

   B. Sets should be **well defined** so that an object either does or does not belong to the set.

   C. An **element** is any **member** of a set.

   D. Sets can be specified by either listing all the elements or using **set-builder notation**.

   E. The **empty set**, written $\varnothing$, contains no elements.

   F. The **universal set** contains all the elements being discussed.

II. Relationships and operations on sets

   A. Two sets are **equal** if, and only if, they have exactly the same elements.

   B. Two sets A and B are in **one-to-one correspondence** if, and only if, each element of A can be paired with exactly one element of B and each element of B can be paired with exactly 1 element of A.

   C. Two sets A and B are **equivalent** if, and only if, their elements can be placed into one-to-one correspondence (written $A \sim B$).

   D. Set A is a **subset** of set B if, and only if, every element of A is an element of B (written $A \subseteq B$).

   E. Set A is a **proper subset** of set B if, and only if, every element of A is an element of B and there is at least one element of B that is not in A (written $A \subset B$).

   F. A set containing n elements has 2^n subsets.

   G. The **union** of two sets A and B is the set of all elements in A, in B, or in both A and B (written $A \cup B$).

   H. The **intersection** of two sets A and B is the set of all elements belonging to both A and B (written $A \cap B$).

   I. The **cardinal number** of a finite set S, $n(S)$ indicates the number of elements in the set.

   J. A set is **finite** if the number of elements in the set is zero or a natural number. Otherwise, the set is **infinite**.

   K. Two sets A and B are **disjoint** if they have no elements in common.

   L. The **complement** of a set A is the set consisting of the elements of the universal set not in A (written $\overline{A}$).

   M. The **complement of set A relative to set B** (set difference) is the set of all elements in B that are not in A (written $B - A$).

   N. The **Cartesian product** of sets A and B, written $A \times B$, is the set of all ordered pairs such that the first element in each pair is from A and the second element of each pair is from B.

   O. Properties of set operations

      1 Commutative property of set union

      2. Commutative property of set intersection

      3. Distributive property of set intersection over union

III. Whole numbers

   A. The set of **whole numbers** W is $\{0, 1, 2, 3, \ldots\}$.

   B. The basic operations for whole numbers are addition, subtraction, multiplication, and division.

      1. *Addition:* If $n(A) = a$ and $n(B) = b$, where $A \cap B = \varnothing$, then $a + b = n(A \cup B)$. The numbers a and b are **addends** and $a + b$ is the **sum**.

      2. *Subtraction:* If a and b are any whole numbers, then $a - b$ is the unique whole number c such that $a = b + c$.

3. *Multiplication:* If a and b are any whole numbers, and $a \neq 0$, then

$$ab = \underbrace{b + b + b + \ldots + b}_{a \text{ terms}}$$

where a and b are **factors** and ab is the **product**.

4. *Multiplication:* If A and B are sets such that $n(A) = a$ and $n(B) = b$, then $ab = n(A \times B)$.

5. *Division:* If a and b are any whole numbers with $b \neq 0$, $a \div b$ is the unique whole number c such that $bc = a$. The number a is the **dividend**, b is the **divisor**, and c is the **quotient**.

6. **Division algorithm:** Given any whole numbers a and b, with $b \neq 0$, there exist unique whole numbers q and r such that $a = bq + r$, with $0 \leq r < b$.

C. Properties of addition and multiplication of whole numbers

1. *Closure:* If $a, b \in W$, then $a + b \in W$ and $ab \in W$.

2. *Commutative:* If $a, b \in W$, then $a + b = b + a$ and $ab = ba$.

3. *Associative:* If $a, b, c \in W$, then $(a + b) + c = a + (b + c)$ and $a(bc) = (ab)c$.

4. *Identity:* 0 is the unique identity element for addition of whole numbers; 1 is the unique identity element for multiplication.

5. *Distributive property of multiplication over addition:* If $a, b, c \in W$, then $a(b + c) = ab + ac$.

6. *Zero multiplication property:* For any whole number a, $a \cdot 0 = 0 = 0 \cdot a$.

D. Relations on whole numbers

1. $a < b$ if, and only if, there is a natural number c such that $a + c = b$.

2. $a > b$ if, and only if, $b < a$.

IV. Functions

A. A **function** from set A to B is a correspondence in which each element $a \in A$ is paired with one, and only one, element $b \in B$. If the function is denoted by f, we write $f(a) = b$. The element $a \in A$ is the input, and $f(a)$ is the output. A is the **domain** of the function. B is any set containing all the outputs. The set of all the outputs is the **range** of the function.

B. A function can be represented by a table, an equation, a function machine, a set of ordered pairs, or a graph.

C. A sequence is a function whose domain is N, the set of natural numbers.

CHAPTER REVIEW

1. List all the subsets of $\{m, a, t, h\}$.

2. Let
   $U = \{u, n, i, v, e, r, s, a, l\}$,
   $A = \{r, a, v, e\}$, $C = \{l, i, n, e\}$, and
   $B = \{a, r, e\}$, $D = \{s, a, l, e\}$.
   Find each of the following:

   a. $A \cup B$ b. $C \cap D$
   c. $\overline{D}$ d. $A \cap \overline{D}$
   e. $\overline{B \cup C}$ f. $(B \cup C) \cap D$
   g. $(\overline{A \cup B}) \cap (C \cap \overline{D})$ h. $(C \cap D) \cap A$
   i. $n(\overline{C})$ j. $n(C \times D)$

3. Indicate the following sets by shading the figure:

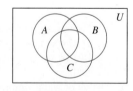

   (a) $A \cap (B \cup C)$ (b) $\overline{(A \cup B)} \cap C$

4. Suppose you are playing a word game with seven distinct letters. How many seven-letter words can there be?

5. a. Show one possible one-to-one correspondence between sets D and E if $D = \{t, h, e\}$ and $E = \{e, n, d\}$.
   b. How many one-to-one correspondences between sets D and E are possible?

6. Use a Venn diagram to determine whether $A \cap (B \cup C) = (A \cap B) \cup C$ for all sets A, B, and C.

7. According to a student survey, 16 students liked history, 19 liked English, 18 liked mathematics, 8 liked mathematics and English, 5 liked history and English, 7 liked history and mathematics, 3 liked all three subjects, and every student liked at least one of the subjects. Draw a Venn diagram describing this information and answer the following questions:

   a. How many students were in the survey?
   b. How many students liked only mathematics?
   c. How many students liked English and mathematics but not history?

8. Describe, using symbols, the shaded portion in each of the following figures:

   (a)   (b)

9. Classify each of the following as true or false. If false, tell why.
   a. For all sets A and B, either $A \subseteq B$ or $B \subseteq A$.
   b. The empty set is a proper subset of every set.
   c. For all sets A and B, if $A \sim B$, then $A = B$.
   d. The set $\{5, 10, 15, 20, \ldots\}$ is a finite set.
   e. No set is equivalent to a proper subset of itself.
   f. If A is an infinite set and $B \subseteq A$, then B also is an infinite set.
   g. For all finite sets A and B, if $A \cap B \neq \varnothing$, then $n(A \cup B) \neq n(A) + n(B)$.
   h. If A and B are sets such that $A \cap B = \varnothing$, then $A = \varnothing$ or $B = \varnothing$.

10. Use Venn diagrams to decide whether each of the following is always true.
    a. $n(A \cup B) = n(A - B) + n(B - A) + n(A \cap B)$.
    b. $n(A \cup B) = n(A - B) + n(B) = n(B - A) + n(A)$.

11. Suppose P and Q are equivalent sets and $n(P) = 17$.
    a. What is the minimum number of elements in $P \cup Q$?
    b. What is the maximum number of elements in $P \cup Q$?
    c. What is the minimum number of elements in $P \cap Q$?
    d. What is the maximum number of elements in $P \cap Q$?

12. Case Eastern Junior College awarded 26 varsity letters in crew, 15 in swimming, and 16 in soccer. If awards went to 46 students and only 2 lettered in all sports, how many students lettered in two of the three sports?

13. Consider the set of northwestern states or provinces {Montana, Washington, Idaho, Oregon, Alaska, British Columbia, Alberta}. If a person chooses one element, show that in three yes or no questions, we can determine the element.

14. For each of the following, identify the properties of the operation(s) for whole numbers illustrated:
    a. $3 \cdot (a + b) = 3 \cdot a + 3 \cdot b$
    b. $2 + a = a + 2$
    c. $16 \cdot 1 = 1 \cdot 16 = 16$
    d. $6 \cdot (12 + 3) = 6 \cdot 12 + 6 \cdot 3$
    e. $3 \cdot (a \cdot 2) = 3 \cdot (2 \cdot a)$
    f. $3 \cdot (2 \cdot a) = (3 \cdot 2) \cdot a$

15. Using the definitions of less than or greater than, prove that each of the following inequalities is true:
    a. $3 < 13$ b. $12 > 9$

16. For each of the following, find all possible replacements to make the following statements true for whole numbers:
    a. $4 \cdot \square - 37 < 27$
    b. $398 = \square \cdot 37 + 28$
    c. $\square \cdot (3 + 4) = \square \cdot 3 + \square \cdot 4$
    d. $42 - \square \geq 16$

17. Use the distributive property of multiplication and addition facts, if possible, to rename each of the following:
    a. $3a + 7a + 5a$
    b. $3x^2 + 7x^2 - 5x^2$
    c. $x(a + b + y)$
    d. $(x + 5)3 + (x + 5)y$

18. How many 12-oz cans of juice would it take to give 60 people one 8-oz serving each?

19. Heidi has a brown and a gray pair of slacks; a brown, a yellow, and a white blouse; and a blue and a white sweater. How many different outfits does she have if each outfit she wears consists of slacks, a blouse, and a sweater?

20. I am thinking of a whole number. If I divide it by 13, then multiply the answer by 12, then subtract 20, and then add 89, I end up with 93. What was my original number?

21. A ski resort offers a weekend ski package for $80 per person or $6000 for a group of 80 people. Which would be the cheaper option for a group of 80?

22. Josi has a job in which she works 30 hr/wk and gets paid $5/hr. If she works more than 30 hr in a week, she receives $8/hr for each hour over 30 hr. If she worked 38 hr this week, how much did she earn?

23. In a television game show, there are five questions to answer. Each question is worth twice as much as the previous question. If the last question was worth $6400, what was the first question worth?

24. Which of the following sets of ordered pairs are functions from the set of first components to the set of second components?
    a. $\{(a, b), (c, d), (e, a), (f, g)\}$
    b. $\{(a, b), (a, c), (b, b), (b, c)\}$
    c. $\{(a, b), (b, a)\}$

25. Given the following function rules and the domains, find the associated ranges:
    a. $f(x) = x + 3$; domain $= \{0, 1, 2, 3\}$
    b. $f(x) = 3x - 1$; domain $= \{5, 10, 15, 20\}$
    c. $f(x) = x^2$; domain $= \{0, 1, 2, 3, 4\}$
    d. $f(x) = x^2 + 3x + 5$; domain $= \{0, 1, 2\}$

26. Which of the following correspondences from A to B describe a function? If a correspondence is a function, find its range. Justify your answers.
    a. A is the set of college students, and B is the set of majors. To each college student corresponds his or her major.
    b. A is the set of books in the library, and B is the set N of natural numbers. To each book corresponds the number of pages in the book.
    c. $A = \{(a, b) \mid a \in N \text{ and } b \in N\}$, and $B = N$. To each element of A corresponds the number $4a + 2b$.
    d. $A = N$ and $B = N$. If x is even, then $f(x) = 0$ and if x is odd, then $f(x) = 1$.
    e. $A = N$ and $B = N$. To each natural number corresponds the sum of its digits.

27. A health club charges an initiation fee of $200 that gives 1 month of free membership, and then charges $55 per month.
    a. If $C(x)$ is the total cost of membership in the club for x months, express $C(x)$ in terms of x.
    b. Graph $C(x)$ for the first 12 months.
    c. Use the graph in (b) to find when the total cost of membership in the club will exceed $600.
    d. When will the total cost of membership exceed $6000?

SELECTED BIBLIOGRAPHY

Beckman, C., and E. Billings. "Menu Problems" Problem 11. *Mathematics Teaching in the Middle School* 6 (April 2001): 465.

Cantlon, D. "Kids + Conjecture = Mathematics Power." *Teaching Children Mathematics* 5 (October 1998): 108–112.

Crouse, R., and A. Alison. "Tips for Beginners: The Human Coordinate System." *Mathematics Teacher* 84 (February 1991): 108–109.

Fleege, P., and D. Thompson. "From Habitat to Legs: Using Science-Themed Counting Books to Foster Connections." *Teaching Children Mathematics* 7 (October 2000): 74–78.

Ginsburg, H., A. Klein, and P. Starkey. "The Development of Children's Mathematical Thinking: Connecting Research with Practice." In *Child Psychology in Practice*, edited by Irving E. Sigel and K. Ann Renninger, pp. 401–476, vol. 4 of *Handbook of Child Psychology*, edited by William Damon. New York: John Wiley & Sons, 1998.

Greenwood, J. "Name That Graph." *Mathematics Teacher* 88 (January 1995): 8–11.

Hines, E. "Exploring Functions with Dynamic Physical Models." *Mathematics Teaching in the Middle School* 7 (January 2002): 274–278.

Huinker, D. "Calculators as Learning Tools for Young Children's Explorations of Number." *Teaching Children Mathematics* 8 (February 2002): 316–321.

Johnston, A. "Introducing Function and Its Notation." *Mathematics Teacher* 80 (October 1987): 558–560.

Kline, K. "Kindergarten Is More Than Counting." *Teaching Children Mathematics* 5 (October 1998): 84–87.

Koirala, H., and P. Goodwin. "Teaching Algebra in the Middle Grades Using Mathmagic." *Mathematics Teaching in the Middle School* 5 (May 2000): 563–566.

Lambdin, D., R. Lynch, and H. McDaniel. "Algebra in the Middle Grades." *Mathematics Teaching in the Middle School* 6 (November 2000): 195–198.

Mercer, J. "Teaching Graphing Concepts with Graphing Calculators." *Mathematics Teacher* 88 (April 1995): 268–273.

Miller, C., and T. Veenstra. "Fibonacci: Beautiful Patterns, Beautiful Mathematics." *Mathematics Teaching in the Middle School* 7 (January 2002): 298–300, 304–305.

Muller, G. "Menu of Problems" Problems 9 and 12. *Mathematics Teaching in the Middle School* 5 (January 2000): 306–307.

Rubenstein, R. "The Function Game." *Mathematics Teaching in the Middle School* 2 (November-December 1996): 74–78.

Sakshaug, L., and K. Wohlhuter. "Responses to the Which Graph Is Which Problem." *Teaching Children Mathematics* 7 (February 2001): 352–353.

Sand, M. "A Function Is a Mail Carrier." *Mathematics Teacher* 89 (September 1996): 468–469.

Schloemer, C. "Tips for Teaching Cartesian Graphing: Linking Concepts and Procedures." *Teaching Children Mathematics* 1 (September 1994): 20–23.

Schneider, S., and C. Thompson. "Incredible Equations Develop Incredible Number Sense." *Teaching Children Mathematics* 7 (November 2000): 146–148, 165–168.

Schulman, L., and R. Eston. "A Problem Worth Revisiting." *Teaching Children Mathematics* 5 (October 1998): 72–77.

Shealy, B. "Becoming Flexible with Functions: Investigating United States Population Growth." *Mathematics Teacher* 89 (May 1996): 414–418.

Siegler, R., *Emerging Minds: The Process of Change in Children's Thinking*. New York: Oxford University Press, 1996.

Smith, E. "Patterns, Functions, and Algebra." In *A Research Companion to NCTM's Standards*, edited by J. Kirkpatrick, W. G. Martin, and D. S. Schifter. Reston, VA: NCTM, 2000.

White, J., ed. "Counting Sheep" cartoon by Blair. *Mathematics Teaching in the Middle School* 5 (March 2000): 445.

−3−
Numeration Systems and Whole-Number Computation

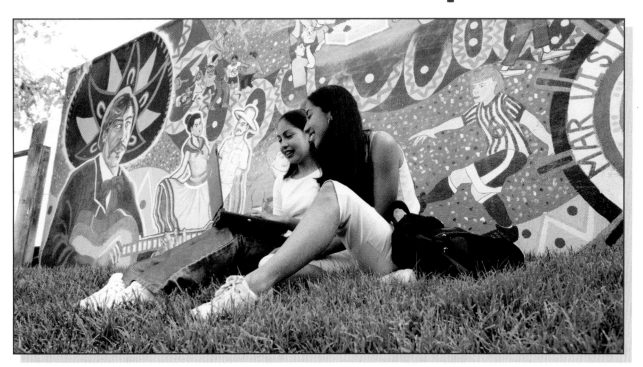

P R E L I M I N A R Y   P R O B L E M

Marcy bets that if you do a series of mathematical computations and activities, she can guess your color. First you must find your special number by completing the following.

Take the number of your birth month.
Add 24.
Add the difference you obtain when you subtract the
number of your birth month from 12.
Divide by 3.
Add 13.
The result is your special number.

To each letter in the alphabet, assign a number that is the letter's order when alphabetical; that is, $a = 1$, $b = 2$, $c = 3$, $d = 4$, and so on. Find the letter that corresponds to your special number. Next write the name of a color that starts with this letter. What color will Marcy predict is your color? Why does this work?

The NCTM's *Principles and Standards* Number and Operations Standard is given below.

Instructional programs from prekindergarten through grade 12 should enable all students to

- *understand numbers, ways of representing numbers, relationships among numbers, and number systems;*
- *understand meanings of operations and how they relate to one another;*
- *compute fluently and make reasonable estimates.* (p. 32)

Further, *Principles and Standards* states that:

The Number and Operations Standard describes deep and fundamental understanding of, and proficiency with, counting, numbers, and arithmetic, as well as an understanding of number systems and their structures. The concepts and algorithms of elementary arithmetic are part of number and operations, as are the properties and characteristics of the classes of numbers that form the beginnings of number theory. (p. 32)

Also, in *Principles and Standards* we find:

In these Standards, understanding number and operations, developing number sense, and gaining fluency in arithmetic computation form the core of mathematics education for the elementary grades. As they progress from prekindergarten through grade 12, students should attain a rich understanding of numbers—what they are; how they are represented with objects, numerals, or on number lines; how they are related to one another; how numbers are embedded in systems that have structures and properties; and how to use numbers and operations to solve problems. (p. 32)

Number and Operation Expectations

The *Principles and Standards* Number and Operations Standard has implications for the expectations of students at various levels. The expectations covered in this chapter include the following.

In grades preK–2, children should learn about number systems and use multiple models to develop understanding of place value and the base-ten number system. Children should develop fluency in adding, subtracting, multiplying, and dividing whole numbers. (p. 392)

In grades 3–5, children should master the expectations of grades preK–2 and use the properties of operations such as the distributive property of multiplication over addition. Children should develop and use strategies for estimating the results of whole-number computations and they should be able to judge if their estimates are reasonable. They should be able to select and use appropriate methods and tools for computing with whole numbers from among mental math, estimation, calculator, and paper and pencil. (p. 392)

Numeration Systems

In the first section of this chapter, we introduce various number systems and compare them to the Hindu-Arabic system of numbers that we use today. By comparing the Hindu-Arabic system with ancient systems that used other bases, we may develop a clearer picture of how we do whole-number computation. The Hindu-Arabic system relies on ten digits: 0, 1, 2, 3, 4, 5, 6, 7, 8, and 9 that represent the cardinal numbers of sets equivalent to those shown in Table 3-1.

Table 3-1

Digits for Cardinal Number of Set	Set
0	∅
1	{a}
2	{a, b}
3	{a, b, c}
4	{a, b, c, d}
5	{a, b, c, d, e}
6	{a, b, c, d, e, f}
7	{a, b, c, d, e, f, g}
8	{a, b, c, d, e, f, g, h}
9	{a, b, c, d, e, f, g, h, i}

numerals The written symbols in Table 3-1, such as 2 or 5, are **numerals**. Different cultures developed different numerals over the years to represent cardinal numbers. Table 3-2 shows other representations along with how they relate to the Hindu-Arabic digits 0 through 9 or 10.

Table 3-2

Babylonian		▼	▼▼	▼▼▼	▼▼▼▼	▼▼▼ ▼▼	▼▼▼ ▼▼▼	▼▼▼▼ ▼▼▼	▼▼▼▼ ▼▼▼▼	▼▼▼▼▼ ▼▼▼▼	<
Egyptian		I	II	III	IIII	III II	III III	IIII III	IIII IIII	III III III	∩
Mayan	⬯	•	••	•••	••••	—	•̲	•̲•̲	•̲•̲•̲	•̲•̲•̲•̲	=
Greek		α	β	γ	δ	ε	φ	ζ	η	θ	ι
Roman		i	ii	iii	IV	V	VI	VII	VIII	IX	X
Hindu	o	1	2	3	8	9	6	Λ	8	9	
Arabic	•	1	٢	٣	٤	٥	٦	٧	٨	٩	
Hindu-Arabic	0	1	2	3	4	5	6	7	8	9	10

numeration system As seen in Table 3-2, in the Hindu-Arabic system, using numerals to represent numbers greater than 9 requires a numeration system. A **numeration system** is a collection of properties and symbols agreed upon to represent numbers systematically. We will examine various numeration systems that have been used throughout history. Through the study of these systems, we can explore the evolution of the Hindu-Arabic system.

Hindu-Arabic Numeration System

The *Hindu-Arabic numeration system* that we use today was developed by the Hindus and transported to Europe by the Arabs; hence, the name *Hindu-Arabic*. The Hindu-Arabic system relies on the following properties.

1. All numerals are constructed from the ten digits.
2. Place value is based on powers of 10, the number base of the system.

place value

face value

Because the Hindu-Arabic system is based on powers of 10, the system is sometimes called a base-ten, or a decimal, system. **Place value** assigns a value of a digit depending on its placement in a numeral. To find the value of a digit in a whole number, we multiply the place value of the digit by its **face value**, where the face value is a digit. For example, in the numeral 5984, the 5 has place value "thousands," the 9 has place value "hundreds," the 8 has place value "tens," and the 4 has place value "units," as seen in Figure 3-1.

FIGURE 3-1

expanded form

factor

We could write 5984 in **expanded form** as $5 \cdot 10^3 + 9 \cdot 10^2 + 8 \cdot 10 + 4 \cdot 1$. In the expanded form of 5984, exponents have been used. For example, 1000, or $10 \cdot 10 \cdot 10$, is written as 10^3. In this case, 10 is a **factor** of the product. In general, we have the following definition.

> ### Definition of a^n
>
> If a is any number and n is any natural number, then
> $$a^n = \underbrace{a \cdot a \cdot a \cdot \ldots \cdot a}_{n \text{ factors}}.$$

A set of base-ten blocks, shown in Figure 3-2 consists of *units, longs, flats,* and *blocks,* representing 1, 10, 100, and 1000, respectively. Such base-ten blocks, a subset of multibase blocks, can be used to teach place value.

1 long $\rightarrow 10^1 = 1$ row of 10 units

1 flat $\rightarrow 10^2 = 1$ row of 10 longs, or 100 units

1 block $\rightarrow 10^3 = 1$ row of 10 flats, or 100 longs, or 1000 units

Students trade blocks by regrouping. That is, they take a set of base-ten blocks representing a number and trade them until they have the fewest possible pieces representing the same number. For example, suppose you have 58 units and want to trade them. The units can be grouped into tens to form longs. Five sets of 10 units each can be traded for 5 longs. Thus, 58 units can be traded for 5 longs and 8 units. In terms of numbers, this is analogous to rewriting 58 as $5 \cdot 10 + 8$.

FIGURE 3-2

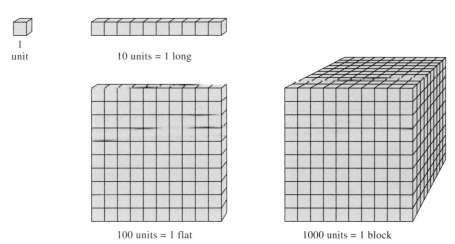

1
unit

10 units = 1 long

100 units = 1 flat

1000 units = 1 block

E X A M P L E
3-1

What is the fewest number of pieces you can receive in a fair exchange for 11 flats, 17 longs, and 16 units?

Solution   The 16 units can be traded for 1 long and 6 units.

11 flats	17 longs	16 units	(16 units = 1 long and 6 units)
	1 long	6 units	(Trade)
11 flats	18 longs	6 units	(After the first trade)

11 flats	18 longs	6 units	(18 longs = 1 flat and 8 longs)
1 flat	8 longs		(Trade)
12 flats	8 longs	6 units	(After the second trade)

12 flats	8 longs	6 units	(12 flats = 1 block and 2 flats)
1 block	2 flats		(Trade)
1 block	2 flats	8 longs	6 units	(After the third trade)

Therefore, the fewest number of pieces is $1 + 2 + 8 + 6 = 17$. This trading is analogous to rewriting $11 \cdot 10^2 + 17 \cdot 10 + 16$ as $1 \cdot 10^3 + 2 \cdot 10^2 + 8 \cdot 10 + 6$, which implies that there are 1286 units.

Next, we discuss other numeration systems. The study of such systems will give us a historical perspective of the development of numeration systems and will help us better understand our own Hindu-Arabic numeration system.

Tally Numeration System

tally numeration system

The **tally numeration system** used single strokes, or tally marks, to represent each object that was counted; for example, the numerals representing the first ten counting numbers are given below.

|, ||, |||, ||||, |||||, ||||||, |||||||, ||||||||, |||||||||, ||||||||||

In a tally system there is a one-to-one correspondence between the marks and the items being counted. The system is simple but it requires many symbols, especially when numbers become greater. Also as numbers become greater, it is harder to read the numerals.

As we see in the "Wizard of Id" cartoon, the tally system can be improved by *grouping*. In the first frame, we see that the tallies are grouped into fives by placing a diagonal across four tallies to make a group of five. Grouping makes it easier to read the numeral. Later, as we see in the second frame, shortened numerals were made in another system (Roman).

Egyptian Numeration System

The Egyptian numeration system, which dates back to about 3400 B.C., used tally marks. The first nine numerals in the Egyptian system in Table 3-2 show the use of tally marks. The Egyptians improved on the system based only on tally marks by developing a *grouping system* to represent certain sets of numbers. This makes the numbers easier to record. For example, the Egyptians used a heel bone symbol, ∩, to stand for a grouping of ten tally marks.

$$||||||||| \rightarrow \cap$$

Table 3-3 shows other numerals that the Egyptians used in their system.

Table 3-3

Egyptian Numeral	Description	Hindu-Arabic Equivalent
I	Vertical staff	1
∩	Heel bone	10
9	Scroll	100
⌇	Lotus flower	1,000
⌀	Pointing finger	10,000
⌔	Polliwog or burbot	100,000
⚰	Astonished man	1,000,000

additive property   In its simplest form, the Egyptian system involved an **additive property**; that is, the value of a number was the sum of the face values of the numerals. The Egyptians customarily wrote the numerals in decreasing order from left to right as in ⌒999∩∩||. The number can be converted to base ten as shown below.

⌒	represents	100,000
999	represents	300 (100 + 100 + 100)
∩∩	represents	20 (10 + 10)
||	represents	___?___ (1 + 1)
⌒999∩∩||	represents	100,322

NOW TRY THIS 3-1

a. Use the Egyptian system to represent 1,312,322.
b. Use the Hindu-Arabic system to represent ⌒⌒𝄃𝄃𝄃∩∩||||.
c. What disadvantages do you see of the Egyptian system compared to the Hindu-Arabic system?

Babylonian Numeration System

The Babylonian numeration system was developed at about the same time as the Egyptian system. The symbols in Table 3-4 were made using a stylus either vertically or horizontally on clay tablets. The Babylonian system has been well preserved because clay tablets were used rather than papyrus, which was used by the Egyptians.

Table 3-4

Babylonian Numeral	Hindu-Arabic Equivalent
▼	1
＜	10

The Babylonian numerals 1 through 59 were similar to the Egyptian numerals, but the vertical staff and the heel bone were replaced by the symbols shown in Table 3-4. For example, ＜＜ ▼▼ represented 22.

The Babylonian numeration system used a *place value system*. Numbers greater than 59 were represented by repeated groupings of 60, much as we use groupings of 10 today. For example ▼▼ ＜＜ might represent $2 \cdot 60 + 20$, or 140. The space indicates that ▼▼ represents $2 \cdot 60$ rather than 2. It is thought that the Babylonians chose to work with 60 because it can be evenly divided by many numbers. This simplifies division and operations with fractions.

Numerals immediately to the left of a second space have a value $60 \cdot 60$ times their face value, and so on.

<< ▼   represents $20 \cdot 60 + 1$, or 1201

<▼ <▼ ▼   represents $11 \cdot 60 \cdot 60 + 11 \cdot 60 + 1$, or $11 \cdot 60^2 + 11 \cdot 60 + 1$, or 40,261

▼ <▼ <▼ ▼   represents $1 \cdot 60 \cdot 60 \cdot 60 + 11 \cdot 60 \cdot 60 + 11 \cdot 60 + 1$, or $1 \cdot 60^3 + 11 \cdot 60^2 + 11 \cdot 60 + 1$, or 256,261

The initial Babylonian system was inadequate by today's standards. For example, the symbol ▼▼ could have represented 2 or $2 \cdot 60$. Later, the Babylonians introduced the symbol ♦ as a placeholder for missing position values. Using this symbol < <<▼ represents $10 \cdot 60 + 21$ and < ♦ <<▼ represents $10 \cdot 60^2 + 0 \cdot 60 + 21$. In this sense, ♦ represented 0.

NOW TRY THIS 3-2

   a. Use the Babylonian system to represent 12,321.
   b. Use the Hindu-Arabic system to represent ▼▼ <▼ ▼.
   c. What advantages does the Hindu-Arabic system have over the Babylonian system?

Mayan Numeration System

In the early development of numeration systems, people frequently used parts of their bodies to count. Fingers could be matched to objects to stand for one, two, three, four, or five objects. Two hands could then stand for a set of ten objects. In warmer climates where people went barefoot, people may have used their toes as well as their fingers for counting. The Mayans introduced an attribute that was not present in the Egyptian or early Babylonian systems, namely, a symbol for zero. The Mayan system used only three symbols, which Table 3-5 shows, and based their system on 20.

Table 3-5

Mayan Numeral	Hindu-Arabic Equivalent
•	1
—	5
👁	0

The symbols for the first ten numerals in the Mayan system are shown in Table 3-2. Notice the groupings of five, where each horizontal bar represents a group of five. Thus the symbol for 19 was ‖‖‖‖, or 3 fives and 4 ones. The symbol for 20 was 👁, which represents 1 group of twenty plus 0 ones. The Mayans wrote numbers vertically with the greatest place value on top. In Figure 3-3(a), we have $2 \cdot 5 + 3 \cdot 1$, or 13 groups of twenty plus $2 \cdot 5 + 1 \cdot 1$, or 11 ones, for a total of 271. In Figure 3-3(b), we have $3 \cdot 5 + 1 \cdot 1$, or 16, groups of twenty and 0 ones, for a total of 320.

FIGURE 3-3

(a)   (b)

In a true base-twenty system, the place value of the symbols in the third position vertically from the bottom should be 20^2, or 400. However, the Mayans used $20 \cdot 18$, or 360, instead of 400. (The number 360 is an approximation of the length of a calendar year, which consisted of 18 months of 20 days each, plus 5 "unlucky" days.) Thus, instead of place values of 1, 20, 20^2, 20^3, 20^4, and so on, the Mayans used 1, 20, $20 \cdot 18$, $20^2 \cdot 18$, $20^3 \cdot 18$, and so on. For example, in Figure 3-4(a), we have $5 + 1$ (or 6) groups of 360, plus $5 + 5 + 2$ (or 12) groups of 20, plus $5 + 4$ (or 9) groups of 1, for a total of 2409. In Figure 3-4(b), we have $2 \cdot 5$ (or 10) groups of 360, plus 0 groups of 20, plus 2 ones, for a total of 3602. Spacing is important in the Mayan system. For example, if two horizontal bars are placed close together, as in ▬, the symbols represent $5 + 5 = 10$. If the bars are spaced apart, as in ▬, then the value is $5 \cdot 20 + 5 \cdot 1 = 105$.

FIGURE 3-4

(a)   (b)

Roman Numeration System

The Roman numeration system was used in Europe in its early form from the third century B.C. It remains in use today, as seen on cornerstones, on the opening pages of books, and on faces of some clocks. The Roman system uses only a few symbols, as shown in Table 3-6.

Table 3-6

Roman Numeral	Hindu-Arabic Equivalent
I	1
V	5
X	10
L	50
C	100
D	500
M	1000

Roman numerals can be combined by using an additive property. For example, MDCLXVI represents $1000 + 500 + 100 + 50 + 10 + 5 + 1 = 1666$, CCCXXVIII represents 328, and VI represents 6.

subtractive property

To avoid repeating a symbol more than three times, as in IIII, a **subtractive property** was introduced in the Middle Ages. For example, I is less than V, so if it is to the left of V, it is subtracted. Thus IV has a value of $5 - 1$, or 4, and XC represents $100 - 10$, or 90.

Some extensions of the subtractive property could lead to ambiguous results. For example, IXC could be 91 or 89. By custom, 91 is written XCI and 89 is written LXXXIX. In general, only one smaller number symbol can be to the left of a larger number symbol, and the pair must be one of those listed in Table 3-7.

Table 3-7

Roman Numeral	Hindu-Arabic Equivalent
IV	$5 - 1$, or 4
IX	$10 - 1$, or 9
XL	$50 - 10$, or 40
XC	$100 - 10$, or 90
CD	$500 - 100$, or 400
CM	$1000 - 100$, or 900

multiplicative property

In the Middle Ages, a bar was placed over a Roman number to multiply it by 1000. The use of bars is based on a **multiplicative property**. For example, $\overline{V}$ represents $5 \cdot 1000$, or 5000, and $\overline{CDX}$ represents $410 \cdot 1000$, or 410,000. To indicate even greater numbers, more bars appear. For example, $\overline{\overline{V}}$ represents $(5 \cdot 1000) \cdot 1000$, or 5,000,000; $\overline{\overline{CXI}}$ represents $111 \cdot 1000^3$, or 111,000,000,000; and $\overline{CXI}$ represents $110 \cdot 1000 + 1$, or 110,001.

Several properies might be used to represent some numbers, for example:

$$\overline{DCLIX} = \underbrace{(500 \cdot 1000)}_{\text{Multiplicative}} + \underbrace{(100 + 50)}_{\text{Additive}} + \underbrace{(10 - 1)}_{\text{Subtractive}} = 500{,}159.$$
$$\underbrace{}_{\text{Additive}}$$

Other Number Base Systems

To understand our base-ten system better and to investigate some of the problems that students might have when learning the Hindu-Arabic system, we will investigate similar systems but with different number bases.

Base Five

The Luo peoples of Kenya used a *quinary*, or base-five, system. A system of this type can be modeled by counting with only one hand. The digits available for counting are 0, 1, 2, 3, and 4. In the "one-hand system," or base-five system, you count 1, 2, 3, 4, 10, where 10 represents one hand and no fingers. Counting in base five proceeds as shown in Figure 3-5. We write the small "five" below the numeral as a reminder that the number is written in base five. If no base is written, a number is assumed to be in base ten.

FIGURE 3-5

One-Hand System	Base-Five Symbol	Base-Five Blocks
0 fingers	0_{five}	
1 finger	1_{five}	
2 fingers	2_{five}	
3 fingers	3_{five}	
4 fingers	4_{five}	
1 hand and 0 fingers	10_{five}	
1 hand and 1 finger	11_{five}	
1 hand and 2 fingers	12_{five}	
1 hand and 3 fingers	13_{five}	
1 hand and 4 fingers	14_{five}	
2 hands and 0 fingers	20_{five}	
2 hands and 1 finger	21_{five}	

Counting in base five is similar to counting in base ten. Because we have only five digits (0, 1, 2, 3, and 4), 4_{five} plays the role of 9 in base ten. Figure 3-6 shows how we can find the number that comes after 34_{five} by using base-five blocks.

FIGURE 3-6

$$34_{\text{five}} \xrightarrow{+1} 34_{\text{five}} + 1_{\text{five}} = 40_{\text{five}}$$

What number follows 44_{five}? There are no more two-digit numbers in the system after 44_{five}. In base ten, the same situation occurs at 99. We use 100 to represent 10 tens, or 1 hundred. In the base-five system, we need a symbol to represent 5 fives. To continue the analogy with base ten, we use 100_{five} to represent 1 group of 5 fives, 0 groups of five, and 0 units. To distinguish from "one hundred" in base ten, the name for 100_{five} is read "one-zero-zero base five." The number 100 means $1 \cdot 10^2 + 0 \cdot 10^1 + 0$, whereas the number 100_{five} means $(1 \cdot 10^2 + 0 \cdot 10^1 + 0)_{\text{five}}$, or $(1 \cdot 5^2 + 0 \cdot 5^1 + 0)_{\text{ten}}$, or 25.

Examples of base-five numerals along with their base-five block representations and conversions to base ten are given in Figure 3-7. Multibase blocks will be used throughout the text to illustrate various concepts.

FIGURE 3-7

Base-Five Numeral	Base-Five Blocks	Base-Ten Numeral
14_{five}		$1 \cdot 5 + 4 = 9$
124_{five}		$1 \cdot 5^2 + 2 \cdot 5 + 4 = 39$
1030_{five}		$1 \cdot 5^3 + 0 \cdot 5^2 + 3 \cdot 5 + 0 \cdot 1 = 140$

EXAMPLE 3-2

Convert 11244_{fiiv} to base ten.

Solution $11244_{five} = 1 \cdot 5^4 + 1 \cdot 5^3 + 2 \cdot 5^2 + 4 \cdot 5^1 + 4 \cdot 1$
$\qquad\qquad\qquad = 1 \cdot 625 + 1 \cdot 125 + 2 \cdot 25 + 4 \cdot 5 + 4 \cdot 1$
$\qquad\qquad\qquad = 625 + 125 + 50 + 20 + 4$
$\qquad\qquad\qquad = 824$

Example 3-2 suggests a method for changing a base-ten number to a base-five number using powers of five. To convert 824 to base five, we divide by successive powers of five. A shorthand method for illustrating this conversion is in the following:

$$5^4 = 625 \quad \rightarrow \quad 625 \overline{)\ 824\ }\ 1 \qquad \text{How many groups of 625 in 824?}$$
$$-625$$
$$5^3 = 125 \quad \rightarrow \quad 125 \overline{)\ 199\ }\ 1 \qquad \text{How many groups of 125 in 199?}$$
$$-125$$
$$5^2 = 25 \quad \rightarrow \quad 25 \overline{)\ 74\ }\ 2 \qquad \text{How many groups of 25 in 74?}$$
$$-50$$
$$5^1 = 5 \quad \rightarrow \quad 5 \overline{)\ 24\ }\ 4 \qquad \text{How many groups of 5 in 24?}$$
$$-20$$
$$5^0 = 1 \quad \rightarrow \quad 1 \overline{)\ 4\ }\ 4 \qquad \text{How many 1s in 4?}$$
$$\underline{-4}$$
$$0$$

Thus $824 = 11244_{fiiv}$.

NOW TRY THIS 3-3

A different method of converting 824 to base five is shown using successive divisions by 5. The quotient in each case is placed below the dividend and the remainder is placed on the right, on the same line with the quotient. The answer is read from bottom to top, that is, as 11244_{five}.

5	824	
5	164	4
5	32	4
5	6	2
	1	1

a. Why does this method work?

b. Use the above method to convert 728 to base five.

Calculators with the integer division feature—$\boxed{\text{INT}\div}$ on a Texas Instrument calculator or $\boxed{\div\text{R}}$ on a Casio—can be used to change base-ten numbers to different number bases. For example, to convert 8 to base five, we enter $\boxed{8}\boxed{\text{INT}\div}\boxed{5}\boxed{=}$ and obtain $\underset{Q}{\llcorner 1 \lrcorner}\,\underset{R}{\llcorner 3 \lrcorner}$. This implies that $8 = 13_{\text{fiv}}$. Will this technique work to convert 34 to base five? Why or why not?

Base Two

binary system

Historians tell of early tribes that used base two. Some aboriginal tribes still count "one, two, two and one, two twos, two twos and one, ..." Because base two has only two digits, it is called the **binary system**. Base two is especially important because of its use in computers. One of the two digits is represented by the presence of an electrical signal and the other by the absence of an electrical signal. Although base two works well for some purposes, it is inefficient for everyday use because multidigit numbers are reached very rapidly in counting in this system, as seen in the following cartoon where Peter is reading Jason's counting to five.

NOW TRY THIS 3-4

In the "Foxtrot" cartoon, Jason has listed the first five counting numbers in base two. Continue the list until you have the first twenty counting numbers.

Conversions from base two to base ten, and vice versa, can be accomplished in a manner similar to that used for base-five conversions.

EXAMPLE 3-3

a. Convert 10111_{two} to base ten.
b. Convert 27 to base two.

Solution **a.** $10111_{\text{two}} = 1 \cdot 2^4 + 0 \cdot 2^3 + 1 \cdot 2^2 + 1 \cdot 2^1 + 1$
$= 16 + 0 + 4 + 2 + 1$
$= 23$

Alternative Solution:

b. 16 ⌐ 27 ⌐ 1   How many groups of 16 in 27?
　 −16

　 8 ⌐ 11 ⌐ 1   How many groups of 8 in 11?
　 −8

　 4 ⌐ 3 ⌐ 0   How many groups of 4 in 3?
　 −0

　 2 ⌐ 3 ⌐ 1   How many groups of 2 in 3?
　 −2

　 1 ⌐ 1 ⌐ 1   How many 1s in 1?
　 −1
　　 0

2 ⌐ 27
2 ⌐ 13   1
2 ⌐ 6   1
2 ⌐ 3   0
　 1   1

Thus 27 is equivalent to 11011_{two}.

Base Twelve

Another commonly used number base system is the base-twelve, or the duodecimal ("dozens"), system. Eggs are bought by the dozen, and pencils are bought by the *gross* (a dozen dozen). In base twelve, there are twelve digits, just as there are ten digits in base ten, five digits in base five, and two digits in base two. In base twelve, new symbols are needed to represent the following groups of x's:

$$10\ x\text{'s} \quad \text{and} \quad 11\ x\text{'s}$$

$$\underbrace{xxxxxxxxxx} \qquad \underbrace{xxxxxxxxxxx}$$

The new symbols chosen are T and E, respectively, so that the base-twelve digits are 0, 1, 2, 3, 4, 5, 6, 7, 8, 9, T, and E. Thus in base twelve we count "1, 2, 3, 4, 5, 6, 7, 8, 9, T, E, 10, 11, 12, . . . , 17, 18, 19, $1T$, $1E$, 20, 21, 22, . . . , 28, 29, $2T$, $2E$, 30, ..."

E X A M P L E 3-4

a. Convert $E2T_{\text{twelve}}$ to base ten.   **b.** Convert 1277 to base twelve.

Solution

a. $E2T_{\text{twelve}} = 11 \cdot 12^2 + 2 \cdot 12^1 + 10 \cdot 1$
$= 11 \cdot 144 + 24 + 10$
$= 1584 + 24 + 10$
$= 1618$

b. 144 ⌐ 1277 ⌐ 8   How many groups of 144 in 1277?
　 −1152

　 12 ⌐ 125 ⌐ T How many groups of 12 in 125?
　 −120

　 1 ⌐ 5 ⌐ 5   How many 1s in 5?
　 −5
　　 0

Thus $1277 = 8T5_{\text{twelve}}$.

**EXAMPLE
3-5**

Rob used base twelve to write the following:

$$g36_{twelve} = 1050_{ten}$$

What is the value of g?

Solution Using expanded form we could write the following equations

$$g \cdot 12^2 + 3 \cdot 12 + 6 \cdot 1 = 1050$$
$$144g + 36 + 6 = 1050$$
$$144g + 42 = 1050$$
$$144g = 1008$$
$$g = 7$$

O N G O I N G   A S S E S S M E N T   3 - 1

1. For each of the following, tell which numeral represents the greater number and why:
   a. $\overline{M}$CDXXIV and $\overline{\overline{M}}$CDXXIV
   b. 4632 and 46,032
   c. **⟨▼▼** and **⟨ ▼▼**
   d. 999∩∩|| and 𝄞∩|
   e. ☰ and 👁

2. For each of the following, name both the succeeding and preceding numbers (one more and one less):
   a. MCMXLIX   **b.** $\overline{M}$I   c. CMXCIX
   d. **⟨⟨ ⟨▼**   e. 𝄞99   f. ☱

3. If the cornerstone represents when a building was built and it reads MCMXXII, when was this building built?

4. Write each of the following in Roman symbols:
   a. 121   **b.** 42
   c. 89   **d.** 5282

5. Write each of the following in Egyptian symbols:
   a. 52   **b.** 103
   c. 100,003   **d.** 38

6. Complete the following table, which compares symbols for numbers in different numeration systems:

Hindu-Arabic	Babylonian	Egyptian	Roman	Mayan
a. 72				
b.	**⟨ ▼▼**			
c.		𝄞99∩∩|||		

7. For each of the following decimal numerals, give the place value of the underlined numeral:
   a. 827,3<u>6</u>7   **b.** 8,421,0<u>0</u>0
   c. 9<u>7</u>,998   **d.** <u>8</u>10,485

8. Rewrite each of the following as a base-ten numeral:
   a. $3 \cdot 10^6 + 4 \cdot 10^3 + 5$ **b.** $2 \cdot 10^4 + 1$
   c. $3 \cdot 10^3 + 5 \cdot 10^2 + 6 \cdot 10$ **d.** $9 \cdot 10^6 + 9 \cdot 10 + 9$

9. A certain three-digit whole number has the following properties: The hundreds digit is greater than 7; the tens digit is an odd number; and the sum of the digits is 10. What could the number be?

10. Study the following counting frame. In the frame, the value of each dot is represented by the number in the box below the dot. For example, the following figure represents the number 154:

••	•••	••
64	8	1

What numbers are represented in the frames in (a) and (b)?

a.
•••	••	•
25	5	1

b.
•		•	•
8	4	2	1

11. Write the base-four numeral for the base-four blocks shown below.

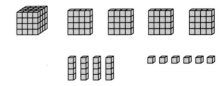

12. Write the first 15 counting numbers for each of the following bases:
   a. Base two   **b.** Base three
   c. Base four   **d.** Base eight

13. How many different digits are needed for base twenty?

14. Write 2032_{four} in expanded base-four notation.

15. Determine the greatest three-digit number in each of the following bases:
    a. Base two   b. Base six
    c. Base ten   d. Base twelve

16. Find the numbers preceding and succeeding each of the following:
    a. $EE0_{\text{twelve}}$ b. 100000_{two} c. 555_{six}
    d. 100_{seven} e. 1000_{fiiv} f. 110_{two}

17. What, if anything, is wrong with the following numerals:
    a. 204_{four} b. 607_{fiiv} c. $T12_{\text{three}}$

18. The smallest number of base-four blocks needed to represent 214 is
    _____ blocks   _____ flats   _____ longs   _____ units

19. Draw multibase blocks to represent
    a. 231_{fiiv} b. 1101_{two}

20. Complete each of the following:
    a. $111_{\text{two}} + 1_{\text{two}} =$
    b. $444_{\text{fiiv}} + 1_{\text{fiiv}} =$
    c. $TTT_{\text{twelve}} + 1_{\text{twelve}} =$
    d. $EEE_{\text{twelve}} + 1_{\text{twelve}} =$
    e. Based on parts (a–d), write a general statement for any base.

21. Convert each of the following base-ten numbers to numbers in the indicated bases:
    a. 432 to base five   b. 1963 to base twelve
    c. 404 to base four   d. 37 to base two

22. Change 42_{eight} to base two.

23. Write each of the following numbers in base ten:
    a. 432_{fiiv} b. 101101_{two} c. $92E_{\text{twelve}}$
    d. $T0E_{\text{twelve}}$ e. 111_{twelve} f. 346_{seven}

24. Suppose you have two quarters, four nickels, and two pennies. What is the value of your money in cents? Write a base-five representation of this amount.

25. You are asked to distribute $900 in prize money. The dollar amounts for the prizes are $625, $125, $25, $5, and $1. How should this $900 be distributed in order to give the fewest number of prizes?

26. What is the minimum number of quarters, nickels, and pennies necessary to make 97¢?

27. Convert each of the following:
    a. 58 days to weeks and days
    b. 54 months to years and months
    c. 29 hours to days and hours
    d. 68 inches to feet and inches

28. A bookstore ordered 11 gross, 6 dozen, and 6 pencils. Express the number of pencils in base twelve and in base ten.

29. For each of the following, find b if possible. If not possible, tell why.
    a. $b2_{\text{seven}} = 44_{\text{ten}}$ b. $5b2_{\text{twelve}} = 734_{\text{ten}}$
    c. $23_{\text{ten}} = 25_b$ d. $b2_{\text{seven}} = 2b_{\text{ten}}$

30. Write $12^5 + 25 \cdot 12^4 + 23$ in base-twelve notation without multiplying out 12^5 and 12^4.

31. The Chinese abacus, depicted as follows, shows the number 5857. (Hint: The beads above the bar represent 5s, 50s, 500s, and 5000s.)

Discuss how the number 5857 is depicted and show how the number 4869 could be depicted.

32. On a calculator, use only the keys $\boxed{1}$, $\boxed{2}$, $\boxed{3}$, $\boxed{4}$, $\boxed{5}$, $\boxed{6}$, $\boxed{7}$, $\boxed{8}$, and $\boxed{9}$, and fill the calculator's display to show each of the following:
    a. The greatest number possible if each key may be used only once
    b. The least number possible if each key may be used only once
    c. The greatest number possible if a key may be used more than once
    d. The least number possible if a key may be used more than once

33. In a game called WIPEOUT, we are to "wipe out" digits from a calculator's display without changing any of the other digits. "Wipeout" in this case means to replace the chosen digit(s) with a 0. For example, if the initial number is 54,321 and we are to wipe out the 4, we could subtract 4000 to obtain 50,321. Complete the following two problems and then try other numbers or challenge another person to wipe out a number from the number you have placed on the screen:
    a. Wipe out the 2s from 32,420.
    b. Wipe out the 5 from 67,357.

Communication

34. Ben claims that zero is the same as nothing. Explain how you as a teacher would respond to Ben's statement.

35. What are the major drawbacks to each of the following systems?
    a. Egyptian   b. Babylonian   c. Roman

36. a. Why are large numbers in the United States written with commas separating groups of three digits?
    b. Find examples from other countries that do not use commas to separate groups of three digits.

37. *I Can Count the Petals of a Flower* (NCTM, 1985) is a picture counting book for young children. How might you use this book with students in the first grade?

38. a. Discuss how you could use pennies, nickels, and quarters to teach base five.
    b. Explain how to use these coins to convert 88 to base five.

Open-Ended

39. An inspector of weights and measures uses a special set of weights to check the accuracy of scales. Various weights are placed on a scale to check accuracy of any amount from 1 oz through 15 oz. What is the least number of weights the inspector needs? What weights are needed to check the accuracy of scales from 1 oz through 15 oz? From 1 oz through 31 oz?

Cooperative Learning

40. **a.** Create a numeration system with unique symbols and write a paragraph explaining the properties of the system.

b. Complete the following table using the system:

Hindu-Arabic Numeral	Your System Numeral
1	
5	
10	
50	
100	
5,000	
10,000	
115,280	

BRAIN
T E A S E R

There are 3 nickels and 3 dimes concealed in 3 boxes. Two coins are placed in each of the boxes, which are labeled 10¢, 15¢, and 20¢. The coins are placed in such a way that no box contains the amount of money shown on its label; for example, the box labeled 10¢ does not really have a total of 10¢ in it. What is the minimum number of coins that you would have to remove from a box, and from which box or boxes, to determine which coins are in which boxes?

3-2 Algorithms for Whole-Number Addition and Subtraction

According to the *Principles and Standards*,

As children in prekindergarten through grade 2 develop an understanding of whole numbers and the operations of addition and subtraction, instructional attention should focus on strategies for computing with whole numbers so that students develop flexibility and computational fluency. Students will generate a range of interesting and useful strategies for solving computational problems, which should be shared and discussed. By the end of grade 2, students should know the basic addition and subtraction combinations, should be fluent in adding two-digit numbers, and should have methods for subtracting two-digit numbers. At the grades 3–5 level, as students develop the basic number combinations for multiplication and division, they should also develop reliable algorithms to solve arithmetic problems efficiently and accurately. These methods should be applied to larger numbers and practiced for fluency.

Researchers and experienced teachers alike have found that when children in the elementary grades are encouraged to develop, record, explain, and critique one another's strategies for solving computational problems, a number of important kinds of learning can occur (see, e.g., Hiebert [1999]; Kamii, Lewis, and Livingston [1993]; Hiebert et al. [1997]). The efficiency of various strategies can be discussed. So can generalizability: Will this work for any numbers or only the two involved here? And experience suggests that in classes focused on the development and discussion of strategies, various "standard" algorithms either arise naturally or can be introduced by the teacher as appropriate. The point is that students must become fluent in arithmetic computation—they must have efficient and accurate methods that are supported by an understanding of numbers and operations. "Standard" algorithms for arithmetic computation are one means of achieving this fluency. (p. 35)

algorithm

The previous chapter introduced the operations of addition and subtraction of whole numbers and now, as pointed out in the *Standards*, it is time to focus on *computational fluency*—having and using efficient and accurate methods for computing. The *Standards* suggest that "standard algorithms" are one means to achieve this fluency. An **algorithm** (named for the ninth-century Arabian mathematician Mohammed al Khowarizmi) is a systematic procedure used to accomplish an operation. This section focuses on developing and understanding algorithms involving addition and subtraction. Alternative algorithms as well as standard algorithms will be developed.

Addition Algorithms

Paper-and-pencil algorithms need to be taught developmentally; that is, they must proceed from the concrete stage to the abstract stage at appropriate times. The use of concrete teaching aids—such as chips, bean sticks, an abacus, or base-ten blocks—helps provide insight into the creation of algorithms for addition.

We now use base-ten blocks to help develop an algorithm for whole-number addition. Suppose we wish to add 14 + 23. We show this computation with a concrete model in Figure 3-8(a), with the expanded algorithm in Figure 3-8(b) and the standard algorithm in Figure 3-8(c).

FIGURE 3-8

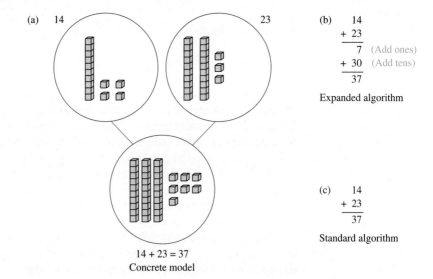

$$\begin{array}{r} 14 \\ +\ 23 \\ \hline 7 \quad \text{(Add ones)} \\ +\ 30 \quad \text{(Add tens)} \\ \hline 37 \end{array}$$

Expanded algorithm

$$\begin{array}{r} 14 \\ +\ 23 \\ \hline 37 \end{array}$$

Standard algorithm

14 + 23 = 37
Concrete model

A more formal justification for this addition not usually presented at the elementary level is the following:

$14 + 23 = (1 \cdot 10 + 4) + (2 \cdot 10 + 3)$ Expanded form

$= (1 \cdot 10 + 2 \cdot 10) + (4 + 3)$ Commutative and associative properties of addition

$= (1 + 2) \cdot 10 + (4 + 3)$ Distributive property of multiplication over addition

$= 3 \cdot 10 + 7$ Single-digit addition facts

$= 37$ Place value

An example using base-ten blocks with regrouping is shown on the student page. After using concrete models with regrouping as on the student page, children should be ready to use the expanded and standard algorithms. Figure 3-9 shows the computation $37 + 28$ using both algorithms. Notice in Figure 3-9(b) that when there were more than ten ones, we regrouped ten ones as a ten and then added the tens. This process could be repeated. Notice that the word *regroup* was used rather than *carry*. The words *regroup* or *trade* are used in the elementary school to describe the actions that take place.

FIGURE 3-9

(a)
```
    37
  + 28
    15   (Add ones)
  + 50   (Add tens)
    65
```
Expanded algorithm

(b)
```
     1
    37
  + 28
    65   (Add the ones, regroup, and add the tens)
```
Standard algorithm

Students often develop algorithms on their own and learning can occur by investigating how and if various algorithms work. Next we explore several algorithms that have been used throughout history.

Left-to-Right Algorithm for Addition

When working with base-ten blocks, some students may combine the larger pieces first and then proceed to combine the smaller pieces. This might seem natural; because children learn to read from left to right, they might try to add from left to right. This left-to-right algorithm is introduced below.

```
    568              568
  + 757            + 757
    12              12̸1̸5
    11      ⟶       32      →   1325
    15
  1325
```

Explain why this technique works and try it with $9076 + 4689$.

Sample School Book Page:
ADDING WITH REGROUPING

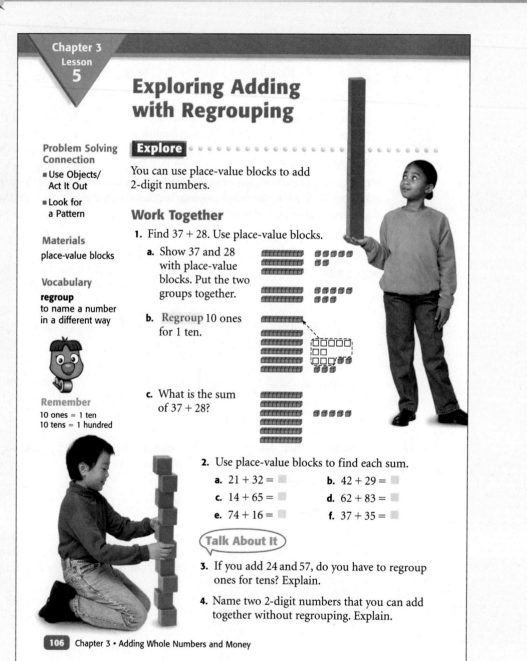

Chapter 3 Lesson 5

Exploring Adding with Regrouping

Problem Solving Connection

- Use Objects/ Act It Out
- Look for a Pattern

Materials
place-value blocks

Vocabulary
regroup
to name a number in a different way

Remember
10 ones = 1 ten
10 tens = 1 hundred

Explore

You can use place-value blocks to add 2-digit numbers.

Work Together

1. Find 37 + 28. Use place-value blocks.

   a. Show 37 and 28 with place-value blocks. Put the two groups together.

   b. Regroup 10 ones for 1 ten.

   c. What is the sum of 37 + 28?

2. Use place-value blocks to find each sum.

   a. 21 + 32 =
   b. 42 + 29 =
   c. 14 + 65 =
   d. 62 + 83 =
   e. 74 + 16 =
   f. 37 + 35 =

Talk About It

3. If you add 24 and 57, do you have to regroup ones for tens? Explain.

4. Name two 2-digit numbers that you can add together without regrouping. Explain.

106 Chapter 3 • Adding Whole Numbers and Money

Source: Scott Foresman–Addison Wesley Math, Grade 3, 2002 (p. 106).

Lattice Algorithm for Addition

We introduce this algorithm by working through an addition involving two four-digit numbers. For example,

$$\begin{array}{r} 3\ 5\ 6\ 7 \\ +\ 5\ 6\ 7\ 8 \\ \hline \end{array}$$

To use this algorithm you need only to add a single-digit number to a single-digit number and record the results in a *lattice* as shown above. Then the sums are added along the diagonals as shown. Notice that this is very similar to the expanded algorithm introduced earlier. Try this technique with 4578 + 2691.

Scratch Algorithm for Addition

The scratch algorithm for addition is often referred to as a low-stress algorithm because it allows students to perform complicated additions by doing a series of additions that involve only two single digits. An example follows:

1.
$$\begin{array}{r} 87 \\ 6\,5_2 \\ +\ 49 \\ \end{array}$$
Add the numbers in the units place starting at the top. When the sum is 10 or more, record this sum by scratching a line through the last digit added and writing the number of units next to the scratched digit. For example, since 7 + 5 = 12, the "scratch" represents 10 and the 2 represents the units.

2.
$$\begin{array}{r} 87 \\ 6\,5_2 \\ +\ 49_1 \\ \end{array}$$
Continue adding the units, including any new digits written down. When the addition again results in a sum of 10 or more, as with 2 + 9 = 11, repeat the process described in (1).

3.
$$\begin{array}{r} {}^2 87 \\ 6\,5_2 \\ +\ 49_1 \\ \hline 1 \end{array}$$
When the first column of additions is completed, write the number of units, 1, below the addition line. Count the number of scratches, 2, and add this number to the second column.

4.
$$\begin{array}{r} {}^2 8_0 7 \\ 6\,5_2 \\ 4_0 9_1 \\ \hline 2\ 0\ 1 \end{array}$$
Repeat the procedure for each successive column.

Subtraction Algorithms

As with addition, base-ten blocks can provide a concrete model for subtraction. Consider how the base-ten blocks are used to perform the subtraction 243 − 61.

First we represent 243 with 2 flats, 4 longs, and 3 units, as shown in Figure 3-10.

FIGURE 3-10

To subtract 61 from 243, we try to remove 6 longs and 1 unit from the blocks in Figure 3-10. We can remove 1 unit, as in Figure 3-11.

FIGURE 3-11

To remove 6 longs from Figure 3-11, we have to trade 1 flat for 10 longs, as shown in Figure 3-12.

FIGURE 3-12

Now we can remove, or "take away," 6 longs leaving 1 flat, 8 longs, and 2 units, or 182, as shown in Figure 3-13.

FIGURE 3-13

How can you use your base-ten blocks and addition to check your subtraction? Discuss how you would perform $332 - 193$ using base-ten blocks.

After students have worked with base-ten blocks for subtraction, they are ready to proceed to the standard algorithm as shown on the partial student page on page 155.

Equal Addends Algorithm

The equal addends algorithm for subtraction is based on the fact that the difference between two numbers does not change if we add the same amount to both numbers. For example, $93 - 27 = (93 + 3) - (27 + 3)$. Thus the difference can be computed as $96 - 30 = 66$. Using this approach the subtraction on the student page could be performed as follows.

$$
\begin{array}{c}
213 \\
\underline{-\ 42}
\end{array}
\rightarrow
\begin{array}{c}
213 + 8 \\
\underline{-\ 42 + 8}
\end{array}
\rightarrow
\begin{array}{c}
221 \\
\underline{-\ 50}
\end{array}
\rightarrow
\begin{array}{c}
221 + 50 \\
\underline{-\ 50 + 50}
\end{array}
\rightarrow
\begin{array}{c}
271 \\
\underline{-100} \\
171
\end{array}
$$

Sample School Book Page:
SUBTRACTION

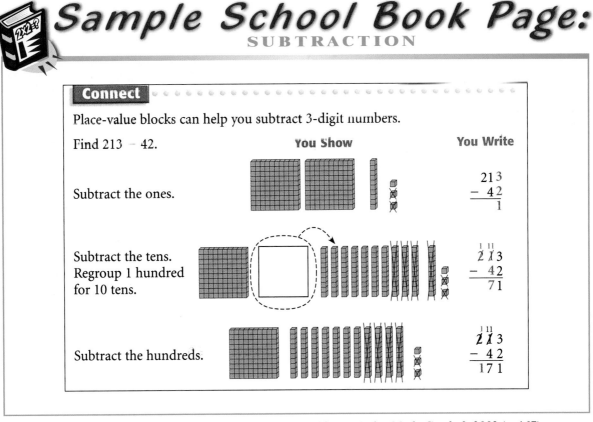

Connect

Place-value blocks can help you subtract 3-digit numbers.

Find 213 – 42.

You Show   **You Write**

Subtract the ones.

$$\begin{array}{r} 213 \\ -\ 42 \\ \hline 1 \end{array}$$

Subtract the tens.
Regroup 1 hundred
for 10 tens.

$$\begin{array}{r} {\scriptstyle 1\ 11} \\ 2\ \not{1}\ 3 \\ -\ 42 \\ \hline 71 \end{array}$$

Subtract the hundreds.

$$\begin{array}{r} {\scriptstyle 1\ 11} \\ \not{2}\ \not{1}\ 3 \\ -\ 42 \\ \hline 171 \end{array}$$

Source: Scott Foresman–Addison Wesley Math, Grade 3, 2002 (p. 167).

Addition and Subtraction in Bases Other Than Ten

A look at computation in other bases may provide insight into computation in base ten. Use of multibase blocks may be helpful in building an addition table for different bases and is highly recommended. Table 3-8 is a base-five addition table.

Table 3-8   Base-Five
Addition Table

+	0	1	2	3	4
0	0	1	2	3	4
1	1	2	3	4	10
2	2	3	4	10	11
3	3	4	10	11	12
4	4	10	11	12	13

NOW TRY THIS 3-5

a. Determine how a number line might be used to model addition in base five.
b. Write each of the following as numerals in base five:
    i. $444_{\text{five}} + 1_{\text{five}}$ ii. $4444_{\text{five}} + 1_{\text{five}}$

Using the addition facts in Table 3-8, we develop algorithms for base-five addition similar to those for base-ten addition. Suppose we wish to add $12_{\text{five}} + 31_{\text{five}}$. We show the computation using a concrete model in Figure 3-14(a), an expanded algorithm in Figure 3-14(b), and the standard algorithm in Figure 3-14(c). Additions in other number bases can be handled similarly.

FIGURE 3-14

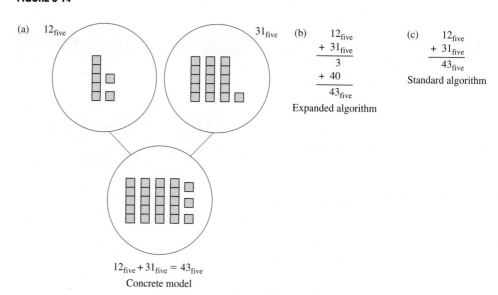

(b)
$$\begin{array}{r} 12_{\text{five}} \\ + \ 31_{\text{five}} \\ \hline 3 \\ + \ 40 \\ \hline 43_{\text{five}} \end{array}$$
Expanded algorithm

(c)
$$\begin{array}{r} 12_{\text{five}} \\ + \ 31_{\text{five}} \\ \hline 43_{\text{five}} \end{array}$$
Standard algorithm

$12_{\text{five}} + 31_{\text{five}} = 43_{\text{five}}$
Concrete model

The subtraction facts for base five can also be derived from the addition-facts table by using the definition of subtraction. For example, to find $12_{\text{five}} - 4_{\text{five}}$, recall that $12_{\text{five}} - 4_{\text{five}} = c_{\text{five}}$ if, and only if, $c_{\text{five}} + 4_{\text{five}} = 12_{\text{five}}$. From Table 3-8, we see that $c = 3_{\text{five}}$. An example of subtraction involving regrouping, $32_{\text{five}} - 14_{\text{five}}$, is developed in Figure 3-15.

FIGURE 3-15

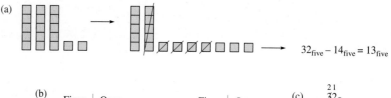

$32_{\text{five}} - 14_{\text{five}} = 13_{\text{five}}$

(b)

Fives	Ones
3	2
– 1	4

Fives	Ones
2	12
– 1	4
1	3

(c)
$$\begin{array}{r} \overset{2\,1}{\cancel{3}2}_{\text{five}} \\ - \ 14_{\text{five}} \\ \hline 13_{\text{five}} \end{array}$$

NOW TRY THIS 3-6

a. Build an addition table for base two.

b. Perform the subtraction $1101_{two} - 111_{two}$.

BRAIN
TEASER

The number on a license plate consists of five digits. When the license plate is looked at upside down, you can still read it, but the value of the upside-down number is 78,633 greater than the real license number. What is the license number?

ONGOING ASSESSMENT 3-2

1. Find the missing digits in each of the following:

   a.
   ```
      _ _ 1
   +  4 2 _
   _ 4 0 2
   ```

   b.
   ```
     _ 0 2 5
     1 1 _ 6
   + 3 1 4 8
     6 _ 6 _
   ```

2. Find the missing digits in each of the following:

   a.
   ```
      3 _ _
   -  1 5 9
      _ 2 4
   ```

   b.
   ```
     1 _ _ _ 6
   -   8 3 0 9
       4 9 8 7
   ```

3. Place the digits 7, 6, 8, 3, 5, and 2 in the boxes to obtain

   a. the greatest sum. **b.** the least sum.

4. Place the digits 7, 6, 8, 3, 5, and 2 in the boxes to obtain

   a. the greatest difference. **b.** the least difference.

5. Tom's diet allows only 1500 calories per day. For breakfast, Tom had skim milk (90 calories), a waffle with no syrup (120 calories), and a banana (119 calories). For lunch, he had $\frac{1}{2}$ cup of salad (185 calories) with mayonnaise (110 calories), and tea (0 calories). Then he had pecan pie (570 calories). Can he have dinner consisting of steak (250 calories), a salad with no mayonnaise, and tea?

6. Wally kept track of last week's money transactions. His salary was $150 plus $54 in overtime and $260 in tips. His transportation expenses were $22, his food expenses were $60, his laundry costs were $15, his entertainment expenditures were $58, and his rent was $185. After expenses, did he have any money left? If so, how much?

7. In the following problem, the sum is correct but the order of the digits in each addend has been scrambled. Correct the addends to obtain the correct sum.

   ```
     2 8 3 4
   + 6 3 1 5
     9 0 5 9
   ```
   ```
   □ □ □ □
 + □ □ □ □
   9 0 5 9
   ```

8. Use the equal addends approach to compute each of the following:

   a.
   ```
     93
   - 37
   ```

   b.
   ```
     321
   -  38
   ```

9. Janet worked her addition problems by placing the partial sums as shown here:

   ```
        569
   +    645
         14
         10
         11
       1214
   ```

   a. Use this method to work the following:

   (i)
   ```
     687
   + 549
   ```
   (ii)
   ```
     359
   + 673
   ```

   b. Explain why this algorithm works.

10. Analyze the following computations. Explain what is wrong in each case.

    a.
    ```
      135
    +  47
      172
    ```
    b.
    ```
      87
    + 25
    1012
    ```
    c.
    ```
      57
    - 38
      21
    ```
    d.
    ```
      56
    - 18
      48
    ```

11. George is cooking an elaborate meal for Thanksgiving. He can cook only one thing at a time in his microwave oven. His turkey takes 75 min; the pumpkin pie takes 18 min; rolls take 45 sec; and a cup of coffee takes 30 sec to heat. How much time does he need to cook the meal?

12. Give reasons for each of the following steps.
$$16 + 31 = (1 \cdot 10 + 6) + (3 \cdot 10 + 1)$$
$$= (1 \cdot 10 + 3 \cdot 10) + (6 + 1)$$
$$= (1 + 3) \cdot 10 + (6 + 1)$$
$$= 4 \cdot 10 + 7$$
$$= 47$$

13. Perform each of the following operations using the bases shown:

a. $43_{five} + 23_{five}$ b. $43_{five} - 23_{five}$
c. $432_{five} + 23_{five}$ d. $42_{five} - 23_{five}$
e. $110_{two} + 11_{two}$ f. $10001_{two} - 111_{two}$

14. Construct an addition table for base eight.

15. Perform each of the following operations:

a.   3 hr 36 min 58 sec
  + 5 hr 56 min 27 sec

b.   5 hr 36 min 38 sec
  − 3 hr 56 min 58 sec

16. Perform each of the following operations (2 c = 1 pt, 2 pt = 1 qt, 4 qt = 1 gal):

a.   1 qt 1 pt 1 c   b.   1 qt 1 c
  +   1 pt 1 c   −   1 pt 1 c

c.   1 gal 3 qt 1 c
   −   4 qt 2 c

17. A palindrome is any number that reads the same backward as forward, for example, 121 and 2332. Try the following. Begin with any number. Is it a palindrome? If not, reverse the digits and add this reversed number to the original number. Is the result a palindrome? If not, repeat the above procedure until a palindrome is obtained. For example, start with 78. Because 78 is not a palindrome, we add: $78 + 87 = 165$. Because 165 is not a palindrome, we add: $165 + 561 = 726$. Again, 726 is not a palindrome, so we add $726 + 627$ to obtain 1353. Finally, $1353 + 3531$ yields 4884, which is a palindrome.

a. Try this method with the following numbers:
(i) 93   (ii) 588   (iii) 2003

b. Find a number for which the procedure described takes more than five steps to form a palindrome.

18. a. Place the numbers 24 through 32 in the following circles so that the sums are the same in each direction:

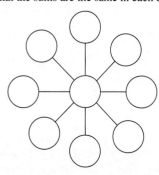

b. How many different numbers can be placed in the middle to obtain a solution?

19. Andrew's calculator was not functioning properly, When he pressed $\boxed{8}\ \boxed{+}\ \boxed{6}\ \boxed{=}$, the numeral 20 appeared on the display. When he pressed $\boxed{5}\ \boxed{+}\ \boxed{4}\ \boxed{=}$, 13 was displayed. When he pressed, $\boxed{1}\ \boxed{5}\ \boxed{-}\ \boxed{3}\ \boxed{=}$, 9 was displayed. What do you think Andrew's calculator was doing?

20. The following is a supermagic square taken from an engraving called *Melancholia* by Dürer that includes the year (1514) it was constructed:

16	3	2	13
5	10	11	8
9	6	7	12
4	15	14	1

a. Find the sum of each row, the sum of each column, and the sum of each diagonal.

b. Find the sum of the four numbers in the center.

c. Find the sum of the four numbers in each corner.

d. Add 11 to each number in the square. Is the square still a magic square? Explain your answer.

e. Subtract 11 from each number in the square. Is the square still a magic square?

21. Use scratch addition to perform the following:

a.   432   b. 32_{five}
      976   13_{five}
 + 1418 22_{five}
                43_{five}
                23_{five}
            + 12_{five}

22. Perform each of the following operations:

a.   4 gross 4 dz 6 ones
  −   5 dz 9 ones

b.   2 gross 9 dz 7 ones
  + 3 gross 5 dz 9 ones

23. Determine what is wrong with the following:
    22_{five}
  + 33_{five}
   $\overline{55_{five}}$

24. Fill in the missing numbers in each of the following:

a.   2 _ _ $_{five}$ b.   2 0 0 1 0$_{three}$
  −   2 2$_{five}$ −   2 _ 2 _ $_{three}$
   $\overline{\text{_ 0 3}_{five}}$ $\overline{\text{1 _ 2 _ 1}_{three}}$

25. The Hawks played the Elks in a basketball game. Based on the information below, complete the scoreboard showing the number of points scored by each team during each quarter and the final score of the game.

TEAMS	QUARTERS				FINAL SCORE
	1	2	3	4	
Hawks					
Elks					

a. The Hawks scored 15 points in the first quarter.

b. The Hawks were behind by 5 points at the end of the first quarter.

c. The Elks scored 5 more points in the second quarter than they did in the first quarter.

d. The Hawks scored 7 more points than the Elks in the second quarter.

e. The Elks outscored the Hawks by 6 points in the fourth quarter.

f. The Hawks scored a total of 120 points in the game.

g. The Hawks scored twice as many points in the third quarter as the Elks did in the first quarter.

h. The Elks scored as many points in the third quarter as the Hawks did in the first two quarters combined.

Communication

26. Tira, a fourth grader, performs addition by adding and subtracting the same number. She added as follows:

$$\begin{array}{c} 39 \\ + 84 \\ \hline \end{array} \rightarrow \begin{array}{c} 39 + 1 \\ + 84 - 1 \\ \hline \end{array} \rightarrow \begin{array}{c} 40 \\ 83 \\ \hline 123 \end{array}$$

How would you respond if you were her teacher?

27. Cathy found her own algorithm for subtraction. She subtracted as follows:

$$\begin{array}{c} 97 \\ -28 \\ \hline -1 \\ +70 \\ \hline 69 \end{array}$$

How would you respond if you were her teacher?

28. Discuss why the words *regroup* and *trade* are used rather than *carry* and *borrow* for whole-number addition and subtraction algorithms.

29. Discuss whether children should be encouraged to develop and use their own algorithms for whole-number addition and subtraction or whether they should be taught only one algorithm per operation and all students should use only the one algorithm.

30. Explain why the scratch addition algorithm works.

31. The *equal addends* algorithm was introduced in this section. The following shows how this algorithm works for $1464 - 687$.

$$\begin{array}{r} 1\,4\,6^{1}4 \\ -\ 6^{9}8\,7 \\ \hline 7 \end{array}$$ (Add 10 to the 4 ones to get 14 ones.)
(Add 1 ten to the 8 tens to get 9 tens.)
(Subtract the ones.)

Now we move to the next column.

$$\begin{array}{r} 1\,4^{1}6^{1}4 \\ -\ ^{7}6^{9}8\,7 \\ \hline 7\,7\,7 \end{array}$$ (Add 10 tens to the 6 tens to get 16 tens.)
(Add 1 hundred to the 6 hundreds to get 7 hundreds.)
(Subtract the 9 tens from the 16 tens and then the 7 hundreds from the 14 hundreds.)

a. Try the technique on three more subtractions.

b. Explain why the equal addends algorithm works.

Open-Ended

32. Search for or develop an algorithm for whole-number addition or subtraction and write a description of your algorithm so that others can understand and use it.

Cooperative Learning

33. Investigate our money system and decide whether the system is a base-ten system.

Review Problems

34. Investigate the measuring of lengths in the metric system. Develop a plan for using place value with lengths to convert among different metric units.

35. Write 5280 in expanded form.

36. What is the value of MCDX in Hindu-Arabic numerals?

37. Convert each of the following to base ten.
   a. $E0T_{twelve}$ b. 1011_{two} c. 43_{five}

38. If 1 mo is approximately 4 wk and 1 yr is approximately 365 days or 52 wk, answer the following:
   a. Lewis and Clark spent approximately 2 yr, 4 mo, and 9 days exploring the territory in the Northwest. What is this time in weeks?
   b. It took Magellan 1126 days to circle the world. How many years is this?
   c. How many seconds old are you?
   d. Approximately how many times does your heart beat in 1 yr?

LABORATORY
A C T I V I T Y

1. One type of Japanese abacus, *soroban*, is shown in Figure 3-16(a). In this abacus, a bar separates two sets of bead counters. Each counter above the bar represents five times the counter below the bar. Numbers are illustrated by moving the counter toward the bar. The number 7632 is pictured. Practice demonstrating and adding numbers on this abacus.

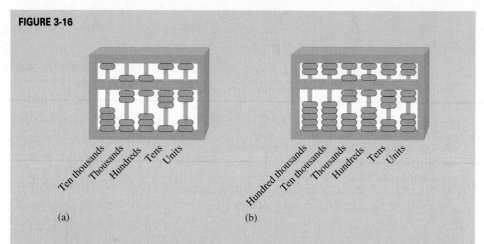

FIGURE 3-16

(a)   (b)

2. The Chinese abacus, *suan pan* (see Figure 3-16(b)), is still in use today. This abacus is similar to the Japanese abacus but has two counters above the bar. The number 7632 is also pictured on it. Practice demonstrating and adding numbers on this abacus. Compare the ease of using the two versions.

Algorithms for Whole-Number Multiplication and Division

In the *Principles and Standards*, we find the following regarding multiplication and division of whole numbers.

In grades 3–5, students should focus on the meanings of, and relationship between, multiplication and division. It is important that students understand what each number in a multiplication or division expression represents. For example, in multiplication, unlike addition, the factors in the problem can refer to different units. If students are solving the problem 29 × 4 to find out how many legs are on 29 cats, 29 is the number of cats (or number of groups), 4 is the number of legs on each cat (or number of items in each group), and 116 is the total number of legs on all the cats. Modeling multiplication problems with pictures, diagrams, or concrete materials helps students learn what the factors and their product represent in various contexts. (p. 151)

In this section, multiplication and division algorithms will be introduced using various models.

Multiplication Algorithms

To develop algorithms for multiplying multidigit whole numbers, we use the strategy of *examining simpler computations first*. Consider $4 \cdot 12$. This computation could be pictured as in Figure 3-17(a) with 4 rows of 12 blocks, or 48 blocks. The blocks in Figure 3-17(a) can also be partitioned to show that $4 \cdot 12 = 4 \cdot (10 + 2) = 4 \cdot 10 + 4 \cdot 2$. The numbers $4 \cdot 10$ and $4 \cdot 2$ are *partial products*.

FIGURE 3-17

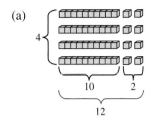

(b)

Tens	Ones
1	2
×	4

$\rightarrow$

$$\begin{array}{r} 10 + 2 \\ \times\quad 4 \\ \hline 40 + 8 \end{array}$$

$\rightarrow$

$$\begin{array}{r} 12 \\ \times 4 \\ \hline \end{array}$$

$\rightarrow$

$$\begin{array}{r} 12 \\ \times 4 \\ \hline 48 \end{array}$$

$40 + 8 \dashrightarrow 8$

$\dashrightarrow 40$

$\dashrightarrow 48$

$\dfrac{}{48}$

Figure 3-17(a) illustrates the distributive property of multiplication over addition on the set of whole numbers. The process leading to an algorithm for multiplying $4 \cdot 12$ is seen in Figure 3-17(b).

Multiplication by 10^n

Next we consider multiplication by powers of 10. First consider what happens when we multiply a given number by 10, such as $23 \cdot 10$. If we start out with the base-ten block representation of 23, we have 2 longs and 3 units. To multiply by 10, we must replace each piece with a base-ten piece that represents the next higher power of 10. This is shown in Figure 3-18. From Figure 3-18, we can see that in general if we multiply any number by 10 we annex a 0 at the end of the number.

FIGURE 3-18

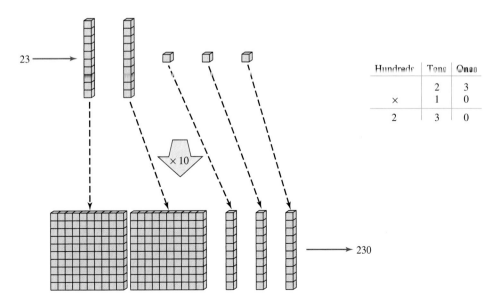

The approach in Figure 3-18 can be explained by using the distributive property of multiplication over addition.

$$
\begin{aligned}
23 \cdot 10 &= (2 \cdot 10 + 3) \cdot 10 \\
&= (2 \cdot 10) \cdot 10 + 3 \cdot 10 \\
&= 2 \cdot (10 \cdot 10) + 3 \cdot 10 \\
&= 2 \cdot 10^2 + 3 \cdot 10 \\
&= 2 \cdot 10^2 + 3 \cdot 10 + 0 \cdot 1 \\
&= 230
\end{aligned}
$$

To compute products such as $3 \cdot 200$, we proceed as follows:

$$
\begin{aligned}
3 \cdot 200 &= 3 \cdot (2 \cdot 10^2) \\
&= (3 \cdot 2) \cdot 10^2 \\
&= 6 \cdot 10^2 \\
&= 6 \cdot 10^2 + 0 \cdot 10^1 + 0 \cdot 1 \\
&= 600
\end{aligned}
$$

We see that multiplying 6 by 10^2 results in annexing two zeros to 6. This idea can be generalized to the statement that *multiplication of any natural number by* 10^n, *where n is a natural number, results in annexing n zeros to the number.*

When multiplying powers of 10, an extension of the definition of exponents is used. For example, $10^2 \cdot 10^1 = (10 \cdot 10) \cdot 10 = 10^3$, or 10^{2+1}. In general, where a is a natural number and m and n are whole numbers, $a^m \cdot a^n$ is given by the following:

$$
\begin{aligned}
a^m \cdot a^n &= \underbrace{(a \cdot a \cdot a \cdot \ldots \cdot a)}_{m \text{ factors}} \cdot \underbrace{(a \cdot a \cdot a \cdot \ldots \cdot a)}_{n \text{ factors}} \\
&= \underbrace{a \cdot a \cdot a \cdot \ldots \cdot a}_{m + n \text{ factors}} = a^{m+n}
\end{aligned}
$$

Consequently, $a^m \cdot a^n = a^{m+n}$.

NOW TRY THIS 3-7

Does $a^n + a^m$ ever equal a^{m+n}? If so, when?

Multiplication with Two-Digit Factors

Consider $14 \cdot 23$. We first model this computation using base-ten blocks, as shown in Figure 3-19(a), and then showing all the partial products and adding, as shown in Figure 3-19(b).

Another approach is to write 14 as $10 + 4$ and use the distributive property of multiplication over addition, as follows:

$$
\begin{aligned}
14 \cdot 23 &= (10 + 4) \cdot 23 \\
&= 10 \cdot 23 + 4 \cdot 23 \\
&= 230 + 92 \\
&= 322
\end{aligned}
$$

FIGURE 3-19

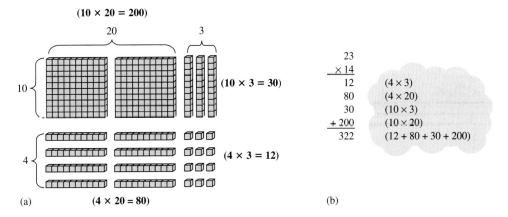

(a)

(b)

This last approach leads to an algorithm for multiplication:

$$
\begin{array}{r}
23 \\
\times\ 14 \\
\hline
92 \\
230 \\
\hline
322
\end{array}
\qquad
\begin{array}{l}
10 + 4 \\
(4 \cdot 23) \\
(10 \cdot 23)
\end{array}
\qquad \text{or} \qquad
\begin{array}{r}
23 \\
\times\ 14 \\
\hline
92 \\
23 \\
\hline
322
\end{array}
$$

We are accustomed to seeing the partial product 230 written without the zero, as 23. The placement of 23 with 3 in the tens column obviates having to write the 0 in the units column. When children first learn multiplication algorithms, they should be encouraged to include the zero in order to avoid errors and promote better understanding. Children should also be encouraged to *estimate* whether their answers are reasonable. In this exercise, we know that the answer must be between $10 \cdot 20 = 200$ and $20 \cdot 30 = 600$ because $10 < 14 < 20$ and $20 < 23 < 30$. Also because 14 and 23 are closer to 10 and 20 than to 20 and 30, the product must be closer to 200 than 600.

Lattice Multiplication

lattice multiplication

The **lattice multiplication** algorithm for multiplying 14 and 23 is shown in Figure 3-20. (Determining the reasons why lattice multiplication works is left as an exercise.)

FIGURE 3-20

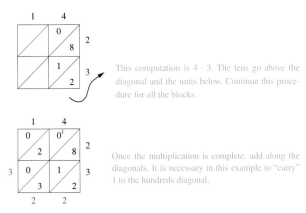

This computation is 4 · 3. The tens go above the diagonal and the units below. Continue this procedure for all the blocks.

Once the multiplication is complete, add along the diagonals. It is necessary in this example to "carry" 1 to the hundreds diagonal.

Division Algorithms

Using Repeated Subtraction to Develop the Standard Division Algorithm

Algorithms for division of whole numbers can also be developed by using repeated subtraction. Consider the following:

A shopkeeper is packaging juice in cartons that hold 6 bottles each. She has 726 bottles. How many cartons does she need?

We might reason that if 1 carton holds 6 bottles, then 10 cartons hold 60 bottles and 100 cartons hold 600 bottles. If 100 cartons are filled, there are $726 - 100 \cdot 6$, or 126, bottles remaining. If 10 more cartons are filled, then $126 - 10 \cdot 6$, or 66, bottles remain. Similarly, if 10 more cartons are filled, $66 - 10 \cdot 6$, or 6, bottles remain. Finally, 1 carton will hold the remaining 6 bottles. The total number of cartons necessary is $100 + 10 + 10 + 1$, or 121. This procedure is summarized in Figure 3-21(a). A more efficient method is shown in Figure 3-21(b).

FIGURE 3-21

$$
\begin{array}{ll}
\text{(a)} \quad 6)\overline{726} & \\
\quad \underline{-600} & \quad 100 \text{ sixes} \\
\quad 126 & \\
\quad \underline{-\ 60} & \quad 10 \text{ sixes} \\
\quad 66 & \\
\quad \underline{-\ 60} & \quad 10 \text{ sixes} \\
\quad 6 & \\
\quad \underline{-6} & \quad \underline{1 \text{ six}} \\
\quad 0 & \quad 121 \text{ sixes}
\end{array}
\qquad
\begin{array}{ll}
\text{(b)} \quad 6)\overline{726} & \\
\quad \underline{-600} & \quad 100 \text{ sixes} \\
\quad 126 & \\
\quad \underline{-120} & \quad 20 \text{ sixes} \\
\quad 6 & \\
\quad \underline{-6} & \quad \underline{1 \text{ six}} \\
\quad 0 & \quad 121 \text{ sixes}
\end{array}
$$

Divisions such as the one in Figure 3-21 are usually shown in elementary school texts in the most efficient form, as in Figure 3-22(b), in which the numbers in color in Figure 3-22(a) are omitted. The technique used in Figure 3-22(a) is often called "scaffolding" and may be used as a preliminary step to achieving the standard algorithm, as in Figure 3-22(b).

FIGURE 3-22

$$
\begin{array}{ll}
\text{(a)} & \dfrac{121}{1} \\
& 20 \\
& 100 \\
& 6)\overline{726} \\
& \underline{-600} \\
& 126 \\
& \underline{-120} \\
& 6 \\
& \underline{-6} \\
& 0
\end{array}
\qquad
\begin{array}{ll}
\text{(b)} & 121 \\
& 6)\overline{726} \\
& \underline{-6} \\
& 12 \\
& \underline{-12} \\
& 6 \\
& \underline{-6} \\
& 0
\end{array}
$$

Using Base-ten Blocks to Develop the Standard Division Algorithm

The development of the division algorithm introduced above used repeated subtraction. This next approach leading to the standard division algorithm uses base-ten blocks. Consider again the problem $6)\overline{726}$.

Base-ten Blocks	Algorithm
1. First we represent 726 with base-ten blocks.	$6\overline{)726}$
2. We next determine how many sets of 6 flats (hundreds) there are in the representation. There is 1 set of 6 flats with 1 flat, 2 longs (tens), and 6 units (ones) left over.	1 set of 6 flats $$\begin{array}{r} 1 \\ 6\overline{)726} \\ -6 \\ \hline 1 \end{array}$$ 1 flat 2 longs 6 units left over
3. Next, we convert the one leftover flat to 10 longs (tens). Now we have 12 longs (tens) and 6 units (ones).	1 set of 6 flats $$\begin{array}{r} 1 \\ 6\overline{)726} \\ -6 \\ \hline 12 \end{array}$$ 12 longs 6 units left over
4. Next we determine how many sets of 6 longs (tens) there are in 12 longs and 6 units. We have 2 sets of 6 longs and 6 units left over.	1 set of 6 flats 2 sets of 6 longs $$\begin{array}{r} 12 \\ 6\overline{)726} \\ -6 \\ \hline 12 \\ -12 \\ \hline 6 \end{array}$$ 6 units left over
5. Next we determine how many sets of 6 units (ones) there are in the 6 remaining units. There is 1 set of 6 units with no units left over (the remainder is 0).	1 set of 6 flats 2 sets of 6 longs 1 set of 6 units $$\begin{array}{r} 121 \\ 6\overline{)726} \\ -6 \\ \hline 12 \\ -12 \\ \hline 6 \\ -6 \\ \hline 0 \end{array}$$ 0 remainder

Therefore we see that in the base-ten block representation of 726, there is 1 group of 6 flats (hundreds), 2 groups of 6 longs (tens), and 1 group of 6 units (ones) with none left over. Hence the quotient is 121 with a remainder of 0. The steps in the algorithm are shown alongside the work with the base-ten blocks.

Short Division

The process used in Figure 3-22(b) is usually referred to as "long" division. Another technique, called "short" division, can be used when the divisor is a one-digit number and most of the work is done mentally. An example of short division is given in Figure 3-23.

FIGURE 3-23

Decide where to start.	Divide the hundreds. Write the remainder by the tens.	Divide the tens. Write the remainder by the ones.	Divide the ones.

$$5 \atop 5)\overline{2\ 8\ 8\ 0}$$

$$5 \atop 5)\overline{2\ 8^3 8\ 0}$$

$$5\ 7 \atop 5)\overline{2\ 8^3 8^3 0}$$

$$5\ 7\ 6 \atop 5)\overline{2\ 8^3 8^3 0}$$

Not enough thousands, so divide the hundreds.

$28 \div 5 = 5\ \text{R}3$

$38 \div 5 = 7\ \text{R}3$

$30 \div 5 = 6\ \text{R}0$

Division in many elementary texts is taught using a four-step algorithm: *estimate, multiply, subtract,* and *compare.* This is demonstrated in the student page. Study the student page and answer the questions at the bottom of the page.

Division by a Two-Digit Divisor

An example of division by a divisor of more than one digit is given next. Consider $32)\overline{2618}$.

1. Estimate the quotient in $32)\overline{2618}$. Because $1 \cdot 32 = 32$, $10 \cdot 32 = 320$, $100 \cdot 32 = 3200$, we see that the quotient is between 10 and 100.
2. Find the number of tens in the quotient. Because $26 \div 3$ is approximately 8, then 26 hundreds divided by 3 tens is approximately 8 tens. We then write the 8 in the tens place, as shown:

$$
\begin{array}{r}
80 \\
32)\overline{2618} \\
-\ 2560 \quad (32 \cdot 80) \\
\hline
58
\end{array}
$$

Sample School Book Page:
DIVISION

Chapter 7
Lesson 7

2- or 3-Digit Quotients

You Will Learn

how to find 2- or 3-digit quotients

Math Tip

Always estimate the quotient to see if you can start dividing a 3-digit dividend in the hundreds place.

Learn • • • • • • • •

What does a lime fruit drink have in common with a coral reef in Florida? How about a mango drink and a rain forest? Lots of cents!

The fruit drink company that Catherine Page works for gives part of its profits to environmental groups. The money will help save endangered sites.

Catherine Page works for a natural fruit drink company in Charlotte, North Carolina.

Example

Catherine's company stacks 114 cases onto pallets. Cases are stacked 6 layers high. How many cases are in each layer?

Find 114 ÷ 6.

Step 1	Step 2	Step 3
Estimate to decide where to start dividing.	Divide the tens.	Bring down the ones and divide.
Think: 114 is close to 120.	$\begin{array}{r} 1 \\ 6\overline{)114} \\ -6 \\ \hline 5 \end{array}$ Multiply. $1 \times 6 = 6$ Subtract. $11 - 6 = 5$ Compare. $5 < 6$	$\begin{array}{r} 19 \\ 6\overline{)114} \\ -6 \\ \hline 54 \\ -54 \\ \hline 0 \end{array}$ Multiply. $9 \times 6 = 54$ Subtract. $54 - 54 = 0$ Compare. $0 < 6$
$\begin{array}{r} 20 \\ 6\overline{)120} \end{array}$		
Start by dividing tens. Your quotient will have 2 digits.		

There are 19 cases in each layer on the pallet.

Talk About It

1. How did estimating help you make sure you divided in the right place?

2. How can you tell that 375 ÷ 7 will have a 2-digit quotient?

310

Chapter 7 • Dividing by 1-Digit Divisors

Source: Scott Foresman–Addison Wesley, Grade 4, 2002 (p. 310).

3. Find the number of units in the quotient. Because $5 \div 3$ is approximately 1, then 5 tens divided by 3 tens is approximately 1. This is shown below on the left, with the standard algorithm shown on the right.

$$
\begin{array}{r}
81 \\
\hline
1 \\
80 \\
32\overline{)2618} \\
-2560 \\
\hline
58 \\
-32 \quad (32 \cdot 1) \\
\hline
26
\end{array}
\qquad
\begin{array}{r}
81\ \text{R}26 \\
32\overline{)2618} \\
-256 \\
\hline
58 \\
-32 \\
\hline
26
\end{array}
$$

4. Check: $32 \cdot 81 + 26 = 2618$.

Normally in grade-school books, we see the format shown on the right, which places the remainder beside the quotient.

Using the division algorithm introduced in Chapter 2, we can write the above division as

$$2618 = 32 \cdot 81 + 26.$$

Use the ideas of division and the division algorithm to work through Now Try This 3-8.

NOW TRY THIS 3-8

a. Suppose $a = 173 \cdot 34 + 40$. Without multiplying $173 \cdot 34$, find the remainder when
  i. a is divided by 173.
  ii. a is divided by 34.
  iii. a is divided by 17.
  iv. a is divided by 2.
b. Suppose $a = 3291 \cdot 17 - 5$. Without performing the multiplication, find the remainder when a is divided by 17.

Multiplication and Division in Different Bases

As with addition and subtraction, we need to identify the basic facts of multiplication before we can use algorithms. The multiplication facts for base five are given in Table 3–9. These facts can be derived by using repeated addition.

Table 3-9 Base-Five Multiplication Table

×	0	1	2	3	4
0	0	0	0	0	0
1	0	1	2	3	4
2	0	2	4	11	13
3	0	3	11	14	22
4	0	4	13	22	31

There are various ways to do the multiplication $21_{\text{five}} \cdot 3_{\text{five}}$.

Five	Ones
2	1
$\times$	3

$\rightarrow$

$$\begin{array}{r} (20 + 1)_{\text{five}} \\ \times \qquad 3_{\text{five}} \\ \hline (110 + 3)_{\text{five}} \end{array}$$

$\rightarrow$

$$\begin{array}{r} 21_{\text{five}} \\ \times\ 3_{\text{five}} \\ \hline 3 \\ 110 \\ \hline 113_{\text{five}} \end{array}$$

$\rightarrow$

$$\begin{array}{r} 21_{\text{five}} \\ \times\ 3_{\text{five}} \\ \hline 113_{\text{five}} \end{array}$$

The multiplication of a two-digit number by a two-digit number is developed next:

$$\begin{array}{r} 23_{\text{five}} \\ \times 14_{\text{five}} \\ \hline 22 \\ 130 \\ 30 \\ 200 \\ \hline 432_{\text{five}} \end{array}$$

$$\begin{array}{l} 10 + 4\ _{\text{five}} \\ (4 \cdot 3)_{\text{five}} \\ (4 \cdot 20)_{\text{five}} \\ (10 \cdot 3)_{\text{five}} \\ (10 \cdot 20)_{\text{five}} \end{array}$$

$$\begin{array}{r} 23_{\text{five}} \\ \times\ 14_{\text{five}} \\ \hline 202 \\ 230 \\ \hline 432_{\text{five}} \end{array}$$

Lattice multiplication can also be used to multiply numbers in various number bases. This is explored in Ongoing Assessment 3-3.

Division in different bases can be performed using the multiplication facts and the definition of division. For example, $22_{\text{five}} \div 3_{\text{five}} = c$ if, and only if, $c \cdot 3_{\text{five}} = 22_{\text{five}}$. From Table 3-9, we see that $c = 4_{\text{five}}$. As in base ten, computing multidigit divisions efficiently in different bases requires practice. The ideas behind the algorithms for division can be developed by using repeated subtraction. For example, $3241_{\text{five}} \div 43_{\text{five}}$ is computed by means of the repeated-subtraction technique in Figure 3-24(a) and by means of the conventional algorithm in Figure 3-24(b). Thus $3241_{\text{five}} \div 43_{\text{five}} = 34_{\text{five}}$ with remainder 14_{five}.

FIGURE 3-24

(a)
$$\begin{array}{r} 43_{\text{five}}\overline{)3241}_{\text{five}} \\ -\ 430 \qquad (10 \cdot 43)_{\text{five}} \\ \hline 2311 \\ -\ 430 \qquad (10 \cdot 43)_{\text{five}} \\ \hline 1331 \\ -\ 430 \qquad (10 \cdot 43)_{\text{five}} \\ \hline 401 \\ -\ 141 \qquad (2 \cdot 43)_{\text{five}} \\ \hline -\ 210 \\ -\ 141 \qquad (2 \cdot 43)_{\text{five}} \\ \hline 14 \qquad (34 \cdot 43)_{\text{five}} \end{array}$$

(b)
$$\begin{array}{r} 34_{\text{five}} \\ 43_{\text{five}}\overline{)3241}_{\text{five}} \\ -234 \\ \hline 401 \\ -\ 332 \\ \hline 14 \end{array}$$

Computations involving base two are demonstrated in Example 3-6.

E X A M P L E
3-6

a. Multiply:

$$\begin{array}{r} 101_{\text{two}} \\ \times\ 11_{\text{two}} \end{array}$$

b. Divide:

$$101_{\text{two}}\overline{)110110}_{\text{two}}$$

Solution   **a.** 101_{two}
$$\underline{\times\ 11_{two}}$$
$$101$$
$$\underline{101\ \ \ }$$
$$1111_{two}$$

b.
$$\begin{array}{r} 1010_{two} \\ 101_{two}\overline{)110110_{two}} \\ -101\ \ \ \ \ \ \ \ \\ \hline 111\ \ \ \ \ \\ -101\ \ \ \ \ \\ \hline 100\ \ \ \end{array}$$

ONGOING ASSESSMENT 3-3

1. Fill in the missing numbers in each of the following:

 a.
$$\begin{array}{r} 4\_6 \\ \underline{\times\ 783} \\ 1\_78 \\ 3408\ \\ \underline{\ 982\ \ \ } \\ 3335\_8 \end{array}$$

 b.
$$\begin{array}{r} 327 \\ \underline{\times\ 9\_1} \\ 327 \\ 1\_08\ \\ \underline{\ 9\_3\ \ } \\ 30\_\_07 \end{array}$$

2. Perform the following multiplications using the lattice multiplication algorithm:

 a.
$$\begin{array}{r} 728 \\ \underline{\times\ 94} \end{array}$$

 b.
$$\begin{array}{r} 306 \\ \underline{\times\ 24} \end{array}$$

3. Explain why the lattice multiplication algorithm works.

4. The following chart gives average water usage for 1 person for one day:

Use	Average Amount
Taking bath	110 L (liters)
Taking shower	75 L
Flushing toilet	22 L
Washing hands, face	7 L
Getting a drink	1 L
Brushing teeth	1 L
Doing dishes (one meal)	30 L
Cooking (one meal)	18 L

 a. Use the chart to calculate how much water you use each day.
 b. The average American uses approximately 200 L of water per day. Are you average?
 c. If there are 290,000,000 people in the United States, on average approximately how much water is used in the United States per day?

5. Simplify each of the following using properties of exponents. Leave answers as powers.
 a. $5^7 \cdot 5^{12}$
 b. $6^{10} \cdot 6^2 \cdot 6^3$
 c. $10^{296} \cdot 10^{17}$
 d. $2^7 \cdot 10^5 \cdot 5^7$

6. a. Which is greater, $2^{80} + 2^{80}$ or 2^{100}? Why?
 b. Which is greatest, 2^{101}, $3 \cdot 2^{100}$, or 2^{102}? Why?

7. The following model illustrates $22 \cdot 13$:

 a. Explain how the partial products are shown in the figure.
 b. Draw a similar model for $15 \cdot 21$.

8. Consider the following:

$$\begin{array}{r} 476 \\ \underline{\times\ 293} \\ 952 \\ 4284\ \\ \underline{1428\ \ } \\ 139468 \end{array} \quad \begin{array}{l} (2 \cdot 476) \\ (9 \cdot 476) \\ (3 \cdot 476) \end{array}$$

 a. Use the conventional algorithm to show that the answer is correct.
 b. Explain why the algorithm works.
 c. Try the method to multiply 84×363.

9. The Russian peasant algorithm for multiplying 27×68 follows. (Disregard remainders when halving.)

	Halves	Doubles	
	→ 27 ×	68	
Halve 27	→ 13	136	Double 68.
Halve 13	→ 6	272	Double 136.
Halve 6	→ 3	544	Double 272.
Halve 3	→ 1	1088	Double 544.

In the "Halves" column, choose the odd numbers. In the "Doubles" column, circle the numbers paired with the odds from the "Halves" column. Add the circled numbers.

68
136
544
1088
1836   This is the product of 27 · 68.

Try this algorithm for 17 · 63 and other numbers.

10. Complete the following table:

a	b	$a \cdot b$	$a + b$
	56	3752	
32			110
		270	33

11. Answer the following questions based on the activity chart given next:

Activity	Calories Burned per Hour
Playing tennis	462
Snowshoeing	708
Cross-country skiing	444
Playing volleyball	198

   a. How many calories are burned during 3 hr of cross-country skiing?

   b. Jane played tennis for 2 hr while Carolyn played volleyball for 3 hr. Who burned more calories, and how many more?

   c. Lyle went snowshoeing for 3 hr and Maurice went cross-country skiing for 5 hr. Who burned more calories, and how many more?

12. On a 14-day vacation, Glenn increased his caloric intake by 1500 calories per day. He also worked out more than usual by swimming 2 hr a day. Swimming burns 666 calories per hour, and a net gain of 3500 calories adds 1 lb of weight. Did Glenn gain at least 1 lb during his vacation?

13. Sue purchased a $20,000 life insurance policy at the price of $24 for each $1000 of coverage. If she pays the premium in 12 monthly installments, how much is each installment?

14. Perform each of the following divisions using both the repeated-subtraction and standard algorithms:
   a. 8)623   **b.** 36)298   **c.** 391)4001

15. Place the digits 7, 6, 8, and 3 in the boxes □)□□□ to obtain
   a. the greatest quotient.   **b.** the least quotient.

16. Using a calculator, Ralph multiplied by 10 when he should have divided by 10. The display read 300. What should the correct answer be?

17. Twenty members of the band plan to attend a festival. The band members washed 245 cars at $2 per car to help cover expenses. The school will match every dollar the band raises with a dollar from the school budget. The cost of renting the bus to take the band is 72¢ per mile and the round trip is 350 mi. The band members can stay in the dorm for 2 nights at $5 per person per night. Meals for the trip will cost $28 per person. Has the band raised enough money yet? If not, how many more cars do they have to wash?

18. The following figure shows four function machines. The output from one machine becomes the input for the one below it. Complete the accompanying chart.

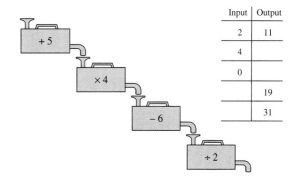

Input	Output
2	11
4	
0	
	19
	31

19. Choose three different digits.
   a. Form six different two-digit numbers from the numbers you chose. Each number can be used only once.
   b. Add the six numbers.
   c. Add the three digits you chose.
   d. Divide the answer in (b) by the answer in (c).
   e. Repeat (a) through (d) with three different numbers.
   f. Is the final result always the same? Why?

20. Consider the following multiplications. Notice that when the digits in the factors are reversed, the products are the same.

$$\begin{array}{r} 36 \\ \times\ 42 \\ \hline 1512 \end{array} \qquad \begin{array}{r} 63 \\ \times\ 24 \\ \hline 1512 \end{array}$$

   a. Find other multiplications where this procedure works.
   b. Find a pattern for the numbers that work in this way.

21. Molly read 160 pages in her book in 4 hr. Her sister Karly took 4 hr to read 100 pages in the same book. If the book is 200 pages long and if the two girls continued to read at these rates, how much longer would it take Karly to read the book than Molly?

22. Discuss possible error patterns in each of the following:

   a. $\begin{array}{r} 34 \\ \times\ 8 \\ \hline 2432 \end{array}$ **b.** $\begin{array}{r} 35 \\ \times\ 26 \\ \hline 90 \end{array}$ **c.** $\begin{array}{r} 34 \\ \times\ 6 \\ \hline 114 \end{array}$ **d.** $\begin{array}{r} 5\ 3 \\ 5)\overline{2515} \\ -\ 25 \\ \hline 15 \\ -\ 15 \\ \hline 0 \end{array}$

23. a. Give reasons for each of the following steps.

$$56 \cdot 10 = (5 \cdot 10 + 6) \cdot 10$$
$$= (5 \cdot 10) \cdot 10 + 6 \cdot 10$$
$$= 5 \cdot (10 \cdot 10) + 6 \cdot 10$$
$$= 5 \cdot 10^2 + 6 \cdot 10$$
$$= 5 \cdot 10^2 + 6 \cdot 10 + 0 \cdot 1$$
$$= 560$$

b. Give reasons for each step in computing $34 \cdot 10^2$?

24. To transport the complete student body of 1672 students to a talk given by the governor, the school plans to rent buses that can hold 29 students each. How many buses are needed? Will all the buses be full?

25. a. If $a = 131 \cdot 4789 + 200$, without multiplying mentally find the quotient and remainder when a is divided by 131.
b. Write the answer for part (a) in the form $a = bq + r$ where $0 \le r < 131$.

26. What happens when you multiply any two-digit number by 101? Discuss why this happens.

27. Perform each of these operations using the bases shown:
   a. $32_{\text{fiiv}} \cdot 4_{\text{fiiv}}$
   b. $32_{\text{fiiv}} \div 4_{\text{fiiv}}$
   c. $43_{\text{fiiv}} \cdot 23_{\text{fiiv}}$
   d. $143_{\text{fiiv}} \div 3_{\text{fiiv}}$
   e. $10010_{\text{two}} \div 11_{\text{two}}$
   f. $10110_{\text{two}} \cdot 101_{\text{two}}$

28. For what possible bases are each of the following computations correct?

a.
$$\begin{array}{r} 213 \\ + 308 \\ \hline 522 \end{array}$$
b.
$$\begin{array}{r} 322 \\ - 233 \\ \hline 23 \end{array}$$
c.
$$\begin{array}{r} 213 \\ \times 32 \\ \hline 430 \\ 1043 \\ \hline 11300 \end{array}$$
d.
$$\begin{array}{r} 101 \\ 11\overline{)1111} \\ -11 \\ \hline 11 \\ -11 \\ \hline 11 \\ -11 \\ \hline 0 \end{array}$$

29. a. Use lattice multiplication to compute $323_{\text{fiiv}} \cdot 42_{\text{fiiv}}$.
b. Find the smallest values of a and b so that $32_a = 23_b$.

30. Place the digits 7, 6, 8, and 3 in the boxes to obtain

☐☐☐
× ☐

   a. the greatest product.   **b.** the least product.

31. Place the digits 7, 6, 8, 3, and 2 in the boxes to obtain

☐☐☐
×☐☐

   a. the greatest product.   **b.** the least product.

32. Find the missing numbers in the following:

a.
$$\begin{array}{r} 37 \\ \times 43 \\ \hline \text{---} \\ \text{----} \\ \underline{591} \end{array}$$
b.
$$\begin{array}{r} \text{--} \\ \times 36 \\ \hline 558 \\ 2790 \\ \hline \text{----} \end{array}$$
c.
$$\begin{array}{r} \overline{)123} \\ -9 \\ \hline 33 \\ -27 \\ \hline 6 \end{array}$$

33. Find the products of the following and describe the pattern that emerges:

a.
1×1
11×11
111×111
1111×1111

b.
99×99
999×999
9999×9999

c. Test the patterns discovered for 30 products using a spreadsheet. If the patterns do not continue as expected, determine when the patterns stop.

Communication

34. Do you think it is valuable for students to see more than one method of doing computation problems? Why or why not?

35. Choose what you consider the "best" algorithm studied in this section. Explain the reasoning behind your choice.

36. Tom claims that long division should receive reduced attention in elementary classrooms. Do you agree or disagree? Defend your answer.

37. Pick a number. Double it. Multiply the result by 3. Add 24. Divide by 6. Subtract your original number. Is the result always the same? Write a convincing argument for your answer.

Open-Ended

38. If a student presented a new "algorithm" for computing with whole numbers, describe the process you would recommend to the student to determine if the algorithm would always work.

Cooperative Learning

39. The traditional sequence for teaching operations in the elementary school is first addition, then subtraction, followed by multiplication, and finally division. Some educators advocate teaching addition followed by multiplication, then subtraction followed by division. Within your group prepare arguments for teaching the operations in either order listed.

Review Problems

40. Write the number succeeding 673 in Egyptian numerals.

41. Write $3 \cdot 10^5 + 2 \cdot 10^2 + 6 \cdot 10$ as a Hindu-Arabic numeral.

42. Illustrate the identity property of addition for whole numbers.

43. Rename each of the following using the distributive property of multiplication over addition:
   a. $ax + bx + 2x$
   b. $3(a + b) + x(a + b)$

44. At the beginning of a trip, the odometer registered 52,281. At the end of the trip, the odometer registered 59,260. How many miles were traveled on this trip?

BRAIN
T E A S E R

For each of the following, replace the letters with digits in such a way that the computation is correct. Each letter may represent only one digit.

a. LYNDON
 × B
 ―――――――
 JOHNSON

b. MA
 MA
 + MA
 ―――――
 EEL

LABORATORY
A C T I V I T Y

1. Messages can be coded on paper tape in base two. A hole in the tape represents 1, whereas a space represents 0. The value of each hole depends on its position; from left to right, 16, 8, 4, 2, 1 (all powers of 2). Letters of the alphabet may be coded in base two according to their position in the alphabet. For example, G is the seventh letter. Since $7 = 1 \cdot 4 + 1 \cdot 2 + 1$, the holes appear as they do in Figure 3-25:

FIGURE 3-25

16 8 4 2 1

a. Decode the message in Figure 3-26.

FIGURE 3-26

b. Write your name on a tape using base two.

2. The number game in Figure 3-27 uses base-two arithmetic:

FIGURE 3-27

Card E		Card D		Card C		Card B		Card A	
16	24	8	24	4	20	2	18	1	17
17	25	9	25	5	21	3	19	3	19
18	26	10	26	6	22	6	22	5	21
19	27	11	27	7	23	7	23	7	23
20	28	12	28	12	28	10	26	9	25
21	29	13	29	13	29	11	27	11	27
22	30	14	30	14	30	14	30	13	29
23	31	15	31	15	31	15	31	15	31

a. Suppose a person's age appears on cards E, C, and B, and the person is 22. Can you discover how this works and why?

b. Design card F so that the numbers 1 through 63 can be used in the game. Note that cards A through E must also be changed.

Mental Mathematics and Estimation for Whole-Number Operations

In the *Principles and Standards* we find the following:

 Part of being able to compute fluently means making smart choices about which tools to use and when. Students should have experiences that help them learn to choose among mental computation, paper-and-pencil strategies, estimation, and calculator use. The particular context, the question, and the numbers involved all play roles in those choices. Do the numbers allow a mental strategy? Does the context call for an estimate? Does the problem require repeated and tedious computations? Students should evaluate problem situations to determine whether an estimate or an exact answer is needed, using their number sense to advantage, and be able to give a rationale for their decision. (p. 36)

In the previous sections in this chapter we focused mainly on paper-and-pencil strategies. Next we focus on two other tools, namely, mental mathematics and computational estimation. **Mental mathematics** is the process of producing an answer to a computation without using computational aids. **Computational estimation** is the process of forming an approximate answer to a numerical problem. Estimation strategies can be used to tell whether answers are reasonable or not. In the "Calvin and Hobbes" cartoon we see that Calvin does not have the number sense to tell whether his result was reasonable.

mental mathematics
computational estimation

Calvin and Hobbes   by Bill Watterson

Proficiency in mental mathematics can help in your everyday estimation skills. It is essential that you have these skills even in a time when calculators are readily available. You must be able to judge the reasonableness of answer obtained on a calculator.

Mental mathematics makes use of a variety of strategies and properties. Next we consider several of the most common strategies for performing operations mentally on whole numbers.

Mental Mathematics: Addition

1. *Adding from the left*

a.   67 $60 + 30 = 90$ (Add the tens.)   **b.**   36 $30 + 30 = 60$ (Double 30.)
       $+ 36$ $7 + 6 = 13$ (Add the units.) $+ 36$ $6 + 6 = 12$ (Double 6.)
              $90 + 13 = 103$ (Add the two $60 + 12 = 72$ (Add the
                              sums.)   doubles.)

2. *Breaking up and bridging*

67	$67 + 30 = 97$	(Add the first number to the tens in the second number.)
+ 36	$97 + 6 = 103$	(Add this sum to the units in the second number.)

3. *Trading off*

a.

67	$67 + 3 = 70$	(Add 3 to make a multiple of 10.)
+ 36	$36 - 3 = 33$	(Subtract 3 to compensate for the 3 that was added.)
	$70 + 33 = 103$	(Add the two numbers.)

b.

67	$67 + 30 = 97$	(Add 30 (next multiple of 10 greater then 29).)
+ 29	$97 - 1 = 96$	(Subtract 1 to compensate for the extra 1 that was added.)

4. *Using compatible numbers*
Compatible numbers are numbers whose sums are easy to calculate mentally.

$$130 + 70 = 200$$
$$50 + 50 = 100$$
$$100 + 200 = 300$$
$$300 + 20 = 320$$

5. *Making compatible numbers*

25	$25 + 75 = 100$	(25 + 75 adds to 100.)
+ 79	$100 + 4 = 104$	(Add 4 more units.)

Mental Mathematics: Subtraction

1. *Breaking up and bridging*

67	$67 - 30 = 37$	(Subtract the tens in the second number from the first number.)
- 36	$37 - 6 = 31$	(Subtract the units in the second number from the difference.)

2. *Trading off*

71	$(71 + 1) = 72; (39 + 1) = 40$	(Add 1 to both numbers. Perform the subtraction, which is easier than the original problem.)
- 39	$(72 - 40) = 32$	

Notice that adding 1 to both numbers does not change the answer. Why?

3. *Drop the zeros*

8700	$87 - 5 = 82$	(Notice that there are two zeros in each number. Drop these zeros and perform the computation. Then replace the two zeros to obtain proper place value.)
- 500	$82 \rightarrow 8200$	

Another mental-mathematics technique for subtraction is called "adding up." This method is based on the *missing addend* approach and is sometimes referred to as the "cashier's algorithm." An example of the cashier's algorithm follows.

E X A M P L E
3.7

Noah owed $11 for his groceries. He used a $50 check to pay the bill. While handing Noah the change, the cashier said, "$11, $12, $13, $14, $15, $20, $30, $50." How much change did Noah receive?

Solution   Table 3-10 shows what the cashier said and how much money Noah received each time. Since $11 plus $1 is $12, Noah must have received $1 when the cashier said $12. The same reasoning follows for $13, $14, and so on. Thus the total amount of change that Noah received is given by $1 + $1 + $1 + $1 + $5 + $10 + $20 = $39. In other words, $50 − $11 = $39 because $39 + $11 = $50.

Table 3-10

What the Cashier Said	$11	$12	$13	$14	$15	$20	$30	$50
Amount of Money Noah Received Each Time	0	$1	$1	$1	$1	$5	$10	$20

NOW TRY THIS 3-9

Perform each of the following computations mentally and explain what technique you used to find the answer.

a.   40 + 160 + 29 + 31
b.   3679 − 474
c.   75 + 28
d.   2500 − 700

Mental Mathematics: Multiplication

As with addition and subtraction, mental mathematics is useful for multiplication. For example, consider 8 × 26. Students may think of this computation in a variety of ways, as shown below.

8 × 20 is 160 and 8 × 6 is 48, so 8 × 26 is 160 + 48, or 208.	8 × 25 is 200, then 8 × 1 is 8 more, so 8 × 26 is 200 + 8, or 208.	8 × 30 is 240, then take off 8 × 4 = 32, so 8 × 26 is 240 − 32 = 208.

Next we consider several of the most common strategies for performing mental mathematics using multiplication.

1. *Front-end multiplying*

$$
\begin{array}{r}
64 \\
\times\,5 \\
\end{array}
\qquad
\begin{array}{l}
60 \times 5 = 300 \\
\ \ 4 \times 5 = \ \ 20 \\
\overline{300 + 20 = 320}
\end{array}
\qquad
\begin{array}{l}
\text{(Multiply the number of tens in the first number by 5.)} \\
\text{(Multiply the number of units in the first number by 5.)} \\
\text{(Add the two products.)}
\end{array}
$$

2. *Using compatible numbers*

$2 \times 9 \times 5 \times 20 \times 5$ Rearrange as $9 \times (2 \times 5) \times (20 \times 5) =$
$9 \times 10 \times 100 = 9000$

3. *Thinking money*

a. $\begin{array}{r} 64 \\ \times\ 5 \\ \hline \end{array}$ Think of the product as 64 nickels, which can be thought of as 32 dimes, which is $32 \times 10 = 320$ cents.

b. $\begin{array}{r} 64 \\ \times\ 50 \\ \hline \end{array}$ Think of the product as 64 half-dollars, which is 32 dollars, or 3200 cents.

c. $\begin{array}{r} 64 \\ \times\ 25 \\ \hline \end{array}$ Think of the product as 64 quarters, which is 32 half-dollars, or 16 dollars. Thus we have 1600 cents.

Mental Mathematics: Division

1. *Breaking up the dividend*

$7\overline{)4256}$ $7\overline{)42\,|\,56}$ (Break up the dividend into parts.)

$\begin{array}{r} 600\ +\ \ 8 \\ \hline 7\overline{)4200 + 56} \end{array}$ (Divide both parts by 7.)

$600 + 8 = 608$ (Add the answers together.)

2. *Using compatible numbers*

a. $3\overline{)105}$ $105 \qquad = 90 + 15$ (Look for numbers that you recognize as divisible by 3 and having a sum of 105.)

$\dfrac{30\ +\ \ 5}{3\overline{)90 + 15}} = 35$ (Divide both parts and add the answers.)

b. $8\overline{)232}$ $232 \qquad = 240 - 8$ (Look for numbers that are easily divisible by 8 and whose difference is 232.)

$\dfrac{30\ -\ 1}{8\overline{)240 - 8}} = 29$ (Divide both parts and take the difference.)

NOW TRY THIS 3-10

Perform each of the following computations mentally and explain what technique you used to find the answer.
a. $25 \cdot 32 \cdot 4$ **b.** $123 \cdot 3$
c. $25 \cdot 35$ **d.** $5075 \div 25$

Computational Estimation

Computational estimation may help determine whether an answer is reasonable or not. This is especially useful when the computation is done on a calculator. Some of the common estimation strategies for addition are given next.

1. *Front-end*

   Front-end estimation begins by focusing on the lead, or front, digits of the addition. These front, or lead, digits are added and assigned an appropriate place value. At this point we may have an underestimate that needs to be adjusted. The adjustment is made by focusing on the next group of digits. The following example shows how front-end estimation works.

   $$4 + 3 + 5$$
   12 hundred

   $$\begin{array}{r} 423 \\ 338 \\ + 561 \end{array}$$

   Steps: **(1.) Add front-end digits**
   $4 + 3 + 5 = 12$.
   (2.) Place value $= 1200$.
   (3.) Adjust $61 + 38 \approx 100$ and $20 + 100$ is 120.
   (4.) Adjusted estimate is $1200 + 120 = 1320$.

The student page shows how front-end estimation can be used to check whether computations are reasonable. Answer the *Talk About It* question on the student page.

2. *Grouping to nice numbers*

   The strategy used to obtain the adjustment in the preceding example is the *grouping to nice numbers* strategy, which means that numbers that "nicely" fit together are grouped. Another example is given here.

   About 100
   $$\begin{array}{r} 23 \\ 39 \\ 32 \\ 64 \\ + 49 \end{array}$$
   About 100

   Therefore the sum is about $100 + 100$, or 200.

3. *Clustering*

   Clustering is used when a group of numbers cluster around a common value. This strategy is limited to certain kinds of computations. In the next example, the numbers seem to cluster around 6000.

   $$\begin{array}{r} 6200 \\ 5842 \\ 6512 \\ 5521 \\ + 6319 \end{array}$$

   (1.) Estimate the "average"—about 6000.
   (2.) Multiply the "average" by the number of values to obtain $5 \cdot 6000 = 30{,}000$.

4. *Rounding*

   Rounding is a way of cleaning up numbers so that they are easier to handle. Rounding enables us to find approximate answers to calculations, as follows:

4724	5000	Round 4724 to 5000.
+ 3192	+ 3000	Round 3192 to 3000.
	8000	Add the rounded numbers.
1267	1300	Round 1267 to 1300.
− 510	− 500	Round 510 to 500.
	800	Subtract the rounded numbers.

   Performing estimations requires a knowledge of place value and rounding techniques. We illustrate a rounding procedure that can be generalized to all rounding situations. For example, suppose we wish to round 4724 to the nearest thousand. We may proceed in four steps (see also Figure 3-28).

Sample School Book Page:
COLUMN ADDITION

Chapter 3
Lesson 6

Column Addition

You Will Learn
how to add 3 or 4 addends

Vocabulary
addends
numbers that are added together to make a sum

front-end estimation
a way to estimate by first looking at the leading digits

Learn

"Don't get in over your head," reads Jonathan's ad. His ad reaches many people who don't know how to use computers. Jonathan prints 442 flyers, 339 brochures, and 628 bookmarks. How many items does he print in all?

Jonathan runs a desktop publishing business in Farmersville, Illinois.

You can add three **addends** to find the total number of items. Use **front-end estimation** to check.

Example
Find 442 + 339 + 628.

Step 1	Step 2	Step 3
Add the ones. Regroup as needed.	Add the tens. Regroup as needed.	Add the hundreds.

Step 1:
$$\begin{array}{r} \overset{1}{4}42 \\ 339 \\ +628 \\ \hline 9 \end{array}$$

Step 2:
$$\begin{array}{r} \overset{1\,1}{4}42 \\ 339 \\ +628 \\ \hline 09 \end{array}$$

Step 3:
$$\begin{array}{r} \overset{1\,1}{4}42 \\ 339 \\ +628 \\ \hline 1,409 \end{array}$$

Round to the front-end, or leading, digits.

$$\begin{array}{rcl} 442 & \longrightarrow & 400 \\ 339 & \longrightarrow & 300 \\ +628 & \longrightarrow & +600 \\ \hline & & 1,300 \end{array}$$

Adjust your estimate.

$$\begin{array}{rcl} 442 & \longrightarrow & 40 \\ 339 & \longrightarrow & 40 \\ +628 & \longrightarrow & +30 \\ \hline & & 110 \end{array}$$

1,300 + 110 = 1,410
Since 1,409 is close to 1,410, the answer is reasonable.
Jonathan needs to print 1,409 items.

Talk About It

Why do you line up the ones, tens, and hundreds before you add?

108 Chapter 3 • Adding and Subtracting Whole Numbers and Money

Source: Scott Foresman–Addision Wesley Math, Grade 4, 2002 (p. 108).

FIGURE 3-28

a. Determine between which two consecutive thousands the number lies.

b. Determine the midpoint between the thousands.

c. Determine which thousand the number is closer to by observing whether it is greater than or less than the midpoint. (Not all texts use the same rule for rounding when a number falls at a midpoint.)

d. If the number to be rounded is greater than or equal to the midpoint, round the given number to the greater thousand; otherwise, round to the lesser thousand. In this case, we round 4724 to 5000.

5. *Using the range*

It is often useful to know into what *range* an answer falls. The range is determined by finding a low estimate and a high estimate and reporting that the answer falls in this interval. An example follows:

Problem	Low Estimate	High Estimate
378	300	400
+ 524	+ 500	+ 600
	800	1000

Thus a range for this problem is from 800 to 1000.

Estimation: Multiplication and Division

Examples of estimation strategies for multiplication and division are given next.

1. *Front-end*

$$524$$
$$\times 8$$

$500 \times 8 = 4000$ (Start multiplying at the front to obtain a first estimate.)

$20 \times 8 = 160$ (Multiply the next important digit 8 times.)
$4000 + 160 = 4160$ (Adjust the first estimate by adding the two numbers.)

2. *Compatible numbers*

$5\overline{)4163}$

$5\overline{)4000}$ (Change 4163 to a number close to it that you know is divisible by 5.)

$$\dfrac{800}{5\overline{)4000}}$$ (Carry out the division and obtain the first estimate of 800. Various techniques can be used to adjust the first estimate.)

NOW TRY THIS 3-11

Estimate each of the following mentally and explain what technique you used to find the answer.

a. A sold-out concert was held in a theater with a capacity of 4,525 people. Tickets were sold for $9 each. How much money was collected?

b. Fliers are to be delivered to 3,625 houses and there are 42 people who will be doing the distribution. If distributed equally, how many houses will each person visit?

ONGOING ASSESSMENT 3-4

1. Compute each of the following mentally.
   a. $180 + 97 - 23 + 20 - 140 + 26$
   b. $87 - 42 + 70 - 38 + 43$
2. Use compatible numbers to compute each of the following mentally.
   a. $2 \cdot 9 \cdot 5 \cdot 6$
   b. $8 \cdot 25 \cdot 7 \cdot 4$
   c. $5 \cdot 11 \cdot 3 \cdot 20$
   d. $82 + 37 + 18 + 13$
3. Supply reasons for each of the first four steps given below.

   $$
   \begin{aligned}
   (525 + 37) + 75 &= 525 + (37 + 75) \\
   &= 525 + (75 + 37) \\
   &= (525 + 75) + 37 \\
   &= 600 + 37 \\
   &= 637
   \end{aligned}
   $$

4. Use breaking and bridging or front-end multiplying to compute each of the following mentally.
   a. $567 + 38$ b. $321 \cdot 3$
   c. $997 - 32$ d. $56 \cdot 30$
5. Use trading off to compute each of the following mentally.
   a. $85 - 49$ b. $87 + 33$
   c. $19 \cdot 6$ d. $58 + 39$
6. A car trip took 8 hours of driving at an average of 62 mph. Mentally compute the total number of miles traveled. Describe your method.
7. Compute each of the following using the cashier's algorithm.
   a. $53 - 28$ b. $63 - 47$
8. Round each number to the place value indicated by the digit in bold.
   a. 5**2**80   b. **1**15,234
   c. 1**1**5,234   d. 2,3**2**5
9. Estimate each answer by rounding.
   a. $878 \div 29$
   b. $25,201 - 19,987$
   c. $32 \cdot 28$
   d. $2215 + 3023 + 5967 + 975$
10. Use front-end estimation with adjustment to estimate each of the following:
    a. $2215 + 3023 + 5987 + 975$
    b. $234 + 478 + 987 + 319 + 469$
11. a. Would the clustering strategy of estimation be a good one to use in each of the following cases? Why or why not?

   (i) $\begin{array}{r} 474 \\ 1467 \\ 64 \\ +\,2445 \end{array}$ (ii) $\begin{array}{r} 483 \\ 475 \\ 530 \\ 503 \\ +\,528 \end{array}$

   b. Estimate each part of (a) using the following strategies:
      (i)   Front-end
      (ii) Grouping to nice numbers
      (iii) Rounding
12. Use the range strategy to estimate each of the following. Explain how you arrived at your estimates.
    a. $22 \cdot 38$ b. $145 + 678$ c. $278 + 36$
13. Tom estimated $31 \cdot 179$ in the three ways shown below.
    (i) $30 \cdot 200 = 6000$
    (ii) $30 \cdot 180 = 5400$
    (iii) $31 \cdot 200 = 6200$
    Without finding the actual product, which estimate do you think is closer to the actual product? Why?
14. About 3,540 calories must be burned to lose 1 pound of body weight. Estimate how many calories must be burned to lose 6 pounds.
15. Suppose you had a balance of $3287 in your checking account and you wrote checks for $85, $297, $403, and $523. Estimate your balance and tell what you did and tell whether you think your estimate is too high or too low.
16. A theater has 38 rows with 23 seats in each row. Estimate the number of seats in the theater and tell how you arrived at your estimate.
17. Without computing tell which of the following have the same answer. Describe your reasoning.
    a. $44 \cdot 22$ and $22 \cdot 11$
    b. $22 \cdot 32$ and $11 \cdot 64$
    c. $13 \cdot 33$ and $39 \cdot 11$
18. The following is a list of the areas in square miles of Europe's largest countries. Mentally use this information to decide if each of the given statements is true.

    | France | 211,207 |
    | Spain | 194,896 |
    | Sweden | 173,731 |
    | Finland | 130,119 |
    | Norway | 125,181 |

    a. Sweden is less than 40,000 mi^2 larger than Finland.
    b. France is more than twice the size of Norway.
    c. France is more than 100,000 mi^2 larger than Norway.
    d. Spain is about 21,000 mi^2 larger than Sweden.
19. The attendance at a World's Fair for one week is given below.

    | Monday | 72,250 |
    | Tuesday | 63,891 |
    | Wednesday | 67,490 |
    | Thursday | 73,180 |
    | Friday | 74,918 |
    | Saturday | 68,480 |

    Estimate the week's attendance and tell what strategy you used and why you used it.

20. Use your calculator to calculate 25^2, 35^2, 45^2, and 55^2 and then see if you can find a pattern that will let you find 65^2 and 75^2 mentally.

21. Use your calculator to multiply several two-digit numbers times 99. Then see if you can find a pattern that will let you find the product of any two-digit number and 99 mentally.

Communication

22. What is the difference between mental mathematics and computational estimation?

23. Is the front-end estimate for addition before adjustment always less than the exact sum? Explain why or why not.

24. In the new textbooks, there is an emphasis on mental mathematics and estimation. Do you think these topics are important for today's students? Why?

25. Suppose x and y are positive (greater than 0) whole numbers. If x is greater than y and you estimate $x - y$ by rounding x up and y down, will your estimate always be too high or too low or could it be either? Explain.

Open-Ended

26. Give several examples from real-world situations where an estimate, rather than an exact answer, is sufficient.

27. Give a numerical example of when front-end estimation and rounding can produce the same estimate. Give an example of when they can produce a different estimate.

Cooperative Learning

28. In a group have each person choose a different grade (3–6) textbook and make a list of mental math or estimation strategies done for each grade level. How do the lists compare?

29. As a group, and without actually finding the answers, find whether $19{,}876 \cdot 43$ or $19{,}875 \cdot 44$ is greater. Prepare a group response to present to the rest of the class.

BRAIN
T E A S E R

The Washington School PTA set up a phone tree in order to reach all of its members. Each person's responsibility, after receiving a call, is to call two other assigned members until all members have been called. Assume that everyone is home and answers the phone, and that each phone call takes 30 seconds. If one of the 85 members makes the first phone call and starts the clock, what is the least amount of time necessary to reach all 85 members of the group?

Hint for Solving the Preliminary Problem

To get a feel for the problem, go through it with your birth month to see what happens and what color you choose. Next, try it with other birth months or compare your outcome with that of others. Next, let b represent any birth month and use algebra to investigate the general case. Now that you know the special number and the letter corresponding to it, what color do you think people will think of when given this letter?

Q U E S T I O N S   F R O M   T H E   C L A S S R O O M

1. **a.** A student asks if $39 + 41 = 40 + 40$, is it true that $39 \cdot 41 = 40 \cdot 40$. How do you reply?

   b. Another student says that he knows that $39 \cdot 41 \neq 40 \cdot 40$ but he found that $39 \cdot 41 = 40 \cdot 40 - 1$. He also found that $49 \cdot 51 = 50 \cdot 50 - 1$. He wants to know if this pattern continues. How would you respond?

2. A student asks why he has to learn about any estimation strategy other than rounding. What is your response?

3. While studying different number bases a student asks if it is possible to have a negative number for a base. What do you tell this student?

4. A student divides as follows. How would you help?

$$
\begin{array}{r}
4\ 5 \\
3\overline{)1215} \\
-12 \\
\hline
15 \\
-15 \\
\hline
0
\end{array}
$$

5. A student claims that the Roman system is a base-ten system since it has symbols for 10, 100, and 1000. How do you respond?

6. A student divides as follows. How do you help?

$$\begin{array}{r} 15 \\ 6\overline{)36} \\ \underline{6} \\ 30 \\ 30 \end{array}$$

7. When using Roman numerals, a student asks whether it is correct to write $\overline{\text{II}}$, as well as MI, for 1001. How do you respond?

8. A parent complains about the use of manipulatives in the classroom and likens their use to the use of fingers to count. How do you respond?

9. A student asks how you can find the quotient and the remainder in a division problem like $592 \div 36$ using a calculator without an integer division button.

10. A student claims that studying different number bases is a waste of time because they are not used. What do you tell him?

11. In order to finish her homework quickly, an elementary student does her estimation problems by using a calculator to find the exact answers and then rounds them to get her estimate. What do you tell her?

CHAPTER OUTLINE

I. Numeration systems
  A. Properties of numeration systems give basic structure to the systems
    1. Additive property
    2. Place-value property
    3. Subtractive property
    4. Multiplicative property
II. Exponents
  A. For any whole number a and any natural number n,

$$a^n = \underbrace{a \cdot a \cdot a \cdot \ldots \cdot a,}_{n \text{ factors}}$$

where a is the **base** and n is the **exponent**.
  B. $a^0 = 1, a \in N$
  C. For any natural number a, with whole numbers m and n, $a^m \cdot a^n = a^{m+n}$.
III. Algorithms for whole-number operations
  A. Addition and subtraction algorithms
    1. Concrete models
    2. Expanded algorithms
    3. Standard algorithms
    4. Addition and subtraction with regrouping
    5. Scratch addition
    6. Addition and subtraction in different number bases
  B. Multiplication and division algorithms
    1. Concrete models
    2. Expanded algorithms
    3. Standard algorithms
    4. Lattice multiplication
    5. Scaffolding with division
    6. Short division
    7. Multiplication and division in different number bases
IV. Mental mathematics and computational estimation strategies
  A. Mental mathematics
    1. Adding from the left
    2. Breaking up and bridging
    3. Trading off
    4. Using compatible numbers
    5. Making compatible numbers
    6. Dropping the zeroes
    7. Using the cashier's algorithm
    8. Front-end multiplying
    9. Thinking money
    10. Breaking up the dividend
  B. Computational estimation strategies
    1. Front-end
    2. Grouping to nice numbers
    3. Clustering
    4. Rounding
    5. Range
    6. Compatible numbers

CHAPTER REVIEW

1. For each of the following base-ten numbers, tell the place value for each of the circled digits:
  a. 4③2   **b.** ③432   **c.** 19③24
2. Convert each of the following to base ten:
  a. *CD*XLIV   **b.** 432_{five} **c.** $ET0_{\text{twelve}}$
  d. 1011_{two} **e.** 4136_{seven}

3. Convert each of the following numbers to numbers in the indicated system:
  a. 999 to Roman
  b. 86 to Egyptian
  c. 123 to Mayan
  d. 346_{ten} to base five
  e. 27_{ten} to base two

4. Simplify each of the following, if possible. Write your answers in exponential form, a^b.
   a. $3^4 \cdot 3^7 \cdot 3^6$ b. $2^{10} \cdot 2^{11}$ c. $3^4 + 2 \cdot 3^4$
   d. $2^{80} + 3 \cdot 2^{80}$ e. $2^{100} + 2^{100}$

5. Write the base-three numeral for the base-three blocks shown below.

6. The smallest number of base three blocks needed to represent 51 is ____ blocks ____ flats ____ longs ____ units

7. Draw multibase blocks to represent
   a. 123_{four} b. 24_{five}

8. Use both the scratch and the traditional algorithms to perform the following:

$$\begin{array}{r} 316 \\ 712 \\ + \; 91 \\ \hline \end{array}$$

9. Use both the traditional and the lattice multiplication algorithms to perform the following:

$$\begin{array}{r} 613 \\ \times \; 98 \\ \hline \end{array}$$

10. Use both the repeated-subtraction and the conventional algorithms to perform the following:
    a. $912\overline{)4803}$ b. $11\overline{)1011}$
    c. $23_{\text{five}}\overline{)3312_{\text{five}}}$ d. $11_{\text{two}}\overline{)1011_{\text{two}}}$

11. Use the division algorithm to check your answers in problem 10.

12. You had a balance in your checking account of $720 before writing checks for $162, $158, and $33 and making a deposit of $28. What is your new balance?

13. Jim was paid $320 a month for 6 mo and $410 a month for 6 mo. What were his total earnings for the year?

14. A soft drink manufacturer produces 15,600 cans of his product each hour. Cans are packed 24 to a case. How many cases could be filled with the cans produced in 4 hr?

15. A limited partnership of 120 investors sold a piece of land for $461,040. If divided equally, how much did each investor receive?

16. How many 12-oz cans of juice would it take to give 60 people one 8-oz serving each?

17. I am thinking of a whole number. If I divide it by 13, then multiply the answer by 12, then subtract 20, and then add 89, I end up with 93. What was my original number?

18. Apples normally sell for 32¢ each. They go on sale for 3 for 69¢. How much money is saved if you purchase 2 dz apples while they are on sale?

19. A ski resort offers a weekend ski package for $80 per person or $6000 for a group of 80 people. Which would be the cheaper option for a group of 80?

20. The owner of a bicycle shop reported his inventory of bicycles and tricycles in an unusual way. He said he counted 126 wheels and 108 pedals. How many bikes and how many trikes did he have?

21. Josi has a job in which she works 30 hr/wk and gets paid $5/hr. If she works more than 30 hr in a week, she receives $8/hr for each hour over 30 hr. If she worked 38 hr at her job this week, how much did she earn?

22. In a television game show, there are five questions to answer. Each question is worth twice as much as the previous question. If the last question was worth $6400, what was the first question worth?

23. Write an example of a base other than ten used in a real-life situation. How is it used?

24. Describe the important characteristics of each of the following systems:
    a. Egyptian   b. Babylonian
    c. Roman   d. Hindu-Arabic

25. Write 128 in each of the following bases:
    a. five   b. two   c. twelve

26. Perform each of the following computations:
    a. $\begin{array}{r} 123_{\text{five}} \\ + \; 34_{\text{five}} \\ \hline \end{array}$ b. $\begin{array}{r} 1010_{\text{two}} \\ - \; 101_{\text{two}} \\ \hline \end{array}$
    c. $\begin{array}{r} 23_{\text{five}} \\ \times \; 34_{\text{five}} \\ \hline \end{array}$ d. $\begin{array}{r} 1001_{\text{two}} \\ \times \; 101_{\text{two}} \\ \hline \end{array}$

27. Tell how to use compatible numbers mentally to perform each of the following:
    a. $26 + 37 + 24 - 7$ b. $4 \cdot 7 \cdot 9 \cdot 25$

28. Compute each of the following mentally. Name the strategy you used to perform your mental math.
    a. $63 \cdot 7$ b. $85 - 49$
    c. $(18 \cdot 5) \cdot 2$ d. $2436 \div 6$

29. Estimate the following addition using (a) front-end estimation with adjustment and (b) rounding. Compare your answers and tell which you think is closer to the exact answer.

$$\begin{array}{r} 543 \\ 398 \\ 255 \\ 408 \\ + \; 998 \\ \hline \end{array}$$

30. Using clustering, estimate the sum $2345 + 2854 + 2234 + 2203$.

31. Explain how the standard division algorithm works for the division given below.

$$\begin{array}{r} 23 \\ 14\overline{)322} \\ -\;28 \\ \hline 42 \\ -\;42 \\ \hline 0 \end{array}$$

32. How can you tell if a numeration system has place value?

33. List some advantages and disadvantages of lattice multiplication versus the standard algorithm.

SELECTED BIBLIOGRAPHY

Berg, R. "Multiplication from Lilavati to the Summa." *Mathematics Teaching in the Middle School* 7 (December 2001): 226–231.

Bobis, J. "Using a Calculator to Develop Number Sense." *Arithmetic Teacher* 38 (January 1991): 42–45.

Bohan, H., and S. Bohan. "Extending the Regular Curriculum Through Creative Problem Solving." *Arithmetic Teacher* 41 (October 1993): 83–87.

Broadent, F. "Lattice Multiplication and Division." *Arithmetic Teacher* 34 (January 1987): 28–31.

Burns, M. "Introducing Division Through Problem-Solving Experiences." *Arithmetic Teacher* 38 (April 1991): 14–18.

Curcio, F., and S. Schwartz. "There Are No Algorithms for Teaching Algorithms." *Teaching Children Mathematics* 5 (September 1998): 26–30.

Englert, G., and R. Sinicrope. "Making Connections with Two-Digit Multiplication." *Arithmetic Teacher* 41 (April 1994): 446–448.

Gluck, D. "Helping Students Understand Place Value." *Arithmetic Teacher* 38 (March 1991): 10–13.

Graeber, A. "Misconceptions about Multiplication and Division." *Arithmetic Teacher* 40 (March 1993): 408–411.

Greenes, C., L. Schulman, and R. Spungin. "Developing Sense About Numbers." *Arithmetic Teacher* 40 (January 1993): 279–284.

Guershon, H., and M. Behr. "Ed's Strategy for Solving Division Problems." *Arithmetic Teacher* 39 (November 1991): 38–40.

Huinker, D. "Multiplication and Division Word Problems: Improving Students' Understanding." *Arithmetic Teacher* 37 (October 1989): 8–12.

Kami, C., and L. Joseph. "Teaching Place Value and Double-Column Addition." *Arithmetic Teacher* 35 (February 1998): 48–52.

Kami, C., and B. Lewis. "The Harmful Effects of Algorithms." *Teaching K–8* 23 (January 1993): 36–38.

Kami, C., B. Lewis, and S. Livingston. "Primary Arithmetic: Children Inventing Their Own Procedures." *Arithmetic Teacher* 41 (December 1993): 200–203.

Kouba, V., and K. Franklin. "Multiplication and Division: Sense Making and Meaning." *Teaching Children Mathematics* 1 (May 1995): 574–577.

Moldavan, C. "Culture in the Curriculum: Enriching Numeration and Number Operations." *Teaching Children Mathematics* 8 (December 2001): 238–243.

Nagel, N., and C. Swingen. "Students' Explanations of Place Value in Addition and Subtraction." *Teaching Children Mathematics* 5 (November 1998): 164–170.

National Council of Teachers of Mathematics. www.figurethis.org, 2002.

Randolph, T., and H. Sherman. "Alternative Algorithms: Increasing Options, Reducing Errors." *Teaching Children Mathematics* 7 (April 2001): 480–484.

Reys, R. "Computation Versus Number Sense." *Mathematics Teaching in the Middle School* 4 (October 1998): 110–112.

Reys, B., and R. Reys. "Computation in the Elementary Curriculum: Shifting the Emphasis." *Teaching Children Mathematics* 5 (December 1998): 236–241.

Reys, R., and D. Yang. "Relationships Between Computational Performance and Number Sense Among Sixth- and Eighth-Grade Students in Taiwan." *Journal for Research in Mathematics Education* 29 (March 1998): 225–237.

Ross, S. "Place Value: Problem Solving and Written Assessment." *Teaching Children Mathematics* 8 (March 2002): 419–423.

Russell, S. "Developing Computational Fluency with Whole Numbers." *Teaching Children Mathematics* 7 (November 2000): 154–158.

Simonsen, L., and A. Teppo. "Using Alternative Algorithms with Preservice Teachers." *Teaching Children Mathematics* 5 (May 1999): 516–519.

Sowder, J. "Mental Computation and Number Sense." *Arithmetic Teacher* 37 (March 1990): 18–20.

Tepper, J. "Basing a Career on Base Two." *Mathematics Teaching in the Middle School* 6 (October 2000): 116–119.

Thornton, C., G. Jones, and J. Neal. "The 100's Chart: A Stepping Stone to Mental Mathematics." *Teaching Children Mathematics* 1 (April 1995): 480–483.

Van de Walle, J. "Redefining Computation." *Arithmetic Teacher* 38 (January 1991): 46–51.

Wearne, D., and J. Hiebert. "Place Value and Addition and Subtraction." *Arithmetic Teacher* 41 (January 1994): 272–274.

Whitenack, J., N. Knipping, S. Novinger, and G. Underwood. "Second Graders Circumvent Addition and Subtraction Difficulties." *Teaching Children Mathematics* 8 (December 2001): 228–233.

Zaslavsky, C. "Developing Number Sense: What Can Other Cultures Tell Us?" *Teaching Children Mathematics* 7 (February 2001): 312–319.

—4—
Integers and Number Theory

P R E L I M I N A R Y   P R O B L E M

One Saturday Jody cut short her visit with her friend Natasha to take three other friends to a movie. "How old are they? " asked Natasha. "The product of their ages is 2450 and the sum is exactly twice your age," replied Jody. Natasha thought for a moment and said: "I need more information." To that Jody replied, "I should have mentioned that I am at least one year younger than the oldest of my three friends." With this information Natasha immediately found the ages of the friends. How did Natasha figure the ages of the friends and what were their ages?

Trhe *Principles and Standards* expectations for students in grades 3–5 include the following:

- explore numbers less than 0 by extending the number line and through familiar applications;
- describe classes of numbers according to characteristics such as the nature of their factors. (p. 148)

The expectations for students in grades 6–8 are:

- use factors, multiples, prime factorization, and relatively prime numbers to solve problems;
- develop meaning for integers and represent and compare quantities with them. (p. 214)

In addition, the *Principles and Standards* point out that in grades 6–8:

Students can also work with whole numbers in their study of number theory. Tasks, such as the following, involving factors, multiples, prime numbers, and divisibility can afford opportunities for problem solving and reasoning.

1. Explain why the sum of the digits of any multiple of 3 is itself divisible by 3.
2. A number of the form abcabc always has several prime-number factors. Which prime numbers are always factors of a number of this form? Why?

Middle-grades students should also work with integers. In lower grades, students may have connected negative integers in appropriate ways to informal knowledge derived from everyday experiences, such as below-zero winter temperatures or lost yards on football plays. In the middle grades, students should extend these initial understandings of integers. Positive and negative integers should be seen as useful for noting relative changes or values. Students can also appreciate the utility of negative integers when they work with equations whose solution requires them, such as 2x + 7 = 1. (pp. 217–18)

In this chapter, we develop the necessary understanding that teachers need to help students reach these expectations. We start with the system of integers and develop an understanding of number theory.

Negative numbers are useful in everyday life. For example, Mount Everest is 29,028 ft above sea level, and the Dead Sea is 1293 ft below sea level. We may symbolize these elevations as 29,028 and ⁻1293. In mathematics, the need for integers, with a sea level being 0, arises because subtractions cannot always be performed in only the set of whole numbers. To compute $4 - 6$ using the definition of subtraction for whole numbers, we must find a whole number *n* such that $6 + n = 4$. Because there is no such whole number *n*, the subtraction cannot be completed in the set of whole numbers. To perform the computation, we must invent a new number. This new number is a *negative integer*. If we attempt to calculate $4 - 6$ on a number line, then we must draw intervals to the left of 0. In Figure 4-1, $4 - 6$ is pictured as an arrow that starts at 0 and ends 2 units to the left of 0. The new number that corresponds to a point 2 units to the left of 0 is *negative two*, symbolized by ⁻2. Other numbers to the left of 0 are created similarly. The new set of numbers {⁻1, ⁻2, ⁻3, ⁻4, . . . } is the set of **negative integers**.

negative integers

FIGURE 4-1

integers   The union of the set of negative integers and the set of whole numbers is the set of **integers**. The set of integers is denoted *I*:

$$I = \{ \ldots, \ ^-4, \ ^-3, \ ^-2, \ ^-1, 0, 1, 2, 3, 4, \ldots \}$$

The mathematical treatment of questions concerning the integers is the subject of elementary number theory. As a field of study, number theory started to flourish in the seventeenth century with the work of Pierre de Fermat (1605–1665). Topics in number theory that occur in the elementary school curriculum include factors, multiples, divisibility tests, prime numbers, prime factorizations, greatest common divisors, and least common multiples. The topic of congruences, introduced by Carl Gauss (1777–1855), is also incorporated into the elementary curriculum through clock arithmetic and modular arithmetic. This topic of congruences gives students a look at a mathematical system.

The Hindu mathematician Bhramagupta (ca. A.D. 598–A.D. 665) provided the first systematic treatment of negative numbers and of zero. The European mathematicians, not being aware of Bhramagupta's work for almost 1000 years after his death, shunned negative numbers. The Italian mathematician Gerolamo Cardano (1501–1576) was the first among European mathematicians to consider negative solutions to certain equations, but, still being uncomfortable with the concept of negative numbers, he called them "fictitious" numbers.

4-1   Integers and the Operations of Addition and Subtraction

Representations of Integers

In the set of integers, the symbol "$-$" unfortunately is used to indicate both a subtraction and a negative sign. To reduce confusion between the uses of this symbol in this text, a raised "$^-$" sign is used for negative numbers, as in $^-2$, in contrast to the lower sign for subtraction. To emphasize that an integer is positive, some people use a raised plus sign, as in $^+3$. In this text, we use the plus sign for addition only and write $^+3$ simply as 3.

opposites   The negative integers are **opposites** of the positive integers. For example, the opposite of 5 is $^-5$. Similarly, the positive integers are the opposites of the negative integers. Because the opposite of 4 is denoted $^-4$, the opposite of $^-4$ can be denoted $^-(^-4)$, or 4. The opposite of 0 is 0. In the set of integers *I*, every element has an opposite that is also in *I*.

E X A M P L E
4-1

For each of the following, find the opposite of *x*:
a. $x = 3$.   **b.** $x = \ ^-5$.   **c.** $x = 0$.

Solution   **a.** $^-x = \ ^-3$.   **b.** $^-x = \ ^-(^-5) = 5$.   **c.** $^-x = \ ^-0 = 0$.

The value of ^-x in Example 4-1(b) is 5. Note that ^-x is the opposite of *x* and may *not represent a negative number*. In other words, *x* is a variable that can be replaced by some number either positive, zero, or negative.

HISTORICAL
N O T E

The dash has not always been used for both the subtraction operation and the negative sign. Other notations were developed but never adopted universally. One such notation was used by Mohammed al-Khowârizmî (ca. 825), who indicated a negative number by placing a small circle over it. For example, ⁻4 was recorded as 4̊. The Hindus denoted a negative number by enclosing it in a circle; for example, ⁻4 was recorded as ④. The symbols + and − first appeared in print in European mathematics in the late fifteenth century. The symbols referred not to addition or subtraction or positive or negative numbers, but to surpluses and deficits in business problems.

Integer Addition

There are many ways to introduce operations on integers. Before formally defining the operations, we consider a more informal approach.

FIGURE 4-2

Chip Model

In the chip model, positive integers are represented by black chips and negative integers by red chips. One red chip neutralizes one black chip. Hence, the integer ⁻1 can be represented by 1 red chip, or 2 red and 1 black, or 3 red and 2 black, and so on. Similarly, every integer can be represented in many ways using chips. Figure 4-2 shows a chip model for the addition ⁻4 + 3. We put four red chips together with 3 black chips. Because 3 red chips neutralize 3 black ones, Figure 4-2 represents the equivalent of 1 red chip, or ⁻1.

FIGURE 4-3

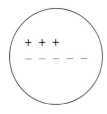

Charged-Field Model

A model similar to the chip model uses positive and negative charges. A field has 0 charge if it has the same number of positive (+) and negative (−) charges. As in the chip model, a given integer can be represented in many ways using the charged-field model. Figure 4-3 uses the model for 3 + ⁻5. Because 3 positive charges "neutralize" 3 negative charges, the net result is 2 negative ones. Hence, 3 + ⁻5 = ⁻2.

Pattern Model

Addition of whole numbers was established in Chapter 2. Addition of integers can also be motivated by using patterns of addition of whole numbers. Notice that in the left column, the first four facts are known from whole-number addition. Also notice that the 4 stays fixed and as the numbers added to 4 decrease by 1, the sum decreases by 1. Following this pattern, 4 + ⁻1 = 3 and we can complete the remainder of the first column. Similar reasoning can be used to complete the computations in the right column, where ⁻2 stays fixed and the other numbers decrease by 1 each time.

$$4 + 3 = 7 \qquad ⁻2 + 4 = 2$$
$$4 + 2 = 6 \qquad ⁻2 + 3 = 1$$
$$4 + 1 = 5 \qquad ⁻2 + 2 = 0$$
$$4 + 0 = 4 \qquad ⁻2 + 1 = ⁻1$$
$$4 + ⁻1 = 3 \qquad ⁻2 + 0 = ⁻2$$
$$4 + ⁻2 = 2 \qquad ⁻2 + ⁻1 = ⁻3$$
$$4 + ⁻3 = 1 \qquad ⁻2 + ⁻2 = ⁻4$$
$$4 + ⁻4 = 0 \qquad ⁻2 + ⁻3 = ⁻5$$
$$4 + ⁻5 = ⁻1 \qquad ⁻2 + ⁻4 = ⁻6$$
$$4 + ⁻6 = ⁻2 \qquad ⁻2 + ⁻5 = ⁻7$$

<u>TECHNOLOGY</u>
C O R N E R

On a spreadsheet, in column A enter 4 and fill down 20 rows. (For help on spreadsheets see Appendix I.) In column B, enter 3 as the first entry and then write a formula to add $^-1$ to 3 for the second entry, add $^-1$ to the second entry to get the third entry, and fill down continuing the pattern. In column C, find the sum of the respective entries in columns A and B. What patterns do you observe? Repeat the problem by changing the entries in column A to $^-4$ and repeating the process.

Number-Line Model

Another model for addition of integers involves a number line used with a moving object. For example, the car in Figure 4-4(a) starts at 0, facing in a positive direction (to the right). To represent a positive integer, the car moves forward, and to represent a negative integer, it moves in reverse. For example, Figure 4-4(a) through (d) illustrates four different additions.

FIGURE 4-4

$5 + 3$ is seen as moving the car forward 5 units and then 3 more units forward for a net move of 8 units to the right from 0. Thus $5 + 3 = 8$.

(a)

$^-5 + 3$ is seen as moving the car 5 units in reverse and then moving it forward 3 units for a net move of 2 units to the left from 0. Thus $^-5 + 3 = ^-2$.

(b)

$3 + ^-5$ is seen as moving the car 3 units forward and then 5 units in reverse for a net move of 2 units to the left from 0. Thus $3 + ^-5 = ^-2$.

(c)

$^-3 + ^-5$ is seen as moving the car 3 units in reverse and then 5 more units in reverse for a net move of 8 units to the left from 0. Thus $^-3 + ^-5 = ^-8$.

(d)

Without the car, $^-3 + {}^-5$ can be pictured as in Figure 4-5.

FIGURE 4-5

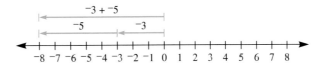

Figure 4-6 similarly depicts integer addition of $3 + {}^-5$.

FIGURE 4-6

Example 4-2 involves a thermometer with a scale in the form of a vertical number line.

E X A M P L E 4-2

FIGURE 4-7

The temperature was $^-4°C$. In an hour, it rose $10°C$. What is the new temperature?

Solution Figure 4-7 shows that the new temperature is $6°C$ and that $^-4 + 10 = 6$.

Absolute Value

Because 4 and $^-4$ are opposites, they are on opposite sides of 0 on the number line and are the same distance (4 units) from 0, as shown in Figure 4-8.

FIGURE 4-8

absolute value

Distance is always a positive number or zero. The distance between the points corresponding to an integer and 0 is called the **absolute value** of the integer. Thus the absolute value of both 4 and $^-4$ is 4, written $|4| = 4$ and $|{}^-4| = 4$, respectively. Notice that if $x \geq 0$ then $|x| = x$, and if $x < 0$ then ^-x is positive. Therefore we have the following:

> **Definition of Absolute Value**

$$|x| = x \quad \text{if } x \geq 0,$$
$$|x| = {}^-x \quad \text{if } x < 0.$$

EXAMPLE 4-3

Evaluate each of the following:

a. $|20|$ **b.** $|^-5|$ **c.** $|0|$ **d.** $^-|^-3|$ **e.** $|2 - 5|$

Solution   **a.** $|20| = 20$ **b.** $|^-5| = 5$ **c.** $|0| = 0$ **d.** $^-|^-3| = ^-3$
e. $|2 - 5| = |^-3| = 3$

REMARK   It is possible to describe addition of integers as the process of finding the difference or the sum of the absolute values of the integers and attaching an appropriate sign.

Properties of Integer Addition

Integer addition has all the properties of whole-number addition. These properties are summarized next.

> ## Properties

Given integers *a, b,* and *c*:
Closure property of addition of integers $a + b$ is a unique integer.
Commutative property of addition of integers $a + b = b + a$.
Associative property of addition of integers $(a + b) + c = a + (b + c)$.
Identity element of addition of integers   0 is the unique integer such that, for all integers *a*,
$0 + a = a = a + 0$.

Notice the name *identity element* in the above properties. Zero is an identity element of addition because when it is added to any integer it does not change the result; it leaves the integer unchanged.

additive inverse   We have seen that every integer has an opposite. This opposite is the **additive inverse** of the integer. The fact that each integer has a unique (one and only one) additive inverse is recorded below.

> ## Uniqueness Property of the Additive Inverse

For every integer *a*, there exists a unique integer ^-a, the additive inverse of *a*, such that $a + {}^-a = 0 = {}^-a + a$.

REMARK   Notice that by definition of the additive inverse, ^-a, is the solution of the equation $x + a = 0$. The fact that the additive inverse is unique is equivalent to saying that the above equation has only one solution. In fact, for any integers *a* and *b* the equation $x + a = b$ has a unique solution.

The uniqueness of additive inverses can be used to justify other properties. For example, the opposite, or the additive inverse, of ^-a can be written $^-(^-a)$. However, because $a + {}^-a = 0$, the additive inverse of ^-a is also a. Because the additive inverse of ^-a must be unique, we have $^-(^-a) = a$. Other properties of addition of integers can be investigated by considering previously developed notions. For example, we saw that $^-2 + {}^-4 = {}^-6$, and we know that $^-6$ is the additive inverse of 6, or $2 + 4$. This leads us to the following:

$$^-2 + {}^-4 - {}^-(2 + 4).$$

This relationship is true in general and is stated along with its proof.

▷ Properties of the Additive Inverse

For any integers, a and b:

1. $^-(^-a) = a$.
2. $^-a + {}^-b = {}^-(a + b)$.

We prove the second property of the additive inverse as follows: By definition $^-(a + b)$ is the additive inverse of $a + b$. If we could show that $^-a + {}^-b$ is also the additive inverse of $a + b$, the uniqueness of the additive inverse implies that $^-(a + b)$ and $^-a + {}^-b$ are equal. To show that $^-a + {}^-b$ is the additive inverse of $a + b$, we need only to show that their sum is 0. This can be shown using the associative and commutative properties of integer addition and the definition of the additive inverse as follows:

$$(^-a + {}^-b) + (a + b) = (^-a + a) + (^-b + b)$$
$$= 0 + 0$$
$$= 0.$$

Hence $^-(a + b) = {}^-a + {}^-b$.

REMARK Notice that in the above proof some of the steps involving the commutative and associative properties of integer addition were omitted. A more detailed proof showing all the steps follows.

$$(^-a + {}^-b) + (a + b) = (^-a + {}^-b) + (b + a)$$
$$= [(^-a + {}^-b) + b] + a$$
$$= [^-a + (^-b + b)] + a$$
$$= (^-a + 0) + a$$
$$= {}^-a + a$$
$$= 0$$

EXAMPLE
4-4

Find the additive inverse of each of the following:

a. $^-(3 + x)$ **b.** $(a + ^-4)$ **c.** $^-3 + (^-x)$

Solution   **a.** $3 + x$

b. $^-(a + ^-4)$, which by the above listed property (2), applied from right to left, can be written $^-a + ^-(^-4)$, or $^-a + 4$.

c. $^-[^-3 + (^-x)]$, which can be written $^-(^-3) + ^-(^-x)$, or $3 + x$.

Integer Subtraction

As with integer addition, we explore several models for integer subtraction.

Chip Model

FIGURE 4-9

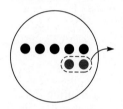

To find $3 - ^-2$, we want to subtract $^-2$ (or remove 2 red chips) from 3 black chips. We need to represent 3 so that at least 2 red chips are present. In Figure 4-9, 3 is represented using 2 red and 5 black chips. When the 2 red chips are removed, 5 black ones are left and, hence, $3 - ^-2 = 5$.

Charged-Field Model

Integer subtraction can be modeled with a charged field. For example, consider $^-3 - ^-5$. To subtract $^-5$ from $^-3$, we first represent $^-3$ so that at least 5 negative charges are present. An example is shown in Figure 4-10(a). To subtract $^-5$, remove the 5 negative charges, leaving 2 positive charges, as in Figure 4-10(b). Hence, $^-3 - ^-5 = 2$.

FIGURE 4-10

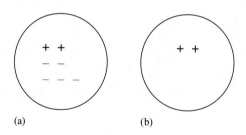

(a)   (b)

Patterns Model

We can find the difference of two integers by considering the following patterns, where we start with subtractions that we already know how to do. Both the following pattern on the left and the pattern on the right start with $3 - 2 = 1$.

$$3 - 2 = 1 \qquad 3 - 2 = 1$$
$$3 - 3 = 0 \qquad 3 - 1 = 2$$
$$3 - 4 = ? \qquad 3 - 0 = 3$$
$$3 - 5 = ? \qquad 3 - ^-1 = ?$$

In the pattern on the left, the difference decreases by 1. If we continue the pattern, we have $3 - 4 = {}^-1$ and $3 - 5 = {}^-2$. In the pattern on the right, the difference increases by 1. If we continue the pattern, we have $3 - {}^-1 = 4$ and $3 - {}^-2 = 5$.

Number-Line Model

The number-line model used for integer addition can also be used to model integer subtraction. In Figure 4-11, the car starts at 0 and is pointed in a positive direction (to the right). In this model, the operation of subtraction corresponds to facing the car in a negative direction. We subtract a positive integer by moving the car forward and a negative integer by moving the car in reverse. Figure 4-11 shows some examples.

FIGURE 4-11

$5 - 3$ first tells you to move the car forward 5 units. The subtraction sign tells you to face the car in the negative direction. Finally, move forward 3 units for a net move of 2 units to the right from 0. Thus $5 - 3 = 2$.

(a)

$5 - {}^-3$ first tells you to move the car forward 5 units. Then face it in a negative direction and move it in reverse 3 units. The net move is 8 units to the right of 0. Thus $5 - {}^-3 = 8$.

(b)

In ${}^-5 - {}^-3$, move the car 5 units in reverse. Then face it in a negative direction and move it in reverse 3 units. The net move is 2 units to the left of 0. Thus ${}^-5 - {}^-3 = {}^-2$.

(c)

NOW TRY THIS 4-1

Suppose a mail carrier brings you three letters, one with a check for $25 and the other two with bills for $15 and $20, respectively. You record this as $25 + {}^-15 + {}^-20$ or $^-10$; that is, you are $10 poorer. Suppose that the next day you find out that the bill for $20 was actually intended for someone else and therefore you give it back to the delivery person. You record your new balance as:

$$^-10 - {}^-20$$

or as,

$$25 + {}^-15 + {}^-20 - {}^-20$$

which equals $25 + {}^-15$, or 10.

For each of the following, make up a mail delivery story and explain how your story can help to find the answer.

a. $23 + {}^-13 + {}^-12$　　　　**b.** $18 - {}^-37$

Subtraction as the Inverse of Addition

Subtraction of integers, like subtraction of whole numbers, can be defined in terms of addition. Recall that $5 - 3$ can be computed by finding a whole number n as follows:

$$5 - 3 = n \qquad \text{if, and only if,} \qquad 5 = 3 + n.$$

Because $3 + 2 = 5$, then $n = 2$.

Similarly, we compute $3 - 5$ as follows:

$$3 - 5 = n \qquad \text{if, and only if,} \qquad 3 = 5 + n.$$

Because $5 + {}^-2 = 3$, then $n = {}^-2$. In general, for integers a and b, we have the following definition of *subtraction*.

> ### Definition of Subtraction

For integers a and b, $a - b$ is the unique integer n such that $a = b + n$.

REMARK Addition "undoes" subtraction; that is, $(a - b) + b = a$. Also, subtraction "undoes" addition; that is, $(a + b) - b = a$.

EXAMPLE 4-5

Use the definition of subtraction to compute the following:

a. $3 - 10$　　**b.** $^-2 - 10$

Solution　**a.** Let $3 - 10 = n$. Then $10 + n = 3$, so $n = {}^-7$. Therefore $3 - 10 = {}^-7$.

　　　　　　b. Let $^-2 - 10 = n$. Then $10 + n = {}^-2$, so $n = {}^-12$. Therefore $^-2 - 10 = {}^-12$.

From our previous work with addition of integers, we know that $3 - 5 = {}^-2$ and $3 + {}^-5 = {}^-2$. Hence, $3 - 5 = 3 + {}^-5$. In general, the following is true.

> **Property**
>
> For all integers a and b, $a - b = a + ({}^-b)$.

The above property can be justified using the fact that the equation $b + x = a$ has a unique solution. From the definition of subtraction, the solution of the above equation is $a - b$. To show that $a - b = a + {}^-b$, we only need to show that $a + {}^-b$ is also a solution. For that purpose, we substitute $a + {}^-b$ for x and check if $b + (a + {}^-b) = a$:

$$b + (a + {}^-b) = b + ({}^-b + a)$$
$$= (b + {}^-b) + a$$
$$= 0 + a$$
$$= a.$$

Consequently, $a - b = a + {}^-b$.

NOW TRY THIS 4-2

a. Is the set of integers closed under subtraction? Why?

b. Do the commutative, associative, or identity properties hold for subtraction of integers? Why or why not?

Many early calculators had a change-of-sign key, either $\boxed{\text{CHS}}$ or $\boxed{{}^+\!/\!-}$. Later generations of calculators use $\boxed{(-)}$, a key that allows computation with integers. For example, to compute $8 - ({}^-3)$, we would press $\boxed{8}\,\boxed{-}\,\boxed{3}\,\boxed{{}^+\!/\!-}\,\boxed{=}$. Investigate what happens if you press $\boxed{8}\,\boxed{-}\,\boxed{-}\,\boxed{3}\,\boxed{=}$.

E X A M P L E
4-6

Using the fact that $a - b = a + ({}^-b)$, compute each of the following:

a. $2 - 8$ **b.** $2 - ({}^-8)$ **c.** ${}^-12 - ({}^-5)$ **d.** ${}^-12 - 5$

Solution   **a.** $2 - 8 = 2 + {}^-8 = {}^-6$

b. $2 - ({}^-8) = 2 + {}^-({}^-8) = 2 + 8 = 10$

c. ${}^-12 - ({}^-5) = {}^-12 + {}^-({}^-5) = {}^-12 + 5 = {}^-7$

d. ${}^-12 - 5 = {}^-12 + {}^-5 = {}^-17$

EXAMPLE 4-7

Use the fact that $a - b = a + (^-b)$ and the properties of additive inverse to write expressions equal to each of the following without using parentheses:

a. $^-(b - c)$ **b.** $a - (b + c)$

Solution   **a.** $^-(b - c) = {}^-(b + {}^-c) = {}^-b + {}^-({}^-c) = {}^-b + c$
b. $a - (b + c) = a + {}^-(b + c) = a + ({}^-b + {}^-c) = (a + {}^-b) + {}^-c = a + {}^-b + {}^-c$

REMARK   It is possible to simplify the answers in parts (a) and (b) further, as follows: $^-b + c = c + {}^-b = c - b$, and $a + {}^-b + {}^-c = (a - b) - c$.

EXAMPLE 4-8

Simplify each of the following:

a. $2 - (5 - x)$ **b.** $5 - (x - 3)$ **c.** $^-(x - y) - y$

Solution   **a.** $\begin{aligned} 2 - (5 - x) &= 2 + {}^-(5 + {}^-x) \\ &= 2 + {}^-5 + {}^-({}^-x) \\ &= 2 + {}^-5 + x \\ &= {}^-3 + x \end{aligned}$

b. $\begin{aligned} 5 - (x - 3) &= 5 + {}^-(x + {}^-3) \\ &= 5 + {}^-x + {}^-({}^-3) \\ &= 5 + {}^-x + 3 \\ &= 8 + {}^-x \\ &= 8 - x \end{aligned}$

c. $\begin{aligned} {}^-(x - y) - y &= {}^-(x + {}^-y) + {}^-y \\ &= [{}^-x + {}^-({}^-y)] + {}^-y \\ &= ({}^-x + y) + {}^-y \\ &= {}^-x + (y + {}^-y) \\ &= {}^-x + 0 \\ &= {}^-x \end{aligned}$

Order of Operations

Subtraction on the set of integers is neither commutative nor associative, as illustrated in these counterexamples:

$$5 - 3 \neq 3 - 5 \qquad \text{because} \qquad 2 \neq {}^-2$$
$$(3 - 15) - 8 \neq 3 - (15 - 8) \qquad \text{because} \qquad {}^-20 \neq {}^-4$$

Remember, computations within parentheses must be completed before other computations.

An expression such as $3 - 15 - 8$ is ambiguous unless we know in which order to perform the subtractions. Mathematicians agree that $3 - 15 - 8$ means $(3 - 15) - 8$; that is, the subtractions in $3 - 15 - 8$ are performed in order from left to right. Similarly, $3 - 4 + 5$ means $(3 - 4) + 5$ and not $3 - (4 + 5)$. Thus $(a - b) - c$ may be written without parentheses as $a - b - c$.

EXAMPLE
4-9

Compute each of the following:

a. $2 - 5 - 5$ **b.** $3 - 7 + 3$ **c.** $3 - (7 - 3)$

Solution   **a.** $2 - 5 - 5 = {}^-3 - 5 = {}^-8$
b. $3 - 7 + 3 = {}^-4 + 3 = {}^-1$
c. $3 - (7 - 3) = 3 - 4 = {}^-1$

TECHNOLOGY
C O R N E R

a. On a graphing calculator, graph the function with equation $y = x - {}^-4$.
b. Using the graph in (a), describe what happens as x takes on values that are less than ${}^-4$, equal to ${}^-4$, and greater than ${}^-4$.

O N G O I N G   A S S E S S M E N T   4 - 1

1. Find the additive inverse of each of the following integers. Write your answer in the simplest possible form.
   a. 2 b. ${}^-5$ c. m
   d. 0 e. ${}^-m$ f. $a + b$

2. Simplify each of the following:
   a. ${}^-({}^-2)$ b. ${}^-({}^-m)$ c. ${}^-0$

3. Evaluate each of the following:
   a. $|{}^-5|$ b. $|10|$ c. ${}^-|{}^-5|$ d. ${}^-|5|$

4. Demonstrate each of the following additions using the charged-field or chip model:
   a. $5 + {}^-3$ b. ${}^-2 + 3$ c. ${}^-3 + 2$
   d. ${}^-3 + {}^-2$

5. Compute each of the following using $a - b = a + {}^-b$.
   a. $3 - {}^-2$ b. ${}^-3 - 2$ c. ${}^-3 - {}^-2$

6. Demonstrate each of the additions in problem 4 above using a number-line model.

7. Write an addition fact that corresponds to each of the following sentences and then answer the question:
   a. A certain stock dropped 17 points and the following day gained 10 points. What was the net change in the stock's worth?
   b. The temperature was ${}^-10°C$ and then it rose by $8°C$. What is the new temperature?
   c. The plane was at 5000 ft and dropped 100 ft. What is the new altitude of the plane?
   d. A visitor in a Las Vegas casino lost $200, won $100, and then lost $50. What is the change in the gambler's net worth?
   e. In four downs, the football team lost 2 yd, gained 7 yd, gained 0 yd, and lost 8 yd. What is the total gain or loss?

8. On January 1, Jane's bank balance was $300. During the month, she wrote checks for $45, $55, $165, $35, and $100 and made deposits of $75, $25, and $400.
   a. If a check is represented by a negative integer and a deposit by a positive integer, express Jane's transactions as a sum of positive and negative integers.
   b. What was the balance in Jane's account at the end of the month?

9. Use a number-line model to find the following:
   a. ${}^-4 - {}^-1$ b. ${}^-4 - {}^-3$

10. Use patterns to show the following:
   a. ${}^-4 - {}^-1 = {}^-3$ b. ${}^-2 - 1 = {}^-3$

11. Perform each of the following:
   a. ${}^-2 + (3 - 10)$ b. $[8 - ({}^-5)] - 10$
   c. $({}^-2 - 7) + 10$ d. ${}^-2 - (7 + 10)$
   e. $8 - 11 - 10$ f. ${}^-2 - 7 + 3$

12. In each of the following, write a subtraction problem that corresponds to the question and an addition problem that corresponds to the question and then answer the questions:
   a. The temperature is $55°F$ and is supposed to drop $60°F$ by midnight. What is the expected midnight temperature?
   b. Moses has overdraft privileges at his bank. If he had $200 in his checking account and he wrote a $220 check, what is his balance?

13. Answer each of the following:
   a. In a game of Triominoes, Jack's scores in five successive turns are 17, ${}^-8$, ${}^-9$, 14, and 45. What is his total at the end of five turns?
   b. The largest bubble chamber in the world is 15 ft in diameter and contains 7259 gal of liquid hydrogen at a temperature of ${}^-247°C$. If the temperature is dropped by $11°C$ per hour for 2 consecutive hours, what is the new temperature?
   c. The greatest recorded temperature ranges in the world are around the "cold pole" in Siberia. Temperatures in Verkhoyansk have varied from ${}^-94°F$ to $98°F$. What is the difference between the high and low temperatures in Verkhoyansk?

14. Motor oils protect car engines over a range of temperatures. These oils have names like 10W–40 or 5W–30. The following graph shows the temperatures, in degrees Fahrenheit, at which the engine is protected by a particular oil. Using the graph, find which oils can be used for the following temperatures:
    a. Between $^-5°$ and 90°   b. Below $^-20°$
    c. Between $^-10°$ and 50°   d. From $^-20°$ to over 100°
    e. From $^-8°$ to 90°

15. Apply the properties discussed in this section to simplify each of the following as much as possible. Show all work.
    a. $3 - (2 - 4x)$ b. $x - (^-x - y)$
    c. $4x - 2 - 3x$ d. $4x - (2 - 3x)$
16. For which integers a, b, c does $a - b - c = a - (b - c)$? Justify your answer.
17. Let W stand for the set of whole numbers, I the set of integers, I^+ the set of positive integers, and I^- the set of negative integers. Find each of the following:
    a. $W \cup I$ b. $W \cap I$ c. $I^+ \cup I^-$
    d. $I^+ \cap I^-$ e. $W - I$ f. $I - W$
    g. $W - I^+$ h. $W - I^-$ i. $I \cap I$
18. Complete the magic square using the following integers: $^-13, ^-10, ^-7, ^-4, 2, 5, 8, 11$.

19. Let $f(x) = ^-x - 1$ with domain I. Find the following:
    a. $f(^-1)$ b. $f(100)$ c. $f(^-2)$ d. $f(^-a)$ in terms of a
    e. For which values of x will the output be 3?
20. Find all integers x, if there are any, such that the following are true:
    a. ^-x is positive.
    b. ^-x is negative.
    c. $^-x - 1$ is positive.
    d. $|x| = 2$.
    e. $^-|x| = 2$.
    f. $^-|x|$ is negative.
    g. $^-|x|$ is positive.
21. Let $f(x) = |1 - x|$ with domain I. Find the following:
    a. $f(10)$ b. $f(^-1)$
    c. All the inputs for which the output is 1
    d. The range

22. a. For each of the following functions find $f(f(x))$
       i. $f(x) = x$
       ii. $f(x) = ^-x$
       iii. $f(x) = ^-x + 2$
    b. Interpret your answers in part (a) using the function machine model.
    ★c. Find other functions for which $f(f(x)) = x$. Justify your answer.
23. Determine how many integers there are between the following given integers (not including the given integers):
    a. 10 and 100   b. $^-30$ and $^-10$
    c. $^-10$ and 10   d. x and y (if $x < y$)
24. Suppose $a = 6, b = 5, c = 4$, and $d = ^-3$. Insert parentheses in the expression $a - b - c - d$ to obtain the greatest possible and the least possible values. What are these values?
25. An arithmetic sequence may have a positive or negative difference. In each of the following arithmetic sequences, find the difference and write the next two terms:
    a. $0, ^-3, ^-6, ^-9$ b. $7, 3, ^-1, ^-5$
    c. $x + y, x, x - y$ d. $1 - 3x, 1 - x, 1 + x$
26. Find the sums of the following arithmetic sequences:
    a. $^-20 + ^-19 + ^-18 + \ldots + 18 + 19 + 20$
    b. $100 + 99 + 98 + \ldots + ^-50$
    c. $100 + 98 + 96 + \ldots + ^-6$
27. In an arithmetic sequence, the eighth term minus the first term equals 21. The sum of the first and the eighth term is $^-5$. Find the fifth term of the sequence.
28. Classify each of the following as true or false. If false, give a counterexample.
    a. $|^-x| = |x|$
    b. $|x - y| = |y - x|$
    c. $|^-x + ^-y| = |x + y|$
    d. $|x^2| = x^2$
    e. $|x^3| = x^3$
    f. $|x^3| = x^2|x|$
29. Assume gear A has 56 teeth and gear B has 14 teeth. Suppose that number of counterclockwise rotations is designated by a positive number and number of clockwise rotations by a negative number. If gear A rotates 7 times per minute, how many times per minute does gear B rotate? Explain your reasoning.

30. Complete each of the following integer arithmetic problems on your calculator, making use of the key change of sign key. For example, on some calculators to find $^-5 + ^-4$, press $\boxed{5}\ \boxed{^+/_-}\ \boxed{+}\ \boxed{4}\ \boxed{^+/_-}\ \boxed{=}$.
    a. $^-12 + ^-6$
    b. $^-12 + 6$
    c. $27 + ^-5$
    d. $^-12 - 6$
    e. $16 - ^-7$

31. Estimate each of the following and then use a calculator to find the actual answer:
    a. $343 + ^-42 - 402$
    b. $^-1992 + 3005 - 497$
    c. $992 - ^-10003 - 101$
    d. $^-301 - ^-1303 + 4993$

Communication

32. A turnpike driver had car trouble. He knew that he had driven 12 mi from milepost 68 before the trouble started. Assuming he is confused and disoriented when he calls on his cellular phone for help, how can he determine his possible location? Explain.

33. Dolores claims that the best way to understand that $a - b = a + (^-b)$, for all integers a and b, is to show that when you add b to each expression you get the same answer.
    a. Explain why you think Dolores is making this claim.
    b. Do you agree with Dolores that her approach is the "best way"? If not, what is a better approach?

34. Addition of integers with like signs can be described using absolute values as follows:
    To add integers with like signs, add the absolute values of the integers. The sum has the same sign as the integers.
    Describe in a similar way how to add integers with unlike signs.

35. Explain why $b - a$ and $a - b$ are additive inverses of each other.

36. The absolute value of an integer is never negative. Does this contradict the fact that the absolute value of x could be equal to ^-x? Explain why or why not.

Open-Ended

37. Describe a realistic word problem that models $^-50 + (^-85) - (^-30)$.

38. In a library some floors are below ground level and others are above ground level. If the ground-level floor is designated the zero floor, design a system for using integers to number the floors and then design an operation system for the elevator to model addition and subtraction with integers.

Cooperative Learning

39. Examine several elementary mathematics textbooks. Report on how addition and subtraction of integers is treated, and on how various properties are justified. Discuss in your group how the treatment of addition and subtraction of integers presented in this section compares to the treatment in elementary textbooks.

BRAIN
T E A S E R

If the digits 1 through 9 are written in order, it is possible to place plus and minus signs between the numbers or to use no operation symbol at all to obtain a total of 100. For example,

$$1 + 2 + 3 + ^-4 + 5 + 6 + 78 + 9 = 100.$$

Can you obtain a total of 100 using fewer plus or minus signs than in the given example? Note that digits, such as 7 and 8 in the example, may be combined.

Multiplication and Division of Integers

We approach multiplication of integers through a variety of models: *patterns, charged-field, chip,* and *number-line.*

Patterns Model

First, we approach multiplication of integers by using repeated addition. For example, if a running back lost 2 yd on each of three carries in a football game, then he had a net loss of $^-2 + ^-2 + ^-2$, or $^-6$, yards. Since $^-2 + ^-2 + ^-2$ can be written as $3 \cdot (^-2)$, using repeated addition, we have $3 \cdot (^-2) = ^-6$.

Consider $(^-2) \cdot 3$. It is meaningless to say that there are $^-2$ threes in a sum.

But if the commutative property of multiplication is to hold for all integers, we must have $(^-2) \cdot 3 = 3 \cdot (^-2) = ^-6$.

Next, consider $(^-3) \cdot (^-2)$. We can develop the following pattern:

$$3 \cdot (^-2) = ^-6$$
$$2 \cdot (^-2) = ^-4$$
$$1 \cdot (^-2) = ^-2$$
$$0 \cdot (^-2) = 0$$
$$(^-1) \cdot (^-2) = ?$$
$$(^-2) \cdot (^-2) = ?$$
$$(^-3) \cdot (^-2) = ?$$

The first four products, $^-6$, $^-4$, $^-2$, and 0, are terms in an arithmetic sequence with fixed difference of 2. If the pattern continues, the next 3 terms in the sequence are 2, 4, and 6. Thus it appears that $(^-3) \cdot (^-2) = 6$. Likewise, $(^-2) \cdot (^-3) = 6$.

TECHNOLOGY
C O R N E R

On a spreadsheet, in column A enter 5 as the first entry and then write a formula to add $^-1$ to 5 for the second entry. Then add $^-1$ to the second entry and fill down continuing the pattern. In column B, repeat the process. In column C, find the product of the respective entries in columns A and B. What patterns do you observe?

Charged-Field Model and Chip Model

The *charged-field model* and the *chip model* can be used to illustrate multiplication of integers, although an interpretation must be given to the signs. Consider Figure 4-12, where $3 \cdot (^-2)$ is pictured using a chip model. The product $3 \cdot (^-2)$ is interpreted as adding 3 groups of 2 red chips each.

FIGURE 4-12

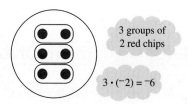

3 groups of 2 red chips

$3 \cdot (-2) = ^-6$

To find $(^-3) \cdot (^-2)$ using the charged-field model, we interpret the signs as follows: $^-3$ is taken to mean "*remove 3 groups of* "; $^-2$ is taken to mean "*2 negative charges.*" To do this, we start with a 0 charged field that includes at least 6 negative charges, as shown in Figure 4-13.

FIGURE 4-13

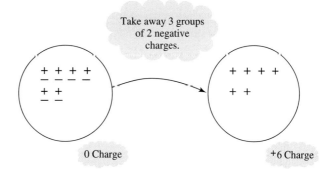

Take away 3 groups
of 2 negative
charges.

```
+  +  +  +          +  +  +  +
-  -  -  -          -  -  -  -
+  +                +  +
-  -                -  -
```

0 Charge $^+6$ Charge

The result is a charge of positive 6, so $(^-3) \cdot (^-2) = 6$.

Number-Line Model

As with addition and subtraction, we demonstrate multiplication by using a car moving along a number line, according to the following rules:

1. Traveling to the left (west) means moving in the negative direction, and traveling to the right (east) means moving in the positive direction.
2. Time in the future is denoted by a positive value, and time in the past is denoted by a negative value.

Consider the number line shown in Figure 4-14. Various cases using this number line are given next.

FIGURE 4-14

W ◄—┼——┼——┼——┼——┼——┼——┼——┼——┼——┼——┼——┼——┼——► E
  $^-150$ $^-125$ $^-100$ $^-75$ $^-50$ $^-25$ 0   25   50   75 100 125 150

1. If you are now at 0 and move east at 50 km/hr, where will you be 3 hr from now?

    50 × 3 = 150

    Move east at 50 km/hr.   3 hr from now   You will be 150 km east of 0.

2. If you are now at 0, moving east at 50 km/hr, where were you 3 hr ago?

    50 × $^-3$ = $^-150$

    Moving east at 50 km/hr.   3 hr ago   You were 150 km west of 0.

3. If you are now at 0 and move west at 50 km/hr, where will you be 3 hr from now?

    $^-50$ × 3 = $^-150$

    Move west at 50 km/hr.   3 hr from now   You will be 150 km west of 0.

4. If you are now at 0, moving west at 50 km/hr, where were you 3 hr ago?

    $^-50$ × $^-3$ = 150

    Moving west at 50 km/hr.   3 hr ago   You were 150 km east of 0.

These models illustrate the following:

> ## Properties
>
> For any whole numbers a and b, the following hold:
>
> **1.** $(^-a)(^-b) = ab$.
> **2.** $(^-a)b = b(^-a) = {}^-(ab)$.

REMARK We will show later in this section that the above are true for all integers a and b.

Properties of Integer Multiplication

The set of integers has properties under multiplication analogous to those of the set of whole numbers under multiplication. These properties are summarized next.

> ## Properties of Integer Multiplication
>
> The set of integers I satisfies the following properties of multiplication for all integers a, b, $c \in I$:
>
> **Closure property of multiplication of integers** ab is a unique integer.
> **Commutative property of multiplication of integers** $ab = ba$.
> **Associative property of multiplication of integers** $(ab)c = a(bc)$.
> **Multiplicative identity property**   1 is the unique integer such that for all integers a, $1 \cdot a = a = a \cdot 1$.
> **Distributive properties of multiplication over addition for integers** $a(b + c) = ab + ac$ and $(b + c)a = ba + ca$.
> **Zero multiplication property of integers**   0 is the unique integer such that for all integers a, $a \cdot 0 = 0 = 0 \cdot a$.

HISTORICAL NOTE

Emmy Noether (1882–1935) is one of the outstanding mathematicians of the twentieth century. She made lasting contributions to the study of *rings,* algebraic systems among which is the set of integers. When she entered the University of Erlanger (Germany) in 1900, Emmy Noether was one of only two women enrolled. After completing her doctorate in 1907 and despite her outstanding achievements, she could not find a suitable job because she was a woman. In 1919 she got a university appointment without pay and, only later, a very modest salary. In 1933, along with many other scholars, she was dismissed from the University at Göttingen because she was Jewish. She emigrated to the United States and taught at Bryn Mawr College until her untimely death only 18 months after arriving in the United States.

An approach to showing that $(^-2) \cdot 3 = {}^-(2 \cdot 3)$ uses the uniqueness property of additive inverses. If we can show that $(^-2) \cdot 3$ and $^-(2 \cdot 3)$ are additive inverses of the same number, then they must be equal. By definition, the additive inverse of $(2 \cdot 3)$ is $^-(2 \cdot 3)$. That $(^-2) \cdot 3$ is also the additive inverse of $2 \cdot 3$ can be proved by showing that $(^-2) \cdot 3 + 2 \cdot 3 = 0$. The proof follows.

$$
\begin{aligned}
(^-2) \cdot 3 + 2 \cdot 3 &= (^-2 + 2) \cdot 3 \qquad &\text{Distributive property of multiplication over addition} \\
&= 0 \cdot 3 &\text{Additive inverse} \\
&= 0 &\text{Zero multiplication}
\end{aligned}
$$

Because $(^-2) \cdot 3$ and $^-(2 \cdot 3)$ are both additive inverses of $(2 \cdot 3)$ and because the additive inverse must be unique, $(^-2) \cdot 3 = {}^-(2 \cdot 3)$.

Using this approach, we could show the following property (whose justification is explored in Ongoing Assessment 4-2):

> ## Property
>
> For every integer a, $(^-1)a = {}^-a$.

It is important to keep in mind that $(^-1)a = {}^-a$ is true for all integers a. Thus if we substitute $^-1$ for a, we get $(^-1) \cdot (^-1) = {}^-(^-1)$. Because $^-(^-1) = 1$, we have yet another justification for the fact that $(^-1) \cdot (^-1) = 1$. Using this result, the above property, and the properties of integers listed earlier, we can show that $(^-a)b = {}^-(ab)$ and that $(^-a)(^-b) = ab$ for all integers a and b as follows:

$$
\begin{aligned}
(^-a)b &= [(^-1)a]b \\
&= (^-1)(ab) \\
&= {}^-(ab).
\end{aligned}
$$

Also:

$$
\begin{aligned}
(^-a)(^-b) &= [(^-1)a] \cdot [(^-1)b] \\
&= [(^-1) \cdot (^-1)](ab) \\
&= 1(ab) \\
&= ab.
\end{aligned}
$$

We have established the following properties:

> ## Properties
>
> For all integers a and b,
>
> $$(^-a)b = {}^-(ab).$$
> $$(^-a)(^-b) = ab.$$

REMARK   It is important to note that in these properties, ^-a and ^-b are not necessarily negative and a and b are not necessarily positive.

The distributive property of multiplication over subtraction follows from the distributive property of multiplication over addition:

$$a(b - c) = a(b + {}^-c)$$
$$= ab + a({}^-c)$$
$$= ab + {}^-(ac)$$
$$= ab - ac.$$

Consequently, $a(b - c) = ab - ac$. Similarly, we can show that $(b - c)a = ba - ca$.

> **Property**

Distributive property of multiplication over subtraction for integers   For any integers a, b, and c,

$$a(b - c) = ab - ac \qquad \text{and} \qquad (b - c)a = ba - ca.$$

EXAMPLE 4-10

Simplify each of the following so that there are no parentheses in the final answer:

a. $({}^-3)(x - 2)$ **b.** $(a + b)(a - b)$

Solution   **a.** $({}^-3)(x - 2) = ({}^-3)x - ({}^-3)(2) = {}^-3x - ({}^-6) = {}^-3x + {}^-({}^-6) = {}^-3x + 6$.

b. $(a + b)(a - b) = (a + b)a - (a + b)b$
$$= (a^2 + ba) - (ab + b^2)$$
$$= a^2 + ab - ab - b^2$$
$$= a^2 - b^2$$
Thus $(a + b)(a - b) = a^2 - b^2$.

difference-of-squares   The result $(a + b)(a - b) = a^2 - b^2$ in Example 4-10(b) is the **difference-of-squares** formula.

EXAMPLE 4-11

Use the difference-of-squares formula to simplify the following:

a. $(4 + b)(4 - b)$ **b.** $({}^-4 + b)({}^-4 - b)$ **c.** $(x + 3)^2 - (x - 3)^2$

Solution   **a.** $(4 + b)(4 - b) = 4^2 - b^2 = 16 - b^2$
b. $({}^-4 + b)({}^-4 - b) = ({}^-4)^2 - b^2 = 16 - b^2$
c. $(x + 3)^2 - (x - 3)^2 = (x + 3 + x - 3)(x + 3 - (x - 3)) = 2x(x + 3 - x + 3)$
$$= 2x \cdot 6$$
$$= 12x$$

NOW TRY THIS 4-3

Determine how to use the difference-of-squares formula to compute the following mentally:

a. $22 \cdot 18$ **b.** $24 \cdot 36$ **c.** $998 \cdot 1002$

When the distributive property of multiplication over subtraction is written in reverse order as

$$ab - ac = a(b - c) \qquad \text{and} \qquad ba - ca = (b - c)a,$$

and similarly for addition, the expressions on the right of each equation are in *factored* form. We say that the common factor a has been *factored out*.

Both the difference-of-squares formula and the distributive properties of multiplication over addition and subtraction can be used for factoring.

EXAMPLE 4-12

Factor each of the following completely:

a. $x^2 - 9$ **b.** $(x + y)^2 - z^2$ **c.** $^{-}3x + 5xy$ **d.** $3x - 6$ **e.** $5x^2 - 2x^2$

Solution   **a.** $x^2 - 9 = x^2 - 3^2 = (x + 3)(x - 3)$
b. $(x + y)^2 - z^2 = (x + y + z)(x + y - z)$
c. $^{-}3x + 5xy = x(^{-}3 + 5y)$
d. $3x - 6 = 3(x - 2)$
e. $5x^2 - 2x^2 = (5 - 2)x^2 = 3x^2$

Integer Division

In the set of whole numbers, $a \div b$, where $b \neq 0$, is the unique whole number c such that $a = bc$. If such a whole number c does not exist, then $a \div b$ is undefined. Division on the set of integers is defined analogously.

Definition of Integer Division

If a and b are any integers, with $b \neq 0$, then $a \div b$ is the unique integer c, if it exists, such that $a = bc$.

EXAMPLE 4-13

Use the definition of integer division, if possible, to evaluate each of the following:

a. $12 \div (^{-}4)$ **b.** $^{-}12 \div 4$ **c.** $^{-}12 \div (^{-}4)$ **d.** $^{-}12 \div 5$

Solution   **a.** Let $12 \div (^{-}4) = c$. Then, $12 = {}^{-}4c$, and consequently, $c = {}^{-}3$. Thus $12 \div (^{-}4) = {}^{-}3$.
b. Let $^{-}12 \div 4 = c$. Then, $^{-}12 = 4c$, and therefore $c = {}^{-}3$. Thus $^{-}12 \div 4 = {}^{-}3$.

c. Let $^-12 \div (^-4) = c$. Then, $^-12 = ^-4c$, and consequently, $c = 3$. Thus $^-12 \div (^-4) = 3$.

d. Let $^-12 \div 5 = c$. Then, $^-12 = 5c$. Because no integer c exists to satisfy this equation (why?), we say that $^-12 \div 5$ is undefined over the integers.

Example 4-13 suggests that *the quotient of two negative integers, if it exists, is a positive integer and the quotient of a positive and a negative integer, if it exists, or of a negative and a positive integer, if it exists, is negative.*

Order of Operations on Integers

The following rules apply to the order in which arithmetic operations are performed. Recall that when addition and multiplication appear in a problem without parentheses, multiplication is done first.

When addition, subtraction, multiplication, division, and exponentiation appear without parentheses, exponentiation is done first, then multiplications and divisions in the order of their appearance from left to right, and then additions and subtractions in the order of their appearance from left to right. Arithmetic operations that appear inside parentheses must be done first.

E X A M P L E
4-14

Evaluate each of the following:

a. $2 - 5 \cdot 4 + 1$
b. $(2 - 5) \cdot 4 + 1$
c. $2 - 3 \cdot 4 + 5 \cdot 2 - 1 + 5$
d. $2 + 16 \div 4 \cdot 2 + 8$
e. $(^-3)^4$
f. $^-3^4$

Solution
   a. $2 - 5 \cdot 4 + 1 = 2 - 20 + 1 = ^-18 + 1 = ^-17$
   b. $(2 - 5) \cdot 4 + 1 = ^-3 \cdot 4 + 1 = ^-12 + 1 = ^-11$
   c. $2 - 3 \cdot 4 + 5 \cdot 2 - 1 + 5 = 2 - 12 + 10 - 1 + 5 = 4$
   d. $2 + 16 \div 4 \cdot 2 + 8 = 2 + 4 \cdot 2 + 8 = 2 + 8 + 8 = 10 + 8 = 18$
   e. $(^-3)^4 = (^-3)(^-3)(^-3)(^-3) = 81$
   f. $^-3^4 = ^-(3^4) = ^-(81) = ^-81$

REMARK   Notice that from Example 4-14(e) and (f), we have $(^-3)^4 \neq ^-3^4$. By convention, $(^-3)^4$ means $(^-3)(^-3)(^-3)(^-3)$ and $^-3^4$ means $^-(3^4)$, or $^-(3 \cdot 3 \cdot 3 \cdot 3)$.

Ordering Integers

As with whole numbers, a number line can be used to describe greater-than and less-than relations for a set of integers. Because $^-5$ is to the left of $^-3$ on the number line in Figure 4-15, we say that "$^-5$ is less than $^-3$," and we write $^-5 < ^-3$. We can also say that "$^-3$ is greater than $^-5$," and we can write $^-3 > ^-5$.

FIGURE 4-15

$$\begin{array}{c} {}^-5 \ {}^-4 \ {}^-3 \ {}^-2 \ {}^-1 \ 0 \ 1 \ 2 \ 3 \ 4 \ 5 \end{array}$$

Notice that since $^-5$ is to the left of $^-3$ there is a positive integer that can be added to $^-5$ to get $^-3$, namely, 2. Thus $^-5 < {}^-3$ because $^-5 + 2 = {}^-3$. The definition of *less than* for integers is similar to that for whole numbers.

> ### Definition of *Less Than* for Integers

For any integers a and b, a is less than b, written $a < b$, if and only if there exists a positive integer k such that $a + k = b$.

The last equation implies that $k = b - a$. Thus we have the following property.

> ### Property

$a < b$ (or equivalently, $b > a$) if, and only if, $b - a$ is equal to a positive integer; that is, $b - a$ is greater than 0.

Using the above property $^-5 < {}^-3$ because $^-3 - ({}^-5) = {}^-3 + {}^-({}^-5) = {}^-3 + 5 = 2 > 0$. (Note that $a \le b$ means that $a < b \ or \ a = b$. Also $b \ge a$ if, and only if, $a \le b$)

EXAMPLE 4-15

Use the above property to justify each of the following for integers x, y, and n.

a. If $x < y$ and n is any integer, then $x + n < y + n$.
b. If $x < y$, then $^-x > {}^-y$.
c. If $x < y$ and $n > 0$, then $n \cdot x < n \cdot y$.
d. If $x < y$ and $n < 0$, then $n \cdot x > n \cdot y$.

Solution   **a.** Because $x < y$ we have $y - x > 0$. We need to show that $(y + n) - (x + n) > 0$. We have $y + n - (x + n) = y + n - x - n = y - x$. Because $y - x > 0$, we have $y + n - (x + n) > 0$, and hence $x + n < y + n$.

b. Because $x < y$, $y - x > 0$. We need to show $^-x - ({}^-y) > 0$. We have $^-x - ({}^-y) = {}^-x + {}^-({}^-y) = {}^-x + y = y - x$. Because $y - x > 0$ we have $^-x - ({}^-y) > 0$, and hence $^-x > {}^-y$.

c. Because $x < y$, $y - x > 0$. We need to show that $ny - nx > . 0$. We have $ny - nx = n(y - x)$. Because n is a positive integer and $y - x$ is positive, $n \cdot (y - x)$ must also be positive. Because $ny - nx > 0$, we have $nx < ny$.

d. To show that $nx > ny$ we need only show that $nx - ny > 0$. We have $nx - ny = n(x - y)$. Since $y - x > 0$, $x - y < 0$ (why?). Because $n < 0$ and $x - y < 0$, $n(x - y)$ is positive. Thus $nx - ny > 0$ and hence, $nx > ny$.

Sample School Book Page:
THE COORDINATE SYSTEM

Melina made a coordinate grid and plotted the points (4, 3), (⁻3, 1), (⁻4, ⁻5), and (3, ⁻3). Study her work, and see if you can figure out what she did.

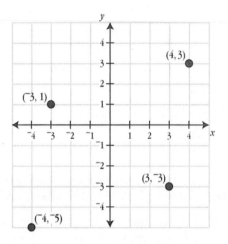

Recall that the two numbers that describe a point are called the *coordinates* of the point. The first number is the *x-coordinate*, and the second number is the *y-coordinate*. For example, the first point Melina plotted has coordinates (4, 3); the *x*-coordinate is 4, and the *y*-coordinate is 3.

Problem 5.1

A. Describe how Melina located each of the four points on the coordinate grid.

B. What polygon could you make by connecting the four points? Justify your answer.

C. On a coordinate grid, plot four points that are the vertices of a square, such that both coordinates of each point are positive integers.

D. On a coordinate grid, plot four points that are the vertices of a square, such that both coordinates of each point are negative integers.

E. On a coordinate grid, plot four points that are the vertices of a square, such that one point has two negative-integer coordinates, one point has two positive-integer coordinates, and each of the other points has one positive-integer coordinate and one negative-integer coordinate.

F. Two vertices of a square are (3, 1) and (⁻1, 1). Find the coordinates for every pair of points that could be the other two vertices.

Source: Connected Mathematics, "Accentuate the Negative Integers." Prentice-Hall 2002 (p. 69).

Extending the Coordinate System

We extended a number line to include all integers. This new extended number line can become the *x*- and *y*-axes of a coordinate system. In Chapter 10 we investigate the coordinate system for all real numbers. Meanwhile look at the student page where the coordinate system is extended to include negative integers. Answer questions C through F on the student page.

BRAIN TEASER

Express each of the numbers from 1 through 10 using 4 fours and any operations. For example,

$$1 = 44 \div 44, \text{ or}$$
$$1 = (4 \div 4)^{44}, \text{ or}$$
$$1 = {}^{-}4 + 4 + (4 \div 4).$$

A S S E S S M E N T   4 - 2

1. Use patterns to show that $({}^{-}1)({}^{-}1) = 1$.
2. Use the charged-field model to show that $({}^{-}4)({}^{-}2) = 8$.
3. Use the number-line model to show that $({}^{-}4)2 = {}^{-}8$.
4. The number of students eating in the school cafeteria has been decreasing at the rate of 20 per year. Assuming this trend continues, write a multiplication problem that describes the change in the number of students eating in the school cafeteria for each of the following:
   a. The change over the next 4 years
   b. The situation 4 years ago
   c. The change over the next *n* years
   d. The situation *n* years ago
5. Use the definition of division to find each quotient, if possible. If a quotient is not defined, explain why.
   a. ${}^{-}40 \div {}^{-}8$ b. $143 \div ({}^{-}11)$
   c. ${}^{-}143 \div 13$ d. $0 \div ({}^{-}5)$
   e. ${}^{-}5 \div 0$ f. $0 \div 0$
6. Evaluate each of the following, if possible:
   a. $({}^{-}10 \div {}^{-}2)({}^{-}2)$ b. $(a \div b)b$
   c. $({}^{-}10 \cdot 5) \div 5$ d. $(ab) \div b$
   e. ${}^{-}8 \div ({}^{-}8 + 8)$ f. $({}^{-}8 + 8) \div 8$
   g. $({}^{-}6 + 6) \div ({}^{-}2 + 2)$ h. $({}^{-}23 - {}^{-}7) \div 4$
   i. $|{}^{-}24| \div 4 \cdot (3 - 15)$
7. Evaluate each of the following products and then if possible, write two division statements that are equivalent to your multiplication statements. If two division statements are not possible, explain why.
   a. $({}^{-}6) \cdot 5$
   b. $({}^{-}5) \cdot ({}^{-}4)$
   c. $({}^{-}3) \cdot 0$
   d. $0 \cdot 0$

8. In a lab, the temperature of various chemical reactions was changing by a fixed number of degrees per minute. Write a multiplication problem that describes each of the following:
   a. The temperature at 8:00 P.M. was 32°C. If it dropped 3°C per minute, what is the temperature at 8:30 P.M.?
   b. The temperature at 8:20 P.M. was 0°C. If it dropped 4°C per minute, what is the temperature at 7:55 P.M.?
   c. The temperature at 8:00 P.M. was ${}^{-}20$°C. If it dropped 4°C per minute, what is the temperature at 7:30 P.M.?
   d. The temperature at 8:00 P.M. was 25°C. If it increased every minute by 3°C, what is the temperature at 7:40 P.M.?
   e. The temperature at 8:00 A.M. was ${}^{-}5$°C. If it increases by *d* degrees per minute, what will the temperature be *m* minutes later?
   f. The temperature at 8:00 P.M. was 0°C. If it dropped *d* degrees per minute, what was the temperature *m* minutes before?
   g. The temperature at 8:00 P.M. was 20°C. If it increased every minute by *d* degrees, what was the temperature *m* minutes before?
9. a. On each of four consecutive plays in a football game, a team lost 11 yd. If lost yardage is interpreted as a negative integer, write the information as a product of integers and determine the total number of yards lost.
   b. If Jack Jones lost a total of 66 yd in 11 plays, how many yards, on the average, did he lose on each play?
10. In 2003, it was predicted that the farmland acreage lost to family dwellings over the next 9 years would be 12,000 acres per year. If this prediction were true and if this pattern were to continue, how much acreage would be lost to homes by the end of 2011?

11. Show that the distributive property of multiplication over addition, $a(b + c) = ab + ac$ is true for each of the following values of a, b, and c:
    a. $a = {}^-1, b = {}^-5, c = {}^-2$
    b. $a = {}^-3, b = {}^-3, c = 2$
    c. $a = {}^-5, b = 2, c = {}^-6$

12. Compute each of the following:
    a. $({}^-2)^3$
    b. $({}^-2)^4$
    c. $({}^-10)^5 \div ({}^-10)^2$
    d. $({}^-3)^5 \div ({}^-3)$
    e. $({}^-1)^{50}$
    f. $({}^-1)^{151}$
    g. ${}^-2 + 3 \cdot 5 - 1$
    h. $10 - 3 \cdot 7 - 4({}^-2) + 3$
    i. $10 - 3 - 12$
    j. $10 - (3 - 12)$
    k. $({}^-3)^2$
    l. ${}^-3^2$
    m. ${}^-5^2 + 3({}^-2)^2$
    n. ${}^-2^3$
    o. $({}^-2)^5$
    p. ${}^-2^4$

13. If x is an integer and $x \neq 0$, which of the following are always positive and which are always negative?
    a. ${}^-x^2$
    b. x^2
    c. $({}^-x)^2$
    d. ${}^-x^3$
    e. $({}^-x)^3$
    f. ${}^-x^4$
    g. $({}^-x)^4$
    h. x^4
    i. x
    j. ${}^-x$

14. Which of the expressions in problem 13 are equal to each other for all values of x?

15. Identify the property of integers being illustrated in each of the following:
    a. $({}^-3) \cdot (4 + 5) = (4 + 5) \cdot ({}^-3)$
    b. $({}^-4) \cdot ({}^-7) \in I$
    c. $5 \cdot [4 \cdot ({}^-3)] = (5 \cdot 4) \cdot ({}^-3)$
    d. $({}^-9) \cdot [5 + ({}^-8)] = ({}^-9) \cdot 5 + ({}^-9) \cdot ({}^-8)$

16. Simplify each of the following:
    a. $({}^-x)({}^-y)$
    b. ${}^-2x({}^-y)$
    c. ${}^-2({}^-x + y) + x + y$
    d. ${}^-1 \cdot x$
    e. $x - 2({}^-y)$
    f. $a - (a - b)({}^-1)$
    g. $y - (y - x)({}^-2)$
    h. ${}^-1(x - y) + x$

17. Multiply each of the following and combine terms where possible:
    a. ${}^-2(x - y)$
    b. $x(x - y)$
    c. ${}^-x(x - y)$
    d. ${}^-2(x + y - z)$
    e. ${}^-x(x - y - 3)$
    f. $({}^-5 - x)(5 + x)$
    g. $(x - y - 1)(x + y + 1)$
    h. $({}^-x^2 + 2)(x^2 - 1)$

18. Find all integers x (if possible) that make each of the following true:
    a. ${}^-3x = 6$
    b. ${}^-3x = {}^-6$
    c. ${}^-2x = 0$
    d. $5x = {}^-30$
    e. $x \div 3 = {}^-12$
    f. $x \div ({}^-3) = {}^-2$
    g. $x \div ({}^-x) = {}^-1$
    h. $0 \div x = 0$
    i. $x \div 0 = 1$
    j. $x^2 = 9$
    k. $x^2 = {}^-9$
    l. ${}^-x \div {}^-x = 1$
    m. ${}^-x^2$ is negative.
    n. ${}^-(1 - x) = x - 1$
    o. $x - 3x = {}^-2x$

19. Use the difference-of-squares formula to simplify each of the following, if possible:
    a. $52 \cdot 48$
    b. $(5 - 100)(5 + 100)$
    c. $({}^-x - y)({}^-x + y)$
    d. $(2 + 3x)(2 - 3x)$
    e. $(x - 1)(1 + x)$
    f. $213^2 - 13^2$

20. Factor each of the following expressions completely and then simplify, if possible:
    a. $3x + 5x$
    b. $ax + 2x$
    c. $xy + x$
    d. $ax - 2x$
    e. $x^2 + xy$
    f. $3x - 4x + 7x$
    g. $3xy + 2x - xz$
    h. $3x^2 + xy - x$
    i. $abc + ab - a$
    j. $(a + b)(c + 1) - (a + b)$
    k. $16 - a^2$
    l. $x^2 - 9y^2$
    m. $4x^2 - 25y^2$
    n. $(x^2 - y^2) + x + y$

21. a. Use the distributive property of multiplication over addition or over subtraction to show that:
    $$(a - b)^2 = a^2 - 2ab + b^2$$
    b. Use your results from (a) to compute each of the following in your head:
    (i) 98^2 (*Hint:* Write $98 = 100 - 2$.)
    (ii) 99^2
    (iii) 997^2

22. If x and y are integers, classify each of the following as true or false. If true, explain why. If false, give a counterexample.
    a. $|x + y| = |x| + |y|$
    b. $|xy| = |x|\,|y|$
    c. $|x^2| = x^2$
    d. $|x|^2 = x^2$

23. a. Given a calendar for any month of the year, such as the one that follows, pick several 3×3 groups of numbers and find the sum of these numbers. How are the obtained sums related to the middle number?

JULY						
S	M	T	W	T	F	S
		1	2	3	4	5
6	7	8	9	10	11	12
13	14	15	16	17	18	19
20	21	22	23	24	25	26
27	28	29	30	31		

   ★b. Prove that the sum of any 9 digits in any 3×3 set of numbers selected from a monthly calendar will always be equal to 9 times the middle number.

24. In each of the following, find the next two terms. If a sequence is arithmetic or geometric, find its difference or ratio and the nth term.
    a. ${}^-10, {}^-7, {}^-4, {}^-1, 2, 5, \_, \_$
    b. $10, 7, 4, 1, {}^-2, {}^-5, \_, \_$
    c. ${}^-2, {}^-4, {}^-8, {}^-16, {}^-32, {}^-64, \_, \_$
    d. ${}^-2, 4, {}^-8, 16, {}^-32, 64, \_, \_$
    e. $2, {}^-2^2, 2^3, {}^-2^4, 2^5, {}^-2^6, \_, \_$

25. Find the sum of the first 100 terms in parts (a) and (b) of problem 24.

26. Find the first five terms of the sequences whose nth term is:
    a. $n^2 - 10$
    b. ${}^-5n + 3$
    c. $({}^-2)^n - 1$
    d. $({}^-2)^n + 2^n$
    e. $n^2({}^-1)^n$
    f. $|10 - n^2|$

27. Find the first two terms of an arithmetic sequence in which the fourth term is ${}^-8$ and the 101st term is ${}^-493$.

28. Tira noticed that every 30 sec, the temperature of a chemical reaction in her lab was decreasing by the same number of degrees. Initially, the temperature was 28°C and 5 min later, $^-12$°C. In a second experiment, Tira noticed that the temperature of the chemical reaction was initially $^-57$°C and was decreasing by 3°C every minute. If she started the two experiments at the same time, when were the temperatures of the reactions the same? What was that temperature?

29. If x and y are integers, classify each of the following as always true, sometimes true, or never true. Justify your answers.

    a. $xy = {}^-|x|\,|y|$ **b.** $({}^-x)^3 = {}^-x^3$
    c. ${}^-x^2 = x^2$ **d.** $|x| > {}^-1$
    e. If $x > y$, then $x^2 > y^2$.

Communication

30. Can $({}^-x - y)(x + y)$ be multiplied by using the difference-of-squares formula? Explain why or why not.

31. Kahlil said that using the equation $(a + b)^2 = a^2 + 2ab + b^2$, he can find a similar equation for $(a - b)^2$. Examine his argument. If it is correct, supply any missing steps or justifications; if it is incorrect, point out why.

$$(a - b)^2 = [a + ({}^-b)]^2$$
$$= a^2 + 2a({}^-b) + ({}^-b)^2$$
$$= a^2 - 2ab + b^2$$

32. **a.** Use the distributive property of multiplication over addition to show that $({}^-1) \cdot a + a = 0$. (*Hint:* Write $a = 1 \cdot a$.)
    b. Use part (a) to show that $({}^-1)a = {}^-a$.

33. Seventh-grader Nancy gave the following argument to show that $({}^-a)b = {}^-(ab)$ for all integers a and b: *I know that $({}^-1)a = {}^-a$; hence:*

$$({}^-a)b = [({}^-1)a] \cdot b$$
$$= ({}^-1) \cdot (ab)$$
$$= {}^-(ab).$$

If the argument is valid, complete its details; if it is not valid, explain why not.

34. Hoani gave the following argument that ${}^-(a + b) = {}^-a + {}^-b$ for all integers a and b. If the argument is correct, supply the missing reasons. If it is incorrect, explain why not.

$$^-(a + b) = ({}^-1) \cdot (a + b)$$
$$= ({}^-1)a + ({}^-1)b$$
$$= {}^-a + {}^-b$$

35. The Swiss mathematician Leonhard Euler (1707–1783) argued that $({}^-1)({}^-1) = 1$ as follows. "The result must be either $^-1$ or 1. If it is $^-1$, then $({}^-1)({}^-1) = {}^-1$. Because $^-1 = ({}^-1) \cdot 1$, we have $({}^-1)({}^-1) = ({}^-1) \cdot 1$. Now dividing both sides of the last equation by $^-1$ we get $^-1 = 1$, which of course cannot be true. Hence $({}^-1)({}^-1)$ must be equal to 1."

    a. What is your reaction to the above argument? Is it logical? Why or why not?
    b. Can Euler's approach be used to justify other properties of integers? Explain.

36. The following graph shows the development of mathematics in different cultures. Explain the use of positive and negative numbers in the graph.

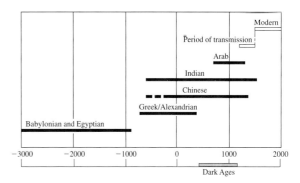

Open-Ended

37. On a national mathematics competition, scoring is accomplished using the formula 4 times the number done correctly minus the number done incorrectly. In this scheme, problems left blank are considered neither correct nor incorrect. Devise a scenario that would allow a student to have a negative score.

38. Select a current middle-school text that introduces multiplication and division of integers and discuss any models that were used and how effective you think they would be with a group of students.

Cooperative Learning

39. Devise a scheme for determining a grade-point average for a college student that allows negative quality points for a failing grade.
    a. Use your scheme to determine possible grades for students with positive, zero, and negative grade-point averages.
    b. Compare your scheme with that of another class group and write a rationale for the best scheme.

40. **a.** How would you introduce multiplication of integers in a middle-school class and how would you explain that a product of two negative numbers is positive? Write a rationale for your approach.
    b. Present your answers and compare them to those of another class group and together decide about the most appropriate way to introduce the concepts. Write a rationale for your approach.

Review Problems

41. Illustrate $^-8 + {}^-5$ on a number line.
42. Find the additive inverse of each of the following:
    a. $^-5$ **b.** 7   **c.** 0

43. Compute each of the following:
    a. $|{}^-14|$ b. $|{}^-14| + 7$
    c. $8 - |{}^-12|$ d. $|11| + |{}^-11|$
44. In the 1400s, European merchants used positive and negative numbers to label barrels of flour. For example, a barrel labeled $^+3$ meant the barrel was 3 lb overweight, whereas a barrel labeled $^-5$ meant the barrel was 5 lb underweight. If the following numbers were found on 100-lb barrels, what was the total weight of the barrels?

BRAIN TEASER

If $a, \ldots, z$ are integers, find the product

$$(x - a)(x - b)(x - c) \ldots (x - z).$$

4-3   Divisibility

The concepts of *even* and *odd* integers are commonly used. For example, during water shortages in the summer in some parts of the country, houses with even number addresses can water on even-numbered days of the month and houses with odd number addresses can water on odd-numbered days. An even integer is an integer that has 0 remainder when divided by 2. We say that it is divisible by 2. An odd integer is an integer that is not divisible by 2. The fact that 12 is divisible by 2 can be stated in the following equivalent statements in the left column:

Example	General Statement
12 is divisible by 2.	a is divisible by b.
2 is a divisor of 12.	b is a divisor of a.
12 is a multiple of 2.	a is a multiple of b.
2 is a factor of 12.	b is a factor of a.
2 divides 12.	b divides a.

divides   The statement that "2 divides 12" is written with a vertical segment as in $2\,|\,12$, where the vertical segment means **divides**. Likewise, "b divides a" can be written $b\,|\,a$. Each statement in the previous right column can be written $b\,|\,a$. We write $5 \nmid 12$ to symbolize that 5 does not divide 12 or that 12 is not divisible by 5. The notation $5 \nmid 12$ also implies that 12 is not a multiple of 5 and 5 is not a factor of 12.

> ### Definition
>
> If a and b are any integers, then b divides a, written $b\,|\,a$, if, and only if, there is a unique integer c such that $a = bc$.

factor ◆ divisor ◆ multiple   If $b\,|\,a$, then b is a **factor**, or a **divisor**, of a, and a is a **multiple** of b.
Do not confuse $b\,|\,a$ with b/a, which is interpreted as $b \div a$. The former, a relation, is either true or false. The latter, an operation, has a numerical value if $a \neq 0$. Note that if b/a is an integer then $b\,|\,a$.

HISTORICAL
N O T E Pierre de Fermat (1601–1665) was a lawyer and a magistrate who served in the provincial parliament in Toulouse, France. He devoted his leisure time to mathematics—a subject in which he had no formal training. After his death, his son decided to publish a new edition of Diophantus's *Arithmetica* with Fermat's notes. One of the notes in the margin of Fermat's copy asserted that the equation $x^n + y^n = z^n$ has no positive integer solutions if n is an integer greater than 2 and commented, "I have found an admirable proof of this, but the margin is too narrow to contain it." Many great mathematicians spent years trying to prove Fermat's assertion, now called "Fermat's last theorem." In 1995 Andrew Wiles, a Princeton University mathematician, proved Fermat's last theorem.

EXAMPLE
4-16

Classify each of the following as true or false. Explain your answers.

a. $^-3|12$ **b.** $0|2$ **c.** 0 is even.   **d.** $8 \nmid 2$ **e.** For all integers, a, $1|a$.
f. For all integers a, $^-1|a$.   **g.** $3|6n$ for all integers n
h. $(a - b)|(a^2 - b^2)$ if a and b are integers and $a \neq b$.

Solution   **a.** $^-3|12$ is true because $12 = {}^-4(^-3)$.
  b. $0|2$ is false because there is no integer c such that $2 = c \cdot 0$.
  c. $2|0$ is true because $0 = 0 \cdot 2$; therefore 0 is even.
  d. $8 \nmid 2$ is true because there is no integer c such that $2 = c \cdot 8$.
  e. $1|a$ is true for all integers a because $a = a \cdot 1$.
  f. $^-1|a$ is true for all integers a because $a = (^-a)(^-1)$.
  g. $3|6n$ is true. Because $6n = 3 \cdot 2n$, $6n$ is a multiple of 3 and hence $3|6n$.
  h. $(a - b)|(a^2 - b^2)$ is true because $a^2 - b^2 = (a - b)(a + b)$ and $a \neq b$.

In Example 4-16(g), because $3|6$ we were able to show that $3|6n$ for all integers n. This can be generalized. If instead of $3|6$ we have $3|a$, then we can conclude that 3 divides any multiple of a. Even more generally, if $d|a$ then d divides any multiple of a. We state this fact in the following theorem.

▷ **Theorem 4-1**

For any integers a and d, if $d|a$ and n is any integer, then $d|na$.

The above theorem can be stated in an equivalent form:
If d is a factor of a (that is, a equals some integer times d), then d is a factor of any multiple of a.

FIGURE 4-16

We can deduce other notions of divisibility from everyday models. Consider two packages of chewing gum each having five pieces, as in Figure 4-16. We can divide each package of gum evenly among five students. In addition, if we opened both packages and put all of the pieces in a bag, we could still divide the pieces of gum evenly among the five students. To generalize this notion, if we buy gum in larger packages with a pieces in one package and b pieces in a second package with both a and b divisible by 5, we can record the preceding discussion as follows:

If $5|a$ and $5|b$, then $5|(a + b)$.

If the number, a, of pieces of gum in one package is divisible by 5, but the number, b, of pieces in the other package is not, then the total, $a + b$, cannot be divided evenly among the five students. This can be recorded as follows:

$$\text{If } 5|a \text{ and } 5\nmid b, \text{ then } 5\nmid(a + b).$$

What, if anything, can you conclude if $5\nmid a$ and $5\nmid b$?

Since subtraction can be defined in terms of addition, results similar to addition hold for subtraction. These ideas are listed in Theorem 4-2.

> **Theorem 4-2**
>
> For any integers a, b, and d, the following holds:
>
> **a.** If $d|a$ and $d|b$, then $d|(a + b)$.
> **b.** If $d|a$ and $d\nmid b$, then $d\nmid(a + b)$.
> **c.** If $d|a$ and $d|b$, then $d|(a - b)$.
> **d.** If $d|a$ and $d\nmid b$, then $d\nmid(a - b)$.

The proofs of most theorems in this section are left as exercises, but the proof of Theorem 4-2(a) is given as an illustration.

Proof.   Theorem 4-2(a) is equivalent to the following:

If a is a multiple of d and b is a multiple of d, then $a + b$ is a multiple of d.

Notice that "a is a multiple of d" means $a = m \cdot d$, for some integer m. Similarly "b is a multiple of d" means $b = n \cdot d$ for some integer n. To show that $a + b$ is a multiple of d, we add the above equations as follows:

$$a + b = md + nd.$$

Is $md + nd$ a multiple of d? Notice that $md + nd = (m + n)d$, so $a + b = (m + n)d$. Because $m + n$ is an integer, $a + b$ is a multiple of d and therefore $d|(a + b)$.

EXAMPLE
4-17

Classify each of the following as true or false, where x, y, and z are integers. If a statement is true, prove it. If a statement is false, provide a counterexample.

a. If $3|x$ and $3|y$, then $3|xy$.
b. If $3|(x + y)$, then $3|x$ and $3|y$.
c. If $9\nmid a$, then $3\nmid a$.

Solution   **a.** True. By Theorem 4-1, if $3|x$, then, for any integer y, $3|yx$ or $3|xy$.
      b. False. For example, $3|(7 + 2)$, but $3\nmid 7$ and $3\nmid 2$.
      c. False. For example, $9\nmid 21$, but $3|21$.

NOW TRY THIS 4-4

If $3|x$, is it true that $3|xy$ regardless of whether $3|y$ or $3\nmid y$? Why?

EXAMPLE
4-18

FIGURE 4-17

$ 0.00

Five students found a padlocked money box that had a deposit slip attached to it. The deposit slip was water-spotted, so the currency total appeared as shown in Figure 4-17. One student remarked that if the money listed on the deposit slip was in the box, it could easily be divided equally among the 5 students without using coins. How did the student know this?

Solution Because the units digit of the amount of the currency is 0, the solution to the problem is to determine whether all natural numbers whose units digit is 0 are divisible by 5. To solve this problem, *look for a pattern*. Natural numbers whose units digit is 0 form a pattern, that is, 10, 20, 30, 40, 50, ... These numbers are multiples of 10. We are to determine whether 5 divides all multiples of 10. Since $5|10$, by Theorem 4-1, 5 divides any multiple of 10. Hence, 5 divides the amount of money in the box, and the student is correct.

Divisibility Rules

As shown in Example 4-18, sometimes it is handy to know if one number is divisible by another just by looking at it or by performing a simple test. We discovered that if a number ends in 0, then the number is divisible by 5. The same argument can be used to show that if a number ends in 5, it is divisible by 5. This is an example of a divisibility rule. Moreover, if the last digit of a number is neither 0 nor 5, then the number is not divisible by 5.

    Elementary texts frequently state divisibility rules. However, such rules have limited use except for mental arithmetic. It is possible to determine whether 1734 is divisible by 17, either by using pencil and paper or a calculator. To check divisibility and avoid decimals, we can use a calculator with an integer division button, $\boxed{\text{INT}\div}$. On such a calculator, integer division can be performed using the following sequence of buttons:

$$\boxed{1}\,\boxed{7}\,\boxed{3}\,\boxed{4}\,\boxed{\text{INT}\div}\,\boxed{1}\,\boxed{7}\,\boxed{=}$$

to obtain the display $\underset{Q}{\lfloor\ 102\ \rfloor}$ $\underset{R}{\lfloor\ 0\ \rfloor}$.

This implies $1734/17 = 102$ with a remainder of 0, which, in turn, implies $17|1734$.

    We could have determined this same result mentally by considering the following:

$$1734 = 1700 + 34$$

Because $17|1700$ and $17|34$, by Theorem 4-2(a), we have $17|(1700 + 34)$, or $17|1734$. Similarly, we could determine mentally that $17 \nmid 1735$.

REMARK Notice that $17|1734$ implies $17|(^-1)1734$; that is, $17|^-1734$. In general, $d|^-a$ if, and only if, $d|a$.

Divisibility Tests for 2, 5, and 10

To determine mentally whether a given integer n is divisible by another integer d, we think of n as the sum or difference of two integers where d divides at least one of these numbers. We try to choose numbers such that one of them is close to n and divisible by d, and the other number is relatively small. As an example, consider the divisibility of 358 by 2:

$$358 = 350 + 8$$
$$= 35(10) + 8.$$

We know that $2|10$, so that $2|35(10)$. We also know that $2|8$, which tells us that $2|(35(10) + 8)$. Because $2|10$, 2 divides any multiple of 10, so to determine the divisibility of any integer by 2, we consider only whether the units digit is divisible by 2. If it is, then by Theorem 4-2(a) the number is divisible by 2. If not, then by Theorem 4-2(b) the number is not divisible by 2.

We can develop a similar test for divisibility by 10. In general, we have the following divisibility rules.

Divisibility Test for 2

An integer is divisible by 2 if, and only if, its units digit is divisible by 2.

Divisibility Test for 5

An integer is divisible by 5 if, and only if, its units digit is divisible by 5, that is, if, and only if, the units digit is 0 or 5.

Divisibility Test for 10

An integer is divisible by 10 if, and only if, its units digit is divisible by 10, that is, if, and only if, the units digit is 0.

Divisibility Tests for 4 and 8

When we consider divisibility rules for 4 and 8, we see that $4 \nmid 10$ and $8 \nmid 10$, so it is not a matter of checking the units digit for divisibility by 4 and 8. However, 4 (which is 2^2) divides 10^2, and 8 (which is 2^3) divides 10^3.

We first develop a divisibility rule for 4. Consider any four-digit number n such that $n = a \cdot 10^3 + b \cdot 10^2 + c \cdot 10 + d$. Our *subgoal* is to *write the given number as a sum of two numbers*, one of which is as great as possible and divisible by 4. We know that $4|10^2$ because $10^2 = 4 \cdot 25$ and, consequently, $4|10^3$. Because $4|10^2$, then $4|b \cdot 10^2$ and because $4|10^3$, then $4|a \cdot 10^3$. Finally, $4|a \cdot 10^3$ and $4|b \cdot 10^2$ imply $4|(a \cdot 10^3 + b \cdot 10^2)$. Now the divisibility of $a \cdot 10^3 + b \cdot 10^2 + c \cdot 10 + d$ by 4 depends on the divisibility of $(c \cdot 10 + d)$ by 4. Notice that $c \cdot 10 + d$ is the number represented by the last two digits in the given number n. We summarize this in the following test.

Divisibility Test for 4

An integer is divisible by 4 if, and only if, the last two digits of the integer represent a number divisible by 4.

To investigate divisibility by 8, we note that the least positive power of 10 divisible by 8 is 10^3 since $10^3 = 8 \cdot 125$. Consequently, all integral powers of 10 greater than 10^3 also are divisible by 8. Hence, the following is a divisibility test for 8.

Divisibility Test for 8

An integer is divisible by 8 if, and only if, the last three digits of the integer represent a number divisible by 8.

EXAMPLE 4-19

a. Determine whether 97,128 is divisible by 2, 4, and 8.
b. Determine whether 83,026 is divisible by 2, 4, and 8.

Solution   **a.** $2|97,128$ because $2|8$.
$4|97,128$ because $4|28$.
$8|97,128$ because $8|128$.

b. $2|83,026$ because $2|6$.
$4 \nmid 83,026$ because $4 \nmid 26$.
$8 \nmid 83,026$ because $8 \nmid 026$.

REMARK   In Example 4-19(a), it would have been sufficient to check that the given number is divisible by 8 because if $8|a$, then $2|a$ and $4|a$. (Why?) This relationship is shown in Figure 4-18.

FIGURE 4-18

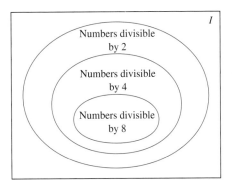

Notice that if $8 \nmid a$, we cannot conclude from this that $4 \nmid a$ or $2 \nmid a$. (Why?)

Divisibility Tests for 3 and 9

Next, we consider a divisibility test for 3. No power of 10 is divisible by 3, but the numbers 9, and 99, and 999, and others of this type are close to powers of 10 and are divisible by 3. For example, to determine whether 5721 is divisible by 3, we rewrite the number using 999, 99, and 9, as follows:

$$5721 = 5 \cdot 10^3 + 7 \cdot 10^2 + 2 \cdot 10 + 1$$
$$= 5(999 + 1) + 7(99 + 1) + 2(9 + 1) + 1$$
$$= 5 \cdot 999 + 5 \cdot 1 + 7 \cdot 99 + 7 \cdot 1 + 2 \cdot 9 + 2 + 1$$
$$= (5 \cdot 999 + 7 \cdot 99 + 2 \cdot 9) + (5 + 7 + 2 + 1)$$

The sum in the first set of parentheses in the last line above is divisible by 3, so the divisibility of 5721 by 3 depends on the sum in the second set of parentheses. In this case, $5 + 7 + 2 + 1 = 15$ and $3|15$, so $3|5721$. Hence, to test 5721 for divisibility by 3, we test

$5 + 7 + 2 + 1$ for divisibility by 3. Notice that $5 + 7 + 2 + 1$ is the sum of the digits of 5721. The example suggests the following test for divisibility by 3.

Divisibility Test for 3

An integer is divisible by 3 if, and only if, the sum of its digits is divisible by 3.

We can use an argument similar to the one used to demonstrate that $3|5721$ to prove the test for divisibility by 3 on any integer and in particular for any 4-digit number $n = a \cdot 10^3 + b \cdot 10^2 + c \cdot 10 + d$. Even though $a \cdot 10^3 + b \cdot 10^2 + c \cdot 10 + d$ is not necessarily divisible by 3, the number $a \cdot 999 + b \cdot 99 + c \cdot 9$ is close to n and *is* divisible by 3. We have the following:

$$a \cdot 10^3 + b \cdot 10^2 + c \cdot 10 + d = a \cdot 1000 + b \cdot 100 + c \cdot 10 + d$$
$$= a(999 + 1) + b(99 + 1) + c(9 + 1) + d$$
$$= (a \cdot 999 + b \cdot 99 + c \cdot 9) + (a \cdot 1 + b \cdot 1 + c \cdot 1 + d)$$
$$= (a \cdot 999 + b \cdot 99 + c \cdot 9) + (a + b + c + d).$$

Because $3|9$, $3|99$, and $3|999$, it follows that $3|(a \cdot 999 + b \cdot 99 + c \cdot 9)$. If $3|(a + b + c + d)$, then $3|[(a \cdot 999 + b \cdot 99 + c \cdot 9) + (a + b + c + d)]$; that is, $3|n$. If, on the other hand, $3\nmid(a + b + c + d)$, it follows from Theorem 4-2(b) that $3\nmid n$.

Since $9|9$, $9|99$, $9|999$, and so on, a test similar to that for divisibility by 3 applies to divisibility by 9. (Why?)

Divisibility Test for 9

An integer is divisible by 9 if, and only if, the sum of the digits of the integer is divisible by 9.

EXAMPLE 4-20

Use divisibility tests to determine whether each of the following numbers is divisible by 3 and divisible by 9:

a. 1002   **b.** 14,238

Solution   **a.** Because $1 + 0 + 0 + 2 = 3$ and $3|3$, it follows that $3|1002$. Because $9\nmid 3$, it follows that $9\nmid 1002$.

b. Because $1 + 4 + 2 + 3 + 8 = 18$ and $3|18$, it follows that $3|14,238$. Because $9|18$, it follows that $9|14,238$.

EXAMPLE 4-21

The store manager has an invoice for 72 four-function calculators. The first and last digits on the receipt are illegible. The manager can read

$$\$\blacksquare 67.9\blacksquare.$$

What are the missing digits, and what is the cost of each calculator?

Solution   Let the missing digits be x and y so that the number is $x67.9y$ dollars, or $x679y$ cents. Because there were 72 calculators sold, the number on the invoice must be divisible by 72. Because the number is divisible by 72 and $72 = 8 \cdot 9$, it must be divisible by 8 and 9, which are factors of 72. For the number on the invoice to be divisible by 8, the three-digit number 79*y* must be divisible by 8. Because 79*y* must be divisible by 8, it is an even number. Therefore 79*y* must be either 790, 792, 794, 796, or 798. Only the number 792 is divisible by 8, so we know the last digit, *y*, on the invoice must be 2.

Because the number on the invoice must be divisible by 9, we know that 9 must divide $x + 6 + 7 + 9 + 2$, or $(x + 24)$. Since 3 is the only single digit that will make $(x + 24)$ divisible by 9, then *x* must be 3. Therefore the number on the invoice must be $367.92. The calculators must cost $367.92/72, or $5.11, each.

Divisibility Tests for 11 and 6

The divisibility test for 7 is usually harder to use than actually performing the division, so we omit the test. We state the divisibility test for 11 but omit the proof. Interested readers might try to find a proof.

Divisibility Test for 11

An integer is divisible by 11 if, and only if, the sum of the digits in the places that are even powers of 10 minus the sum of the digits in the places that are odd powers of 10 is divisible by 11.

For example, to test whether 8,471,986 is divisible by 11, we check whether 11 divides the difference $(6 + 9 + 7 + 8) - (8 + 1 + 4)$, or 17. Because $11 \nmid 17$, it follows from the divisibility test for 11 that $11 \nmid 8,471,986$. A number like 2772 is divisible by 11 because $(2 + 7) - (7 + 2) = 9 - 9 = 0$ and 0 is divisible by 11.

The divisibility test for 6 is related to the divisibility tests for 2 and 3. In Section 4-4, we showed that if $2|n$ and $3|n$, then $(2 \cdot 3)|n$. Consequently, the following divisibility test is true.

Divisibility Test for 6

An integer is divisible by 6 if, and only if, the integer is divisible by both 2 and 3.

Divisibility tests for other numbers are explored in the Ongoing Assessment 4-3.

EXAMPLE 4-22

The number 57,729,364,583 has too many digits for most calculator displays. Determine whether it is divisible by each of the following:

a. 2   **b.** 3   **c.** 5   **d.** 6   **e.** 8   **f.** 9   **g.** 10   **h.** 11

Solution   **a.** No, the last digit, 3, is not divisible by 2.
   b. No, the sum of the digits is 59, which is not divisible by 3.
   c. No, the last digit is neither 0 nor 5.
   d. No, because the number is not divisible by 2 and by 3. (Actually, just the fact that the number is not divisible by 2 implies that it is not divisible by 6. Why?)
   e. No, because the number formed by the last 3 digits, 583, is not divisible by 8.
   f. No, because the sum of the digits is 59, which is not divisible by 9.
   g. No, because the units digit is not 0.
   h. Yes, because $(3 + 5 + 6 + 9 + 7 + 5) - (8 + 4 + 3 + 2 + 7) = 35 - 24 = 11$ and 11 is divisible by 11.

NOW TRY THIS 4-5

> Fill in the following blanks so that the number is divisible by 9. List all possibilities.
> 12,506,5_ _.

PROBLEM SOLVING   ### A Mistake in the Inventory

A class from Washington School visited a neighborhood cannery warehouse. The warehouse manager told the class that there were 11,368 cans of juice in the inventory and that the cans were packed in boxes of 6 or 24, depending on the size of the can. One of the students, Sam, thought for a moment and announced that there was a mistake in the inventory. Is Sam's statement correct? Why or why not?

Understanding the Problem   The problem is to determine if the manager's inventory of 11,368 cans was correct. To solve the problem, we must assume there are no partial boxes of cans; that is, a box must contain exactly 6 or exactly 24 cans of juice.

Devising a Plan   We know that the boxes contain either 6 cans or 24 cans, but we do not know how many boxes of each type there are. One strategy for solving this problem is to *find an equation* that involves the total number of cans in all the boxes.

The total number of cans, 11,368, equals the number of cans in all the 6-can boxes plus the number of cans in all the 24-can boxes. If there are n boxes containing 6 cans each, there are $6n$ cans altogether in those boxes. Similarly, if there are m boxes with 24 cans each, those boxes contain a total of $24m$ cans. Because the total was reported to be 11,368 cans, we have the equation $6n + 24m = 11,368$. Sam claimed that $6n + 24m \neq 11,368$.

One way to show that $6n + 24m \neq 11,368$ is to show that $6n + 24m$ and 11,368 do not have the same divisors. Both $6n$ and $24m$ are divisible by 6. This implies that $6n + 24m$ must be divisible by 6. If 11,368 is not divisible by 6, then Sam is correct.

Carrying Out the Plan   The divisibility test for 6 states that a number is divisible by 6 if, and only if, the number is divisible by both 2 and 3. Because 11,368 is an even number, it is divisible by 2. Is it divisible by 3?

The divisibility test for 3 states that a number is divisible by 3 if, and only if, the sum of the digits in the number is divisible by 3. We see that $1 + 1 + 3 + 6 + 8 = 19$, which is not divisible by 3, so 11,368 is not divisible by 3. Hence, Sam is correct.

Looking Back   Suppose 11,368 had been divisible by 6. Would that have implied that the manager was correct? The answer is no; it would have implied only that we would have to change our approach to the problem.

As a further Looking Back activity, suppose that, given different data, the manager is correct. Can we determine values for m and n? In fact, this can be done. If a computer is available, a program can be written to determine all possible natural-number values of m and n.

HISTORICAL NOTE

A modern mathematician who worked in the area of number theory was American Julia Robinson (1919–1985). Robinson's work with the Russian mathematician Yuri Matijaseviĉ on Diophantine equations led directly to the solution of the tenth of the famous set of 23 problems the German mathematician David Hilbert posed. Robinson was the first woman mathematician to be elected to the National Academy of Sciences and the first woman president of the American Mathematical Society. She died of leukemia at the age of sixty-five.

BRAIN
T E A S E R

The following is an argument to show that an ant weighs as much as an elephant. What is wrong?

Let e be the weight of the elephant and a the weight of the ant. Let $e - a = d$. Consequently, $e = a + d$. Multiply each side of $e = a + d$ by $e - a$. Then simplify.

$$e(e - a) = (a + d)(e - a)$$
$$e^2 - ea = ae + de - a^2 - da$$
$$e^2 - ea - de = ae - a^2 - da$$
$$e(e - a - d) = a(e - a - d)$$
$$e = a$$

Thus the weight of the elephant equals the weight of the ant.

O N G O I N G   A S S E S S M E N T   4 - 3

1. Classify each of the following as true or false. If false, tell why.
   a. 6 is a factor of 30.　　b. 6 is a divisor of 30.
   c. 6|30.　　　　　　　　d. 30 is divisible by 6.
   e. 30 is a multiple of 6.　f. 6 is a multiple of 30.

2. Using divisibility tests, answer each of the following:
   a. There are 1379 children signed up to play in a baseball league. If exactly 9 players are to be placed on each team, will any team be short of players?
   b. A forester has 43,682 seedlings to be planted. Can these be planted in an equal number of rows with 11 seedlings in each row?
   c. There are 261 students to be assigned to 9 teachers so that each teacher has the same number of students. Is this possible?
   d. Six friends win with a lottery ticket. The payoff is $242,800. Can the money be divided evenly?
   e. Jack owes $7812 on a new car. Can this amount be paid in 12 equal monthly installments?

3. Without using a calculator, test each of the following numbers for divisibility by 2, 3, 4, 5, 6, 8, 9, 10, and 11:
   a. 746,988
   b. 81,342
   c. 15,810
   d. 4,201,012
   e. 1,001
   f. 10,001

4. Determine each of the following without actually performing the division. Explain how you did it in each case.
   a. Is 34,015 divisible by 17?
   b. Is 34,051 divisible by 17?
   c. Is 19,031 divisible by 19?
   d. Is $2 \cdot 3 \cdot 5 \cdot 7$ divisible by 5?
   e. Is $(2 \cdot 3 \cdot 5 \cdot 7) + 1$ divisible by 5?

5. Justify each of the given statements, assuming that a, b, and c are integers. If a statement cannot be justified by one of the theorems in this section, answer "none."
   a. $4|20$ implies $4|113 \cdot 20$.
   b. $4|100$ and $4 \nmid 13$ imply $4 \nmid (100 + 13)$.
   c. $4|100$ and $4 \nmid 13$ imply $4 \nmid 1300$.
   d. $3|(a + b)$ and $3 \nmid c$ imply $3 \nmid (a + b + c)$.
   e. $3|a$ implies $3|a^2$.

6. Classify each of the following as true or false:
   a. If every digit of a number is divisible by 3, the number itself is divisible by 3.
   b. If a number is divisible by 3, then every digit of the number is divisible by 3.
   c. A number is divisible by 3 if, and only if, every digit of the number is divisible by 3.
   d. If a number is divisible by 6, then it is divisible by 2 and by 3.
   e. If a number is divisible by 2 and 3, then it is divisible by 6.
   f. If a number is divisible by 2 and 4, then it is divisible by 8.
   g. If a number is divisible by 8, then it is divisible by 2 and 4.

7. Classify each of the statements in problem 6 as sometimes, always, or never true.

8. Devise a test for divisibility by each of the following numbers:
   a. 16
   b. 25

9. When the two missing digits in the following number are replaced, the number is divisible by 99. What is the number?

85_ _1

10. Fill each of the following blanks with the greatest digit that makes the statement true:
    a. $3|74\_$
    b. $9|83\_45$
    c. $11|6\_55$

11. Place a digit in the square, if possible, so that the number

    $$527,4\square2$$

    is divisible by
    a. 2   b. 3
    c. 4   d. 9
    e. 11

12. The bookstore marked some notepads down from $2.00 but still kept the price over $1.00. It sold all of them. The total amount of money from the sale of the pads was $31.45. How many notepads were sold?

13. A group of people ordered No-Cal candy bars. The bill was $2.09. If the original price of each was 12¢ but the price has been inflated, how much does each cost?

14. Leap years occur in years that are divisible by 4. However, if the year ends in two zeros, in order for the year to be a leap year, it must be divisible by 400. Determine which of the following are leap years:
    a. 1776   b. 1986   c. 2000   d. 2024

15. In a football game, a touchdown with an extra point is worth 7 points and a field goal is worth 3 points. Suppose that in a game the only scoring done by teams are touchdowns with extra points and field goals.
    a. Which of the scores 1 to 25 are impossible for a team to score?
    b. List all possible ways for a team to score 40 points.
    c. A team scored 57 points with 6 touchdowns and 6 extra points. How many field goals did the team score?

16. Complete the following table where n is the given integer.

	n	Remainder when n is divided by 9	Sum of the digits of n	Remainder when the sum of the digits of n is divided by 9
a.	31			
b.	143			
c.	345			
d.	2987			
e.	7652			

     f. Make a conjecture about the remainder and the sum of the digits in an integer when it is divided by 9.

17. A test for checking computations is called *casting out nines*. Consider the sum $193 + 24 + 786 = 1003$. The remainders when 193, 24, and 786 are divided by 9 are 4, 6,

and 3, respectively. The sum of the remainders, 13, has a remainder of 4 when divided by 9, as does 1003. Checking the remainders in this manner provided a quasi-check for the computation. Find the following sums and use casting out nines to check your sums:
    a. $12,343 + 4546 + 56$
    b. $987 + 456 + 8765$
    c. $10,034 + 3004 + 400 + 20$
    d. Will this check always work for addition? Give an example to illustrate your answer.
    e. Try the check on the subtraction, $1003 - 46$.
    f. Try the check on the multiplication, $345 \cdot 56$.
    g. Would it make sense to try the check on division? Why or why not?

18. a. If 21 divides n, what other natural numbers divide n? Why?
    b. If 16 divides n, what other natural numbers divide n? Why?

19. A palindrome is a number that reads the same forward as backward.
    a. Check the following four-digit palindromes for divisibility by 11:
       i. 4554   ii. 9339   iii. 2002   iv. 2222
    b. Are all four-digit palindromes divisible by 11? Why or why not?
    c. Are all five-digit palindromes divisible by 11? Why or why not?
    d. Are all six-digit palindromes divisible by 11? Why or why not?

20. The numbers 5872 and 2785 are a palindromic pair of numbers because reversing the order of the digits of one number gives the other number. Explain why in a palindromic pair, if one number is divisible by 3, then so is the other.

21. The numbers x and y are divisible by 5.
    a. Is the sum of x and y divisible by 5? Why?
    b. Is the difference of x and y divisible by 5? Why?
    c. Is the product of x and y divisible by 5? Why?
    d. Is the quotient of x and y divisible by 5? Why?

22. Using only divisibility tests, explain whether 6,868,395 is divisible by 15.

23. Classify each of the following as true or false, assuming that $a, b, c,$ and d are integers and $d \neq 0$. If a statement is false, give a counterexample.
    a. If $d|(a + b)$, then $d|a$ and $d|b$.
    b. If $d|(a + b)$, then $d|a$ or $d|b$.
    c. If $d|ab$, then $d|a$ or $d|b$.
    d. If $ab|c$, $a \neq 0$, and $b \neq 0$, then $a|c$ and $b|c$.
    e. If $a|b$ and $b|a$, then $a = b$.
    f. If $d|a$ and $d|b$, then $d|(ax + by)$ for any integers x and y.
    g. If $d \nmid a$ and $d \nmid b$, then $d \nmid (a + b)$.
    h. If $d|a^2$, then $d|a$.
    i. If $d \nmid a$, then $d \nmid a^2$.

★**24.** Prove Theorem 4-2(b).

25. Prove the test for divisibility by 9 for any five-digit number.

26. **a.** Choose a two-digit number such that the number in the tens place is one greater than the number in the units place. Reverse the digits in your number, and subtract this number from your original number; for example, $87 - 78 = 9$. Make a conjecture concerning the results of performing these kinds of operations.

b. Choose any two-digit number such that the number in the tens place is two greater than the number in the units place. Reverse the digits in your number, and subtract this number from your original number; for example, $31 - 13 = 18$. Make a conjecture concerning the results of performing these kinds of operations.

★**c.** Prove that for any two-digit number, if the digits are reversed and the numbers subtracted, the difference is a multiple of 9.

d. Investigate what happens whenever two-digit numbers with equal digit sums are subtracted; for example, $62 - 35 = 27$.

Communication

27. A customer wants to mail a package. The postal clerk determines the cost of the package to be $18.95, but only 6¢ and 9¢ stamps are available. Can the available stamps be used for the exact amount of postage for the package? Why or why not?

28. **a.** Jim uses his calculator to see if a number n having eight or fewer digits is divisible by a number d. He finds that $n \div d$ has a display of 32. Does $d \,|\, n$? Why?

b. If $n \div d$ gives a display of 16.8, does $d \,|\, n$? Why?

29. Is the area of each of the following rectangles divisible by 4? Explain why or why not.

a.

52,832 cm

324,518 cm

b.

52,834 cm

324,514 cm

30. Can you find three consecutive natural numbers none of which is divisible by 3? Explain your answer.

31. Answer each of the following and justify your answers.

a. If a number is not divisible by 5, can it be divisible by 10?

b. If a number is not divisible by 10, can it be divisible by 5?

32. A number in which each digit except 0 appears exactly 3 times is divisible by 3. For example, 777,555,222 and 414,143,313 are divisible by 3. Explain why this statement is true.

33. Enter any three-digit number on the calculator; for example, enter 243. Repeat it: 243,243. Divide by 7. Divide by 11. Divide by 13. What is the answer? Try it again with any other three-digit number. Will this always work? Why?

34. Alexa claims that she can justify the divisibility test by 11. She says: *I noticed that each even power of 10 can be written as a multiple of 11 plus 1 and every odd power of 10 can be written as a multiple of 11 minus 1. In fact:*

$$10 = 11 - 1$$
$$10^2 = 99 + 1 = 9 \cdot 11 + 1$$
$$10^3 = 10 \cdot 10^2 = 10(9 \cdot 11 + 1) = 90 \cdot 11 + 10$$
$$= 90 \cdot 11 + 11 - 1 = 91 \cdot 11 - 1$$
$$10^4 = 10^2 \cdot 10^2 = 100(9 \cdot 11 + 1)$$
$$= 900 \cdot 11 + 9 \cdot 11 + 1 = 909 \cdot 11 + 1$$

and so on.

Now I look at a four-digit number abcd *and proceed as in the divisibility by 3. I collect the parts that are divisible by 11 regardless of what the digits are and put together the rest, which is*

$$d - c + b - a.$$

Complete the details of Alexa's argument and justify the test for divisibility by 11.

Open-Ended

35. A breakfast food company had a contest in which numbers were placed in breakfast food boxes. A prize of $1000 was awarded to anyone who could collect numbers whose sum was 100. The company had thousands of cards made with the following numbers on them:

3 12 15 18 27 33 45 51 66 75 84 90

a. If the company did not make any more cards, is there a winning combination?

b. If the company is going to add one more number to the list and they want to make sure the contest has at most 1000 winners, suggest a strategy for them to use.

Cooperative Learning

36. In your group, discuss the value of teaching various divisibility tests in middle school. If a teacher decides to discuss the various tests, how should they be introduced?

Review Problems

37. Find all integers x (if possible) that make each of the following true:

a. $3(^-x) = 6$

b. $(^-2)|x| = 6$

c. $(^-x) \div 0 = {}^-1$

d. $^-(x - 1) = 1 - x$

e. $^-|^-x| = 5$

f. $^-x < 0$

38. Simplify each of the following.
    a. $3x - (1 - 2x)$
    b. $(^-2x)^2 - 3x^2$
    c. $y - x - 2(y - x)$
    d. $(x - 1)^2 - x^2 + 2x$

39. Consider the function $y = f(x) = {}^-2x - 3$ whose domain is the set of integers and answer the following questions.
    a. Find $f(^-5)$.
    b. For what value of x will the value of y be 17?
    c. Is 2 a possible output? Explain your answer.
    d. Find all possible outputs.

40. Jerry decides to start a juice bar. He figures out that his startup cost will be $1,800 (to buy the equipment and pay for permits.) If he charges $2 for each cup of juice, answer the following.
    a. What will his profit (or loss) be after he sells 700 cups of juice?
    b. If he sells x cups of juice and his profit is $P(x)$, write an equation that will show $P(x)$ as a function of x (in terms of x).
    c. What is Jerry's *break-even point*; that is, how many cups of juice must he sell before he makes a profit?

BRAIN
T E A S E R

Dee finds that she has an extraordinary social security number. Its nine digits contain all the numbers from 1 through 9. They also form a number with the following characteristics: when read from left to right, its first two digits form a number divisible by 2, its first three digits form a number divisible by 3, its first four digits form a number divisible by 4, and so on, until the complete number is divisible by 9. What is Dee's social security number?

4-4 Prime and Composite Numbers

One method used in elementary schools to determine the positive divisors of a number is to use squares of paper and to represent the number as a rectangle. Such a rectangle resembles a candy bar formed with small squares. The dimensions of the rectangle are divisors of the number. For example, Figure 4-19 shows rectangles to represent 12.

FIGURE 4-19

FIGURE 4-20

As the figure shows, the number 12 has six positive divisors: 1, 2, 3, 4, 6, and 12. If rectangles were used to find the divisors of 7, then we would find only a 1×7 rectangle, as Figure 4-20 shows. Thus 7 has exactly two divisors: 1 and 7.

To illustrate further the number of divisors of a number, we construct Table 4-1. Below each number listed across the top, we identify numbers less than or equal to 37 that have that number of positive divisors. For example, 12 is in the 6 column because it has six positive divisors, and 7 is in the 2 column because it has only two positive divisors.

Table 4-1 Number of Factors

1	2	3	4	5	6	7	8	9
1	2	4	6	16	12		24	36
	3	9	8		18		30	
	5	25	10		20			
	7		14		28			
	11		15		32			
	13		21					
	17		22					
	19		26					
	23		27					
	29		33					
	31		34					
	37		35					

NOW TRY THIS 4-6

a. What patterns do you see forming in Table 4-1?

b. Will there be other entries in the 1 column? Why?

c. What are the next three numbers in the 3 column?

d. Find an entry for the 7 column.

e. What kinds of numbers have an odd number of factors? Why?

The numbers in the 2 column in Table 4-1 are of particular importance. Notice that they have exactly two positive divisors, namely, 1 and themselves. Any positive integer with exactly two distinct, positive divisors is a *prime number*, or a **prime**. Any integer greater than 1 that has a positive factor other than 1 and itself is a *composite number*, or a **composite**. For example, 4, 6, and 16 are composites because they have positive factors other than 1 and themselves. The number 1 has only one positive factor, so it is neither prime nor composite. From the 2 column in Table 4-1, we see that the first 12 primes are 2, 3, 5, 7, 11, 13, 17, 19, 23, 29, 31, and 37. Other patterns in the table are explored in the problem set.

prime
composite

EXAMPLE 4-23

Show that the following numbers are composite:

a. 1564   b. 2781   c. 1001   d. $3 \cdot 5 \cdot 7 \cdot 11 \cdot 13 + 1$

Solution a. Since $2|4$, 1564 is divisible by 2 and is composite.

b. Since $3|(2 + 7 + 8 + 1)$, 2781 is divisible by 3 and is composite.

c. Since $11|[(1 + 0) - (0 + 1)]$, 1001 is divisible by 11 and is composite.

d. Because a product of odd numbers is odd (why?), $3 \cdot 5 \cdot 7 \cdot 11 \cdot 13$ is odd. If we add 1 to an odd number, the sum is even. An even number (other than 2) has a factor of 2 and is therefore composite.

Prime Factorization

Composite numbers can be expressed as products of two or more whole numbers greater than 1. For example, $18 = 2 \cdot 9$, $18 = 3 \cdot 6$, or $18 = 2 \cdot 3 \cdot 3$. Each expression of 18 as a product of factors is a **factorization**.

factorization

prime factorization

A factorization containing only prime numbers is a **prime factorization**. To find a prime factorization of a given composite number, first rewrite the number as a product of two smaller numbers greater than 1. Continue the process, factoring the lesser numbers until all factors are primes. For example, consider 260:

$$260 = 26 \cdot 10 = 2 \cdot 13 \cdot 2 \cdot 5 = 2 \cdot 2 \cdot 5 \cdot 13 = 2^2 \cdot 5 \cdot 13.$$

factor tree

The procedure for finding a prime factorization of a number can be organized using a **factor tree**, as Figure 4-21(a) demonstrates. The last branches of the tree display the prime factors of 260.

A second way to factor 260 is shown in Figure 4-21(b). The two trees produce the same prime factorization, except for the order in which the primes appear in the products.

FIGURE 4-21

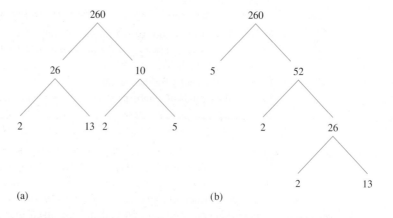

(a)   (b)

The *Fundamental Theorem of Arithmetic*, or the *Unique Factorization Theorem*, states that in general, if order is disregarded, the prime factorization of a number is unique.

> ### Theorem 4-3

Fundamental Theorem of Arithmetic   Each composite number can be written as a product of primes in one, and only one, way except for the order of the prime factors in the product.

The Fundamental Theorem of Arithmetic assures us that once we find a prime factorization of a number, a different prime factorization of the same number cannot be found. For example, consider 260. We start with the least prime, 2, and see whether it divides 260. If not, we try the next greater prime and check for divisibility by this prime. Once we find a prime that divides the number in question, we must find the quotient of the number divided by the prime. This step in the prime factorization of 260 is shown in Figure 4-22(a). Next we check whether the prime divides the quotient. If so, we repeat the process; if not, we try the next greater prime, 3, and check to see if it divides the quotient. We see that 260 divided by 2 yields 130, as shown in Figure 4-22(b). We continue the procedure, using greater primes, until a quotient of 1 is reached. The original number is the product of all the prime divisors used. The complete procedure for 260 is shown in Figure 4-22(c). An alternative form is shown in Figure 4-22(d).

FIGURE 4-22

$$
\begin{array}{r|l}
2 & 260 \\ \hline
  & 130
\end{array}
\qquad
\begin{array}{r|l}
2 & 260 \\ \hline
2 & 130 \\ \hline
  & 65
\end{array}
\qquad
\begin{array}{r|l}
2 & 260 \\ \hline
2 & 130 \\ \hline
5 & 65 \\ \hline
13 & 13 \\ \hline
 & 1
\end{array}
\qquad
\begin{array}{r|l}
 & 260 \\ \hline
2 & 130 \\ \hline
2 & 65 \\ \hline
5 & 13 \\ \hline
13 & 1
\end{array}
$$

(a)   (b)   (c)   (d) Alternative form

The primes in the prime factorization of a number are typically listed in increasing order from left to right and if a prime appears in a product more than once, exponential notation is used. Thus the factorization of 260 is written as $2^2 \cdot 5 \cdot 13$.

Prime factorization is demonstrated in the partial student page on page 230. Read the page and answer problem 6.

NOW TRY THIS 4-7

Colored rods are used in the elementary school classroom to teach many concepts. The rods vary in length from 1 cm to 10 cm. Various lengths have colors associated with them. For example, the 5 rod is yellow. Rods are shown in Figure 4-23 with their appropriate colors. A row with all the same color rods is called a one-color train.

a. What rods can be used to form a one-color train for 18?
b. What one-color trains are possible for 24?
c. How many one-color trains of 2 or more rods are possible for each prime number?
d. If a number can be represented by an all-red train, an all-green train, and an all-yellow train, what is the least number of factors it must have? What are they?

FIGURE 4-23

Sample School Book Page:
PRIME FACTORIZATION

Every human being has a unique fingerprint. Similarly, every composite number has a unique "factorprint." It is called the **prime factorization**. It's the set of prime numbers whose product equals the number.

You can use a "factor tree" to find a prime factorization. Find two numbers whose product equals the original number and write them below. If a number is prime, circle it. If a number is composite, continue to break it apart until you only have prime numbers left. Rewrite the prime factors at the bottom from least to greatest.

$$30 = 2 \times 3 \times 5$$

Example

Find the prime factorization of 630.

Use the divisibility rules to find factors and draw "branches."

630 ends in 0, so it's divisible by 10.
$630 \div 10 = 63$

Circle prime factors when you find them.

Stop when the "leaves" at ends of branches are all circled.

The prime factorization is $2 \times 3 \times 3 \times 5 \times 7$, or $2 \times 3^2 \times 5 \times 7$.

Remember

3^2 is in exponential notation. It means 3×3. The exponent, in this case 2, tells you how many times the base, in this case 3, is used as a factor.

Check

Find the prime factorization of each number.

1. 12   **2.** 20   **3.** 36   **4.** 45   **5.** 210

6. Reasoning Rachel says 121 is prime, since it is odd and she can't find a number that divides into it without a remainder. Is she right? Explain.

Source: Scott Foresman–Addison Wesley Math 2002, Grade 6 (p. 271).

Number of Divisors

How many positive divisors does 24 have? Note that the question asks for the number of divisors, not just prime divisors. To aid in the listing, we group divisors as follows:

$$1, 2, 3, 4, 6, 8, 12, 24$$

The divisors of 24 occur in pairs, where the product of the divisors in each pair is 24. If 3 is a divisor of 24, then 24/3, or 8, is also a divisor of 24. In general, if a natural number k is a divisor of 24, then $24/k$ is also a divisor of 24.

Another way to think of the number of divisors of 24 is to consider the prime factorization $24 = 2^3 \cdot 3$. The divisors of 2^3 are 2^0, 2^1, 2^2, and 2^3. The divisors of 3 are 3^0 and 3^1. We know that 2^3 has $(3 + 1)$, or 4, divisors and 3^1 has $(1 + 1)$, or 2, divisors. Because each divisor of 24 is the product of a divisor of 2^3 and a divisor of 3^1, then we use the Fundamental Counting Principle (discussed in Section 2-1) to conclude that 24 has $4 \cdot 2$, or 8, divisors. This is summarized in Table 4-2.

Table 4-2

Divisors of 2^3	$2^0 = 1$	$2^1 = 2$	$2^2 = 4$	$2^3 = 8$
Divisors of 3^1	$3^0 = 1$	$3^1 = 3$		
Divisors of $3^1 \cdot$ Divisors of 2^3 (Divisors of 24)	$3^0 \cdot 2^0 = 1$ $3^1 \cdot 2^0 = 3$	$3^0 \cdot 2^1 = 2$ $3^1 \cdot 2^1 = 6$	$3^0 \cdot 2^2 = 4$ $3^1 \cdot 2^2 = 12$	$3^0 \cdot 2^3 = 8$ $3^1 \cdot 2^3 = 24$

This discussion can be generalized as follows: If p is any prime and n is any natural number, then the divisors of p^n are $p^0, p^1, p^2, p^3, \ldots, p^n$. Therefore there are $(n + 1)$ divisors of p^n. Now, using the Fundamental Counting Principle, we can find the number of divisors of any number whose prime factorization is known. For example, if p and q are different primes, then we use the Fundamental Counting Principle to find that $p^n q^m$ will have $(n + 1)(m + 1)$ divisors.

E X A M P L E
4-24

Find the number of divisors of each of the following:

a. 1,000,000   **b.** 210^{10}

Solution   **a.** We first find the prime factorization of 1,000,000.

$$1,000,000 = 10^6 = (2 \cdot 5)^6 = (2 \cdot 5)(2 \cdot 5)(2 \cdot 5)(2 \cdot 5)(2 \cdot 5)(2 \cdot 5)$$
$$= (2 \cdot 2 \cdot 2 \cdot 2 \cdot 2 \cdot 2) \cdot (5 \cdot 5 \cdot 5 \cdot 5 \cdot 5 \cdot 5)$$
$$= 2^6 \cdot 5^6$$

Because 2^6 has $6 + 1$ divisors and 5^6 has $6 + 1$ divisors, then by the Fundamental Counting Principle $2^6 \cdot 5^6$ has $(6 + 1)(6 + 1)$, or 49, divisors.

b. The prime factorization of 210 is

$$210 = 21 \cdot 10 = 3 \cdot 7 \cdot 2 \cdot 5 = 2 \cdot 3 \cdot 5 \cdot 7,$$
$$210^{10} = (2 \cdot 3 \cdot 5 \cdot 7)^{10} = 2^{10} \cdot 3^{10} \cdot 5^{10} \cdot 7^{10}.$$

By the Fundamental Counting Principle, the number of divisors of 210^{10} is $(10 + 1)(10 + 1)(10 + 1)(10 + 1)$, or 11^4, or 14,641.

NOW TRY THIS 4-8

Is it necessary to divide 97 by 2, 3, 4, 5, 6, . . . , 96 to check if it is prime? Consider the following:

a. If 2 is not a divisor of 97, could any multiple of 2 be a divisor of 97? Why?

b. If 3 is not a divisor of 97, what other numbers could not be divisors of 97? Why?

c. If 5 is not a divisor of 97, what other numbers could not be divisors of 97? Why?

d. If 7 is not a divisor of 97, what other numbers could not be divisors of 97?

e. Conjecture what numbers we have to check for divisibility in order to determine if 97 is prime.

Determining if a Number Is Prime

As depicted in the following cartoon by Sidney Harris, prime numbers have fascinated people of various backgrounds.

In Now Try This 4-8, you might have found that to determine if a number is prime, you must check only divisibility by prime numbers less than the given number. (Why?) However, do we need to check all the primes less than the number? Suppose we want to check if 97 is prime and we find that 2, 3, 5, and 7 do not divide 97. Could a greater prime divide 97? If p is a prime greater than 7, then $p \geq 11$. If $p|97$, then $97/p$ also divides 97. However, because $p > 11$ then $97/p$ must be less than 10 and hence cannot divide 97. (Why?) So we see that there is no need to check for divisibility by numbers other than 2, 3, 5, and 7. These ideas are generalized in the following theorems.

> ### Theorem 4-4

If d is a divisor of n, then $\dfrac{n}{d}$ is also a divisor of n.

Suppose that p is the *least* divisor of n (greater than 1). Such a divisor must be prime (why?). Then by Theorem 4-4, n/p is also a divisor of n, and because p is the least divisor of n, then $p \leq n/p$. If $p \leq n/p$, then $p^2 \leq n$. This idea is summarized in the following theorem.

> ### Theorem 4-5

If n is composite, then n has a prime factor p such that $p^2 \leq n$.

Theorem 4-5 can be used to help determine whether a given number is prime or composite. For example, consider the number 109. If 109 is composite, it must have a prime divisor p such that $p^2 \leq 109$. The primes whose squares do not exceed 109 are 2, 3, 5, and 7. Mentally, we can see that $2 \nmid 109$, $3 \nmid 109$, $5 \nmid 109$, and $7 \nmid 109$. Hence, 109 is prime. The argument used leads to the following theorem.

> ### Theorem 4-6

If n is an integer greater than 1 and not divisible by any prime p, such that $p^2 \leq n$, then n is prime.

REMARK Because $p^2 \leq n$ implies that $p \leq \sqrt{n}$, Theorem 4-6 says that to determine if a number n is prime, it is enough to check if any prime less than or equal to $\sqrt{n}$ is a divisor of n.

a. Is 397 composite or prime?   **b.** Is 91 composite or prime?

Solution   **a.** The possible primes p such that $p^2 \leq 397$ are 2, 3, 5, 7, 11, 13, 17, and 19. Because $2 \nmid 397$, $3 \nmid 397$, $5 \nmid 397$, $7 \nmid 397$, $11 \nmid 397$, $13 \nmid 397$, $17 \nmid 397$, and $19 \nmid 397$, the number 397 is prime.

   b. The possible primes p such that $p^2 \leq 91$ are 2, 3, 5, and 7. Because 91 is divisible by 7, it is composite.

More About Primes

One way to find all the primes less than a given number is to use the *Sieve of Eratosthenes*, named after the Greek mathematician Eratosthenes (276–194 or 192 B.C.). If all the natural numbers greater than 1 are considered (or placed in the sieve), the numbers that are not prime are methodically crossed out (or drop through the holes of the sieve). The remaining numbers are prime. The following student page illustrates this process. Before reading on, answer questions 1, 2, and 3 on the student page.

Notice that we can stop crossing out multiples of primes after all the multiples of 5 and all the multiples of 7 have been crossed out because 7 is the greatest prime whose square, 49, is less than 100. All the numbers remaining in the list and not crossed out are prime.

Eratosthenes (276–194 B.C.), a Greek scholar, was born in Cyrene, a Greek colony in North Africa, but spent most of his life in Alexandria as the chief librarian at the museum there. He wrote treatises on a variety of topics including geography, philosophy, astronomy, poetry, and mathematics. In his work *Geographica* he gave arguments for the spherical shape of the earth. Today Eratosthenes is best known for his "sieve"—a systematic procedure for isolating the prime numbers, and for a simple method for calculating the circumference of the earth.

Primes have been treasured since antiquity, as the following cartoon depicts.

There are infinitely many whole numbers, infinitely many odd whole numbers, and infinitely many even whole numbers. Are there infinitely many primes? Because prime numbers do not appear in any known pattern, the answer to this question is not obvious. Euclid was the first to prove that there are infinitely many primes.

Sample School Book Page:
PRIME AND COMPOSITE NUMBERS

Chapter 4
Lesson
14

Exploring Prime and Composite Numbers

Problem Solving Connection

■ Look for a Pattern

■ Use Logical Reasoning

Materials
hundred chart

Vocabulary

prime number
whole number with exactly two different factors

composite number
whole number greater than 1 that is not prime

Explore • • • • • • • • • • • •

Eratosthenes (*ehr uh TAHS thuh neez*) was a mathematician from Cyrene (now known as Libya) who lived about 2,200 years ago. He studied **prime numbers**. The number 3 is an example of a prime number. It has only two factors, 1 and 3.

Composite numbers have more than two factors. An example of a composite number is 8. Its factors are 1, 2, 4, and 8.

Cyrene was the capital of ancient Cyrenaica.

1×8 • • • • • • • • 2×4 • • • •
                                                                    • • • •

You tell whether a number is prime by testing possible factors. There are no other factors for 7 besides 7 and 1. So, 7 is a prime number.

1×7 • • • • • • •

Eratosthenes' Sieve is a process that "strains" out composite numbers and leaves prime numbers behind. Use it to find the prime numbers between 1 and 100.

Did You Know?
A computer has been used to find a prime number that, if printed in a newspaper, would fill 12 pages.

Work Together

1. Use a hundred chart. Follow the directions to cross out composite numbers and circle prime numbers.

   a. Cross out 1. It has only 1 factor.

   b. Circle 2, the least prime number. Cross out all numbers divisible by 2.

   c. Repeat this step with 3, the next prime number.

2. Continue this process until you reach 100.

3. List all of the circled numbers. There should be 25.

What pattern can you see in the list of prime numbers?

Source: Scott Foresman–Addison Wesley Math, Grade 5 (p. 204).

Mathematicians have long looked for a formula that produces only primes, but no one has found one. One result was the expression $n^2 - n + 41$, where n is a whole number. Substituting 0, 1, 2, 3, . . . , 40 for n in the expression always results in a prime number. However, substituting 41 for n gives $41^2 - 41 + 41$, or 41^2, a composite number.

In 1998 Roland Clarkson, a 19-year-old student at California State University, showed that $2^{3021377} - 1$ is prime. The number has 909,526 digits. The full decimal expansion of the number would fill several hundred pages. Since then at least two more large primes have been discovered: $2^{6972593} - 1$ and $2^{13466917} - 1$. These are examples of *Mersenne primes*. A Mersenne prime, named after the French monk Marin Mersenne (1588–1648), is a prime of the form $2^n - 1$, where n is prime.

Searching for large primes has led to advances in *distributed computing*, that is, using the Internet to use the unused computing power of great numbers of computers. Searching for Mersenne primes has been used as a test for computer hardware.

Another type of interesting prime is a *Sophie Germain prime*, which is an odd prime p for which $2p + 1$ is also a prime. Notice that $p = 3$ is a Sophie Germain prime, since $2 \cdot 3 + 1$, or 7, is also a prime. Check that 5, 11, and 23 are also such primes. The primes were named after the French mathematician Sophie Germain. In 2003 the greatest Sophie Germain prime discovered had 34,547 digits.

H I S T O R I C A L
N O T E

Sophie Germain (1776–1831) was born in Paris and grew up during the French Revolution. She wanted to study at the prestigious École Polytechnique but women were not allowed as students. Consequently, she studied from lecture notes and Gauss's monograph on number theory. In addition to her work in number theory, she made major contributions to the mathematical theory of elasticity, for which she was awarded the prize of the French Academy of Sciences. Germain's work was highly regarded by Gauss, who recommended her for an honorary degree from the University of Göttingen. She died before the degree could be awarded.

PROBLEM SOLVING   **How Many Bears?**

A large toy store carries one kind of stuffed bear. On Monday the store sold a certain number of the stuffed bears for a total of $1,843 and on Tuesday, without changing the price, the store sold a certain number of the stuffed bears for a total of $1,957. How many toy bears were sold each day if the price of each bear is a whole number and greater than $1?

Understanding the Problem   One day a store sold a number of stuffed bears for $1,843 and on the next day a number of them for a total of $1,957. We need to find the number of bears sold on each day.

Devising a Plan   If x bears were sold the first day and y bears the second day, and if the price of each bear was c dollars, we would have $cx = 1843$ and $cy = 1957$. Thus 1843 and 1957 should have a common factor—the price c. We could factor each number and find the possible factors. If the problem is to have a unique solution, the two numbers should have only one common factor other than 1. Any common factor of 1957 and 1843 will also be a factor of $1957 - 1843 = 114$ and the factors of 114 are easier to find.

Carrying Out the Plan   We have $114 = 2 \cdot 57 = 2 \cdot 3 \cdot 19$. Thus if 1957 and 1843 have a common prime factor, it must be 2, 3, or 19. But neither 2 nor 3 divides the number, hence the only possible common factor is 19. We divide each number by 19 and find:

$$1843 = 19 \cdot 97.$$
$$1957 = 19 \cdot 103.$$

Notice that neither 97 nor 103 is divisible by 2, 3, 5, or 7. Hence 97 and 103 are primes (why?) and therefore the only common factor (greater than 1) of 1843 and 1957 is 19. Consequently, the price of each bear was $19. The first day 97 bears were sold and the next day 103 bears were sold.

Looking Back   Notice that the problem had a unique solution because the only common factor (greater than 1) of the two numbers was 19. We could create similar problems by having the price of the item be a prime number and the number of items sold each day also be prime numbers. For example, the total sale on the first day could have been $23 \cdot 101$ or $2,323 and on the second day $23 \cdot 107$ or $2,461 (notice that 23, 101, and 107 are prime numbers).

To find a common factor of 1957 and 1843, we found all the common factors of $1957 - 1843 = 114 = 2 \cdot 3 \cdot 19$ and checked which of the factors of the difference was a common factor of the original numbers. We have used the following property: If $d|a$ and $d|b$, then $d|(a - b)$. The property assures us that every common factor of a and b will also be a factor of $a - b$.

HISTORICAL NOTE

During World War II, Alan Turing (1912–1954), Peter Hilton, and other British analysts helped crack the codes developed on the German Enigma cipher machine. In the 1970s, determining large prime numbers became extremely useful in coding and decoding secret messages. In all coding and decoding, the letters of an alphabet correspond in some way to nonnegative integers. A "safe" coding system, in which messages are unintelligible to everyone except the intended receiver, was devised by three Massachusetts Institute of Technology scientists (Ronald Rivest, Adi Shamir, and Leonard Adleman) and is referred to as the RSA (their initials) system. The secret deciphering key consists of two large prime numbers chosen by the user. The enciphering key is the product of these two primes. Because it is extremely difficult and time consuming to factor large numbers, it was practically impossible to recover the deciphering key from a known enciphering key. In 1982, new methods for factoring large numbers were invented, which resulted in the use of even greater primes to prevent the breaking of decoding keys.

ONGOING ASSESSMENT 4-4

1. Find the least positive number that is divisible by three primes.
2. Determine which of the following numbers are primes:
   a. 109
   b. 119
   c. 33
   d. 101
   e. 463
   f. 97
3. Use a factor tree to find the prime factorization for each of the following:
   a. 504
   b. 2475
   c. 11,250

4. a. Fill in the missing numbers in the following factor tree:

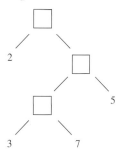

   b. How could you find the top number without finding the other two numbers?

5. What is the greatest prime you must consider to test whether 5669 is prime?

6. a. When the U.S. flag had 48 stars, the stars formed a 6 × 8 rectangular array. In what other rectangular arrays could they have been arranged?

   b. How many rectangular arrays of stars could there be if there were only 47 states?

7. If the Spanish Armada had consisted of 177 galleons, could it have sailed in an equal number of small flotillas? If so, how many ships would have been in each?

8. Suppose the 435 members of the House of Representatives are placed on committees consisting of more than 2 members but fewer than 30 members. Each committee is to have an equal number of members and each member is to be on only one committee.

   a. What size committees are possible?

   b. How many committees are there of each size?

9. Mr. Arboreta wants to plant fruit trees in a rectangular array. For each of the following numbers of trees, find all possible numbers of rows if each row is to have the same number of trees:

   a. 36   b. 28   c. 17   d. 144

10. Find the least number divisible by each natural number less than or equal to 12.

11. Some of the divisors of a locker number are 2, 5, and 9. If there are exactly nine additional divisors, what is the locker number?

12. a. Use the Fundamental Theorem of Arithmetic to justify that if $2|n$ and $3|n$, then $6|n$.

    b. Is it always true that if $a|n$ and $b|n$, then $ab|n^2$? Either prove the statement or give a counterexample.

13. Find the greatest four-digit number that has exactly three factors.

14. Extend the Sieve of Eratosthenes to find all primes less than 200.

15. The prime numbers 11 and 13 are called *twin primes* because they differ by 2. Find all the twin primes less than 200. (The existence of infinitely many twin primes has not been proven.)

16. Show that if 1 were considered a prime, every number would have more than one prime factorization.

17. If $42|n$, what other positive integers divide n?

18. Is it possible to find positive integers x, y, and z such that $2^x \cdot 3^y = 5^z$? Why or why not?

19. It is not known whether there are infinitely many primes in the infinite sequence consisting only of ones: 1, 11, 111, 1111, ... Find infinitely many composite numbers in the sequence.

20. Show that there are infinitely many composite numbers in the arithmetic sequence 1, 5, 9, 13, 17, ...

21. If $2N = 2^6 \cdot 3^5 \cdot 5^4 \cdot 7^3 \cdot 11^7$, explain why $2 \cdot 3 \cdot 5 \cdot 7 \cdot 11$ is a factor of N.

22. Is $3^2 \cdot 2^4$ a factor of $3^4 \cdot 2^7$? Explain why or why not.

23. Explain why each of the following numbers is composite:
    a. $3 \cdot 5 \cdot 7 \cdot 11 \cdot 13$ b. $(3 \cdot 4 \cdot 5 \cdot 6 \cdot 7 \cdot 8) + 2$
    c. $(3 \cdot 5 \cdot 7 \cdot 11 \cdot 13) + 5$
    d. $10! + 7$ (*Note:* $10! = 1 \cdot 2 \cdot 3 \cdot 4 \cdot 5 \cdot 6 \cdot 7 \cdot 8 \cdot 9 \cdot 10$.)
    e. $10! + k$, where $k = 2, 3, 4, 5, 6, 7, 8, 9,$ or 10

24. Explain why $2^3 \cdot 3^2 \cdot 25^3$ is not a prime factorization and find the prime factorization of the number.

25. A prime such as 7331 is a *superprime* because any integers obtained by deleting digits from the right of 7331 are prime; for example, 733, 73, and 7.

    a. For a prime to be a superprime, what digits cannot appear in the number?

    b. Of the digits that can appear in a superprime, what digit cannot be the left-most digit of a superprime?

    c. Find all of the two-digit superprimes.

    d. Find a three-digit superprime.

26. Is the following always true? (Justify your answer) If $m|ab$ then $m|a$ or $m|b$.

27. Find the prime factorizations of each of the following:
    a. $36^{10} \cdot 49^{20} \cdot 6^{15}$
    b. $100^{60} \cdot 300^{40}$
    c. $2 \cdot 3^4 \cdot 5^{110} \cdot 7 + 4 \cdot 3^4 \cdot 5^{110}$
    d. $2 \cdot 3 \cdot 5 \cdot 7 \cdot 11 + 1$

★28. Use the Fundamental Theorem of Arithmetic to justify the following statement for whole numbers a and b greater than 1. If p is prime and $p|ab$, then $p|a$ or $p|b$.

Communication

29. Explain why the product of any three consecutive integers is divisible by 6.

30. Explain why the product of any four consecutive integers is divisible by 24.

31. In order to test for divisibility by 12, one student checked to determine divisibility by 3 and 4, while another checked for divisibility by 2 and 6. Are both students using a correct approach to divisibility by 12? Why or why not?

32. In the Sieve of Eratosthenes for numbers less than 100, explain why, after we cross out all the multiples of 2, 3, 5, and 7, the remaining numbers are primes.

33. Let $M = 2 \cdot 3 \cdot 5 \cdot 7 + 11 \cdot 13 \cdot 17 \cdot 19$. Without multiplying, show that none of the primes less than or equal to 19 divides M.

★34. A woman with a basket of eggs finds that if she removes the eggs from the basket 3 or 5 at a time, there is always 1 egg left. However, if she removes the eggs 7 at a time, there are no eggs left. If the basket holds up to 100 eggs, how many eggs does she have? Explain your reasoning.

35. Explain why, when a number is composite, its least positive divisor, other than 1, must be prime.

36. a. An eighth grader at the Roosevelt Middle School claims that because there are as many even numbers as odd numbers between 1 and 1000, there must be as many numbers that have an even number of divisors

as numbers that have an odd number of divisors between 1 and 1000. Is the student correct? Why or why not?

  b. How many numbers between 1 and 1000 have an odd number of divisors?

★ **37.** Euclid proved that, given any finite list of primes, there exists a prime not in the list. Read the following argument and answer the questions that follow.

Let 2, 3, 5, 7, . . . , p be a list of all the primes less than or equal to a certain prime p. We will show that there exists a prime not on the list. Consider the product

$$2 \cdot 3 \cdot 5 \cdot 7 \cdot \ldots \cdot p.$$

Notice that every prime in our list divides that product. However, if we add 1 to the product, that is, form the number $N = (2 \cdot 3 \cdot 5 \cdot 7 \cdot \ldots \cdot p) + 1$, then none of the primes in the list will divide N. Notice that whether N is prime or composite, some prime q must divide N. Because no prime in our list divides N, q is not one of the primes in our list. Consequently $q > p$. We have shown that there exists a prime greater than p.

  a. Explain why no prime in the list will divide N.

  b. Explain why some prime must divide N.

  c. Someone discovered a prime that has 65,050 digits. How does the above argument assure us that there exists an even larger prime?

  d. Does the above argument show that there are infinitely many primes? Why or why not?

  e. Let $M = 2 \cdot 3 \cdot 5 \cdot 7 \cdot 11 \cdot 13 \cdot 17 \cdot 19 + 1$. Without multiplying, explain why some prime greater than 19 will divide M.

Open-Ended

38. a. In which of the following intervals do you think there are the most primes? Why? Check to see if you were correct.

  i. 0–99   **ii.** 100–199
  iii. 200–299   **iv.** 300–399

  b. What is the longest string of consecutive composite numbers in the intervals?

  c. How many twin primes (see problem 15 above) are there in each interval?

  d. What patterns, if any, do you see for any of the questions above? Predict what might happen in other intervals.

39. One of the recently discovered primes has 65,050 digits. If you wrote this number out, how long a sheet of paper would you need?

40. A number is a *perfect number* if the sum of its factors (other than the number itself) is equal to the number. For example, 6 is a perfect number because its factors sum to 6, that is, $1 + 2 + 3 = 6$. An *abundant number* has factors whose sum is greater than the number itself. A *deficient number* is a number with factors whose sum is less than the number itself.

  a. Classify each of the following numbers as perfect, abundant, or deficient:

  i. 12   **ii.** 28   **iii.** 35

  b. Find at least one more number that falls in each class.

Cooperative Learning

41. A class of 23 students was using square tiles to build rectangular shapes. Each student had more than 1 tile and each had a different number of tiles. Each student was able to build only one shape of rectangle. All tiles had to be used to build a rectangle and the rectangle could not have holes. For example, a 2 by 6 rectangle uses 12 tiles and is considered the same as a 6 by 2 rectangle but is different from a 3 by 4 rectangle. The class did the activity using the least number of tiles. How many tiles did the class use? Divide the work among the members of your group to explore the various rectangles that could be made.

Review Problems

42. Classify the following as true or false:

  a. 11 is a factor of 189.

  b. 1001 is a multiple of 13.

  c. $7 | 1001$ and $7 \nmid 12$ imply $7 \nmid (1001 - 12)$.

  d. If a number is divisible by both 7 and 11, then its prime factorization contains 7 and 11.

43. Test each of the following for divisibility by 2, 3, 4, 5, 6, 7, 8, 9, 10, and 11:

  a. 438,162   **b.** 2,345,678,910

44. Prove that if a number is divisible by 12, then it is divisible by 3.

45. Could $9976 be divided exactly among either 7 or 8 people?

LABORATORY
A C T I V I T Y

In Figure 4-24, a spiral starts with 41 at its center and continues in a counterclockwise direction. Primes are written in and squares that represent composites are shaded. Continue the spiral until you reach the prime 439. Check the primes along the diagonal. Can you find each of the primes from the formula $n^2 + n + 41$ by substituting appropriate values for n?

FIGURE 4-24

421	419							409					
	347						337					331	401
	281		277			271	269						
	349	223							211				
	283	173		167			163						
		131		127						263	397		
		97											
	353	227	71		67	89							
			53										
	229		73	43				157					
431		179	101	(41)									
		137			47			257					
433		181	103		59	61							
	359	233	139		79		83			389			
	293			107	109		113	199	317				
						149	151						
					191	193		197					
		239	241					251					
439						307		311	313				
		367		373			379		383				

Greatest Common Divisor and Least Common Multiple

Consider the following situation:

Two bands are to be combined to march in a parade. A 24-member band will march behind a 30-member band. The combined bands must have the same number of columns and the same number of members in each column. What is the greatest number of columns in which they can march?

The bands could each march in two columns, and we would have the same number of columns, but this does not satisfy the condition of having the greatest number of columns. The number of columns must divide both 24 and 30. (Why?) Numbers that divide both 24 and 30 are 1, 2, 3, and 6. The greatest of these numbers is 6, so the bands should each march in columns of 6. The first band would have 6 columns with 4 members in each column, and the second band would have 6 columns with 5 members in each column.

In this problem, we have found the greatest number that divides both 24 and 30, that is, the **greatest common divisor (GCD)**.

greatest common divisor

> **Definition**

The **greatest common divisor (GCD)** of two integers a and b is the greatest integer that divides both a and b.

We can find the GCD in many ways. We show several ways next.

Colored Rods Model

We can build a model of two or more integers with colored rods to determine the GCD of two positive integers. For example, consider finding the GCD of 6 and 8 using the 6 rod and the 8 rod, as in Figure 4-25.

FIGURE 4-25

(a)   (b)

To find the GCD of 6 and 8, we must find the longest rod such that we can use multiples of that rod to build both the 6 rod and the 8 rod. The 1 rods and the 2 rods can be used to build both the 6 and 8 rods, as shown in Figure 4-25(b); the 3 rods can be used to build the 6 rod but not the 8 rod; the 4 rods can be used to build the 8 rod but not the 6 rod; the 5 rods can be used to build neither; and the 6 rods cannot be used to build the 8 rod. Therefore GCD(6,8) = 2.

NOW TRY THIS 4-9

> Explain how you could use colored rods to solve the marching bands' problem.

The Intersection-of-Sets Method

In the *intersection-of-sets* method, we list all members of the set of positive divisors of the two integers, then find the set of all *common divisors*, and, finally, pick the *greatest* element in that set. For example, to find the GCD of 20 and 32, denote the sets of divisors of 20 and 32 by D_{20} and D_{32}, respectively.

$$D_{20} = \{1, 2, 4, 5, 10, 20\}.$$
$$D_{32} = \{1, 2, 4, 8, 16, 32\}.$$

The set of all common positive divisors of 20 and 32 is

$$D_{20} \cap D_{32} = \{1, 2, 4\}.$$

Because the greatest number in the set of common positive divisors is 4, the GCD of 20 and 32 is 4, written GCD(20, 32) = 4.

The Prime Factorization Method

The intersection-of-sets method is rather time consuming and tedious if the numbers have many divisors. Another, more efficient, method is the prime factorization method. To find GCD(180, 168), first notice that

$$180 = 2 \cdot 2 \cdot 3 \cdot 3 \cdot 5$$

and
$$168 = 2 \cdot 2 \cdot 2 \cdot 3 \cdot 7.$$

We see that 180 and 168 have two factors of 2 and one of 3 in common. These common primes divide both 180 and 168. In fact, the only numbers other than 1 that divide both 180 and 168 must have no more than two 2s and one 3 and no other prime factors in their prime factorizations. The possible common divisors are 1, 2, 2^2, 3, $2 \cdot 3$, and $2^2 \cdot 3$. Hence, the greatest common divisor of 180 and 168 is $2^2 \cdot 3$. The procedure for finding the GCD of two or more numbers by using the prime factorization method is summarized as follows:

To find the GCD of two or more positive integers, first find the prime factorizations of the given numbers and then identify each common prime factor of the given numbers. The GCD is the product of the common factors, each raised to the lowest power of that prime that occurs in either of the prime factorizations.

If we apply the prime factorization technique to finding GCD(4,9), we see that 4 and 9 have no common prime factors. But that does not mean there is no GCD. We still have 1 as a common divisor, so GCD(4,9) = 1. Numbers, such as 4 and 9, whose GCD is 1, are

relatively prime

relatively prime. Both the intersection-of-sets method and the prime factorization method are found on the student page. (GCF in the student page stands for *Greatest Common Factor* which is the same as GCD.)

E X A M P L E
4-26

Find each of the following:

a. GCD(108, 72)
b. GCD(0, 13)
c. GCD(x, y) if $x = 2^3 \cdot 7^2 \cdot 11 \cdot 13$ and $y = 2 \cdot 7^3 \cdot 13 \cdot 17$
d. GCD(x, y, z) if $z = 2^2 \cdot 7$, using x and y from (c)
e. GCD(x, y) where $x = 5^4 \cdot 13^{10}$ and $y = 3^{10} \cdot 11^{20}$

Solution **a.** Since $108 = 2^2 \cdot 3^3$ and $72 = 2^3 \cdot 3^2$, it follows that GCD(108, 72) = $2^2 \cdot 3^2 = 36$.
b. Because $13 | 0$ and $13 | 13$, it follows that GCD(0, 13) = 13.
c. GCD(x, y) = $2 \cdot 7^2 \cdot 13 = 1274$.
d. Because $x = 2^3 \cdot 7^2 \cdot 11 \cdot 13$, $y = 2 \cdot 7^3 \cdot 13 \cdot 17$, and $z = 2^2 \cdot 7$, then GCD(x, y, z) = $2 \cdot 7 = 14$. Notice that GCD(x, y, z) can also be obtained by finding the GCD of z and 1274, the answer from (c).
e. Because x and y have no common prime factors, GCD(x, y) = 1.

Calculator Method

Calculators with a ⌐Simp⌐ key can be used to find the GCD of two numbers. For example, to find the GCD(120, 180), use the following sequence of buttons to start: First, press ⌐1⌐⌐2⌐⌐0⌐⌐/⌐⌐1⌐⌐8⌐⌐0⌐ ⌐Simp⌐ ⌐=⌐ to obtain the display ⌐N/D→n/d 60/90⌐. By pressing the ⌐x◯y⌐ button, we see ⌐2⌐ on the display as a common divisor of 120 and 180. By pressing the ⌐x◯y⌐ button again and pressing ⌐Simp⌐ ⌐=⌐ ⌐x◯y⌐, we see 2 again as a factor. The process is repeated to reveal 3 and 5 as other common factors. The GCD(120, 180) is the product of the common prime factors $2 \cdot 2 \cdot 3 \cdot 5$, or 60.

Sample School Book Page:
FINDING THE GCF

Example 1

Find the GCF of 36 and 48.

1, 2, 3, 4, 6, 9, 12, 18, 36

1, 2, 3, 4, 6, 8, 12, 16, 24, 48

1, 2, 3, 4, 6, 12

The GCF of 36 and 48 is 12.

Making a list to find the GCF for larger numbers can be impractical.

The GCF can also be found using prime factorization.

The GCF is found by multiplying together the smallest power of each common prime factor.

Example 2

Use prime factorization to find the GCF of 378 and 180.

$378 = 3 \times 3 \times 2 \times 3 \times 7 = 2 \times 3^3 \times 7$

$180 = 2 \times 3 \times 3 \times 2 \times 5 = 2^2 \times 3^2 \times 5$

2 and 3^2 are the smallest power of each common prime factor.

$2 \times 3^2 = 18$

The GCF of 378 and 180 is 18.

Try It

Use prime factorization to find the GCF of each pair of numbers.

a. 72 and 138   **b.** 49 and 21   **c.** 276 and 136

You would use the same procedure of multiplying the smallest power of each common prime factor to find the GCF of more than two numbers.

7-2 • Greatest Common Factors (GCF) **331**

Source: Scott Foresman–Addison Wesley Middle School Math Course 3, 2002 (p. 223).

Euclidean Algorithm Method

Large numbers may be hard to factor. For these numbers, another method is more efficient than factorization for finding the GCD. For example, suppose we want to find GCD(676, 221). If we could find two smaller numbers whose GCD is the same as GCD(676, 221), our task would be easier. From Theorem 4-2(c), every divisor of 676 and 221 is also a divisor of $676 - 221$ and 221. Conversely, every divisor of $676 - 221$ and 221 is also a divisor of 676 and 221. Thus the set of all the common divisors of 676 and 221 is the same as the set of all common divisors of $676 - 221$ and 221. Consequently, GCD(676, 221) = GCD($676 - 221$, 221). This process can be continued to subtract three 221s from 676 so that GCD(676, 221) = GCD($676 - 3 \cdot 221$, 221) = GCD(13, 221). To determine how many 221s can be subtracted from 676, we could have divided as follows:

$$
\begin{array}{r}
3 \\
221\overline{)676} \\
663 \\
\hline
13
\end{array}
$$

Continuing, we see that GCD(13, 221) = GCD(0, 13) from the following division:

$$
\begin{array}{r}
17 \\
13\overline{)221} \\
13 \\
\hline
91 \\
91 \\
\hline
0
\end{array}
$$

Because GCD(0, 13) = 13, the GCD(676, 221) = 13. Based on this illustration, we make the generalization outlined in the following theorem.

> ### Theorem 4-7

If a and b are any whole numbers greater than 0 and $a \geq b$, then GCD(a, b) = GCD(r, b), where r is the remainder when a is divided by b.

REMARK Because GCD(x, y) = GCD(y, x) for all integers x and y not both 0, Theorem 4-7 can be written

$$\text{GCD}(a, b) = \text{GCD}(b, r).$$

Euclidean algorithm Finding the GCD of two numbers by repeatedly using Theorem 4-7 until the remainder 0 is reached is referred to as the **Euclidean algorithm**.

E X A M P L E
4-27

Use the Euclidean algorithm to find GCD(10,764, 2300).

Solution

$$\begin{array}{r} 4 \\ 2300\overline{)10764} \\ 9200 \\ \hline 1564 \end{array}$$ Thus GCD(10,764, 2300) = GCD(2300, 1564).

$$\begin{array}{r} 1 \\ 1564\overline{)2300} \\ 1564 \\ \hline 736 \end{array}$$ Thus GCD(2300, 1564) = GCD(1564, 736).

$$\begin{array}{r} 2 \\ 736\overline{)1564} \\ 1472 \\ \hline 92 \end{array}$$ Thus GCD(1564, 736) = GCD(736, 92)

$$\begin{array}{r} 8 \\ 92\overline{)736} \\ 736 \\ \hline 0 \end{array}$$ Thus GCD(736, 92) = GCD(92, 0).

Because GCD(92, 0) = 92, it follows that GCD(10,764, 2300) = 92.

REMARK The procedure for finding the GCD by using the Euclidean algorithm can be stopped at any step at which the GCD is obvious.

 A calculator with the integer division feature can also be used to perform the Euclidean algorithm. This feature yields the quotient and the remainder when doing a division. For example, if the integer division key looks like $\boxed{\text{INT}÷}$, then to find GCD(10,764, 2300) we proceed as follows:

$\boxed{1}\boxed{0}\boxed{7}\boxed{6}\boxed{4}\boxed{\text{INT}÷}\boxed{2}\boxed{3}\boxed{0}\boxed{0}\boxed{=}$ which displays $\underset{Q}{4}$ $\underset{R}{1564}$.

$\boxed{2}\boxed{3}\boxed{0}\boxed{0}\boxed{\text{INT}÷}\boxed{1}\boxed{5}\boxed{6}\boxed{4}\boxed{=}$ which displays $\underset{Q}{1}$ $\underset{R}{736}$.

$\boxed{1}\boxed{5}\boxed{6}\boxed{4}\boxed{\text{INT}÷}\boxed{7}\boxed{3}\boxed{6}\boxed{=}$ which displays $\underset{Q}{2}$ $\underset{R}{92}$.

$\boxed{7}\boxed{3}\boxed{6}\boxed{\text{INT}÷}\boxed{9}\boxed{2}\boxed{=}$ which displays $\underset{Q}{8}$ $\underset{R}{0}$.

The last number we divided by when we obtained a 0 remainder is 92, so

$$\text{GCD}(10764, 2300) = 92.$$

Sometimes shortcuts can be used to find the GCD of two or more numbers, as in the following example.

EXAMPLE
4-28

Find each of the following:

a. GCD(134791, 6341, 6339)
b. The GCD of any two consecutive integers

Solution   **a.** Any common divisor of three numbers is also a common divisor of any two of them (why?). Consequently, the GCD of three numbers cannot be greater than the GCD of any two of the numbers. The numbers 6341 and 6339 are close to each other and therefore it is easy to find their GCD:

$$GCD(6341, 6339) = GCD(6341 - 6339, 6339)$$
$$= GCD(2, 6339)$$
$$= 1.$$

Because GCD(134791, 6341, 6339) cannot be greater than 1, it follows that it must equal 1.

b. Notice that GCD(4, 5) = 1, GCD(5,6) = 1, GCD(6, 7)= 1, and GCD(99, 100) = 1. It seems that the GCD of any two consecutive integers is 1. To justify this conjecture, we need to show that for all integers n, GCD($n, n + 1$) = 1. We have

$$GCD(n, n + 1) = GCD(n + 1, n) = GCD(n + 1 - n, n)$$
$$= GCD(1, n)$$
$$= 1.$$

Least Common Multiple

Hot dogs are usually sold 10 to a package, while hot dog buns are usually sold 8 to a package. This mismatch causes troubles when one is trying to match hot dogs and buns. What is the least number of packages of each you could order so that there is an equal number of hot dogs and buns? The numbers of hot dogs that we could have are just the multiples of 10, that is, 10, 20, 30, 40, 50, ... Likewise the possible numbers of buns are 8, 16, 24, 32, 40, 48, ... We can see that the number of hot dogs matches the number of buns whenever 10 and 8 have multiples in common. This occurs at 40, 80, 120, ... In this problem, we are interested in the least of these multiples, 40. Therefore we could obtain the same number of hot dogs and buns in the least amount by buying 4 packages of **least common multiple**   hot dogs and 5 packages of buns. The answer 40 is the **least common multiple (LCM)** of 8 and 10.

> Definition

Suppose that a and b are positive integers. Then the least common multiple (LCM) of a and b is the least positive integer that is simultaneously a multiple of a and a multiple of b.

As with GCDs, there are several methods for finding least common multiples.

Colored Rods Method

We can use colored rods to determine the LCM of two numbers. For example, consider the 3 rod and the 4 rod in Figure 4-26(a). We build trains of 3 rods and 4 rods until they are the same length, as shown in Figure 4-26(b). The LCM is the common length of the train.

FIGURE 4-26

NOW TRY THIS 4-10

Explain how to use colored rods to solve the hot dog problem, that is, to find LCM(8, 10).

The Intersection-of-Sets Method

In the *intersection-of-sets* method, we first find the set of all positive *multiples* of both the first and second numbers, then find the set of all *common multiples* of both numbers, and finally pick the *least* element in that set. For example, to find the LCM of 8 and 12, denote the sets of positive multiples of 8 and 12 by M_8 and M_{12}, respectively.

$$M_8 = \{8, 16, 24, 32, 40, 48, 56, 64, 72, \ldots\}.$$
$$M_{12} = \{12, 24, 36, 48, 60, 72, 84, 96, 108, \ldots\}.$$

The set of common multiples is

$$M_8 \cap M_{12} = \{24, 48, 72, \ldots\}.$$

Because the least number in $M_8 \cap M_{12}$ is 24, the LCM of 8 and 12 is 24, written LCM(8, 12) = 24.

The Prime Factorization Method

The intersection-of-sets method for finding the LCM is often lengthy, especially when it is used to find the LCM of three or more natural numbers. Another, more efficient method for finding the LCM of several numbers is the *prime factorization method*. For example, to find LCM(40, 12), first find the prime factorizations of 40 and 12, namely, $2^3 \cdot 5$ and $2^2 \cdot 3$, respectively.

    If $m = \text{LCM}(40, 12)$, then m is a multiple of 40 and must contain both 2^3 and 5 as factors. Also, m is a multiple of 12 and must contain 2^2 and 3 as factors. Since 2^3 is a multiple of 2^2, then $m = 2^3 \cdot 5 \cdot 3 = 120$. In general, we have the following:

To find the LCM of two natural numbers, first find the prime factorization of each number. Then take each of the primes that are factors of either of the given numbers. The LCM is the product of these primes, each raised to the greatest power of the prime that occurs in either of the prime factorizations.

E X A M P L E
4-29

Find the LCM of 2520 and 10,530.

Solution

$$2520 = 2^3 \cdot 3^2 \cdot 5 \cdot 7.$$
$$10{,}530 = 2 \cdot 3^4 \cdot 5 \cdot 13.$$
$$\text{LCM}(2520, 10530) = 2^3 \cdot 3^4 \cdot 5 \cdot 7 \cdot 13 = 294{,}840.$$

The prime factorization method can also be used to find the LCM of more than two numbers. For example, to find LCM(12, 108, 120), we can proceed as follows:

$$12 = 2^2 \cdot 3$$
$$108 = 2^2 \cdot 3^3$$
$$120 = 2^3 \cdot 3 \cdot 5$$

Then, LCM(12, 108, 120) = $2^3 \cdot 3^3 \cdot 5$ = 1080.

To see the connection between the GCD and LCM, consider the GCD and LCM of 6 and 9. Because $6 = 2 \cdot 3$ and $9 = 3^2$, it follows that GCD(6, 9) = 3 and LCM(6, 9) = 18. Notice that GCD(6, 9) $\cdot$ LCM(6, 9) = $3 \cdot 18 = 54$, and 54 is the product of the original numbers 6 and 9. In general, for any two natural numbers a and b, the connection between their GCD and LCM is given by Theorem 4-8.

> Theorem 4-8

For any two natural numbers a and b,

$$\text{GCD}(a, b) \cdot \text{LCM}(a, b) = ab.$$

Theorem 4-8 can be justified in several ways. Here is a specific example that suggests how the theorem might be proved.

Suppose $a = 5^{13} \cdot 7^{20} \cdot 11^4$ and
$b = 5^{10} \cdot 7^{25} \cdot 11^6 \cdot 13.$

Then LCM$(a, b) = 5^{13} \cdot 7^{25} \cdot 11^6 \cdot 13$ and
GCD$(a, b) = 5^{10} \cdot 7^{20} \cdot 11^4.$

Now we have

$$\text{LCM}(a, b) \cdot \text{GCD}(a, b) = 5^{13+10} \cdot 7^{25+20} \cdot 11^{6+4} \cdot 13 \quad \text{and}$$
$$ab = 5^{13+10} \cdot 7^{20+25} \cdot 11^{4+6} \cdot 13.$$

For the above values of *a* and *b*, Theorem 4-8 is true. Notice, however, that in the product LCM(a, b) · GCD(a, b) we have all the powers of the primes appearing in *a* or in *b*, because for the LCM we take the greater of the powers of the common primes and for GCD the lesser. Also in *ab* we have all the powers. Hence Theorem 4-8 is true in general.

The Euclidean Algorithm Method

Theorem 4–8 is useful for finding the LCM of two numbers *a* and *b* when their prime factorizations are not easy to find. GCD(a, b) can be found by the Euclidean algorithm, the product *ab* can be found by simple multiplication, and LCM(a, b) can be found by division.

EXAMPLE 4-30

Find LCM(731, 952).

Solution   By the Euclidean algorithm, GCD(731, 952) = 17. By Theorem 4-8,

$$17 \cdot \text{LCM}(731, 952) = 731 \cdot 952.$$

Consequently,

$$\text{LCM}(731, 952) = \frac{731 \cdot 952}{17} = 40{,}936.$$

The Division-by-Primes Method

Another procedure for finding the LCM of several natural numbers involves *division by primes*. For example, to find LCM(12, 75, 120), we start with the least prime that divides at least one of the given numbers and divide as follows:

$$\frac{2 \,\lfloor 12,\, 75,\, 120}{6,\, 75,\ \ 60}$$

Because 2 does not divide 75, simply bring down the 75. To obtain the LCM using this procedure, continue the division process until the row of answers consists of relatively prime numbers.

$$
\begin{array}{r|lll}
2 & 12, & 75, & 120 \\
\hline
2 & 6, & 75, & 60 \\
\hline
2 & 3, & 75, & 30 \\
\hline
3 & 3, & 75, & 15 \\
\hline
5 & 1, & 25, & 5 \\
\hline
  & 1, & 5, & 1
\end{array}
\qquad \longrightarrow \qquad \text{GCD is 3 (Why?)}
$$

Thus LCM(12, 75, 120) = $2 \cdot 2 \cdot 2 \cdot 3 \cdot 5 \cdot 1 \cdot 5 \cdot 1 = 2^3 \cdot 3 \cdot 5^2 = 600$.

Problems related to the LCM or GCD appear on the following student page. Solve them.

Sample School Book Page:
LCM AND GCD

4.3 Planning a Picnic

Common factors and common multiples can be used to figure out how many people can share things equally.

Problem 4.3

Miriam's uncle donated 120 cans of juice and 90 packs of cheese crackers for the school picnic. Each student is to receive the same number of cans of juice and the same number of packs of crackers.

What is the largest number of students that can come to the picnic and share the food equally? How many cans of juice and how many packs of crackers will each student receive? Explain how you got your answers.

■ Problem 4.3 Follow-Up

If Miriam's uncle eats two packs of crackers before he sends the supplies to the school, what is the largest number of students that can come to the picnic and share the food equally? How many cans of juice and how many packs of crackers will each receive?

Source: Connected Mathematics, "Prime Time." Prentice-Hall 2002, (p. 39).

ONGOING ASSESSMENT 4-5

1. Find the GCD and the LCM for each of the following using the intersection-of-sets method:
   a. 18 and 10
   b. 24 and 36
   c. 8, 24, and 52
   d. 7 and 9
2. Find the GCD and the LCM for each of the following using the prime factorization method:
   a. 132 and 504
   b. 65 and 1690
   c. 900, 96, and 630
   d. 108 and 360
   e. 11 and 19
3. Find the GCD for each of the following using the Euclidean algorithm:
   a. 220 and 2924
   b. 14,595 and 10,856
   c. 122,368 and 123,152
4. Find the LCM for each of the following using any method:
   a. 24 and 36
   b. 72 and 90 and 96
   c. 90 and 105 and 315
   d. 9^{100} and 25^{100}
5. Find the LCM for each of the following pairs of numbers using Theorem 4–8 and the answers from problem 3 above:
   a. 220 and 2924
   b. 14,595 and 10,856
   c. 122,368 and 123,152
6. Use colored rods to find the GCD and the LCM of 6 and 10.
7. In Quinn's dormitory room, there are three snooze-alarm clocks, each of which is set at a different time. Clock A goes off every 15 min, clock B goes off every 40 min, and clock C goes off every 60 min. If all three clocks go off at 6:00 A.M., answer the following:
   a. How long will it be before the clocks go off together again after 6:00 A.M.?
   b. Would the answer to (a) be different if clock B went off every 15 min and clock A went off every 40 min?
8. Midas has 120 gold coins and 144 silver coins. He wants to place his gold coins and his silver coins in stacks so that there are the same number of coins in each stack. What is the greatest number of coins that he can place in each stack?
9. Bill and Sue both work at night. Bill has every sixth night off and Sue has every eighth night off. If they are both off tonight, how many nights will it be before they are both off again?
10. By selling cookies at 24¢ each, José made enough money to buy several cans of pop costing 45¢ per can. If he had no money left over after buying the pop, what is the least number of cookies he could have sold?

11. Bijous I and II start their movies at 7:00 P.M. The movie at Bijou I takes 75 min, while the movie at Bijou II takes 90 min. If the shows run continuously, when will they start at the same time again?
12. Two bike riders ride around in a circular path. The first rider completes one round in 12 min and the second rider completes it in 18 min. If they both start at the same place and the same time and go in the same direction, after how many minutes will they meet again at the starting place?
13. Assume a and b are natural numbers and answer the following:
    a. If GCD(a, b) = 1, find LCM(a, b).
    b. Find GCD(a, a) and LCM(a, a).
    c. Find GCD(a^2, a) and LCM(a^2, a).
    d. If $a|b$, find GCD(a, b) and LCM(a, b).
    e. If a and b are two primes, find GCD(a, b) and LCM(a, b).
    f. What is the relationship between a and b if GCD(a, b) = a?
    g. What is the relationship between a and b if LCM(a, b) = a?
14. Classify each of the following as true or false.
    a. If GCD(a, b) = 1, then a and b cannot both be even.
    b. If GCD(a, b) = 2, then both a and b are even.
    c. If a and b are even, then GCD(a, b) = 2.
    d. For all natural numbers a and b, LCM(a, b)|GCD(a, b).
    e. For all natural numbers a and b, LCM(a, b)|ab.
    f. GCD(a, b) $\leq a$.
    g. LCM(a, b) $\geq a$.
15. To find GCD(24, 20, 12), it is possible to find GCD(24, 20), which is 4, and then find GCD(4, 12), which is 4. Use this approach and the Euclidean algorithm to find
    a. GCD(120, 75, 105).
    b. GCD(34578, 4618, 4619).
16. a. Show that 97,219,988,751 and 4 are relatively prime.
    b. Show that 181,345,913 and 11 are relatively prime.
17. The radio station gave away a discount coupon for every twelfth and thirteenth caller. Every twentieth caller received free concert tickets. Which caller was first to get both a coupon and a concert ticket?
18. Jackie spent the same amount of money on DVDs that she did on compact discs. If DVDs cost $12 and CDs $16, what is the least amount she could have spent on each?
19. Larry and Mary bought a special 360-day joint membership to a tennis club. Larry will use the club every other day, and Mary will use the club every third day. They both use the club on the first day. How many days will neither person use the club in the 360 days?
20. At the Party Store, paper plates come in packages of 30, paper cups in packages of 15, and napkins in packages of 20. What is the least number of plates, cups, and napkins that can be purchased so that there is an equal number of each?

21. Determine how many complete revolutions gear 2 in the following must make before the arrows are lined up again.

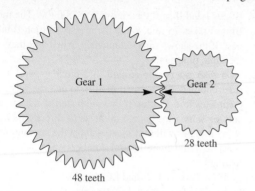

48 teeth

28 teeth

22. Determine how many complete revolutions each gear in the following must make before the arrows are lined up again.

Gear 1

Gear 2

Gear 3

24 teeth

40 teeth

60 teeth

23. Venn diagrams can be used to show factors of two or more numbers. Draw Venn diagrams to show the common prime factors for each of the following sets of three numbers:
  a. 10, 15, 60
  b. 8, 16, 24
24. What are the factors of 4^{10}?
25. Find all natural numbers x such that GCD$(25, x) = 1$ and $1 \le x \le 25$.

Communication

26. Can two whole numbers have a greatest common multiple? Explain your answer.
27. Describe to a sixth-grade student the difference between a divisor and a multiple.
28. Is it true that GCD$(a, b, c) \cdot$ LCM$(a, b, c) = abc$? Explain your answer.
29. A rectangular plot of land is 558 meters by 1212 meters. A surveyor needs to divide the plot into the largest possible square plots of the same size, being a whole number of meters long. What is the size of each square and how many square plots can be created? Explain your reasoning.

30. Suppose that GCD$(a, b, c) = 1$. Is it necessarily true that GCD$(a, b) = $ GCD$(b, c) = 1$? Explain your reasoning.
31. Suppose GCD$(a, b) = $ GCD$(b, c) = 2$. Does that always imply that GCD$(a, b, c) = 2$? Justify your answer.
32. How can you tell from the prime factorization of two numbers if their LCM equals the product of the numbers? Explain your reasoning?
33. Can the LCM of two numbers ever be greater than the product of the numbers? Explain your reasoning.

Open-Ended

34. Examine three elementary school textbooks and report on how the introduction of the topics of GCD and LCM differ in the different textbooks.
35. Make up a word problem that can be solved by finding the GCD and another that can be solved by finding the LCM. Solve your problems and explain why you are sure that your approach is correct.
36. Find three pairs of numbers for which the LCM of the numbers in a pair is smaller than the product of the two numbers.
37. Describe infinitely many pairs of numbers whose GCD is
  a. 2
  b. 6
  c. 91

Cooperative Learning

38. a. In your group, discuss whether the Euclidean algorithm for finding the GCD of two numbers should be introduced in middle school (to all students? to some?) Why or why not?
  b. If you decide that it should be introduced in middle school, discuss how it should be introduced. Report your group's decision to the class.

Review Problems

39. Find two whole numbers x and y such that

$$x \cdot y = 1{,}000{,}000$$

and neither x nor y contains any zeros as digits.
40. Fill each blank space with a single digit that makes the corresponding statement true. Find all possible answers.
  a. $3|83\_51$ **b.** $11|8\_691$ **c.** $23|103\_6$
41. Is 3111 a prime? Prove your answer.
42. Find a number that has exactly six prime factors.
43. Produce the least positive number that is divisible by 2, 3, 4, 5, 6, 7, 8, 9, 10, and 11.
44. What is the greatest prime that must be used to determine if 2089 is prime?

1. Write a spreadsheet to generate the first 50 multiples of 3 and the first 50 multiples of 4. Describe the intersection of the 2 sets.

2. Use a spreadsheet to find the factors of 2486. How far down do you need to copy the formula to be sure you have found all the divisors?

	A	**B**
1	1	= 2486/A1
2	2	
3	3	

3. Make a spreadsheet with four columns:
   Column A—the multiples of 6
   Column B—the multiples of 9
   Column C—the multiples of 12
   Column D—the multiples of 15

   a. What is the least number that appears in all four columns?
   b. Explain how to find this number without using a spreadsheet.

For any $n \times m$ rectangle such that $GCD(n, m) = 1$, find a rule for determining the number of unit squares (1×1) that a diagonal passes through. For example, in the drawings in Figure 4-27 the diagonal passes through 8 and 6 unit squares, respectively.

FIGURE 4-27

(a)   (b)

*Clock and Modular Arithmetic

In this section, we investigate clock arithmetic. Consider the following:

a. A doctor's prescription says to take a pill every 8 hr. If you take the first pill at 7:00 A.M., when should you take the next two pills?

b. Suppose you are following a bean soup recipe that calls for letting the beans soak for 12 hr. If you begin soaking them at 8:00 P.M., when should you take them out?

c. The odometer on a car gives the total miles traveled up to 99,999 miles and then starts counting from 0. If the odometer shows 99,124 miles, what will it show after a trip of 2,116 miles?

Some of these situations involve the ability to solve arithmetic problems using clocks. Most people can solve these problems without thinking much about what they are doing. It is possible to use the clock in Figure 4-28 to determine that 8 hr after 7:00 A.M. is 3:00 P.M., and 8 hr after that is 11:00 P.M. Also, 12 hr after 8:00 P.M. is 8:00 A.M. We could record these additions on the clock as

$$7 \oplus 8 = 3, \qquad 3 \oplus 8 = 11, \qquad 8 \oplus 12 = 8,$$

where $\oplus$ indicates addition on a 12-hr clock.

FIGURE 4-28

You probably noticed the special role of 12 when you found that $8 \oplus 12 = 8$. In 12-hr clock arithmetic, 12 acts like a 0 if you were adding in the set of whole numbers. An addition table for the finite system based on the clock is shown in Table 4-3.

Table 4-3

+	12	1	2	3	4	5	6	7	8	9	10	11
12	12	1	2	3	4	5	6	7	8	9	10	11
1	1	2	3	4	5	6	7	8	9	10	11	12
2	2	3	4	5	6	7	8	9	10	11	12	1
3	3	4	5	6	7	8	9	10	11	12	1	2
4	4	5	6	7	8	9	10	11	12	1	2	3
5	5	6	7	8	9	10	11	12	1	2	3	4
6	6	7	8	9	10	11	12	1	2	3	4	5
7	7	8	9	10	11	12	1	2	3	4	5	6
8	8	9	10	11	12	1	2	3	4	5	6	7
9	9	10	11	12	1	2	3	4	5	6	7	8
10	10	11	12	1	2	3	4	5	6	7	8	9
11	11	12	1	2	3	4	5	6	7	8	9	10

NOW TRY THIS 4-11

Examine Table 4-3 to determine if the following properties hold for $\oplus$ on the set of numbers in the table:
   a. Commutative property of addition
   b. Identity property of addition
   c. Inverse property of addition

When we allow numbers other than those on the 12-hr clock to be added, such as $8 \oplus 24 = 8$, we find that numbers such as 24, 36, 48, . . . act like 12 (or 0). Likewise, the numbers 13, 25, 37, . . . act like the number 1. Similarly, we can generate classes of numbers that act like each of the numbers on the 12-hr clock. The members of any one class differ by multiples of 12. Consequently, to perform additions on a 12-hr clock we perform regular addition, divide by 12, and record the remainder as the answer. For example, we can find $11 \oplus 8$ and $8 \oplus 12$ as follows:

$11 + 8 = 19$. Next divide $19 \div 12$. The quotient is 1 with a remainder of 7, which is the answer.

$8 + 12 = 20$. Next divide $20 \div 12$. The quotient is 1 with a remainder of 8, which is the answer.

Whenever the sum of digits on a 12-hr clock exceeds 12, add the numbers normally and then obtain the remainder when the sum is divided by 12.

To perform other operations on the clock, such as $2 \ominus 9$, where $\ominus$ denotes clock subtraction, we could interpret it as the time 9 hr before 2 o'clock. Counting backward (counterclockwise) 9 units from 2 reveals that $2 \ominus 9 = 5$. If subtraction on the clock is defined in terms of addition, we have $2 \ominus 9 = x$ if, and only if, $2 = 9 \oplus x$. Consequently, $x = 5$.

EXAMPLE 4-31

Perform each of the following computations on a 12-hr clock:

a. $8 \oplus 8$ **b.** $4 \ominus 12$ **c.** $4 \ominus 4$ **d.** $4 \ominus 8$

Solution   **a.** $(8 + 8) \div 12$ has remainder 4. Hence, $8 \oplus 8 = 4$.
   b. $4 \ominus 12 = 4$, since, by counting forward or backward 12 hr, you arrive at the original position.
   c. $4 \ominus 4 = 12$. This should be clear from looking at the clock, but it can also be found by using the definition of subtraction in terms of addition.
   d. $4 \ominus 8 = 8$ because $8 \oplus 8 = 4$.

Clock multiplication can be defined using repeated addition, as with whole numbers. For example, $2 \otimes 8 = 8 \oplus 8 = 4$, where $\otimes$ denotes clock multiplication. Similarly, $3 \otimes 5 = (5 \oplus 5) \oplus 5 = 10 \oplus 5 = 3$.

Clock division can be defined in terms of multiplication. For example, $8 \oslash 5 = x$, where $\oslash$ denotes clock division, if, and only if, $8 = 5 \otimes x$ for a unique x in the set $\{1, 2, 3, \ldots, 12\}$. Because $5 \otimes 4 = 8$, then $8 \oslash 5 = 4$.

EXAMPLE 4-32

Perform the following operations on a 12-hr clock, if possible:

a. $3 \otimes 11$ **b.** $2 \oslash 7$ **c.** $3 \oslash 2$ **d.** $5 \oslash 12$

Solution   **a.** $3 \otimes 11 = (11 \oplus 11) \oplus 11 = 10 \oplus 11 = 9$.
   b. $2 \oslash 7 = x$ if, and only if, $2 = 7 \otimes x$. Consequently, $x = 2$.

c. $3 \oslash 2 = x$ if, and only if, $3 = 2 \otimes x$. Multiplying each of the numbers 1, 2, 3, 4, . . . , 12 by 2 shows that none of the multiplications yields 3. Thus the equation $3 = 2 \otimes x$ has no solution, and consequently, $3 \oslash 2$ is undefined.

d. $5 \oslash 12 = x$ if, and only if, $5 = 12 \otimes x$. However, $12 \otimes x = 12$ for every x in the set $\{1, 3, 4, . . . , 12\}$. Thus $5 = 12 \otimes x$ has no solution on the clock; and therefore $5 \oslash 12$ is undefined.

FIGURE 4-29

Adding or subtracting 12 on a 12-hr clock gives the same result. Thus 12 behaves as 0 does in a base-ten addition or subtraction and is the additive identity for addition on the 12-hr clock. Similarly, on a 5-hr clock 5 behaves as 0 does.

Addition, subtraction, and multiplication on a 12-hr clock can be performed for any two numbers but, as shown in Example 4-32(d), not all divisions can be performed. Division by 12, the additive identity, on a 12-hr clock either can never be performed or is not meaningful, since it does not yield a unique answer. However, there are clocks on which all divisions can be performed, except by the corresponding additive identities. One such clock is a 5-hr clock, shown in Figure 4-29.

On this clock, $3 \oplus 4 = 2$, $2 \ominus 3 = 4$, $2 \otimes 4 = 3$, and $3 \oslash 4 = 2$. Since adding 5 to any number yields the original number, 5 is the additive identity for this 5-hr clock, as seen in Table 4-4(a). Consequently, you might suspect that division by 5 is not possible on a 5-hour clock. To determine which divisions are possible, consider Table 4-5(b), a multiplication table for 5-hr clock arithmetic. To find $1 \oslash 2$, we write $1 \oslash 2 = x$, which is equivalent to $1 = 2 \otimes x$. The second row of Table 4-4(b) shows that $2 \otimes 1 = 2$, $2 \otimes 2 = 4$, $2 \otimes 3 = 1$, $2 \otimes 4 = 3$, and $2 \otimes 5 = 5$. The solution of $1 = 2 \otimes x$ is $x = 3$, so $1 \oslash 2 = 3$. The information given in the second row of the table can be used to determine the following divisions:

$2 \oslash 2 = 1$	because	$2 = 2 \otimes 1$
$3 \oslash 2 = 4$	because	$3 = 2 \otimes 4$
$4 \oslash 2 = 2$	because	$4 = 2 \otimes 2$
$5 \oslash 2 = 5$	because	$5 = 2 \otimes 5$

Table 4-4

(a)

$\oplus$	1	2	3	4	5
1	2	3	4	5	1
2	3	4	5	1	2
3	4	5	1	2	3
4	5	1	2	3	4
5	1	2	3	4	5

(b)

$\otimes$	1	2	3	4	5
1	1	2	3	4	5
2	2	4	1	3	5
3	3	1	4	2	5
4	4	3	2	1	5
5	5	5	5	5	5

Because every element occurs in the second row, division by 2 is always possible. Similarly, division by all other numbers, except 5, is always possible. In the problem set, you are asked to perform arithmetic on different clocks and to investigate for which clocks all computations, except division by the additive identity, can be performed.

FIGURE 4-30

Modular Arithmetic

Many of the concepts for clock arithmetic can be used to work problems that involve a calendar. On the calendar in Figure 4-30, the five Sundays have dates 1, 8, 15, 22, and 29. Any two of these dates for Sunday differ by a multiple of 7. The same property is true for any other day of the week. For example, the second and thirtieth days fall on the same day, since $30 - 2 = 28$ and 28 is a multiple of 7. We say that 30 is congruent to 2, modulo 7, and we write $30 \equiv 2 \pmod{7}$. Similarly, because 18 and 6 differ by a multiple of 12, we write $18 \equiv 6 \pmod{12}$. This leads to the following definition.

> ## Definition of Modular Congruence

For integers a and b, **a is congruent to b modulo m**, written $a \equiv b \pmod{m}$, if, and only if, $a - b$ is a multiple of m, where m is a positive integer greater than 1.

REMARK   This definition could be written as $a \equiv b \pmod{m}$ if, and only if, $m \mid (a - b)$, where m is a positive whole number greater than 1.

Notice 18 and 25 are congruent modulo 7 and each number leaves the same remainder, 4, upon division by 7. Indeed, $18 = 2 \cdot 7 + 4$ and $25 = 3 \cdot 7 + 4$. In general, we have the following property: *Two whole numbers are congruent modulo m if, and only if, their remainders on division by m are the same.* On the student page modular arithmetic modulo 7 is introduced through remainders. Answer the questions that follow the explanation on page 258.

**E X A M P L E
4-33**

Tell why each of the following is true:

a. $23 \equiv 3 \pmod{10}$
b. $23 \equiv 3 \pmod{4}$
c. $23 \not\equiv 3 \pmod{7}$
d. $10 \equiv {}^{-}1 \pmod{11}$
e. $m \equiv 0 \pmod{m}$

Solution   **a.** $23 \equiv 3 \pmod{10}$ because $23 - 3$ is a multiple of 10, or because 23 and 3 leave the same remainder, 3, upon division by 10.
　　　　　b. $23 \equiv 3 \pmod{4}$ because $23 - 3$ is a multiple of 4.
　　　　　c. $23 \not\equiv 3 \pmod{7}$ because $23 - 3$ is not a multiple of 7.
　　　　　d. $10 \equiv {}^{-}1 \pmod{11}$ because $10 - ({}^{-}1) = 11$ is a multiple of 11.
　　　　　e. $m \equiv 0 \pmod{m}$ because $m - 0$ is a multiple of m, or because m and 0 have the same remainder, 0, upon division by m.

REMARK   Example 4-33(e) shows that m behaves like 0 modulo m. This is also evident for $m = 12$ in Table 4-3 and for $m = 5$ in Table 4-4.

Sample School Book Page:
MODULAR ARITHMETIC

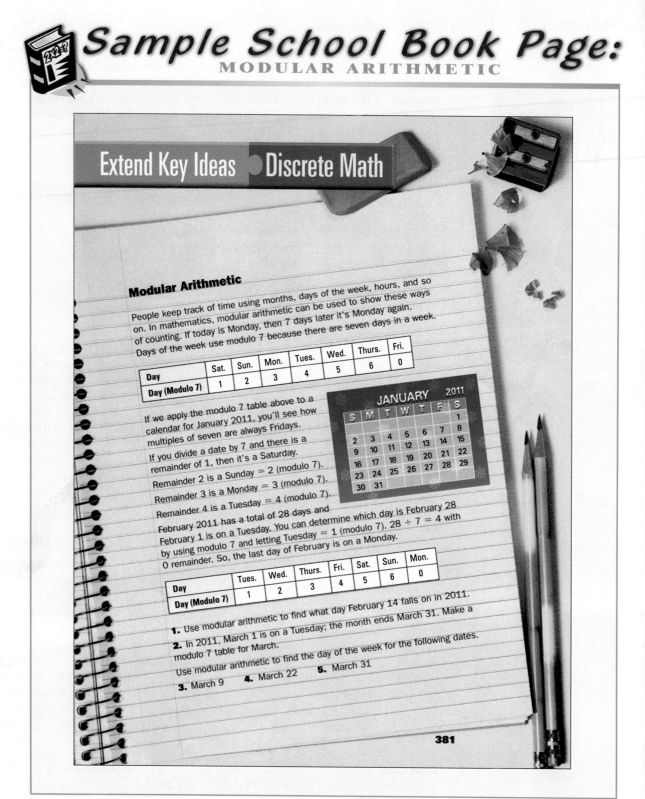

Extend Key Ideas ● Discrete Math

Modular Arithmetic

People keep track of time using months, days of the week, hours, and so on. In mathematics, modular arithmetic can be used to show these ways of counting. If today is Monday, then 7 days later it's Monday again. Days of the week use modulo 7 because there are seven days in a week.

Day	Sat.	Sun.	Mon.	Tues.	Wed.	Thurs.	Fri.
Day (Modulo 7)	1	2	3	4	5	6	0

If we apply the modulo 7 table above to a calendar for January 2011, you'll see how multiples of seven are always Fridays.

If you divide a date by 7 and there is a remainder of 1, then it's a Saturday.

Remainder 2 is a Sunday = 2 (modulo 7).

Remainder 3 is a Monday = 3 (modulo 7).

Remainder 4 is a Tuesday = 4 (modulo 7).

February 2011 has a total of 28 days and February 1 is on a Tuesday. You can determine which day is February 28 by using modulo 7 and letting Tuesday = 1 (modulo 7). 28 ÷ 7 = 4 with 0 remainder. So, the last day of February is on a Monday.

JANUARY 2011

S	M	T	W	T	F	S
						1
2	3	4	5	6	7	8
9	10	11	12	13	14	15
16	17	18	19	20	21	22
23	24	25	26	27	28	29
30	31					

Day	Tues.	Wed.	Thurs.	Fri.	Sat.	Sun.	Mon.
Day (Modulo 7)	1	2	3	4	5	6	0

1. Use modular arithmetic to find what day February 14 falls on in 2011.

2. In 2011, March 1 is on a Tuesday; the month ends March 31. Make a modulo 7 table for March.

Use modular arithmetic to find the day of the week for the following dates.

3. March 9   4. March 22   5. March 31

381

Source: Scott Foresman–Addison-Wesley Middle School Math Course 3, 2002 (p. 381).

EXAMPLE 4-34

Find all integers x such that $x \equiv 1 \pmod{10}$.

Solution $x \equiv 1 \pmod{10}$ if, and only if, $x - 1 = 10k$, where k is any integer. Consequently, $x = 10k + 1$. Letting $k = 0, 1, 2, 3, \ldots$ yields the sequence $1, 11, 21, 31, 41, \ldots$. Likewise, letting $k = {}^{-}1, {}^{-}2, {}^{-}3, {}^{-}4, \ldots$ yields the negative integers ${}^{-}9, {}^{-}19, {}^{-}29, {}^{-}39, \ldots$. The two sequences can be combined to give the solution set

$$\{ \ldots, {}^{-}39, {}^{-}29, {}^{-}19, {}^{-}9, 1, 11, 21, 31, 41, 51, \ldots \}.$$

The $\boxed{\text{INT} \div}$ button on a calculator can be used to work with modular arithmetic. If we press the following sequence of buttons, we see that $4325 \equiv 5 \pmod 9$ because the remainder when 4325 is divided by 9 is 5:

$$\boxed{4}\,\boxed{3}\,\boxed{2}\,\boxed{5}\,\boxed{\text{INT}\div}\,\boxed{9}\,\boxed{=},$$

and the display shows a remainder of 5.

EXAMPLE 4-35

Heidi signed a promissory note that will become due in 90 days. She is worried that it will become due on a weekend. She signed the note on a Monday. On what day of the week will it be due?

Solution Because $90 = 7 \cdot 12 + 6$, we know that $90 \equiv 6 \pmod 7$. On a fraction calculator, you could enter $\boxed{9}\,\boxed{0}\,\boxed{\text{INT}\div}\,\boxed{7}\,\boxed{=}$, and a quotient of 12 with remainder 6 would be displayed. Therefore the note will come due 12 wk and 6 days after Monday, which is a Sunday.

EXAMPLE 4-36

a. If it is now Monday, October 14, on what day of the week will October 14 fall next year if next year is not a leap year?
b. If Christmas falls on Thursday this year, on what day of the week will Christmas fall next year if next year is a leap year?

Solution a. Because next year is not a leap year, we have 365 days in the year. Because $365 = 52 \cdot 7 + 1$, we have $365 \equiv 1 \pmod 7$. Thus 365 days after October 14 will be 52 wk and one day later. Thus October 14 will be on a Tuesday.
b. Because there are 366 days in a leap year, we have $366 \equiv 2 \pmod 7$. Thus Christmas will be 2 days after Thursday, on Saturday.

ONGOING ASSESSMENT 4-6

1. Dr. Harper prescribed some medicine for Camile. She is supposed to take a dose every 6 hr. If she takes her first dose at 8:00 A.M., when should she take her next dose?

2. Perform each of the following operations on a 12-hr clock, if possible:
   a. $7 \oplus 8$
   b. $4 \oplus 10$
   c. $3 \ominus 9$
   d. $4 \ominus 8$
   e. $3 \otimes 9$
   f. $4 \otimes 4$
   g. $1 \ominus 3$
   h. $2 \oplus 5$

3. Perform each of the following operations on a 5-hr clock:
   a. $3 \oplus 4$
   b. $3 \oplus 3$
   c. $3 \otimes 4$
   d. $1 \otimes 4$
   e. $4 \otimes 4$
   f. $2 \otimes 3$
   g. $3 \ominus 4$
   h. $1 \ominus 4$

4. a. Construct an addition table for a 7-hr clock.
   b. Using the addition table in (a), find $5 \ominus 6$ and $2 \ominus 5$.
   c. Using the definition of subtraction in terms of addition, show that subtraction can always be performed on a 7-hr clock.

5. a. Construct a multiplication table for a 7-hr clock.
   b. Use the multiplication table in (a) to find $3 \oslash 5$ and $4 \oslash 6$.
   c. Use the multiplication table to find whether division by numbers different from 7 is always possible.

6. On a 12-hr clock, find each of the following:
   a. Additive inverse of 2
   b. Additive inverse of 3
   c. $(^-2) \oplus (^-3)$
   d. $^-(2 \oplus 3)$
   e. $(^-2) \ominus (^-3)$
   f. $(^-2) \otimes (^-3)$

7. a. If April 23 falls on Tuesday, what are the dates of the other Tuesdays in April?
   b. If July 2 falls on Tuesday, list the dates of the Wednesdays in July.
   c. If September 3 falls on Monday, on what day of the week will it fall next year if next year is a leap year?

8. Fill in each of the following blanks so that the answer is nonnegative and the least possible number:
   a. $29 \equiv$ _____ (mod 5)
   b. $3498 \equiv$ _____ (mod 3)
   c. $3498 \equiv$ _____ (mod 11)
   d. $^-23 \equiv$ _____ (mod 10)

9. a. Find all x such that $x \equiv 0$ (mod 2).
   b. Find all x such that $x \equiv 1$ (mod 2).
   c. Find all x such that $x \equiv 3$ (mod 5).

Communication

10. Explain how the odometer on a car uses modular arithmetic. What is the mod?

Open-Ended

11. On a clock we define the additive inverse of a in the same way as the additive inverse was defined for integers. Having this definition in mind, list some similarities and some differences between the number system on the clock and the set of integers. Justify your answers.

Cooperative Learning

12. a. Have members of your group construct the multiplication tables for 3-hr, 4-hr, 6-hr, and 11-hr clocks.
    b. Compare your results. On which of the clocks in (a) can divisions by numbers other than the additive identity always be performed?
    c. How do the multiplication tables of clocks for which division can always be performed (except by an additive identity) differ from the multiplication tables of clocks for which division is not always meaningful?

BRAIN
T E A S E R

How many primes are in the following sequence?
$9, 98, 987, 9876, \ldots, 987654321, 9876543219, 98765432198, \ldots$

Hint for Solving the Preliminary Problem

Factor 2450 into prime factors. Find all the triples of three positive integers that could reasonably represent ages and whose product is 2450. Then find the corresponding sums (e.g., $1 \cdot 49 \cdot 50 = 2450$ and $1 + 49 + 50 = 100$). After listing all possible triples and the corresponding sums, it will be clear that the need for more information implies two possible triples with the same sum. From the final information, we deduce Jody's age and differentiate between two possible cases.

QUESTIONS FROM THE CLASSROOM

1. A fourth-grade student devised the following subtraction algorithm for subtracting $84 - 27$.
   Four minus seven equals negative three.

$$\begin{array}{r} 84 \\ -\ 27 \\ \hline ^-3 \end{array}$$

   Eighty minus twenty equals sixty,

$$\begin{array}{r} 84 \\ -\ 27 \\ \hline ^-3 \\ 60 \end{array}$$

   Sixty plus negative three equals fifty-seven.

$$\begin{array}{r} 84 \\ -\ 27 \\ \hline ^-3 \\ +\ 60 \\ \hline 57 \end{array}$$

   Thus the answer is 57. What is your response as a teacher?

2. A seventh-grade student does not believe that $^-5 < ^-2$. The student argues that a debt of \$5 is greater than a debt of \$2. How do you respond?

3. An eighth-grade student claims she can prove that subtraction of integers is commutative. She points out that if a and b are integers, then $a - b = a + {}^-b$. Since addition is commutative, so is subtraction. What is your response?

4. A student computes $^-8 - 2(^-3)$ by writing $^-10(^-3) = 30$. How would you help this student?

5. A student says that his father showed him a very simple method for dealing with expressions like $^-(a - b + 1)$ and $x - (2x - 3)$. The rule is, if there is a negative sign before the parentheses, change the signs of the expressions inside the parentheses. Thus, $^-(a - b + 1) = {}^-a + b - 1$ and $x - (2x - 3) = x - 2x + 3$. What is your response?

6. A student had the following picture of an integer and its opposite. Other students in the class objected, saying that ^-a should be to the left of 0. How do you respond?

7. A student found that addition of integers can be performed by finding the sum or the difference of the absolute values of these integers. She would like to know if this is always true. How do you respond?

8. A student claims that $a|a$ and $a|a$ implies $a|(a - a)$, and hence, $a|0$. Is the student correct?

9. A student writes, "If $d \nmid a$ and $d \nmid b$, then $d \nmid (a + b)$." How do you respond?

10. Your seventh-grade class has just completed a unit on divisibility rules. One of the better students asks why divisibility by numbers other than 3 and 9 cannot be tested by dividing the sum of the digits by the tested number. How should you respond?

11. A student says that a number with an even number of digits is divisible by 7 if, and only if, each of the numbers formed by pairing the digits into groups of two is divisible by 7. For example, 49,562,107 is divisible by 7, since each of the numbers 49, 56, 21, and 07 is divisible by 7. Is this true?

12. A sixth-grade student argues that there are infinitely many primes because "there is no end to numbers." How do you respond?

13. A student claims that a number is divisible by 21 if, and only if, it is divisible by 3 and by 7, and, in general, a number is divisible by $a \cdot b$ if, and only if, it is divisible by a and by b. What is your response?

14. A student says that for any two integers a and b, GCD(a, b) divides LCM(a, b) and, hence, GCD$(a, b) <$ LCM(a, b). Is the student correct? Why or why not?

15. A student asks about the relation between least common multiple and least common denominator. How do you respond?

16. A student found that all three digit numbers of the form aba where $a + b$ is a multiple of 7 are divisible by 7. She would like to know why this is so. How do you respond?

17. A student wants to know how many integers between 1 and 10,000 are either multiples of 3 or multiples of 5. She wonders if it is correct to find the number of those integers that are multiples of 3 and add the number of those that are multiples of 5. How do you respond?

18. A student claims that every prime greater than 3 is a term in the arithmetic sequence whose nth term is $6n + 1$, or in the arithmetic sequence whose nth term is $6n - 1$. Is this true? If so why?

CHAPTER OUTLINE

I. Basic concepts of integers
   A. The set of **integers**, I, is { . . . , $^-3$, $^-2$, $^-1$, 0, 1, 2, 3, . . . }.
   B. The distance from any integer to 0 is the **absolute value** of the integer. The absolute value of an integer x is denoted $|x|$. If $x \geq 0$ then $|x| = x$ and if $x < 0$ then $|x| = {}^-x$.
   C. Operations with integers
      1. **Addition:** For any integers a and b,
      $$^-a + {}^-b = {}^-(a + b).$$

2. **Subtraction**
   a. If a and b are any integers, then $a - b = n$ if, and only if, $a = b + n$.
   b. For all integers a and b, $a - b = a + {}^-b$.
3. **Multiplication:** For any integers a and b,
   a. $({}^-a) \cdot ({}^-b) = ab$.
   b. $({}^-a) \cdot b = b \cdot ({}^-a) = {}^-(ab)$.
4. **Division:** If a and b are any integers with $b \neq 0$, then $a \div b$ is the unique integer c, if it exists, such that $a = bc$.
5. **Order of operations:** When addition, subtraction, multiplication, and division appear without parentheses, multiplications and divisions are done first in the order of their appearance from left to right and then additions and subtractions are done in the order of their appearance from left to right. Any arithmetic in parentheses is done first.

II. The system of integers
   A. The set of integers, $I = \{ \ldots, {}^-3, {}^-2, {}^-1, 0, 1, 2, 3, \ldots \}$, along with the operations of addition and multiplication, satisfy the following properties:

Property	+	×
Closure	Yes	Yes
Commutative	Yes	Yes
Associative	Yes	Yes
Identity	Yes, 0	Yes, 1
Inverse	Yes	No
Distributive Property of Multiplication over Addition		

   B. **Zero multiplication property of integers**
   For any integer a, $a \cdot 0 = 0 = 0 \cdot a$.
   C. **Addition property of equality:** For any integers a, b, and c, if $a = b$, then $a + c = b + c$.
   D. **Multiplication property of equality:** For any integers a, b, and c, if $a = b$, then $ac = bc$.
   E. **Substitution property:** Any number may be substituted for its equal.
   F. **Cancellation properties of equality**
      1. For any integers a, b, and c, if $a + c = b + c$, then $a = b$.
      2. For any integers a, b, and c, if $c \neq 0$ and $ac = bc$, then $a = b$.
   G. For all integers a, b, and c,
      1. ${}^-({}^-a) = a$.
      2. $a - (b - c) = a - b + c$.
      3. $(a + b)(a - b) = a^2 - b^2$ (**difference-of-squares formula**).

III. Divisibility
   A. If a and b are any integers, then b **divides** a, denoted $b|a$, if, and only if, there is a unique integer c such that $a = cb$.

   B. The following are basic divisibility theorems for integers a, b, and d:
      1. If $d|a$ and k is any integer, then $d|ka$.
      2. If $d|a$ and $d|b$, then $d|(a + b)$ and $d|(a - b)$.
      3. If $d|a$ and $d \nmid b$, then $d \nmid (a + b)$ and $d \nmid (a - b)$.
   C. Divisibility tests
      1. An integer is divisible by 2, 5, or 10 if, and only if, its units digit is divisible by 2, 5, or 10, respectively.
      2. An integer is divisible by 4 if, and only if, the last 2 digits of the integer represent a number divisible by 4.
      3. An integer is divisible by 8 if, and only if, the last 3 digits of the integer represent a number divisible by 8.
      4. An integer is divisible by 3 or by 9 if, and only if, the sum of its digits is divisible by 3 or 9, respectively.
      5. An integer is divisible by 11 if, and only if, the sum of the digits in the places that are even powers of 10 minus the sum of the digits in the places that are odd powers of 10 is divisible by 11.
      6. An integer is divisible by 6 if, and only if, the integer is divisible by both 2 and 3.

IV. Prime and composite numbers
   A. Positive integers that have exactly two positive divisors are **primes**. Integers greater than 1 and not primes are **composites**.
   B. **Fundamental Theorem of Arithmetic:** Every composite number has one and only one prime factorization, aside from variation in the order of the prime factors.
   C. Criterion for determining if a given number n is prime: *If n is not divisible by any prime p such that $p^2 \leq n$, then n is prime.*
   D. If the prime factorization of a number is $p^n q^m$, where p and q are prime, then the number of divisors of n is $(n + 1)(m + 1)$.

V. Greatest common divisor and least common multiple
   A. The **greatest common divisor (GCD)** of two or more natural numbers is the greatest divisor, or factor, that the numbers have in common.
   B. **Euclidean algorithm:** If a and b are positive integers and $a \geq b$, then $\text{GCD}(a, b) = \text{GCD}(b, r)$, where r is the remainder when a is divided by b. The procedure of finding the GCD of two numbers a and b by using the above result repeatedly is the *Euclidean algorithm*.
   C. The **least common multiple (LCM)** of two or more natural numbers is the least positive multiple that the numbers have in common.
   D. $\text{GCD}(a, b) \cdot \text{LCM}(a, b) = ab$.
   E. If $\text{GCD}(a, b) = 1$, then a and b are **relatively prime**.

* VI. Modular arithmetic
   A. For any integers a and b, a **is congruent to** b **modulo** m if, and only if, $a - b$ is a multiple of m, where m is a positive integer greater than 1.
   B. Two integers are congruent modulo m if, and only if, their remainders upon division by m are the same.

CHAPTER REVIEW

1. Find the additive inverse of each of the following:
   a. 3   **b.** ^-a **c.** 0   **d.** $x + y$
   e. $^-x + y$ **f.** $^-x - y$ **g.** $(^-2)^5$ **h.** $^-2^5$

2. Perform each of the following operations:
   a. $(^-2 + {^-8}) + 3$ **b.** $^-2 - (^-5) + 5$
   c. $^-3(^-2) + 2$ **d.** $^-3(^-5 + 5)$
   e. $^-40 \div (^-5)$ **f.** $(^-25 \div 5)(^-3)$

3. For each of the following, find all integer values of x (if there are any) that make the given equation true:
   a. $^-x + 3 = 0$ **b.** $^-2x = 10$
   c. $0 \div (^-x) = 0$ **d.** $^-x \div 0 = {^-1}$
   e. $3x - 1 = {^-124}$ **f.** $^-2x + 3x = x$

4. Use a pattern approach to explain why $(^-2)(^-3) = 6$.

5. In each of the following chip models, the encircled chips are removed. Write the corresponding integer problem with its solution.

   (a)   (b)

6. Simplify each of the following expressions:
   a. ^-1x **b.** $(^-1)(x - y)$
   c. $2x - (1 - x)$ **d.** $(^-x)^2 + x^2$
   e. $(^-x)^3 + x^3$ **f.** $(^-3 - x)(3 + x)$
   g. $(^-2 - x)(^-2 + x)$

7. Factor each of the following expressions and then simplify, if possible:
   a. $x - 3x$ **b.** $x^2 + x$
   c. $x^2 - 36$ **d.** $81y^6 - 16x^4$
   e. $5 + 5x$ **f.** $(x - y)(x + 1) - (x - y)$

8. Classify each of the following as true or false (all letters represent integers). Justify your answers.
   a. $|x|$ always is positive.
   b. For all x and y, $|x + y| = |x| + |y|$.
   c. If $a < {^-b}$, then $a < 0$.
   d. For all x and y, $(x - y)^2 = (y - x)^2$.

9. Find a counterexample to disprove each of the following properties on the set of integers:
   a. Commutative property of division
   b. Associative property of subtraction
   c. Closure property for division
   d. Distributive property of division over subtraction

10. Classify each of the following as true or false:
    a. $8|4$ **b.** $0|4$ **c.** $4|0$
    d. If a number is divisible by 4 and by 6, then it is divisible by 24.
    e. If a number is not divisible by 12, then it is not divisible by 3.

11. Classify each of the following as true or false. If false, show a counterexample.
    a. If $7|x$ and $7 \nmid y$, then $7 \nmid xy$.
    b. If $d \nmid (a + b)$, then $d \nmid a$ and $d \nmid b$.
    c. If $16|10^4$, then $16|10^6$.
    d. If $d|(a + b)$ and $d \nmid a$, then $d \nmid b$.
    e. If $d|(x + y)$ and $d|x$, then $d|y$.
    f. If $4 \nmid x$ and $4 \nmid y$, then $4 \nmid xy$.

12. Test each of the following numbers for divisibility by 2, 3, 4, 5, 6, 8, 9, and 11:
    a. 83,160   **b.** 83,193

13. Assume that 10,007 is prime. Without actually dividing 10,024 by 17, prove that 10,024 is not divisible by 17.

14. Fill each blank with 1 digit to make each of the following true (find all the possible answers):
    a. $6|87\_4$
    b. $24|4\_856$
    c. $29|87\_\_4$

15. A student claims that the sum of 5 consecutive positive integers is always divisible by 5.
    a. Check the student's claim for a few cases.
    b. Prove or disprove the student's claim.

16. Determine whether each of the following numbers is prime or composite:
    a. 143   **b.** 223

17. How can you tell if a number is divisible by 24? Check 4152 for divisibility by 24.

18. Find the GCD for each of the following:
    a. 24 and 52
    b. 5767 and 4453

19. Find the LCM for each of the following:
    a. $2^3 \cdot 5^2 \cdot 7^3$, $2 \cdot 5^3 \cdot 7^2 \cdot 13$, and $2^4 \cdot 5 \cdot 7^4 \cdot 29$
    b. 278 and 279

20. Construct a number that has exactly five divisors. Explain your construction.

21. Find all divisors of 144.

22. Find the prime factorization of each of the following:
    a. 172   **b.** 288   **c.** 260   **d.** 111

23. Find the least positive number that is divisible by every positive integer less than or equal to 10.

24. Candy bars priced at 50¢ each were not selling, so the price was reduced. Then they all sold in one day for a total of $31.93. What was the reduced price of each candy bar?

25. Two bells ring at 8:00 A.M. For the remainder of the day, one bell rings every half hour and the other bell rings every 45 min. What time will it be when the bells ring together again?

26. If the GCD of two positive whole numbers is 1, what can you say about the LCM of the two numbers? Explain your reasoning.

27. If there were to be 9 boys and 6 girls at a party and the host wanted each to be given exactly the same number of

candies that could be bought in packages containing 12 candies, what is the fewest number of packages that could be bought?

28. Jane and Ramon are running laps on a track. If they start at the same time and place and go in the same direction, with Jane running a lap in 5 min and Ramon running a lap in 3 min, how long will it take for them to be at the starting place at the same time if they continue to run at these speeds?

29. June, an owner of a coffee stand, marked down the price of a latte between 7:00 A.M. and 8:00 A.M. from $2.00 a cup. If she grossed $98.69 from the latte sale and we know that she never sells a latte for less than a dollar, how many lattes did she sell between 7:00 A.M. and 8:00 A.M.? Explain your reasoning. (*Note:* 71|9869)

★ 30. The triplet 3, 5, 7 consists of consecutive odd integers that are all prime. Give a convincing argument that this is the only triplet of consecutive odd integers that are all prime. (*Hint:* Use the Division Algorithm.)

31. Prove the test for divisibility by 9 using a 3-digit number n such that $n = a \cdot 10^2 + b \cdot 10 + c$.

★ 32. The length of a week was probably inspired by the need for market days and religious holidays. The Romans, for example, once used an 8-day week. Assuming April still had 30 days but was based on an 8-day week, if the first day of the month was on Sunday and the extra day after Saturday was called Venaday, on what day would the last day of the month fall?

*33. To measure angles of rotation that a light on a small island lighthouse sweeps, what mod system would be used and why?

SELECTED BIBLIOGRAPHY

Ball, J. "A Perfect Formula." *Mathematics Teaching in the Middle School* 2 (February 1997): 200.

Bay, J. "Developing Number Sense on the Number Line." *Mathematics Teaching in the Middle School* 6 (April 2001): 448–451.

Bennett, A., and L. Nelson. "Divisibility Tests: So Right for Discoveries." *Mathematics Teaching in the Middle School* 7 (April 2002): 460–464.

Bezuszka, S., and M. Kenney. "Even Perfect Numbers: (Update)[2]." *Mathematics Teacher* 90 (November 1997): 628–633.

Borlaug, V. "Building Equations Using M&M's." *Mathematics Teaching in the Middle School* 2 (February 1997): 290–292.

Christensen, E. "The Thinking of Students: Pythagorean Triples Served for Supper." *Mathematics Teaching in the Middle School* 3 (September 1997): 60–62.

Ewbank, W. "LCM—Let's Put It in Its Place." *Arithmetic Teacher* 35 (November 1987): 45–47.

Florence, H., Ed. "Pythagorean Triples Revisited." *Mathematics Teaching in the Middle School* 3 (May 1998): 478–479.

Georgeson, J., and C. Laughlin. "March's Menu of Problems." *Mathematics Teaching in the Middle School* 2 (March–April 1997): 332–333.

Georgeson, J., and C. Laughlin. "December's Menu of Problems." *Mathematics Teaching in the Middle School* 4 (November–December 1998): 180–181.

Koirala, H., and P. Goodwin. "Teaching Algebra in the Middle Grades Using Mathmagic." *Mathematics Teaching in the Middle School* 5 (May 2000): 562–566.

Lamdin, D., R. Lynch and H. McDaniel. "Algebra in the Middle Grades." *Mathematics Teaching in the Middle School* 6 (November 2000): 195–198.

Peterson, J. "Fourteen Different Strategies for Multiplication of Integers, or Why $(^-1)(^-1) = (+1)$." *Arithmetic Teacher* 19 (May 1972): 396–403.

Petrella, G. "Subtracting Integers: An Affective Lesson." *Mathematics Teaching in the Middle School* 7 (November 2001): 150–151.

Pollack, P. "The Thinking of Students: My Application of the Pythagorean Theorem." *Mathematics Teaching in the Middle School* 1 (May 1996): 814–816.

Schneider, S., and C. Thompson. "Incredible Equations Develop Incredible Number Sense." *Teaching Children Mathematics* 7 (November 2000): 146–148, 165–168.

Shultz, H. "The Postage-Stamp Problem, Number Theory, and the Programmable Calculator." *Mathematics Teacher* 92 (January 1999): 20–22.

Smith, J., and E. Phillips. "Listening to Middle School Students' Algebraic Thinking." *Mathematics Teaching in the Middle School* 6 (November 2000): 156–161.

Stallings, L., and P. Bullock. "Juniper Green." *Mathematics Teaching in the Middle School* 4 (April 1999): 438–440.

Tent, M. "Inequalities: Part of Every Child's Life." *Mathematics Teaching in the Middle School* 5 (January 2000): 292–295.

–5–
Rational Numbers as Fractions

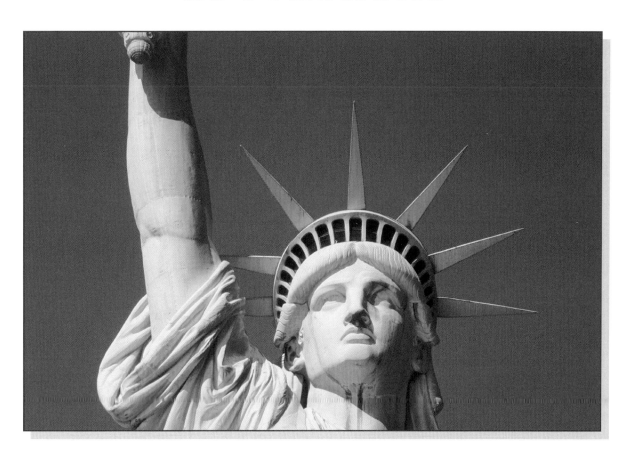

P R E L I M I N A R Y   P R O B L E M

Mandy read that the arm of the Statue of Liberty is 42 feet long. She would like to know approximately how long the Statue of Liberty's nose is. How would you advise her to proceed?

I ntegers such as ⁻5 were invented to solve equations like $x + 5 = 0$. Similarly, a new type of number is needed to solve an equation like $2x = 1$. Because there is no integer that satisfies this equation, we need to invent a number that does. The new number must be such that it is between 0 and 1 because $2 \cdot 0 = 0$, $2 \cdot 1 = 2$, and $0 < 1 < 2$. Thus, $2 \cdot 0 < 2x < 2 \cdot 1$, or $0 < x < 1$. There are no integers between 0 and 1 that meet these conditions. Therefore, similar to the development of new notation for negative integers, we need notation for this new number. If multiplication is to work with this new number as with multiplication of whole numbers and $2x = 1$, then $x + x = 1$. In other words, the number created must be added to itself to get 1. The number invented to solve the equation is *one half*, denoted 1/2. It is an element of the set of numbers of the form a/b, where **rational numbers** $b \neq 0$ and a and b are integers. Moreover, numbers of the form a/b are solutions to equations of the form $bx = a$. This set, denoted Q, is the set of **rational numbers** and is defined as follows:

$$Q = \{a/b \mid a \text{ and } b \text{ are integers and } b \neq 0\}.$$

Q is a subset of another set of numbers called *fractions*. Fractions are of the form a/b where $b \neq 0$ but a and b are not necessarily integers. For example, $1/\sqrt{2}$ is a fraction but not a rational number. (In this text we restrict ourselves to fractions where a and b are real numbers, but that restriction is not necessary.) The fact that $b \neq 0$ is always necessary because division by 0 is impossible.

In the *Principles and Standards* we find the following:

Beyond understanding whole numbers, young children can be encouraged to understand and represent commonly used fractions in context, such as 1/2 of a cookie or 1/8 of a pizza, and to see fractions as part of a unit whole or of a collection. Teachers should help students develop an understanding of fractions as division of numbers. And in the middle grades, in part as a basis for their work with proportionality, students need to solidify their understanding of fractions as numbers. (p. 33)

Rational Numbers as Fractions Expectations

The *Principles and Standards* expectations of students that are covered in this chapter include the following:

In grades K–2, children should understand and represent commonly used fractions such as 1/4, 1/3, and 1/2. (p. 392)

In grades 3–5, children should develop an understanding of fractions to include them as parts of unit wholes, as parts of a collection, as locations on number lines, and as divisions of whole numbers. Children should use models, benchmarks, and equivalent forms to judge the size of fractions. They should be able to develop and use strategies to estimate computations involving fractions. (p. 392)

In grades 6–8, children work flexibly with fractions to solve problems, compare and order fractions, and find their locations on a number line. They understand and use ratios and proportions to represent quantitative relationships. Children understand the meanings and effects of arithmetic operations with fractions. They select appropriate methods and tools for computing with fractions from among mental computation, estimation, calculators, or paper and pencil and apply the selected method. (p. 393)

The early Egyptian numeration system had symbols for fractions with numerators of 1. Most fractions with numerators other than 1 were expressed as a sum of different fractions with numerators of 1, for example, $\frac{7}{12} = \frac{1}{3} + \frac{1}{4}$.

Fractions with denominator 60 or powers of 60 were common in ancient Babylon about 2000 B.C., where 12,35 meant $12 + \frac{35}{60}$. The method was later adopted by the Greek astronomer Ptolemy (approximately A.D. 125). The same method was also used in Islamic and European countries and is presently used in the measurements of angles, where 13°19′ 47″ means $13 + \frac{19}{60} + \frac{47}{60^2}$ degrees.

The modern notation for fractions—a bar between numerator and denominator—is of Hindu origin. It came into general use in Europe in sixteenth-century books.

5-1   The Set of Rational Numbers

numerator ◆ denominator

In the rational number $\frac{a}{b}$, a is the **numerator** and b is the **denominator**. The rational number $\frac{a}{b}$ may also be represented as a/b or as $a \div b$. The word *fraction* is derived from the Latin word *fractus* meaning "to break." The word *numerator* comes from a Latin word meaning "numberer," and *denominator* comes from a Latin word meaning "namer." Table 5-1 shows several ways in which we use rational numbers.

Table 5-1   *Uses of Rational Numbers*

Use	Example
Division problem or solution to a multiplication problem	The solution to $2x = 3$ is $\frac{3}{2}$.
Partition, or part, of a whole	Joe received $\frac{1}{2}$ of Mary's salary each month for alimony.
Ratio	The ratio of Republicans to Democrats in the Senate is three to five.
Probability	When you toss a fair coin, the probability of getting heads is $\frac{1}{2}$.

FIGURE 5-1

(a)

0   1

(b)

(c)

Figure 5-1 illustrates the use of rational numbers as part of a whole and as part of a given set. For example, in the area model in Figure 5-1(a), one part out of three congruent parts, or $\frac{1}{3}$ of the largest rectangle, is shaded. In Figure 5-1(b), two parts out of three congruent parts, or $\frac{2}{3}$ of the unit segment, are shaded. In Figure 5-1(c), three circles out of five congruent circles, or $\frac{3}{5}$ of the circles, are shaded.

Our early exposure to fractions, or rational numbers, usually takes the form of oral description rather than mathematical notation. We hear phrases such as "one half of a pizza," "one third of a cake," or "three fourths of a pie." We encounter such questions as "If three identical fruit bars are distributed equally among four friends, how much does each get?" The answer is that each receives $\frac{3}{4}$ of a bar.

Rational numbers can be represented on a number line. Once the integers 0 and 1 are assigned to points on a line, every other rational number is assigned to a specific point. For example, to represent $\frac{3}{4}$ on the number line, we divide the segment from 0 to 1 into 4 segments of equal length. Then, starting from 0, we count 3 of these segments and stop at the mark corresponding to the right endpoint of the third segment to obtain the point assingend to the rational number $\frac{3}{4}$. Figure 5-2 shows the points that correspond to $^-2, \frac{-5}{4}, {^-1}, \frac{-3}{4}, 0, \frac{3}{4}, 1, \frac{5}{4}$, and 2.

FIGURE 5-2

NOW TRY THIS 5-1

a.   If ▭ represents $\frac{3}{4}$, draw rectangles for $\frac{1}{4}, \frac{1}{2}, \frac{3}{2}, \frac{2}{3}$, and $\frac{4}{3}$.

b.   In Figure 5-2, locate points that correspond to $\frac{1}{2}, \frac{-1}{2}, \frac{3}{2}$, and $\frac{-7}{4}$.

proper fraction

improper fraction

A fraction $\frac{a}{b}$, where $0 \le |a| < |b|$, is a **proper fraction**. For example, $\frac{4}{7}$ is a proper fraction, but $\frac{7}{4}, \frac{4}{4}$, and $\frac{-9}{7}$ are not; $\frac{7}{4}$ is an **improper fraction**. In general $\frac{a}{b}$ is an improper fraction if $|a| \ge |b| > 0$.

NOW TRY THIS 5-2

Draw a Venn diagram to show the relationship among natural numbers, whole numbers, integers, and rational numbers.

Equivalent or Equal Fractions

Fractions can be introduced in the classroom through a concrete activity such as paper folding. In Figure 5-3(a), one of three congruent parts, or $\frac{1}{3}$, is shaded. In Figure 5-3(b), each of the thirds has been folded in half so that now we have six sections, and two of six congruent parts, or $\frac{2}{6}$, are shaded. Thus both $\frac{1}{3}$ and $\frac{2}{6}$ represent exactly the same shaded

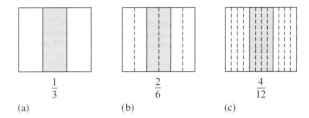

portion. Although the symbols $\frac{1}{3}$ and $\frac{2}{6}$ do not look alike, they represent the same rational

equivalent fractions ◆   number and are **equivalent fractions** or **equal fractions**. Because they represent equal
equal fractions

amounts, we write $\frac{1}{3} = \frac{2}{6}$ and say that $\frac{1}{3}$ equals $\frac{2}{6}$.

FIGURE 5-3

	$\dfrac{1}{3}$		$\dfrac{2}{6}$		$\dfrac{4}{12}$
	(a)		(b)		(c)

Figure 5-3(c) shows the rectangle with each of the original thirds folded into 4 equal

parts with 4 of the 12 parts now shaded. Thus $\frac{1}{3}$ is equal to $\frac{4}{12}$ because the same portion of

the model is shaded. Similarly, we could illustrate that $\frac{1}{3}, \frac{2}{6}, \frac{3}{9}, \frac{4}{12}, \frac{5}{15}, \ldots$ are equal.

The paper-folding example illustrates the Fundamental Law of Fractions. It can be
stated as follows: *The value of a fraction does not change if its numerator and denominator are multiplied by the same nonzero whole number.*

> ## Fundamental Law of Fractions

Let $\frac{a}{b}$ be any fraction and n a nonzero whole number, then $\frac{a}{b} = \frac{an}{bn}$.

REMARK   It can be shown that n can be any nonzero number. This version of
the Fundamental Law of Fractions is used later in this book.

NOW TRY THIS 5-3

Explain why in the Fundamental Law of Fractions n must be nonzero.

From the Fundamental Law of Fractions, $\dfrac{7}{-15} = \dfrac{^{-}7}{15}$ because $\dfrac{7}{-15} = \dfrac{7 \cdot (^{-}1)}{-15 \cdot (^{-}1)} = \dfrac{^{-}7}{15}$.

Similarly, $\dfrac{a}{-b} = \dfrac{^{-}a}{b}$. The form $\dfrac{^{-}a}{b}$, where b is a positive number, is usually preferred.

EXAMPLE
5-1

Find a value for x so that $\dfrac{12}{42} = \dfrac{x}{210}$.

Solution   By the Fundamental Law of Fractions, $\dfrac{12}{42} = \dfrac{12 \cdot 5}{42 \cdot 5} = \dfrac{60}{210}$. Hence, $\dfrac{x}{210} = \dfrac{60}{210}$,
and $x = 60$.

Simplifying Fractions

simplifying fractions

The Fundamental Law of Fractions justifies the process of **simplifying fractions**. Consider the following:

$$\frac{60}{210} = \frac{6 \cdot 10}{21 \cdot 10} = \frac{6}{21}.$$

Also,

$$\frac{6}{21} = \frac{2 \cdot 3}{7 \cdot 3} = \frac{2}{7}.$$

We can simplify $\frac{60}{210}$ because the numerator and denominator have a common factor of 10. We can simplify $\frac{6}{21}$ because 6 and 21 have a common factor of 3. However, we cannot simplify $\frac{2}{7}$ because 2 and 7 have no common factor other than 1. The fraction $\frac{2}{7}$ is the

simplest form

lowest terms

simplest form of $\frac{60}{210}$ because both 60 and 210 have been divided by their greatest common divisor, 30. To write a fraction $\frac{a}{b}$ in simplest form, that is, in **lowest terms**, we divide both a and b by the GCD(a, b).

> ## Definition of Simplest Form

A rational number $\frac{a}{b}$ is in simplest form if a and b have no common factor greater than 1, that is, if a and b are relatively prime.

We can use scientific/fraction calculators to simplify fractions. For example, to simplify $\frac{6}{12}$, we enter $\boxed{6}\ \boxed{/}\ \boxed{1}\ \boxed{2}$ and press $\boxed{\text{SIMP}}\ \boxed{=}$, and $\frac{3}{6}$ appears on the screen. At this point, an indicator tells us that this is not in simplest form, so we press $\boxed{\text{SIMP}}\ \boxed{=}$ again to obtain $\frac{1}{2}$. At any time, we can view the factor that was removed by pressing the $\boxed{x \circlearrowright y}$ key.

E X A M P L E
5-2

Write each of the following in simplest form if not already in simplest form.

a. $\dfrac{28ab^2}{42a^2b^2}$ **b.** $\dfrac{(a + b)^2}{3a + 3b}$ **c.** $\dfrac{x^2 + x}{x + 1}$ **d.** $\dfrac{3 + x^2}{3x^2}$ **e.** $\dfrac{3 + 3x^2}{3x^2}$

f. $\dfrac{a^2 - b^2}{a - b}$ **g.** $\dfrac{a^2 + b^2}{a + b}$

Solution   **a.** $\dfrac{28ab^2}{42a^2b^2} = \dfrac{2(14ab^2)}{3a(14ab^2)} = \dfrac{2}{3a}$

b. $\dfrac{(a + b)^2}{3a + 3b} = \dfrac{(a + b)(a + b)}{3(a + b)} = \dfrac{a + b}{3}$

c. $\dfrac{x^2 + x}{x + 1} = \dfrac{x(x + 1)}{x + 1} = \dfrac{x(x + 1)}{1(x + 1)} = \dfrac{x}{1} = x$

d. $\dfrac{3 + x^2}{3x^2}$ cannot be simplified because $3 + x^2$ and $3x^2$ have no factors in common except 1.

e. $\dfrac{3 + 3x^2}{3x^2} = \dfrac{3(1 + x^2)}{3 \cdot x^2} = \dfrac{1 + x^2}{x^2}$

f. $\dfrac{a^2 - b^2}{a - b} = \dfrac{(a - b)(a + b)}{(a - b) \cdot 1} = \dfrac{a + b}{1} = a + b$

g. Already in simplest form because $a^2 + b^2$ does not have $(a + b)$ as a factor.

Equality of Fractions

We can use three methods to show that two fractions, such as $\dfrac{12}{42}$ and $\dfrac{10}{35}$, are equal.

1. Simplify both fractions to the same simplest form:

$$\frac{12}{42} = \frac{2^2 \cdot 3}{2 \cdot 3 \cdot 7} = \frac{2}{7} \quad \text{and} \quad \frac{10}{35} = \frac{5 \cdot 2}{5 \cdot 7} = \frac{2}{7}.$$

Thus

$$\frac{12}{42} = \frac{10}{35}.$$

2. Rewrite both fractions with the same least common denominator. Since LCM(42, 35) = 210, then

$$\frac{12}{42} = \frac{60}{210} \quad \text{and} \quad \frac{10}{35} = \frac{60}{210}.$$

Thus

$$\frac{12}{42} = \frac{10}{35}.$$

3. Rewrite both fractions with a common denominator (not necessarily the least). A common multiple of 42 and 35 may be found by finding the product $42 \cdot 35$, or 1470. Now,

$$\frac{12}{42} = \frac{420}{1470} \quad \text{and} \quad \frac{10}{35} = \frac{420}{1470}.$$

Hence,

$$\frac{12}{42} = \frac{10}{35}.$$

The third method suggests a general algorithm for determining if two fractions $\dfrac{a}{b}$ and $\dfrac{c}{d}$ are equal. Rewrite both fractions with common denominator bd. That is,

$$\frac{a}{b} = \frac{ad}{bd} \quad \text{and} \quad \frac{c}{d} = \frac{bc}{bd}.$$

Because the denominators are the same, $\dfrac{ad}{bd} = \dfrac{bc}{bd}$ if, and only if, $ad = bc$. For example, $\dfrac{24}{36} = \dfrac{6}{9}$ because $24 \cdot 9 = 216 = 36 \cdot 6$. In general, the following property results.

> ## Property

Two fractions $\dfrac{a}{b}$ and $\dfrac{c}{d}$ are equal if, and only if, $ad = bc$.

Using a calculator, we can determine if two fractions are equal by using the above property. Since both $\boxed{2}\;\boxed{\times}\;\boxed{2}\;\boxed{1}\;\boxed{9}\;\boxed{6}\;\boxed{=}$ and $\boxed{4}\;\boxed{\times}\;\boxed{1}\;\boxed{0}\;\boxed{9}\;\boxed{8}\;\boxed{=}$ yield a display of 4392, we see that $\dfrac{2}{4} = \dfrac{1098}{2196}$.

Ordering Rational Numbers

As discussed in the *Principles and Standards*, students in lower grades should experience comparing fractions between 0 and 1 in relation to such benchmarks as $0, \dfrac{1}{2}, \dfrac{3}{4}$, and 1. In the middle grades the comparison of fractions becomes more difficult. We first consider the comparison of fractions with like denominators.

Children know that $\dfrac{7}{8} > \dfrac{5}{8}$ because if a pizza is divided into 8 parts, then 7 parts of a pizza is more than 5 parts. Similarly, $\dfrac{3}{7} < \dfrac{4}{7}$. Thus given two fractions with common positive denominators and nonnegative numerators, the one with the greater numerator is the greater fraction. This can be stated as follows.

> ## Theorem 5-1

If a, b, and c are integers and $b > 0$, then $\dfrac{a}{b} > \dfrac{c}{b}$ if, and only if, $a > c$.

NOW TRY THIS 5-4

Determine if Theorem 5-1 is true if $b < 0$.

FIGURE 5-4

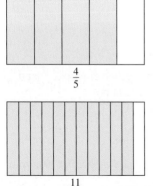

$\dfrac{4}{5}$

$\dfrac{11}{12}$

Comparing fractions with unlike denominators may be aided by using fraction strips to compare the fractions visually. For example, consider the fractions 4/5 and 11/12 shown in Figure 5-4.

From Figure 5-4, students see that each fraction is one piece less than the same size whole unit. However, they see that the missing piece for 11/12 is smaller than the missing piece for 4/5 so 11/12 must be greater than 4/5.

Comparing fractions with unlike denominators can be accomplished by rewriting the fractions with the same denominator. Then we can compare them using a previously learned technique. Using the common denominator bd, we can write the fractions $\dfrac{a}{b}$ and $\dfrac{c}{d}$ as $\dfrac{ad}{bd}$ and $\dfrac{bc}{bd}$. Because $b > 0$ and $d > 0$, we can apply Theorem 5-1 as follows.

$$\frac{a}{b} > \frac{c}{d} \quad \text{if, and only if,} \quad \frac{ad}{bd} > \frac{bc}{bd} \quad \text{and} \quad \frac{ad}{bd} > \frac{bc}{bd} \quad \text{if, and only if,} \quad ad > bc.$$

Therefore we have the following.

> ## Theorem 5-2

If a, b, c, and d are integers and $b > 0$, $d > 0$, $\frac{a}{b} > \frac{c}{d}$ if, and only if, $ad > bc$.

NOW TRY THIS 5-5

Order the fractions 3/4, 9/16, 5/8, and 2/3 from least to greatest.

Denseness of Rational Numbers

The set of rational numbers has a property that the set of whole numbers and the set of integers do not have. Consider $\frac{1}{2}$ and $\frac{2}{3}$. To find a rational number between $\frac{1}{2}$ and $\frac{2}{3}$, we first rewrite the fractions with a common denominator, as $\frac{3}{6}$ and $\frac{4}{6}$. Because there is no whole number between the numerators 3 and 4, we next find two fractions equal respectively to $\frac{1}{2}$ and $\frac{2}{3}$ with greater denominators. For example, $\frac{1}{2} = \frac{6}{12}$ and $\frac{2}{3} = \frac{8}{12}$, and $\frac{7}{12}$ is between the two fractions $\frac{6}{12}$ and $\frac{8}{12}$. So $\frac{7}{12}$ is between $\frac{1}{2}$ and $\frac{2}{3}$.

This property is generalized as follows.

> ## Denseness Property for Rational Numbers

Given rational numbers $\frac{a}{b}$ and $\frac{c}{d}$, there is another rational number between these two numbers.

NOW TRY THIS 5-6

Explain why there are infinitely many rational numbers between any two rational numbers.

EXAMPLE 5-3

Find two fractions between $\frac{7}{18}$ and $\frac{1}{2}$.

Solution Because $\frac{1}{2} = \frac{1 \cdot 9}{2 \cdot 9} = \frac{9}{18}$, we see that $\frac{8}{18}$, or $\frac{4}{9}$, is between $\frac{7}{18}$ and $\frac{9}{18}$. To find another fraction between the given fractions, we find two fractions equal to $\frac{7}{18}$ and $\frac{9}{18}$, respectively, but with greater denominators. For example, $\frac{7}{18} = \frac{14}{36}$ and $\frac{9}{18} = \frac{18}{36}$.

We now see that $\frac{15}{36}, \frac{16}{36}$, and $\frac{17}{36}$ are all between $\frac{14}{36}$ and $\frac{18}{36}$ and thus between $\frac{7}{18}$ and $\frac{1}{2}$.

Some students incorrectly add $\frac{a}{b} + \frac{c}{d}$ as $\frac{a+c}{b+d}$. Although the technique does not produce the correct sum, as will be seen in Section 5-2, it provides a way to find a number between any two rational numbers. In Example 5-3, to find a number between $\frac{7}{18}$ and $\frac{1}{2}$ we could add the numerators and add the denominators to produce $\frac{7+1}{18+2} = \frac{8}{20}$. We see that $\frac{7}{18} < \frac{8}{20}$ because $140 < 144$. Also $\frac{8}{20} < \frac{1}{2}$ because $16 < 20$. We state the general property in the following theorem, whose proof is explored in Now Try This 5-7.

> ### Theorem 5-3
>
> Let $\frac{a}{b}$ and $\frac{c}{d}$ be any rational numbers with positive denominators where $\frac{a}{b} < \frac{c}{d}$. Then $\frac{a}{b} < \frac{a+c}{b+d} < \frac{c}{d}$.

NOW TRY THIS 5-7

Prove Theorem 5-3, that is, if $\frac{a}{b}$ and $\frac{c}{d}$ are any rational numbers where $\frac{a}{b} < \frac{c}{d}$, then $\frac{a}{b} < \frac{a+c}{b+d} < \frac{c}{d}$. (*Hint:* If $\frac{a}{b} < \frac{c}{d}$, then $ad < bc$. Now add ab to both sides and use this to show that $\frac{a}{b} < \frac{a+c}{b+d}$. Then finish the proof in a similar way.)

LABORATORY
A C T I V I T Y

Obtain tangram pieces or build them and cut them out as shown in Figure 5-5. Answer each of the following.

a. If the area of the entire square is 1 square unit, find the area of each tangram piece.
b. If the area of piece a is 1 square unit, find the area of each tangram piece.

FIGURE 5-5

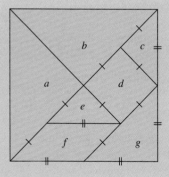

ONGOING ASSESSMENT 5-1

1. Write a sentence that illustrates the use of $\frac{7}{8}$ in each of the following ways:
   a. As a division problem
   b. As part of a whole
   c. As a ratio

2. For each of the following, write a fraction to represent the shaded portion:

(a)　　　　　(b)

(c)　　　　　(d)

(e)　　　　　(f)

3. For each of the following four squares, write a fraction to represent the shaded portion. What property of fractions does the diagram illustrate?

(a)　　　(b)　　　(c)　　　(d)

4. Complete each of the following figures so that it shows $\frac{3}{5}$:

0　　　1

(a)　　　　　(b)

(c)

(d)

(e)　　　　　(f)

5. Could the shaded portions in the figures below represent the indicated fractions?

  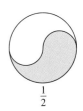

$\frac{1}{4}$　　　$\frac{3}{4}$　　　$\frac{1}{2}$

(a)　　　　　(b)　　　　　(c)

6. Refer to the following figure and represent each of the following as a fraction:

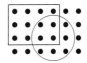

   a. The dots inside the circle as a part of all the dots
   b. The dots inside the rectangle as a part of all the dots
   c. The dots in the intersection of the rectangle and the circle as a part of all the dots
   d. The dots outside the circle but inside the rectangle as part of all the dots

7. For each of the following, write three fractions equal to the given fraction:
   a. $\frac{2}{9}$　　b. $\frac{-2}{5}$　　c. $\frac{0}{3}$　　d. $\frac{a}{2}$

8. Find the simplest form for each of the following fractions:
   a. $\frac{156}{93}$　　b. $\frac{27}{45}$　　c. $\frac{-65}{91}$
   d. $\frac{0}{68}$　　e. $\frac{84^2}{91^2}$　　f. $\frac{662}{703}$

9. Mr. Gonzales and Ms. Price gave the same test to their fifth-grade classes. In Mr. Gonzales's class, 20 out of 25 students passed the test, and in Ms. Price's class, 24 out of 30 students passed the test. One of Ms. Price's students heard about the results of the tests and claimed that the classes did equally well. Is the student right? Explain.

10. For each of the following, choose the expression in parentheses that equals or describes best the given fraction:

    a. $\frac{0}{0}$ (1, undefined, 0)   b. $\frac{5}{0}$ (undefined, 5, 0)

    c. $\frac{0}{5}$ (undefined, 5, 0)

    d. $\frac{2+a}{a}$ (2, 3, cannot be simplified)

    e. $\frac{15+x}{3x}$ $\left(\frac{5+x}{x}, 5,\text{ cannot be simplified}\right)$

    f. $\frac{2^6+2^5}{2^4+2^7}$ $\left(1, \frac{2}{3},\text{ cannot be simplified}\right)$

    g. $\frac{2^{100}+2^{98}}{2^{100}-2^{98}}$ $\left(2^{196}, \frac{5}{3},\text{ too large to simplify}\right)$

11. Find the simplest form for each of the following fractions:

    a. $\frac{a^2-b^2}{3a+3b}$ b. $\frac{14x^2y}{63xy^2}$ c. $\frac{a^2+ab}{a+b}$ d. $\frac{a}{3a+ab}$

12. Determine if the following pairs are equal:

    a. $\frac{3}{8}$ and $\frac{375}{1000}$ b. $\frac{18}{54}$ and $\frac{23}{69}$

    c. $\frac{6}{10}$ and $\frac{600}{1000}$ d. $\frac{17}{27}$ and $\frac{25}{45}$

13. Determine if the following pairs are equal by changing both to the same denominator:

    a. $\frac{10}{16}$ and $\frac{12}{18}$ b. $\frac{3}{12}$ and $\frac{41}{154}$

    c. $\frac{3}{-12}$ and $\frac{-36}{144}$ d. $\frac{-21}{86}$ and $\frac{-51}{215}$

14. A board is needed that is exactly $\frac{11}{32}$ in. wide to fill a hole. Can a board that is $\frac{3}{8}$ in. be shaved down to fit the hole? If so, how much must be shaved from the board?

15. Draw an area model to show that $\frac{3}{4}=\frac{6}{8}$.

16. If a fraction is equal to $\frac{3}{4}$ and the sum of the numerator and denominator is 84, what is the fraction?

17. The following two parking meters are next to each other with the times left as shown. Which meter has more time left on it? How much more?

Meter A

Meter B

18. Mr. Gomez filled his car's 16-gal gas tank. He took a short trip and used 6 gal of gas. Draw an arrow in the following figure to show what his gas gauge looked like after the trip:

19. Read each measurement as shown on the following ruler:

20. Determine if each of the following is correct. Explain.

    a. $\frac{ab+c}{b}=a+c$ b. $\frac{a+b}{a+c}=\frac{b}{c}$ c. $\frac{ab+ac}{ac}=\frac{b+c}{c}$

21. Solve for x in each of the following:

    a. $\frac{2}{3}=\frac{x}{16}$ b. $\frac{3}{4}=\frac{-27}{x}$ c. $\frac{3}{x}=\frac{3x}{x^2}$

22. a. If $\frac{a}{c}=\frac{b}{c}$, what must be true?

    b. If $\frac{a}{b}=\frac{a}{c}$, what must be true?

23. Let W be the set of whole numbers, N be the set of natural numbers, I be the set of integers, and Q the set of rational numbers.

    a. Write sentences to describe the relationships among $N, W, I,$ and Q.

    b. Draw a Venn diagram showing the relationships.

24. In Amy's algebra class, 6 of the 31 students received A's on a test. The same test was given to Bren's class and 5 of the 23 students received A's. Which class had the higher rate of A's?

25. For each of the following pairs of fractions, replace the comma with the correct symbol ($<, =, >$) to make a true statement:

    a. $\frac{7}{8}, \frac{5}{6}$ b. $2\frac{4}{5}, 2\frac{3}{6}$ c. $\frac{-7}{8}, \frac{-4}{5}$

    d. $\frac{1}{-7}, \frac{1}{-8}$ e. $\frac{2}{5}, \frac{4}{10}$ f. $\frac{0}{7}, \frac{0}{17}$

26. Arrange each of the following in decreasing order:

    a. $\frac{11}{22}, \frac{11}{16}, \frac{11}{13}$ b. $\frac{-1}{5}, \frac{-19}{36}, \frac{-17}{30}$

27. If $\frac{a}{b}<1$ and $\frac{c}{d}>0$, compare the size of $\frac{c}{d}$ with $\frac{ac}{bd}$.

28. Show that the sequence $\frac{1}{2}, \frac{2}{3}, \frac{3}{4}, \frac{4}{5}, \frac{5}{6}, \frac{6}{7}, \ldots$ is an increasing sequence; that is, show that each term in the sequence is greater than the preceding one.

29. For each of the following, find two rational numbers between the given fractions:

a. $\frac{3}{7}$ and $\frac{4}{7}$ **b.** $\frac{^-7}{9}$ and $\frac{^-8}{9}$

c. $\frac{5}{6}$ and $\frac{83}{100}$ **d.** $\frac{^-1}{3}$ and $\frac{3}{4}$

30. Consider the following number grid. The circled numbers form a rhombus (that is, all sides are the same length).

1	2	3	4	5	6	7	8	9	10
11	12	13	14	15	16	17	18	19	20
21	22	23	24	25	26	27	28	29	30
31	32	33	34	35	36	37	38	39	40
41	42	43	44	45	46	47	48	49	50

a. If A is the sum of the four circled numbers and B is the sum of the four interior numbers, find A/B.

b. Form a rhombus by circling the numbers 6, 18, 25, and 37. Compute A and B as in (a) and then find A/B.

c. How do the answers in (a) and (b) compare? Why does this happen?

31. A scale on a map is 12 mi to the inch. What is the airline mileage between two cities that are 38 in. apart on the map?

32. **a.** Six ounces is what part of a pound? A ton?

b. A dime is what fraction of a dollar?

c. 15 minutes is what fraction of an hour?

d. 8 hours is what fraction of a day?

Communication

33. Explain why there are 24 time zones on earth.

34. If $\frac{1}{3}$ of each of two classes is female, explain whether each class must contain the same number of females.

35. Consider the set of all fractions equal to $\frac{1}{2}$. If you take any ten of those fractions, add their numerators to obtain the numerator of a new fraction and add their denominators to obtain the denominator of a new fraction, how does the new fraction relate to $\frac{1}{2}$? Generalize what you found and explain.

36. Should fractions always be reduced to their simplest form? Why or why not?

37. How would you respond to each of the following students?

a. Iris claims that if we have two positive rational numbers, the one with the greatest numerator is the greatest.

b. Shirley claims that if we have two positive rational numbers, the one with the greatest denominator is the least.

38. If we take the set of fractions equivalent to $\frac{1}{3}$ and graph them as points on a coordinate system so that the numerator becomes the x-coordinate and the denominator becomes the y-coordinate for that point, explain what type of graph we would get.

39. Write an explanation of how to convert inches to yards and vice versa.

Open-Ended

40. List three types of measure that require rational numbers as the appropriate number of units in the measurements.

41. Some people have argued that the system of integers is more understandable than the system of positive rational numbers. If you could decide which should be taught first in school, which would you choose and why?

Cooperative Learning

42. Assume the tallest person in your group is 1 unit tall and do the following:

a. Find rational numbers to approximately represent other members of the group.

b. Make a number line using the rational numbers for each person ordered according to height.

BRAIN TEASER

In an old Sam Loyd puzzle, a watch is described as having stopped when the minute and hour hands formed a straight line, and the second hand was not on 12. At what times can this happen?

5-2 Addition and Subtraction of Rational Numbers

Addition and subtraction of rational numbers is very much like addition and subtraction of whole numbers and integers. We first demonstrate the addition of two rational numbers with like denominators using both an area model and a number-line model. The sum $\frac{2}{5} + \frac{1}{5}$ is illustrated in Figure 5-6.

FIGURE 5-6

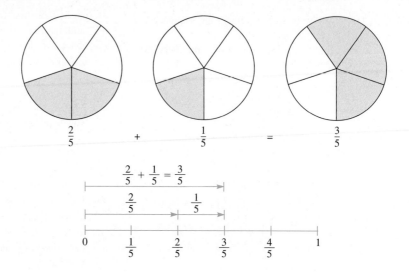

The ideas illustrated in Figure 5-6 can be applied to the sum of two rational numbers with like denominators and are summarized in the definition below.

> ### Definition of Addition of Rational Numbers
>
> If $\dfrac{a}{b}$ and $\dfrac{c}{b}$ are rational numbers, then $\dfrac{a}{b} + \dfrac{c}{b} = \dfrac{a+c}{b}$.

Next we consider the addition of two rational numbers with unlike denominators, using Polya's four-step, problem-solving process.

PROBLEM SOLVING   **Adding Rational Numbers Problem**

Determine how to add the rational numbers 2/3 and 1/4.

Understanding the Problem   We can model $\dfrac{2}{3}$ and $\dfrac{1}{4}$ as parts of a whole, as seen in Figure 5-7, but we need a way to combine the two drawings to find the sum.

FIGURE 5-7

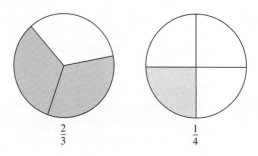

■ **Devising a Plan** We use the strategy of *solving a simpler problem* and consider adding rational numbers with the same denominators. We can find the sum by writing each fraction with a common denominator and then completing the computation.

FIGURE 5-8

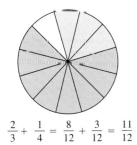

$$\frac{2}{3} + \frac{1}{4} = \frac{8}{12} + \frac{3}{12} = \frac{11}{12}$$

Carrying Out the Plan From earlier work in the chapter, we know that 2/3 is equal to infinitely many representations of the rational numbers 2/3, including 4/6, 6/9, 8/12, and so on. Also 1/4 is equal to an infinite set of rational numbers, including 2/8, 3/12, 4/16, and so on. By comparing the two sets of rational numbers, we see that 8/12 and 3/12 have the same denominator. One is 8 parts of 12 while the other is 3 parts of 12. Consequently, the sum is 2/3 + 1/4 = 8/12 + 3/12 = 11/12. Figure 5-8 illustrates the addition.

Looking Back To add two rational numbers of unlike denominators, we considered equal rational numbers with like denominators. The common denominator for 2/3 and 1/4 is 12. This is also the least common denominator, or the LCM(3, 4). To add two fractions with unequal denominators such as 5/12 and 7/18, we could find equal fractions with the denominator as the LCM(12, 18), or 36. However, any common denominator will work as well, for example, 72 or even 12 · 18. ▩

By considering the sum $\frac{2}{3} + \frac{1}{4} = \frac{2 \cdot 4}{3 \cdot 4} + \frac{1 \cdot 3}{4 \cdot 3} = \frac{8}{12} + \frac{3}{12} = \frac{11}{12}$, we can generalize to

the sum of two rational numbers with unlike denominators, as in the following property.

> **Property**

> If $\frac{a}{b}$ and $\frac{c}{d}$ are any two rational numbers, then $\frac{a}{b} + \frac{c}{d} = \frac{ad + bc}{bd}$.

EXAMPLE 5-4

Find each of the following sums:

a. $\frac{1}{15} + \frac{4}{21}$ **b.** $\frac{2}{^-3} + \frac{1}{5}$ **c.** $\left(\frac{3}{4} + \frac{1}{5}\right) + \frac{1}{6}$ **d.** $\frac{3}{x} + \frac{4}{y}$

Solution   **a.** Because LCM(15, 21) = 3 · 5 · 7, then $\frac{2}{15} + \frac{4}{21} = \frac{2 \cdot 7}{15 \cdot 7} + \frac{4 \cdot 5}{21 \cdot 5}$

$= \frac{14}{105} + \frac{20}{105} = \frac{34}{105}$

b. $\frac{2}{^-3} + \frac{1}{5} = \frac{(2)(5) + (^-3)(1)}{(^-3)(5)} = \frac{10 + ^-3}{^-15} = \frac{7}{^-15} = \frac{7(^-1)}{^-15(^-1)} = \frac{^-7}{15}$

c. $\frac{3}{4} + \frac{1}{5} = \frac{3 \cdot 5 + 4 \cdot 1}{4 \cdot 5} = \frac{19}{20}$. Hence, $\left(\frac{3}{4} + \frac{1}{5}\right) + \frac{1}{6} = \frac{19}{20} + \frac{1}{6} =$

$\frac{19 \cdot 6 + 20 \cdot 1}{20 \cdot 6} = \frac{134}{120}$, or $\frac{67}{60}$.

d. $\frac{3}{x} + \frac{4}{y} = \frac{3y}{xy} + \frac{4x}{xy} = \frac{3y + 4x}{xy}$

Mixed Numbers

mixed numbers

In everyday life, we often use **mixed numbers**, that is, numbers that are made up of an integer and a fractional part of an integer. For example, Figure 5-9 shows that the nail is $2\frac{3}{4}$ in. long. The mixed number $2\frac{3}{4}$ means $2 + \frac{3}{4}$. It is sometimes inferred that $2\frac{3}{4}$ means

2 times $\frac{3}{4}$, since xy means $x \cdot y$, but this is not correct. Also, the number $^-4\frac{3}{4}$ means $-\left(4\frac{3}{4}\right)$, or $^-4 - \frac{3}{4}$, not $^-4 + \frac{3}{4}$.

FIGURE 5-9

A mixed number is a rational number, and therefore it can always be written in the form $\frac{a}{b}$. For example,

$$2\frac{3}{4} = 2 + \frac{3}{4} = \frac{2}{1} + \frac{3}{4} = \frac{2 \cdot 4 + 1 \cdot 3}{1 \cdot 4} = \frac{8 + 3}{4} = \frac{11}{4}.$$

EXAMPLE 5-5

Change each of the following mixed numbers to the form $\frac{a}{b}$, where a and b are integers:

a. $4\frac{1}{3}$ **b.** $^-3\frac{2}{5}$

Solution **a.** $4\frac{1}{3} = 4 + \frac{1}{3} = \frac{4}{1} + \frac{1}{3} = \frac{4 \cdot 3 + 1 \cdot 1}{1 \cdot 3} = \frac{12 + 1}{3} = \frac{13}{3}$

b. $^-3\frac{2}{5} = -\left(3 + \frac{2}{5}\right) = -\left(\frac{3}{1} + \frac{2}{5}\right) = -\left(\frac{3 \cdot 5 + 1 \cdot 2}{1 \cdot 5}\right) = \frac{^-17}{5}$

NOW TRY THIS 5-8

Use the ideas in Example 5-5 to convert a general mixed number $A\frac{b}{c}$ (notation for $A + \frac{b}{c}$) to an improper fraction.

Now that we know how to change a mixed number to an improper fraction, we consider the following student page, which explores the changing of an improper fraction to a mixed number. The page in the student book that preceded this student page discussed the "universal language" of trade and how the Spanish dollar was the main money used for trade in colonial America. It talked about how the dollar coin was often cut into 2, 4, or 8 equal pieces to make change. Many of us have probably referred to a quarter as "two bits" but never understood where this term came from. The example on the student page of converting 21 bits for whole dollars and bits is equivalent to converting $\frac{21}{8}$ to a mixed number.

$$\frac{21}{8} = \frac{8}{8} + \frac{8}{8} + \frac{5}{8} = 1 + 1 + \frac{5}{8} = 2\frac{5}{8}$$

Next try problem 5 on the student page on your own.

Sample School Book Page:
FRACTIONS AND MIXED NUMBERS

GOAL
LEARN HOW TO...
◆ write fractions as mixed numbers
◆ write mixed numbers as fractions
AS YOU...
◆ exchange colonial money
KEY TERM
◆ mixed number

Exploration 1

Renaming Fractions and Mixed Numbers

If you had lived in colonial America, a knowledge of fractions and *mixed numbers* would have helped you when you made purchases with Spanish dollars.

4 Suppose a colonial merchant had 11 bits.

    a. If the merchant combined bits to make Spanish dollars, how many Spanish dollars and how many leftover bits did the merchant have?

    b. What fraction represents the leftover bits?

▶ **Fractions as Mixed Numbers** You can use the same thinking as in Question 4 to write fractions as *mixed numbers*. A **mixed number** is the sum of a nonzero whole number and a fraction between 0 and 1.

EXAMPLE

Suppose you have 21 bits and you want to exchange the bits for whole Spanish dollars and bits.

21 bits is the same as 21 eighths of a Spanish dollar.

$$\frac{21}{8} = \frac{8}{8} + \frac{8}{8} + \frac{5}{8}$$

$$= 2 + \frac{5}{8}$$

$$= 2\frac{5}{8}$$

Think: How many eighths make a **whole**? How many eighths are left?

5 What mixed number is equal to $\frac{15}{4}$? If necessary, use the coins or make a sketch.

Source: Middle Grade Mathematics, Book 2, McDougal Littell Publishing Co., 2002 (p. 178).

EXAMPLE 5-6

Change $\dfrac{29}{5}$ to a mixed number.

Solution $\dfrac{29}{5} = \dfrac{5 \cdot 5 + 4}{5} = \dfrac{5 \cdot 5}{5} + \dfrac{4}{5} = 5 + \dfrac{4}{5} = 5\dfrac{4}{5}$

REMARK In elementary schools, problems like Example 5-6 are usually solved using division, as follows:

$$\begin{array}{r} 5 \\ 5{\overline{\smash{\big)}\,29}} \\ \underline{25} \\ 4 \end{array}$$

Hence, $\dfrac{29}{5} = 5 + \dfrac{4}{5} = 5\dfrac{4}{5}$.

We can use scientific/fraction calculators to change improper fractions to mixed numbers. For example, if we enter $\boxed{2}\,\boxed{9}\,\boxed{/}\,\boxed{5}$ and press $\boxed{Ab/c}$, then 5 ⊔ 4/5 appears, which means $5\dfrac{4}{5}$.

Because mixed numbers are rational numbers, the methods of adding rationals can be extended to include mixed numbers. The following student page shows a method of estimating sums of mixed numbers.

We can also use scientific/fraction calculators to add mixed numbers. For example, to add $2\dfrac{4}{5} + 3\dfrac{5}{6}$, we enter $\boxed{2}\,\boxed{Unit}\,\boxed{4}\,\boxed{/}\,\boxed{5}\,\boxed{+}\,\boxed{3}\,\boxed{Unit}\,\boxed{5}\,\boxed{/}\,\boxed{6}\,\boxed{=}$, and the display reads 5 ⊔ 49/30. We then press $\boxed{Ab/c}$ to obtain 6 ⊔ 19/30, which means $6\dfrac{19}{30}$.

Properties of Addition for Rational Numbers

Rational numbers have the following properties for addition: *closure, commutative, associative, additive identity,* and *additive inverse.* To emphasize the additive inverse property of rational numbers, we state it explicitly, as follows.

> ## Property

Additive inverse property of rational numbers For any rational number $\dfrac{a}{b}$, there exists a unique rational number $-\dfrac{a}{b}$, the additive inverse of $\dfrac{a}{b}$, such that

$$\frac{a}{b} + \left(-\frac{a}{b}\right) = 0 = \left(-\frac{a}{b}\right) + \frac{a}{b}.$$

Another form of $-\dfrac{a}{b}$ can be found by considering the sum $\dfrac{a}{b} + \dfrac{^-a}{b}$. Because

$$\frac{a}{b} + \frac{^-a}{b} = \frac{a + {}^-a}{b} = \frac{0}{b} = 0,$$

it follows that $-\dfrac{a}{b}$ and $\dfrac{^-a}{b}$ are both additive inverses of $\dfrac{a}{b}$, so $-\dfrac{a}{b} = \dfrac{^-a}{b}$.

Sample School Book Page:
ADDING MIXED NUMBERS

6-5 Adding Mixed Numbers

You'll Learn ...

■ to add mixed numbers

... How It's Used

Farmers add mixed numbers when working with rainfall data.

▶ **Lesson Link**   In the last lesson, you estimated sums of mixed numbers. Now you'll learn how to find mixed number sums exactly. ◀

Explore | **Adding Mixed Numbers**

Another Fine Mix!

Materials: Fraction Bars®

Adding Mixed Numbers

- Draw and label the whole number for the first mixed number.
- Next to that, draw and label the fraction for the first number.
- Next to that, draw and label the whole number for the second mixed number.
- Next to that, draw and label the fraction for the second number.
- Using a whole number and a fraction less than 1, describe the model.

$$1\frac{3}{4} + 1\frac{1}{2} = 3\frac{1}{4}$$

1. Model each problem.

   a. $1\frac{1}{4} + 2\frac{1}{2}$ **b.** $1\frac{2}{3} + 1\frac{3}{6}$ **c.** $1\frac{3}{8} + 2\frac{1}{8}$ **d.** $1\frac{3}{6} + 2\frac{1}{2}$

2. Does the whole number in the answer always equal the sum of the two whole numbers in the problem? Explain.

3. Is the sum of two mixed numbers always a mixed number? Explain.

Source: Middle School Math, Course: Scott Foresman–Addison Wesley, 2002 (p. 346).

E X A M P L E 5-7

Find the additive inverses for each of the following:

a. $\dfrac{3}{5}$ **b.** $\dfrac{^-5}{11}$ **c.** $4\dfrac{1}{2}$

Solution   **a.** $-\dfrac{3}{5}$ or $\dfrac{^-3}{5}$ **b.** $-\left(\dfrac{^-5}{11}\right) = \dfrac{^-(^-5)}{11} = \dfrac{5}{11}$ **c.** $^-4\dfrac{1}{2}$, or $\dfrac{^-9}{2}$

Properties of the additive inverse for rational numbers are analogous to those of the additive inverse for integers, as shown in Table 5-2. As with the set of integers, the set of rational numbers also has the addition property of equality.

Table 5-2

Integers		Rational Numbers	
1. $^-(^-a) = a$		1. $-\left(-\dfrac{a}{b}\right) = \dfrac{a}{b}$	
2. $^-(a + b) = {}^-a + {}^-b$		2. $-\left(\dfrac{a}{b} + \dfrac{c}{d}\right) = \dfrac{^-a}{b} + \dfrac{^-c}{d}$	

> **Property**

Addition property of equality   If $\dfrac{a}{b}$ and $\dfrac{c}{d}$ are any rational numbers such that $\dfrac{a}{b} = \dfrac{c}{d}$, and if $\dfrac{e}{f}$ is any rational number, then $\dfrac{a}{b} + \dfrac{e}{f} = \dfrac{c}{d} + \dfrac{e}{f}$.

Subtraction of Rational Numbers

In elementary school, subtraction of rational numbers is usually introduced by using a take-away model. If we have $\dfrac{6}{7}$ of a pizza and $\dfrac{2}{7}$ of the original pizza is taken away, $\dfrac{4}{7}$ of the pizza remains: that is, $\dfrac{6}{7} - \dfrac{2}{7} = \dfrac{6 - 2}{7} = \dfrac{4}{7}$. In general, subtraction of rational numbers with like denominators is determined as follows:

$$\frac{a}{b} - \frac{c}{b} = \frac{a - c}{b}.$$

Subtraction of rational numbers, like subtraction of integers, can be defined in terms of addition as follows.

> **Definition of Subtraction of Rational Numbers in Terms of Addition**

If $\dfrac{a}{b}$ and $\dfrac{c}{d}$ are any rational numbers, then $\dfrac{a}{b} - \dfrac{c}{d}$ is the unique rational number $\dfrac{e}{f}$ such that $\dfrac{a}{b} = \dfrac{c}{d} + \dfrac{e}{f}$.

As with integers, we can see that subtraction of rational numbers can be performed by adding the additive inverses. The following theorem states this.

> **Theorem 5-4**

If $\frac{a}{b}$ and $\frac{c}{d}$ are any rational numbers, then $\frac{a}{b} - \frac{c}{d} = \frac{a}{b} + \frac{{}^{-}c}{d}$.

Now, using the definition of addition of rational numbers, we obtain the following:

$$\frac{a}{b} - \frac{c}{d} = \frac{a}{b} + \frac{{}^{-}c}{d}$$
$$= \frac{ad + b({}^{-}c)}{bd}$$
$$= \frac{ad + {}^{-}(bc)}{bd}$$
$$= \frac{ad - bc}{bd}.$$

We summarize this result in the following theorem.

> **Theorem 5-5**

If $\frac{a}{b}$ and $\frac{c}{d}$ are any rational numbers, then $\frac{a}{b} - \frac{c}{d} = \frac{ad - bc}{bd}$.

EXAMPLE 5-8

Find each difference in the following:

a. $\frac{5}{8} - \frac{1}{4}$ **b.** $5\frac{1}{3} - 2\frac{3}{4}$

Solution   **a.** One approach is to find the LCM for the fractions. Because LCM(8, 4) = 8, we have

$$\frac{5}{8} - \frac{1}{4} = \frac{5}{8} - \frac{2}{8} = \frac{3}{8}.$$

An alternative approach is as follows:

$$\frac{5}{8} - \frac{1}{4} = \frac{5 \cdot 4 - 8 \cdot 1}{8 \cdot 4} = \frac{20 - 8}{32} = \frac{12}{32}, \text{ or } \frac{3}{8}.$$

b. Two methods of solution are given:

$$
\begin{array}{l}
5\frac{1}{3} = \ 5\frac{4}{12} = 4 + 1\frac{4}{12} = \ 4\frac{16}{12} \\
-2\frac{3}{4} = -2\frac{9}{12} = -2\frac{9}{12} \ \ = -2\frac{9}{12} \\
\hline
\hspace{5cm} 2\frac{7}{12}
\end{array}
$$

$$
\begin{aligned}
5\frac{1}{3} - 2\frac{3}{4} &= \frac{16}{3} - \frac{11}{4} \\
&= \frac{16 \cdot 4 - 3 \cdot 11}{3 \cdot 4} \\
&= \frac{64 - 33}{12} \\
&= \frac{31}{12}, \text{ or } 2\frac{7}{12}
\end{aligned}
$$

Estimation with Rational Numbers

Estimation helps us make practical decisions in our everyday lives. For example, suppose we need to double a recipe that calls for $\frac{3}{8}$ of a cup of flour. Will we need more or less than a cup of flour? Many of the estimation and mental math techniques that we learned to use with whole numbers also work with rational numbers.

Estimation plays an important role in judging the reasonableness of computations. Students do not necessarily have this skill. For example, when asked to estimate $\frac{12}{13} + \frac{7}{8}$, only 24 percent of thirteen-year-old students on a national assessment said the answer was close to 2. Most said it was close to 1, 19, or 21. These incorrect estimates suggest common computational errors in adding fractions and suggest a lack of understanding of the operation being carried out. These incorrect estimates also suggest a lack of number sense.

NOW TRY THIS 5-9

A student added $\frac{3}{4} + \frac{1}{2}$ and obtained $\frac{4}{6}$. How would you use estimation to show this student that his answer could not be correct?

Sometimes to obtain an estimate it is desirable to round fractions to a *convenient* fraction, such as $\frac{1}{2}, \frac{1}{3}, \frac{1}{4}, \frac{1}{5}, \frac{2}{3}, \frac{3}{4}$, or 1. For example, if a student had 59 correct answers out of 80 questions, the student answered $\frac{59}{80}$ of the questions correctly, which is approximately $\frac{60}{80}$, or $\frac{3}{4}$. Intuitively, we know $\frac{60}{80}$ is greater than $\frac{59}{80}$. On a number line, the greater fraction is to the right of the lesser. The estimate $\frac{3}{4}$ for $\frac{59}{80}$ is a high estimate. In a similar way, we can estimate $\frac{31}{90}$ by $\frac{30}{90}$, or $\frac{1}{3}$. In this case, the estimate of $\frac{1}{3}$ is a low estimate.

EXAMPLE 5-9

A sixth-grade class is collecting cans to take to the recycling center. Becky's group brought the following amounts (in pounds). About how many pounds does her group have all together?

$$1\frac{1}{8}, 3\frac{4}{10}, 5\frac{7}{8}, \frac{6}{10}$$

Solution We can estimate the amount by using front-end estimation and then adjusting by using $0, \frac{1}{2}$, and 1 as reference points. The front-end estimate is $(1 + 3 + 5)$, or 9. The adjustment is $\left(0 + \frac{1}{2} + 1 + \frac{1}{2}\right)$, or 2. An adjusted estimate would be 11 lb.

E X A M P L E
5-10

Estimate each of the following:

a. $\dfrac{27}{13} + \dfrac{10}{9}$ **b.** $3\dfrac{9}{10} + 2\dfrac{7}{8} + \dfrac{11}{12}$

Solution   **a.** Because $\dfrac{27}{13}$ is more than 2 and $\dfrac{10}{9}$ is more than 1, an estimate is a number close to but more than 3.

b. We first add the whole-number parts to obtain $3 + 2$, or 5. Because each of the fractions, $\dfrac{9}{10}, \dfrac{7}{8},$ and $\dfrac{11}{12},$ is close to but less than 1, their sum is less than 3. The approximate answer is a number close to but less than 8.

O N G O I N G   A S S E S S M E N T   5 - 2

1. Compute each of the following using any method:

   a. $\dfrac{1}{2} + \dfrac{2}{3}$ b. $\dfrac{4}{12} - \dfrac{2}{3}$

   c. $\dfrac{5}{x} + \dfrac{^-3}{y}$ d. $\dfrac{^-3}{2x^2y} + \dfrac{5}{2xy^2} + \dfrac{7}{x^2}$

   e. $\dfrac{5}{6} + 2\dfrac{1}{8}$ f. $^-4\dfrac{1}{2} - 3\dfrac{1}{6}$

2. Change each of the following fractions to mixed numbers:

   a. $\dfrac{56}{3}$ b. $\dfrac{14}{5}$

   c. $-\dfrac{293}{100}$ d. $-\dfrac{47}{8}$

3. Change each of the following mixed numbers to fractions in the form $\dfrac{a}{b}$, where a and b are integers:

   a. $6\dfrac{3}{4}$ b. $7\dfrac{1}{2}$

   c. $^-3\dfrac{5}{8}$ d. $^-4\dfrac{2}{3}$

4. Place the numbers 2, 5, 6, and 8 in the following boxes to make the equation true:

   $$\dfrac{\square}{\square} + \dfrac{\square}{\square} = \dfrac{23}{24}$$

5. Approximate each of the following situations with a convenient fraction. Explain your reasoning. Tell whether your estimate is high or low.

   a. Giorgio had 15 base hits out of 46 times at bat.

   b. Ruth made 7 goals out of 41 shots.

   c. Laura answered 62 problems correctly out of 80.

   d. Jonathan made 9 baskets out of 19.

6. Use the information in the following table to answer each of the following questions:

Team	Games Played	Games Won
Ducks	22	10
Beavers	19	10
Tigers	28	9
Bears	23	8
Lions	27	7
Wildcats	25	6
Badgers	21	5

   a. Which team won just over $\dfrac{1}{2}$ of its games?

   b. Which team won just under $\dfrac{1}{2}$ of its games?

   c. Which team won just over $\dfrac{1}{3}$ of its games?

   d. Which team won just under $\dfrac{1}{3}$ of its games?

   e. Which team won just over $\dfrac{1}{4}$ of its games?

   f. Which team won just under $\dfrac{1}{4}$ of its games?

7. Sort the following fraction cards into the ovals by estimating in which oval the fraction belongs:

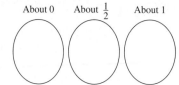

Sort these fraction cards   About 0   About $\frac{1}{2}$ About 1

8. Approximate each of the following fractions by 0, $\frac{1}{4}, \frac{1}{2}, \frac{3}{4}$, or 1. Tell whether your estimate is high or low.

   a. $\dfrac{19}{39}$ **b.** $\dfrac{3}{197}$ **c.** $\dfrac{150}{201}$ **d.** $\dfrac{8}{9}$

   e. $\dfrac{113}{100}$ **f.** $\dfrac{-2}{117}$ **g.** $\dfrac{150}{198}$ **h.** $\dfrac{999}{2000}$

9. Without actually finding the exact answer, state which of the numbers given in parentheses in the following is the best approximation for the given sum or difference:

   a. $\dfrac{6}{13} + \dfrac{7}{15} + \dfrac{11}{23} + \dfrac{17}{35} \left(1, 2, 3, 3\frac{1}{2}\right)$

   b. $\dfrac{30}{41} + \dfrac{1}{1000} + \dfrac{3}{2000} \left(\frac{3}{8}, \frac{3}{4}, 1, 2\right)$

   c. $\dfrac{103}{300} + \dfrac{203}{601} - \dfrac{602}{897} \left(1, \frac{1}{3}, \frac{2}{3}, 0\right)$

   d. $\dfrac{1}{100} - \dfrac{1}{101} + \dfrac{1}{102} - \dfrac{1}{103} \left(\frac{1}{2}, 1, 0\right)$

10. Compute each of the following mentally:

   a. $1 - \dfrac{3}{4}$ **b.** $6 - \dfrac{7}{8}$

   c. $3\dfrac{3}{8} + 2\dfrac{1}{4} - 5\dfrac{5}{8}$ **d.** $2\dfrac{3}{5} + 4\dfrac{1}{10} + 3\dfrac{3}{10}$

11. The following ruler has regions marked M, A, T, H:

Use mental mathematics and estimation to determine which region each of the following falls into (for example, $\dfrac{12}{5}$ in. falls in region A).

   a. $\dfrac{20}{8}$ in.   **b.** $\dfrac{36}{8}$ in.

   c. $\dfrac{60}{16}$ in.   **d.** $\dfrac{18}{4}$ in.

12. Use *clustering* to estimate the following sum.
$$3\frac{1}{3} + 3\frac{1}{5} + 2\frac{7}{8} + 2\frac{2}{9}$$

13. A class consists of $\frac{2}{5}$ freshmen, $\frac{1}{4}$ sophomores, and $\frac{1}{10}$ juniors; the rest are seniors. What fraction of the class is seniors?

14. The Naturals Company sells its products in many countries. The following two circle graphs show the fractions of the company's earnings for 1990 and 2000. Based on this information, answer the following questions:

   a. In 1990, how much greater was the fraction of sales for Japan than for Canada?

   b. In 2000, how much less was the fraction of sales for England than for the United States?

   c. How much greater was the fraction of total sales for the United States in 2000 than in 1990?

   d. Is it true that the amount of sales in dollars in Australia was less in 1990 than in 2000? Why?

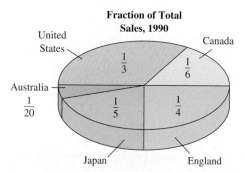

Fraction of Total Sales, 1990

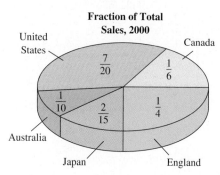

Fraction of Total Sales, 2000

15. A clerk sold three pieces of one type of ribbon to different customers. One piece was $\frac{1}{3}$ yd long, another was $2\frac{3}{4}$ yd long, and the third was $3\frac{1}{2}$ yd long. What was the total length of that type of ribbon sold?

16. A recipe requires $3\frac{1}{2}$ c of milk. Ran put in $1\frac{3}{4}$ c and emptied the container. How much more milk does he need to put in?

17. Martine bought $8\frac{3}{4}$ yd of fabric. She wants to make a skirt using $1\frac{7}{8}$ yd, pants using $2\frac{3}{8}$ yd, and a vest using $1\frac{2}{3}$ yd. How much fabric will be left over?

18. A $15\frac{3}{4}$-in. board is cut from a $38\frac{1}{4}$-in. board. The saw cut takes $\frac{3}{8}$ in. How much of the $38\frac{1}{4}$-in. board is left after cutting?

19. Students from Rattlesnake School formed four teams to collect cans for recycling during the months of April and May. The students received 10¢ for each 5 lb of cans. A record of their efforts follows:

Number of Pounds Collected

	Team 1	Team 2	Team 3	Team 4
April	$28\frac{3}{4}$	$32\frac{7}{8}$	$28\frac{1}{2}$	$35\frac{3}{16}$
May	$33\frac{1}{3}$	$28\frac{5}{12}$	$25\frac{3}{4}$	$41\frac{1}{2}$

   a. Which team collected the most for the 2-mo period? How much did they collect?

   b. What was the difference in the total amounts collected by all the teams during the 2 mo?

20. Demonstrate by example that each of the following properties of rational numbers holds:

   a. Closure property of addition

   b. Commutative property of addition

   c. Associative property of addition

21. For each of the following sequences, discover a pattern and write three more terms of the sequence if the pattern continues. Which of the sequences are arithmetic, and which are not? Justify your answers.

   a. $\frac{1}{4}, \frac{1}{2}, \frac{3}{4}, 1, \frac{5}{4}, \ldots$ **b.** $\frac{1}{2}, \frac{2}{3}, \frac{3}{4}, \frac{4}{5}, \frac{5}{6}, \ldots$

   c. $\frac{2}{3}, \frac{5}{3}, \frac{8}{3}, \frac{11}{3}, \frac{14}{3}, \ldots$ **d.** $\frac{5}{4}, \frac{3}{4}, \frac{1}{4}, \frac{^-1}{4}, \frac{^-3}{4}, \ldots$

22. Find the nth term in each of the sequences in problem 21.

23. Insert five fractions between the numbers 1 and 2 so that the seven numbers (including 1 and 2) constitute an arithmetic sequence.

24. Let $f(x) = x + \frac{3}{4}$ where the domain is the set of rational numbers.

   a. Find the outputs if the inputs are the following:

      (i) 0 **(ii)** $\frac{4}{3}$ **(iii)** $\frac{^-3}{4}$

   b. For which inputs will the outputs be the following?

      (i) 1 **(ii)** $^-1$ **(iii)** $\frac{1}{2}$

25. Let $f(x) = \frac{x+2}{x-1}$ and let the domain of the function be the set of all integers except 1. Find the following:

   a. $f(0)$ **b.** $f(^-2)$ c. $f(^-5)$ **d.** $f(5)$

26. **a.** Check that each of the following is true:

      (i) $\frac{1}{3} = \frac{1}{4} + \frac{1}{3 \cdot 4}$ **(ii)** $\frac{1}{4} = \frac{1}{5} + \frac{1}{4 \cdot 5}$

     (iii) $\frac{1}{5} = \frac{1}{6} + \frac{1}{5 \cdot 6}$

   b. Based on the examples in (a), write $\frac{1}{n}$ as a sum of two unit fractions, that is, as a sum of fractions with numerator 1.

Communication

27. Sally claims that it is easier to add two fractions if she adds the numerators and then adds the denominators. How can you help her?

28. Does each of the following properties hold for subtraction of rational numbers? Justify your answer.

   a. Closure   **b.** Commutative

   c. Associative   **d.** Identity

   e. Inverse

29. Explain an error pattern in each of the following.

   a. $\frac{13}{35} = \frac{1}{5}, \quad \frac{27}{73} = \frac{2}{3}, \quad \frac{16}{64} = \frac{1}{4}$

   b. $\frac{4}{5} + \frac{2}{3} = \frac{6}{8}, \quad \frac{2}{5} + \frac{3}{4} = \frac{5}{9}, \quad \frac{7}{8} + \frac{1}{3} = \frac{8}{11}$

   c. $8\frac{3}{8} - 6\frac{1}{4} = 2\frac{2}{4}, \quad 5\frac{3}{8} - 2\frac{2}{3} = 3\frac{1}{5}, \quad 2\frac{2}{7} - 1\frac{1}{3} = 1\frac{1}{4}$

   d. $\frac{2}{3} \cdot 3 = \frac{6}{9}, \quad \frac{1}{4} \cdot 6 = \frac{6}{24}, \quad \frac{4}{5} \cdot 2 = \frac{8}{10}$

Open-Ended

30. **a.** With the exception of $\frac{2}{3}$, the Egyptians used only unit fractions (fractions that have numerators of 1). For example, the Egyptians had the following symbols:

$$\frac{1}{4} = \overset{\frown}{||||}, \quad \frac{1}{10} = \cap, \quad \frac{1}{15} = \cap||||| .$$

Every unit fraction can be expressed as the sum of two unit fractions in more than one way, for example, $\frac{1}{2} = \frac{1}{4} + \frac{1}{4}$ and $\frac{1}{2} = \frac{1}{3} + \frac{1}{6}$. Find at least two different unit fraction representations for each of the following.

      (i) $\frac{1}{3}$ **(ii)** $\frac{1}{7}$

   b. Compute $\frac{1}{n} - \frac{1}{n+1}$ and simplify your answer.

   c. How does your answer in part (b) help to answer the question in part (a)? Use the ideas of part (b) to write $\frac{1}{17}$ as a sum of two different unit fractions.

Cooperative Learning

31. Interview 10 people and ask them if and when they add and subtract fractions in their lives. Combine their responses with those of the rest of the class to get a view of how "ordinary" people must use computation of rational numbers in their daily lives.

Review Problems

32. Simplify if possible.

   a. $\frac{14}{21}$ **b.** $\frac{117}{153}$ c. $\frac{5^2}{7^2}$

   d. $\frac{a^2 + a}{1 + a}$ e. $\frac{a^2 + 1}{a + 1}$

33. Determine if the fractions in each of the following pairs are equal:

a. $\dfrac{a^2}{b}$ and $\dfrac{a^2 b^2}{b^3}$

b. $\dfrac{377}{400}$ and $\dfrac{378}{401}$

c. $\dfrac{0}{10}$ and $\dfrac{0}{-10}$

d. $\dfrac{a}{b}$ and $\dfrac{a+1}{b+1}$, where $a \neq b$

34. a. What month of the year has the smallest fraction of days of the year?

b. What fraction of days of the year occur before July 4?

c. How many days are actually in a year? Express this as a mixed number and as an improper fraction.

35. If the same positive number is added to the numerator and denominator of a positive proper fraction, is the new fraction greater than, less than, or equal to the original fraction? Justify your answer.

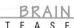

T E A S E R

When Professor Sum was asked by Mr. Little how many students were in his classes, he answered, "All of them study either languages, physics, or not at all. One half of them study languages only, one fourth of them study French, one seventh of them study physics only, and 20 do not study at all." How many students does Professor Sum have?

Multiplication and Division of Rational Numbers

Multiplication of Rational Numbers

To motivate the definition of multiplication of rational numbers, we use the interpretation of multiplication as repeated addition. Using repeated addition, we can interpret $3 \cdot \left(\dfrac{3}{4}\right)$ as follows:

$$3 \cdot \left(\frac{3}{4}\right) = \frac{3}{4} + \frac{3}{4} + \frac{3}{4} = \frac{9}{4} = 2\frac{1}{4}.$$

The area model in Figure 5-10 is another way to show this calculation.

FIGURE 5-10

$$3 \quad \cdot \quad \frac{3}{4} \quad = \quad \frac{3}{4} \quad + \quad \frac{3}{4} \quad + \quad \frac{3}{4} \quad = \quad \frac{9}{4}, \quad \text{or} \quad 2\frac{1}{4}$$

We next consider $\left(\dfrac{3}{4}\right) \cdot 3$. How should this product be interpreted? If the commutative property of multiplication of rational numbers is to hold, then $\left(\dfrac{3}{4}\right) \cdot 3 = 3 \cdot \left(\dfrac{3}{4}\right) = \dfrac{9}{4}$.

Next, we consider what happens when neither factor in the product is an integer. If forests once covered about $\dfrac{3}{5}$ of Earth's land and only about $\dfrac{1}{2}$ of these forests remain, what fraction of Earth is covered with forests today? We can use an area model to find out.

FIGURE 5-11

$$\frac{3}{5}$$

(a)

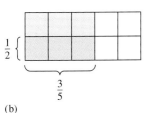

$\frac{1}{2}\left\{\right.$

$$\frac{3}{5}$$

(b)

Figure 5-11(a) shows a one-unit rectangle separated into fifths, with $\frac{3}{5}$ shaded. To find $\frac{1}{2}$ of $\frac{3}{5}$, we divide the shaded portion of the rectangle in Figure 5-11(a) into two equal parts and take one of those parts. The result would be the green portion of Figure 5-11(b). However, the green portion represents three parts out of 10, or $\frac{3}{10}$, of the one-unit rectangle. Thus

$$\frac{1}{2} \cdot \frac{3}{5} = \frac{3}{10} = \frac{1 \cdot 3}{2 \cdot 5}.$$

This discussion leads to the following definition of multiplication for rational numbers.

> ## Definition of Multiplication of Rational Numbers
>
> If $\frac{a}{b}$ and $\frac{c}{d}$ are any rational numbers, then $\frac{a}{b} \cdot \frac{c}{d} = \frac{a \cdot c}{b \cdot d}.$

**E X A M P L E
5-11**

Answer the following:

If $\frac{5}{6}$ of the population of a certain city are college graduates and $\frac{7}{11}$ of the city's college graduates are female, what fraction of the population of that city is female and college graduates?

Solution The fraction should be $\frac{7}{11}$ of $\frac{5}{6}$ or $\frac{7}{11} \cdot \frac{5}{6} = \frac{7 \cdot 5}{11 \cdot 6} = \frac{35}{66}.$

The fraction of the population that is college-graduated females is $\frac{35}{66}.$

Properties of Multiplication of Rational Numbers

Multiplication of rational numbers has properties analogous to the properties of addition of rational numbers. These include the following properties for multiplication: closure, commutative, associative, multiplicative identity, and multiplicative inverse. For emphasis, we list the last two properties.

> ## Properties
>
> **Multiplicative identity of rational numbers** The number 1 is the unique number such that for every rational number $\frac{a}{b}$,
>
> $$1 \cdot \left(\frac{a}{b}\right) = \frac{a}{b} = \left(\frac{a}{b}\right) \cdot 1.$$
>
> **Multiplicative inverse of rational numbers** For any nonzero rational number $\frac{a}{b}$, $\frac{b}{a}$ is the unique rational number such that $\frac{a}{b} \cdot \frac{b}{a} = 1 = \frac{b}{a} \cdot \frac{a}{b}$. The multiplicative inverse of $\frac{a}{b}$ is also called the **reciprocal** of $\frac{a}{b}$.

reciprocal

EXAMPLE
5-12

Find the multiplicative inverse, if possible, for each of the following rational numbers:

a. $\dfrac{2}{3}$ **b.** $\dfrac{-2}{5}$ **c.** 4   **d.** 0   **e.** $6\dfrac{1}{2}$

Solution   **a.** $\dfrac{3}{2}$

b. $\dfrac{5}{-2}$, or $\dfrac{-5}{2}$

c. Because $4 = \dfrac{4}{1}$, the multiplicative inverse of 4 is $\dfrac{1}{4}$.

d. Even though $0 = \dfrac{0}{1}, \dfrac{1}{0}$ is undefined; there is no multiplicative inverse of 0.

e. Because $6\dfrac{1}{2} = \dfrac{13}{2}$, the multiplicative inverse of $6\dfrac{1}{2}$ is $\dfrac{2}{13}$.

Multiplication and addition are connected through the distributive property of multiplication over addition. Also there is a multiplication property of equality for rational numbers and a multiplication property of zero similar to those for whole numbers and integers.

> ## Properties

Distributive property of multiplication over addition for rational numbers.   If $\dfrac{a}{b}, \dfrac{c}{d}$, and $\dfrac{e}{f}$ are any rational numbers, then

$$\frac{a}{b}\left(\frac{c}{d} + \frac{e}{f}\right) = \left(\frac{a}{b} \cdot \frac{c}{d}\right) + \left(\frac{a}{b} \cdot \frac{e}{f}\right).$$

Multiplication property of equality for rational numbers.   If $\dfrac{a}{b}$ and $\dfrac{c}{d}$ are any rational numbers such that $\dfrac{a}{b} = \dfrac{c}{d}$, and $\dfrac{e}{f}$ is any rational number, then $\dfrac{a}{b} \cdot \dfrac{e}{f} = \dfrac{c}{d} \cdot \dfrac{e}{f}$.

Multiplication property of zero for rational numbers.   If $\dfrac{a}{b}$ is any rational number, then

$$\frac{a}{b} \cdot 0 = 0 = 0 \cdot \frac{a}{b}.$$

EXAMPLE
5-13

A bicycle is on sale at $\dfrac{3}{4}$ of its original price. If the sale price is $330, what was the original price?

Solution   Let x be the original price. Then $\dfrac{3}{4}$ of the original price is $\dfrac{3}{4}x$. Because the sale price is $330, we have $\dfrac{3}{4}x = 330$. Solving for x gives

$$\frac{4}{3} \cdot \frac{3}{4}x = \frac{4}{3} \cdot 330$$
$$1 \cdot x = 440$$
$$x = 440.$$

Thus the original price was $440.

An alternative approach, which does not use algebra, follows. Because $\frac{3}{4}$ of the original price is \$330, $\frac{1}{4}$ of the original price is $\frac{1}{3} \cdot 330$, or \$110; thus $4 \cdot \frac{1}{4}$ of the original price is $4 \cdot 110$, or \$440.

Multiplication with Mixed Numbers

In the "Peanuts" cartoon, Sally is having trouble multiplying two mixed numbers. If she used an estimate to check whether her answer was reasonable, she would notice that if she multiplies two numbers that are both less than 3, the answer must be less than 9.

One way to multiply $2\frac{1}{2} \cdot 2\frac{1}{2}$ is to change the mixed numbers to improper fractions and use the definition of multiplication, as shown below.

$$2\frac{1}{2} \cdot 2\frac{1}{2} = \frac{5}{2} \cdot \frac{5}{2} = \frac{25}{4}$$

We could then change $\frac{25}{4}$ to the mixed number $6\frac{1}{4}$.

Another way to multiply mixed numbers uses the distributive property of multiplication over addition. For example,

$$2\frac{1}{2} \cdot 2\frac{1}{2} = \left(2 + \frac{1}{2}\right) \cdot \left(2 + \frac{1}{2}\right)$$
$$= \left(2 + \frac{1}{2}\right) \cdot 2 + \left(2 + \frac{1}{2}\right) \cdot \frac{1}{2}$$
$$= 2 \cdot 2 + \frac{1}{2} \cdot 2 + 2 \cdot \frac{1}{2} + \frac{1}{2} \cdot \frac{1}{2}$$
$$= 4 + 1 + 1 + \frac{1}{4}$$
$$= 6 + \frac{1}{4}$$
$$= 6\frac{1}{4}.$$

> **PROBLEM SOLVING**   <u>Sonja's Deck</u>

Sonja wants to build a square deck with the floor made out of 1-in.-by-6-in. boards. She wants the deck to be 30 boards wide. Boards come in lengths of 6, 8, 10, 12, 14, 16, 18, and 20 ft and sell for 32¢ per ft. How many boards of what length must Sonja order to make the floor? What is the minimum cost of the floor if she orders only complete boards?

Understanding the Problem   In reality a 1-in.-by-6-in. board is $5\frac{1}{2}$ in. wide and $\frac{3}{4}$ in. thick. Only complete boards can be used. We need to find the minimum cost.

Devising a Plan   Because the deck is a square and the deck is 30 boards wide, the length of the deck must be $30 \cdot \left(5\frac{1}{2}\right) = 165$ in. From this information, we can find the length of the boards Sonja needs and the cost.

Carrying Out the Plan   Since the length of the deck is 165 in., we divide by 12 to convert to feet and obtain $13\frac{3}{4}$ ft. Hence, we need to order 30 of the 14-ft boards. This gives $30 \cdot 14$, or 420 ft, at 32¢ per ft. Thus Sonja's bill would be $32¢ \cdot 420 = \$134.40$. This is the minimum cost because boards shorter than 14 ft will not work, boards longer than 14 ft cost more, and two lengths cannot be cut from any board.

Looking Back   We could vary this problem by changing the sizes of the deck or the boards. We could also work on *related problems* such as which size nail is needed to nail together three 1-in.-by-6-in. boards so that the nail would go through two boards and go $\frac{1}{2}$ in. into the third board. (Nail sizes increase by $\frac{1}{4}$ in. For example, a 2-penny nail is 1 in. long; a 3-penny nail is $1\frac{1}{4}$ in. long; a 4-penny nail is $1\frac{1}{2}$ in. long, and so forth.) How many nails would be needed to nail down the deck?

Division of Rational Numbers

In the *Principles and Standards* we find the following statement concerning division of rational numbers.

> *The division of fractions has traditionally been quite vexing for students. Although "invert and multiply" has been a staple of conventional mathematics instruction and although it seems to be a simple way to remember how to divide fractions, students have for a long time had difficulty doing so. Some students forget which number is to be inverted, and others are confused about when it is appropriate to apply the procedure. A common way of formally justifying the "invert and multiply" procedure is to use sophisticated arguments involving the manipulation of algebraic rational expressions—arguments beyond the reach of many middle-grades students. This process can seem very remote and mysterious to many students. Lacking an understanding of the underlying rationale, many students are therefore unable to repair their errors and clear up their confusions about division of fractions on their own. An alternative approach involves helping students understand the division of fractions by building on what they know about the division of whole numbers.* (p. 219)

We try to follow that advice in developing the concept of division of rational numbers.

Recall that $6 \div 3$ means "How many 3s are there in 6?" We found that $6 \div 3 = 2$ because $3 \cdot 2 = 6$. Consider $3 \div \left(\dfrac{1}{2}\right)$, which is equivalent to finding how many halves there are in 3. We see from the area model in Figure 5-12 that there are 6 half pieces in the 3 whole pieces. We record this as $3 \div \left(\dfrac{1}{2}\right) = 6$. This is true because $\left(\dfrac{1}{2}\right) \cdot 6 = 3$.

FIGURE 5-12

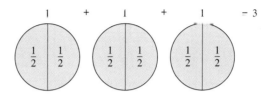

Next, consider $\left(\dfrac{3}{4}\right) \div \left(\dfrac{1}{8}\right)$. This means "How many $\dfrac{1}{8}$s are in $\dfrac{3}{4}$?" Figure 5-13 shows that there are six $\dfrac{1}{8}$s in the shaded portion, which represents $\dfrac{3}{4}$ of the whole. Therefore $\left(\dfrac{3}{4}\right) \div \left(\dfrac{1}{8}\right) = 6$. This is true because $\left(\dfrac{1}{8}\right) \cdot 6 = \dfrac{3}{4}$.

FIGURE 5-13

In the previous examples, we saw a relationship between division and multiplication of rational numbers. We can define division for rational numbers formally in terms of multiplication in the same way that we define division for whole numbers.

> ### Definition of Division of Rational Numbers

If $\dfrac{a}{b}$ and $\dfrac{c}{d}$ are any rational numbers and $\dfrac{c}{d}$ is not zero, then $\dfrac{a}{b} \div \dfrac{c}{d} = \dfrac{e}{f}$ if, and only if, $\dfrac{e}{f}$ is the unique rational number such that $\dfrac{c}{d} \cdot \dfrac{e}{f} = \dfrac{a}{b}$.

REMARK   In the definition of division, $\dfrac{c}{d}$ is not zero because division by zero is impossible. Also, $\dfrac{c}{d} \neq 0$ implies that $c \neq 0$.

Algorithm for Division of Rational Numbers

As we see in the "Peanuts" cartoon, Sally doesn't understand why the algorithm for division of fractions works. She is not alone in her confusion and we will explain why "to divide fractions we use the reciprocal and multiply."

To develop an algorithm for division of rational numbers, we consider what such a division might mean. For example,

$$\frac{2}{3} \div \frac{5}{7} = x \quad \text{implies} \quad \frac{2}{3} = \frac{5}{7}x.$$

We multiply both sides of the equation by $\frac{7}{5}$. Thus,

$$\frac{7}{5} \cdot \frac{2}{3} = \frac{7}{5} \cdot \left(\frac{5}{7}x\right) = x.$$

A traditional justification of the division algorithm also follows. The algorithm for division of fractions is usually justified in the middle grades by using the Fundamental Law of Fractions, $\frac{a}{b} = \frac{ac}{bc}$, where a, b, and c are all fractions. For example,

$$\frac{2}{3} \div \frac{5}{7} = \frac{\frac{2}{3}}{\frac{5}{7}} = \frac{\frac{2}{3} \cdot \frac{7}{5}}{\frac{5}{7} \cdot \frac{7}{5}} = \frac{\frac{2}{3} \cdot \frac{7}{5}}{1} = \frac{2}{3} \cdot \frac{7}{5}.$$

Thus

$$\frac{2}{3} \div \frac{5}{7} = \frac{2}{3} \cdot \frac{7}{5}.$$

We summarize the algorithm as follows:

> **Algorithm for Division of Fractions**
>
> $$\frac{a}{b} \div \frac{c}{d} = \frac{a}{b} \cdot \frac{d}{c}, \quad \text{where} \quad \frac{c}{d} \neq 0.$$

An alternative algorithm for division of fractions can be found by first dividing fractions that have equal denominators. For example, $\frac{9}{10} \div \frac{3}{10} = 9 \div 3$ and $\frac{15}{23} \div \frac{5}{23} = 15 \div 5$. These examples suggest that when two fractions with the same denominator are divided, the result can be obtained by dividing the numerator of the first fraction by the numerator of the second. To divide fractions with different denominators, we rename the fractions so that the denominators are equal. Thus

$$\frac{a}{b} \div \frac{c}{d} = \frac{ad}{bd} \div \frac{bc}{bd} = ad \div bc = \frac{ad}{bc}.$$

EXAMPLE 5-14

A radio station provides 36 min for Public Service Announcements for every 24 hr of broadcasting.

a. What part of the broadcasting day is allotted to Public Service Announcements?
b. How many 3/4-min Public Service Announcements can be allowed in the 36 min?

Solution   **a.** There are 60 min in an hour and 60 · 24 min in a day. Thus 36/(60 · 24), or 1/40, of the day is allotted for the announcements.
   b. 36/(3/4) = 36(4/3), or 48, announcements are allowed.

EXAMPLE 5-15

We have $35\frac{1}{2}$ yd of material available to make shirts. Each shirt requires $\frac{3}{8}$ yd of material.

a. How many shirts can be made?
b. How much material will be left over?

Solution   **a.** We need to find the integer part of the answer to $35\frac{1}{2} \div \frac{3}{8}$. The division follows:

$$35\frac{1}{2} \div \frac{3}{8} = \frac{71}{2} \cdot \frac{8}{3} = \frac{284}{3} = 94\frac{2}{3}.$$

Thus we can make 94 shirts.
   b. Because the division in (a) was by $\frac{3}{8}$, the amount of material left over is $\frac{2}{3}$ of $\frac{3}{8}$, or $\frac{2}{3} \cdot \frac{3}{8}$, or $\frac{1}{4}$ yd. This can also be answered by noting that the $\frac{2}{3}$ in part (a) is two-thirds of a shirt, which requires $\frac{2}{3}$ of $\frac{3}{8}$ yd of material.

Estimation and Mental Math with Rational Numbers

Estimation and mental math strategies that were developed with whole numbers can also be used with rational numbers.

EXAMPLE 5-16

Use mental math to find

a. $(12 \cdot 25) \cdot \frac{1}{4}$ **b.** $5\frac{1}{6} \cdot 12$ **c.** $\frac{4}{5} \cdot 20$

Solution   Each of the following is a possible approach.

a. $(12 \cdot 25) \cdot \frac{1}{4} = 25 \cdot \left(12 \cdot \frac{1}{4}\right) = 25 \cdot 3 = 75$

b. $5\frac{1}{6} \cdot 12 = 5 \cdot 12 + \frac{1}{6} \cdot 12 = 60 + 2 = 62$

c. $\frac{4}{5} \cdot 20 = 4\left(\frac{1}{5} \cdot 20\right) = 4 \cdot 4 = 16$

EXAMPLE 5-17

Estimate each of the following:

a. $3\frac{1}{4} \cdot 7\frac{8}{9}$ **b.** $24\frac{5}{7} \div 4\frac{1}{8}$

Solution   **a.** Using rounding, the product will be close to $3 \cdot 8 = 24$. If we use the range strategy, we can say the product must be between $3 \cdot 7 = 21$ and $4 \cdot 8 = 32$.

b. We can use compatible numbers and think of the estimate as $24 \div 4 = 6$ or $25 \div 5 = 5$.

Extending the Notion of Exponents

Recall that a^m was defined for any number a and any natural number m as follows.

> ### Definition of *a* to the *m*th Power
>
> $a^m = \underbrace{a \cdot a \cdot a \cdot \ldots \cdot a}_{m \text{ factors}}$, where a is any rational number and m is any natural number.

From the definition, $a^3 \cdot a^2 = (a \cdot a \cdot a) \cdot (a \cdot a) = a^{3+2}$. In a similar way, it follows that

$$(1) \qquad\qquad\qquad a^m \cdot a^n = a^{m+n},$$

where a is any number and m and n are natural numbers. If (1) is true for all whole numbers m and n, then because $a^1 \cdot a^0 = a^{1+0} = a^1$, we must have $a^0 = 1$. Hence, it is useful to give meaning to a^0 when $a \neq 0$ as follows:

$$(2) \qquad\qquad\qquad a^0 = 1, \qquad \text{if } a \neq 0.$$

These notions can be extended for rational number values of a. For example, consider the following:

$$\left(\frac{2}{3}\right)^4 = \frac{2}{3} \cdot \frac{2}{3} \cdot \frac{2}{3} \cdot \frac{2}{3}$$

$$\left(\frac{2}{3}\right)^2 \cdot \left(\frac{2}{3}\right)^3 = \left(\frac{2}{3} \cdot \frac{2}{3}\right) \cdot \left(\frac{2}{3} \cdot \frac{2}{3} \cdot \frac{2}{3}\right) = \left(\frac{2}{3}\right)^{2+3} = \left(\frac{2}{3}\right)^5.$$

Exponents can also be extended to negative integers. Notice that as the exponents decrease by 1, the numbers on the right are divided by 10. Thus the pattern might be continued, as shown.

$$10^3 = 10 \cdot 10 \cdot 10$$
$$10^2 = 10 \cdot 10$$
$$10^1 = 10$$
$$10^0 = 1$$
$$10^{-1} = \frac{1}{10} = \frac{1}{10^1}$$
$$10^{-2} = \frac{1}{10} \cdot \frac{1}{10} = \frac{1}{10^2}$$
$$10^{-3} = \frac{1}{10^2} \cdot \frac{1}{10} = \frac{1}{10^3}$$

If the pattern is extended, then we would predict that $10^{-n} = \frac{1}{10^n}$. This is true, and in general, for any nonzero number a, $a^{-n} = \frac{1}{a^n}$.

Consider whether the property $a^m \cdot a^n = a^{m+n}$ can be extended to include all powers of a, where the exponents are integers. For example, is it true that $2^4 \cdot 2^{-3} = 2^{4+^-3} = 2^1$? The definitions of 2^{-3} and the properties of nonnegative exponents ensure this is true, as shown next:

$$2^4 \cdot 2^{-3} = 2^4 \cdot \frac{1}{2^3} = \frac{2^4}{2^3} = \frac{2^1 \cdot 2^3}{2^3} = 2^1.$$

Also, $2^{-4} \cdot 2^{-3} = 2^{-4+^-3} = 2^{-7}$ is true because

$$2^{-4} \cdot 2^{-3} = \frac{1}{2^4} \cdot \frac{1}{2^3} = \frac{1 \cdot 1}{2^4 \cdot 2^3} = \frac{1}{2^{4+3}} = \frac{1}{2^7} = 2^{-7}.$$

In general, with integer exponents, the following property holds.

> **Property**

For any nonzero rational number a and any integers m and n, $a^m \cdot a^n = a^{m+n}$.

Other properties of exponents can be developed by using the properties of rational numbers. For example,

$$\frac{2^5}{2^3} = \frac{2^3 \cdot 2^2}{2^3} = 2^2 = 2^{5-3} \qquad \frac{2^5}{2^8} = \frac{2^5}{2^5 \cdot 2^3} = \frac{1}{2^3} = 2^{-3} = 2^{5-8}.$$

With integer exponents, the following property holds.

> **Property**

For any rational number a such that $a \neq 0$ and for any integers m and n, $\dfrac{a^m}{a^n} = a^{m-n}$.

At times, we may encounter an expression like $(2^4)^3$. This expression can be written as a single power of 2 as follows:

$$(2^4)^3 = 2^4 \cdot 2^4 \cdot 2^4 = 2^{4+4+4} = 2^{3 \cdot 4} = 2^{12}.$$

In general, if a is a nonzero rational number and m and n are positive integers, then

$$\overbrace{(a^m)^n = \underbrace{a^m \cdot a^m \cdot a^m \cdot ... \cdot a^m}_{n \text{ factors}} = a^{m+m+ \cdots +m}}^{n \text{ terms}} = a^{nm} = a^{mn}.$$

Does this property hold for negative-integer exponents? For example, does $(2^3)^{-4} = 2^{(3)(-4)} = 2^{-12}$? The answer is yes because $(2^3)^{-4} = \dfrac{1}{(2^3)^4} = \dfrac{1}{2^{12}} = 2^{-12}$. Also, $(2^{-3})^4 = \left(\dfrac{1}{2^3}\right)^4 = \dfrac{1}{2^3} \cdot \dfrac{1}{2^3} \cdot \dfrac{1}{2^3} \cdot \dfrac{1}{2^3} = \dfrac{1^4}{(2^3)^4} = \dfrac{1}{2^{12}} = 2^{-12}.$

> **Property**

For any rational number $a \neq 0$ and any integers m and n,
$$(a^m)^n = a^{mn}.$$

Using the definitions and properties developed, we can derive additional properties. Notice, for example, that

$$\left(\frac{2}{3}\right)^4 = \frac{2}{3} \cdot \frac{2}{3} \cdot \frac{2}{3} \cdot \frac{2}{3} = \frac{2 \cdot 2 \cdot 2 \cdot 2}{3 \cdot 3 \cdot 3 \cdot 3} = \frac{2^4}{3^4}.$$

This property can be generalized as follows.

> **Property**

For any nonzero rational number $\dfrac{a}{b}$ and any integer m,
$$\left(\frac{a}{b}\right)^m = \frac{a^m}{b^m}.$$

From the definition of negative exponents, the preceding property, and division of fractions, we have

$$\left(\frac{a}{b}\right)^{-m} = \frac{1}{\left(\dfrac{a}{b}\right)^m} = \frac{1}{\dfrac{a^m}{b^m}} = \frac{b^m}{a^m} = \left(\frac{b}{a}\right)^m.$$

> **Property**

For any nonzero rational number $\dfrac{a}{b}$ and any integer m, $\left(\dfrac{a}{b}\right)^{-m} = \left(\dfrac{b}{a}\right)^m.$

A property similar to this holds for multiplication. For example,

$$(2 \cdot 3)^{-3} = \frac{1}{(2 \cdot 3)^3} = \frac{1}{2^3 \cdot 3^3} = \left(\frac{1}{2^3}\right) \cdot \left(\frac{1}{3^3}\right) = 2^{-3} \cdot 3^{-3},$$

and in general, it is true that $(a \cdot b)^m = a^m \cdot b^m$ if a and b are rational numbers and m is an integer.

The definitions and properties of exponents are summarized in the following list. For any rational numbers a and b and integers m and n (as long as 0^0 does not appear), we have the following:

> ## Properties of Exponents

1. $a^m = \underbrace{a \cdot a \cdot a \cdot \ldots \cdot a}_{m \text{ factors}}$, where m is a positive integer

2. $a^0 = 1$, where $a \neq 0$

3. $a^{-m} = \dfrac{1}{a^m}$, where $a \neq 0$

4. $a^m \cdot a^n = a^{m+n}$

5. $\dfrac{a^m}{a^n} = a^{m-n}$, where $a \neq 0$

6. $(a^m)^n = a^{mn}$

7. $\left(\dfrac{a}{b}\right)^m = \dfrac{a^m}{b^m}$, where $b \neq 0$

8. $(ab)^m = a^m \cdot b^m$

9. $\left(\dfrac{a}{b}\right)^{-m} = \left(\dfrac{b}{a}\right)^m$, where $a \neq 0, b \neq 0$

Observe that all the properties of exponents refer to powers with either the same base or the same exponent. To evaluate expressions using exponents where different bases or powers are used, perform all the computations or rewrite the expressions in either the same base or the same exponent if possible. For example, $\dfrac{27^4}{81^3}$ can be rewritten $\dfrac{27^4}{81^3} = \dfrac{(3^3)^4}{(3^4)^3} = \dfrac{3^{12}}{3^{12}} = 1.$

E X A M P L E
5-18

Write each of the following in simplest form using positive exponents in the final answer:

a. $16^2 \cdot 8^{-3}$ **b.** $20^2 \div 2^4$ **c.** $(10^{-1} + 5 \cdot 10^{-2} + 3 \cdot 10^{-3}) \cdot 10^3$

Solution   **a.** $16^2 \cdot 8^{-3} = (2^4)^2 \cdot (2^3)^{-3} = 2^8 \cdot 2^{-9} = 2^{8+-9} = 2^{-1} = \dfrac{1}{2}$

b. $\dfrac{20^2}{2^4} = \dfrac{(2^2 \cdot 5)^2}{2^4} = \dfrac{2^4 \cdot 5^2}{2^4} = 5^2$

c. $(10^{-1} + 5 \cdot 10^{-2} + 3 \cdot 10^{-3}) \cdot 10^3 = 10^{-1} \cdot 10^3 + 5 \cdot 10^{-2} \cdot 10^3 + 3 \cdot 10^{-3} \cdot 10^3$
$= 10^{-1+3} + 5 \cdot 10^{-2+3} + 3 \cdot 10^{-3+3}$
$= 10^2 + 5 \cdot 10^1 + 3 \cdot 10^0$
$= 153$

BRAIN
T E A S E R

A castle in the faraway land of Aluossim was surrounded by four moats. One day, the castle was attacked and captured by a fierce tribe from the north. Guards were stationed at each bridge. Prince Juan was allowed to take a number of bags of gold from the castle as he went into exile. However, the guard at the first bridge demanded half the bags of gold plus one more bag. Juan met this demand and proceeded to the next bridge. The guards at the second, third, and fourth bridges made identical demands, all of which the prince met. When Juan finally crossed all the bridges, a single bag of gold was left. With how many bags did Juan start?

O N G O I N G   A S S E S S M E N T   5 - 3

1. In the following figures, a unit rectangle is used to illustrate the product of two fractions. Name the fractions and their products.

   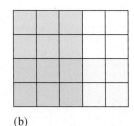

   (a)   (b)

2. Use a rectangular region to illustrate each of the following products:

   a. $\dfrac{3}{4} \cdot \dfrac{1}{3}$ b. $\dfrac{1}{5} \cdot \dfrac{2}{3}$ c. $\dfrac{2}{5} \cdot \dfrac{1}{3}$

3. Find each of the following products. Write your answers in simplest form.

   a. $\dfrac{49}{65} \cdot \dfrac{26}{98}$ b. $\dfrac{a}{b} \cdot \dfrac{b^2}{a^2}$ c. $\dfrac{xy}{z} \cdot \dfrac{z^2 a}{x^3 y^2}$

   d. $2\dfrac{1}{3} \cdot 3\dfrac{3}{4}$ e. $\dfrac{22}{7} \cdot 4\dfrac{2}{3}$ f. $\dfrac{-5}{2} \cdot 2\dfrac{1}{2}$

4. Use the distributive property to find each product.

   a. $4\dfrac{1}{2} \cdot 2\dfrac{1}{3}$ $\left[Hint: \left(4 + \dfrac{1}{2}\right) \cdot \left(2 + \dfrac{1}{3}\right). \right]$

   b. $3\dfrac{1}{3} \cdot 2\dfrac{1}{2}$ c. $248\dfrac{2}{5} \cdot 100\dfrac{1}{8}$

5. Find the multiplicative inverse of each of the following:

   a. $\dfrac{-1}{3}$ b. $3\dfrac{1}{3}$

   c. $\dfrac{x}{y}$, if $x \neq 0$ and $y \neq 0$ d. $^-7$

6. Compute the following mentally. Find the exact answers.

   a. $3\dfrac{1}{4} \cdot 8$ b. $7\dfrac{1}{4} \cdot 4$ c. $9\dfrac{1}{5} \cdot 10$ d. $8 \cdot 2\dfrac{1}{4}$

   e. $3 \div \dfrac{1}{2}$ f. $3\dfrac{1}{2} \div \dfrac{1}{2}$ g. $3 \div \dfrac{1}{3}$ h. $4\dfrac{1}{2} \div 2$

7. Choose the number from among the numbers in parentheses that best approximates each of the following:

   a. $3\dfrac{11}{12} \cdot 5\dfrac{3}{100}$ (8, 20, 15, 16)

   b. $2\dfrac{1}{10} \cdot 7\dfrac{7}{8}$ (16, 14, 4, 3)

   c. $20\dfrac{2}{3} \div 9\dfrac{7}{8}$ $\left(2, 180, \dfrac{1}{2}, 10 \right)$

   d. $\dfrac{1}{101} \div \dfrac{1}{103}$ $\left(0, 1, \dfrac{1}{2}, \dfrac{1}{4} \right)$

8. Estimate the following:

   a. $5\dfrac{4}{5} \cdot 3\dfrac{1}{10}$ b. $4\dfrac{10}{11} \cdot 5\dfrac{1}{8}$

   c. $\dfrac{20\dfrac{8}{9}}{3\dfrac{1}{12}}$ d. $\dfrac{12\dfrac{1}{3}}{1\dfrac{7}{8}}$

9. Without actually doing the computations, choose the number in parentheses that correctly describes each:

   a. $\dfrac{13}{14} \cdot \dfrac{17}{19}$ (greater than 1, less than 1)

   b. $3\dfrac{2}{7} \div 5\dfrac{1}{9}$ (greater than 1, less than 1)

   c. $4\dfrac{1}{3} \div 2\dfrac{3}{100}$ (greater than 2, less than 2)

   d. $16 \div 4\dfrac{3}{18}$ (greater than 4, less than 4)

   e. $16 \div 3\dfrac{8}{9}$ (greater than 4, less than 4)

10. A sewing project requires $6\dfrac{1}{8}$ yd of material that sells for 62¢ per yard and $3\dfrac{1}{4}$ yd that sells for 81¢ per yard. Choose from the following the best estimate for the cost of the project:

   a. Between $2 and $4   b. Between $4 and $6
   c. Between $6 and $8   d. Between $8 and $10

11. When you multiply a certain number by 3 and then subtract $\frac{7}{18}$, you get the same result as when you multiply the number by 2 and add $\frac{5}{12}$. What is the number?

12. Five-eighths of the students at Salem State College live in dormitories. If 6000 students at the college live in dormitories, how many students are there in the college?

13. Di Paloma University had a faculty reduction and lost $\frac{1}{5}$ of its faculty. If 320 faculty members were left after the reduction, how many members were there originally?

14. Alberto owns $\frac{5}{9}$ of the stock in the N.W. Tofu Company. His sister Renatta owns half as much stock as Alberto. What part of the stock is owned by neither Alberto nor Renatta?

15. A person has $29\frac{1}{2}$ yd of material available to make doll uniforms. Each uniform requires $\frac{3}{4}$ yd of material.
    a. How many uniforms can be made?
    b. How much material will be left over?

16. A suit is on sale for $180. What was the original price of the suit if the discount was $\frac{1}{4}$ of the original price?

17. Every employee's salary at the Sunrise Software Company increases each year by $\frac{1}{10}$ of that person's salary the previous year.
    a. If Martha's present annual salary is $100,000, what will her salary be in 2 yr?
    b. If Aaron's present salary is $99,000, what was his salary 1 yr ago?
    c. If Juanita's present salary is $363,000, what was her salary 2 yr ago?

18. Jasmine is reading a book. She has finished $\frac{3}{4}$ of the book and has 82 pages left to read. How many pages has she read?

19. John took all his money out of his bank savings account. He spent $50 on a radio and $\frac{3}{5}$ of what remained on presents. Half of what was left he put back in his checking account, and the remaining $35 he donated to charity. How much money did John originally have in his savings account?

20. Peter, Paul, and Mary start at the same time walking around a circular track in the same direction. Peter takes $\frac{1}{2}$ hr to walk around the track. Paul takes $\frac{5}{12}$ hr, and Mary takes $\frac{1}{3}$ hr.
    a. How many minutes does it take each person to walk around the track?
    b. How many times will each person go around the track before all three meet again at the starting line?

21. The formula for converting degrees Celsius (C) to degrees Fahrenheit (F) is $F = \left(\frac{9}{5}\right) \cdot C + 32$.
    a. If Samantha reads that the temperature is 32°C in Spain, what is the Fahrenheit temperature?
    b. If the temperature dropped to $^{-}40°F$ in West Yellowstone, what is the temperature in degrees Celsius?

22. Glenn bought 175 shares of stock at $48\frac{1}{4}$ a share. A year later, he sold it at $35\frac{3}{8}$ a share. How much did Glenn lose on the transaction?

23. Al gives $\frac{1}{2}$ of his marbles to Bev. Bev gives $\frac{1}{2}$ of these to Carl. Carl gives $\frac{1}{2}$ of these to Dani. If Dani has four marbles, how many did Al have originally?

24. The normal brain weight for an African bull elephant is 9 1/4 lb. Approximately how much would be the weight of the brains of 13 of these elephants?

25. Write each of the following in simplest form using positive exponents in the final answer:
    a. $3^{-7} \cdot 3^{-6}$ b. $3^7 \cdot 3^6$
    c. $5^{15} \div 5^4$ d. $5^{15} \div 5^{-4}$
    e. $(^{-}5)^{-2}$ f. $\frac{a^2}{a^{-3}}$, where $a \neq 0$
    g. $\frac{a}{a^{-1}}$, where $a \neq 0$ h. $\frac{a^{-3}}{a^{-2}}$, where $a \neq 0$

26. Write each of the following in simplest form using positive exponents in the final answer:
    a. $\left(\frac{1}{2}\right)^3 \cdot \left(\frac{1}{2}\right)^7$ b. $\left(\frac{1}{2}\right)^9 \div \left(\frac{1}{2}\right)^6$ c. $\left(\frac{2}{3}\right)^5 \cdot \left(\frac{4}{9}\right)^2$
    d. $\left(\frac{3}{5}\right)^7 \div \left(\frac{3}{5}\right)^7$ e. $\left(\frac{3}{5}\right)^7 \div \left(\frac{5}{3}\right)^4$ f. $\left[\left(\frac{5}{6}\right)^7\right]^3$

27. If a and b are rational numbers, with $a \neq 0$ and $b \neq 0$, and if m and n are integers, which of the following are true and which are false? Justify your answers.
    a. $a^m \cdot b^n = (ab)^{m+n}$ b. $a^m \cdot b^n = (ab)^{mn}$
    c. $a^m \cdot b^m = (ab)^{2m}$ d. $a^0 = 0$
    e. $(a + b)^m = a^m + b^m$ f. $(a + b)^{-m} = \frac{1}{a^m} + \frac{1}{b^m}$
    g. $a^{mn} = a^m \cdot a^n$ h. $\left(\frac{a}{b}\right)^{-1} = \frac{b}{a}$

28. Solve for the integer n in each of the following:
    a. $2^n = 32$ b. $n^2 = 36$
    c. $2^n \cdot 2^7 = 2^5$ d. $2^n \cdot 2^7 = 8$
    e. $(2 + n)^2 = 2^2 + n^2$ f. $3^n = 27^3$

29. A human being has approximately 25 trillion $(25 \cdot 10^{12})$ red blood cells, and each has an average radius of $4 \cdot 10^{-3}$ mm (millimeters).
    a. If these cells were placed end to end in a line, how long would the line be in millimeters?
    b. If 1 km is 10^6 mm, how long would the line be in kilometers?

30. Solve each of the following inequalities for x, where x is an integer:
    a. $3^x \leq 81$ b. $4^x < 8$ c. $3^{2x} > 27$ d. $2^x > 1$

31. Determine which fraction in each of the following pairs is greater:
    a. $\left(\frac{1}{2}\right)^3$ or $\left(\frac{1}{2}\right)^4$ b. $\left(\frac{3}{4}\right)^{10}$ or $\left(\frac{3}{4}\right)^8$

c. $\left(\dfrac{4}{3}\right)^{10}$ or $\left(\dfrac{4}{3}\right)^{8}$ d. $\left(\dfrac{3}{4}\right)^{10}$ or $\left(\dfrac{4}{5}\right)^{10}$

e. $\left(\dfrac{4}{3}\right)^{10}$ or $\left(\dfrac{5}{4}\right)^{10}$ f. $\left(\dfrac{3}{4}\right)^{100}$ or $\left(\dfrac{3}{4} \cdot \dfrac{9}{10}\right)^{100}$

32. Suppose the amount of bacteria in a certain culture is given as a function of time by $Q(t) = 10^{10}(6/5)^{t}$, where t is the time in seconds and $Q(t)$ is the amount of bacteria after t seconds. Find the following:
    a. The initial number of bacteria (that is, the number of bacteria at $t = 0$)
    b. The number of bacteria after 2 sec

33. Let $S = \dfrac{1}{2} + \dfrac{1}{2^2} + \dfrac{1}{2^3} + \ldots + \dfrac{1}{2^{64}}$.
    a. Use the distributive property of multiplication over addition to find an expression for $2S$.
    b. Show that $2S - S = S = 1 - \left(\dfrac{1}{2}\right)^{64}$.
    c. Find a simple expression for the sum
    $$\dfrac{1}{2} + \dfrac{1}{2^2} + \dfrac{1}{2^3} + \ldots = \dfrac{1}{2^n}.$$

34. In an arithmetic sequence, the first term is 1 and the hundredth term is 2. Find the following:
    a. The fiftieth term
    b. The sum of the first 50 terms

35. If $f(n) = \dfrac{3}{4} \cdot 2^n$, find the following:
    a. $f(0)$ b. $f(5)$ c. $f(^-5)$
    d. The greatest integer value of n for which $f(n) < \dfrac{3}{1400}$

36. If the nth term of a sequence is given by $a_n = 3 \cdot 2^{-n}$, answer the following:
    a. Find the first 5 terms.
    b. Show that the first 5 terms are in a geometric sequence.
    c. Find the first term that is less than $\dfrac{3}{1000}$.

37. In the following, determine which number is greater:
    a. 32^{50} or 4^{100} b. $(^-27)^{15}$ or $(^-3)^{75}$

38. There is a simple method for squaring any number that consists of a whole number and $\dfrac{1}{2}$. For example $\left(3\dfrac{1}{2}\right)^{2} =$
    $3 \cdot 4 + \left(\dfrac{1}{2}\right)^{2} = 12\dfrac{1}{4}$; $\left(4\dfrac{1}{2}\right)^{2} = 4 \cdot 5 + \left(\dfrac{1}{2}\right)^{2} = 20\dfrac{1}{4}$;
    $\left(5\dfrac{1}{2}\right)^{2} = 5 \cdot 6 + \left(\dfrac{1}{2}\right)^{2} = 30\dfrac{1}{4}$.
    a. Write a statement for $\left(n + \dfrac{1}{2}\right)^{2}$ that generalizes these examples, where n is a whole number.
    ★b. Justify this procedure.

39. Consider these products:
    First product: $\left(1 + \dfrac{1}{1}\right)\left(1 + \dfrac{1}{2}\right)$
    Second product: $\left(1 + \dfrac{1}{1}\right)\left(1 + \dfrac{1}{2}\right)\left(1 + \dfrac{1}{3}\right)$

Third product: $\left(1 + \dfrac{1}{1}\right)\left(1 + \dfrac{1}{2}\right)\left(1 + \dfrac{1}{3}\right)\left(1 + \dfrac{1}{4}\right)$
    a. Calculate the value of each product. Based on the pattern in your answers, guess the value of the fourth product. Then check to determine if your guess is correct.
    b. Guess the value of the hundredth product.
    c. Find as simple an expression as possible for the nth product.

40. Show that the arithmetic mean of two rational numbers is between the two numbers; that is, for $0 < \dfrac{a}{b} < \dfrac{c}{d}$, prove that $0 < \dfrac{a}{b} < \dfrac{1}{2}\left(\dfrac{a}{b} + \dfrac{c}{d}\right) < \dfrac{c}{d}$.

Communication

41. Suppose you divide a natural number, n, by a positive rational number less than 1. Will the answer always be less than n, sometimes less than n, or never less than n? Why?

42. If the fractions represented by points C and D on the following number line are multiplied, what point best represents the product? Explain why.

43. If the product of two numbers is 1 and one of the numbers is greater than 1, what do you know about the other number? Explain your answer.

44. Show that the following properties do *not* hold for the division of rational numbers:
    a. Commutative   b. Associative
    c. Identity   d. Inverse

Open-Ended

45. Would you use the problem in the following cartoon in your class? Why or why not? Solve the problem.

Cooperative Learning

46. Choose a brick building on your campus. Measure the height of one brick and the thickness of mortar between bricks. Estimate the height of the building and then calculate the height of the building. Were rational numbers used in your computations?

Review Problems

47. Perform each of the following computations. Leave your answers in simplest form.

a. $\dfrac{^-3}{16} + \dfrac{7}{4}$

b. $\dfrac{1}{6} + \dfrac{^-4}{9} + \dfrac{5}{3}$

c. $\dfrac{^-5}{2^3 \cdot 3^2} - \dfrac{^-5}{2 \cdot 3^3}$

d. $3\dfrac{4}{5} + 4\dfrac{5}{6}$

e. $5\dfrac{1}{6} - 3\dfrac{5}{8}$

f. $^-4\dfrac{1}{3} - 5\dfrac{5}{12}$

48. Each student at Sussex Elementary School takes one foreign language. Two-thirds of the students take Spanish, $\dfrac{1}{9}$ take French, $\dfrac{1}{18}$ take German, and the rest take some other foreign language. If there are 720 students in the school, how many do not take Spanish, French, or German?

 BRAIN
T E A S E R

A woman's will decreed that her cats be shared among her three daughters as follows: $\dfrac{1}{2}$ of the cats to the eldest daughter, $\dfrac{1}{3}$ of the cats to the middle daughter, and $\dfrac{1}{9}$ of the cats to the youngest daughter. Since the woman had 17 cats, the daughters decided that they could not carry out their mother's wishes. The judge who held the will agreed to lend the daughters a cat so that they could share the cats as their mother wished. Now, $\dfrac{1}{2}$ of 18 is 9; $\dfrac{1}{3}$ of 18 is 6; and $\dfrac{1}{9}$ of 18 is 2. Since 9 + 6 + 2 = 17, the daughters were able to divide the 17 cats and return the borrowed cat. They obviously did not need the extra cat to carry out their mother's bequest, but they could not divide 17 into halves, thirds, and ninths. Has the woman's will really been followed?

 Proportional Reasoning

In the *Principles and Standards* we find the following:

◆ *Working with proportions is a major focus proposed in these* Standards *for the middle grades. Students should become proficient in creating ratios to make comparisons in situations that involve pairs of numbers, as in the following problem:*
*   If three packages of cocoa make fifteen cups of hot chocolate, how many packages are needed to make sixty cups?* (p. 34)

As seen in the quote from the *Standards*, ratios and proportions are a very important part of the middle-grades curriculum. Ratios are encountered in everyday life. For example, there may be a 2-to-3 ratio of Democrats to Republicans on a certain legislative committee, a friend may be given a speeding ticket for driving 69 miles per hour, or eggs may **ratio** cost 98¢ a dozen. Each of these illustrates a **ratio**. Ratios are written $\dfrac{a}{b}$ or $a:b$ and are usually used to compare quantities.

A ratio of 1:3 for boys to girls in a class means that the number of boys is 1/3 that of girls; that is, there is one boy for every 3 girls. Notice we could also say that the ratio of girls to boys is 3:1 or that there are 3 times as many girls as boys. Some ratios give **part-to-part** comparisons such as the ratio of the number of students to one teacher. For example, a school might say that the average ratio of students to teachers cannot exceed 24:1. Ratios can also represent **part-to-whole** or **whole-to-part** comparisons. For example, if the ratio of boys to girls in a class is 1:3, then the ratio of boys (part) to children (whole) is 1:4. We could also say that the ratio of children (whole) to boys (part) is 4:1.

part-to-part comparison

part-to-whole comparison ◆
whole-to-part comparison

Notice that the ratio of 1:3 for boys to girls in a class does not tell us how many boys and how many girls there are in the class. It only tells us the relative size of the groups. There could be 2 boys and 6 girls or 3 boys and 9 girls or 4 boys and 12 girls or some other number that gives a fraction equivalent to 1/3.

EXAMPLE
5-19

There were 7 males and 12 females in the Dew Drop Inn on Monday evening. In the Game Room next door were 14 males and 24 females.

a. Express the number of males to females at the Inn as a ratio.
b. Express the number of males to females at the Game Room as a ratio.

Solution   **a.** The ratio is $\frac{7}{12}$.   **b.** The ratio is $\frac{14}{24}$.

In Example 5-19, the ratios $\frac{7}{12}$ and $\frac{14}{24}$ are equal and proportional to each other. In general, two ratios are **proportional** if, and only if, the fractions representing them are equal. Two equal ratios form a **proportion**.

proportional
proportion

For example, $\frac{2}{3}$ and $\frac{8}{12}$ form a proportion because $\frac{2}{3} = \frac{8}{12}$, since $2 \cdot 12 = 8 \cdot 3$. Also $\frac{3}{4} \neq \frac{4}{5}$ because $3 \cdot 5 \neq 4 \cdot 4$. In general, we have the following property, that follows directly from the property on page 272.

> **Property of Proportions**
>
> If a, b, c, and d are all real numbers and $b \neq 0$ and $d \neq 0$, then the proportion
>
> $$\frac{a}{b} = \frac{c}{d} \quad \text{is true if, and only if,} \quad ad = bc.$$

This property can be justified by multiplying each side of the proportion by bd.

Frequently, as in the problem introduced in the quote from the *Principles and Standards*, one term in a proportion is missing

$$\frac{3}{15} = \frac{x}{60}.$$

This equation is a proportion if, and only if,

$$3 \cdot 60 = 15 \cdot x$$
$$180 = 15 \cdot x$$
$$12 = x.$$

Therefore, 12 packages of cocoa are needed to make 60 cups of hot chocolate.

Another way to solve the equation is to multiply both sides by 60, as follows:

$$\frac{3}{15} \cdot 60 = \frac{x}{60} \cdot 60$$
$$3 \cdot 4 = x$$
$$12 = x.$$

EXAMPLE 5-20

If there should be 3 tractors for every 4 farmers on a collective farm, how many tractors are needed for 44 farmers on the farm?

Solution   We use the strategy of *setting up a table*, as shown in Table 5-3.

Table 5-3

Number of Tractors	3	x
Number of Farmers	4	44

The ratio of tractors to farmers should always be the same.

$$\begin{array}{c} \text{Tractors} \rightarrow \\ \text{Farmers} \rightarrow \end{array} \frac{3}{4} = \frac{x}{44}$$
$$3 \cdot 44 = 4 \cdot x$$
$$132 = 4x$$
$$33 = x$$

Thus 33 tractors are needed.

It is important to remember that in the ratio $a \div b$, a and b do not have to be integers. For example, if in Eugene, Oregon, $\frac{7}{10}$ of the population exercises regularly, then $\frac{3}{10}$ of the population does not exercise regularly, and the ratio of those who do to those who do not is $\frac{7}{10} : \frac{3}{10}$. This ratio can be written $7 : 3$.

It is also important to notice units of measure when we work with proportions. For example, if a turtle travels 5 in. every 10 sec, how many feet does it travel in 50 sec? If units of measure are ignored, we might set up the following proportion:

$$\frac{5}{10} = \frac{x}{50}.$$

This statement is incorrect. A correct statement must involve the same units in each ratio. We may write the following:

$$\frac{5 \text{ in.}}{10 \text{ sec}} = \frac{x \text{ in.}}{50 \text{ sec}}.$$

This implies that $x = 25$. Consequently, since 12 in. = 1 ft, the turtle travels $\frac{25}{12}$ ft, or $2\frac{1}{12}$ ft, or 2 ft 1 in.

The *Principles and Standards* point out the following concerning the cross-multiplication method of solving proportions.

Instruction in solving proportions should include methods that have a strong intuitive basis. The so-called cross-multiplication method can be developed meaningfully if it arises naturally in students' work, but it can also have unfortunate side effects when students do not adequately understand when the method is appropriate to use. Other approaches to solving proportions are often more intuitive and also quite powerful. For example, when trying to decide which is the better buy—12 tickets for 15.00 or 20 tickets for $23.00—students might choose to use a scaling strategy (finding the cost for a common number of tickets) or a unit-rate strategy (finding the cost for one ticket). (p. 221)

scaling strategy   The **scaling strategy** for solving the problem would involve finding the cost for a common number of tickets. Because LCM(12, 20) = 60, we could choose to find the cost of 60 tickets under each plan.

> *In the first plan, since 12 tickets cost $15, then 60 tickets cost $75.*

> *In the second plan, since 20 tickets cost $23, then 60 tickets cost $69.*

Therefore, the second plan is a better buy.

unit-rate strategy   The **unit-rate strategy** for solving this problem involves finding the cost of one ticket under each plan and then comparing the unit cost.

> *In the first plan, since 12 tickets cost $15, then one ticket costs $1.25.*

> *In the second plan, since 20 tickets cost $23, then one ticket costs $1.15.*

Therefore the second plan is the better buy.

EXAMPLE 5-21

Kai, Paulus, and Judy made $2520 for painting a house. Kai worked 30 hr, Paulus worked 50 hr, and Judy worked 60 hr. They divided the money in proportion to the number of hours worked. How much did each earn?

Solution   If we use $30x$ to denote the amount of money that Kai received, then the amount of money Paulus received must be $50x$ because then, and only then, will the ratios of the amounts be the same as 30:50, as required. Similarly, Judy received $60x$. Because the total amount of money received is $30x + 50x + 60x$, we have

$$30x + 50x + 60x = 2520$$
$$140x = 2520$$
$$x = 18.$$

Hence,

Kai received $30x = 30 \cdot 18$, or \$540.

Paulus received $50x = 50 \cdot 18$, or \$900.

Judy received $60x = 60 \cdot 18$, or \$1080.

Dividing each of the amounts by 18 shows that the proportion is as required. Note that x is the rate of pay per hour; that is, \$18 per hour (why?).

Consider the proportion $\frac{15}{30} = \frac{3}{6}$. Because the ratios in the proportion are equal fractions and because equal nonzero fractions have equal reciprocals, it follows that $\frac{30}{15} = \frac{6}{3}$. Also notice that the proportions are true because each results in $15 \cdot 6 = 30 \cdot 3$. In general, we have the following property.

> **Property**

For any rational numbers $\frac{a}{b}$ and $\frac{c}{d}$, with $a \neq 0$ and $c \neq 0$, $\frac{a}{b} = \frac{c}{d}$ if, and only if, $\frac{b}{a} = \frac{d}{c}$.

Consider $\frac{15}{30} = \frac{3}{6}$ again. Notice that $\frac{15}{3} = \frac{30}{6}$; that is, the ratio of the numerators is proportional to the ratio of the corresponding denominators. In general we have the following property.

> **Property**

For any rational numbers $\frac{a}{b}$ and $\frac{c}{d}$, with $b, c, d \neq 0$, $\frac{a}{b} = \frac{c}{d}$ if, and only if, $\frac{a}{c} = \frac{b}{d}$.

PROBLEM SOLVING   <u>**Dog Cartoon Problem**</u>

Analyze the statements in the "Mother Goose and Grimm" cartoon. How did the author arrive at the ratio of 21 meals per day based on the information in the first two frames?

Understanding the Problem   The dog in the cartoon makes the following three statements:

1. One year to a person is like seven years to a dog.
2. One day to a person is like one week to a dog.
3. I can eat 21 meals every day.

We need to determine if the ratio in **3** follows from the ratios in **1** or **2** or both.

Devising a Plan   We need to translate each statement into its mathematical form and check the computations.

From the cartoon Mother Goose and Grimm

Carrying Out the Plan   The first frame of the cartoon leads to the following ratio:

$$\frac{1 \text{ year to a person}}{7 \text{ years to a dog}} \text{ or the ratio of person time to dog time is } 1/7$$

If we translate the next frame into a ratio, we have the following:

$$\frac{1 \text{ day to a person}}{1 \text{ week to a dog}}$$

which also implies that the ratio of person time to dog time is

$$\frac{1 \text{ day to a person}}{7 \text{ days to a dog}}.$$

If a person eats 3 meals per day and the author of the cartoon assumes that the ratio of person time to dog time carries over to meals, then we have the following:

$$\frac{3 \text{ meals for a person}}{x \text{ meals for a dog}} = \frac{1 \text{ day for a person}}{7 \text{ days for a dog}}.$$

Solving for x, we have $x = 21$ meals for a dog. Thus the ratio in the cartoon's last frame follows from the ratio in the first frames.

Looking Back   Each statement in the cartoon appears to be consistent with the other statements. Either frame 1 or frame 2 of the cartoon is not needed to analyze the problem. ▨

Scale Drawings

Ratio and proportions are used in scale drawings. For example, if the scale is $1:300$ then the length of 1 cm in such a drawing represents 300 cm, or 3 m in true size. The **scale** is the ratio of the size of the drawing to the size of the object. The following example shows the use of scale drawings.

scale

**EXAMPLE
5-22**

The floor plan of the main floor of a house in Figure 5-14 is drawn in the scale of 1:300. Find the dimensions in meters of the living room.

FIGURE 5-14

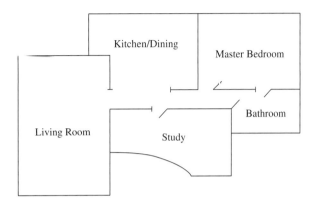

Solution   In Figure 5-14, the dimensions of the living room measured with a centimeter ruler are approximately 3.7 cm by 2.5 cm. Because the scale is 1:300, 1 cm in the drawing represents 300 cm, or 3 m in true size. Hence, 3.7 cm represents 3.7 · 3, or 11.1 m, and 2.5 cm represents 2.5 · 3, or 7.5 m. Hence the dimensions of the living room are approximately 11.1 m by 7.5 m.

ONGOING ASSESSMENT 5-4

1. Answer the following regarding the English alphabet:
   a. Determine the ratio of vowels to consonants.
   b. What is the ratio of consonants to vowels?
   c. What is the ratio of consonants to letters in the English alphabet?
   d. Write a word that has a ratio of 2:3 of vowels to consonants.

2. Solve for x in each of the following proportions:
   a. $\dfrac{12}{x} = \dfrac{18}{45}$

   b. $\dfrac{x}{7} = \dfrac{^-10}{21}$

   c. $\dfrac{5}{7} = \dfrac{3x}{98}$

   d. $3\dfrac{1}{2}$ is to 5 as x is to 15.

3. There are approximately 2 lb of muscle for every 5 lb of body weight. For a 90-lb person, how much of the weight is muscle?

4. There are 5 adult drivers to each teenage driver in Aluossim. If there are 12,345 adult drivers in Aluossim, how many teenage drivers are there?

5. If 4 grapefruits sell for 79¢, how much do 6 grapefruits cost?

6. On a map, $\dfrac{1}{3}$ in. represents 5 mi. If New York and Aluossim are 18 in. apart on the map, what is the actual distance between them?

7. David read 40 pages of a book in 50 min. How many pages should he be able to read in 80 min if he reads at a constant rate?

8. A candle is 30 in. long. After burning for 12 min, the candle is 25 in. long. How long will it take for the whole candle to burn at the same rate?

9. Two numbers are in the ratio 3:4. Find the numbers if
   a. their sum is 98.
   b. their product is 768.

10. A rectangular yard has a width-to-length ratio of 5:9. If the distance around the yard is 2800 ft, what are the dimensions of the yard?

11. Gary, Bill, and Carmella invested in a corporation in the ratio of 2:4:5, respectively. If they divide the profit of $82,000 proportionally to their investment, how much will each receive?

12. Sheila and Dora worked $3\frac{1}{2}$ hr and $4\frac{1}{2}$ hr, respectively, on a programming project. They were paid $176 for the project. How much did each earn?

13. Vonna scored 75 goals in her soccer kicking practice. If her success-to-failure rate is 5:4, how many times did she attempt a goal?

14. Express each of the following as a ratio whose terms are whole numbers.

    a. $\frac{1}{6}:1$ b. $\frac{1}{3}:\frac{1}{3}$ c. $\frac{1}{6}:\frac{2}{7}$

15. Write three other proportions that follow from the following proportion.

$$\frac{12¢}{36\ oz} = \frac{16¢}{48\ oz}$$

16. The rise and span for a house roof are identified as follows. The pitch of a roof is the ratio of the rise to the half-span.

    a. If the rise is 10 ft and the span is 28 ft, what is the pitch?

    b. If the span is 16 ft and the pitch is $\frac{3}{4}$, what is the rise?

17. A grasshopper can jump 20 times its length. If jumping ability in humans were proportional to a grasshopper's, how far could a 6-ft-tall person jump?

18. Jim found out that after working for 9 mo he had earned 6 days of vacation time. How many days per year does he earn at this rate?

19. Gear ratios are used in industry. A gear ratio is the comparison of the number of teeth on two gears. When two gears are meshed, the revolutions per minute (rpm) are inversely proportional to the number of teeth; that is,

$$\frac{\text{rpm of large gear}}{\text{rpm of small gear}} = \frac{\text{number of teeth on small gear}}{\text{number of teeth on large gear}}.$$

    a. The rpm ratio of the large gear to the small gear is 4:6. If the small gear has 18 teeth, how many teeth does the large gear have?

    b. The large gear revolves at 200 rpm and has 60 teeth. How many teeth are there on the small gear that has an rpm of 600?

20. A Boeing 747 jet is approximately 230 ft long and has a wingspan of 195 ft. If a scale model of the plane is about 40 cm long, what is the model's wingspan?

21. Jennifer weighs 160 lb on Earth and 416 lb on Jupiter. Find Amy's weight on Jupiter if she weighs 120 lb on Earth.

22. a. If the ratio of boys to girls in a class is 2:3, what is the ratio of boys to all the students in the class? Why?

    b. If the ratio of boys to girls in a class is $m:n$, what is the ratio of boys to all the students in the class?

23. A recipe calls for 1 tsp of mustard seeds, 3 c of tomato sauce, 1 1/2 c of chopped scallions, and 3 1/4 c of beans. If one ingredient is altered as specified, how must the other ingredients be changed to keep the proportions the same? Explain your reasoning.

    a. 2 c of tomato sauce

    b. 1 c of chopped scallions

    c. 1 3/4 c of beans

24. The electrical resistance of a wire, measured in ohms (Ω), is equal to a constant times the length of the wire. If the electrical resistance of a 5-ft wire is 4.2 Ω, what is the resistance of 18 ft of the same wire?

25. At Rattlesnake School the teacher-student ratio is 1:30. If the school has 1200 students, how many additional teachers must be hired to reduce the ratio to 1:20?

26. At a particular time, the ratio of the height of an object that is perpendicular to the ground to the length of its shadow is the same for all objects. If a 30-ft tree casts a shadow of 12 ft, how tall is a tree that casts a shadow of 14 ft?

27. In a photograph of a father and his daughter, the daughter's height is 2.3 cm and the father's height is 5.8 cm. If the father is actually 188 cm tall, how tall is the daughter?

28. The amount of gold jewelry and other products is measured in karats (K), where 24K represents pure gold. The mark 14K on a chain indicates that the ratio between the mass of the gold in the chain and the mass of the chain is 14:24. If a gold ring is marked 18K and it weighs 0.4 oz, what is the value of the gold in the ring if pure gold is valued at $300 per oz?

29. The following table shows several possible widths W and corresponding lengths L of a rectangle whose area is 10 ft².

Width (W) (Feet)	Length (L) (Feet)	Area (Square Feet)
0.5	20	$0.5 \cdot 20 = 10$
1	10	$1 \cdot 10 = 10$
2	5	$2 \cdot 5 = 10$
2.5	4	$2.5 \cdot 5 = 10$
4	2.5	$4 \cdot 2.5 = 10$
5	2	$5 \cdot 2 = 10$
10	1	$10 \cdot 1 = 10$
20	0.5	$20 \cdot 0.5 = 10$

Area = 10 ft² with length L and width W

a. Use the values in the table and some additional values to graph the length L on the vertical axis versus the width W on the horizontal axis.

b. What is the algebraic relationship between L and W?

c. Write W as a function of L; that is, express W in terms of L.

d. Write L as a function of W; that is, express L in terms of W.

30. a. In Room A of the University Center are one man and two women; in Room B are two men and four women; and in Room C are five men and ten women. If all the people in Rooms B and C go to Room A, what will be the ratio of men to women in Room A?

★**b.** Prove the following generalization of the proportions used in (a):

If $\dfrac{a}{b} = \dfrac{c}{d} = \dfrac{e}{f}$,   then $\dfrac{a}{b} = \dfrac{c}{d} = \dfrac{e}{f} = \dfrac{a+c+e}{b+d+f}$.

★ **31.** Prove that if $\dfrac{a}{b} = \dfrac{c}{d}$, then the following are true:

a. $\dfrac{a+b}{b} = \dfrac{c+d}{d}$ $\left(\text{Hint: } \dfrac{a}{b} + 1 = \dfrac{c}{d} + 1\right)$

b. $\dfrac{a}{a+b} = \dfrac{c}{c+d}$

c. $\dfrac{a-b}{a+b} = \dfrac{c-d}{c+d}$

Communication

32. Iris has found some dinosaur bones and a fossil footprint. The length of the footprint is 40 cm, the length of the thigh bone is 100 cm, and the length of the body is 700 cm.

a. What is the ratio of the footprint's length to the dinosaur's length?

b. Iris found a new track that she believes was made by the same species of dinosaur. If the footprint was 30 cm long and if the same ratio of foot length to body length holds, how long is the dinosaur?

c. In the same area, Iris also found a 50-cm thigh bone. Do you think this thigh bone belonged to the same dinosaur that made the 30-cm footprint that Iris found? Why or why not?

33. Suppose a 10-in. pizza costs $4. For you to find the price x of a 14-in. pizza, is it correct to set up the proportion $\dfrac{x}{4} = \dfrac{14}{10}$? Why or why not?

34. Amy's friend told her the ratio of girls to boys in her new class is $5:6$. Amy was very surprised to think her class would only have 11 students. What do you tell her?

35. Write a paragraph in which you use the terms *ratio* and *proportion* correctly.

Open-Ended

36. List three real-world situations that involve ratio and proportion.

37. Boyle's law states that at a given temperature, the product of the volume V of a gas and the pressure P is a constant c as follows:

$$PV = c$$

a. If at a given temperature, a pressure of 48 lb/in^2 compresses a certain gas to a volume of 960 in^3, what pressure would be necessary to compress the gas to a volume of 800 in^3 at the same temperature?

b. Find three other real-world situations in which the variables are related mathematically like the variables in Boyle's law. In each case, describe how the variables are related using ratio and proportion.

Cooperative Learning

38. Look at various elementary science and mathematics books and determine both if and how *dimensional analysis* is treated in those texts. How is dimensional analysis related to ratio and proportion?

39. Consider the stock market pages of a newspaper. Each person in a group should determine the profit-to-earnings ratio for at least five companies. Discuss with your group how you would rate stocks based on this indicator.

Review Problems

40. Find all values of x that satisfy the following equations or inequalities:

a. $\dfrac{x}{3} = \dfrac{3x}{4}$

b. $3^x = 243$

c. $\dfrac{1}{3}x + \dfrac{3}{4}x = 49$

d. $\dfrac{1}{3}x \le 49 - \dfrac{3}{4}x$

41. Do all rational numbers have a multiplicative inverse?

42. Find three rational numbers between 2 and 3 so that the numbers, including 2 and 3, form an arithmetic sequence.

43. If a geometric sequence has 4/9 as its seventh term, and the ratio of the sequence is 1/2, what is the first term?

44. Determine what, if anything, is wrong with each of the following:

a. $2 = \dfrac{6}{3} = \dfrac{3+3}{3} = \dfrac{3}{3} + 3 = 1 + 3 = 4$

b. $1 = \dfrac{4}{2+2} = \dfrac{4}{2} + \dfrac{4}{2} = 2 + 2 = 4$

c. $\dfrac{ab+c}{a} = \dfrac{\not{a}b + c}{\not{a}} = b + c$

d. $\dfrac{a^2 - b^2}{a - b} = \dfrac{a \cdot \not{a} - b \cdot \not{b}}{\not{a} - \not{b}} = a - b$

e. $\dfrac{a+c}{b+c} = \dfrac{a+\not{c}}{b+\not{c}} = \dfrac{a}{b}$

Hint for Solving the Preliminary Problem

It is possible to set up a proportion to solve the problem if you know what the arm length and nose length of a typical person might be. You might determine this from collecting data in your class.

QUESTIONS FROM THE CLASSROOM

1. Is $\frac{0}{6}$ in simplest form? Why or why not?

2. A student says that taking one half of a number is the same as dividing the number by one half. Is this correct?

3. A student writes $\frac{15}{53} < \frac{1}{3}$ because $3 \cdot 15 < 53 \cdot 1$. Another student writes $\frac{1\cancel{5}}{\cancel{5}3} = \frac{1}{3}$. Where is the fallacy?

4. A student claims that the following is an arithmetic sequence. How would you respond?

$$\frac{1}{2}, \frac{2}{3}, \frac{3}{4}, \frac{4}{5}, \frac{5}{6}, \frac{6}{7}, \frac{7}{8}, \cdots$$

5. A student claims that there are no numbers between $\frac{999}{1000}$ and 1 because they are so close together. What is your response?

6. When working on the problem of simplifying

$$\frac{3}{4} \cdot \frac{1}{2} \cdot \frac{2}{3},$$

a student did the following:

$$\frac{3}{4} \cdot \frac{1}{2} \cdot \frac{2}{3} = \left(\frac{3 \cdot 1}{4 \cdot 2}\right)\left(\frac{3 \cdot 2}{4 \cdot 3}\right) = \frac{3}{8} \cdot \frac{6}{12} = \frac{19}{96}.$$

What was the error, if any?

7. A student claims that division always makes things smaller so $5 \div \left(\frac{1}{2}\right)$ can't be 10 because that is greater than the number she started with. How do you respond?

8. A student simplified the fraction $\frac{m+n}{p+n}$ to $\frac{m}{p}$. How would you help this student?

9. Without thinking, a student argued that a pizza cut into 12 pieces was more than a pizza cut into 6 pieces. How would you respond?

10. A student asks if adding the same very large number to both the numerator and the denominator of a fraction yields a quotient of 1. How do you respond?

11. A student asks whether it is easier to add fractions or multiply fractions. What is your response?

12. A student claimed that $\frac{9}{-11}$ is an improper fraction. How do you respond?

13. If $2^{-1} = \frac{1}{2}$, a student said that 3^{-2} should equal $\frac{2}{3}$. How do you respond?

14. Joe reported that if $\frac{a}{b} = \frac{c}{d}$, then $\frac{a}{a-b} = \frac{c}{c-d}$. Joan said she didn't believe it. How do you respond?

15. Al is 5 ft tall and has a shadow that is 18 in long. At the same time, a tree has a shadow that is 15 ft long. Al sets up and solves the proportion as follows:

$$\frac{5 \text{ ft}}{15 \text{ ft}} = \frac{18 \text{ in}}{x \text{ in}}, \quad \text{so } x = 54 \text{ in}.$$

How would you help him?

CHAPTER OUTLINE

I. Fractions and rational numbers

  A. Numbers of the form $\frac{a}{b}$, where a and b are integers and $b \neq 0$, are **rational numbers**. a is the numerator and b is the denominator.

  B. A rational number can be used as follows:

    1. A division problem or the solution to a multiplication problem

    2. A partition, or part, of a whole

    3. A ratio

    4. A probability

  C. Fundamental Law of Fractions: For any fraction $\frac{a}{b}$ and any number $c \neq 0$, $\frac{a}{b} = \frac{ac}{bc}$.

  D. Two fractions $\frac{a}{b}$ and $\frac{c}{d}$ are **equal** (**eqivalent**) if, and only if, $ad = bc$.

  E. If GCD$(a, b) = 1$, then $\frac{a}{b}$ is said to be in **simplest form**.

  F. If $0 \leq |a| < |b|$, then $\frac{a}{b}$ is a **proper fraction**. If $|a| \geq |b| > 0$, $\frac{a}{b}$ is an **improper fraction**.

  G. $\frac{a}{b} > \frac{c}{d}$ if, and only if, $ad > bc$.

H. If $\frac{a}{b} < \frac{c}{d}$, then $\frac{a}{b} < \frac{a+c}{b+d} < \frac{c}{d}$.

II. Operations on rational numbers

A. $\frac{a}{b} + \frac{c}{b} = \frac{a+c}{b}$

B. $\frac{a}{b} + \frac{c}{d} = \frac{ad+bc}{bd}$

C. $\frac{a}{b} - \frac{c}{d} = \frac{ad-bc}{bd}$

D. $\frac{a}{b} \cdot \frac{c}{d} = \frac{ac}{bd}$

E. $\frac{a}{b} \div \frac{c}{d} = \frac{a}{b} \cdot \frac{d}{c} = \frac{ad}{bc}$, where $c \neq 0$

III. Properties of rational numbers

A.

	Addition	Subtraction	Multiplication	Division
Closure	Yes	Yes	Yes	Yes, except for division by 0
Commutative	Yes	No	Yes	No
Associative	Yes	No	Yes	No
Identity	Yes	No	Yes	No
Inverse	Yes	No	Yes, except 0	No

B. Distributive property of multiplication over addition for rational numbers x, y, and z:

$$x(y + z) = xy + xz.$$

C. Denseness property: Between any two rational numbers, there is another rational number.

D. Multiplication property of equality: If $\frac{a}{b}$ and $\frac{c}{d}$ are any rational numbers such that $\frac{a}{b} = \frac{c}{d}$, and $\frac{e}{f}$ is any rational number, then $\frac{a}{b} \cdot \frac{e}{f} = \frac{c}{d} \cdot \frac{e}{f}$.

E. Multiplication property of zero for rational numbers: If $\frac{a}{b}$ is any rational number, then $\frac{a}{b} \cdot 0 = 0 = 0 \cdot \frac{a}{b}$.

IV. Exponents

A. $a^m = \underbrace{a \cdot a \cdot a \cdot \ldots \cdot a}_{m \text{ factors}}$, where m is a positive integer and a is a rational number

B. Properties of exponents involving rational numbers

1. $a^0 = 1$, where $a \neq 0$
2. $a^{-m} = \frac{1}{a^m}$, where $a \neq 0$
3. $a^m \cdot a^n = a^{m+n}$
4. $\frac{a^m}{a^n} = a^{m-n}$, where $a \neq 0$
5. $(a^m)^n = a^{mn}$
6. $\left(\frac{a}{b}\right)^m = \frac{a^m}{b^m}$, where $b \neq 0$
7. $(ab)^m = a^m \cdot b^m$
8. $\left(\frac{a}{b}\right)^{-m} = \left(\frac{b}{a}\right)^m$

V. Ratio and Proportion

A. A fraction a/b is a **ratio**.

B. A **proportion** is an equation of two ratios.

C. Properties of proportions

1. If $\frac{a}{b} = \frac{c}{d}$, then $\frac{b}{a} = \frac{d}{c}$, where $a \neq 0$ and $c \neq 0$.
2. If $\frac{a}{b} = \frac{c}{d}$, then $\frac{a}{c} = \frac{b}{d}$, where $c \neq 0$.

CHAPTER REVIEW

1. For each of the following, draw a diagram illustrating the fraction:

a. $\frac{3}{4}$ b. $\frac{2}{3}$ c. $\frac{3}{4} \cdot \frac{2}{3}$

2. Write three rational numbers equal to $\frac{5}{6}$.

3. Reduce each of the following rational numbers to simplest form:

a. $\frac{24}{28}$ b. $\frac{ax^2}{bx}$ c. $\frac{0}{17}$ d. $\frac{45}{81}$ e. $\frac{b^2+bx}{b+x}$ f. $\frac{16}{216}$

4. Replace the comma with $>$, $<$, or $=$ in each of the following pairs to make a true statement:

a. $\frac{6}{10}, \frac{120}{200}$ b. $\frac{-3}{4}, \frac{-5}{6}$

c. $\left(\frac{4}{5}\right)^{10}, \left(\frac{4}{5}\right)^{20}$ d. $\left(1+\frac{1}{3}\right)^2, \left(1+\frac{1}{3}\right)^3$

5. Find the additive and multiplicative inverses for each of the following:

a. 3 b. $3\frac{1}{7}$ c. $\frac{5}{6}$ d. $-\frac{3}{4}$

6. Order the following numbers from least to greatest:

$$-1\frac{7}{8}, 0, -2\frac{1}{3}, \frac{69}{140}, \frac{71}{140}, \left(\frac{71}{140}\right)^{300}, \frac{1}{2}, \left(\frac{74}{73}\right)^{300}$$

7. Can $\frac{4}{5} \cdot \frac{7}{8} \cdot \frac{5}{14}$ be written as $\frac{4}{8} \cdot \frac{7}{14} \cdot \frac{5}{5}$ to obtain the same answer? Why or why not?

8. Use mental math to compute the following. Explain your method.

    a. $\frac{1}{3} \cdot (8 \cdot 9)$ **b.** $36 \cdot 1\frac{5}{6}$

9. John has $54\frac{1}{4}$ yd of material. If he needs to cut the cloth into pieces that are $3\frac{1}{12}$ yd long, how many pieces can he cut? How much material will be left over?

10. Without actually performing the given operations, choose the most appropriate estimation (among the numbers in parentheses) for the following expressions:

    a. $\dfrac{30\frac{3}{8}}{4\frac{1}{9}} \cdot \dfrac{8\frac{1}{3}}{3\frac{8}{9}}$ (15, 20, 8)

    b. $\left(\dfrac{3}{800} + \dfrac{4}{5000} + \dfrac{15}{6} \right) \cdot 6$ (15, 0, 132)

    c. $\dfrac{1}{407} \div \dfrac{1}{1609}$ $\left(\dfrac{1}{4}, 4, 0 \right)$

11. Justify the invert-and-multiply algorithm for division of rational numbers.

12. The ratio of boys to girls in Mr. Good's class is 3 to 5, the ratio of boys to girls in Ms. Garcia's is the same, and you know that there are 15 girls in Ms. Garcia's class. How many boys are in Ms. Garcia's class?

13. Find two rational numbers between $\frac{3}{4}$ and $\frac{4}{5}$.

14. Suppose the $\boxed{\div}$ button on your calculator is broken, but the $\boxed{1/x}$ button works. Explain how you could compute 504792/23.

15. Jim is starting a diet. When he arrived home, he ate $\frac{1}{3}$ of the half of pizza that was left from the previous night. The whole pizza contains approximately 2000 calories. How many calories did Jim consume?

16. If a person got heads on a flip of a fair coin one half the time and obtained 376 heads, how many times was the coin flipped?

17. If a person obtained 240 heads when flipping a coin 1000 times, what fraction of the time did the person obtain heads? Put the answer in simplest form.

18. If the University of New Mexico won 3/4 of its women's basketball games and 5/8 of its men's basketball games, explain whether it is reasonable to say that the university won 3/4 + 5/8 of its basketball games.

19. Explain why a negative rational number times a negative rational number is a positive rational number.

20. A student argues that the following fraction is not a rational number because it is not the quotient of two integers:

$$\frac{\frac{2}{3}}{\frac{3}{4}}$$

How would you respond?

21. Molly wants to fertilize 12 acres of park land. If it takes $9\frac{1}{3}$ bags for each acre, how many bags does she need?

22. If 2/3 of all students in the academy are female and 2/5 of those are blondes, what fraction describes the number of blond females in the academy?

23. Explain which is greater: $^{-}11/9$ or $^{-}12/10$.

24. Solve for x.

    a. $7^x = 343$

    b. $2^{-3x} = \dfrac{1}{512}$

25. In water (H_2O), the ratio of the weight of oxygen to the weight of hydrogen is approximately 8:1. How many ounces of hydrogen is in 1 lb of water?

26. To estimate the number of fish in a lake, scientists use a tagging and recapturing technique. A number of fish are captured, tagged, and then released back into the lake. After a while, some fish are captured and the number of tagged fish is counted.

    Let T be the total number of fish captured, tagged, and released into the lake, n the number of fish in a recaptured sample, and t the number of fish found tagged in that sample. Finally let x be the number of fish in the lake. The assumption is that the ratio between tagged fish and the total number of fish in any sample is approximately the same and hence scientists assume $t/n = T/x$. Suppose 173 fish were captured, tagged, and released. Then 68 fish were recaptured and among them 21 were found to be tagged. Estimate the number of fish in the lake.

27. A manufacturer produces the same kind of computer chip in two plants. In the first plant, the ratio of defective chips to good chips is 15:100, and in the second plant, that ratio is 12:100. A buyer of a large number of chips is aware that some come from the first plant and some from the second. However, she is not aware of how many come from each. The buyer would like to know the ratio of defective chips to good chips in any given order. Can she determine that ratio? If so, explain how. If not, explain why not.

28. Suppose the ratio of the lengths of the sides in two squares is $1:r$. What is the ratio of their areas?

SELECTED BIBLIOGRAPHY

Alcoro, P., A. Alston, and N. Katjims. "Fractions Attack! Children Thinking and Talking Mathematically." *Teaching Children Mathematics* 6 (May 2000): 562–567.

Anderson, C., E. Anderson, and E. Wenzel. "Oil and Water Don't Mix, But They Teach Fractions." *Teaching Children Mathematics* 7 (November 2000): 174–178.

Barnett, J. "A Brief History of Algorithms in Mathematics " *The Teaching and Learning of Algorithms in School Mathematics*, edited by L. Morrow and M. Kenny, pp. 69–77. Reston, Va: National Council of Teachers of Mathematics, 1998.

Ben-Chaim, D., J. Fey, W. Fitzgerald, C. Benedetto, and J. Miller. "Proportional Reasoning among 7th Grade Students with Different Curricular Experiences." *Educational Studies in Mathematics* 36 (1998): 247–273.

Billings, E., "Problems That Encourage Proportion Sense." *Mathematics Teaching in the Middle School* 5 (January 2000): 310–313.

Brinker, L. "Using Recipes and Ratio Tables." *Teaching Children Mathematics* 5 (December 1998): 218–224.

Burrill, G., et al. *Figure This!* Washington, DC: Widmeyer Corporation, 2002. (www.figurethis.org)

Caldwell, J. "Communicating about Fractions with Pattern Blocks." *Teaching Children Mathematics* 2 (November 1995): 156–161.

Conaway, B., and R. Midkiff. "Connecting Literature, Language, and Fractions." *Arithmetic Teacher* 41 (April 1994): 430–434.

Cramer, K., and N. Bezuk. "Multiplication of Fractions: Teaching for Understanding." *Arithmetic Teacher* 39 (November 1991): 34–37.

Cramer, K., and T. Post. "Proportional Reasoning." *Mathematics Teacher* 86 (May 1993): 404–407.

Curcio, F., and N. Bezuk. "Understanding Rational Numbers and Proportions." *Curriculum and Evaluation Standards for School Mathematics Addenda Series Grades 5–8*. Reston, VA: National Council of Teachers of Mathematics, 1994.

Edelman, L. "The Fractions of a Day." *Mathematics Teaching in the Middle School* 3 (November–December 1997): 192–195.

Empson, S. "Equal Sharing and the Roots of Fraction Equivalence." *Teaching Children Mathematics* 7 (March 2001): 421–425.

Friel, J., and G. Gannon. "'What If . . . ?' A Case in Point." *Mathematics Teacher* 88 (April 1995): 320–322.

Greeley, N., and T. R. Offerman. "Now & Then Dancing in Time and Space." *Mathematics Teaching in the Middle School* 4 (November–December 1998): 192–199.

Groff, P. "On My Mind: It Is Time to Question Fraction Teaching." *Mathematics Teaching in the Middle School* 1 (January–February 1996): 604–607.

Kieren, T., B. Davis, and R. Mason. "Fraction Flags: Learning from Children to Help Children Learn." *Mathematics Teaching in the Middle School* 2 (September–October 1996): 14–19.

Kuhns, C. "Half-Time Day." *Teaching Children Mathematics* 3 (January 1997): 218–221, 235.

Lappan, G., and M. Bouck. "Developing Algorithms for Adding and Subtracting Fractions." *The Teaching and Learning of Algorithms in School Mathematics*, edited by L. Morrow and M. Kenny, pp. 69–77. Reston, Va: National Council of Teachers of Mathematics, 1998.

Mack, N. "Making Connections to Understand Fractions." *Arithmetic Teacher* 40 (February 1993): 362–364.

Middleton, J., M. van den Heuvel-Panhuizen. "The Ratio Table." *Mathematics Teaching in the Middle School* 1 (January–March 1995): 282–288.

Middleton, J., M. van den Heuvel-Panhuizen, and J. Shew. "Using Bar Representations as a Model for Connecting Concepts of Rational Numbers." *Mathematics Teaching in the Middle School* 3 (January 1998): 302–312.

Miller, J., and J. Fey. "Proportional Reasoning." *Mathematics Teaching in the Middle School* 5 (January 2000): 310–313.

Nowlin, D. "Division with Fractions." *Mathematics Teaching in the Middle School* 2 (November–December 1996): 116–119.

Ott, J. "A Unified Approach to Multiplying Fractions." *Arithmetic Teacher* 37 (March 1990): 47–49.

Reys, B. "Promoting Number Sense in the Middle Grades." *Mathematics Teaching in the Middle School* 1 (September–October, 1994): 114–120.

Warrington, M. "How Children Think about Division with Fractions." *Mathematics Teaching in the Middle School* 2 (May 1997): 390–394.

Warrington, M., and C. Kamii. "Multiplication with Fractions: A Piagetian, Constructivist Approach." *Mathematics Teaching in the Middle School* 3 (February 1998): 339–343.

Watanabe, T. "Ben's Understanding of One-Half." *Teaching Children Mathematics* 2 (April 1996): 460–464.

Watanabe, T. "Let's Eliminate Fractions from the Primary Curricula." *Teaching Children Mathematics* 8 (October 2001): 70–72.

Watanabe, T. "Representations in Teaching and Learning Fractions." *Teaching Children Mathematics* 8 (April 2002): 457–463.

Wu, Z. "Multiplying Fractions." *Teaching Children Mathematics* 8 (November 2001): 174–177.

Yang, D., and R. Reys, "One Fraction Problem, Many Solution Paths." *Mathematics Teaching in the Middle School* 7 (September 2001): 10–14.

–6–
Decimals, Percents, and Real Numbers

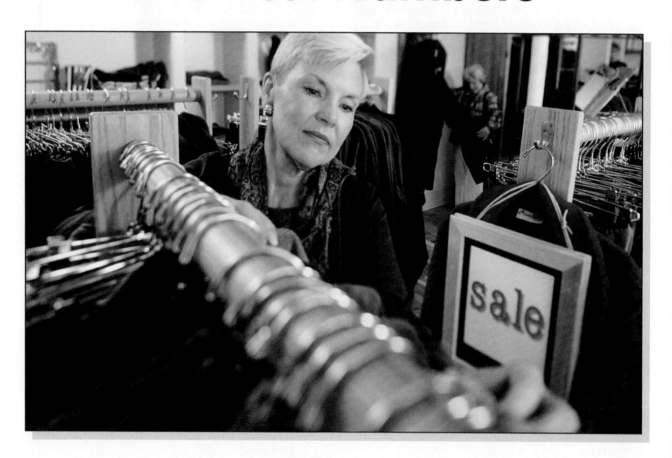

PRELIMINARY PROBLEM

When a store had a 60% off sale, and Dori had a coupon for an additional 40% off any item, she thought she should be able to obtain the dress that she wanted free. If you were the store manager, how would you explain the mathematics of the situation to her?

I n *Principles and Standards* (NCTM 2000), we find that students in grades 6–8 should

- work flexibly with fractions, decimals, and percents to solve problems;
- compare and order fractions, decimals, and percents efficiently and find their approximate locations on a number line;
- develop meaning for percents greater than 100 and less than 1;
- develop an understanding of large numbers and recognize and appropriately use exponential, scientific and calculator notation;
- understand the meaning and effects of arithmetic operations with fractions, decimals, and integers. (p. 214)

In this chapter, we develop the necessary understanding that teachers must have to help students reach these expectations. To begin, we look at a brief history of decimals.

Although the Hindu-Arabic numeration system discussed in Chapter 3 was perfected around the sixth century, the extension of the system to decimals by the Dutch scientist Simon Stevin did not take place until about a thousand years later. The only significant improvement in the system since Stevin's time has been in notation. Even today there is no universally accepted form of writing a decimal. For example, in the United States, we write 6.75; in England, this number is written 6 · 75; and in Germany and France, it is written 6,75.

Decimals play an important part in the mathematics education of students in grades 5 through 8. In Section 6-1, we explore relationships between fractions and decimals and see how decimals are an extension of the base-ten system. Later in the chapter, we consider operations on decimals, properties of decimals, percents and applications of percents, and finally real numbers.

HISTORICAL NOTE

In 1584, Simon Stevin (1548–1620), a quartermaster general in the Dutch army, wrote *La Thiende (The Tenth)*, a work that gave rules for computing with decimals. He not only stated rules for decimal computations but also suggested practical applications for decimals and recommended that his government adopt a system similar to the metric system. To show place value, Stevin used circled numerals between digits. For example, he wrote 0.4789 as 4 ①7 ②8 ③9 ④.

THIENDE.   13

HET ANDER DEEL
DER THIENDE VANDE
WERCKINCHE.

I. VOORSTEL VANDE
VERGADERINGHE.

*Wefende ghegeven Thiendetalen te ver-
gaderen: hare Somme te vinden.*

T'GHEGHEVEN. Het fijn drie oirdens van
Thiendetalen, welcker eerſte 27 ③ 8 ① 4 ③
7 ③, de tweede, 37 ③ 6 ① 7 ② 5 ③, de derde,
875 ③ 7 ① 8 ② 2 ③. TBEGHEERDE. Wy
moeten haer Somme vinden. WERCKING.
Men ſal de ghegheven ghe-
talen in oirden ſtellen als   ③ ① ② ③
hier neven, die vergaderen-   2 7 8 4 7
de naer de ghemeene manie   3 7 6 7 5
re der vergaderinghe van   8 7 5 7 8 2
heelegetalen aldus: ──────────
                               9 4 1 3 0 4

Introduction to Decimals

decimal point

The word *decimal* comes from the Latin *decem*, meaning "ten." Most people first encounter decimals when dealing with money. For example, on a sign that says a bike costs $128.95, the dot in $128.95 is the **decimal point**. Because $0.95 is $\frac{95}{100}$ of a dollar, we have $128.95 = 128 + \frac{95}{100}$ dollars. Because $0.95 is 9 dimes and 5 cents, one dime is $\frac{1}{10}$ of a dollar, 1 cent is $\frac{1}{100}$ of a dollar, so $0.95 is $9 \cdot \frac{1}{10} + 5 \cdot \frac{1}{100}$ of a dollar.

Consequently,

$$128.95 = 1 \cdot 10^2 + 2 \cdot 10 + 8 \cdot 1 + 9 \cdot \frac{1}{10} + 5 \cdot \frac{1}{10^2}.$$

The digits in 128.95 correspond to the following place values: 10^2, 10, 1, $\frac{1}{10}$, and $\frac{1}{10^2}$, respectively. (Each term in the sequence of place values after the first is $\frac{1}{10}$ of the previous term.) Thus, 12.61843 represents

$$1 \cdot 10 + 2 \cdot 1 + \frac{6}{10^1} + \frac{1}{10^2} + \frac{8}{10^3} + \frac{4}{10^4} + \frac{3}{10^5}, \quad \text{or} \quad 12\frac{61,843}{100,000}.$$

The decimal 12.61843 is read "twelve and sixty-one thousand eight hundred forty-three hundred-thousandths." Each place of a decimal may be named by its power of 10. For example, the places of 12.61843 can be named as shown in Table 6-1.

Table 6-1

1	2	.	6	1	8	4	3
Tens	Units	*and*	Tenths	Hundredths	Thousandths	Ten-thousandths	Hundred-thousandths

Decimals can be introduced with concrete materials. We can use a set of base-ten blocks and decide that 1 flat represents 1 unit, 1 long represents $\frac{1}{10}$, and 1 cube represents $\frac{1}{100}$, as in Figure 6-1(a). In this model, Figure 6-1(b) represents 1.23.

FIGURE 6-1

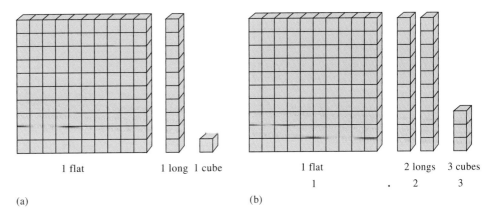

1 flat   1 long 1 cube   1 flat   2 longs 3 cubes

                                            1   .   2   3

(a)   (b)

To represent a decimal such as 2.235, we can think of the block shown in Figure 6-2(a) as a unit. Then a flat represents $\frac{1}{10}$, a long represents $\frac{1}{100}$, and a cube represents $\frac{1}{1000}$. Using these objects, we show a representation of 2.235 in Figure 6-2(b).

FIGURE 6-2

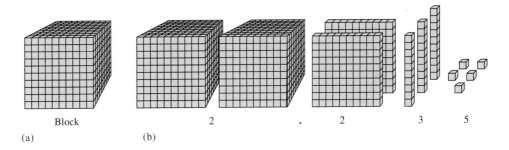

Block   2   .   2   3   5

(a)   (b)

Table 6-2 shows other examples of decimals, their fractional meanings, and their common fraction notations.

Table 6-2

Decimal	Fractional Meaning	Common Fraction Notation
5.3	$5 + \dfrac{3}{10}$	$5\dfrac{3}{10}$, or $\dfrac{53}{10}$
0.02	$0 + \dfrac{0}{10} + \dfrac{2}{100}$	$\dfrac{2}{100}$
2.0103	$2 + \dfrac{0}{10} + \dfrac{1}{100} + \dfrac{0}{1000} + \dfrac{3}{10,000}$	$2\dfrac{103}{10,000}$, or $\dfrac{20,103}{10,000}$
$^{-}3.6$	$-\left(3 + \dfrac{6}{10}\right)$	$^{-}3\dfrac{6}{10}$, or $-\dfrac{36}{10}$

Decimals can also be written in expanded form using place value and negative exponents. Thus

$$12.61843 = 1 \cdot 10^1 + 2 \cdot 10^0 + 6 \cdot 10^{-1} + 1 \cdot 10^{-2} + 8 \cdot 10^{-3} + 4 \cdot 10^{-4} + 3 \cdot 10^{-5}.$$

NOW TRY THIS 6-1

Decimals can sometimes cause confusion. In the "Blondie" cartoon below, the writers probably intended the price of the prime rib to be half that of the steak. Is that what the cartoon says? Give other examples of this type of mistake involving dollars and cents.

Example 6-1 shows how to convert rational numbers whose denominators are powers of 10 to decimals.

EXAMPLE 6-1

Convert each of the following to decimals:

a. $\dfrac{56}{100}$ **b.** $\dfrac{205}{10,000}$ **c.** $\dfrac{3.85}{1000}$

Solution

a. $\dfrac{56}{100} = \dfrac{5 \cdot 10 + 6}{10^2} = \dfrac{5 \cdot 10}{10^2} + \dfrac{6}{10^2} = 0 + \dfrac{5}{10} + \dfrac{6}{10^2} = 0.56$

b. $\dfrac{205}{10,000} = \dfrac{2 \cdot 10^2 + 0 \cdot 10 + 5}{10^4} = \dfrac{2 \cdot 10^2}{10^4} + \dfrac{0 \cdot 10}{10^4} + \dfrac{5}{10^4}$

$= \dfrac{2}{10^2} + \dfrac{0}{10^3} + \dfrac{5}{10^4} = 0 + \dfrac{0}{10^1} + \dfrac{2}{10^2} + \dfrac{0}{10^3} + \dfrac{5}{10^4} = 0.0205$

c. $\dfrac{3.85}{1000} = \dfrac{3 + \dfrac{8}{10} + \dfrac{5}{10^2}}{10^3} = \dfrac{3}{10^3} + \dfrac{8}{10^4} + \dfrac{5}{10^5}$

$= 0 + \dfrac{0}{10^1} + \dfrac{0}{10^2} + \dfrac{3}{10^3} + \dfrac{8}{10^4} + \dfrac{5}{10^5} = 0.00385$

We reinforce the ideas in Example 6-1 through the use of a calculator. In Example 6-1(a), press $\boxed{5}\;\boxed{6}\;\boxed{\div}\;\boxed{1}\;\boxed{0}\;\boxed{0}\;\boxed{=}$ and watch the display. Divide by 10 and look at the new placement of the decimal point. Once more, divide by 10 (which amounts to dividing the original number, 56, by 10,000) and note the placement of the decimal point. This leads to the following general rule for dividing a decimal by a positive integer power of 10:

To divide a decimal by 10^n, start at the decimal point, count n digits from right to left, annexing zeros if necessary, and insert the decimal point to the left of the nth digit.

The fractions in Example 6-1 are easy to convert to decimals because the denominators are powers of 10. If the denominator of a fraction is not a power of 10, as in $\frac{3}{5}$, we use the problem-solving strategy of *converting the problem to one we already know how to do.* First, we rewrite $\frac{3}{5}$ as a fraction in which the denominator is a power of 10, and then we convert the fraction to a decimal.

$$\frac{3}{5} = \frac{3 \cdot 2}{5 \cdot 2} = \frac{6}{10} = 0.6$$

The reason for multiplying the numerator and the denominator by 2 is apparent when we observe that $10 = 2 \cdot 5$. In general, because $10^n = (2 \cdot 5)^n = 2^n \cdot 5^n$, the prime factorization of the denominator must be $2^n \cdot 5^n$ in order for the denominator of a rational number in simplest form to be 10^n. We use these ideas to write each fraction in Example 6-2 as a decimal.

EXAMPLE 6-2

Express each of the following as decimals:

a. $\frac{7}{2^6}$ **b.** $\frac{1}{2^3 \cdot 5^4}$ **c.** $\frac{1}{125}$ **d.** $\frac{7}{250}$

Solution   **a.** $\dfrac{7}{2^6} = \dfrac{7 \cdot 5^6}{2^6 \cdot 5^6} = \dfrac{7 \cdot 15{,}625}{(2 \cdot 5)^6} = \dfrac{109{,}375}{10^6} = 0.109375$

b. $\dfrac{1}{2^3 \cdot 5^4} = \dfrac{1 \cdot 2^1}{2^3 \cdot 5^4 \cdot 2^1} = \dfrac{2}{2^4 \cdot 5^4} = \dfrac{2}{(2 \cdot 5)^4} = \dfrac{2}{10^4} = 0.0002$

c. $\dfrac{1}{125} = \dfrac{1}{5^3} = \dfrac{1 \cdot 2^3}{5^3 \cdot 2^3} = \dfrac{8}{(5 \cdot 2)^3} = \dfrac{8}{10^3} = 0.008$

d. $\dfrac{7}{250} = \dfrac{7}{2 \cdot 5^3} = \dfrac{7 \cdot 2^2}{(2 \cdot 5^3)2^2} = \dfrac{28}{(2 \cdot 5)^3} = \dfrac{28}{10^3} = 0.028$

A calculator can quickly convert some fractions to decimals. For example, to find $\frac{7}{2^6}$, press $\boxed{7}$ $\boxed{\div}$ $\boxed{2}$ $\boxed{y^x}$ $\boxed{6}$ $\boxed{=}$; to convert $\frac{1}{125}$ to a decimal, press $\boxed{1}$ $\boxed{\div}$ $\boxed{1}$ $\boxed{2}$ $\boxed{5}$ $\boxed{=}$, or press $\boxed{1}$ $\boxed{2}$ $\boxed{5}$ $\boxed{1/x}$ $\boxed{=}$. The display for $\frac{1}{125}$ on some calculators may show $\boxed{8\quad-03}$, which is the calculator's notation for $\frac{8}{10^3}$, or $8 \cdot 10^{-3}$. (This *scientific notation* is discussed in more detail later in this section.)

terminating decimals   The answers in Example 6-2 are illustrations of **terminating decimals**—*decimals that can be written with only a finite number of places to the right of the decimal point.* (*Note:* Not every rational number can be written as a terminating decimal.) If we attempt to rewrite $\frac{2}{11}$ as a terminating decimal using the method just developed, we first try to find a natural number b such that the following holds:

$$\frac{2}{11} = \frac{2b}{11b}, \quad \text{where } 11b \text{ is a power of 10.}$$

By the Fundamental Theorem of Arithmetic (discussed in Chapter 4), the only prime factors of a power of 10 are 2 and 5. Because $11b$ has 11 as a factor, we cannot write $11b$ as a power of 10, and therefore it seems that $\frac{2}{11}$ cannot be written as a terminating decimal. A similar argument using the Fundamental Theorem of Arithmetic holds in general, so we have the following result.

> ### Theorem 6-1
>
> A rational number $\frac{a}{b}$ in simplest form can be written as a terminating decimal if, and only if, the prime factorization of the denominator contains no primes other than 2 or 5.

**E X A M P L E
6-3**

Which of the following fractions can be written as terminating decimals?

a. $\frac{7}{8}$ **b.** $\frac{11}{250}$ **c.** $\frac{21}{28}$ **d.** $\frac{37}{768}$

Solution **a.** Because the denominator, 8, is 2^3 and the fraction is in simplest form, then $\frac{7}{8}$ can be written as a terminating decimal.

b. Because the denominator, 250, is $2 \cdot 5^3$ and the fraction is in simplest form, then $\frac{11}{250}$ can be written as a terminating decimal.

c. First, $\frac{21}{28}$ can be written in simplest form as $\frac{21}{28} = \frac{3 \cdot 7}{2^2 \cdot 7} = \frac{3}{2^2}$. The denominator is now 2^2, so $\frac{21}{28}$ can be written as a terminating decimal.

d. In simplest form, the fraction $\frac{37}{768} = \frac{37}{2^8 \cdot 3}$ has a denominator with a factor of 3, so $\frac{37}{768}$ cannot be written as a terminating decimal.

REMARK   As Example 6-3(c) shows, to determine whether a rational number $\frac{a}{b}$ can be represented as a terminating decimal, we consider the prime factorization of the denominator *only* if the fraction is in simplest form.

Ordering Terminating Decimals

Two decimals can be ordered by converting each to rational numbers in the form $\frac{a}{b}$, where a and b are integers, and determine which is greater. For example, because $0.36 = \frac{36}{100}$, $0.9 = 0.90 = \frac{90}{100}$ and $\frac{90}{100} > \frac{36}{100}$, it follows that $0.9 > 0.36$. One could also tell that $0.9 > 0.36$ because $\$0.90$ is 90¢ and $\$0.36$ is 36¢ and 90¢ $>$ 36¢. This suggests a way to order decimals without conversion to fractions. The steps we use to compare decimals are like those for comparing whole numbers:

1. Line up the numbers by place value.
2. Start at the left and find the first place where the face values are different.
3. Compare these digits. The number containing the greater face value in this place is the greater of the two original numbers.

For example, to compare 0.532 and 0.54, we could do the following:

0.532

0.54

The digits in the hundredths place are different and $4 > 3$, so $0.532 < 0.54$.

O N G O I N G   A S S E S S M E N T   6 - 1

1. Write each of the following as a sum, using powers of 10 to show place value.
   a. 0.023
   b. 206.06
   c. 312.0103
   d. 0.000132

2. Rewrite each of the following as decimals:
   a. $4 \cdot 10^3 + 3 \cdot 10^2 + 5 \cdot 10 + 6 + 7 \cdot 10^{-1} + 8 \cdot 10^{-2}$
   b. $4 \cdot 10^3 + 6 \cdot 10^{-1} + 8 \cdot 10^{-3}$
   c. $4 \cdot 10^4 + 3 \cdot 10^{-2}$
   d. $2 \cdot 10^{-1} + 4 \cdot 10^{-4} + 7 \cdot 10^{-7}$

3. Write each of the following as numerals:
   a. Five hundred thirty-six and seventy-six ten-thousandths
   b. Three and eight thousandths
   c. Four hundred thirty-six millionths
   d. Five million and two tenths

4. Write each of the following terminating decimals in common fraction notation:
   a. 0.436
   b. 25.16
   c. $^-$316.027
   d. 28.1902
   e. $^-$4.3
   f. $^-$62.01

5. Mentally determine which of the following represent terminating decimals:
   a. $\dfrac{4}{5}$
   b. $\dfrac{61}{2^2 \cdot 5}$
   c. $\dfrac{3}{6}$
   d. $\dfrac{1}{2^5}$
   e. $\dfrac{36}{5^5}$
   f. $\dfrac{133}{625}$
   g. $\dfrac{1}{3}$
   h. $\dfrac{2}{25}$
   i. $\dfrac{1}{13}$
   j. $\dfrac{26}{65}$

6. Where possible, write each of the numbers in problem 5 as a terminating decimal.

7. In each of the following, order the decimals from greatest to least:
   a. 13.4919, 13.492, 13.49183, 13.49199
   b. $^-$1.453, $^-$1.45, $^-$1.4053, $^-$1.493

8. Write the numbers in each of the following sentences as decimals in symbols.
   a. A mite has body length about fourteen thousandths of an inch.

   b. The earth goes around the sun once every three hundred sixty-five and twenty-four hundredths days.

9. Use a grid with 100 squares and represent 0.32. Explain your representation.

10. If the decimals 0.804, 0.84, and 0.8399 are arranged on a typical number line, which is furthest to the right?

11. Write a decimal number that has a ten-thousandths place and is between 8.34 and 8.341.

12. Given any reduced rational number $\dfrac{a}{b}$ with $0 < a < b$, where b is of the form $2^m \cdot 5^n$ (m and n are whole numbers), determine a relationship between m and/or n and the number of digits in the terminating decimal. Justify your answer.

13. Which of the following numbers is the greatest: $100{,}000^3$, 1000^5, $100{,}000^2$? Justify your answer.

14. A baseball player's batting average was reported as "three-twenty-two." A batting average is essentially determined when you divide the number of times that the player has hits by the number of time at bat. Explain why the reported batting average is not mathematically correct.

15. If "decimals" in other number bases work the same as in base 10, explain the meaning of the following:
    a. 3.145_{six}
    b. 0.00334_{seven}

16. The five top swimmers in an event had the following times.
Emily	64.54 seconds
Molly	64.46 seconds
Martha	63.59 seconds
Kathy	64.02 seconds
Rhonda	63.54 seconds
    List them in the order they placed.

Communication

17. Explain how you would use base-ten blocks to represent two and three hundred forty-five thousandths.

18. Explain why in Theorem 6-1 the rational number must be in simplest form before examining the denominator.

19. In your own words, explain what a decimal point is and what it does.

Open-Ended

20. Determine how decimal notation is symbolized in different countries.

21. Examine three elementary school textbooks and report how the introductions of the topics of exponents and decimals differ, if they do.

Cooperative Learning

22. Based on a system similar to that of base 10, determine how you might introduce a "decimal" notation in base 5.

BRAIN
T E A S E R

A U.S. Post Office advertised stamps for $.37¢ each. Was this "true" advertising?

6-2 ▸ Operations on Decimals

To develop an algorithm for addition of terminating decimals, consider the sum 2.16 + 1.73. In elementary school, base-ten blocks are recommended to demonstrate such an addition problem. Figure 6-3 shows how the addition can be performed.

FIGURE 6-3

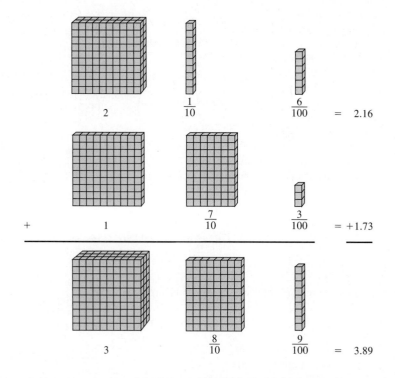

The computation in Figure 6-3 can be explained by *changing it to a problem we already know how to solve*, that is, to a sum involving fractions. We then use the commutative and associative properties of addition to aid in the computation, as follows:

$$2.16 + 1.73 = \left(2 + \frac{1}{10} + \frac{6}{100}\right) + \left(1 + \frac{7}{10} + \frac{3}{100}\right)$$

$$= (2 + 1) + \left(\frac{1}{10} + \frac{7}{10}\right) + \left(\frac{6}{100} + \frac{3}{100}\right)$$

$$= 3 + \frac{8}{10} + \frac{9}{100}$$

$$= 3.89$$

In the computation of Figure 6-3, we see that we are adding units to units, tenths to tenths, and hundredths to hundredths. This can be accomplished most efficiently by keeping the numbers in their decimal forms, lining up the decimal points, and adding as if the numbers were whole numbers. This technique works for both addition and subtraction, as demonstrated on the student page. Try the problems on the bottom of the student page using this technique, and answer problem 9.

Multiplying Decimals

Just as we explained an algorithm for adding and subtracting terminating decimals by representing them as fractions, we can develop and explain an algorithm for multiplication of decimals. Consider the product $4.62 \cdot 2.4$:

$$(4.62)(2.4) = \frac{462}{100} \cdot \frac{24}{10} = \frac{462}{10^2} \cdot \frac{24}{10^1} = \frac{462 \cdot 24}{10^2 \cdot 10^1} = \frac{11{,}088}{10^3} = 11.088$$

The answer to this computation was obtained by multiplying the whole numbers 462 and 24 and then dividing the result by 10^3.

The algorithm for multiplying decimals can be stated as follows:

If there are n digits to the right of the decimal point in one number and m digits to the right of the decimal point in a second number, multiply the two numbers, ignoring the decimals, and then place the decimal point so that there are n + m digits to the right of the decimal point in the product.

REMARK   There are $n + m$ digits to the right of the decimal point in the product because $10^n \cdot 10^m = 10^{n+m}$.

**EXAMPLE
6-4**

Compute each of the following:

a. $(6.2)(1.43)$ **b.** $(0.02)(0.013)$ **c.** $(1000)(3.6)$

Solution   **a.**
$$\begin{array}{r} 1.4\,3 \\ \times\ 6.2 \\ \hline 2\,8\,6 \\ 8\,5\,8 \\ \hline 8.8\,6\,6 \end{array}$$
(2 digits after the decimal point)
(1 digit after the decimal point)

(3 digits after the decimal point)

b.
$$\begin{array}{r} 0.0\,1\,3 \\ \times\quad 0.0\,2 \\ \hline 0.0\,0\,0\,2\,6 \end{array}$$

c.
$$\begin{array}{r} 3.6 \\ \times\quad 1\,0\,0\,0 \\ \hline 3\,6\,0\,0.0 \end{array}$$

Sample School Book Page:
MULTIPLYING DECIMALS

Connect and Learn

When you add, you must make sure you're adding tenths to tenths, hundredths to hundredths, and so on. To do this, make sure to line up the decimal points. Then add as if you were adding whole numbers.

Example 1

Add 1.7 and 2.49.

```
  1.7     Line up the decimal points.
+ 2.49
  4.19
```

Estimate: $2 + 2 = 4$

Since 4.19 is close to the estimate of 4, the answer is reasonable.

Use the same plan when subtracting decimals. Line up the decimal points and then subtract as if you were subtracting whole numbers. Annex zeros if the second number has more digits after the decimal point than the first.

Example 2

The United Kingdom uses a decimal currency based on the pound (£). Paul has £1.8. Edmund has only £1.38. How many more pounds does Paul have?

Subtract to find the difference.

```
  1.80    Line up the decimal points.
- 1.38    Annex zeros.
  0.42
```

Paul has £0.42 more than Edmund.

Estimate to tenths: $1.8 - 1.4 = 0.4$

Since 0.42 is close to 0.4, the answer is reasonable.

Remember

Annexing zeros to the right of a decimal number does not change the value of the number.

Check

Find each sum or difference.

1. $4.631 + 3.986$
2. $8.592 - 4.635$
3. $5.6 + 1.973$
4. $7.3 - 4.45$
5. $0.04 + 18.6$
6. $9.72 - 1.80$
7. $2.5 - 0.25$
8. $0.198 + 1.18$

9. **Reasoning** Will drew this grid to model $0.4 + 0.25$. Is he correct? Explain.

Source: Scott Foresman–Addison Wesley Math, Grade 6, 2002 (p. 163).

NOW TRY THIS 6-2

Example 6-4(c) suggests that multiplication by 1000 or 10^3 results in moving the decimal point in the multiplicand 3 places to the right. **(a)** Explain why this is true using expanded notation and the distributive property of multiplication over addition. **(b)** In general, how does multiplication by 10^n, where n is a positive integer, affect the multiplicand? Why?

Scientific Notation

Many calculators will display the decimals for the fractions $\dfrac{3}{45,689}$ or $\dfrac{5}{76,146}$ as

 $\boxed{6.5661319 \quad -05}$ and $\boxed{6.566333 \quad -05}$, respectively. The displays are in *scientific notation*. The first display is a notation for $6.5661319 \cdot 10^{-5}$ and the second for $6.566333 \cdot 10^{-5}$.

Scientists use scientific notation to handle either very small or very large numbers. For example, "the sun is 93,000,000 mi from Earth" is expressed as "the sun is $9.3 \cdot 10^7$ mi from Earth." A micron, a metric unit of measure that is 0.000001 m, is written $1 \cdot 10^{-6}$ m.

> ### Definition of Scientific Notation

> In **scientific notation**, a positive number is written as the product of a number greater than or equal to 1 and less than 10 and an integer power of 10.

The following numbers are in scientific notation:

$$8.3 \cdot 10^8, \qquad 1.2 \cdot 10^{10}, \qquad \text{and } 7.84 \cdot 10^{-6}$$

The numbers $0.43 \cdot 10^9$ and $12.3 \cdot 10^{-6}$ are not in scientific notation because 0.43 and 12.3 are not greater than or equal to 1 and less than 10. To write a number like 934.5 in scientific notation, we divide by 10^2 to get 9.345 and then multiply by 10^2 to retain the value of the original number:

$$934.5 = (934.5/10^2) \cdot 10^2 = 9.345 \cdot 10^2$$

This amounts to moving the decimal point two places to the left (dividing by 10^2) and then multiplying by 10^2. Similarly to write 0.000078 in scientific notation, we first multiply by 10^5 to obtain 7.8 and then divide by 10^5 (or multiply by 10^{-5}) to keep the original value:

$$0.000078 = (0.000078 \cdot 10^5) \cdot 10^{-5} = 7.8 \cdot 10^{-5}.$$

This amounts to moving the decimal point five places to the right and multiplying by 10^{-5}.

EXAMPLE 6-5   Write each of the following in scientific notation:

a. 413,682,000   **b.** 0.0000231   **c.** 83.7   **d.** 10,000,000

Solution   **a.** $413,682,000 = (413,682,000/10^8) \cdot 10^8 = 4.13682 \cdot 10^8$
b. $0.0000231 = (0.0000231 \cdot 10^5) \cdot 10^{-5} = 2.31 \cdot 10^{-5}$
c. $83.7 = (83.7/10^1) \cdot 10^1 = 8.37 \cdot 10^1$
d. $10,000,000 = (10,000,000/10^7) \cdot 10^7 = 1 \cdot 10^7$

E X A M P L E
6-6

Convert each of the following to standard numerals:

a. $6.84 \cdot 10^{-5}$ **b.** $3.12 \cdot 10^{7}$

Solution   **a.** $6.84 \cdot 10^{-5} = 6.84 \cdot \left(\dfrac{1}{10^{5}}\right) = 0.0000684$

b. $3.12 \cdot 10^{7} = 31,200,000$

Numbers in scientific notation are easy to manipulate using the laws of exponents. For example, $(5.6 \cdot 10^{5})(6 \cdot 10^{4})$ can be rewritten $(5.6 \cdot 6)(10^{5} \cdot 10^{4}) = 33.6 \cdot 10^{9}$, which is $3.36 \cdot 10^{10}$ in scientific notation. Also,

$$(2.35 \cdot 10^{-15})(2 \cdot 10^{8}) = (2.35 \cdot 2)(10^{-15} \cdot 10^{8}) = 4.7 \cdot 10^{-7}.$$

Calculators with an $\boxed{\text{EE}}$ key can be used to represent numbers in scientific notation. For example, to find $(5.2 \cdot 10^{16}) \cdot (9.37 \cdot 10^{4})$, press

$$\boxed{5}\,\boxed{.}\,\boxed{2}\,\boxed{\text{EE}}\,\boxed{1}\,\boxed{6}\,\boxed{\times}\,\boxed{9}\,\boxed{.}\,\boxed{3}\,\boxed{7}\,\boxed{\text{EE}}\,\boxed{4}\,\boxed{=}.$$

Dividing Decimals

Next we develop an algorithm for division of decimals. As with the other operations, we use fractions to represent a division that involves decimals and see if it suggests an algorithm to handle the division. Consider $75.45 \div 3$:

$$75.45 \div 3 = \frac{7545}{100} \div \frac{3}{1} = \frac{7545}{100} \cdot \frac{1}{3} = \frac{7545}{3} \cdot \frac{1}{100} = 2515 \cdot \frac{1}{100} = 25.15$$

This computation is shown using the algorithm on the following student page.

From the student page, we see that when the divisor is a whole number, the division can be handled as with whole numbers and the decimal point placed directly over the decimal point in the dividend. Notice the role of estimation in the algorithm and that the division can be checked using the inverse operation of multiplication. When the divisor is not a whole number, as in $1.2032 \div 0.32$, we can obtain a whole-number divisor by expressing the quotient as a fraction and then multiplying the numerator and denominator of the fraction by 100. This corresponds to rewriting the division problem in form (a) as an equivalent problem in form (b), as follows:

(a) $0.32 \overline{)1.2032}$ (b) $32 \overline{)120.32}$

In elementary school texts, this process is usually described as "moving" the decimal point two places to the right in both the dividend and the divisor. This process is usually indicated with arrows, as shown in the following.

$$
\begin{array}{r}
3.76 \\
0.3\,2\,\overline{)1.2\,0\,3\,2} \\
\underline{9\,6} \\
2\,4\,3 \\
\underline{2\,2\,4} \\
1\,9\,2 \\
\underline{1\,9\,2} \\
0
\end{array}
$$

Multiply divisor and dividend by 100.

Sample School Book Page:
DIVIDING DECIMALS

Connect and Learn ●

A problem with a decimal divisor can be changed to one without a decimal divisor.

Multiply both divisor and dividend by a power of 10 that will make the divisor a whole number.

Dividend Divisor
$2.618 \div 0.34 = 261.8 \div 34.$
$\times 100 \quad \times 100$

Math Tip
To multiply a number by 100 move the decimal two places to the right.

Example 1
Find the quotient $5.832 \div 1.62$
$5.832 \div 1.62 = 583.2 \div 162.$

$$
\begin{array}{r}
3.6 \\
162\overline{)583.2} \\
-486 \\
\hline
972 \\
-972 \\
\hline
0
\end{array}
$$

The quotient is 3.6

Multiply dividend and divisor by 100 to make the divisor a whole number.

Divide.

Source: Scott Foresman–Addison Wesley Math, Grade 6, 2002 (p. 191).

EXAMPLE 6-7

Compute each of the following:
a. $13.169 \div 0.13$ **b.** $9 \div 0.75$

Solution **a.**
$$
\begin{array}{r}
101.3 \\
0.13\overline{)13.169} \\
13 \\
\hline
16 \\
13 \\
\hline
39 \\
39 \\
\hline
0
\end{array}
$$

b.
$$
\begin{array}{r}
12 \\
0.75\overline{)9.00} \\
75 \\
\hline
150 \\
150 \\
\hline
0
\end{array}
$$

In Example 6-7(b), we annexed two zeros in the dividend because $\dfrac{9}{0.75} = \dfrac{9 \cdot 100}{0.75 \cdot 100} = \dfrac{900}{75}$.

EXAMPLE
6-8

An owner of a gasoline station must collect a gasoline tax of $0.11 on each gallon of gasoline sold. One week, the owner paid $1595 in gasoline taxes. The pump price of a gallon of gas that week was $1.35.

a. How many gallons of gas were sold during the week?
b. What was the revenue after taxes for the week?

Solution   **a.** To find the number of gallons of gas sold during the week, we must divide the total gas tax bill by the amount of the tax per gallon:

$$\frac{1595}{0.11} = 14,500$$

Thus 14,500 gallons were sold.

b. To obtain the revenue after taxes, first determine the revenue before taxes. Then multiply the number of gallons sold by the cost per gallon:

$$(14,500)(\$1.35) = \$19,575$$

Next, subtract the gasoline taxes from the total revenue:

$$\$19,575 - \$1595 = \$17,980$$

Thus the revenue after gasoline taxes is $17,980.

NOW TRY THIS 6-3

Use decimal division to help Hi, in the "Hi & Lois" cartoon, determine the best buy.

Mental Computation

Some of the tools used for mental computations with whole numbers can be used to perform mental computations with decimals, as seen in the following:

1. *Breaking and bridging*

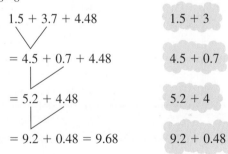

$$1.5 + 3.7 + 4.48$$

$$= 4.5 + 0.7 + 4.48$$

$$= 5.2 + 4.48$$

$$= 9.2 + 0.48 = 9.68$$

1.5 + 3

4.5 + 0.7

5.2 + 4

9.2 + 0.48

2. *Using compatible numbers*
(Decimal numbers are compatible when they add up to a whole number.)

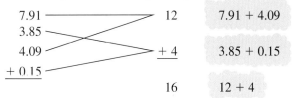

3. *Making compatible numbers*

$$
\begin{aligned}
9.27 &= 9.25 + 0.02 \\
+\,3.79 &= 3.75 + 0.04 \\
\hline
& \, 13.00 + 0.06 = 13.06
\end{aligned}
$$

4. *Balancing with decimals in subtraction*

$$
\begin{aligned}
4.63 &= & 4.63 + 0.03 &= & 4.66 \\
-\,1.97 &= & -(1.97 + 0.03) &= & -2.00 \\
\hline
& & & & 2.66
\end{aligned}
$$

5. *Balancing with decimals in division*

$$0.25\overline{)8}$$

$$\times 4 \qquad \times 4$$

$$1\overline{)32} \quad 32$$

REMARK   Balancing with decimals in division uses the property $\dfrac{a}{b} = \dfrac{a \cdot c}{b \cdot c}$ if $c \neq 0$.

Rounding Decimals

Frequently, it is not necessary to know the exact numerical answer to a question. For example, if we want to know the distance to the moon or the population of New York City, the approximate answers of 239,000 mi and 16,640,000 people, respectively, may be adequate.

Often a situation determines how you should round. For example, suppose a purchase came to $38.65 and the cashier used a calculator to figure out the 6% sales tax by multiplying $0.06 \cdot 38.65$. The display showed 2.319. Because the display is between 2.31 and 2.32 and it is closer to 2.32, the cashier rounds up the sales tax to $2.32.

Suppose a display of 8.7345649 needs to be reported to the nearest hundredth. The display is between 8.73 and 8.74 but is closer to 8.73, so we round it down to 8.73. Next suppose the number 6.8675 needs to be rounded to the nearest thousandth. Notice that 6.8675 is exactly halfway between 6.867 and 6.868. In such cases, it is common practice to round up and therefore the answer to the nearest thousandth is 6.868. We write this $6.8675 \doteq 6.868$ and say 6.8675 is approximately equal to 6.868.

E X A M P L E
6-9

Round each of the following numbers:

a. 7.456 to the nearest hundredth
b. 7.456 to the nearest tenth
c. 7.456 to the nearest unit
d. 7456 to the nearest thousand
e. 745 to the nearest ten
f. 74.56 to the nearest ten

Solution **a.** $7.456 \doteq 7.46$
b. $7.456 \doteq 7.5$
c. $7.456 \doteq 7$
d. $7456 \doteq 7000$
e. $745 \doteq 750$
f. $74.56 \doteq 70$

 Rounding can also be done on some calculators using the $\boxed{\text{FIX}}$ key. If you want the number 2.3669 to be rounded to thousandths, you enter $\boxed{\text{FIX}}$ $\boxed{3}$. The display will show 0.000. If you then enter 2.3669 and press the $\boxed{=}$ key, the display will show 2.367.

Estimating Decimal Computations Using Rounding

Rounded numbers can be useful for estimating answers to computations. For example, consider each of the following:

1. Karly goes to the grocery store to buy items that cost the following amounts. She estimates the total cost by rounding each amount to the nearest dollar and adding the rounded numbers.

$$
\begin{array}{rcr}
\$2.39 & \rightarrow & \$2 \\
0.89 & \rightarrow & 1 \\
6.13 & \rightarrow & 6 \\
4.75 & \rightarrow & 5 \\
+\,5.05 & \rightarrow & 5 \\
\hline
 & & \$19
\end{array}
$$

Thus Karly's estimate for her grocery bill is $19.

2. Karly's bill for car repairs was $72.80, and she has a coupon for $17.50 off. She can estimate her total cost by rounding each amount to the nearest ten dollars and subtracting.

$$
\begin{array}{rr}
\$72.80 & \$70 \\
-\,17.50 & -\,20 \\
\hline
 & \$50
\end{array}
$$

Thus an estimate for the repair bill is $50.

3. Karly sees a flash of lightning and hears the thunder 3.2 sec later. She knows that sound travels at 0.33 km/sec. She may estimate the distance she is from the lightning by rounding the time to the nearest unit and the speed to the nearest tenth and multiplying.

$$
\begin{array}{ccc}
0.33 & \rightarrow & 0.3 \\
\times\, 3.2 & \rightarrow & \times\, 3 \\
\hline
& & 0.9
\end{array}
$$

Thus Karly estimates that she is approximately 0.9 km from the lightning.

An alternative approach is to recognize that $0.33 \doteq \dfrac{1}{3}$ and 3.2 is close to 3.3, so an approximation using compatible numbers is $\left(\dfrac{1}{3}\right) \cdot 3.3$, or 1.1 km.

4. Karly wants to estimate the number of miles she gets per gallon of gas. If she had driven 298 mi and it took 12.4 gal to fill the gas tank, she rounds and divides as follows:

$$
12.4\overline{)298} \rightarrow 12\overline{)300} \;\; \text{(25)}
$$

Thus she got about 25 mi/gal.

When computations are performed with rounded numbers, the results may be significantly different from the actual answer.

NOW TRY THIS 6-4

Other estimation strategies, such as front-end, clustering, and grouping to nice numbers, that you investigated with whole numbers also work with decimals. Take the grocery store bill in part 1 on the preceding page and use a front-end-with-adjustment strategy to estimate the bill.

Round-off Errors

Round-off errors are typically compounded when computations are involved. For example, if two distances are 42.6 mi and 22.4 mi rounded to the nearest tenth, then the sum of the distances appears to be $42.6 + 22.4$, or 65 mi. To the nearest hundredth, the distances might have been more accurately reported as 42.55 and 22.35 mi, respectively. The sum of these distances is 64.9 mi. Alternatively, the original distances may have been rounded from 42.64 and 22.44 mi. The sum now is 65.08, or 65.1 rounded to the nearest tenth. The original sum of 65 mi is between 64.9 and 65.1 mi, but the simple rounding process used is not precise.

Similar errors arise in other arithmetic operations. *When computations are done with approximate numbers, the final result should not be reported using more decimal places than the number used with the fewest decimal places.* In other words, an answer can be "no more accurate" than "the least accurate" number used to find it.

ONGOING ASSESSMENT 6-2

1. If Maura went to the store and bought a chair for $17.95, a lawn rake for $13.59, a spade for $14.86, a lawn mower for $179.98, and two six-packs of mineral water for $2.43 each, what was the bill?

2. A stock's price dropped from 63.28 per share to 27.45. What was the loss on a single share of the stock?

3. Complete the following magic square; that is, make the sum of every row, column, and diagonal the same:

8.2		
3.7	5.5	
	9.1	2.8

4. Keith bought 30 lb of nuts at $3.00/lb and 20 lb of nuts at $5.00/lb. If he wanted to buy 10 more pounds of a different kind of nut to make the average price per pound equal to $4.50, what price should he pay for the additional 10 lb?

5. A kilowatt hour means 1000 watts of electricity are being used continuously for 1 hr. The electric utility company in Laura's town charges $0.03715 for each kilowatt hour used. Laura heats her house with three electric wall heaters that use 1200 watts per hour each.
   a. How much does it cost to heat her house for one day?
   b. How many hours would a 75-watt light bulb have to stay on to result in $1 for electricity charges?

6. Automobile engines were once measured in cubic inches (in.^{3}) but are now usually measured in cubic centimeters (cm^3). If 2.54 cm is equivalent to 1 in., answer the following:
   a. Susan's 1963 Thunderbird has a 390 in.^{3} engine. Approximately how many cubic centimeters is this?
   b. Dan's 1991 Taurus has a 3000 cm^3 engine. Approximately how many cubic inches is this?

7. Florence Griffith-Joyner set a world record for the women's 100-m dash at the 1988 Summer Olympics in Seoul, South Korea. She covered the distance in 10.49 sec. If 1 m is equivalent to 39.37 in., express Griffith-Joyner's speed in terms of miles per hour.

8. If each of the following sequences is either arithmetic or geometric, continue the following decimal patterns:
   a. 0.9, 1.8, 2.7, 3.6, 4.5, ____, ____, ____
   b. 0.3, 0.5, 0.7, 0.9, 1.1, ____, ____, ____
   c. 1, 0.5, 0.25, 0.125, ____, ____, ____
   d. 0.2, 1.5, 2.8, 4.1, 5.4, ____, ____, ____

9. A bank statement from a local bank shows that a checking account has a balance of $83.62. The balance recorded in the checkbook shows only $21.69. After checking the canceled checks against the record of these checks, the cus-

tomer finds that the bank has not yet recorded six checks in the amounts of $3.21, $14.56, $12.44, $6.98, $9.51, and $7.49. Is the bank record correct? (Assume the person's checkbook records *are* correct.)

10. Convert each of the following to standard numerals:
    a. $3.2 \cdot 10^{-9}$
    b. $3.2 \cdot 10^9$
    c. $4.2 \cdot 10^{-1}$
    d. $6.2 \cdot 10^5$

11. Write the numerals in each of the following sentences in scientific notation:
    a. The diameter of Earth is about 12,700,000 m.
    b. The distance from Pluto to the sun is about 4,486,000,000 km.
    c. Each year, about 50,000,000 cans are discarded in the United States.

12. Write the numerals in each of the following sentences in standard form:
    a. A computer requires $4.4 \cdot 10^{-6}$ sec to do an addition problem.
    b. There are about $1.99 \cdot 10^4$ km of coastline in the United States.
    c. Earth has existed for approximately $3 \cdot 10^9$ yr.

13. Write the results of each of the following in scientific notation:
    a. $(8 \cdot 10^{12}) \cdot (6 \cdot 10^{15})$
    b. $(16 \cdot 10^{12}) \div (4 \cdot 10^5)$
    c. $(5 \cdot 10^8) \cdot (6 \cdot 10^9) \div (15 \cdot 10^{15})$

14. Round each of the following numbers as specified:
    a. 203.651 to the nearest hundred
    b. 203.651 to the nearest ten
    c. 203.651 to the nearest unit
    d. 203.651 to the nearest tenth
    e. 203.651 to the nearest hundredth

15. Jane's car travels 224 mi on 12 gal of gas. Rounded to the nearest mile how many miles to the gallon does her car get?

16. Audrey wants to buy some camera equipment to take pictures on her daughter's birthday. To estimate the total cost, she rounds each price to the nearest dollar and adds the rounded prices. What is her estimate for the items listed?

Camera	$54.56
Film	$ 4.50
Case	$17.85

17. Estimate the sum or difference in each of the following by using (i) rounding and (ii) front-end estimation. Then perform the computations to see how close your estimates are to the actual answers.

a.	65.84	b.	89.47	c.	5.85	d.	223.75
	24.29		− 32.16		6.13		− 87.60
	12.18				9.10		
	+ 19.75				+ 4.32		

18. Mary Kim invested $964 in 18 shares of stock. A month later, she sold the 18 shares at $61.48 per share. She also invested in 350 shares of stock for a total of $27,422.50. She sold this stock for $85.35 a share and paid $495 in total commissions. What was Mary Kim's profit or loss on the transactions to the nearest dollar?

19. Luisa is traveling in Switzerland where the exchange rate is U.S. $1 = 1.59 Swiss francs for cash and U.S. $1 = 1.60 Swiss francs for traveler's checks.
    a. Luisa is exchanging $235 in cash. How many Swiss francs will she get?
    b. Luisa wants to buy a watch that costs 452.85 Swiss francs and hiking boots that cost 284.65 Swiss francs. What is the minimum number of dollars in cash that Luisa needs to exchange to purchase both?
    c. Luisa wants to buy a suit that costs 687.75 Swiss francs. She has traveler's checks in U.S. dollars in denominations of $100 and $20. What is the least amount of dollars in traveler's checks she needs to exchange? Explain your solution.

20. Find the least and the greatest possible products for each expression using the digits 1 through 9. Each digit may be used only once in each part.
    a. ☐.☐ × ☐   b. ☐.☐ × ☐.☐

21. Some digits in the following number are covered by squares:

    4☐3☐.☐☐8☐

    If each of the digits 1 through 9 is used exactly once in the number, determine the number in each of these cases:
    a. The number is the greatest possible.
    b. The number is the least possible.

22. Iris worked a 40-hour week at $6.25/hr. Mentally compute her salary for the week and explain how you did it.

23. Mentally compute the number to fill in the blank in each of the following.
    a. $8.4 \cdot 6 = 4.2 \cdot$ ____
    b. $10.2 \div 0.3 = 20.4 \div$ ____
    c. $a \cdot b = (a/2) \cdot$ ____
    d. $a \div b = 2a \div$ ____

24. Which of the following result in equal quotients?
    a. $7 \div 0.25$
    b. $70 \div 2.5$
    c. $0.7 \div 0.25$
    d. $700 \div 25$

25. Use estimation to place the decimal point in the correct position in each of the following products:
    a. $534 \cdot 0.34 = 18156$
    b. $5.07 \cdot 29.3 = 148551$

26. Is subtracting 0.3 the same as (a) subtracting 0.30? (b) subtracting 0.03? Explain.

27. Use estimation to choose a decimal to multiply by 9 in order to get within 1 of 93. Explain how you made your choice and check your estimate.

28. a. Fill in the parentheses in each of the following to write a true equation:
    $$1 \cdot 2 + 0.25 = (\quad)^2 \qquad 2 \cdot 3 + 0.25 = (\quad)^2$$
    Conjecture what the next two equations in this pattern will be.
    b. Do the computations to determine if your next two equations are correct.
    c. Generalize your answer in part (a) by filling in an appropriate expression in the equation
    $$n \cdot (n + 1) + 0.25 = (\quad)^2,$$
    where n is the number of the terms in this sequence of equations.

Communication

29. How is multiplication of decimals like multiplication of whole numbers? How is it different?

30. Why are estimation skills important in dividing decimals?

31. In the text, multiplication and division were done using both fractional and decimal forms. Discuss the advantages and disadvantages of each.

32. Explain why subtraction of terminating decimals can be accomplished by lining up the decimal points, subtracting as if the numbers were whole numbers, and then placing the decimal point in the difference.

Open-Ended

33. Find several examples of the use of decimals in the newspaper. Tell whether you think the numbers are exact or estimates. Also tell why you think decimals were used instead of fractions.

34. How could a calculator be used to develop or reinforce the understanding of multiplication of decimals?

Cooperative Learning

35. In your group, decide on all the prerequisite skills that students need before learning to perform arithmetic operations on decimals.

 36. You will need a calculator and a partner to play the game described on page 338 on the student page from McDougal Littell *Middle Grades MATH Thematics, Book 1*, 2002.

Review Problems

37. Write 14.0479 in expanded form.

38. Without dividing, determine which of the following represent terminating decimals:
    a. 24/36   b. 35/56

39. If the denominator of a fraction is 26, is it possible that the fraction could be written as a terminating decimal? Why or why not?

40. 35/56 can be written as a decimal that terminates. Explain why.

Sample School Book Page:
ESTIMATING DECIMAL PRODUCTS

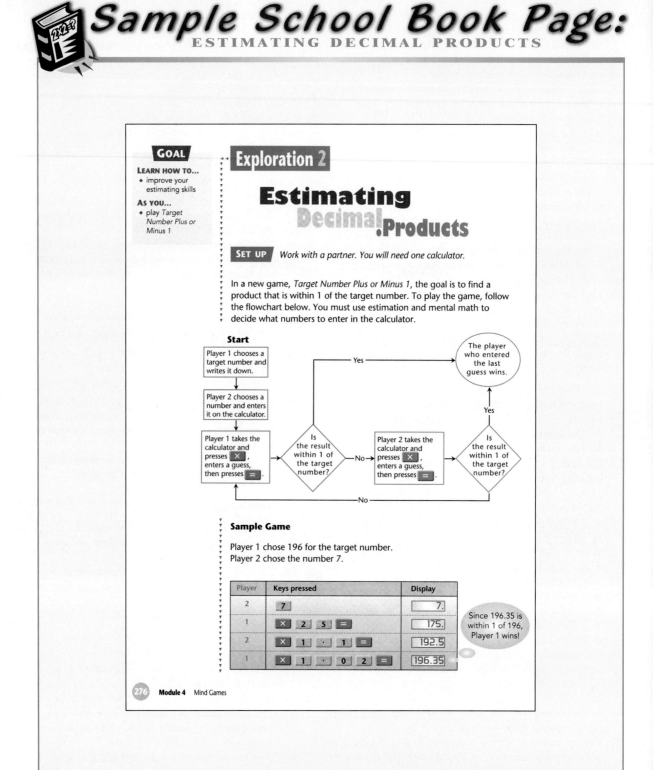

GOAL

LEARN HOW TO...
- improve your estimating skills

AS YOU...
- play *Target Number Plus or Minus 1*

Exploration 2

Estimating Decimal Products

SET UP Work with a partner. You will need one calculator.

In a new game, *Target Number Plus or Minus 1*, the goal is to find a product that is within 1 of the target number. To play the game, follow the flowchart below. You must use estimation and mental math to decide what numbers to enter in the calculator.

Start

Player 1 chooses a target number and writes it down.

Player 2 chooses a number and enters it on the calculator.

Player 1 takes the calculator and presses ×, enters a guess, then presses =.

Is the result within 1 of the target number?

— Yes →

The player who entered the last guess wins.

Player 2 takes the calculator and presses ×, enters a guess, then presses =.

Is the result within 1 of the target number?

— No —

— Yes —

— No —

Sample Game

Player 1 chose 196 for the target number.
Player 2 chose the number 7.

Player	Keys pressed	Display
2	7	7.
1	× 2 5 =	175.
2	× 1 · 1 =	192.5
1	× 1 · 0 2 =	196.35

Since 196.35 is within 1 of 196, Player 1 wins!

276 **Module 4** Mind Games

Source: McDougal Littell, Middle Grades MATH Thematics, Book 1, 2002 (p. 276).

Nonterminating Decimals

Earlier in the text, procedures for converting some rational numbers to decimals were developed. For example, 7/8 can be written as a terminating decimal as follows:

$$\frac{7}{8} = \frac{7}{2^3} = \frac{7 \cdot 5^3}{2^3 \cdot 5^3} = \frac{875}{1000} = 0.875$$

The decimal for 7/8 can also be found by division, as shown below:

$$\begin{array}{r} 0.875 \\ 8\overline{)7.000} \\ \underline{6\,4} \\ 60 \\ \underline{56} \\ 40 \\ \underline{40} \\ 0 \end{array}$$

Repeating Decimals

If we use a calculator to find a decimal representation for 2/11, the calculator may display 0.1818181. It seems that 18 repeats itself. To examine what digits, if any, the calculator did not display, consider the following division:

$$\begin{array}{r} 0.18 \\ 11\overline{)2.00} \\ \underline{1\,1} \\ 90 \\ \underline{88} \\ 2 \end{array}$$

repeating decimal ◆ repetend

At this point, if the division is continued, the division pattern would repeat, since the remainder 2 divided by 11 repeats the division. Thus the quotient is 0.181818 . . . . A decimal of this type is a **repeating decimal**, and the repeating block of digits is the **repetend**. The repeating decimal is written $0.\overline{18}$, where the bar indicates that the block of digits underneath is repeated continuously.

E X A M P L E
6-10

Convert the following to decimals:

a. $\dfrac{1}{7}$ **b.** $\dfrac{2}{13}$

Solution   We use a calculator to divide, and it seems that the division pattern repeats.

a. $\dfrac{1}{7} = 0.\overline{142857}$

b. $\dfrac{2}{13} = 0.\overline{153846}$

To see why in Example 6-10 the division pattern repeats as predicted, consider the following divisions:

$$
\begin{array}{r}
\textbf{a.} \quad 0.142857 \\
7\overline{)1.000000} \\
\underline{7} \\
30 \\
\underline{28} \\
20 \\
\underline{14} \\
60 \\
\underline{56} \\
40 \\
\underline{35} \\
50 \\
\underline{49} \\
1
\end{array}
\qquad
\begin{array}{r}
\textbf{b.} \quad 0.153846 \\
13\overline{)2.000000} \\
\underline{1\,3} \\
70 \\
\underline{65} \\
50 \\
\underline{39} \\
110 \\
\underline{104} \\
60 \\
\underline{52} \\
80 \\
\underline{78} \\
2
\end{array}
$$

In $\frac{1}{7}$, the remainders obtained in the division are 3, 2, 6, 4, 5, and 1. These are all the possible nonzero remainders that can be obtained when dividing by 7. If we had obtained a remainder of 0, the decimal would terminate. Consequently, the seventh division cannot produce a new remainder. Whenever a remainder recurs, the process repeats itself. Using similar reasoning, we could predict that the repetend for $\frac{2}{13}$ could not have more than 12 digits, because there are only 12 possible nonzero remainders. However, one of the remainders could repeat sooner than that, which was actually the case in part (b). In general, if $\frac{a}{b}$ is any rational number in simplest form with $b \neq 0$ and $b > a$, and it does not represent a terminating decimal, the repetend has at most $b - 1$ digits. Therefore *a rational number may always be represented either as a terminating decimal or as a repeating decimal.*

NOW TRY THIS 6-5

> **a.** Write 1/9 as a decimal.
> **b.** Based on your answer in part (a), mentally compute the decimal representation for each of the following.
>   (i) 2/9   (ii) 3/9
>   (iii) 5/9   (iv) 8/9

EXAMPLE 6-11

Use a calculator to convert $\frac{1}{17}$ to a repeating decimal.

Solution   In using a calculator, if we press $\boxed{1}\ \boxed{\div}\ \boxed{1}\ \boxed{7}\ \boxed{=}$, we obtain the following, shown as part of a division problem:

$$
\begin{array}{r}
0.0588235 \\
17\overline{)1.}
\end{array}
$$

Without knowing whether the calculator has an internal round-off feature and with the calculator's having an 8-digit display, we find the greatest number of digits to be trusted in the quotient is 6 following the decimal point. (Why?) If we use those 6 places and multiply 0.058823 times 17, we may continue the operation as follows:

$$\boxed{\cdot}\,\boxed{0}\,\boxed{5}\,\boxed{8}\,\boxed{8}\,\boxed{2}\,\boxed{3}\,\boxed{\times}\,\boxed{1}\,\boxed{7}\,\boxed{=}$$

We then obtain 0.999991, which we may place in the preceding division:

$$
\begin{array}{r}
0.058823 \\
17\overline{)1.000000} \\
999991 \\
\hline
9
\end{array}
$$

Next, we divide 9 by 17 to obtain 0.5294118. Again ignoring the rightmost digit, we continue as before, completing the division as follows, where the repeating pattern is apparent:

$$
\begin{array}{r}
0.0588235294117647058235 \\
17\overline{)1.00000000000000000000000} \\
999991 \\
\hline
9000000 \\
8999987 \\
\hline
13000000 \\
12999985 \\
\hline
15
\end{array}
$$

Thus $\dfrac{1}{17} = 0.\overline{0588235294117647}$, and the repetend is 16 digits long.

Writing a Repeating Decimal in the Form $\dfrac{a}{b}$ Where $a, b \in I, b \neq 0$

We have already considered how to write terminating decimals in the form $\dfrac{a}{b}$, where a, b are integers and $b \neq 0$. For example,

$$0.55 = \frac{55}{10^2} = \frac{55}{100}.$$

To write $0.\overline{5}$ in a similar way, we see that because the repeating decimal has infinitely many digits, there is no single power of 10 that can be placed in the denominator. To overcome this difficulty, we must somehow eliminate the infinitely repeating part of the decimal. If we let $n = 0.\overline{5}$, then our *subgoal* is to write an equation for n without a repeating decimal. It can be shown that $10(0.555\ldots) - 5.555\ldots = 5.5$. Hence, $10n = 5.\overline{5}$. Using this information, we subtract the corresponding sides of the equations to obtain an equation whose solution can be written without a repeating decimal.

$$
\begin{array}{r}
10n = 5.\overline{5} \\
-\ n = 0.\overline{5} \\
\hline
9n = 5 \\
n = \dfrac{5}{9}
\end{array}
$$

Thus $0.\overline{5} = \frac{5}{9}$. This result can be checked by performing the division $5 \div 9$. (*Note:* Performing the subtraction gives an equation that contains only integers. The repeating blocks "cancel" each other.)

Suppose a decimal has a repetend of more than one digit, such as $0.\overline{235}$. We can reasonably multiply by 10^3, since there is a three-digit repetend. Let $n = 0.\overline{235}$. Our *subgoal* is again to write an equation for n without the repeating decimal:

$$1000n = 235.\overline{235}$$
$$-\ \ \ \ n = \ \ \ 0.\overline{235}$$
$$999n = 235$$
$$= \frac{235}{999}$$

Hence, $0.\overline{235} = \frac{235}{999}$.

Notice that $0.\overline{5}$ repeats in one-digit blocks. Therefore, to write it in the form $\frac{a}{b}$, we first multiply by 10^1. Because $0.\overline{235}$ repeats in three-digit blocks, we first multiply by 10^3. In general, *if the repetend is immediately to the right of the decimal point, first multiply by 10^m, where m is the number of digits in the repetend, and then continue as in the preceding cases.*

Now, suppose the repeating block does *not* occur immediately after the decimal point. For example, let $n = 2.3\overline{45}$. A strategy for solving this problem is to *change it to a related problem* we already know how to do; that is, change it to a problem where the repeating block immediately follows the decimal point. This is our new *subgoal*. To accomplish this, we multiply both sides by 10:

$$n = 2.3\overline{45}$$
$$10n = 23.\overline{45}$$

We now proceed as with previous problems. Because $10n = 23.\overline{45}$ and the number of digits in the repetend is 2, we multiply by 10^2 as follows:

$$100(10n) = 2345.\overline{45}$$

Thus

$$1000n = 2345.\overline{45}$$
$$-\ 10n = \ \ \ 23.\overline{45}$$
$$990n = 2322$$
$$n = \frac{2322}{990}, \text{ or } \frac{129}{55}$$

Hence, $2.3\overline{45} = \frac{2322}{990}$, or $\frac{129}{55}$.

To find the $\frac{a}{b}$ form of $0.\overline{9}$, we proceed as follows. Let $n = 0.\overline{9}$, then $10n = 9.\overline{9}$. Next we subtract and continue to solve for n:

$$10n = 9.\overline{9}$$
$$-\ n = 0.\overline{9}$$
$$9n = 9$$
$$n = 1$$

Hence, $0.\overline{9} = 1$. This approach to the problem may not be convincing. Another approach to show that $0.\overline{9}$ is really another name for 1 is shown next:

$$\text{(a) } \frac{1}{3} = 0.33333333 \ldots \quad \text{(b) } \frac{2}{3} = 0.66666666 \ldots$$

Adding Equations (a) and (b), we have $1 = 0.99999999 \ldots$, or $0.\overline{9}$. This last decimal represents the infinite sum $\frac{9}{10} + \frac{9}{10^2} + \frac{9}{10^3} + \ldots$. In more advanced mathematics courses, such sums are defined as the limits of finite sums.

NOW TRY THIS 6-6

a. Based on the cartoon below, write Arlo's real age in years as a decimal. Is the decimal terminating or nonterminating? Why?

b. Find Arlo's real age in years and months.

c. Use the 74.9-year life expectancy and your age to determine what date of a one-year life it is for you.

Arlo and Janis *by Johnson*

ARLO & JANIS REPRINTED BY PERMISSION OF NEWSPAPER ENTERPRISE ASSOCIATION, INC. ALL RIGHTS RESERVED.

Ordering Repeating Decimals

We saw in Section 6-1 how to compare terminating decimals. To compare repeating decimals such as $1.\overline{3478}$ and $1.347\overline{821}$, we use a similar procedure. We write the decimals one under the other, in their equivalent forms without the bars, and line up the decimal points, as follows:

$$1.34783478 \ldots$$
$$1.34782178 \ldots$$

The digits to the left of the decimal points and the first four digits after the decimal points are the same in each of the numbers. However, since the digit in the hundred-thousandths place of the top number, which is 3, is greater than the digit 2 in the hundred-thousandths place of the bottom number, $1.\overline{3478}$ is greater than $1.347\overline{821}$.

It is easy to compare two fractions, such as $\frac{21}{43}$ and $\frac{37}{75}$, using a calculator. We convert each to a decimal and then compare the decimals.

$$\boxed{2}\,\boxed{1}\,\boxed{\div}\,\boxed{4}\,\boxed{3}\,\boxed{=} \rightarrow 0.4883721$$
$$\boxed{3}\,\boxed{7}\,\boxed{\div}\,\boxed{7}\,\boxed{5}\,\boxed{=} \rightarrow 0.4933333$$

Examining the digits in the hundredths place, we see that

$$\frac{37}{75} > \frac{21}{43}.$$

EXAMPLE 6-12

Find a rational number in decimal form between $0.\overline{35}$ and $0.\overline{351}$.

Solution First, line up the decimals.

$$0.353535\ldots$$
$$0.351351\ldots$$

Then, to find a decimal between these two, observe that starting from the left, the first place at which the two numbers differ is the thousandths place. Clearly, one decimal between these two is 0.352. Others include 0.3514, 0.3515, and 0.35136. In fact, there are infinitely many others.

ASSESSMENT 6-3

1. Find the decimal representation for each of the following:
   a. $\frac{4}{9}$ b. $\frac{2}{7}$ c. $\frac{3}{11}$ d. $\frac{1}{15}$ e. $\frac{2}{75}$
   f. $\frac{1}{99}$ g. $\frac{5}{6}$ h. $\frac{1}{13}$ i. $\frac{1}{21}$ j. $\frac{3}{19}$

2. Convert each of the following repeating decimals to $\frac{a}{b}$ form where a, b are integers, $b \neq 0$.
   a. $0.\overline{4}$ b. $0.\overline{61}$ c. $1.3\overline{9}$
   d. $0.5\overline{5}$ e. $^-2.3\overline{4}$ f. $^-0.0\overline{2}$

3. Order each of the following decimals from greatest to least:
   $$^-1.4\overline{54},\ ^-1.\overline{454},\ ^-1.4\overline{5},\ ^-1.45\overline{4},\ ^-1.454$$

4. Continue the following patterns for the sequences below.
   a. $0, 0.\overline{3}, 0.\overline{6}, 1, 1.\overline{3},$ ____, ____, ____
   b. $0, 0.5, 0.\overline{6}, 0.75, 0.8, 0.8\overline{3},$ ____, ____, ____

5. Suppose $a = 0.\overline{32}$ and $b = 0.\overline{123}$.
   a. Find $a + b$ by adding from left to right. How many digits are in the repetend of the sum?
   b. Find $a + b$ if $a = 1.2\overline{34}$ and $b = 0.\overline{1234}$. Is the answer a rational number? How many digits are in the repetend?

6. Explain whether you think a terminating decimal could ever be written as a repeating decimal.

7. Find three decimals between each of the two following pairs of decimals:
   a. $3.\overline{2}$ and 3.22   b. $462.\overline{24}$ and 462.243

8. Find the decimal halfway between the two following decimals:
   a. $0.\overline{4}$ and 0.5   b. $0.\overline{9}$ and 1.1

9. a. Find three rational numbers between 3/4 and $0.\overline{75}$.
   b. Find three rational numbers between 1/3 and $0.\overline{34}$.

10. a. What is the 21st digit in the decimal expansion of 3/7?
    b. What is the 5280th digit in the decimal expansion of 1/17?

11. a. Write each of the following as a fraction in the form a/b where a and b are integers, $b \neq 0$.
    (i) $0.\overline{1}$ (ii) $0.\overline{01}$ (iii) $0.\overline{001}$
    b. What fractions would you expect for $0.\overline{0001}$?
    c. Mentally compute the decimal equivalent for 1/90.

12. Use the fact that $0.\overline{1} = 1/9$ to mentally convert each of the following into fractions:
    a. $0.\overline{2}$ b. $0.\overline{3}$ c. $0.\overline{5}$ d. $2.\overline{7}$ e. $9.\overline{9}$

13. Use the fact that $0.\overline{01} = 1/99$ and $0.\overline{001} = 1/999$ to mentally convert each of the following into fractions:
    a. $0.\overline{05}$ b. $0.\overline{003}$ c. $3.\overline{25}$ d. $3.1\overline{25}$

Communication

14. A friend claims that every finite decimal is equal to some infinite decimal. Is the claim true? Explain why or why not.

15. Some addition problems are easier to compute with fractions and some are easier to do with decimals. For example, $1/7 + 5/7$ is easier to compute than $0.\overline{142857} + 0.\overline{714285}$ and $0.4 + 0.25$ is easier to compute than $2/5 + 1/4$. Describe situations in which you think it would be easier to compute the additions with fractions than with decimals, and vice versa.

Open-Ended

16. Notice that $\frac{1}{7} = 0.\overline{142857}$, $\frac{2}{7} = 0.\overline{285714}$, $\frac{3}{7} = 0.\overline{428571}$, $\frac{4}{7} = 0.\overline{571428}$, $\frac{5}{7} = 0.\overline{714285}$, and $\frac{6}{7} = 0.\overline{857142}$.

   a. Describe a common property that all of these repeating decimals share.
   b. Suppose you memorized the decimal form for $\frac{1}{7}$. How could you quickly find the answers for the decimal expansion of the rest of the above fractions? Describe as many ways as you can.
   c. Find the other fractions that behave like $\frac{1}{7}$. In what way is the behavior similar?
   d. Based on your answer in (a), describe shortcuts for writing $\frac{k}{14}$ as a repeating decimal for $k = 1, 2, 3, \ldots, 13$.

Cooperative Learning

17. Choose a partner and play the following game. Write a repeating decimal of the form $0.\overline{abcdef}$. Tell your partner that the decimal is of that form but do not reveal the specific values for the digits. Your partner's objective is to find your repeating decimal. Your partner is allowed to ask you for the values of 6 digits that are at the 100th or greater

places after the decimal point but not the digits in consecutive places. For example, your opponent may ask for the 100th, 200th, 300th, ... digits but may not ask for the 100th and 101st digit. Switch roles at least once. After playing the game, discuss in your group a strategy for asking your partner the least number of questions that will allow one to find the partner's repetend.

Review Problems

18. John is a payroll clerk for a small company. Last month, the employees' gross earnings (earnings before deductions) totaled $27,849.50. John deducted $1520.63 for social security, $723.30 for unemployment insurance, and $2843.62 for federal income tax. What was the employees' net pay (their earnings after deductions)?

19. The speed of light is approximately 186,000 mi/sec. It takes light from the nearest star, Alpha Centauri, approximately 4 yr to reach Earth. How many miles away is Alpha Centauri from Earth? Express the answer in scientific notation.

20. Find the product of 0.22 and 0.35 on a calculator. How does the placement of the decimal point in the answer on the calculator compare with the placement of the decimal point using the rule in this chapter? Explain.

21. Answer the following:
   a. Find a number to add to ¯0.023 to obtain a sum greater than 3 but less than 4.
   b. Find a number to subtract from ¯0.023 to obtain a difference greater than 3 but less than 4.
   c. Find a number to multiply times 0.023 to obtain a product greater than 3 but less than 4.
   d. Find a number to divide into 0.023 to obtain a quotient greater than 3 but less than 4.

Percents

percent

Percents are very useful in conveying information. People hear that there is a 60 percent chance of rain or that their savings accounts are drawing 6 percent interest. The word **percent** comes from the Latin phrase *per centum*, which means *per hundred*. For example, a bank that pays 6 percent simple interest on a savings account pays $6 for each $100 in the account for 1 yr; that is, it pays $\frac{6}{100}$ of whatever amount is in the account for 1 yr. The symbol, %, indicates percent. For example, we write 6% for $\frac{6}{100}$.

In general, we have the following definition.

> ### Definition of Percent

$$n\% = \frac{n}{100}$$

FIGURE 6-4

Thus $n\%$ of a quantity is $\dfrac{n}{100}$ of the quantity. Therefore 1% is one hundredth of a whole and 100% represents the entire quantity, whereas 200% represents $\dfrac{200}{100}$, or 2 times, the given quantity. Percents can be illustrated by using a hundreds grid. For example, what percent of the grid is shaded in Figure 6-4? Because 30 out of the 100, or $\dfrac{30}{100}$, of the squares are shaded, we say that 30% of the grid is shaded.

Because $n\% = \dfrac{n}{100}$, to convert a number to a percent we write it as a fraction with denominator 100; the numerator gives the amount of the percent. For example, $\dfrac{3}{4} = \dfrac{3 \cdot 25}{4 \cdot 25} = \dfrac{75}{100}$. Hence, $\dfrac{3}{4} = 75\%$.

E X A M P L E 6-13

Write each of the following as a percent:

a. 0.03   **b.** $0.\overline{3}$ **c.** 1.2   **d.** 0.00042

e. 1   **f.** $\dfrac{3}{5}$ **g.** $\dfrac{2}{3}$ **h.** $2\dfrac{1}{7}$

Solution   **a.** $0.03 = 100\left(\dfrac{0.03}{100}\right) = \dfrac{3}{100} = 3\%$

b. $0.\overline{3} = 100\left(\dfrac{0.\overline{3}}{100}\right) = \dfrac{33.\overline{3}}{100} = 33.\overline{3}\%$

c. $1.2 = 100\left(\dfrac{1.2}{100}\right) = \dfrac{120}{100} = 120\%$

d. $0.00042 = 100\left(\dfrac{0.00042}{100}\right) = \dfrac{0.042}{100} = 0.042\%$

e. $1 = 100\left(\dfrac{1}{100}\right) = \dfrac{100}{100} = 100\%$

f. $\dfrac{3}{5} = 100\left[\dfrac{\left(\dfrac{3}{5}\right)}{100}\right] = \dfrac{60}{100} = 60\%$

g. $\dfrac{2}{3} = 100\left[\dfrac{\left(\dfrac{2}{3}\right)}{100}\right] = \dfrac{\left(\dfrac{200}{3}\right)}{100} = \dfrac{66.\overline{6}}{100} = 66.\overline{6}\%$

h. $2\dfrac{1}{7} = 100\left[\dfrac{\left(2\dfrac{1}{7}\right)}{100}\right] = \dfrac{\left(\dfrac{1500}{7}\right)}{100} = \dfrac{1500}{7}\%, \text{ or } 214\dfrac{2}{7}\%$

A number can also be converted to a percent by using a *proportion*. For example, to write $\dfrac{3}{5}$ as a percent, find the value of n in the following proportion:

$$\frac{3}{5} = \frac{n}{100}$$

$$\left(\frac{3}{5}\right) \cdot 100 = n$$

$$n = 60$$

Therefore $\frac{3}{5} = 60\%.$

Still another way to convert a number to a percent is to recall that $1 = 100\%$. Thus for example, $\frac{3}{4} = \frac{3}{4}$ of $1 = \frac{3}{4} \cdot 1 = \frac{3}{4} \cdot 100\% = 75\%.$

REMARK The % symbol is crucial in identifying the meaning of a number. For example, $\frac{1}{2}$ and $\frac{1}{2}\%$ are different numbers: $\frac{1}{2} = 50\%$, which is not equal to $\frac{1}{2}\%$. Similarly, 0.01 is different from 0.01%, which is 0.0001.

In our computations, it is sometimes useful to convert percents to decimals. This can be done by writing the percent as a fraction in the form $\frac{n}{100}$ and then converting the fraction to a decimal.

EXAMPLE 6-14

Write each of the following percents as a decimal:

a. 5%   **b.** 6.3%   **c.** 100%   **d.** 250%   **e.** $\frac{1}{3}\%$ **f.** $33\frac{1}{3}\%$

Solution   **a.** $5\% = \frac{5}{100} = 0.05$ **b.** $6.3\% = \frac{6.3}{100} = 0.063$

c. $100\% = \frac{100}{100} = 1$ **d.** $250\% = \frac{250}{100} = 2.50$

e. $\frac{1}{3}\% = \frac{\frac{1}{3}}{100} = \frac{0.\overline{3}}{100} = 0.00\overline{3}$ **f.** $33\frac{1}{3}\% = \frac{33\frac{1}{3}}{100} = \frac{33.\overline{3}}{100} = 0.\overline{3}$

Another approach to writing a percent as a decimal is first to convert 1% to a decimal. Because $1\% = \frac{1}{100} = 0.01$, we can conclude that $5\% = 5 \cdot 0.01 = 0.05$ and that $6.3\% = 6.3 \cdot 0.01 = 0.063$.

NOW TRY THIS 6-7

a. Investigate how your calculator handles percents and tell what the calculator does when the $\boxed{\%}$ key is pushed.

b. Use your calculator to change $\frac{1}{3}$ to a percent.

In the *Principles and Standards* we find the following under the Representation Standard for Grades 6–8.

◆ *Middle-grades students who are taught with this Standard in mind will learn to recognize, compare, and use an array of representational forms for fractions, decimals, percents and integers. They also will learn to use representational forms such as exponential and scientific notation when working with large and small numbers and to use a variety of graphical tools to represent and analyze data sets.* (p. 280)

The *Principles and Standards* also states

◆ *Technology should not be used as a replacement for basic understandings and intuitions; rather, it can and should be used to foster those understandings and intuitions. In mathematics-instruction programs, technology should be used widely and responsibly, with the goal of enriching students' learning of mathematics.* (p. 25)

Applications Involving Percent

Application problems that involve percents usually take one of the following forms:

1. Finding a percent of a number
2. Finding what percent one number is of another
3. Finding a number when a percent of that number is known

Before we consider examples illustrating these forms, recall what it means to find a fraction "of" a number. For example, $\frac{2}{3}$ of 70 means $\frac{2}{3} \cdot 70$. Similarly, to find 40% of 70, we have $\frac{40}{100}$ of 70, which means $\frac{40}{100} \cdot 70$, or $0.40 \cdot 70 = 28$.

EXAMPLE 6-15

A house that sells for $92,000 requires a 20% down payment. What is the amount of the down payment?

Solution   The down payment is 20% of $92,000, or $0.20 \cdot \$92,000 = \$18,400$. Hence, the amount of the down payment is $18,400.

EXAMPLE 6-16

If Alberto has 45 correct answers on an 80-question test, what percent of his answers are correct?

Solution   Alberto has $\frac{45}{80}$ of the answers correct. To find the percent of correct answers, we need to convert $\frac{45}{80}$ to a percent. We can do this by multiplying the fraction by 100 and attaching the % symbol as follows:

$$\frac{45}{80} = 100 \cdot \frac{45}{80}\%$$
$$= 56.25\%$$

Thus 56.25% of the answers are correct.

An alternative solution uses proportion. Let n be the percent of correct answers and proceed as follows:

$$\frac{45}{80} = \frac{n}{100}$$

$$\frac{45}{80} \cdot 100 = n$$

$$n = \frac{4500}{80} = 56.25$$

EXAMPLE 6-17

Forty-two percent of the parents of the school children in the Paxson School District are employed at Di Paloma University. If the number of parents employed by the university is 168, how many parents are in the school district?

Solution Let n be the number of parents in the school district. Then 42% of n is 168. We *translate this information into an equation* and solve for n.

$$42\% \text{ of } n = 168$$

$$\frac{42}{100} \cdot n = 168$$

$$0.42 \cdot n = 168$$

$$n = \frac{168}{0.42} = 400$$

There are 400 parents in the school district.

Example 6-17 can be solved using a proportion. Forty-two percent, or $\frac{42}{100}$, of the parents are employed at the university. If n is the total number of parents, then 168/n also represents the fraction of parents employed there. Thus

$$\frac{42}{100} = \frac{168}{n}$$

$$42n = 100 \cdot 168$$

$$n = \frac{16{,}800}{42} = 400$$

We can also solve the problem as follows:

$$42\% \text{ of } n \text{ is } 168.$$

$$1\% \text{ of } n \text{ is } \frac{168}{42}.$$

$$100\% \text{ of } n \text{ is } 100\left(\frac{168}{42}\right).$$

Therefore,

$$n = 100\left(\frac{168}{42}\right), \text{ or } 400.$$

E X A M P L E
6-18

Kelly bought a bicycle and a year later sold it for 20% less than what she paid for it. If she sold the bike for $144, what did she pay for it?

Solution   We are looking for the original price P that Kelly paid for the bike. We know that she sold the bike for $144 and that this included a 20% loss. Thus we can *write the following equation*:

$$\$144 = P - \text{Kelly's loss}$$

Because Kelly's loss is 20% of P, we proceed as follows:

$$\$144 = P - 20\% \cdot P$$
$$\$144 = P - 0.20 \cdot P$$
$$\$144 = (1 - 0.20)P$$
$$\$144 = 0.80P$$
$$\frac{\$144}{0.80} = P$$
$$\$180 = P$$

Thus, she paid $180 for the bike.

E X A M P L E
6-19

Westerner's Clothing Store advertised a suit for 10% off, for a savings of $15. Later, the manager marked the suit at 30% off the original price. What is the amount of the current discount?

Solution   A 10% discount amounts to a $15 savings. We could find the amount of the current discount if we knew the original price. Thus finding the original price becomes our *subgoal*. Because 10% of P is $15, we have the following:

$$10\% \cdot P = \$15$$
$$0.10 \cdot P = \$15$$
$$P = \$150$$

To find the current discount, we calculate 30% of $150. Because $0.30 \cdot \$150 = \$45$, the amount of the 30% discount is $45.

In the *Looking Back* stage of problem solving, we check the answer and look for other ways to solve the problem. A different approach leads to a more efficient solution and confirms the answer. If 10% of the price is $15, then 30% of the price is 3 times $15, or $45.

Mental Math with Percents

Mental math may be helpful when working with percents. Two techniques follow:

1. *Using fraction equivalents*
   Knowing fraction equivalents for some percents can make some computations easier. Table 6-3 gives several fraction equivalents.

Table 6-3

Percent	25%	50%	75%	$33\frac{1}{3}$%	$66\frac{2}{3}$%	10%	1%
Fraction Equivalent	$\frac{1}{4}$	$\frac{1}{2}$	$\frac{3}{4}$	$\frac{1}{3}$	$\frac{2}{3}$	$\frac{1}{10}$	$\frac{1}{100}$

These equivalents can be used in such computations as the following:

$$50\% \text{ of } \$80 = \left(\frac{1}{2}\right)80 = \$40$$

$$66\frac{2}{3}\% \text{ of } 90 = \left(\frac{2}{3}\right)90 = 60$$

2. *Using a known percent*

   Frequently, we may not know a percent of something, but we know a close percent of it. For example, to find 55% of 62, we might do the following:

$$50\% \text{ of } 62 = \left(\frac{1}{2}\right)(62) = 31$$

$$5\% \text{ of } 62 = \left(\frac{1}{2}\right)(10\%)(62) = \left(\frac{1}{2}\right)(6.2) = 3.1$$

Adding, we see that 55% of 62 is $31 + 3.1 = 34.1$.

Estimations with Percents

Estimations with percents can be used to determine whether answers are reasonable. Following are two examples:

1. To estimate 27% of 598, note that 27% of 598 is a little more than 25% of 598, but 25% of 598 is approximately the same as 25% of 600, or $\frac{1}{4}$ of 600, or 150. Here, we have adjusted 27% downward and 598 upward, so 150 should be a reasonable estimate. A better estimate might be obtained by estimating 30% of 600 and then subtracting 3% of 600 to obtain 27% of 600, giving $180 - 18$, or 162.

2. To estimate 148% of 500, note that 148% of 500 should be slightly less than 150% of 500. 150% of 500 is $1.5(500) = 750$. Thus 148% of 500 should be a little less than 750.

EXAMPLE 6-20

Laura wants to buy a blouse originally priced at $26.50 but now on sale at 40% off. She has $17 in her wallet and wonders if she has enough cash. How can she mentally find out?

Solution   It is easier to find 40% of $25 (versus $26.50) mentally. One way is to find 10% of $25, which is $2.50. Now, 40% is 4 times that much, that is, $4 \cdot \$2.50$, or $10. Thus Laura estimates that the blouse will cost $26.50 - \$10$, or $16.50. Since the actual discount is greater than $10 (40% of 26.50 is greater than 40% of 25), Laura will have to pay less than $16.50 for the blouse and, hence, she has enough cash.

Sometimes it may not be clear which operations to perform with percent. The following example investigates this.

EXAMPLE 6-21

Which of the following statements are true and which are false? Explain your answers.

a. Leonardo got a 10% raise at the end of his first year on the job and a 10% raise after another year. His total raise was 20% of his original salary.

b. Jung and Dina paid 45% of their first department store bill of $620 and 48% of the second department store bill of $380. They paid 45% + 48% = 93% of the total bill of $1000.

c. Bill spent 25% of his salary on food and 40% on housing. Bill spent 25% + 40% = 65% of his salary on food and housing.

d. In Bordertown, 65% of the adult population works in town, 25% works across the border, and 15% is unemployed.

e. In Clean City, the fine for various polluting activities is a certain percentage of one's monthly income. The fine for smoking in public places is 40%, for driving a polluting car is 50%, and for littering is 30%. Mr. Schmutz committed all three polluting crimes in one day and paid a fine of 120% of his monthly salary.

Solution

a. In applications, percent has meaning only when it represents part of a quantity. For example, 10% of a quantity plus another 10% of the same quantity is 20% of that quantity. In Leonardo's case, the first 10% raise was calculated based on his original salary and the second 10% raise was calculated on his new salary. Consequently, the percentages cannot be added, and the statement is false.

b. The answer does not make sense. Jung and Dina paid less than $\frac{1}{2}$ of each bill, so they could not have paid 93% (almost all) of the total. In fact, $\frac{1}{2}$ of one bill plus $\frac{1}{2}$ of the other bill is not the full amount of the total bill, because the bills are different.

c. Because the percentages are of the same quantity, the statement is true.

d. Because the percentages are of the same quantity, that is, the number of adults, we can add them: 65% + 25% + 15% = 105%. But 105% of the population accounts for more (5% more) than the town's population, which is impossible. Hence, the statement is false.

e. Again, the percentages are of the same quantity, that is, the individual's monthly income. Hence, we can add them: 120% of one's monthly income is a stiff fine, but possible.

ONGOING ASSESSMENT 6-4

1. Express each of the following as percents:
   a. 7.89   b. 0.032   c. 193.1   d. 0.2
   e. $\frac{5}{6}$ f. $\frac{3}{20}$ g. $\frac{1}{8}$ h. $\frac{3}{8}$
   i. $\frac{5}{8}$ j. $\frac{1}{6}$ k. $\frac{4}{5}$ l. $\frac{1}{40}$

2. Convert each of the following percents to decimals:
   a. 16%   b. $4\frac{1}{2}\%$ c. $\frac{1}{5}\%$ d. $\frac{2}{7}\%$
   e. $13\frac{2}{3}\%$ f. 125%   g. $\frac{1}{3}\%$ h. $\frac{1}{4}\%$

3. Fill in the following blanks to find other expressions for 4%:
   a. _____ for every 100   b. _____ for every 50
   c. 1 for every _____   d. 8 for every _____
   e. 0.5 for every _____

4. Different calculators compute percents in various ways. To investigate this, consider $5 \cdot 6\%$.
   a. If the following sequence of keys is pressed, is the correct answer of 0.3 displayed on your calculator?

   $\boxed{5}\ \boxed{\times}\ \boxed{6}\ \boxed{\%}\ \boxed{=}$

   b. Press $\boxed{6}\ \boxed{\%}\ \boxed{\times}\ \boxed{5}\ \boxed{=}$. Is the answer 0.3?

5. Answer each of the following:
   a. What is 6% of 34?
   b. 17 is what percent of 34?
   c. 18 is 30% of what number?
   d. What is 7% of 49?
   e. 61.5 is what percent of 20.5?
   f. 16 is 40% of what number?

6. a. Write a fraction representing 5% of *x*.
   b. If 10% of an amount is *a*, what is the amount in terms of *a*?

7. Marc had 84 boxes of candy to sell. He sold 75% of the boxes. How many did he sell?

8. Gail made $16,000 last year and received a 6% raise. How much does she make now?

9. Gail received a 7% raise last year. If her salary is now $27,285, what was her salary last year?

10. Joe sold 180 newspapers out of 200. Bill sold 85% of his 260 newspapers. Ron sold 212 newspapers, 80% of those he had.
    a. Who sold the most newspapers? How many?
    b. Who sold the greatest percentage of his newspapers? What percent?
    c. Who started with the greatest number of newspapers? How many?

11. If a dress that normally sells for $35 is on sale for $28, what is the "percent off"? (This could be called a *percent of decrease*, or a *discount*.)

12. A used car originally cost $1700. One year later, it was worth $1400. What is the percentage of depreciation?

13. On a certain day in Glacier Park, 728 eagles were counted. Five years later, 594 were counted. What was the percentage of decrease in the number of eagles counted?

14. Mort bought his house in 1985 for $59,000. It was recently appraised at $95,000. What is the *percent of increase* in value?

15. Xuan weighed 9 lb when he was born. At 6 mo, he weighed 18 lb. What was the percent of increase in Xuan's weight?

16. Sally bought a dress marked 20% off. If the regular price was $28.00, what was the sale price?

17. What is the sale price of a softball if the regular price is $6.80 and there is a 25% discount?

18. If a $\frac{1}{4}$-c serving of Crunchies breakfast food has 0.5% of the minimum daily requirement of vitamin C, how many cups would you have to eat to obtain the minimum daily requirement of vitamin C?

19. An airline ticket costs $320 without the tax. If the tax rate is 5%, what is the total bill for the airline ticket?

20. Bill got 52 correct answers on an 80-question test. What percent of the questions did he answer incorrectly?

21. A real estate broker receives 4% of an $80,000 sale. How much does the broker receive?

22. A survey reported that $66\frac{2}{3}$% of 1800 employees favored a new insurance program. How many employees favored the new program?

23. Which represents the greater percent: 325/500 or 600/1000? How can you tell?

24. a. How can an estimate of 10% of a number help you estimate 35% of the number?
    b. Mentally compute 35% of $8.00.

25. If 30 is 150% of a number, is the number greater than or less than 30? Why?

26. What is 40% of 50% of a number?

27. If you add 20% of a number to the number itself, what percent of the result would you have to subtract to get the original number back?

28. An advertisement reads that if you buy 10 items, you get 20% off your total purchase price. You need 8 items that cost $9.50 each.
    a. How much would 8 items cost? 10 items?
    b. Is it more economical to buy 8 items or 10 items?

29. Soda is advertised at 45¢ a can or $2.40 a six-pack. If 6 cans are to be purchased, what percent is saved by purchasing the six-pack?

30. John paid $330 for a new mountain bicycle to sell in his shop. He wants to price it so that he can offer a 10% discount and still make 20% of the price he paid for it. At what price should the bike be marked?

31. The price of a suit that sold for $200 was reduced by 25%. By what percent must the price of the suit be increased to bring the price back to $200?

32. The car Elsie bought 1 yr ago has depreciated by $1116.88, which is 12.13% of the price she paid for it. How much did she pay for the car, to the nearest cent?

33. Solve each of the following using mental mathematics:
    a. 15% of $22
    b. 20% of $120
    c. 5% of $38
    d. 25% of $98

34. If we build a 10 × 10 model with blocks, as shown in the following figure, and paint the entire model, what percent of the cubes will have each of the following?
    a. Four faces painted
    b. Three faces painted
    c. Two faces painted

35. For people to be safe but still achieve a cardiovascular training effect, they should monitor their heart rates while exercising. The maximum heart rate can be approximated by subtracting your age from 220. You can achieve a safe training effect if you maintain your heart rate between 60% and 80% of that number for at least 20 min three times a week.
    a. Determine the range for your age.
    b. At the top of a long hill, Jeannie slows her bike and takes her pulse. She counts 41 beats in 15 sec.
       (i) Express in decimal form the amount of time in seconds between successive beats.
       (ii) Express the amount in terms of minutes.

36. A crew consists of 1 apprentice, 1 journeyman, and 1 master carpenter. The crew receives a check for $4200 for a job they just finished. A journeyman makes 200% of what an apprentice makes, and a master makes 150% of what a journeyman makes. How much does each person in the crew earn?

37. a. In an incoming freshman class of 500 students, only 20 claimed to be math majors. What percent of the freshman class is this?
    b. When the survey was repeated the next year, 5% of nonmath majors had decided to switch and become math majors.
       (i) How many math majors are there now?
       (ii) What percent of the freshman class do they represent?

38. Ms. Price has received a 10% raise in salary in each of the last 2 years. If her annual salary this year is $100,000, what was her salary 2 years ago, rounded to the nearest penny?

Communication

39. Is 40% of 30 equal to 30% of 40? Explain why or why not.

40. Why is it possible to have an increase of 150% in a price but not a 150% decrease in price?

41. A student asks if 90% means 90 out of 100, how can she possibly score 90% on a test that has only 20 questions. How do you answer her?

42. Two equal amounts of money were invested in two different stocks. The value of the first stock increased by 15% the first year and then decreased by 15% the second year. The second stock decreased by 15% the first year and increased by 15% the second year. Was one investment better than the other? Explain your reasoning.

Open-Ended

43. Write and solve a word problem whose solution involves the following. If one of these tasks is impossible, explain why.
    a. Addition of percent
    b. Subtraction of percent

c. Multiplication of percent
d. Division of percent
e. A percent whose decimal representation is raised to the second power
f. A percent greater than 100

44. Look at newspapers and magazines for information given in percents.
    a. Based on your findings, write a problem that involves social science as well as mathematics.
    b. Write a clear solution to your problem in (a).

45. Write a percentage problem whose answer is the solution of the following equations.
    a. $\dfrac{37}{100} = \dfrac{115}{x}$ b. $\dfrac{p}{100} = \dfrac{a}{x}$

Cooperative Learning

46. Find the percentage of students in your class that engage in each of the following activities:
    a. Studying and doing homework   b. Watching TV

Number of Hours per Week (h)	Percent
$h < 1$	
$1 \le h < 3$	
$3 \le h < 5$	
$5 \le h < 10$	
$h \ge 10$	
Total	

Number of Hours per Week (h)	Percent
$h < 1$	
$1 \le h < 5$	
$5 \le h < 10$	
$h \ge 10$	
Total	

c. Did your totals add up to 100%? Why or why not?

Review Problems

47. a Find $0.8 \div 0.32$ by converting these numbers to rational numbers in the form $\dfrac{a}{b}$ where a and b are integers, ($b \ne 0$), dividing the rational numbers, and then changing the quotient back to decimal form.
    b. Find $0.8 \div 0.32$ using decimal division and compare your answer with the answer from part (a).

48. Change $7.27\overline{1}$ to a rational number in the form $\dfrac{a}{b}$ where a and b are integers ($b \ne 0$).

49. Find a repeating decimal between 0.2 and $0.\overline{2}$.

50. Order the following from least to greatest:
    $2.5, \quad 5/3, \quad 2.0\overline{5}, \quad 2.\overline{15}, \quad 7/3$

51. Show that $0.\overline{9} = 1$ in three ways.

BRAIN
T E A S E R

The crust of a certain pumpkin pie is 25% of the pie. By what percent should the amount of crust be reduced in order to make it constitute 20% of the pie?

We can use spreadsheets to solve mixture problems. For example, consider the problem of finding out how many liters of water must be added to 5 L of pure lemon juice to change its concentration from 100% to less than 30% lemon juice.

Six lemonade mixtures were prepared starting from 5 L of pure lemon juice and adding water in 2 L increments. At each step, the percent of lemon juice in the mixture was calculated. The results of the process are summarized in the spreadsheet in Figure 6-5. The formulas used to obtain the results in a particular column are given in row 12.

a. Explain how this spreadsheet can be used to help students solve the problem.

b. Explain the formulas in row 12.

FIGURE 6-5

	A	B	C	D
1	Liters of	Liters of	Total Liters	% Lemon Juice
2	**Lemon Juice**	**Water Added**	**in Mixture**	**in Mixture**
3	(L)	(L)	(L)	
4	5	0	5	100.00
5	5	2	7	71.43
6	5	4	9	55.56
7	5	6	11	45.45
8	5	8	13	38.46
9	5	10	15	33.33
10	5	12	17	29.41
11				
12	5	x	$5 + x$	$5/(5 + x)*100$
13		(where x is a		
14		multiple of 2)		
15				
16				
17				

Sheet1 / Sheet2 / S

 6-5 *Computing Interest*

interest

When a bank advertises a $5\frac{1}{2}\%$ interest rate on a savings account, the **interest** is the amount of money the bank will pay for using that money. The original amount deposited or bor-

principal ◆ interest rate

rowed is the **principal**. The percent used to determine the interest is the **interest rate**. Interest rates are given for specific periods of time, such as years, months, or days. Interest

simple interest

computed on the original principal is **simple interest**. For example, suppose we borrow $5000 from a company at a simple interest rate of 9% for 1 yr. The interest we owe on the loan for 1 yr is 9% of $5000, or $5000 · 0.09. In general, if a principal P is invested at an annual interest rate of r, then the simple interest after 1 yr is $Pr \cdot 1$; after t years, it is Prt. Thus if I represents simple interest, we have

$$I = Prt.$$

The amount needed to pay off a $5000 loan at 9% simple interest is the $5000 borrowed plus the interest on the $5000, that is, $5000 + 5000 \cdot 0.09$, or $5450. In general, *an* **amount** (*or* **balance**) *A is equal to the principal P plus the interest I*; that is,

amount/balance

$$A = P + I = P + Prt = P(1 + rt).$$

EXAMPLE 6-22

Vera opened a savings account that pays simple interest at the rate of $5\frac{1}{4}\%$ per year. If she deposits $2000 and makes no other deposits, find the interest and the final amount for the following time periods:

a. 1 year   **b.** 90 days

Solution   **a.** To find the interest for 1 yr, we proceed as follows:

$$I = \$2000 \cdot 5\frac{1}{4}\% \cdot 1 = \$2000 \cdot 0.0525 \cdot 1 = \$105$$

Her final amount at the end of 1 yr is

$$\$2000 + \$105 = \$2105.$$

b. When the interest rate is annual and the interest period is given in days, we represent the time as a fractional part of a year by dividing the number of days by 365. Thus

$$I = \$2000 \cdot 5\frac{1}{4}\% \cdot \frac{90}{365}$$

$$= \$2000 \cdot 0.0525 \cdot \frac{90}{365} \doteq \$25.89.$$

Hence,

$$A \doteq \$2000 + \$25.89$$
$$A \doteq \$2025.89.$$

Thus Vera's amount after 90 days is approximately $2025.89.

EXAMPLE 6-23

Find the annual interest rate if a principal of $10,000 increased to $10,900 at the end of 1 yr.

Solution   Let the annual interest be $x\%$. We know that $x\%$ of $10,000 is the increase. Because the increase is $10,900 − $10,000 = $900, we use the strategy of *writing an equation* for x as follows:

$$x\% \text{ of } 10{,}000 = 900$$

$$\frac{x}{100} \cdot 10{,}000 = 900$$

$$x = 9$$

Thus the interest is 9%. We can also solve this problem mentally by asking, "What percent of 10,000 is 900?" Because 1% of 10,000 is 100, to obtain 900, we take 9% of 10,000.

Compound Interest

compound interest

In business transactions, interest is sometimes calculated daily (365 times a year). In the case of savings, the earned interest is added daily to the principal, and each day the interest is earned on a different amount; that is, it is earned on the previous interest as well as the principal. When interest is computed in this way, it is called **compound interest**. Compounding usually is done annually (once a year), semiannually (twice a year), quarterly (4 times a year), or monthly (12 times a year). However, even when the interest is compounded, it is given as an annual rate. For example, if the annual rate is 6% compounded monthly, the interest per month is $\frac{6}{12}$%, or 0.5%. If it is compounded daily, the interest per day is $\frac{6}{365}$%. In general, *the interest rate per period is the annual interest rate divided by the number of periods in a year.*

We can use a spreadsheet to compare various compound interest rates. Work through the student page on page 358 and answer the questions in the *TRY IT* and the *ON YOUR OWN* sections.

EXAMPLE
6-24

If you invest $100 at 8% compounded quarterly, how much will you have in the account after 1 yr?

Solution   The quarterly interest rate is $\frac{1}{4} \cdot 8$%, or 2%. It seems that we would have to calculate the interest four times. But we can also reason as follows. If at the beginning of any of the four periods there are x dollars in the account, at the end of that period there will be

$$x + 2\% \text{ of } x = x + 0.02x$$
$$= x(1 + 0.02)$$
$$= x \cdot 1.02 \text{ dollars.}$$

Hence, to find the amount at the end of any period, we need only multiply the amount at the beginning of the period by 1.02. From Table 6-4, we see that the amount at the end of the fourth period is $100 \cdot 1.02^4$. On a scientific calculator, we can find the amount using $\boxed{1}\,\boxed{0}\,\boxed{0}\,\boxed{\times}\,\boxed{1}\,\boxed{.}\,\boxed{0}\,\boxed{2}\,\boxed{y^x}\,\boxed{4}\,\boxed{=}$. The calculator displays 108.24322. Thus the amount at the end of 1 yr is approximately $108.24.

Table 6-4

Period	Initial Amount	Final Amount
1	100	$100 \cdot 1.02$
2	$100 \cdot 1.02$	$(100 \cdot 1.02) \cdot 1.02$ or $100 \cdot 1.02^2$
3	$100 \cdot 1.02^2$	$(100 \cdot 1.02^2) \cdot 1.02$ or $100 \cdot 1.02^3$
4	$100 \cdot 1.02^3$	$(100 \cdot 1.02^3) \cdot 1.02$ or $100 \cdot 1.02^4$

Sample School Book Page:
COMPOUND INTEREST RATES

TECHNOLOGY

Using a Spreadsheet • Compound Interest

Problem: Which investment strategy will cause your $100 investment to increase the most in 4 years: if you earn 4% interest compounded annually or if you earn 3.75% interest compounded monthly?

A spreadsheet can help you find the answer to this problem.

❶ Enter the following information in your spreadsheet as shown.

	A	B	C	D	E	F
1	Year	Amount	Annual Rate	Month	Amount	Monthly Rate
2	0	100		0	100	

❷ Enter the following formulas.
In cell C2, enter =.04.
In cell F2, enter =.0375/12.
In cell A3, enter =A2+1.
In cell B3, enter =B2+B2*C$2.
In cell D3, enter =D2+1.
In cell E3, enter =E2+E2*F$2.

	A	B	C	D	E	F
1	Year	Amount	Annual Rate	Month	Amount	Monthly Rate
2	0	100	0.04	0	100	0.003125
3	1	104		1	100.3125	

❸ Select cells A3 to F50 and use the **Fill Down** command.

	A	B	C	D	E	F
1	Year	Amount	Annual Rate	Month	Amount	Monthly Rate
2	0	100	0.04	0	100	0.003125
3	1	104		1	100.3125	
4	2	108.16		2	100.6259	
5	3	112.4864		3	100.9404	
6	4	116.9858		4	101.2558	
50	48	657.0528		48	116.1562	

Solution: $100 at 4% interest compounded annually is $116.99; $100 at 3.75% interest compounded monthly is only $116.16.

TRY IT

Which investment strategy will cause your $100 investment to increase the most in 4 years: if you earn 5% interest compounded annually or if you earn 5% interest compounded quarterly (4 times a year)?

ON YOUR OWN

▶ Which is easier, computing compound interest by calculator or by using a spreadsheet? Explain.

▶ Why must you divide the interest rate by the number of compounding periods?

▶ Why do you have to enter formulas by using the "=" symbol?

312

Source: Scott Foresman–Addison Wesley Middle School Math, Course 3, 2002 (p. 312).

In Example 6-24, finding the final amount at the end of the nth period amounts to finding the nth term of a geometric sequence whose first term is $100 \cdot 1.02$ (amount at the end of the first period) and whose ratio is 1.02. Thus, the amount at the end of the nth period is given by $(100 \cdot 1.02) \cdot (1.02)^{n-1} = 100 \cdot 1.02^n$. We can generalize this discussion. If the principal is P and the interest rate per period is r, then the amount A after n periods is $P(1 + r) \cdot (1 + r)^{n-1}$ or $P(1 + r)^n$. Therefore, we have a *formula for computing the amount at the end of the nth period, namely $A = P(1 + r)^n$.*

EXAMPLE 6-25

Suppose you deposit $1000 in a savings account that pays 6% interest compounded quarterly.

a. What is the balance at the end of 1 yr?
b. What is the *effective annual yield* on this investment; that is, what is the rate that would have been paid if the amount had been invested using simple interest?

Solution   **a.** An annual interest rate of 6% earns $\frac{1}{4}$ of 6%, or an interest rate of $\frac{0.06}{4}$, in 1 quarter. Because there are 4 periods, we have the following:

$$A = 1000\left(1 + \frac{0.06}{4}\right)^4 \doteq \$1061.36$$

The balance at the end of 1 yr is approximately $1061.36.

b. Because the interest earned is $1061.36 − $1000.00 = $61.36, the effective annual yield can be computed by using the simple interest formula, $I = Prt$.

$$61.36 = 1000 \cdot r \cdot 1$$
$$\frac{61.36}{1000} = r$$
$$0.06136 = r$$
$$6.136\% = r$$

The effective annual yield is 6.136%.

EXAMPLE 6-26

To save for their child's college education, a couple deposits $3000 into an account that pays 7% annual interest compounded daily. Find the amount in this account after 8 yr.

Solution   The principal in the problem is $3000, the daily rate i is 0.07/365, and the number of compounding periods is $8 \cdot 365$, or 2920. Thus we have

$$A = \$3000\left(1 + \frac{0.07}{365}\right)^{2920} \doteq \$5251.74.$$

Thus the amount in the account is approximately $5251.74.

O N G O I N G   A S S E S S M E N T   6 - 5

You will need a calculator to do most of the following problems.

1. Complete the following compound-interest chart.

Compounding Period	Principal	Annual Rate	Length of Time (Years)	Interest Rate per Period	Number of Periods	Amount of Interest Paid
a. Semiannual	$1000	6%	2			
b. Quarterly	$1000	8%	3			
c. Monthly	$1000	10%	5			
d. Daily	$1000	12%	4			

2. Ms. Jackson borrowed $42,000 at 13% annual simple interest to buy her house. If she won the Irish Sweepstakes exactly 1 yr later and was able to repay the loan without penalty, how much interest would she owe?

3. Carolyn went on a shopping spree with her Bankamount card and made purchases totaling $125. If the interest rate is 1.5% per month on the unpaid balance and she does not pay this debt for 1 yr, how much interest will she owe at the end of the year?

4. A man collected $28,500 on a loan of $25,000 he made 4 yr ago. If he charged simple interest, what was the rate he charged?

5. Burger Queen will need $50,000 in 5 yr for a new addition. To meet this goal, the company deposits money in an account today that pays 9% annual interest compounded quarterly. Find the amount that should be invested to total $50,000 in 5 yr.

6. A company is expanding its line to include more products. To do so, it borrows $320,000 at 13.5% annual simple interest for a period of 18 mo. How much interest must the company pay?

7. To save for their retirement, a couple deposits $4000 in an account that pays 9% interest compounded quarterly. What will be the value of their investment after 20 yr?

8. A car company is offering car loans at a simple-interest rate of 9%. Find the interest charged to a customer who finances a car loan of $7200 for 3 yr.

9. Johnny and Carolyn have three savings plans, which accumulated the following amounts of interest for 1 yr.
   a. A passbook savings account that accumulated $53.90 on a principal of $980
   b. A certificate of deposit that accumulated $55.20 on a principal of $600
   c. A money-market certificate that accumulated $158.40 on a principal of $1200
   Which of these accounts paid the best interest rate for the year?

10. A hamburger costs $1.35 and the price continues to rise at a rate of 11% a year for the next 6 yr. What will the price of a hamburger be at the end of 6 yr?

11. If college tuition is $10,000 this year, what will it be 10 yr from now, assuming a constant inflation rate of 9% a year?

12. Sara invested money at a bank that paid 6.5% compounded quarterly. If she had $4650 at the end of 4 yr, what was her initial investment?

13. Adrien and Jarrell deposit $300 on January 1 in a holiday savings account that pays 1.1% per month interest and they withdraw the money on December 1 of the same year. What is the effective annual yield?

14. The number of trees in a rain forest decreases each month by 0.5%. If the forest has approximately $2.34 \cdot 10^9$ trees, how many trees will be left after 20 yr?

15. An amount of $3000 was deposited in a bank at a rate of 5% compounded quarterly for 3 yr. The rate then increased to 8% and was compounded quarterly for the next 3 yr. If no money was withdrawn, what was the balance at the end of this time?

16. A money-market fund pays 14% annual interest compounded daily. What is the value of $10,000 invested in this fund after 15 yr?

17. The New Age Savings Bank advertises 9% interest rates compounded daily, while the Pay More Bank pays 10.5% interest compounded annually. Which bank offers a better rate for a customer who plans to leave her money in for exactly 1 yr?

18. A car is purchased for $15,000. If each year the car depreciates by 10% of its value the preceding year, what will its value be at the end of 3 yr?

Communication

19. Because of a recession, the value of a new house depreciated 10% each year for 3 yr in a row. Then, for the next 3 yr, the value of the house increased 10% each year. Did the value of the house increase or decrease after 6 yr? Explain.

20. Determine the number of years (to the nearest tenth) it would take for any amount of money to double if it were deposited at a 10% interest rate compounded annually. Explain your reasoning.

21. A car parts manufacturer advertised three devices that could be installed in a car to save gas. The first could save 15% on fuel, the second 35%, and the third 50%. Explain whether you could conclude that when all three devices were installed, the savings on fuel would be 100%?

22. Each year a car's value depreciated 20% from the previous year. Mike claims that after 5 years the car would depreciate 100% and would not be worth anything. Is Mike correct? Explain why or why not. If not, find the actual percent the car would depreciate after 5 years.

Open-Ended

23. The effect of depreciation can be computed using a formula similar to the formula for compound interest.
  a. Assume depreciation is the same each month. Write a problem involving depreciation and solve it.
  b. Develop a general formula for depreciation defining what each variable in the formula stands for.

24. Find four large cities around the world and an approximate percentage rate of population growth for the countries in which the cities are located. Estimate the population in each of the four cities in 25 yr.

25. State different situations that do not involve money in which a formula like the one for compound interest is used. In each case, state a related problem and write its solution.

Cooperative Learning

26. The federal *Truth in Lending Act*, passed in 1969, requires lending institutions to quote an annual percentage rate (APR) that helps consumers compare the true cost of loans regardless of how each lending institution computes the interest and adds on costs.
  a. Call different banks and ask for their APR on some loans and the meaning of APR.
  b. Based on your findings in (a), write a clear definition of APR.
  c. Use the information given by your credit card (you may need to call the bank) and compute the APR on cash advances. Is your answer the same as that given by the bank? Compare the APR for different credit cards.

BRAIN TEASER

In the cartoon below, which of the people talking in the first two cells is correct? Why?

Real Numbers

Every rational number can be expressed either as a repeating decimal or as a terminating decimal. The ancient Greeks discovered numbers that are not rational. Such numbers must have a decimal representation that neither terminates nor repeats. To find such decimals, we focus on the characteristics they must have:

1. There must be an infinite number of nonzero digits to the right of the decimal point.

2. There cannot be a repeating block of digits (a repetend).

One way to construct a nonterminating, nonrepeating decimal is to devise a pattern of infinite digits in such a way that there will definitely be no repeated block. Consider the number 0.1010010001 . . . . If the pattern continues, the next groups of digits are four zeros followed by 1, five zeros followed by 1, and so on. It is possible to describe a pattern for this decimal, but there is no repeating block of digits. Because this decimal is nonterminating and nonrepeating, it cannot represent a rational number. Such numbers **irrational numbers** that are not rational numbers are **irrational numbers**.

In the mid-eighteenth century, it was proved that the ratio of the circumference of a circle to its diameter, symbolized by π **(pi)**, is an irrational number. The numbers $\frac{22}{7}$, **π (pi)** 3.14, or 3.14159 are rational-number approximations of π. The value of π has been computed to billions of decimal places with no apparent pattern.

Square Roots

Irrational numbers occur in the study of area. For example, to find the area of a square, we use the formula $A = s^2$, where A is the area and s is the length of a side of the square. If a side of a square is 3 cm long, then the area of the square is 9 cm² (square centimeters). Conversely, we can use the formula to find the length of a side of a square, given its area. If the area of a square is 25 cm², then $s^2 = 25$, so $s = 5$ or $^-5$. Each of these solutions is a **square root** **square root** of 25. However, because lengths are always nonnegative, 5 is the only possi**principal square root** ble solution. The positive solution of $s^2 = 25$ (namely, 5) is the **principal square root** of 25 and is denoted $\sqrt{25}$. Similarly, the principal square root of 2 is denoted $\sqrt{2}$. Note that $\sqrt{16} \neq {}^-4$ because $^-4$ is not the principal square root of 16. Can you find $\sqrt{0}$?

> ### Definition of the Principal Square Root

If a is any nonnegative number, the **principal square root** of a (denoted $\sqrt{a}$) is the nonnegative number b such that $b^2 = a$.

HISTORICAL NOTE

The discovery of irrational numbers by members of the Pythagorean Society (founded by Pythagoras) is one of the greatest events in the history of mathematics. This discovery was very disturbing to the Pythagoreans, who believed that everything depended on whole numbers, so they decided to keep the matter secret. One legend has it that Hippasus, a society member, was drowned because he relayed the secret to persons outside the society. In 1525, Christoff Rudolff, a German mathematician, became the first to use the symbol $\sqrt{}$ for a radical or a root.

**EXAMPLE
6-27**

Find the following:

a. The square roots of 144
b. The principal square root of 144

c. $\sqrt{\dfrac{4}{9}}$

Solution **a.** The square roots of 144 are 12 and $^{-}12$.

b. The principal square root of 144 is 12.

c. $\sqrt{\dfrac{4}{9}} = \dfrac{2}{3}$

Other Roots

We have seen that the positive solution to $s^2 = 25$ is denoted $\sqrt{25}$. Similarly, the positive solution to $s^4 = 25$ is denoted $\sqrt[4]{25}$.

nth root ◆ **index**   In general, if n is even, the positive solution to $x^n = 25$ is $\sqrt[n]{25}$ and is the principal **nth root** of 25. The number n is the **index**. Note that in the expression $\sqrt{25}$, the index 2 is understood and not expressed. In general, the positive solution to $x^n = b$, *where b is non-negative,* is $\sqrt[n]{b}$. Substituting $\sqrt[n]{b}$ for x in the equation $x^n = b$ gives the following:

$$(\sqrt[n]{b})^n = b$$

If b is negative, $\sqrt[n]{b}$ may not be a real number. For example, consider $\sqrt[4]{^{-}16}$. If $\sqrt[4]{^{-}16} = x$, then $x^4 = {}^{-}16$. Because any nonzero real number raised to the fourth power is positive, there is no real-number solution to $x^4 = {}^{-}16$ and therefore $\sqrt[4]{^{-}16}$ is not a real number. Similarly, if we are restricted to real numbers it is not possible to find *any* even root of a negative number. However, the value $^{-}2$ satisfies the equation $x^3 = {}^{-}8$. Hence, $\sqrt[3]{^{-}8} = {}^{-}2$. *In general, the odd root of a negative number is a negative number.*

Because $\sqrt{a}$, if it exists, is positive by definition, $\sqrt{(^{-}3)^2} = \sqrt{9} = 3$ and not $^{-}3$. Many students think that $\sqrt{a^2}$ always equals a. This is true if $a \geq 0$, but false if $a < 0$. *In general, $\sqrt{a^2} = |a|$. Similarly, $\sqrt[4]{a^4} = |a|$ and $\sqrt[6]{a^6} = |a|$, but $\sqrt[3]{a^3} = a$ for all a (why?).*

REMARK   Notice that when n is even and $b > 0$, the equation $x^n = b$ has two real-number solutions, $\sqrt[n]{b}$ and $^{-}\sqrt[n]{b}$. If n is odd, the equation has only one real-number solution $\sqrt[n]{b}$, for any real number b.

Irrationality of Square Roots and Other Roots

Some square roots are rational numbers. Others, like $\sqrt{2}$, are irrational numbers. To see this, note that $1^2 = 1$ and $2^2 = 4$ and that there is no whole number s such that $s^2 = 2$. Is there a rational number $\dfrac{a}{b}$ such that $\left(\dfrac{a}{b}\right)^2 = 2$? We use the strategy of *indirect reasoning.*

If we assume there is such a rational number, then the following must be true:

$$\left(\frac{a}{b}\right)^2 = 2$$

$$\frac{a^2}{b^2} = 2$$

$$a^2 = 2b^2$$

If $a^2 = 2b^2$, then by the Fundamental Theorem of Arithmetic, the prime factorizations of a^2 and $2b^2$ are the same. In particular, the prime 2 appears the same number of times in the prime factorization of a^2 as it does in the factorization of $2b^2$. Because $b^2 = b \cdot b$, no matter how many times 2 appears in the prime factorization of b, it appears twice as many times in $b \cdot b$. Also, a^2 has an even number of 2s for the same reason b^2 does. In $2b^2$, another factor of 2 is introduced, resulting in an odd number of 2s in the prime factorization of $2b^2$ and, hence, of a^2. But 2 cannot appear both an odd number of times and an even number of times in the same prime factorization of a^2. We have a contradiction. This contradiction could have been caused only by the assumption that $\sqrt{2}$ is a rational number. Consequently, $\sqrt{2}$ must be an irrational number. We can use a similar argument to show that $\sqrt{3}$ is irrational or $\sqrt{n}$ is irrational, where n is a whole number but not the square of another whole number.

Pythagorean Theorem

Many irrational numbers can be interpreted geometrically. For example, we can find a point on a number line to represent $\sqrt{2}$ by using the **Pythagorean Theorem**. That is, if a and b are the lengths of the shorter sides (legs) of a right triangle and c is the length of the longer side (hypotenuse), then $a^2 + b^2 = c^2$, as shown in Figure 6-6.

FIGURE 6-6

Figure 6-7 shows a segment one unit long constructed perpendicular to a number line at point P. Thus two sides of the triangle shown are each one unit long. If $a = b = 1$, then $c^2 = 2$ and $c = \sqrt{2}$. To find a point on the number line that corresponds to $\sqrt{2}$, we need to find a point Q on the number line such that the distance from 0 to Q is $\sqrt{2}$. Because $\sqrt{2}$ is the length of the hypotenuse, the point Q can be found by marking an arc with center 0 and radius c. The intersection of the positive number line with the arc is Q.

FIGURE 6-7

Similarly, other square roots can be constructed, as shown in Figure 6-8.

FIGURE 6-8

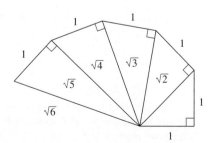

Estimating a Square Root

From Figure 6-7, we see that $\sqrt{2}$ must have a value between 1 and 2; that is, $1 < \sqrt{2} < 2$. To obtain a closer approximation of $\sqrt{2}$, we attempt to "squeeze" $\sqrt{2}$ between two numbers that are between 1 and 2. Because $(1.5)^2 = 2.25$ and $(1.4)^2 = 1.96$, it follows that $1.4 < \sqrt{2} < 1.5$. Because a^2 can be interpreted as the area of a square with side of length a, this discussion can be pictured geometrically, as in Figure 6-9.

FIGURE 6-9

If we desire a more accurate approximation for $\sqrt{2}$, we can continue this squeezing process. We see that $(1.4)^2$, or 1.96, is closer to 2 than is $(1.5)^2$, or 2.25, so we choose numbers closer to 1.4 in order to find the next approximation. We find the following:

$$(1.42)^2 = 2.0164$$
$$(1.41)^2 = 1.9981$$

Thus $1.41 < \sqrt{2} < 1.42$. We can continue this process until we obtain the desired approximation. Note that if your calculator has a square-root key, we can obtain an approximation directly.

The System of Real Numbers

real numbers The set of **real numbers** R is the union of the set of rational numbers and the set of irrational numbers. Real numbers represented as decimals can be terminating, repeating, or nonterminating and nonrepeating.

Every integer is a rational number as well as a real number. Every rational number is a real number, but not every real number is rational, as has been shown with $\sqrt{2}$. The relationships among sets of numbers are summarized in the tree in Figure 6-10.

FIGURE 6-10

The concept of fractions can now be extended to include all numbers of the form $\frac{a}{b}$, where a and b are real numbers with $b \neq 0$, such as $\frac{\sqrt{3}}{5}$. Addition, subtraction, multiplication, and division are defined on the set of real numbers in such a way that all the properties of these operations on rationals still hold. The properties are summarized next.

> ## Properties

Closure properties   For real numbers a and b, $a + b$ and ab are unique real numbers.

Commutative properties   For real numbers a and b, $a + b = b + a$ and $ab = ba$.

Associative properties   For real numbers a, b, and c, $a + (b + c) = (a + b) + c$ and $a(bc) = (ab)c$.

Identity properties   The number 0 is the unique additive identity and 1 is the unique multiplicative identity such that, for any real number a, $0 + a = a = a + 0$ and $1 \cdot a = a = a \cdot 1$.

Inverse properties   (1) For every real number a, ^{-}a is its unique additive inverse; that is, $a + {}^{-}a = 0 = {}^{-}a + a$. (2) For every nonzero real number a, $\frac{1}{a}$ is its unique multiplicative inverse; that is, $a\left(\frac{1}{a}\right) = 1 = \left(\frac{1}{a}\right)a$.

Distributive property of multiplication over addition   For real numbers a, b, and c, $a(b + c) = ab + ac$.

Denseness property   For real numbers a and b, there exists a real number c such that $a < c < b$.

Radicals and Rational Exponents

Scientific calculators have a $\boxed{y^x}$ key with which we can find the values of expressions like $3.41^{2/3}$ and $4^{1/2}$. What does $4^{1/2}$ mean? By extending the properties of exponents previously developed for integer exponents, we have $4^{1/2} \cdot 4^{1/2} = 4^{1/2+1/2} = 4^1$. This implies that $(4^{1/2})^2 = 4$, or $4^{1/2}$, is a square root of 4. The number $4^{1/2}$ is assumed to be the principal square root of 4, that is, $4^{1/2} = \sqrt{4}$. In general, if x is a nonnegative real number, then $x^{1/2} = \sqrt{x}$. Similarly, $(x^{1/3})^3 = x^{(1/3)3} = x^1$, and $x^{1/3} = \sqrt[3]{x}$. This discussion leads to the following:

1. $x^{1/n} = \sqrt[n]{x}$, where $\sqrt[n]{x}$ is meaningful.
2. $(x^m)^{1/n} = \sqrt[n]{x^m}$.
3. $x^{m/n} = \sqrt[n]{x^m}$, if $\frac{m}{n}$ is in simplest form.

More Properties of Exponents

The properties of integer exponents also hold for rational exponents. These properties are equivalent to the corresponding properties of radicals if the expressions involving radicals are meaningful.

Let r and s be any rational numbers, x and y be any real numbers, and n be any nonzero integer.

a. $x^{-r} = \dfrac{1}{x^r}$.

b. $(xy)^r = x^r y^r$ implies $(xy)^{1/n} = x^{1/n} y^{1/n}$ and $\sqrt[n]{xy} = \sqrt[n]{x}\,\sqrt[n]{y}$

c. $\left(\dfrac{x}{y}\right)^r = \dfrac{x^r}{y^r}$ implies $\left(\dfrac{x}{y}\right)^{1/n} = \dfrac{x^{1/n}}{y^{1/n}}$ and $\sqrt[n]{\dfrac{x}{y}} = \dfrac{\sqrt[n]{x}}{\sqrt[n]{y}}$

d. $(x^r)^s = x^{rs}$ implies $(x^{1/n})^s = x^{s/n}$ and hence, $(\sqrt[n]{x})^s = \sqrt[n]{x^s}$

REMARK The preceding properties can be used to write equivalent expressions for the roots of many numbers. For example, $\sqrt{96} = \sqrt{16 \cdot 6} = \sqrt{16} \cdot \sqrt{6} = 4 \cdot \sqrt{6}$. Similarly, $\sqrt[3]{54} = \sqrt[3]{27 \cdot 2} = \sqrt[3]{27} \cdot \sqrt[3]{2} = 3 \cdot \sqrt[3]{2}$.

E X A M P L E
6-28

Simplify each of the following if possible.

a. $16^{1/4}$ **b.** $16^{5/4}$ **c.** $(^{-}8)^{1/3}$ **d.** $125^{-4/3}$ **e.** $(^{-}16)^{1/4}$

Solution   **a.** $16^{1/4} = (2^4)^{1/4} = 2^1 = 2$, or $16^{1/4} = \sqrt[4]{16} = 2$
b. $16^{5/4} = 16^{(1/4)5} = (16^{1/4})^5 = 2^5 = 32$
c. $(^{-}8)^{1/3} = ((^{-}2)^3)^{1/3} = (^{-}2)^1 = {}^{-}2$ or $(^{-}8)^{1/3} = \sqrt[3]{-8} = {}^{-}2$
d. $125^{-4/3} = (5^3)^{-4/3} = 5^{-4} = 1/5^4 = 1/625$
e. Because every real number raised to the fourth power is positive, $\sqrt[4]{-16}$ is not a real number. Consequently, $(^{-}16)^{1/4}$ is not a real number.

NOW TRY THIS 6-8

Compute $\sqrt[8]{10}$ on a calculator using the following sequence of keys:

$$\boxed{10}\ \boxed{\sqrt{\ }}\ \boxed{\sqrt{\ }}\ \boxed{\sqrt{\ }}$$

a. Explain why this approach works.
b. For what values of n can $\sqrt[n]{10}$ be computed using only the $\boxed{\sqrt{\ }}$ key? Why?

O N G O I N G   A S S E S S M E N T   6 - 6

1. Write an irrational number whose digits are twos and threes.
2. Use the Pythagorean Theorem to find x.

   a. **b.** **c.**

3. Arrange the following real numbers in order from greatest to least:

   $0.9,\quad 0.\overline{9},\quad 0.\overline{98},\quad 0.9\overline{88},\quad 0.9\overline{98},\quad 0.\overline{898},\quad \sqrt{0.98}$

4. Determine which of the following represent irrational numbers:
   a. $\sqrt{51}$ **b.** $\sqrt{64}$ c. $\sqrt{324}$
   d. $\sqrt{325}$ e. $2 + 3\sqrt{2}$ **f.** $\sqrt{2} \div 5$

5. If possible find the square roots for each of the following without using a calculator:
   a. 225   **b.** 169   c. $^{-}81$ **d.** 625

6. Find the approximate square roots for each of the following, rounded to hundredths, by using the squeezing method:
   a. 7   **b.** 0.0120   c. 20.3   **d.** 1.64

7. Classify each of the following as true or false. If false, give a counterexample.
   a. The sum of any rational number and any irrational number is a rational number.
   b. The sum of any two irrational numbers is an irrational number.
   c. The product of any two irrational numbers is an irrational number.
   d. The difference of any two irrational numbers is an irrational number.

8. Find three irrational numbers between 1 and 3.

9. Find an irrational number between 0.53 and 0.54.

10. If R is the set of real numbers, Q is the set of rational numbers, I is the set of integers, W is the set of whole numbers, and S is the set of irrational numbers, find each of the following:
   a. $Q \cup S$ **b.** $Q \cap S$ c. $Q \cap R$
   d. $S \cap W$ e. $W \cup R$ **f.** $Q \cup R$

11. If the following letters correspond to the sets listed in problem 10, complete the following table by placing checkmarks in the appropriate columns. (N is the set of natural numbers.)

	N	I	Q	R	S
a. 6.7			✔	✔	
b. 5					
c. $\sqrt{2}$					
d. $^-5$					
e. $3\frac{1}{7}$					

12. If the following letters correspond to the sets listed in problem 10, put a checkmark under each set of numbers for which a solution to the problem exists. (N is the set of natural numbers).

	N	I	Q	R	S
a. $x^2 + 1 = 5$					
b. $2x - 1 = 32$					
c. $x^2 = 3$					
d. $x^2 = 4$					
e. $\sqrt{x} = ^-1$					
f. $\frac{3}{4}x = 4$					

13. Determine for what real values of x, if any, each of the following statements is true:
    a. $\sqrt{x} = 8$ b. $\sqrt{x} = ^-8$ c. $\sqrt{^-x} = 8$
    d. $\sqrt{^-x} = ^-8$ e. $\sqrt{x} > 0$ f. $\sqrt{x} < 0$

14. A diagonal brace is placed in a 4 ft × 5 ft rectangular gate. What is the length of the brace to the nearest tenth of a foot? (*Hint:* Use the Pythagorean Theorem.)

15. Write each of the following square roots in the form $a\sqrt{b}$, where a and b are integers and b has the least value possible:
    a. $\sqrt{180}$ b. $\sqrt{363}$ c. $\sqrt{252}$

16. Write each of the following in the simplest form $a\sqrt[n]{b}$, where a and b are integers, $b > 0$, and b has the least value possible:
    a. $\sqrt[3]{^-54}$ b. $\sqrt[5]{96}$ c. $\sqrt[3]{250}$ d. $\sqrt[5]{^-243}$

17. In each of the following geometric sequences, find the missing terms:
    a. 5, _, _, 10   b. 2, _, _, _, 1

18. The following exponential function approximates the number of bacteria after t hours: $E(t) = 2^{10} \cdot 16^t$.
    a. What is the initial number of bacteria, that is, the number when $t = 0$?
    b. After $\frac{1}{4}$ hr, how many bacteria are there?
    c. After $\frac{1}{2}$ hr, how many bacteria are there?

19. Solve for x in the following, where x is a rational number:
    a. $3^x = 81$ b. $4^x = 8$
    c. $128^{^-x} = 16$ d. $\left(\frac{4}{9}\right)^{3x} = \frac{32}{243}$

20. Classify each of the following numbers as rational or irrational:
    a. $\sqrt{2} - \frac{2}{\sqrt{2}}$ b. $(\sqrt{2})^{^-4}$
    c. $\frac{1}{1 + \sqrt{2}}$ d. $\frac{4}{\sqrt{2}} - \sqrt{2}$

Communication

21. Jim asked, if $\sqrt{2}$ can be written $\sqrt{2}/1$, why it isn't rational? How would you answer him?
22. Find the value of $\sqrt{3}$ on a calculator. Explain why this can't be the exact value of $\sqrt{3}$.
23. Is it true that $\sqrt{a + b} = \sqrt{a} + \sqrt{b}$? Explain.
24. Pi (π) is an irrational number. Could $\pi = \frac{22}{7}$? Why or why not?
25. Without using a calculator or doing any computation, determine if $\sqrt{13} = 3.60\overline{5}$. Explain why or why not.
26. Is $\sqrt{x^2 + y^2} = x + y$ for all values of x and y? Explain your reasoning.
27. Without using a calculator, arrange the following in increasing order. Explain your reasoning.
    $(4/25)^{^-1/3}, (25/4)^{1/3}, (4/25)^{^-1/4}$

Open-Ended

28. The sequence 1, 1.01, 1.001, 1.0001, . . . is an infinite sequence of rational numbers.
    a. Write several other infinite sequences of rational numbers.
    b. Write an infinite sequence of irrational numbers.
29. a. Place five irrational numbers between 1/2 and 3/4.
    b. Write an infinite sequence of irrational numbers all of whose terms are between 1/2 and 3/4.

Cooperative Learning

30. Let each member of a group choose a number between 0 and 1 on a calculator and check what happens when the $\boxed{x^2}$ key is pressed in succession until it is clear that there is no reason to go on.
    a. Compare your answers and write a conjecture based on what you observe.
    b. Use other keys on the calculator in a similar way. Describe the process and state a corresponding conjecture.
    c. Why do you get the result you do?
31. A calculator displays the following: $(3.7)^{2.4} = 23.103838$. In your group, discuss the meaning of the expression $(3.7)^{2.4}$ in view of what you know about exponents. Compare your findings with those of other groups.

Review Problems

32. a. Human bones make up 0.18 of a person's body weight. How much do the bones of a 120-lb person weigh?

b. Muscles make up about 0.4 of a person's body weight. How much do the muscles of a 120-lb person weigh?

33. Write each of the following decimals in the form $\frac{a}{b}$, where $a, b \in I, b \neq 0$:

a. 16.72   b. 0.003   c. ⁻5.07   d. 0.123

34. Write a repeating decimal equal to each of the following without using more than one zero.

a. 5   b. 5.1   c. $\frac{1}{2}$

35. Write 0.00024 as a fraction in simplest form.

36. Write 0.24 as a fraction in simplest form.

37. Write each of the following as a standard numeral.

a. $2.08 \cdot 10^5$ b. $3.8 \cdot 10^{-4}$

BRAIN
TEASER

Many schools celebrate Pi Day as suggested in the cartoon. When do you think it is celebrated? Why?

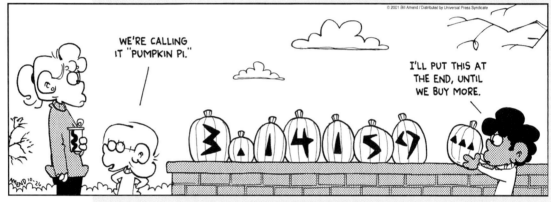

FOXTROT © Bill Amend. Reprinted with permission of UNIVERSAL PRESS SYNDICATE. All rights reserved.

Hint for Solving the Preliminary Problem

If you were the store manager, you might use the example of a dress originally costing $100.00 and lead Dori through the percentages off.

QUESTIONS FROM THE CLASSROOM

1. A student claims that 0.36 is greater than 0.9 because 36 is greater than 9. How do you respond?

2. A student reports that ⁻438,340,000 cannot be written in scientific notation. How do you respond?

3. A student multiplies (6.5)(8.5) to obtain the following:

$$
\begin{array}{r}
8.5 \\
\times\, 6.5 \\
\hline
4\,2\,5 \\
5\,1\,0 \\
\hline
5\,5.2\,5
\end{array}
$$

However, when the student multiplies $8\frac{1}{2} \cdot 6\frac{1}{2}$, she obtains the following:

$$
\begin{array}{r}
8\frac{1}{2} \\
\times\, 6\frac{1}{2} \\
\hline
4\frac{1}{4} \quad \left(\frac{1}{2} \cdot 8\frac{1}{2}\right) \\
48 \quad (6 \cdot 8) \\
\hline
52\frac{1}{4}
\end{array}
$$

How is this possible?

4. A student says that $3\frac{1}{4}\% = 0.03 + 0.25 = 0.28$. Is this correct? Why?

5. A student reports that it is impossible to mark a product up 150% because 100% of something is all there is. What is your response?

6. A student argues that a $p\%$ increase in salary followed by a $q\%$ decrease is equivalent to a $q\%$ decrease followed by a $p\%$ increase because of the commutative property of multiplication. How do you respond?

7. A student argues that $0.01\% = 0.01$ because in 0.01%, the percent is already written as a decimal. How do you respond?

8. A student tries to calculate $0.999^{10,000}$ on a calculator and finds the answer to be $4.5173346 \cdot 10^{-5}$. The student wonders how it could be that a number like 0.999 so close to 1 when raised to some power could result in a number close to 0. How do you respond?

9. Explain how you would respond to the following:

   a. A student claims that $\frac{9443}{9444}$ and $\frac{9444}{9445}$ are equal because both display 0.9998941 on his scientific calculator when the divisions are performed.

   b. Another student claims that the fractions are not equal and wants to know if there is any way the same calculator can determine which is greater.

10. Why is $\sqrt{25} \neq {}^{-}5$?

11. A student claims that $\sqrt{({}^{-}5)^2} = {}^{-}5$ because $\sqrt{a^2} = a$. Is this correct?

12. Another student says that $\sqrt{({}^{-}5)^2} = [({}^{-}5)^2]^{1/2} = ({}^{-}5)^{2/2} = ({}^{-}5)^1 = {}^{-}5$. Is this correct?

13. A student claims that the equation $\sqrt{{}^{-}x} = 3$ has no solution, since the square root of a negative number does not exist. Why is this argument wrong?

14. A student claims that if the value of an item increases by 100% each year from its value the previous year and if the original price is d dollars, then the value after n years will be $d \cdot 2^n$ dollars. Is the student correct? Why or why not?

15. A student argues that in the real world, irrational numbers are never used. How do you respond?

CHAPTER REVIEW

1. a. On the number line, find the decimals that correspond to points *A, B,* and *C.*

   b. Indicate by *D* the point that corresponds to 0.09 and by *E* the point that corresponds to 0.15.

2. Write each of the following using fractions:
   a. 32.012
   b. 0.00103

3. Give a test to determine if a fraction can be written as a terminating decimal without one's actually performing the division. Explain why this test is valid.

4. A board is 442.4 cm long. How many shelves can be cut from it if each shelf is 55.3 cm long? (Disregard the width of the cuts.)

5. Write each of the following as a decimal:

   a. $\frac{4}{7}$ b. $\frac{1}{8}$ c. $\frac{2}{3}$ d. $\frac{5}{8}$

6. Write each of the following as a fraction in simplest form:

   a. 0.28   b. ${}^{-}5.07$ c. $0.\overline{3}$ d. $2.0\overline{8}$

7. Round each of the following numbers as specified:
   a. 307.625 to the nearest hundredth
   b. 307.625 to the nearest tenth
   c. 307.625 to the nearest unit
   d. 307.625 to the nearest hundred

8. Rewrite each of the following in scientific notation:
   a. 426,000   b. $324 \cdot 10^{-6}$
   c. 0.00000237   d. 0.325

9. Order each of the following decimals from greatest to least: $1.45\overline{19}$, $1.451\overline{9}$, 1.4519, $1.4\overline{519}$, ${}^{-}0.134$, ${}^{-}0.13\overline{401}$, 0.13401

10. Each of the following is a geometrical sequence. Find the missing terms.
    a. 5, _, 10   b. 1, _, _, _, 1/4

11. Write each of the following in scientific notation without using a calculator:
    a. 1783411.56   b. $347/10^8$ c. $49.3 \cdot 10^8$
    d. $29.4 \cdot 10^{12}/10^{-4}$ e. $0.47 \cdot 1000^{12}$ f. $3/5^9$

12. a. Find five decimals between 0.1 and 0.11 and order them from greatest to least.

    b. Find four decimals between 0 and 0.1 listed from least to greatest so that each decimal starting from the second is twice as large as the preceding one.

    c. Find four decimals between 0.1 and 0.2 and list them in increasing order so that the first one is halfway between 0.1 and 0.2, the second halfway between the first and 0.2, the third halfway between the second and 0.2, and similarly for the fourth one.

13. Answer each of the following:
    a. 6 is what percent of 24?
    b. What is 320% of 60?
    c. 17 is 30% of what number?
    d. 0.2 is what percent of 1?

14. Change each of the following to percents:

    a. $\frac{1}{8}$ b. $\frac{3}{40}$ c. 6.27

    d. 0.0123   e. $\frac{3}{2}$

15. Change each of the following percents to decimals:

    a. 60%   b. $\frac{2}{3}$%   c. 100%

16. Sandy received a dividend that equals 11% of the value of her investment. If her dividend was $1020.80, how much was her investment?

17. Five computers in a shipment of 150 were found to be defective. What percent of the computers were defective?

18. On a mathematics examination, a student missed 8 of 70 questions. What percent of the questions, rounded to the nearest tenth, did the student do correctly?

19. A microcomputer system costs $3450 at present. This is 60% of the cost 4 yr ago. What was the cost of the system 4 yr ago? Explain your reasoning.

20. If, on a purchase of one new suit, you are offered successive discounts of 5%, 10%, or 20% in any order you wish, what order should you choose?

21. Jane bought a bicycle and sold it for 30% more than she paid for it. She sold it for $104. How much did she pay for it?

*22. A company was offered a $30,000 loan at a 12.5% annual interest rate for 4 yr. Find the simple interest due on the loan at the end of 4 yr.

*23. A money-market fund pays 14% annual interest compounded quarterly. What is the value of a $10,000 investment after 3 yr?

24. Classify each of the following as rational or irrational (assume the patterns shown continue):

    a. 2.19119911999119999119 . . .

    b. $\frac{1}{\sqrt{2}}$

    c. $\frac{4}{9}$

    d. 0.0011001100110011 . . .

    e. 0.001100011000011 . . .

25. Write each of the following in the form $a\sqrt{b}$ or $a\sqrt[n]{b}$, where a and b are integers and b has the least value possible:

    a. $\sqrt{242}$ b. $\sqrt{288}$
    c. $\sqrt{360}$ d. $\sqrt[3]{162}$

26. Answer each of the following and explain your answers:

    a. Is the set of irrational numbers closed under addition?

    b. Is the set of irrational numbers closed under subtraction?

    c. Is the set of irrational numbers closed under multiplication?

    d. Is the set of irrational numbers closed under division?

27. Find an approximation for $\sqrt{23}$ correct to three decimal places without using the $\boxed{y^x}$ or the $\boxed{\sqrt{}}$ keys.

CHAPTER OUTLINE

I. Decimals

   A. Every rational number can be represented as a terminating or repeating decimal.

   B. A rational number $\frac{a}{b}$, in simplest form whose denominator is of the form $2^m \cdot 5^n$, where m and n are whole numbers, can be expressed as a **terminating decimal**.

   C. A **repeating decimal** is a decimal with a block of digits, called the **repetend**, that repeat infinitely many times.

   D. A number is in **scientific notation** if it is written as the product of a number n that is greater than or equal to 1 and less than 10 and an integer power of 10.

II. Percent and interest

   A. **Percent** means *per hundred*. Percent is written using the % symbol: $x\% = \frac{x}{100}$.

   *B. **Simple interest** is computed using the formula $I = Prt$, where I is the interest, P is the principal, r is the annual interest rate, and t is the time in years.

   *C. When **compound interest** is involved, we use the formula $A = P(1 + i)^n$, where A is the balance, P is the principal, i is the interest rate per period, and n is the number of periods.

III. Real numbers

   A. An **irrational number** is represented by a nonterminating, nonrepeating decimal.

   B. The set of **real numbers** is the set of all decimals, namely, the union of the set of rational numbers and the set of irrational numbers.

   C. If a is any whole number, then the **principal square root** of a, denoted by $\sqrt{a}$, is the nonnegative number b such that $b \cdot b = b^2 = a$.

   D. Square roots and nth roots can be found by using the **squeezing method**.

IV. Radicals and rational exponents

   A. $\sqrt[n]{x}$, or $x^{1/n}$, is the **nth root** of x and n is the **index**.

   B. The following properties hold for all radicals if the expressions involving radicals are meaningful:

      a. $\sqrt[n]{xy} = \sqrt[n]{x} \cdot \sqrt[n]{y}$

      b. $\sqrt[n]{\dfrac{x}{y}} = \dfrac{\sqrt[n]{x}}{\sqrt[n]{y}}$

      c. $x^{m/n} = (\sqrt[n]{x})^m = \sqrt[n]{x^m}$, if m/n is in simplest form.

SELECTED BIBLIOGRAPHY

Beigie, D. "Investigating Limits in Number Patterns." *Mathematics Teaching in the Middle School* 7 (April 2002): 438–443.

Bennett, A., and T. Nelson. "A Conceptual Model for Solving Percent Problems." *Mathematics Teaching in the Middle School* 1 (April 1994): 20–25.

Drum, R., and W. Petty, Jr. "2 Is Not the Same as 2.0!" *Mathematics Teaching in the Middle School* 6 (September 2000): 34–38.

Glasgow, R., G. Ragan, W. Fields, R. Reys, and D. Wasman. "The Decimal Dilemma." *Teaching Children Mathematics* 7 (October 2000): 89–93.

Oppenheimer, L., and R. Hunting. "Relating Fractions and Decimals: Listening to Students Talk." *Mathematics Teaching in the Middle School* 4 (February 1999): 318–321.

Reys, B., and F. Arbaugh. "Clearing Up the Confusion over Calculator Use in Grades K–5." *Teaching Children Mathematics* 8 (October 2001): 90–94.

Sweeney, E., and R. Quinn. "Concentration: Connecting Fractions, Decimals, & Percents." *Mathematics Teaching in the Middle School* 5 (January 2000): 324–328.

Thompson, A., and S. Sproule. "Deciding When to Use Calculators." *Mathematics Teaching in the Middle School* 6 (October 2000): 12–129.

Thompson, C., and V. Walker. "Connecting Decimals and Other Mathematical Content." *Teaching Children Mathematics* 2 (April 1996): 496–502.

Weibe, J. "Manipulating Percentages." *Mathematics Teacher* 79 (January 1986): 21, 23–26.

Williams, S., and J. Copley. "Using Calculators to Discover Patterns in Dividing Decimals." *Mathematics Teaching in the Middle School* 1 (April 1994): 72–75.

Yang, D., and R. Reys. "One Fraction Problem, Many Solution Paths." *Mathematics Teaching in the Middle School* 7 (November 2001): 164–166.

–7–
Probability

PRELIMINARY PROBLEM

A manufacturer found that among 500 randomly selected smoke detectors only 450 worked properly. Based on this information, how many smoke detectors would you have to install to be sure that the probability that at least one of them will work will be greater than 99.99%?

P robability, with its roots in gambling, is used in such areas as predicting sales, planning political campaigns, determining insurance premiums, making investment decisions, and testing experimental drugs. Some examples of uses of probability in everyday conversations include the following:

What is the probability that the Braves will win the World Series?

There is no chance you will get a raise.

There is a 50% chance of rain today.

The *Principles and Standards* call for an increased emphasis on data analysis and probability. In the *Standards*, we find the following:

Although the computation of probabilities can appear to be simple work with fractions, students must grapple with many conceptual challenges in order to understand probability. Misconceptions about probability have been held not only by many students but also by many adults (Konold 1989). To correct misconceptions, it is useful for students to make predictions and then compare the predictions with actual outcomes. (p. 254)

Probability Expectations

The *Principles and Standards* Data Analysis and Probability Standard describes its expectations for students with regard to the study of probability. The expectations covered in this chapter include the following:

In grades K–2, children should discuss events related to their experience as likely or unlikely. (p. 400)

In grades 3–5, children should be able to describe events as likely or unlikely and discuss degrees of likelihood using words such as certain, equally likely, *and* impossible. *They should be able to predict the probability of simple experiments and test the predictions. They should understand that the measure of likelihood of an event can be represented by a number from 0 to 1.* (p. 400)

In grades 6–8, children should understand complementary and mutually exclusive events. They should be able to make and test conjectures about the results of experiments and simulations. They should be able to compute probabilities of compound events using methods such as organized lists, tree diagrams, and area models. (p. 401)

In this chapter, we introduce all of the topics in the above expectations along with several others. We use tree diagrams and geometric probabilities (area models) to solve problems and to analyze games that involve spinners, cards, and dice. We introduce counting techniques and discuss the role of simulations in probability.

HISTORICAL NOTE

The first time probability appears to have been mentioned in the western history of mathematics is in a 1477 commentary on Dante's *Divine Comedy*, but most historians think that it originated in an unfinished dice game. The French mathematician Blaise Pascal (1623–1665) received a letter from his friend Chevalier de Méré, a professional gambler, who asked how to divide the stakes if two players start, but fail to complete, a game consisting of five matches in which the winner is the one who wins three out of five matches. The players decided to divide the stakes according to their chances of winning the game. Pascal shared the problem with Pierre de Fermat (1601–1665) and together they solved the problem, which prompted the development of probability.

Since the work of the French mathematician Pierre Simon de Laplace (1749–1827), probability theory has become a major mathematical tool in science. In 1905 Albert Einstein (1879–1955) used the theory of probability in his work in physics.

7-1 How Probabilities Are Determined

Probabilities are ratios, expressed as fractions, decimals, or percents, determined by con

experiment   sidering results or outcomes of experiments. An **experiment** is an activity whose results

outcome   can be observed and recorded. Each of the possible results of an experiment is an **outcome**. If we toss a coin that cannot land on its edge, there are two distinct possible outcomes: heads (*H*) and tails (*T*).

sample space   A set of all possible outcomes for an experiment is a **sample space**. In a single coin toss, the sample space *S* is given by *S* = {*H, T*}. The sample space can be modeled by a tree dia-

FIGURE 7-1   gram, as shown in Figure 7-1. Each outcome of the experiment is designated by a separate branch in the tree diagram. The sample space *S* for rolling the standard die in Figure 7-2(a) is *S* = {1, 2, 3, 4, 5, 6}. Figure 7-2(b) gives a tree diagram for the sample space.

FIGURE 7-2

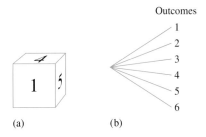

(a)   (b)

event   Any subset of a sample space is an **event**. For example, the set of all even-numbered rolls {2, 4, 6} is a subset of all possible rolls of a die {1, 2, 3, 4, 5, 6} and is an event.

E X A M P L E
7-1

Suppose an experiment consists of drawing one slip of paper from a jar containing 12 slips of paper, each with a different month of the year written on it. Find each of the following:

a. The sample space *S* for the experiment
b. The event *A* consisting of outcomes having a month beginning with J
c. The event *B* consisting of outcomes having the name of a month that has exactly 4 letters
d. The event *C* consisting of outcomes having a month that begins with M or N

Solution   **a.** *S* = {January, February, March, April, May, June, July, August, September, October, November, December}
b. *A* = {January, June, July}
c. *B* = {June, July}
d. *C* = {March, May, November}

**EXAMPLE
7-2**

Suppose we toss a fair coin three times and record the results. Find each of the following:

a. The sample space for this experiment
b. The event A of tossing two heads and one tail
c. The event B of tossing no tails
d. The event C of tossing a head on the last toss

Solution   **a.** $S = \{HHH, HHT, HTH, THH, TTT, TTH, THT, HTT\}$
   b. $A = \{HHT, HTH, THH\}$
   c. $B = \{HHH\}$
   d. $C = \{HHH, HTH, THH, TTH\}$

Determining Probabilities

Around 1900, the English statistician Karl Pearson tossed a coin 24,000 times and recorded 12,012 heads. During World War II, the Dane, John Kerrich, a prisoner of war, tossed a coin 10,000 times. A subset of his results is in Table 7-1. The *relative frequency* column on the right is obtained by dividing the number of heads by the number of tosses of the coin.

Table 7-1

Number of Tosses	Number of Heads	Relative Frequency (rounded)
10	4	0.400
50	25	0.500
100	44	0.440
500	255	0.510
1,000	502	0.502
5,000	2,533	0.507
8,000	4,034	0.504
10,000	5,067	0.507

As the number of Kerrich's tosses increased, he obtained heads close to half the time. The relative frequency for Pearson's 24,000 tosses gives a similar result of 12,012/24,000, or approximately $\frac{1}{2}$.

relative frequency interpretation

Kerrich was using the **relative frequency interpretation** of probability. In this interpretation, a probability is the long-run proportion of times that an event will occur given many repetitions under identical circumstances.

experimentally ◆ **empirically**

When a probability is determined by observing outcomes of experiments, it is said to be determined **experimentally**, or **empirically**. The exact number of heads that occurs when a fair coin is tossed a few times cannot be predicted accurately. A *fair coin* is a coin that is just as likely to land "heads" as it is to land "tails." Probabilities only suggest what will happen in the "long run." When a fair coin is tossed many times and the fraction (or proportion) of heads is near $\frac{1}{2}$, we say that the probability of heads occurring is $\frac{1}{2}$ and write $P(\{H\}) = \frac{1}{2}$, or we shorten the symbolism to $P(H) = \frac{1}{2}$.

theoretical probabilities   We assign **theoretical probabilities** to the outcomes under ideal conditions. For example, we could argue that since an ideal coin is symmetric and has two sides, then each side should appear about the same number of times if the coin is tossed many times. Again we would conclude that

$$P(H) = P(T) = \frac{1}{2}.$$

equally likely   When one outcome is just as likely as another, as in coin tossing, the outcomes are **equally likely**. In this text, by "probability" we mean *theoretical probability*. If an experiment is repeated many times, the experimental probability of the event's occurring should be approximately equal to the theoretical probability of the event's occurring.

A *fair* die is a die that is just as likely to land showing any of the numerals 1 through 6. Its sample space S is given by $S = \{1, 2, 3, 4, 5, 6\}$, and $P(1) = P(2) = P(3) = P(4) = P(5) = P(6) = 1/6$. The probability of rolling an even number, that is, the probability of the event $E = \{2, 4, 6\}$, is 3/6, or 1/2. For a sample space with equally likely outcomes, the probability of an event A can be defined as follows.

> ## Definition of Probability of an Event with Equally Likely Outcomes
>
> For an experiment with sample space S and equally likely outcomes, the **probability of an event A** is given by
>
> $$P(A) = \frac{\text{Number of elements of } A}{\text{Number of elements of } S} = \frac{n(A)}{n(S)}.$$

FIGURE 7-3

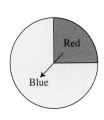

This definition applies only to a sample space that has equally likely outcomes. Applying the definition to a space with outcomes that are not equally likely leads to incorrect conclusions. For example, the sample space for spinning the spinner in Figure 7-3 is given by $S = \{\text{Red, Blue}\}$, but the outcome Blue is more likely to occur than is the outcome Red, so $P(\text{Red})$ is not equal to $\frac{1}{2}$ but $\frac{1}{4}$ (why?). If the spinner were spun 100 times, we could reasonably expect that about $\frac{1}{4}$ of 100, or 25, of the outcomes would be Red, whereas about $\frac{3}{4}$ of 100, or 75, of the outcomes would be Blue.

Notice that $P(\text{Red}) = \dfrac{Area(\text{Red})}{Area(\text{Circle})}$ because $Area(\text{Red}) = \frac{1}{4} Area(\text{Circle})$. Later in this chapter, we investigate more examples of computing probabilities involving areas.

NOW TRY THIS 7-1

> **a.** In an experiment of tossing a fair coin once, what is the sum of the probabilities of all the distinct outcomes in the sample space?
>
> **b.** In an experiment of tossing a fair die once, what is the sum of the probabilities of all the distinct outcomes in the sample space?
>
> **c.** Does the sum of the probabilities of all the distinct outcomes of any sample space always result in the same number? Why?

**E X A M P L E
7-3**

at random

Let $S = \{1, 2, 3, 4, 5, \ldots, 25\}$. If a number is chosen **at random**, that is, with the same chance of being drawn as all other numbers in the set, calculate each of the following probabilities:

a. The event A that an even number is drawn
b. The event B that a number less than 10 and greater than 20 is drawn
c. The event C that a number less than 26 is drawn
d. The event D that a prime number is drawn
e. The event E that a number both even and prime is drawn

Solution   Each of the 25 numbers in set S has an equal chance of being drawn.

a. $A = \{2, 4, 6, 8, 10, 12, 14, 16, 18, 20, 22, 24\}$, so $n(A) = 12$. Thus

$$P(A) = \frac{n(A)}{n(S)} = \frac{12}{25}.$$

b. $B = \emptyset$, so $n(B) = 0$. Thus $P(B) = \dfrac{0}{25} = 0$.

c. $C = S$ and $n(C) = 25$. Thus $P(C) = \dfrac{25}{25} = 1$.

d. $D = \{2, 3, 5, 7, 11, 13, 17, 19, 23\}$, so $n(D) = 9$. Thus

$$P(D) = \frac{n(D)}{n(S)} = \frac{9}{25}.$$

e. $E = \{2\}$, so $n(E) = 1$. Thus $P(E) = \dfrac{1}{25}$.

---

impossible event

certain event

In Example 7-3(b), event B is the empty set. An event such as B that has no outcomes is an **impossible event** *and has probability* 0. If the word *and* were replaced by *or* in Example 7-3(b), then event B would no longer be the empty set. In Example 7-3(c), event C consists of drawing a number less than 26 on a single draw. Because every number in S is less than 26, $P(C) = \dfrac{25}{25} = 1$. An event that has probability 1 is a **certain event**.

In Example 7-3(a), because an event A is a subset of a sample space S, $\emptyset \subseteq A \subseteq S$. Hence, $0 = n(\emptyset) \le n(A) \le n(S)$ and $0 = \dfrac{0}{n(S)} \le \dfrac{n(A)}{n(S)} \le \dfrac{n(S)}{n(S)} = 1$. In general, we have the following property.

FIGURE 7-4

> **Property**

If A is any event and S is the sample space, then $0 \le P(A) \le 1$.

Consider one spin of the wheel shown in Figure 7-4. For this experiment, $S = \{0, 1, 2, 3, 4, 5, 6, 7, 8, 9\}$. If A is the event of spinning a number in the set $\{0, 1, 2, 3, 4\}$ and B is the event of spinning a number in the set $\{5, 7\}$, then using the definition of probability for equally likely events, $P(A) = n(A)/n(S) = 5/10$ and $P(B) = n(B)/n(S) = 2/10$. The probability of an event can be found by adding the probabilities of the events representing the various outcomes in the set. For example, event $B = \{5, 7\}$ can be represented as the union of two disjoint events, that is, spinning a 5 or spinning a 7. Then $P(B)$ can be found by adding the probabilities of each event.

$$P(B) = P(5) + P(7) = 1/10 + 1/10 = 2/10$$

Likewise,

$$P(A) = 1/10 + 1/10 + 1/10 + 1/10 + 1/10 = 5/10.$$

These are special cases of the following property, which holds for all probabilities.

> ### Property

The probability of an event is equal to the sum of the probabilities of the outcomes making up the event.

E X A M P L E
7-4

If we draw a card at random from an ordinary deck of playing cards, what is the probability that

a. the card is an ace?   **b.** the card is an ace or a queen?

Solution **a.** There are 52 cards in a deck, 4 of which are aces. If event A is drawing an ace, then $A = \left\{ \spadesuit, \clubsuit, \diamondsuit, \heartsuit \right\}$. We use the definition of probability for equally likely outcomes to compute the following:

$$P(A) = \frac{n(A)}{n(S)} = \frac{4}{52}$$

An alternative approach is to find the sum of the probabilities of obtaining each of the outcomes in the event, where the probability of drawing any single ace from the deck is $\frac{1}{52}$:

$$P(A) = \frac{1}{52} + \frac{1}{52} + \frac{1}{52} + \frac{1}{52} = \frac{4}{52}$$

b. The event E of getting an ace or a queen consists of 8 cards; 4 aces and 4 queens. Hence,

$$P(E) = \frac{n(E)}{n(S)} = \frac{8}{52}.$$

Mutually Exclusive Events

Consider one spin of the wheel in Figure 7-4. For this experiment, we have $S = \{0, 1, 2, 3, 4, 5, 6, 7, 8, 9\}$. If $A = \{0, 1, 2, 3, 4\}$ and $B = \{5, 7\}$, then $A \cap B = \varnothing$. Two such

mutually exclusive events are **mutually exclusive** events. If event A occurs, then event B cannot occur, and we have the following definition.

> ## Definition of Mutually Exclusive Events

Events A and B are **mutually exclusive** if they have no elements in common; that is, $A \cap B = \varnothing$.

Each outcome in the space $S = \{0, 1, 2, 3, 4, 5, 6, 7, 8, 9\}$ is equally likely, with probability $\frac{1}{10}$. Thus, if we write the probability of A or B as $P(A \cup B)$, we have the following:

$$P(A \cup B) = \frac{n(A \cup B)}{n(S)} = \frac{7}{10} = \frac{5 + 2}{10} = \frac{5}{10} + \frac{2}{10}$$

$$= \frac{n(A)}{n(S)} + \frac{n(B)}{n(S)} = P(A) + P(B)$$

The result developed in this example is true for all mutually exclusive events. In general, we have the following property.

> ## Property

If events A and B are mutually exclusive, then $P(A \text{ or } B) = P(A \cup B) = P(A) + P(B)$.

For a sample space with equally likely outcomes, this property follows immediately from the fact that if $A \cap B = \varnothing$, then $n(A \cup B) = n(A) + n(B)$. In general, the probability of the union of events such that any two are mutually exclusive is the sum of the probabilities of those events.

Complementary Events

complements

complementary events

If the weather forecaster tells us that the probability of rain is 25%, what is the probability that it will not rain? These two events—rain and not rain—are **complements** of each other. Therefore if the probability of rain is 25%, or 1/4, the probability it will not rain is $100\% - 25\% = 75\%$, or $1 - 1/4 = 3/4$. Notice that $P(\text{no rain}) = 1 - P(\text{rain})$. The two events rain and no rain are mutually exclusive because if one happens, the other cannot. Two mutually exclusive events whose union is the sample space are **complementary events**. If A is an event, the complement of A, written $\overline{A}$, is also an event. For example, consider the event $A = \{2, 4\}$ of tossing a 2 or a 4 using a standard die. The complement of A is the set $\overline{A} = \{1, 3, 5, 6\}$. Because the sample space is $S = \{1, 2, 3, 4, 5, 6\}$, we have $P(A) = 2/6$ and $P(\overline{A}) = 4/6$. Notice that $P(A) + P(\overline{A}) = \frac{2}{6} + \frac{4}{6} = 1$. This is true in general for any set A and its complement, $\overline{A}$.

> ## Property

If A is an event and $\overline{A}$ is its complement, then

$$P(A) + P(\overline{A}) = 1,$$
$$P(\overline{A}) = 1 - P(A) \quad \text{or} \quad P(A) = 1 - P(\overline{A}).$$

Non-Mutually Exclusive Events

FIGURE 7-5

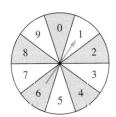

Consider the spinner in Figure 7-5. Let E be the event of spinning an even number and T the event of spinning a number divisible by 3; that is,

$$E = \{0, 2, 4, 6, 8\}$$
$$T = \{0, 3, 6, 9\}.$$

The event of spinning an even number and a number divisible by 3 is denoted $E \cap T$. Because $E \cap T = \{0, 6\}$, E and T are not mutually exclusive and $P(E \cup T) \neq P(E) + P(T)$. However, because each outcome is equally likely we can still use the definition of the probability of an event to compute the probability of E or T as follows:

$$P(E \cup T) = \frac{n(E \cup T)}{n(S)}$$

Because $E \cup T = \{0, 2, 4, 6, 8, 3, 9\}$, $n(E \cup T) = 7$. Also, $n(S) = 10$, and $P(E \cup T) = \frac{7}{10}$.

In general, we can also compute the probability of E or T by using the following result from Chapter 2.

$$n(E \cup T) = n(E) + n(T) - n(E \cap T)$$

Therefore, for a sample space with equally likely outcomes,

$$\begin{aligned} P(E \cup T) &= \frac{n(E \cup T)}{n(S)} \\ &= \frac{n(E) + n(T) - n(E \cap T)}{n(S)} \\ &= \frac{n(E)}{n(S)} + \frac{n(T)}{n(S)} - \frac{n(E \cap T)}{n(S)} \\ &= P(E) + P(T) - P(E \cap T). \end{aligned}$$

This result, although proved for events in a sample space with equally likely outcomes, is true in general. This and other properties of probability are summarized next.

▶ Properties of Probability

1. $P(\emptyset) = 0$ (impossible event).
2. $P(S) = 1$, where S is the sample space (certain event).
3. For any event A, $0 \leq P(A) \leq 1$.
4. If A and B are events and $A \cap B = \emptyset$, then $P(A \cup B) = P(A) + P(B)$.
5. If A and B are events, then $P(A \cup B) = P(A) + P(B) - P(A \cap B)$.
6. If A is an event, then $P(\overline{A}) = 1 - P(A)$.

EXAMPLE 7-5

A golf bag contains 2 red tees, 4 blue tees, and 5 white tees.

a. What is the probability of the event R that a tee drawn at random is red?

b. What is the probability of the event "not R," that is, that a tee drawn at random is not red?

c. What is the probability of the event that a tee drawn at random is either red (R) or blue (B), that is, $P(R \cup B)$?

Solution **a.** Because the bag contains a total of $2 + 4 + 5$, or 11, tees and 2 tees are red,
$$P(R) = \frac{2}{11}.$$

b. The bag contains 11 tees and 9 are not red, so the probability of "not R" is $\frac{9}{11}$. Also, notice that $P(\overline{R}) = 1 - P(R) = 1 - \frac{2}{11} = \frac{9}{11}$.

c. The bag contains 2 red tees and 4 blue tees and $R \cap B = \varnothing$, so $P(R \cup B) = \frac{2}{11} + \frac{4}{11}$, or $\frac{6}{11}$.

EXAMPLE 7-6

Find the probability of rolling a sum of 7 or 11 when rolling a fair pair of dice.

Solution To solve this problem, we use the strategy of *making a table*. Figure 7–6(a) shows all possible outcomes of tossing the dice. We know that there are 6 possible results from tossing the first die and 6 from tossing the second die, so by the Fundamental Counting Principle, there are $6 \cdot 6$, or 36, entries in the table. It may be easier to read the results when they are recorded as ordered pairs, as in Figure 7-6(b), where the first component represents the number on the first die and the second component represents the number on the second die. We show the possible sums from rolling the pair of dice in Figure 7-6(c).

FIGURE 7-6

(a)

Number on Second Die

	1	2	3	4	5	6
1	(1, 1)	(1, 2)	(1, 3)	(1, 4)	(1, 5)	(1, 6)
2	(2, 1)	(2, 2)	(2, 3)	(2, 4)	(2, 5)	(2, 6)
3	(3, 1)	(3, 2)	(3, 3)	(3, 4)	(3, 5)	(3, 6)
4	(4, 1)	(4, 2)	(4, 3)	(4, 4)	(4, 5)	(4, 6)
5	(5, 1)	(5, 2)	(5, 3)	(5, 4)	(5, 5)	(5, 6)
6	(6, 1)	(6, 2)	(6, 3)	(6, 4)	(6, 5)	(6, 6)

Number on First Die

(b)

Number on Second Die

	1	2	3	4	5	6
1	2	3	4	5	6	7
2	3	4	5	6	7	8
3	4	5	6	7	8	9
4	5	6	7	8	9	10
5	6	7	8	9	10	11
6	7	8	9	10	11	12

Number on First Die

Possible Sums

(c)

In Figure 7-6(c) we see that a sum of 7 appears six times. Hence, the event "a sum of 7" arises from the following subset of the set of ordered pairs in Figure 7-6(b):

$$\{(6, 1), (5, 2), (4, 3), (3, 4), (2, 5), (1, 6)\}$$

Each outcome in this set is equally likely and hence P(a sum of 7) = 6/36. Similarly, P(a sum of 11) = 2/36. The probabilities of each of the possible sums can be calculated in the same way and are displayed in Table 7-2 (the numbers in the "Outcome" row represent the sum of the numbers that appear on the two dice).

Table 7-2

Outcome	2	3	4	5	6	7	8	9	10	11	12
Probability	1/36	2/36	3/36	4/36	5/36	6/36	5/36	4/36	3/36	2/36	1/36

The probability of rolling a sum of 7 or 11 is given by P(sum of 7 or sum of 11) = P(sum of 7) + P(sum of 11) = 6/36 + 2/36 = 8/36.

E X A M P L E
7-7

A fair pair of dice is rolled. Let E be the event of rolling a sum that is an even number and P the event of rolling a sum that is a prime number. Find the probability of rolling a sum that is even *or* prime, that is, $P(E \cup P)$.

Solution   To solve this problem, we use Table 7-2. We know that events E and P are not mutually exclusive because $E = \{2, 4, 6, 8, 10, 12\}$, $P = \{2, 3, 5, 7, 11\}$, and $E \cap P = \{2\}$. One way to solve the problem is to note that $E \cup P = \{2, 4, 6, 8, 10, 12, 3, 5, 7, 11\}$. Therefore

$$P(E \cup P) = P(2) + P(4) + P(6) + P(8) + P(10) + P(12) + P(3) + P(5)$$
$$+ P(7) + P(11)$$
$$= 1/36 + 3/36 + 5/36 + 5/36 + 3/36 + 1/36 + 2/36 + 4/36 + 6/36 + 2/36$$
$$= 32/36.$$

Another approach is to use a property of probabilities (Property 5):

$$P(E \cup P) = P(E) + P(P) - P(E \cap P)$$
$$= 18/36 + 15/36 - 1/36$$
$$= 32/36$$

A third approach to finding $P(E \cup P)$ is to find $P(\overline{E \cup P})$ and subtract this probability from 1. Because $E \cup P = \{2, 3, 4, 5, 6, 7, 8, 10, 11, 12\}$, then $\overline{E \cup P} = \{9\}$ and $P(\overline{E \cup P}) = 4/36$. Hence, $P(E \cup P) = 1 - P(\overline{E \cup P}) = 1 - 4/36 = 32/36$.

1. When a thumbtack is dropped, it will land point up (⊥) or point down (人). This experiment was repeated 80 times with the following results:

   Point up: 56 times   Point down: 24 times

   a. What is the experimental probability that the thumbtack will land point up?

   b. What is the experimental probability that the thumbtack will land point down?

   c. If you were to try this experiment another 80 times, would you get the same results? Why?

   d. Would you expect to get nearly the same results on a second trial? Why?

2. Consider the experiment of drawing a single card from a standard deck of cards and determine which of the following are sample spaces with equally likely outcomes:

   a. {face card, not face card}

   b. {club, diamond, heart, spade}

   c. {black, red}

   d. {king, queen, jack, ace, even card, odd card}

3. An experiment consists of selecting the last digit of a telephone number. Assume that each of the 10 digits is equally likely to appear as a last digit. List each of the following:

   a. The sample space

   b. The event consisting of outcomes that the digit is less than 5

   c. The event consisting of outcomes that the digit is odd

   d. The event consisting of outcomes that the digit is not 2

   e. Find the probability of each of the events in (b) through (d).

4. Each letter of the alphabet is written on a separate piece of paper and placed in a box and then one piece is drawn at random.

   a. What is the probability that the selected piece of paper has a vowel written on it?

   b. What is the probability that it has a consonant written on it?

   c. What is the probability that the paper has a vowel on it or a letter from the word "probability"?

5. The following spinner is spun:

   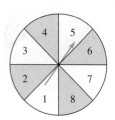

   Find the probabilities of obtaining each of the following:

   a. *P*(factor of 35)   **b.** *P*(multiple of 3)

   c. *P*(even number)   **d.** *P*(6 or 2)

   e. *P*(11)

   f. *P*(composite number)

   g. *P*(neither a prime nor a composite)

6. A card is selected from an ordinary deck of 52 cards. Find the probabilities for each of the following:

   a. A red card   **b.** A face card

   c. A red card or a 10   **d.** A queen

   e. Not a queen   **f.** A face card or a club

   g. A face card and a club

   h. Not a face card and not a club

7. A drawer contains 6 black socks, 4 brown socks, and 2 green socks. Suppose one sock is drawn from the drawer and that it is equally likely that any one of the socks is drawn. Find the probabilities for each of the following:

   a. The sock is brown.

   b. The sock is either black or green.

   c. The sock is red.

   d. The sock is not black.

8. The drawer in the cartoon contains 6 pairs of black socks, 8 pairs of blue socks, and 3 pairs of white socks.

   a. A child reaches in the drawer without looking to pull out four socks. What is the probability that the child gets two socks of the same color?

   b. What is the least number of socks that one must pull out to guarantee getting at least one pair of each color? Justify your answer.

   c. A cat knocks one sock out of the drawer. What is the probability that the sock is not white?

9. Riena has six unmarked CDs in a box, where each is dedicated to exactly one of English, mathematics, French, American history, chemistry, and computer science. Answer the following questions:

a. If she chooses a CD at random, what is the probability she chooses the English CD?

b. What is the probability that she chooses a CD that is neither math nor chemistry?

10. The following questions refer to a very popular dice game, craps, in which a player rolls two dice:

a. Rolling a sum of 7 or 11 on the first roll of the dice is a win. What is the probability of winning on the first roll?

b. Rolling a sum of 2, 3, or 12 on the first roll of the dice is a loss. What is the probability of losing on the first roll?

c. Rolling a sum of 4, 5, 6, 8, 9, or 10 on the first roll is neither a win nor a loss. What is the probability of neither winning nor losing on the first roll?

d. After rolling a sum of 4, 5, 6, 8, 9, or 10, a player must roll the same sum again before rolling a sum of 7. Which sum—4, 5, 6, 8, 9, or 10—has the highest probability of occurring again?

e. What is the probability of rolling a sum of 1 on any roll of the dice?

f. What is the probability of rolling a sum less than 13 on any roll of the dice?

g. If the two dice are rolled 60 times, predict about how many times a sum of 7 will be rolled.

11. According to a weather report, there is a 30% chance it will rain tomorrow. What is the probability it will not rain tomorrow? Explain your answer.

12. A roulette wheel has 38 slots around the rim. The first 36 slots are numbered from 1 to 36. Half of these 36 slots are red, and the other half are black. The remaining 2 slots are numbered 0 and 00 and are green. As the roulette wheel is spun in one direction, a small ivory ball is rolled along the rim in the opposite direction. The ball has an equally likely chance of falling into any one of the 38 slots. Find each of the following:

a. The probability that the ball lands in a black slot

b. The probability that the ball lands on 0 or 00

c. The probability that the ball does not land on a number from 1 through 12

d. The probability that the ball lands on an odd number or on a green slot

13. If the roulette wheel in problem 12 is spun 190 times, predict about how many times the ball will land on 0 or 00.

14. Determine if each player has an equal probability of winning each of the following games:

a. Toss a fair coin. If heads appears, I win; if tails appears, you lose.

b. Toss a fair coin. If heads appears, I win; otherwise, you win.

c. Toss a fair die numbered 1 through 6. If 1 appears, I win; if 6 appears, you win.

d. Toss a fair die numbered 1 through 6. If an even number appears, I win; if an odd number appears, you win.

e. Toss a fair die numbered 1 through 6. If a number greater than or equal to 3 appears, I win; otherwise, you win.

f. Toss two fair dice numbered 1 through 6. If a 1 appears on each die, I win; if a 6 appears on each die, you win.

g. Toss two fair dice numbered 1 through 6. If the sum is 3, I win; if the sum is 2, you win.

h. Toss two dice numbered 1 through 6; one die is red and one is white. If the number on the red die is greater than the number on the white die, I win; otherwise, you win.

15. Suppose a fair coin is tossed twice. Find the probability for each of the following:

a. Exactly one head   **b.** At least one head

c. At most one head

16. In Sentinel High School, there are 350 freshmen, 320 sophomores, 310 juniors, and 400 seniors. If a student is chosen at random from the student body to represent the school, what is the probability that the chosen student is a freshman?

17. In each of the following, sketch a single spinner with the following characteristics:

a. The outcomes are *M, A, T,* and *H,* each with equally likely probability.

b. The outcomes are *R, A,* and *T* with $P(R) = 3/4$, $P(A) = 1/8$, and $P(T) = 1/8$.

18. In the game of "Between," two cards are dealt. You then pick a third card from the deck. To win, you must pick a card that has a value between the other two cards. The order of values is 2, 3, 4, 5, 6, 7, 8, 9, 10, J, Q, K, A, where the letters represent a jack, queen, king, and ace, respectively. Determine the probability of your winning if the first two cards dealt are the following:

a. 5 and a jack   **b.** 2 and a king

c. 5 and a 6

19. Calculators, watches, scoreboards, and many other devices display numbers using arrays like the following. The device lights up different parts of the array (any segment lettered *a* through *g*), to display any single digit 0 through 9. Suppose a digit is chosen at random. Determine the probability for each of the following. (*Hint:* Use a digital watch to see which segments are lit up for the different numbers.)

a. Segment *a* will be lit.

b. Segment *b* will be lit.

c. Segments *e* and *b* will be lit.

d. Segment *e* or *b* will be lit.

20. If A is the set of students taking algebra and C is the set of students taking chemistry at Central High School, describe in words what is meant by each of the following probabilities:
    a. $P(A \cup C)$ b. $P(A \cap C)$ c. $1 - P(C)$

21. If A and B are mutually exclusive and if $P(A) = 0.3$ and $P(B) = 0.4$, what is $P(A \cup B)$?

22. A calculus class is composed of 35 men and 45 women. There are 20 business majors, 30 biology majors, 10 computer science majors, and 20 mathematics majors. No person has a double major. If a single student is chosen from the class, what is the probability that the student is the following:
    a. Female
    b. A computer science major
    c. Not a mathematics major
    d. A computer science major or a mathematics major

23. A box contains 25% black balls and 75% white balls. The same number of black balls as was in the box is added (so the new number of black balls is twice the original number). A ball is now drawn from the box at random. What is the probability that it is black?

24. A box contains 5 white balls, 3 black balls, and 2 red balls.
    a. How many red balls must be added to the box so that the probability of drawing a red ball is 3/4?
    b. How many black balls must be added to the original box so that the probability of drawing a white ball is 1/4?

25. Suppose we have a box containing 5 white balls, 3 black balls, and 2 red balls. Is it possible to add the same number of each color balls to the box so that when a ball is drawn at random the probability that it is a black ball is the following (explain):
    a. $\frac{1}{3}$ b. 0.32

Communication

26. If events A and B are from the same sample space, and if $P(A) = 0.8$ and $P(B) = 0.9$, can events A and B be mutually exclusive? Explain.

27. Bobbie says that when she shoots a free throw in basketball, she will either make it or miss it. Because there are only two outcomes and one of them is making a basket, Bobbie claims the probability of her making a free throw is 1/2. Explain whether Bobbie's reasoning is correct.

28. If the following spinner is spun 100 times, Joe claims that the number 4 will occur most often because the greatest area of the spinner is covered by the number 4. What would you tell Joe about his conjecture? What is the probability that a 4 will occur on any spin?

29. José says that if a family has two children, then the only possibilities are two boys, two girls, or one boy and one girl. Because there are only three possibilities José claims the probability of having two boys is $\frac{1}{3}$. How would you respond to José?

Open-Ended

30. Select any book, go to the first complete paragraph in it, and count the number of words the paragraph has. Now count the number of words that start with a vowel. If the paragraph has fewer than 100 words, continue to count words until there are more than 100 words from where you started. What is the experimental probability that a word chosen at random from the book starts with a vowel? Open the book to any page and choose a paragraph with more than 100 words. Predict how many words will start with a vowel, and then count them to see how close you were.

31. List three real-world situations that do not involve weather or gambling where probability might be used.

32. For each of the following letters, describe an event, if possible, that has the approximate probability marked by a letter on the probability line:

Cooperative Learning

33. Form groups of three or four students. Each group has a pair of dice. Each player needs 18 markers and a sheet of paper with a gameboard drawn on it similar to the following:

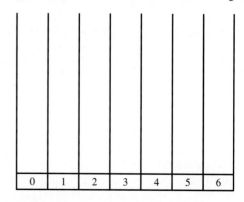

At the beginning of each game, each player places his or her markers on the boards in any arrangement above the numbers. Two players (or teams) then take turns rolling the dice. The result of each roll is the difference between the greater and the smaller of the two numbers. For example, if a 6 and a 4 were rolled, the difference would be $6 - 4$, or 2. All players who have a marker on the number that represents the difference can remove one marker. Only one marker can be removed each roll. The first player to remove all of his or her markers is the winner. The game may be stopped if it is clear that there can be no winner.

a. Play the game twice. What differences seem to occur most often? Least often?

b. Roll the dice 20 times and record how often the various differences occur. Using this information, explain how you would distribute your 18 markers to win.

c. Compute the theoretical probabilities for each possible difference.

d. Use your answers to (c) to explain how you would arrange the markers in order to win the game.

34. The following game is played with two players and a single fair die numbered 1 through 6. The die is rolled and one person receives a score that is the square of the number appearing on the die. The other person will receive a score of four times the value showing on the die. The person with the greatest score wins.

a. Play the game several times to see if it appears to be a *fair game,* that is, a game in which each player has an equal chance of winning.

b. Determine if this is a fair game. If it is not fair, who has the advantage? Explain how you arrived at your answer.

LABORATORY
A C T I V I T Y

1. Suppose a paper cup is tossed in the air. The different ways it can land are shown in Figure 7-7.

FIGURE 7-7

Top   Bottom   Side

Toss a cup 100 times and record each result. From this information, calculate the experimental probability of each outcome. Do the outcomes appear to be equally likely? Using experimental probabilities, predict how many times the cup will land on its side if tossed 100 times.

2. Toss a fair coin 100 times and record the results. From this information, calculate the experimental probability of getting heads on a particular toss. Does the experimental result agree with the expected theoretical probability of $\frac{1}{2}$?

3. Hold a coin upright on its edge under your forefinger on a hard surface and then spin it with your other finger so that it spins before landing. Repeat this experiment 100 times and calculate the experimental probability of the coin's landing on heads on a particular spin. Compare your experimental probabilities with those in activity 2.

Multistage Experiments with Tree Diagrams and Geometric Probabilities

In Section 7-1, we considered one-stage experiments, that is, experiments that were over after one step. For example, drawing one ball at random from the box containing a red, white, and green ball in Figure 7-8(a) is a one-stage experiment. A tree diagram for this experiment is shown in Figure 7-8(b).

FIGURE 7-8

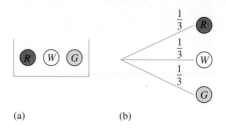

(a)   (b)

Next we consider a two-stage experiment. For example, a ball is drawn from the box in Figure 7-8(a) and its color is recorded. Then the ball is *replaced*, and a second ball is drawn and its color is recorded. A tree diagram for this experiment is given in Figure 7-9.

FIGURE 7-9

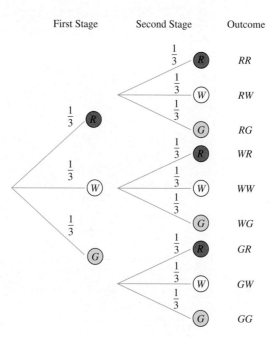

Notice that the tree diagram in Figure 7-9 can be used to generate the sample space. A sample space for this experiment may be written {*RR, RW, RG, WR, WW, WG, GR, GW, GG*}.

Each of the outcomes in the sample space is equally likely and there are nine total outcomes, so the probability of each outcome is 1/9.

An alternative way to generate the sample space is to use a Second Draw table, as shown in Figure 7-10.

FIGURE 7-10

Second Draw

		R	W	G
	R	RR	RW	RG
First Draw	W	WR	WW	WG
	G	GR	GW	GG

NOW TRY THIS 7-2

1. For each of the following use the tree diagram in Figure 7-9 to determine the probability that
   a. both balls are red.
   b. no ball is red.
   c. at least one ball is red.
   d. at most one ball is red.
   e. both balls are the same color.
2. Answer each part of question 1 using the table in Figure 7-10.

The box in Figure 7-11(a) contains one colored ball and two white balls. If a ball is drawn at random and the color recorded, a tree diagram for the experiment might look like the one in Figure 7-11(b). Because each ball has the same chance of being drawn, we may combine the branches and obtain the tree diagram shown in Figure 7-11(c). Combining branches in this way is a common practice because it simplifies tree diagrams.

FIGURE 7-11

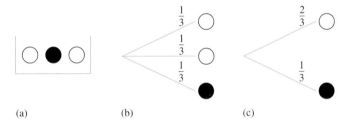

(a) (b) (c)

Suppose a ball is drawn at random from the box in Figure 7-11(a) and its color recorded. The ball is then *replaced*, and a second ball is drawn and its color recorded. The sample space for this two-stage experiment may be recorded using ordered pairs as $\{(\bullet, \bullet), (\bullet, \bigcirc), (\bigcirc, \bullet), (\bigcirc, \bigcirc)\}$ or, more commonly, as $\{\bullet\bullet, \bullet\bigcirc, \bigcirc\bullet, \bigcirc\bigcirc\}$, as shown in the tree diagram in Figure 7-12.

FIGURE 7-12

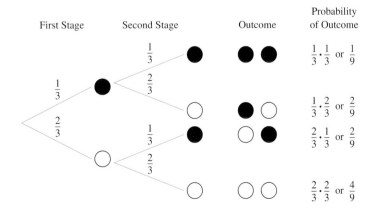

To assign the probability of the outcomes in this experiment, consider, for example, the path for the outcome ● ○. In the first stage, the probability of obtaining a colored ball is $\frac{1}{3}$. Then, the probability of obtaining a white ball in the second stage (second draw) is $\frac{2}{3}$. Thus we expect to obtain a colored ball on the first draw $\frac{1}{3}$ of the time and then on the second draw, to obtain a white ball $\frac{2}{3}$ of those times that we obtained a colored ball on the first draw, that is, $\frac{2}{3}$ of $\frac{1}{3}$, or $\frac{2}{3} \cdot \frac{1}{3}$. Observe that this product can be obtained by multiplying the probabilities along the branches used for the path leading to ● ○, that is, $\frac{1}{3} \cdot \frac{2}{3}$, or $\frac{2}{9}$.

The probabilities shown in Figure 7-12 are obtained by following the paths leading to each of the four outcomes and multiplying the probabilities along the paths. This procedure is an instance of the following general property.

▶ Property: Multiplication Rule for Probabilities for Tree Diagrams

For all multistage experiments, the probability of the outcome along any path of a tree diagram is equal to the product of all the probabilities along the path.

REMARK   The sum of the probabilities on all the branches from any point always equals 1, and the sum of the probabilities for the possible outcomes must also be 1.

Look again at the box pictured in Figure 7-11(a). This time, suppose two balls are drawn one by one *without replacement*. A tree diagram for this experiment, along with the set of possible outcomes, is shown in Figure 7-13. Compare this figure to the one in Figure 7-12. How are they different?

FIGURE 7-13

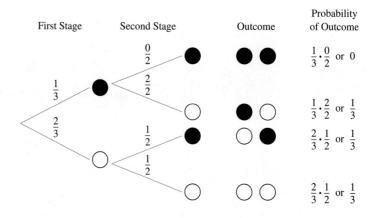

The denominators of the fractions along the second stage are all 2. Because the draws are made without replacement, only two balls remain for the second draw.

Consider event A, consisting of the outcomes for drawing exactly one colored ball in the two draws without replacement. This event is given by $A = \{\bullet \bigcirc, \bigcirc \bullet\}$. Since the outcome $\bullet \bigcirc$ appears $\frac{1}{3}$ of the time, and the outcome $\bigcirc \bullet$ appears $\frac{1}{3}$ of the time, then either $\bullet \bigcirc$ or $\bigcirc \bullet$ will appear $\frac{2}{3}$ of the time. Thus $P(A) = \frac{1}{3} + \frac{1}{3} = \frac{2}{3}$.

Event B, consisting of outcomes for drawing *at least* one colored ball, could be recorded as $B = \{\bullet \bigcirc, \bigcirc \bullet, \bullet \bullet\}$. Because $P(\bullet \bigcirc) = \frac{1}{3}, P(\bigcirc \bullet) = \frac{1}{3}$, and $P(\bullet \bullet) = 0$, then $P(B) = \frac{1}{3} + \frac{1}{3} + 0 = \frac{2}{3}$. Because $\overline{B} = \{\bigcirc \bigcirc\}$ and $P(\overline{B}) = \frac{1}{3}$, the probability of B could have been computed as follows: $P(B) = 1 - P(\overline{B}) = 1 - \frac{1}{3} = \frac{2}{3}$.

Independent Events

independent

In Figure 7-13, the fact that the first ball was not replaced affects the probability of the color of the second ball drawn. When the outcome of one event has no influence on the outcome of a second event, the events are **independent**. For example, if two coins are flipped and event E_1 is obtaining a head on the first coin and E_2 is obtaining a tail on the second coin, then E_1 and E_2 are independent events because one event has no influence on the second. Notice that $P(E_1) = \frac{1}{2}$, $P(E_2) = \frac{1}{2}$, and $P(E_1 \cap E_2) = \frac{1}{4}$. So in this case, $P(E_1 \cap E_2) = P(E_1) \cdot P(E_2)$.

Next, consider two boxes: box 1 contains 2 white and 2 black balls, and box 2 contains 2 white balls and 3 black balls. Let B_1 be the event of drawing a black ball from box 1 and B_2 the event of drawing a black ball from box 2. Notice that the events are independent. Suppose a ball is drawn from each box and we are interested in the probability that each ball is black; that is, $P(B_1 \cap B_2)$. We know that $P(B_1) = \frac{2}{4}$ and $P(B_2) = \frac{3}{5}$. Is $P(B_1 \cap B_2) = P(B_1) \cdot P(B_2)$ in this case as well? We can answer this question by computing $P(B_1 \cap B_2)$ using a familiar approach. If we consider all the black balls to be different and all the white balls to be different, there are $4 \cdot 5$ different pairs of balls. (Why?) Among these pairs, we are interested in pairs consisting only of black balls. There are $2 \cdot 3$ such pairs. (Why?) Hence,

$$P(B_1 \cap B_2) = \frac{2 \cdot 3}{4 \cdot 5} = \frac{2}{4} \cdot \frac{3}{5} = \frac{1}{2} \cdot \frac{3}{5}.$$

Thus we see that for the above independent events B_1 and B_2, we have $P(B_1 \cap B_2) = P(B_1) \cdot P(B_2)$. The property can be generalized as follows:

> ## Property

For any independent events E_1 and E_2,
$$P(E_1 \cap E_2) = P(E_1) \cdot P(E_2).$$

The student page gives examples of problems that involve independent events. Answer questions 2 through 9 on the following student page.

Sample School Book Page:
INDEPENDENT EVENTS

12-7 Exercises and Applications

Practice and Apply

1. **Getting Started** Five red cubes and five green cubes are in a bag. Follow the steps to find *P*(green, green)—the probability that you pull two green cubes out of the bag in a row.

   a. What is the probability that the first cube taken from the bag is green?

   b. After a green cube is taken out of the bag, how many green cubes are left? How many cubes are left all together?

   c. What is the probability that the second cube taken from the bag is green?

   d. Find the product of your answers from **a** and **c**. Write your answer in lowest terms.

Tell whether the events are dependent or independent.

2. One tossed coin landing heads and the next landing tails

3. Rolling two sixes in a row on a number cube

4. Being the tallest person in your class one year, then being the tallest again the next year

Exercises 5–7 refer to rolling a number cube, then spinning the spinner shown. Find each probability.

5. *P*(rolling a 2, spinning an A)

6. *P*(rolling an even number, spinning a vowel)

7. *P*(rolling a number less than 3, spinning a consonant)

8. **Social Studies** During Hanukkah, children play with a *dreidel*. The dreidel has four sides, with the Hebrew letters that correspond to the letters N, G, S, and H. The children spin the dreidel like a top, and the letter that comes up determines the result for each turn.

   a. Are the spins of a dreidel dependent or independent events?

   b. What is the probability of spinning 2 Hs in a row?

9. **Science** Suppose the weather report says there is a 25% chance of rain for the next two days.

   a. If the events are independent, what is the probability that it rains *both* days?

   b. Do you think these events are actually independent? Explain why or why not.

Source: Scott Foresman–Addison Wesley Middle School Math Course 2, 2002 (p. 662).

NOW TRY THIS 7-3

In the cartoon below, assume that the events are independent and that there is a 30% chance of rain tonight and a 60% chance of rain tomorrow.

a. What is the probability that it will rain both times?
b. What is the probability that it will not rain either of the times?
c. What is the probability that it will rain exactly one of the times?
d. What is the probability that it will rain at least one of the times?
e. In real life, do you think that the events of rain tonight and rain tomorrow are independent events? Why or why not?

WIZARD OF ID

ELEVEN O'CLOCK AND TIME FOR THE NEWS

THERE IS A 30% CHANCE OF RAIN TONIGHT...

...A 60% CHANCE OF RAIN TOMORROW...

...AND A 90% CHANCE I'M WRONG ON BOTH COUNTS!

EXAMPLE 7-8

Figure 7-14 shows a box with eleven letters. Some letters are repeated. Suppose four letters are drawn at random from the box one by one without replacement. What is the probability of the outcome *BABY*, with the letters chosen in exactly the order given?

FIGURE 7-14

PROBABILITY

Solution We do not need the entire tree diagram to find this probability because we are interested in only the branch leading to the outcome *BABY*. The portion needed is shown in Figure 7-15.

FIGURE 7-15

Probability of Outcome

$$\xrightarrow{\frac{2}{11}} B \xrightarrow{\frac{1}{10}} A \xrightarrow{\frac{1}{9}} B \xrightarrow{\frac{1}{8}} Y \qquad \frac{2}{11} \cdot \frac{1}{10} \cdot \frac{1}{9} \cdot \frac{1}{8} = \frac{2}{7920}$$

The probability of the first B is $\frac{2}{11}$ because there are 2 B's out of 11 letters. The probability of the second B is $\frac{1}{9}$ because there are nine letters left after 1 B and 1 A have been chosen. Then, $P(BABY)$ is $\frac{2}{7920}$, as shown.

In Example 7-8, suppose four letters are drawn one by one from the box and the letters are replaced after each drawing. In this case, the branch needed to find $P(BABY)$ in the order drawn is pictured in Figure 7-16. Then $P(BABY) = \left(\dfrac{2}{11}\right) \cdot \left(\dfrac{1}{11}\right) \cdot \left(\dfrac{2}{11}\right) \cdot \left(\dfrac{1}{11}\right)$, or $\dfrac{4}{14,641}$.

FIGURE 7-16

Probability of Outcome

$$\xrightarrow{\frac{2}{11}} B \xrightarrow{\frac{1}{11}} A \xrightarrow{\frac{2}{11}} B \xrightarrow{\frac{1}{11}} Y \qquad \frac{2}{11} \cdot \frac{1}{11} \cdot \frac{2}{11} \cdot \frac{1}{11} \text{ or } \frac{4}{14,641}$$

EXAMPLE 7-9

Consider the three boxes in Figure 7-17. A letter is drawn from box 1 and placed in box 2. Then, a letter is drawn from box 2 and placed in box 3. Finally, a letter is drawn from box 3. What is the probability that the letter drawn from box 3 is B?

FIGURE 7-17

AAB	AB	ABBB
1	2	3

Solution   A tree diagram for this experiment is given in Figure 7-18. Notice that the denominators in the second stage are 3 rather than 2 because in this stage, there are now three letters in box 2. The denominators in the third stage are 5 because in this stage, there are five letters in box 3. To find the probability that a B is drawn from box 3, add the probabilities for the outcomes AAB, ABB, BAB, and BBB that make up this event.

FIGURE 7-18

First Stage	Second Stage	Third Stage	Outcome	Probability of Outcome
$\frac{2}{3}$ A	$\frac{2}{3}$ A	$\frac{2}{5}$ A	AAA	$\frac{2}{3} \cdot \frac{2}{3} \cdot \frac{2}{5}$ or $\frac{8}{45}$
		$\frac{3}{5}$ B	AAB	$\frac{2}{3} \cdot \frac{2}{3} \cdot \frac{3}{5}$ or $\frac{12}{45}$
	$\frac{1}{3}$ B	$\frac{1}{5}$ A	ABA	$\frac{2}{3} \cdot \frac{1}{3} \cdot \frac{1}{5}$ or $\frac{2}{45}$
		$\frac{4}{5}$ B	ABB	$\frac{2}{3} \cdot \frac{1}{3} \cdot \frac{4}{5}$ or $\frac{8}{45}$
$\frac{1}{3}$ B	$\frac{1}{3}$ A	$\frac{2}{5}$ A	BAA	$\frac{1}{3} \cdot \frac{1}{3} \cdot \frac{2}{5}$ or $\frac{2}{45}$
		$\frac{3}{5}$ B	BAB	$\frac{1}{3} \cdot \frac{1}{3} \cdot \frac{3}{5}$ or $\frac{3}{45}$
	$\frac{2}{3}$ B	$\frac{1}{5}$ A	BBA	$\frac{1}{3} \cdot \frac{2}{3} \cdot \frac{1}{5}$ or $\frac{2}{45}$
		$\frac{4}{5}$ B	BBB	$\frac{1}{3} \cdot \frac{2}{3} \cdot \frac{4}{5}$ or $\frac{8}{45}$

Thus the probability of obtaining a B on the draw from box 3 in this experiment is

$$\frac{12}{45} + \frac{8}{45} + \frac{3}{45} + \frac{8}{45} = \frac{31}{45}.$$

NOW TRY THIS 7-4

Suppose that in Example 7-9, it is known that the letter *A* was drawn on the first draw. What is the probability that

a. the last letter drawn is a *B*?

b. the last letter drawn is an *A*?

c. the last 2 letters drawn will match, that is, 2 *A*'s or 2 *B*'s?

Modeling Games

We can use models to analyze games that involve probability. Consider the following game, which Arthur and Guinevere play: There are two colored marbles and one white marble in a box. Guinevere mixes the marbles, and Arthur draws two marbles at random without replacement. If the two marbles match, Arthur wins; otherwise, Guinevere wins. Does each player have an equal chance of winning? We *develop a model* to analyze the game. One possible model is a tree diagram, as shown in Figure 7-19(a). Because the outcome ○ ○ can't happen, the tree diagram could also be shortened as in Figure 7-19(b).

FIGURE 7-19

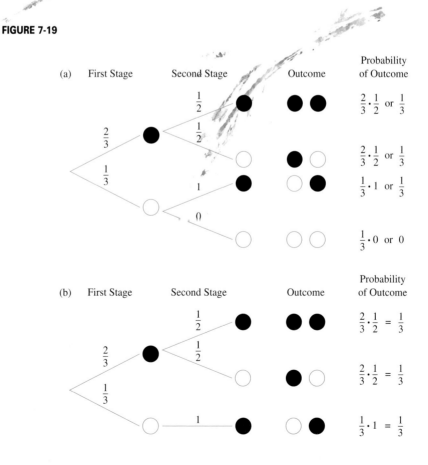

The probability that the marbles are the same color is $\frac{1}{3} + 0$, or $\frac{1}{3}$, and the probability that they are not the same color is $\frac{1}{3} + \frac{1}{3}$, or $\frac{2}{3}$. Because $\frac{1}{3} \neq \frac{2}{3}$, the players do not have the same chance of winning.

An alternative model for analyzing this game is given in Figure 7-20, where the colored and white marbles are shown along with the possible ways of drawing two marbles. Each line segment in the diagram represents one pair of marbles that could be drawn. S indicates that the marbles in the pair are the same color, and D indicates that the marbles are different colors. Because there are two D's in Figure 7-20, we see that the probability of drawing two different-colored marbles is $\frac{2}{3}$. Likewise, the probability of drawing two marbles of the same color is $\frac{1}{3}$. Because $\frac{2}{3} \neq \frac{1}{3}$, the players do not have an equal chance of winning.

Will adding another white marble give each player an equal chance of winning? With two white and two colored marbles, we have the model in Figure 7-21. Therefore $P(D) = \frac{4}{6}$, or $\frac{2}{3}$, and $P(S) = \frac{2}{6}$, or $\frac{1}{3}$. We see that adding a white marble does not change the probabilities.

FIGURE 7-20

FIGURE 7-21

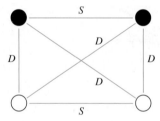

Next, consider a game with the same rules but using three colored marbles and one white marble. Figure 7-22 shows a model for this situation.

FIGURE 7-22

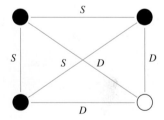

Thus the probability of drawing two marbles of the same color is $\frac{3}{6}$, and the probability of drawing two marbles of different colors is $\frac{3}{6}$. Finally, we have a game in which each player has an equal chance of winning.

NOW TRY THIS 7-5

Referring to the games described on the previous page, answer the following:

a. Does each player have an equal chance of winning if only one white marble and one colored marble are used and the marble is replaced after the first draw?

b. Find games that involve different numbers of marbles in which each player has an equal chance of winning.

c. Find a pattern for the numbers of colored and white marbles that allow each player to have an equal chance of winning.

PROBLEM SOLVING   ### A String-Tying Game

In a party game, a child is handed six strings, as shown in Figure 7-23(a). Another child ties the top ends two at a time, forming three separate knots, and the bottom ends, forming three separate knots, as in Figure 7-23(b). If the strings form one closed ring, as in Figure 7-23(c), the child tying the knots wins a prize. What is the probability that the child wins a prize on the first try? Guess the probability before working the problem.

FIGURE 7-23

(a)   (b)   (c)

Understanding the Problem   The problem is to determine the probability that one closed ring will be formed. One closed ring means that all six pieces are joined end to end to form one, and only one, ring, as shown in Figure 7-23(c).

Devising a Plan   Figure 7-24(a) shows what happens when the ends of the strings of one set are tied in pairs at the top. Notice that no matter in what order those ends are tied, the result appears as in Figure 7-24(a).

FIGURE 7-24

(a)   (b)   (c)

Then, the other ends are tied in a three-stage experiment. If we pick any string in the first stage, then there are five choices for its mate. Four of these choices are favorable choices for forming a ring. (Why?) Thus the probability of forming a favorable first tie is $\frac{4}{5}$. Figure 7-24(b) shows a favorable tie at the first stage.

For any one of the remaining four strings, there are three choices for its mate. Two of these choices are favorable ones. (Why?) Thus the probability of forming a favorable second tie is $\frac{2}{3}$. Figure 7-24(c) shows a favorable tie at the second stage.

Now, two ends remain. Since nothing can go wrong at the third stage, the probability of making a favorable tie is 1. If we use the probabilities completed at each stage and a single branch of a tree diagram, we can calculate the probability of performing three successful ties in a row and hence the probability of forming one closed ring.

Carrying Out the Plan   If we let S represent a successful tie at each stage, then the branch of the tree with which we are concerned is the one shown in Figure 7-25.

FIGURE 7-25

First Tie   Second Tie   Third Tie

$$\xrightarrow{\frac{4}{5}} S \xrightarrow{\frac{2}{3}} S \xrightarrow{\frac{1}{1}} S$$

Thus the probability of forming one ring is $P(\text{ring}) = \frac{4}{5} \cdot \frac{2}{3} \cdot \frac{1}{1} = \frac{8}{13} = 0.5\overline{3}.$

Looking Back   The probability that a child will form a ring on the first try is $\frac{8}{15}$. A class might simulate this problem several times with strings to see how the fraction of successes compares with the theoretical probability of $\frac{8}{15}$.

Related problems that could be posed for solution include the following:

1. If a child fails to get a ring 10 times in a row, the child may not play again. What is the probability of such a streak of bad luck?
2. If the number of strings is reduced to three and the rule is that an upper end must be tied to a lower end, what is the probability of a single ring?
3. If the number of strings is three, but an upper end can be tied to either an upper or a lower end, what is the probability of a single ring?
4. What is the probability of forming three rings in the original problem?
5. What is the probability of forming two rings in the original problem?   ▨

FIGURE 7-26

Geometric Probability (Area Models)

A probability model that uses geometric shapes is called an *area model*. When area models are used to determine probabilities geometrically, outcomes are associated with points chosen at random in a geometric region that represents the sample space. For example, suppose we throw darts at a square target 2 units long on a side and divided into four congruent triangles, as shown in Figure 7-26. If the dart must hit the target somewhere and if all spots can be hit with equal probability, what is the probability that the dart will land in the shaded region? The entire target, which has an area of 4 square units, represents the sample space. The shaded area is the event of a successful toss. The area of the shaded part is $\frac{1}{4}$ of the sample space. Thus the probability of the dart's landing in the shaded region is the ratio of the area of the event to the area of the sample space, or $\frac{1}{4}$.

Another example of a geometric probability is given on the student page. The following problem is solved by using both tree diagrams and an area model.

Sample School Book Page:
GEOMETRIC PROBABILITY

Geometric Models of Probability

You Will Learn

■ to calculate probability from geometric models

Did You Know?

The Coast Guard uses probability when describing the chances of locating a particular ship lost at sea.

Learn •

Suppose you are going to play a game. You must decide which spinner has the better chance of landing on "Move ahead 2 spaces."

Even though the sections are not the same size, you can still determine the probability of landing on "Move ahead 2 spaces" for each spinner.

A   B

☐ Move ahead 2 spaces
▨ Go back 1 space

One Way

Spin each spinner 20 times and record the results in a table.

The probability of landing on "Move ahead 2 spaces" is $\frac{9}{20}$ for Spinner A and $\frac{13}{20}$ for Spinner B.

Spinner B is the better spinner to use.

Spinner	Move Ahead	Go Back
A	卌 IIII	卌 卌 I
B	卌 卌 III	卌 II

Remember, though, probability calculated from sample data is only an estimate.

Another Way

Find out the total area of each spinner covered by sections marked "Move ahead 2 spaces."

Spinner A: Spinner B:

$\frac{1}{8}+\frac{1}{8}+\frac{1}{4}=\frac{1}{8}+\frac{1}{8}+\frac{2}{8}=\frac{4}{8}=\frac{1}{2}$ $\frac{1}{5}+\frac{1}{5}+\frac{1}{5}=\frac{3}{5}$

There is a better chance on landing on "Move ahead 2 spaces" on Spinner B.

Source: Scott Foresman–Addison Wesley MATH, Grade 6, 2002 (p. 634).

A Quiz-Show Game

On a quiz show, a contestant stands at the entrance to a maze that opens into two rooms labeled A and B in Figure 7-27. The master of ceremonies' assistant is to place a new car in one room and a donkey in the other. The contestant must walk through the maze into one of the rooms and will win whatever is in that room. If the contestant makes each decision in the maze at random, in which room should the assistant place the car to give the contestant the best chance to win?

FIGURE 7-27

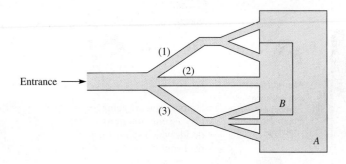

Understanding the Problem   The contestant must first choose one of the paths marked 1, 2, or 3 and then choose other paths as she proceeds through the maze. To determine the room the contestant is most likely to choose, the assistant must be able to determine the probability of the contestant's reaching each room.

■   **Devising a Plan**   One way to determine where the car should be placed is to *model the choices with a tree diagram* and to compute the probabilities along the branches of the tree.

Carrying Out the Plan   A tree diagram for the maze is shown in Figure 7-28, along with the possible outcomes and the probabilities of each branch.

FIGURE 7-28

	Outcome	Probability of Outcome
$\frac{1}{3}$ 1 $\frac{1}{2}$ A	1A	$\frac{1}{3} \cdot \frac{1}{2}$ or $\frac{1}{6}$
$\frac{1}{2}$ B	1B	$\frac{1}{3} \cdot \frac{1}{2}$ or $\frac{1}{6}$
$\frac{1}{3}$ 2 0 A	2A	$\frac{1}{3} \cdot 0$ or 0
1 B	2B	$\frac{1}{3} \cdot 1$ or $\frac{1}{3}$
$\frac{1}{3}$ 3 $\frac{2}{3}$ A	3A	$\frac{1}{3} \cdot \frac{2}{3}$ or $\frac{2}{9}$
$\frac{1}{3}$ B	3B	$\frac{1}{3} \cdot \frac{1}{3}$ or $\frac{1}{9}$

The probability that room A is chosen is $\frac{1}{6} + 0 + \frac{2}{9} = \frac{7}{18}$. Hence the probability that room B is chosen is $1 - \frac{7}{18} = \frac{11}{18}$. Thus room B has the greater probability of being chosen. This is where the car should be placed for the contestant to have the best chance of winning it.

Looking Back An alternative model for this problem and for many probability problems is an area model. The rectangle in Figure 7-29(a) represents the first three choices that the contestant can make. Because each choice is equally likely, each is represented by an equal area. If the contestant chooses the upper path, then rooms *A* and *B* have an equal chance of being chosen. If she chooses the middle path, then only room *B* can be entered. If she chooses the lower path, then room *A* is entered $\frac{2}{3}$ of the time. This can be expressed in terms of the area model shown in Figure 7-29(b). Dividing the rectangle into pieces of equal area, we obtain the model in Figure 7-29(c), in which the area representing room *B* is shaded. Because the area representing room *B* is greater than the area representing room *A*, room *B* has the greater probability of being chosen. Figure 7-29(c) can enable us to find the probability of choosing room *B*. Because the shaded area consists of 11 rectangles out of a total of 18 rectangles, the probability of choosing room *B* is $\frac{11}{18}$. We can vary the problem by changing the maze or by changing the locations of the rooms.

FIGURE 7-29

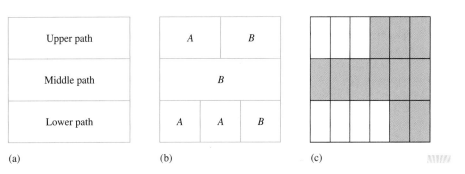

(a) (b) (c)

O N G O I N G   A S S E S S M E N T   7 - 2

1. **a.** A box contains 3 white balls and 2 red balls. A ball is drawn at random from the box and not replaced. Then a second ball is drawn from the box. Draw a tree diagram for this experiment and find the probability that the two balls are of different colors.

   b. Suppose that a ball is drawn at random from the box in part (a), its color is recorded, and then it is put back in the box. Draw a tree diagram for this experiment and find the probability that the two balls are of different colors.

2. Suppose an experiment consists of spinning *X* and then spinning *Y*, as follows:

Find the following:
   a. The sample space *S* for the experiment
   b. The event *A* consisting of outcomes from spinning an even number followed by an even number
   c. The event *B* consisting of outcomes from spinning at least one 2
   d. The event *C* consisting of outcomes from spinning exactly one 2

3. A box contains six letters, shown as follows. What is the probability of the outcome *DAN* in that order if three letters are drawn one by one
   a. with replacement?
   b. without replacement?

   | RANDOM |

4. Following are three boxes containing letters:

   | MATH | | AND | | HISTORY |
   | 1 | | 2 | | 3 |

   a. From box 1, three letters are drawn one by one without replacement and recorded in order. What is the probability that the outcome is *HAT*?
   b. From box 1, three letters are drawn one by one with replacement and recorded in order. What is the probability that the outcome is *HAT*?
   c. One letter is drawn at random from box 1, then another from box 2, and then another from box 3, with the results recorded in order. What is the probability that the outcome is *HAT*?
   d. If a box is chosen at random and then a letter is drawn at random from the box, what is the probability that the outcome is A?

5. An executive committee consisted of 10 members: four women and six men. Three members were selected at random to be sent to a meeting in Hawaii. A blindfolded woman drew three of the 10 names from a hat. All three names drawn were women's. What was the probability of such luck?

6. Two boxes with letters follow. You are to choose a box and draw three letters at random, one by one, without replacement. If the outcome is SOS, you win a prize.

   | SOS | | SOSSOS |
   | 1 | | 2 |

   a. Which box should you choose?
   b. Which box would you choose if the letters are to be drawn with replacement?

7. Following are three boxes containing balls. Draw a ball from box 1 and place it in box 2. Then draw a ball from box 2 and place it in box 3. Finally, draw a ball from box 3.

   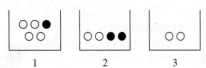

   a. What is the probability that the last ball, drawn from box 3, is white?
   b. What is the probability that the last ball drawn is colored?

8. An assembly line has two inspectors. The probability that the first inspector will miss a defective item is 0.05. If the defective item passes the first inspector, the probability that the second inspector will miss it is 0.01. What is the probability that a defective item will pass by both inspectors?

9. Following are two boxes containing colored and white balls. A ball is drawn at random from box 1. Then a ball is drawn at random from box 2, and the colors of balls from both boxes are recorded in order.

   Find each of the following:
   a. The probability of two white balls
   b. The probability of at least one colored ball
   c. The probability of at most one colored ball
   d. The probability of ● ○ or ○ ●

10. A penny, a nickel, a dime, and a quarter are tossed. What is the probability of obtaining at least three heads?

11. Assume the probability is $\frac{1}{2}$ that a child born is a boy.

    What is the probability that if a family is going to have four children, they will all be boys?

12. Brittany is going to ascend a four-step staircase. At any time, she is just as likely to stride up one step or two steps. Find the probability that she will ascend the four steps in
    a. two strides.   b. three strides.   c. four strides.

13. A box contains five slips of paper. Each slip has one of the numbers 4, 6, 7, 8, or 9 written on it. There are two players for the game. The first player reaches into the box and draws two slips and adds the two numbers. If the sum is even, the player wins. If the sum is odd, the player loses.
    a. What is the probability that the first player wins?
    b. Does the probability change if the two numbers are multiplied? Explain.

14. Suppose we spin the following spinner with the first spin giving the numerator and the second spin giving the denominator of a fraction. What is the probability that the fraction will be greater than 1 1/2?

15. The following shows the numbers of symbols on each of the three dials of a standard slot machine:

Symbol	Dial 1	Dial 2	Dial 3
Bar	1	3	1
Bell	1	3	3
Plum	5	1	5
Orange	3	6	7
Cherry	7	7	0
Lemon	3	0	4
Total	20	20	20

Find the probability for each of the following:

a. Three plums   **b.** Three oranges

c. Three lemons   **d.** No plums

16. You play a game in which you first choose one of the two spinners shown below. You then spin your spinner and a second person spins the other spinner. The one with the greater number wins.

 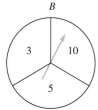

a. Which spinner should you choose? Why?

b. Notice that the sum of the numbers on each spinner is 18. Design two spinners with unequal sums so that choosing the spinner with the least sum will give the player a greater probability of winning.

17. An experiment consists of spinning the spinner shown below and then flipping a coin with sides numbered 1 and 2.

What is the probability that

a. the number on the spinner will be greater than the number on the coin?

b. the outcome will consist of two consecutive integers in any order?

18. If a person takes a five-question true-false test, what is the probability that the score is 100% correct if the person guesses on every question?

19. Rattlesnake and Paxson Colleges play four games against each other in a chess tournament. Rob Fisher, the chess whiz from Paxson, withdrew from the tournament, so the probabilities that Rattlesnake and Paxson will win each game are $\frac{2}{3}$ and $\frac{1}{3}$, respectively. Determine the following probabilities:

a. Paxson loses all four games.

b. The match is a draw with each school winning two games.

20. The combinations on the lockers at the high school consist of three numbers, each ranging from 0 to 39. If a combination is chosen at random, what is the probability that the first two numbers are multiples of 9 and the third number is a multiple of 4?

21. The following box contains the 11 letters shown. The letters are drawn one by one without replacement, and the results are recorded in order. Find the probability of the outcome MISSISSIPPI.

$$\boxed{\text{MIIIIPPSSSS}}$$

22. Consider the following dart board: (Assume that all quadrilaterals are squares and that the x's represent equal measures.)

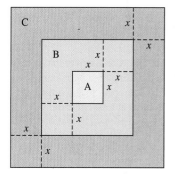

If a dart may hit any point on the board with equal probability, what is the probability that it will land in

a. section A?   **b.** section B?   c. section C?

23. In the following square dart board, suppose a dart is equally likely to land in any region of the board.

Points are given as follows:

Region	Points
A	10
B	8
C	6
D	4
E	2

a. What is the total area of the board?
b. What is the probability of a dart's landing in each region of the board?
c. If two darts are tossed, what is the probability of scoring 20 points?
d. What is the probability that the dart will land in neither *D* nor *E*?

24. The land area of Earth is approximately 57,500,000 mi². The water area of Earth is approximately 139,600,000 mi². If a meteor lands at random on the planet, what is the probability, to the nearest tenth, that it will hit water?

25. An electric clock is stopped by a power failure. What is the probability that the second hand is stopped between the 3 and the 4?

26. A husband and wife discover that there is a 10% probability of their passing on a hereditary disease to one of their children. If they plan to have three children, what is the probability that at least one child will inherit the disease?

27. Let $A = \{x \mid ^-1 < x < 1\}$ and $B = \{x \mid ^-3 < x < 2\}$. If a real number is picked at random from set *B*, what is the probability it will be in set *A*?

28. At a certain hospital, 40 patients have lung cancer, 30 patients smoke, and 25 have lung cancer and smoke. Suppose the hospital contains 200 patients. If a patient chosen at random is known to smoke, what is the probability that the patient has lung cancer?

29. There are 40 employees in a certain firm. We know that 28 of these employees are males, 2 of these males are secretaries, and 10 secretaries are employed by the firm. What is the probability that an employee chosen at random is a secretary, given that the person is a male?

30. In a certain population of caribou, the probability of an animal's being sickly is $\frac{1}{20}$. If a caribou is sickly, the probability of its being eaten by wolves is $\frac{1}{3}$. If a caribou is not sickly, the probability of its being eaten by wolves is $\frac{1}{150}$. If a caribou is chosen at random from the herd, what is the probability that it will be eaten by wolves?

31. Four blue socks, 4 white socks, and 4 gray socks are mixed in a drawer. You pull out two socks, one at a time, without looking.
a. Draw a tree diagram along with the possible outcomes and the probabilities of each branch.
b. What is the probability of getting a pair of socks of the same color?

c. What is the probability of getting two gray socks?
d. Suppose that, instead of pulling out two socks, you pull out 4 socks. What is now the probability of getting two socks of the same color?

32. Solve the Quiz-Show Game in this section by replacing Figure 7-27 with the following maze:

★ 33. Carolyn will win a large prize if she wins two tennis games in a row out of three games. She is to play alternately against Billie and Bobby. She may choose to play Billie-Bobby-Billie or Bobby-Billie-Bobby. She wins against Billie 50% of the time and against Bobby 80% of the time. Which alternative should she choose, and why?

★ 34. Jane has two tennis serves, a hard serve and a soft serve. Her hard serve is in (a good serve) 50% of the time, and her soft serve is in (good) 75% of the time. If her hard serve is in, she wins 75% of her points. If her soft serve is in, she wins 50% of her points. Since she is allowed to re-serve one time if her first serve is out, what should her serving strategy be? That is, should she serve hard followed by soft; both hard; soft followed by hard; or both soft?

Communication

35. Jim rolled a fair die three times and obtained a 3 every time. He concluded that on the next roll, a 3 is more likely to occur than the other numbers. Explain whether this is true.

36. A witness to a crime observed that the criminal had blond hair and blue eyes and drove a red car. When the police look for a suspect, is the probability greater that they will find someone with blond hair and blue eyes or that they will find someone with blond hair and blue eyes who drives a red car? Explain your answer.

37. You are given 3 white balls, 1 red ball, and 2 identical boxes. You are asked to distribute the balls in the boxes in any way you like. You then are asked to select a box (after the boxes have been shuffled) and to pick a ball at random from that box. If the ball is red, you win a prize. How should you distribute the balls in the boxes to maximize your chances of winning? Justify your reasoning.

Open-Ended

38. Make up a game in which the players have an equal chance of winning and that involves rolling two regular dice.

39. How can the faces of two cubes be numbered so that when they are rolled, the resulting sum is a number 1 to 12 inclusive and each sum has the same probability?

40. Use graph paper to design a dart board such that the probability of hitting a certain part of the board is $\frac{3}{5}$. Explain your reasoning.

Cooperative Learning

41. Play the following game in pairs. One player chooses one of four equally likely outcomes from the sample space {*HH, HT, TH, TT*}, obtained by tossing a fair coin twice. The other player then chooses one of the other outcomes. A coin is flipped until either player's choice appears. For example, the first player chooses *TT* and the second player chooses *HT*. If the first two flips yield *TH*, then no one wins and the game continues. If, after five flips, the string *THHHT* appears, the second player is the winner because the sequence *HT* finally appeared. Play the game 10 times. Does each player appear to have the same chance of winning? Analyze the game for the case in which the first player chooses *TT* and the second *HT*, and explain whether the game is fair. (*Hint:* Find the probability that the first player wins the game by showing that the first player will win if and only if "tails" appears on the first and on the second flip.)

42. Consider the three spinners *A, B,* and *C* shown in the following figure:

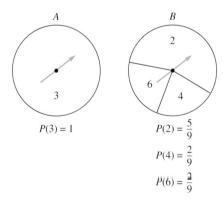

$P(3) = 1$

$P(2) = \frac{5}{9}$

$P(4) = \frac{2}{9}$

$P(6) = \frac{2}{9}$

$P(1) = \frac{6}{11}$

$P(5) = \frac{5}{11}$

a. Suppose there are only two players and that the first player chooses a spinner and then the second player chooses a different spinner and each person spins his or her spinner with the highest number winning. Play the game several times to get a feeling for it. Determine if each player appears to have the same chances of winning the game. If not, which spinner should you choose in order to win?

b. This time play the same game with three players. If each player must choose a different spinner, is the winning strategy the same as it was in (a)? Why or why not?

Review Problems

43. Match the following phrase to the probability that describes it:

 a. A certain event   (i) $\frac{1}{1000}$

 b. An impossible event   (ii) $\frac{999}{1000}$

 c. A very likely event   (iii) 0

 d. An unlikely event   (iv) $\frac{1}{2}$

 e. A 50% chance   (v) 1

44. A date in the month of April is chosen at random. Find the probability of the date's being each of the following:
 a. April 7
 b. April 31
 c. Before April 20

<u>BRAIN</u>
T E A S E R

Bradley Efron, a Stanford University statistician, designed a set of nonstandard dice whose faces are numbered as shown in Figure 7-30. The dice are to be used in a game in which each player chooses a die and then rolls it. Whoever rolls the greatest number is the winner. What strategy should you use so that you have the best chance of winning this game?

FIGURE 7-30

7-3 Using Simulations in Probability

simulation

Students can often use simulations to study phenomena too complex to analyze by other means. A **simulation** is a technique used to act out a problem by conducting experiments whose outcomes are analogous to the original problem. Using simulations, students can estimate rather than determine probabilities theoretically. Simulations can take various forms. For example, consider the simulation on the student page. In this case, the students use a simulation with a globe to find the probability that a meteorite will hit land. Follow the instructions on the student page and then answer the questions in Now Try This 7-6.

NOW TRY THIS 7-6

a. After doing the simulation on the student page, what percentage of the Earth do you think is covered by land?

b. What is the probability that a meteorite will hit water?

c. It is estimated that approximately 500 meteorites hit the Earth each year. How many would you expect to hit land each year?

In the *Principles and Standards*, we find the following:

◆ *If simulations are used, teachers need to help students understand what the simulation data represent and how they relate to the problem situation, such as flipping coins.* (p. 254)

Suppose we want to simulate the results of flipping a coin 100 times. We could do this using random digits, as in Table 7-3. Random-digit tables are lists of digits selected at random, often by a computer or calculator. To simulate the coin toss, pick a number at

Sample School Book Page:
GEOMETRIC PROBABILITY

GOAL

LEARN HOW TO...
- find geometric probabilities
- use probability to predict

AS YOU...
- describe the chance of an object falling in a particular area

KEY TERM
- geometric probability

Exploration 1

GEOMETRIC Probability

SET UP *Work as a class. You will need an inflatable globe.*

▷ A meteorite has an equally likely chance of hitting anywhere on Earth. To find the probability that a meteorite will hit land you will conduct an experiment with a globe.

2 **Try This as a Class** Follow the steps below to simulate a meteorite falling to Earth.

First Make a table like the one shown to record the results of your experiment.

Next Carefully toss an inflated globe from one person to another. Each time the globe is caught, make a tally mark to record whether the left index finger is touching land or touching water before tossing it again. Record the results of 30 tosses.

Then Complete your table by calculating the percent of the tosses that hit land and the percent that hit water.

	Tally	Number of tosses	Percent of tosses
Land			
Water			
Total		30	

FOR ◁ HELP
with *finding probabilities*, see
MODULE 4, p. 242

Source: Middle Grades MATH Thematics, Book 1, McDougal Littell, 2002 (p. 566).

random to start and then read across the table, letting an even digit represent heads and an odd digit represent tails. Continue this process for 100 digits. The simulated probability of heads is the ratio of the number of even digits found (heads) to 100. For example, if we choose the top two rows in Table 7-3 and use the first 100 numbers, we find that there are 44 even numbers. Because even numbers represent heads, the simulated probability of tossing a head is $P(H) = 44/100$. Notice that we did not obtain the theoretical probability of 1/2. However, if the number of random digits chosen was much greater, then the simulated probability should be closer to the theoretical probability.

Similarly, to simulate the probability of a couple's having two girls (GG) in an expected family, we could use the random-digit table with an even digit representing a girl and an odd digit representing a boy. Because there are two children, we need to consider pairs of digits. If we examine 100 pairs, then the simulated probability of GG will be the number of pairs of even digits divided by 100, the total number of pairs considered.

Table 7-3 Random Digits

36422	93239	76046	81114	77412	86557	19549	98473	15221	87856
78496	47197	37961	67568	14861	61077	85210	51264	49975	71785
95384	59596	05081	39968	80495	00192	94679	18307	16265	48888
37957	89199	10816	24260	52302	69592	55019	94127	71721	70673
31422	27529	95051	83157	96377	33723	52902	51302	86370	50452
07443	15346	40653	84238	24430	88834	77318	07486	33950	61598
41348	86255	92715	96656	49693	99286	83447	20215	16040	41085
12398	95111	45663	55020	57159	58010	43162	98878	73337	35571
77229	92095	44305	09285	73256	02968	31129	66588	48126	52700
61175	53014	60304	13976	96312	42442	96713	43940	92516	81421
16825	27482	97858	05642	88047	68960	52991	67703	29805	42701
84656	03089	05166	67571	25545	26603	40243	55482	38341	97782
03872	31767	23729	89523	73654	24626	78393	77172	41328	95633
40488	70426	04034	46618	55102	93408	10965	69744	80766	14889
98322	25528	43808	05935	78338	77881	90139	72375	50624	91385
13366	52764	02407	14202	74172	58770	65348	24115	44277	96735
86711	27764	86789	43800	87582	09298	17880	75507	35217	08352
53886	50358	62738	91783	71944	90221	79403	75139	09102	77826
99348	21186	42266	01531	44325	61042	13453	61917	90426	12437
49985	08787	59448	82680	52929	19077	98518	06251	58451	91140
49807	32863	69984	20102	09523	47827	08374	79849	19352	62726
46569	00365	23591	44317	55054	99835	20633	66215	46668	53587
09988	44203	43532	54538	16619	45444	11957	69184	98398	96508
32916	00567	82881	59753	54761	39404	90756	91760	18698	42852
93285	32297	27254	27198	99093	97821	46277	10439	30389	45372
03222	39951	12738	50303	25017	84207	52123	88637	19369	58289
87002	61789	96250	99337	14144	00027	43542	87030	14773	73087
68840	94259	01961	42552	91843	33855	00824	48733	81297	80411
88323	28828	64765	08244	53077	50897	91937	08871	91517	19668
55170	71062	64159	79364	53088	21536	39451	95649	65256	23950

NOW TRY THIS 7-7

a. Use the random-digit table to estimate the probability that in a family of three, there are two girls and one boy.

b. Determine the theoretical probability of the family's having two girls and one boy and compare the answer to the simulated probability in (a).

c. Should the answers in (a) and (b) always be exactly the same? Why? How can you make sure that the answers are approximately the same?

**E X A M P L E
7-10**

A baseball player, Reggie, has a batting average of 0.400; that is, his probability of getting a hit on any particular time at bat is 0.400. Estimate the probability that he will get at least one hit in his next three times at bat.

Solution We use a random-digit table to simulate this example. We choose a starting point and place the random digits in groups of three. Because Reggie's probability of getting a hit on any particular time at bat is 0.400, we could use the occurrence of four numbers from 0 through 9 to represent a hit. Suppose a hit is represented by the digits 0, 1, 2, and 3. At least one hit is obtained in three times at bat if, in any sequence of three digits, a 0, 1, 2, or 3 appears. Data for 50 trials are given next:

780	862	760	580	783	720	590	506	021	366
848	118	073	077	042	254	063	667	374	153
377	883	573	683	780	115	662	591	685	274
279	652	754	909	754	892	310	673	964	351
803	034	799	915	059	006	774	640	298	961

We see that a 0, 1, 2, or 3 appears in 42 out of the 50 trials. Thus an estimate for the probability of at least one hit on Reggie's next three times at bat is $\frac{42}{50}$. Try to determine the theoretical probability for this experiment.

From a random sample, we can deduce information about the population from which the sample was taken. To see how this can be done, consider Example 7-11.

**E X A M P L E
7-11**

To determine the number of fish in a certain pond, suppose we capture 300 fish, mark them, and throw them back into the pond. Suppose that the next day, 200 fish are caught and 20 of these are already marked. These 200 fish are then thrown back into the pond. Estimate how many fish are in the pond.

Solution Because 20 of the 200 fish are marked, we assume that $\frac{20}{200}$, or $\frac{1}{10}$, of the fish are marked. Thus $\frac{1}{10}$ of the population is marked. If n represents the population, then $\frac{1}{10}n = 300$ and $n = 300 \cdot 10 = 3000$. Hence, an estimate for the fish population of the pond is 3000.

The following "Peanuts" cartoon suggests a simulation problem concerning chocolate chip cookies.

EXAMPLE 7-12

Suppose Lucy makes enough batter for exactly 100 chocolate chip cookies and mixes 100 chocolate chips into the batter. If the chips are distributed at random and Charlie Brown chooses a cookie at random from the 100 cookies, estimate the probability that it will contain exactly one chocolate chip.

Solution   We can use a simulation to estimate the probability of choosing a cookie with exactly one chocolate chip. We construct a 10×10 grid, as shown in Figure 7-31(a), to represent the 100 cookies Lucy made. Each square (cookie) can be associated with some ordered pair, where the first component is for the horizontal scale and the second is for the vertical scale. For example, the squares (0, 2) and (5, 3) are pictured in Figure 7-31(a). Using the random-digit table, close your eyes and then take a pencil and point to one number to start. Look at the number and the number immediately following it. Consider these numbers an ordered pair and continue until you obtain 100 ordered pairs to represent the 100 cookies. For example, suppose we start at a 3 and the numbers following 3 are as follows:

$$39968 \qquad 80495 \qquad 00192 \dots$$

Then the ordered pairs would be given as (3, 9), (9, 6), (8, 8), (0, 4), and so on. Use each pair of numbers as the coordinates for the square (cookie) and place a tally on the grid to represent each chip, as shown in Figure 7-31(b). We estimate the probability that a cookie has exactly one chip by counting the number of squares with exactly one tally and dividing by 100.

FIGURE 7-31

(a)

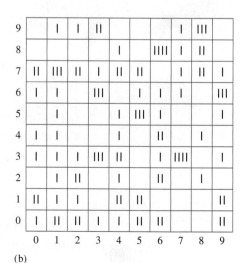

(b)

Table 7-4 shows the results of one simulation. Thus the estimate for the probability of Charlie Brown receiving a cookie with exactly one chip is $\frac{34}{100}$.

Table 7-4

Number of Chips	Number of Cookies
0	38
1	34
2	20
3	6
≥ 4	2

Try a simulation on your own and compare your results with the preceding ones and with the results given in Table 7-5, obtained by theoretical methods.

Table 7-5

Number of Chips	Number of Cookies
0	36.8
1	36.8
2	18.4
3	6.1
≥ 4	1.9

ONGOING ASSESSMENT 7-3

1. How might you use a deck of cards to simulate the birth of boys and girls?
2. The weather forecast for Pelican, Alaska, is for a 90% chance of rain on any given day. (Assume independent events).
   a. How might you simulate the probability of rain in Pelican on any given day?
   b. Use your simulation from (a) to estimate the probability of rain in Pelican for seven days in a row.
   c. What is the theoretical probability that in a 7-day period it does not rain every day?
3. How might you use a random-digit table to simulate each of the following?
   a. Tossing a single die
   b. Choosing three people at random from a group of 20 people

   c. Spinning the spinner, where the probability of each color is as shown in the following figure:

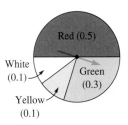

4. A school has 500 students. The principal is to pick 30 students at random from the school to go to the Rose Bowl. How can this be done by using a random-digit table?

5. In a certain city, the probability that it will rain on a certain day is 0.8 if it rained the day before. The probability that it will be dry on a certain day is 0.3 if it was dry the day before. It is now Sunday, and it is raining. Use the random-digit table to simulate the weather for the rest of the week.

6. It is reported that 15% of people who come into contact with a person infected with strep throat contract the disease. How might you use the random-digit table to simulate the probability that at least one child in a three-child family will catch the disease, given that each child has come into contact with the infected person?

7. Pick a block of two digits from the random-digit table. What is the probability that the block picked is less than 30?

8. An estimate of the fish population of a certain pond was found by catching 200 fish and marking and returning them to the pond. The next day, 300 fish were caught, of which 50 had been marked the previous day. Estimate the fish population of the pond.

9. Suppose that in the World Series, the two teams are evenly matched. The two teams play until one team wins four games, and no ties are possible.
   a. What is the maximum number of games that could be played?
   b. Use simulation to approximate the probabilities that the series will end in (i) four games and in (ii) seven games.

10. Assume Carmen Smith, a basketball player, makes free throws with 80% probability of success and is placed in a one-and-one situation where she is given a second foul shot only if the first shot goes through the basket. Simulate the 25 attempts from the foul line in one-and-one situations to determine how many times we would expect Carmen to score 0 points, 1 point, and 2 points.

Communication

11. In an attempt to reduce the growth of its population, China instituted a policy limiting a family to one child. Rural Chinese suggested revising the policy to limit families to one son. Assuming the suggested policy is adopted and that any birth is as likely to produce a boy as a girl, explain how to use simulation to answer the following:
    a. What would be the average family size?
    b. What would be the ratio of newborn boys to newborn girls?

12. Consider a "walk" on the following grid starting out at the origin 0 and "walking" one unit (block) north, and at each intersection turning left with probability $\frac{1}{2}$, turning right with probability $\frac{1}{6}$, and moving straight with probability $\frac{1}{3}$.

    Explain how to simulate the "walk" using a regular six-sided die.

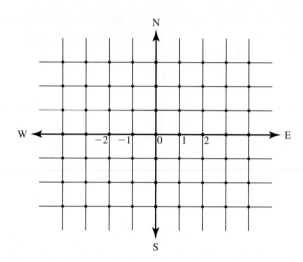

Open-Ended

13. What is the probability that in a group of five people chosen at random, at least two will have birthdays in the same month? Design a simulation for this problem and try your simulation 10 times.

14. The probability of the home team's winning a basketball game is 80%. Describe a simulation of the probability that the home team will win three home games in a row.

15. Montana duck hunters are all perfect shots. Ten Montana hunters are in a duck blind when 10 ducks fly over. All 10 hunters pick a duck at random to shoot at, and all 10 hunters fire at the same time. How many ducks could be expected to escape, on the average, if this experiment were repeated a large number of times? How could this problem be simulated?

Cooperative Learning

16. The sixth-grade class decided that the ideal number of children in a family is four: two boys and two girls.
    a. As a group, design a simulation to determine the probability of two boys and two girls in a family of four.
    b. Have each person in your group try the simulation 25 times and compare the probabilities.
    c. Combine the results of all the members of your group and use this information to find a simulated probability.
    d. Compute the theoretical probability of having two boys and two girls in a family of four and compare your answer to the simulated probability.

17. Have you ever wondered how you would score on a 10-item true-false test if you guessed at every answer?
    a. Simulate your score by tossing a coin 10 times with heads representing true and tails representing false. Check your answers by using the following key and score yourself:

1	2	3	4	5	6	7	8	9	10
F	T	F	F	T	F	T	T	T	F

b. Combine your results with those of others in your group to find the average (mean) number of correct answers for your group.

c. How many items would you expect to get correct if the number of items were 30 instead of 10?

d. What is the theoretical probability of your getting all the answers correct on a 10-item true-false test if all answers were chosen by flipping a coin?

18. a. Estimate how many cards you would expect to have to turn over on the average in an ordinary playing deck before an ace appeared.

b. Have each person in your group repeat the experiment 10 times or simulate it for 10 trials. Then find the average number of aces.

c. Combine the results of all the members of your group and find the average number of cards that needs to be drawn. How does this average compare to your individual estimate?

★ **19.** A cereal company places a coupon bearing a number from 1 to 9 in each box of cereal. If the numbers are distributed at random in the boxes, estimate the number of boxes you would have to purchase in order to obtain all nine numbers. Explain how the random-digit table could be used to estimate the number of coupons. Each person in the group should simulate 10 trials, and the results in the group should be combined to find the estimate.

Review Problems

20. In a two-person game, four coins are tossed. If exactly two heads come up, you win. If anything else comes up, you lose. Does each player have an equal chance of winning the game? Explain why or why not.

21. A single card is drawn from an ordinary deck. What is the probability of obtaining each of the following?

a. A club b. A queen and a spade
c. Not a queen d. Not a heart
e. A spade or a heart f. The 6 of diamonds
g. A queen or a spade h. Either red or black

22. From a sack containing 7 red marbles, 8 blue marbles, and 4 white marbles, marbles are drawn at random for several experiments. Determine the probability of each of the following events:

a. One marble drawn at random is either red or blue.

b. The first draw is red and the second is blue, where one marble is drawn at random, its color is recorded, the marble is replaced, and another marble is drawn.

c. The event in (b) where the first marble is not replaced.

TECHNOLOGY CORNER

RANDINT(or RANDI(

1. On some graphing calculators, if we choose the MATH menu and then select PRB, which stands for PROBABILITY, we find **RANDINT(**, or **RANDI(**, the random integer feature. RANDINT(generates a random integer within a specified range. It requires two inputs that are the upper and lower boundaries for the integers. For example, RANDINT(1, 10) generates a random integer from 1 through 10.

a. How could you use RANDINT(to simulate tossing a single die?

b. How could you use RANDINT(to simulate the sum of the numbers when tossing 2 dice?

RAND

int

2. Some graphing calculators have a **RAND** function, a random-digit generator. RAND generates and returns a random number greater than 0 and less than 1. For example, RAND might produce the numbers .5956605, .049599836, or .876572691. To have RAND produce random numbers from 1 to 10 as in (1), we enter int (10 *RAND) + 1. The **int** (greatest integer) feature is found in the MATH menu under NUM. The feature int returns the greatest integer less than or equal to a number.

a. How could you use RAND to simulate tossing a single die?

b. How could you use RAND to simulate tossing two dice and taking the sum of the numbers?

3. Use one of these random features to simulate tossing two dice 30 times. Based on your simulation, what is the probability that a sum of 7 will occur?

7-4   Odds, Conditional Probability, and Expected Value

Computing Odds

odds in favor

People talk about the *odds in favor of* and the *odds against* a particular event's happening. When the **odds in favor** of the president's being reelected are 4 to 1, this refers to how likely the president is to win the election relative to how likely the president is to lose. The probability of the president's winning is four times the probability of losing. If W represents the event the president wins the election and L represents the event the president loses, then $P(W) = 4P(L)$ or as a proportion, we have

$$\frac{P(W)}{P(L)} = \frac{4}{1}, \text{ or } 4:1.$$

Because W and L are complements of each other, $L = \overline{W}$, we have

$$\frac{P(W)}{P(\overline{W})} = \frac{P(W)}{1 - P(W)} = \frac{4}{1}, \text{ or } 4:1.$$

odds against

The **odds against** the president's winning are how likely the president is to lose relative to how likely the president is to win. Using the information above, we have

$$\frac{P(L)}{P(W)} = \frac{1}{4}, \text{ or } 1:4.$$

Because $L = \overline{W}$, we have

$$\frac{P(\overline{W})}{P(W)} = \frac{1 - P(W)}{P(W)} = \frac{1}{4}, \text{ or } 1:4.$$

Formally, odds are defined as follows.

> ### Definition of Odds
>
> Let $P(A)$ be the probability that A occurs and $P(\overline{A})$ be the probability that A does not occur. Then the **odds in favor** of an event A are
>
> $$\frac{P(A)}{P(\overline{A})}, \quad \text{or} \quad \frac{P(A)}{1 - P(A)},$$
>
> and the **odds against** an event A are
>
> $$\frac{P(\overline{A})}{P(A)}, \quad \text{or} \quad \frac{1 - P(A)}{P(A)}.$$

When odds are calculated for equally likely outcomes, we have the following:

$$\text{Odds in favor of an event } A: \frac{P(A)}{P(\overline{A})} = \frac{n(A)}{n(S)} \div \frac{n(\overline{A})}{n(S)} = \frac{n(A)}{n(S)} \cdot \frac{n(S)}{n(\overline{A})} = \frac{n(A)}{n(\overline{A})}$$

$$\text{Odds against an event } A: \frac{n(\overline{A})}{n(A)}$$

Thus, in the case of equally likely outcomes, we have

$$\text{Odds in favor} = \frac{\text{Number of favorable outcomes}}{\text{Number of unfavorable outcomes}}$$

$$\text{Odds against} = \frac{\text{Number of unfavorable outcomes}}{\text{Number of favorable outcomes}}.$$

When you roll a die, the number of favorable ways of rolling a 4 in one throw of a die is 1, and the number of unfavorable ways is 5. Thus the odds in favor of rolling a 4 are 1 to 5.

EXAMPLE 7-13

For each of the following, find the odds in favor of the event's occurring:

a. Rolling a number less than 5 on a die
b. Tossing heads on a fair coin
c. Drawing an ace from an ordinary 52-card deck
d. Drawing a heart from an ordinary 52-card deck

Solution   **a.** The probability of rolling a number less than 5 is $\frac{4}{6}$; the probability of rolling a number not less than 5 is $\frac{2}{6}$. The odds in favor of rolling a number less than 5 are $\left(\frac{4}{6}\right) \div \left(\frac{2}{6}\right)$, or $4:2$, or $2:1$.

b. $P(H) = \frac{1}{2}$ and $P(\overline{H}) = \frac{1}{2}$. The odds in favor of getting heads are $\left(\frac{1}{2}\right) \div \left(\frac{1}{2}\right)$, or $1:1$.

c. The probability of drawing an ace is $\frac{4}{52}$, and the probability of not drawing an ace is $\frac{48}{52}$. The odds in favor of drawing an ace are $\left(\frac{4}{52}\right) \div \left(\frac{48}{52}\right)$, or $4:48$, or $1:12$.

d. The probability of drawing a heart is $\frac{13}{52}$, or $\frac{1}{4}$, and the probability of not drawing a heart is $\frac{39}{52}$, or $\frac{3}{4}$. The odds in favor of drawing a heart are $\left(\frac{13}{52}\right) \div \left(\frac{39}{52}\right) = \frac{13}{39}$, or $13:39$, or $1:3$.

NOW TRY THIS 7-8

In Example 7-13(a), there are four ways to roll a number less than 5 on a die (favorable outcomes) and two ways of not rolling a number less than 5 (unfavorable outcomes), so the odds in favor of rolling a number less than 5 are $4:2$, or $2:1$. Work the other three parts of Example 7-13 using this approach.

Given the probability of an event, it is possible to find the odds in favor of (or against) the event and vice versa. For example, if the odds in favor of an event A are $5:1$, then we have the following:

$$\frac{P(A)}{1 - P(A)} = \frac{5}{1}$$

$$P(A) = 5[1 - P(A)]$$

$$6P(A) = 5$$

$$P(A) = \frac{5}{6}$$

REMARK The probability $\frac{5}{6}$ is a ratio. The exact number of favorable outcomes and the exact total of all outcomes are not necessarily known.

E X A M P L E
7-14

In the following cartoon, find the probability of making totally black copies if the odds are 3 to 1 against making totally black copies:

TODAY'S ODDS	
Makes totally black copies	3-1
Makes copies with wavy black lines	4-1
Misfeeds	2-1
Gives no change	3-1
Gives double change	8-1
Mystery light appears and 2 or more of the above occur	5-1

COPIES 20¢

Cable

Solution If the odds against making totally black copies are 3 to 1, B represents the event of making a totally black copy and $\overline{B}$ represents not making a totally black copy. We have

$$\frac{P(\overline{B})}{1 - P(\overline{B})} = \frac{3}{1}$$

$$P(B) = 3(1 - P(\overline{B}))$$

$$P(\overline{B}) = \frac{3}{4}$$

$$P(B) = 1 - P(\overline{B}) = 1 - \frac{3}{4}$$

$$P(B) = \frac{1}{4}.$$

In Example 7-14, the odds in favor of making totally black copies are $1:3$. Therefore, the ratio of favorable outcomes to unfavorable outcomes is $\frac{1}{3}$. Thus in a sample space modeling this situation with four elements, there would be 1 favorable outcome and 3 unfavorable outcomes and $P(\text{black copies}) = \frac{1}{1+3} = \frac{1}{4}$. In general, we have the following.

> **Theorem**

If the odds in favor of event E are $m:n$, then $P(E) = \dfrac{m}{m+n}$.

If the odds against event E are $m:n$, then $P(E) = \dfrac{n}{m+n}$.

Conditional Probabilities

When the sample space of an experiment is affected by additional information, the new sample space often is reduced in size. For example, suppose we toss a fair coin three times and consider the following events:

A: getting a tail on the first toss

B: getting a tail on all three tosses

In Figure 7-32 we see that $P(A) = \frac{4}{8} = \frac{1}{2}$ and $P(B) = \frac{1}{8}$.

FIGURE 7-32

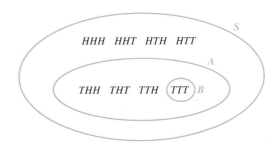

(*S* represents the sample space)

What if we were told that event A has occurred (that is, a tail occurred on the first toss), and we are now asked to find $P(B)$. The sample space is now reduced to {*THH, THT, TTH, TTT*}. Now the probability that all three tosses are tails given that the first toss is a tail is $\frac{1}{4}$. (Note that $A \cap B = \{TTT\}$.) The notation that we use for this situation is $P(B|A)$, read "the probability of B given A," and we write $P(B|A) = \frac{1}{4}$. Notice that

$$P(B|A) = \frac{1}{4} = \frac{\frac{1}{8}}{\frac{4}{8}} = \frac{P(A \cap B)}{P(A)}.$$

This is true in general and we have the following.

> ## Property

If A and B are events in sample space S and $P(A) \neq 0$, then the **conditional probability** that event B occurs given that event A has occurred is given by
$$P(B|A) = \frac{P(A \cap B)}{P(A)}.$$

EXAMPLE 7-15

What is the probability of rolling a 6 on a fair die if you know that the roll is an even number?

Solution If event B is rolling a 6 and event A is rolling an even number, then

$$P(B|A) = \frac{P(A \cap B)}{P(A)} = \frac{\frac{1}{6}}{\frac{1}{2}} = \frac{1}{3}.$$

Note that it is not really necessary to use the formula for conditional probability to answer the question, because the new sample space is {2, 4, 6}, and so $P(6) = \frac{1}{3}$.

Expected Value

Racetracks use odds for betting purposes. If the odds against Fast Jack are 3:1, this means the track will pay $3 for every $1 you bet. If Fast Jack wins, then for a $5 bet, the track will return your $5 plus $15, or $20. The 3:1 odds means the track expects Fast Jack to lose 3 out of 4 times in this situation. If the odds at racetracks were accurate, bettors would receive an even return for their money; that is, bettors would not expect to win or lose money in the long run. For example, if the stated odds of 3:1 against Fast Jack were accurate, then the probability of Fast Jack's losing the race would be 3/4 and for Fast Jack's winning 1/4. If we compute the expected average winnings (expected value) over the long run, the gain is $3 for every $1 bet for a win and a loss of $1 otherwise. The expected value, E, is computed as follows:

$$E = 3(1/4) + {}^{-}1(3/4) = 0$$

Therefore the expected value is $0. If the racetrack gave accurate odds, it could not stay in business because it could not cover its expenses and make a profit. This is why the track overestimates the horses' chances of winning by about 20%.

Consider the spinner in Figure 7-33, with the payoff in each sector of the circle. Using area models, we can assign the following probabilities to each region:

FIGURE 7-33

$$P(\$1.00) = \frac{1}{2} \qquad P(\$2.00) = \frac{1}{4} \qquad P(\$3.00) = \frac{1}{8} \qquad P(\$4.00) = \frac{1}{8}$$

Should the owner of this spinner expect to make money over an extended period of time if the charge is $2.00 per spin?

To determine the average payoff over the long run, we find the product of the probability of landing on the payoff and the payoff itself and then find the sum of the products. This computation is given by

$$E = (1/2)1 + (1/4)2 + (1/8)3 + (1/8)4 = 1.875.$$

The owner can expect to pay out about $1.88 per spin. This is less than the $2.00 charge, so the owner should make a profit if the spinner is used many times. The sum of the products in this example, $1.875, is the **expected value**, or **mathematical expectation**, of the experiment of spinning the wheel in Figure 7-33 once. The owner's expected average earnings are $2.00 − $1.875 = $0.125 per spin and the player's expected average earnings (loss) are $^-$\$.125.

expected value ◆
mathematical expectation

The expected value is an average of winnings over the long run. Expected value can be used to predict the average result of an experiment when it is repeated many times. But *an expected value cannot be used to determine the outcome of any single experiment.*

> ## Definition of Expected Value

If, in an experiment, the possible outcomes are numbers $a_1, a_2, \ldots, a_n$, occurring with probabilities $p_1, p_2, \ldots, p_n$, respectively, then the **expected value (mathematical expectation)** E is given by the equation

$$E = a_1 \cdot p_1 + a_2 \cdot p_2 + a_3 \cdot p_3 + \ldots + a_n \cdot p_n.$$

fair game

When payoffs are involved and the net winning of a game of chance is $0, the game is a **fair game**. Do you think gambling casinos and lotteries make sure that the games are not fair?

REMARK Previously, a *fair game* was defined as a game in which each player has an equal chance of winning the game. If there are two players and each has the same probability of winning a given number of dollars from the other, it follows that the net winning for each player is 0.

E X A M P L E
7-16

Suppose you pay $5.00 to play the following game. Two coins are tossed. You receive $10 if two heads occur, $5 if exactly one head occurs, and nothing if no heads appear. Is this a fair game? That is, are the net winnings $0?

Solution Before we determine the average payoff, recall that $P(HH) = \frac{1}{4}$, $P(HT \text{ or } TH)$ $= \frac{1}{2}$, and $P(TT) = \frac{1}{4}$. To find the expected value, we perform the following computation:

$$E = \left(\frac{1}{4}\right) \cdot (\$10) + \left(\frac{1}{2}\right) \cdot (\$5) + \left(\frac{1}{4}\right) \cdot (0) = \$5$$

Because the price of playing is equal to the average payoff, the net winnings are $0. This is a fair game.

PROBLEM SOLVING   <u>**A Coin-Tossing Game**</u>

Al and Betsy played a coin-tossing game in which a fair coin was tossed until a total of either three heads or three tails occurred. Al was to win when a total of three heads were tossed, and Betsy was to win when a total of three tails were tossed. Each bet $50 on the game. If the coin was lost when Al had two heads and Betsy had one tail, how should the stakes be fairly split if the game is not continued?

Understanding the Problem Al and Betsy each bet $50 on a coin-tossing game in which a fair coin was to be tossed five times. Al was to win when a total of three heads was obtained; Betsy was to win when a total of three tails was obtained. When Al had two heads and Betsy had one tail, the coin was lost. The problem is how to split the stakes fairly.

Different people could have different interpretations of what "splitting fairly" means. Possibly, though, the best is to split the pot in proportion to the probabilities of each player's winning the game when play was halted. We must calculate the expected value for each player and split the pot accordingly.

Devising a Plan A third head would make Al the winner, whereas Betsy needs two more tails to win. A *tree diagram* that simulates the completion of the game allows us to find the probability of each player's winning the game. Once we find the probabilities, all we need do is multiply the probabilities by the amount of the pot, $100, to determine each player's fair share.

Carrying Out the Plan The tree diagram in Figure 7-34 shows the possibilities for game winners if the game is completed. We can find the probabilities of each player's winning as follows:

FIGURE 7-34

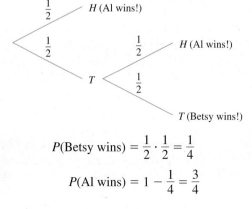

$$P(\text{Betsy wins}) = \frac{1}{2} \cdot \frac{1}{2} = \frac{1}{4}$$

$$P(\text{Al wins}) = 1 - \frac{1}{4} = \frac{3}{4}$$

Hence, the fair way to split the stakes is for Al to receive $\frac{3}{4}$ of $100, or $75, and Betsy should receive $\frac{1}{4}$ of $100, or $25.

Looking Back   The problem could be made even more interesting by assuming that the coin is not fair so that the probability is not $\frac{1}{2}$ for each branch in the tree diagram. Other possibilities arise if the players have unequal amounts of money in the pot or if more tosses are required in order to win. ▨▨

O N G O I N G   A S S E S S M E N T   7 - 4

1. **a.** What are the odds in favor of drawing a face card from an ordinary deck of playing cards?
   b. What are the odds against drawing a face card?
2. On a single roll of a pair of dice, what are the odds against rolling a sum of 7?
3. If the probability of a boy's being born is $\frac{1}{2}$, and a family plans to have four children, what are the odds against having all boys?
4. Diane tossed a coin nine times and got nine tails. Assume that Diane's coin is fair and answer each of the following questions:
   a. What is the probability of tossing a tail on the 10th toss?
   b. What is the probability of tossing 10 more tails in a row?
   c. What are the odds against tossing 10 more tails in a row?
5. If the odds against Deborah's winning first prize in a chess tournament are 3 to 5, what is the probability that she will win first prize?
6. What are the odds in favor of tossing at least two heads if a fair coin is tossed three times?
7. If the probability of rain for the day is 60%, what are the odds against its raining?
8. On an American roulette wheel, half of the slots numbered 1 through 36 are red and half are black. Two slots, numbered 0 and 00, are green. What are the odds against a red slot's coming up on any spin of the wheel?
9. On a tote board at a race track, the odds for Gameylegs are listed as 26:1. Tote boards list the odds that the horse will lose the race. If this is the case, what is the probability of Gameylegs's winning the race?
10. A container has 3 white balls and 2 red balls. A first ball is drawn at random and not replaced. Then a second ball is drawn. Given the following conditions, what is the probability that the second ball was red?
    a. The first ball was white.
    b. The first ball was red.

11. The following spinner is spun. Given the conditions below, what is the probability that it lands on 2?

   a. It lands on an odd number.
   b. It lands on a number divisible by 3.
   c. It does not land on 5, 6, or 7.
   d. It lands on a number less than 4.
12. If $P(A) = \frac{2}{3}$, $P(B) = \frac{1}{2}$, and $P(B|A) = \frac{1}{3}$, find $P(A|B)$.
13. You play a game in which two dice are rolled. If a sum of 7 appears, you win $10; otherwise, you lose $2.00. If you intend to play this game for a long time, should you expect to make money, lose money, or come out about even? Explain.
14. On a roulette wheel are 36 slots numbered 1 through 36 and 2 slots numbered 0 and 00. You can bet on a single number. If the ball lands on your number, you receive 35 chips plus the chip you played.
    a. What is the probability that the ball will land on 17?
    b. What are the odds against the ball landing on 17?
    c. If each chip is worth $1, what is the expected payoff for a player who plays the number 17 for a long time?
15. Suppose five quarters, five dimes, five nickels, and ten pennies are in a box. One coin is selected at random. What is the expected value of this experiment?
16. If the odds in favor of Fast Leg's winning a horse race are 5 to 2 and the first prize is $14,000, what is the expected value of Fast Leg's winning?
17. Sweepstakes are required by law to display the odds of winning as well as the payoffs. That information is sufficient to calculate the expected value of a sweepstakes.

Suppose that mailing the sweepstakes costs $0.37 and the odds in favor of winning the various prizes are as follows:

Odds	Prize	Quantity
1 to 20,000,000	$1,000,000	1
1 to 20,000,000	$100,000	10
1 to 1,000,000	$1,000	100

a. What is the expected value of the sweepstakes for any individual?

b. At what postage rate would the drawing be fair?

18. Suppose it costs $8 to roll a pair of dice. You get paid the sum of the numbers in dollars that appear on the dice.
    a. What is the expected value of the game?
    b. Is it a fair game?

Communication

19. Explain the difference between odds and probability.
20. A prominent newspaper reported that the odds of getting AIDS in June 1991 were 68,000 to 1. Explain why you believe or disbelieve this report.
21. A game involves tossing two coins. A player wins $1.00 if both tosses result in heads. What should you pay to play this game in order to make it a fair game? Explain your answer.

Open-Ended

22. An insurance company sells a policy that pays $50,000 in case of accidental death. According to company figures, the rate of accidental death is 47 per 100,000 population. What annual premium should the company charge for this coverage? Explain how much profit the company will make under your plan, how you determined the amount of profit needed for the company, and how the annual premium was computed.
23. Write a game-type problem about odds and payoffs so that the odds in favor of an event are 2:3 and the game is a fair game.

Cooperative Learning

24. As a group, design a game that involves cards, dice, or spinners.
    a. Write the rules so that any person who wants to play can understand the game.
    b. Write a description explaining whether the game is fair and how you arrived at your conclusion.
    c. Calculate the odds of each player's winning.
    d. If betting is involved, discuss expected values.
    e. Exchange a game with another group and compare your analysis of their game with their analysis of your group's game.

Review Problems

25. Refer to the following spinners and write the sample space for each of the following experiments:

 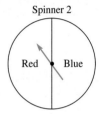

Spinner 1   Spinner 2

a. Spin spinner 1 once.
b. Spin spinner 2 once.
c. Spin spinner 1 once and then spin spinner 2 once.
d. Spin spinner 2 once and then roll a die.
e. Spin spinner 1 twice.
f. Spin spinner 2 twice.

26. Draw a spinner with two sections, red and blue, such that the probability of getting (Blue, Blue) on two spins is $\frac{25}{36}$.
27. Find the probability of getting two vowels when someone draws two letters from the English alphabet with replacement.

It is your first day of class, and your class has 40 students. A friend who does not know any students in your class bets you that at least two of them share a birthday (month and day). What are your friend's chances of winning the bet?

7-5 **Using Permutations and Combinations in Probability**

Permutations of Unlike Objects

permutation An arrangement of things in a definite order with no repetitions is a **permutation**. For example, RAT, RTA, ART, ATR, TRA, and TAR are all different arrangements of the three letters R, A, and T. Notice that order is important and there are no repetitions. Determining the number of possible arrangements of the three letters without making a list can be done using the Fundamental Counting Principle. Because there are three ways to choose the first letter, two ways to choose the second letter, and one way to choose the third letter, there are $3 \cdot 2 \cdot 1$, or 6, ways to arrange the letters. It is common to record the number of permutations of three objects taken three at a time as $_3P_3$. Therefore, $_3P_3 = 6$.

Consider how many ways the owner of an ice cream parlor can display 10 flavors in a row along the front of the display case. The first position can be filled in 10 ways, the second position in 9 ways, the third position in 8 ways, and so on. By the Fundamental Counting Principle, there are $10 \cdot 9 \cdot 8 \cdot 7 \cdot 6 \cdot 5 \cdot 4 \cdot 3 \cdot 2 \cdot 1$, or 3,628,800, ways to display the flavors. If there were 16 flavors, there would be $16 \cdot 15 \cdot 14 \cdot 13 \cdot \ldots \cdot 3 \cdot 2 \cdot 1$ ways to arrange them. In general, *if there are n objects, then the number of possible ways to arrange the objects in a row is the product of all the natural numbers from n to 1, inclu-*

n factorial (*n*!)

sive. This expression is called **n factorial** and is denoted **n!**, as shown next.

$$n! = n \cdot (n - 1) \cdot (n - 2) \cdot \ldots \cdot 3 \cdot 2 \cdot 1$$

For example, $5! = 5 \cdot 4 \cdot 3 \cdot 2 \cdot 1$, $3! = 3 \cdot 2 \cdot 1$, and $1! = 1$. Using factorial notation is helpful in counting and probability problems.

Many calculators have a factorial key such as $\boxed{x!}$. To use this key, enter a whole number and then press the factorial key. For example, to compute 5!, press $\boxed{5}\ \boxed{x!}$ and 120 will appear on the display.

Consider the set of people in a small club, {Al, Betty, Carl, Dan}. For them to elect a president and a secretary, order is important and no repetitions are possible. How many ways are there to elect a committee of two in which one person is president and the other secretary? One way to answer the question is to agree that the choice "Al, Betty" denotes Al as president and Betty as secretary, while the choice "Betty, Al" indicates that Betty is president and Al is secretary. Thus order is important and no repetitions are possible. Consequently, counting the number of possibilities is a permutation problem. Since there are four ways of choosing a president and then three ways of choosing a secretary, by the Fundamental Counting Principle, there are $4 \cdot 3$, or 12, ways of choosing a president and a secretary. Choosing two officers from a club of four is a permutation of four people chosen two at a time. The number of possible permutations of four objects taken two at a time, denoted $_4P_2$, may be counted using the Fundamental Counting Principle, as seen in Figure 7-35. Therefore we have $_4P_2 = 4 \cdot 3$, or 12.

FIGURE 7-35

	·	
4 choices		3 choices
President		Secretary

NOW TRY THIS 7-9

a. Write $_nP_2$, $_nP_3$, and $_nP_4$ in terms of n.

b. Based on your answers in part (a), write $_nP_r$ in terms of n and r.

c. In the club listed above, how many ways are there to choose a president, vice president, and secretary?

The number of permutations can be written in terms of factorials. Consider the number of permutations of 20 objects chosen 3 at a time:

$$\begin{aligned}
{}_{20}P_3 &= 20 \cdot 19 \cdot 18 \\
&= \frac{20 \cdot 19 \cdot 18 \cdot (17 \cdot \ldots \cdot 3 \cdot 2 \cdot 1)}{(17 \cdot \ldots \cdot 3 \cdot 2 \cdot 1)} \\
&= \frac{20!}{17!} \\
&= \frac{20!}{(20 - 3)!}
\end{aligned}$$

This can be generalized as follows:

Permutation of Objects in a Set

If a set has n elements, then the number of permutations of n objects taken r at a time is given by

$$ {}_nP_r = \frac{n!}{(n - r)!} $$

${}_nP_n$ is the number of permutations of n objects chosen n at a time—that is, the number of ways of rearranging n objects in a row. We have seen that this number is $n!$. If we use the formula for ${}_nP_r$ to compute ${}_nP_n$, we obtain

$$ {}_nP_r = \frac{n!}{(n - n)!} = \frac{n!}{0!}. $$

Consequently, $n! = n!/0!$. To make this equation true, we define $0!$ to be 1.

  Many calculators, especially graphing calculators, can calculate the number of permutations of n objects taken r at a time. This feature is usually denoted $\boxed{{}_nP_r}$. To use this key, enter the value of n, then press $\boxed{{}_nP_r}$, followed by the value of r. If you then press $\boxed{=}$ or $\boxed{\text{ENTER}}$, the number of permutations is displayed.

NOW TRY THIS 7-10

---

a. Try to use a factorial key $\boxed{x!}$ on your calculator to compute $\dfrac{100!}{98!}$. What happens? Why?

b. Without using a calculator, use the definition of factorials to compute the expression in part (a).

E X A M P L E
7-17

a. A baseball team has nine players. Find the number of ways the manager can arrange the batting order.

b. Find the number of ways of choosing three initials from the alphabet if none of the letters can be repeated.

Solution **a.** Because there are nine ways to choose the first batter, eight ways to choose the second batter, and so on, there are $9 \cdot 8 \cdot 7 \cdot \ldots \cdot 2 \cdot 1 = 9!$, or 362,880, ways of arranging the batting order. Using the formula for permutations, we have ${}_9P_9 = 9!/0! = 362,880$.

b. There are 26 ways of choosing the first letter, 25 ways of choosing the second letter, and 24 ways of choosing the third letter. Hence, there are $26 \cdot 25 \cdot 24$, or 15,600, ways of choosing the 3 letters. Alternately, if we use the formula for permutations, we have

$$_{26}P_3 = \frac{26!}{23!} = \frac{26 \cdot 25 \cdot 24 \cdot (23 \cdot 22 \cdot 21 \cdot \ldots \cdot 1)}{23 \cdot 22 \cdot 21 \cdot \ldots \cdot 1}$$
$$= 26 \cdot 25 \cdot 24$$
$$= 15,600.$$

NOW TRY THIS 7-11

If the digits 1 through 9 inclusive are used with no repeats to form a 4-digit code, what is the probability that a code number selected at random starts with 9?

Permutations Involving Like Objects

In the previous counting examples, each object to be counted was distinct. Suppose we wanted to rearrange the letters in the word *ZOO*. How many choices would we have? A tree diagram, as in Figure 7-36, suggests that there might be $3 \cdot 2 \cdot 1 = 3!$, or 6, possibilities. However, looking at the list of possibilities shows that *ZOO, OZO,* and *OOZ* each appears twice because the *O*'s are not different. We need to determine how to remove the duplication in arrangements such as this where some objects are the same. To eliminate the duplication, we divide the number of arrangements shown by the number of ways the two *O*'s can be rearranged, which is 2!. Consequently, there are $\frac{3!}{2!}$, or 3, ways of arranging the letters in *ZOO*. The arrangements are *ZOO, OZO,* and *OOZ*.

FIGURE 7-36

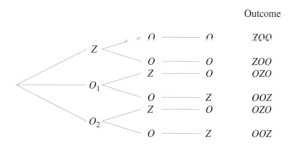

Permutations of Like Objects

If a set contains n elements, of which r_1 are of one kind, r_2 are of another kind, and so on through r_k, then the number of different arrangements of all n elements is equal to

$$\frac{n!}{r_1! \cdot r_2! \cdot r_3! \cdot \ldots \cdot r_k!}.$$

EXAMPLE
7-18

Find the number of rearrangements of the letters in each of the following words:

a. bubble   **b.** statistics

Solution   **a.** There are six letters with *b* repeated three times. Hence, the number of arrangements is

$$\frac{6!}{3!} = 6 \cdot 5 \cdot 4 = 120.$$

b. There are 10 letters in the word *statistics*, with three *s*'s, three *t*'s, and two *i*'s in the word. Hence, the number of arrangements is

$$\frac{10!}{3! \cdot 3! \cdot 2!} = \frac{10 \cdot 9 \cdot 8 \cdot 7 \cdot 6 \cdot 5 \cdot 4 \cdot 3 \cdot 2 \cdot 1}{3 \cdot 2 \cdot 1 \cdot 3 \cdot 2 \cdot 1 \cdot 2 \cdot 1} = 50,400.$$

Combinations

Reconsider the club {Al, Betty, Carl, Dan}. Suppose a two-person committee is selected with no chair. In this case, order is not important, and an Al-Betty choice is the same as a Betty-Al choice. An arrangement of objects in which the order makes no difference is **combination** a **combination**. A comparison of the results of electing a president and a secretary for the club and the results of simply selecting a two-person committee are shown in Figure 7-37. We see that the number of combinations is the number of permutations divided by 2, or

$$\frac{4 \cdot 3}{2} = 6.$$

Because each two-person choice can be arranged in 2!, or 2, ways, we divide the number of permutations by 2.

FIGURE 7-37

Permutations (Election)	Combinations (Committee)
(A, B) (B, A)	$\{A, B\}$
(A, C) (C, A)	$\{A, C\}$
(A, D) (D, A)	$\{A, D\}$
(B, C) (C, B)	$\{B, C\}$
(B, D) (D, B)	$\{B, D\}$
(C, D) (D, C)	$\{C, D\}$

In how many ways can a committee of three people be selected from the club {Al, Betty, Carl, Dan}? To solve this problem, we proceed as we did above and find the number of ways to select three people from a group of four for three offices, say president, vice president, and secretary (a permutation problem) and then use this result to see how many combinations of people are possible for the committee. Figure 7-38 shows a partial list for both problems.

FIGURE 7-38

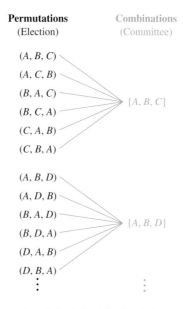

By the Fundamental Counting Principle, if order is important the number of ways to choose three people from the list of four is $4 \cdot 3 \cdot 2$, or 24. However, with each triple chosen, there are 3!, or 6, ways to rearrange the triple, as seen in Figure 7-38. Therefore there are 3! times as many permutations as combinations. To find the number of combinations, we divide the number of permutations, 24, by 3!, or 6, to obtain 4. The four committees are {A, B, C}, {A, B, D}, {B, C, D}, and {A, C, D}.

In general, we use the following rule to count combinations.

Combinations Rule

To find the number of combinations possible in a counting problem, first use the Fundamental Counting Principle to find the number of permutations and then divide by the number of ways in which each choice can be arranged.

Symbolically, the number of combinations of n objects taken r at a time is denoted $_nC_r$. From the preceding rule, we develop the following formula:

$$_nC_r = \frac{_nP_r}{_rP_r} = \frac{\dfrac{n!}{(n-r)!}}{r!} = \frac{n!}{r!(n-r)!}$$

It is not necessary to memorize this formula; we can always find the number of combinations by using the reasoning developed in the committee example.

E X A M P L E
7-19

The Library of Science Book Club offers three free books from a list of 42. If you circle three choices from a list of 42 numbers on a postcard, how many possible choices are there?

Solution By the Fundamental Counting Principle, there are $42 \cdot 41 \cdot 40$ ways to choose the three free books. Because each set of three circled numbers could be rearranged $3 \cdot 2 \cdot 1$ ways, there is an extra factor of 3! in the original $42 \cdot 41 \cdot 40$ ways. Therefore the number of combinations possible for three books is

$$\frac{42 \cdot 41 \cdot 40}{3!} = 11,480.$$

E X A M P L E
7-20

At the beginning of the second quarter of a mathematics class for elementary-school teachers, each of the class's 25 students shook hands with each of the other students exactly once. How many handshakes took place?

Solution Since the handshake between persons A and B is the same as that between persons B and A, this is a problem of choosing combinations of 25 people two at a time. There are

$$_{25}C_2 = \frac{25 \cdot 24}{2!} = 300$$

different handshakes.

E X A M P L E
7-21

Given a class of 12 girls and 10 boys, answer each of the following:

a. In how many ways can a committee of five consisting of 3 girls and 2 boys be chosen?
b. What is the probability that a committee of five, chosen at random from the class, consists of 3 girls and 2 boys?
c. How many of the possible committees of five have no boys?
d. What is the probability that a committee of five, chosen at random from the class, consists only of girls?

Solution **a.** Based on the information in the problem, we do not assign special functions to members on a committee and, hence, the order of the children on a committee does not matter. From 12 girls we can choose 3 girls in $_{12}C_3$ ways. Each of these choices can be paired with $_{10}C_2$ combinations of boys. By the Fundamental Counting Principle, the total number of committees is

$$_{12}C_3 \cdot {}_{10}C_2 = \frac{12 \cdot 11 \cdot 10}{3!} \cdot \frac{10 \cdot 9}{2} = 9900.$$

b. The total number of committees of 5 is $_{22}C_5$ or 26,334. Using part (a), we find the probability that a committee of five will consist of 3 girls and 2 boys to be

$$\frac{_{12}C_3 \cdot {}_{10}C_2}{_{22}C_5} = \frac{9900}{26,334} \doteq 0.3759.$$

c. The number of ways to choose 5 girls from the 12 girls in the class is

$$_{10}C_0 \cdot {}_{12}C_5 = 1 \cdot {}_{12}C_5 = \frac{12 \cdot 11 \cdot 10 \cdot 9 \cdot 8}{5 \cdot 4 \cdot 3 \cdot 2 \cdot 1} = 792.$$

d. $\dfrac{_{12}C_5}{_{22}C_5} = \dfrac{792}{26334} \doteq 0.030075$

PROBLEM SOLVING   **A True-False Test Problem**

In the following "Peanuts" cartoon, suppose Peppermint Patty took a six-question true-false test. If she answered each question true or false at random, what is the probability that she answered 50% of the questions correctly?

Understanding the Problem   A score of 50% indicates that Peppermint Patty answered $\frac{1}{2}$ of the six questions, or three questions, correctly. She answered the questions true or false at random, so the probability that she answered a given question correctly is $\frac{1}{2}$.

We are asked to determine the probability that Patty answered exactly three of the questions correctly.

Devising a Plan   We do not know which three questions Patty missed. She could have missed any three out of six on the test. Suppose she answered questions 2, 4, and 5 incorrectly. In this case, she would have answered questions 1, 3, and 6 correctly. We can compute the probability of this set of answers by *using the branch of a tree diagram*, as in Figure 7-39, where *C* represents a correct answer and *I* represents an incorrect answer.

FIGURE 7-39

Multiplying the probabilities along the branches, we obtain $\left(\frac{1}{2}\right)^6$ as the probability of answering questions 1 through 6 in the following way: *C I C I I C*. There are other ways to answer exactly three questions correctly: for example, *C C C I I I*. The probability of answering questions 1 through 6 in this way is also $\left(\frac{1}{2}\right)^6$. The number of ways to answer the questions is simply the number of ways of arranging three *C*'s and three *I*'s in a row, which is also the number of ways of choosing three correct questions out of six, that is, $_6C_3$. Because all these arrangements give Patty a score of 50%, the desired probability is the sum of the probabilities for each arrangement.

Carrying Out the Plan   There are $_6C_3$, or 20, sets of answers similar to the one in Figure 7-39, with three correct and three incorrect answers. The product of the probabilities for each of these sets of answers is $\left(\frac{1}{2}\right)^6$, so the sum of the probabilities for all 20 sets is $20 \cdot \left(\frac{1}{2}\right)^6$, or approximately 0.3125. Thus Peppermint Patty has a probability of 0.3125 of obtaining a score of exactly 50% on the test.

Looking Back   It seems paradoxical to learn that the probability of obtaining a score of 50% on a six-question true-false test is not close to $\frac{1}{2}$. As an extension of the problem, suppose a passing score is a score of at least 70%. Now what is the probability that Peppermint Patty will pass? What is the probability of her obtaining a score of at least 50% on the test? If the test is a six-question multiple-choice test with five alternative answers for each question, what is the probability of obtaining a score of at least 50% by random guessing?

PROBLEM SOLVING   <u>**Matching Letters to Envelopes**</u>

Stephen placed three letters in envelopes while he was having a telephone conversation. He addressed the envelopes and sealed them without checking if each letter was in the correct envelope. What is the probability that each of the letters was inserted correctly?

Understanding the Problem   Stephen sealed three letters in addressed envelopes without checking to see if each was in the correct envelope. We are to determine the probability that each of the three letters was placed correctly. This probability could be found if we knew the sample space, or at least how many elements are in the sample space.

Devising a Plan   To aid in solving the problem, we represent the respective letters as *a*, *b*, and *c* and the respective envelopes as *A*, *B*, and *C*. For example, a correctly placed letter *a* would be in envelope *A*. To construct the sample space, we use the strategy of *making a table*. The table should show all the possible permutations of letters in envelopes. Once the table is completed, we can determine the probability that each letter is placed correctly.

Carrying Out the Plan   Table 7-6 is constructed by using the envelope labels *A*, *B*, and *C* as headings and listing all ways that letters *a*, *b*, and *c* could be placed in the envelopes. Case 1 is the only case out of 6 in which each of the envelopes is labeled correctly, so the probability that each envelope is labeled correctly is $\frac{1}{6}$.

Table 7-6

Addresses

	A	B	C
1	a	b	c
2	a	c	b
3	b	a	c
4	b	c	a
5	c	a	b
6	c	b	a

(Letters labels rows 1–6 on the left side)

Looking Back   Is the probability of having each letter placed incorrectly the same as the probability of having each letter placed correctly? A first guess might be that the probabilities are the same, but that is not true. Why?

We also could have used a counting argument to solve the problem. Given an envelope, there is only one correct letter to place in the envelope. Thus there is one correct way to place the letters in the envelopes. By the Fundamental Counting Principle, there are $3 \cdot 2 \cdot 1$ ways of choosing the letters to place in the envelopes, so the probability of having the letters correctly placed is $\frac{1}{6}$.

ONGOING ASSESSMENT 7-5

1. The eighth-grade class at a grade school has 16 girls and 14 boys. How many different boy-girl dates can be arranged?

2. If a coin is tossed five times, in how many different ways can the sequence of heads and tails appear?

3. The telephone prefix for a university is 243. The prefix is followed by four digits. How many telephones are possible before a new prefix is needed?

4. Radio stations in the United States have call letters that begin with either K or W. Some have three letters; others have four letters. How many sets of three-letter call letters are possible? How many sets of four-letter call letters are possible?

5. Carlin's Pizza House offers 3 kinds of salad, 15 kinds of pizza, and 4 kinds of dessert. How many different three-course meals can be ordered?

6. Decide whether each of the following is true or false:
   a. $6! = 6 \cdot 5!$ b. $3! + 3! = 6!$
   c. $\dfrac{6!}{3!} = 2!$ d. $\dfrac{6!}{3} = 2!$
   e. $\dfrac{6!}{5!} = 6$ f. $\dfrac{6!}{4!2!} = 15$
   g. $n!(n + 1) = (n + 1)!$

7. In how many ways can the letters in the word *SCRAMBLE* be rearranged?

8. How many two-person committees can be formed from a group of six people?

9. Find the number of ways to rearrange the letters in the following words:
   a. *OHIO*   b. *ALABAMA*
   c. *ILLINOIS*   d. *MISSISSIPPI*
   e. *TENNESSEE*

10. In a car race, there are six Chevrolets, four Fords, and two Pontiacs. In how many ways can the 12 cars finish if we consider only the makes of the cars?

11. Assume a class has 30 members.
    a. In how many ways can a president, a vice president, and a secretary be selected?
    b. How many committees of three people can be chosen?

12. A basketball coach was criticized in the newspaper for not trying out every combination of players. If the team roster has 12 players, how many five-player combinations are possible?

13. A five-volume numbered set of books is placed randomly on a shelf. What is the probability that the books will be numbered in the correct order from left to right?

14. Take 10 points in a plane, no three of them on a line. How many straight lines can be drawn if each line is drawn through a pair of points?

15. Sally has four red flags, three green flags, and two white flags. How many nine-flag signals can she run up a flag-pole?

16. Find the number of shortest paths from point *A* to point *B* along the edges of the cubes in each of the following. (For example, in (a) one shortest path is *A-C-D-B*.)

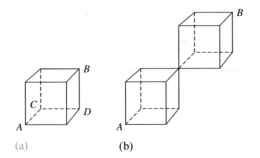

(a)   (b)

17. At a party, 28 handshakes took place. Each person shook hands exactly once with each of the others present. How many people were at the party?

18. A committee of three people is selected at random from a set consisting of seven Americans, five French people, and three English people.
    a. What is the probability that the committee consists of all Americans?
    b. What is the probability that the committee has no Americans?

19. How many different five-card hands can be dealt from a standard deck of 52 playing cards?

20. License plates in a certain state have three letters followed by three digits. How many different plates are possible if no repetitions of letters or numbers are allowed?

21. In a certain lottery game, 54 numbers are randomly mixed and six are selected. A person must pick all six numbers to win. Order is not important. What is the probability of winning?

22. Social Security numbers are in the form ###-##-####, where each symbol represents a number 0 through 9. How many Social Security numbers are possible using this format?

23. The probability of a basketball player's making a free throw successfully at any time in a game is $\frac{2}{3}$. If the player attempts ten free throws in a game, what is the probability that exactly six are made?

24. A fair die is rolled eight times. What is the probability of getting
    a. 1 on each of the eight rolls?
    b. 6 exactly twice in the eight rolls?
    c. 6 at least once in the eight rolls?

25. Two fair dice are rolled five times and the sum of the numbers that come up is recorded. Find the probability of getting
    a. a sum of 7 on each of the five rolls.
    b. a sum of 7 exactly twice in the five rolls.

26. From a group of 10 boys and 12 girls, a committee of 4 students is chosen at random. What is the probability that

    a. all four members on the committee will be girls?
    b. there will be at least one girl on the committee?
    c. all four members of the committee will be boys?

27. From a group of 20 Britons, 21 Italians, and 4 Danes, a committee of 8 people is chosen at random. Find the probability that (Express your answers using notation for combinations.)
    a. the committee will consist of 2 Britons, 4 Italians, and 2 Danes.
    b. the committee will have no Britons.
    c. there will be at least one Briton on the committee.
    d. all members of the committee will be Britons.

28. What are the odds against a royal flush in poker, that is, a ten, jack, queen, king, and ace all of the same suit?

29. How many different 12-person juries can be selected from a pool of 24 people?

Communication

30. The terms *Fundamental Counting Principle, permutations,* and *combinations* are all used to work with counting problems. In your own words, explain how all these terms are related and how they are used.

31. Explain why $0! = 1$.

32. a. A bicycle lock has three reels, each of which contains the numbers 0 through 9. To open the lock, you must enter the numbers in the correct order, such as 369 or 455, where one number is chosen from each reel. How many different possibilities are there for the numbers to open the lock? Explain how you arrived at your answer.
    b. The lock in the cartoon below is called a *combination* lock. Explain why this is probably not a good name for this lock for someone who has studied counting problems.

REAL LIFE ADVENTURES by Gary Wise and Lance Aldrich

The hacksaw industry would be in serious trouble without the combination-lock industry.

33. a. Ten people are to be seated on 10 chairs in a line. Among them is a family of 3 that does not want to be separated. How many different seating arrangements are possible? Explain how you arrived at your answer.
    b. How many possible seating arrangements are there in part (a) in which the family members do not sit all together? Explain how you arrived at your answer.
34. In how many ways can five couples be seated in a row of 10 chairs if no couple is separated? Explain how you arrived at your answer.

Open-Ended

35. Suppose the Department of Motor Vehicles uses only six spaces and the numbers 0 through 9 to create its license plates. Numbers can be repeated.
    a. How many license plates are possible?
    b. Based on the 2000 census, determine whether there are any states in which the answer in (a) might provide enough license plates?
    c. If you were in charge of making license plates for the state of California, describe the method you would use to ensure you would have enough license plates.
36. On a roulette wheel, the probability of winning when you pick a particular number is $\frac{1}{38}$. Suppose your friend pays $1.00 to play the game, and if his number is picked, he wins $36. Is this a fair game? What would happen if you played this game a large number of times. Explain your answers.

Cooperative Learning

37. The following triangular array of numbers is a part of **Pascal's triangle**:

													Row
						1							(0)
					1		1						(1)
				1		2		1					(2)
			1		3		3		1				(3)
		1		4		6		4		1			(4)
	1		5		10		10		5		1		(5)
1		6		15		20		15		6		1	(6)

a. In your group, decide how the triangle was constructed and complete the next two rows.
b. Describe at least three number patterns in Pascal's triangle.
c. Find the sum of the numbers in each row. Predict the sum of the numbers in row ten.
d. The entries in row two are just $_2C_0$, $_2C_1$, and $_2C_2$. Have different members of your group investigate whether a similar pattern holds for other rows in Pascal's triangle.
e. Describe how you could use combinations to find any entry in Pascal's triangle.

Review Problems

38. Two cards are drawn at random without replacement from a deck of 52 cards. What is the probability that
    a. at least one card is an ace?
    b. exactly one card is red?
39. If two regular dice are tossed, what is the probability of tossing a sum greater than 10?
40. Two coins are tossed. You win $5.00 if both coins are heads and $3.00 if both coins are tails and lose $4.00 if the coins do not match. What is the expected value of this game? Is this a fair game?

BRAIN TEASER

An airplane can complete its flight if at least $\frac{1}{2}$ of its engines are working. If the probability that an engine fails is 0.01 and all engine failures do not depend on each other, what is the probability of a successful flight if the plane has

a. two engines?   b. four engines?

Hint for Solving the Preliminary Problem

First we need to use the given data to find the experimental probability that a single smoke detector will work properly. We could then use the complement of this probability and carry out the computations on a branch of a tree diagram until the product of the probabilities is less than 1/10,000.

QUESTIONS FROM THE CLASSROOM

1. A student claims that if a fair coin is tossed and comes up heads five times in a row, then, according to the law of averages, the probability of tails on the next toss is greater than the probability of heads. What is your reply?

2. A student observes the following spinner and claims that the color red has the highest probability of appearing, since there are two red areas on the spinner. What is your reply?

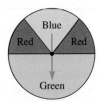

3. A student tosses a coin three times, and tails appears each time. The student concludes that the coin is not fair. What is your response?

4. An experiment consists of tossing a coin twice. The student reasons that there are three possible outcomes: two heads, one head and one tail, or two tails. Thus $P(HH) = \frac{1}{3}$. What is your reply?

5. A student would like to know the difference between two events being independent and two events being mutually exclusive. How would you answer her?

6. In response to the question, "If a fair die is rolled twice, what is the probability of rolling a pair of fives?" a student replies, "One third, because $\frac{1}{6} + \frac{1}{6} = \frac{1}{3}$." How do you respond?

7. A student wonders why probabilities cannot be negative. What is your response?

8. A student claims that "if the probability of an event is $\frac{3}{5}$, then there are three ways the event can occur and only five elements in the sample space." How do you respond?

9. A student claims that if the odds in favor of winning a game are $a:b$, then out of every $a + b$ games she would win a games. Hence the probability of winning the game is $\frac{a}{a + b}$. Is the student's reasoning correct? Why or why not?

10. A student does not understand the meaning of $_4P_0$. The student wants to know how we can consider permutations of four objects chosen zero at a time. How do you respond?

11. A student wants to know why, if we can define 0! as 1, we cannot define $\frac{1}{0}$ as 1. How do you respond?

12. A student is not sure when to add and when to multiply probabilities. How do you respond?

13. Alberto is to spin the spinners shown below and compute the probability of two blacks. He looks at the spinners and says the answer is $\frac{1}{2}$ because $\frac{1}{2}$ of the areas of the circles are black. How do you respond?

CHAPTER OUTLINE

I. Probability
   A. Probabilities can be determined **experimentally (empirically)** or **theoretically**.
   B. A **sample space** is the set of all possible **outcomes** of an **experiment**.
   C. An **event** is a subset of a sample space.
   D. Outcomes are **equally likely** if each outcome is as likely to occur as another.
   E. If all outcomes of an experiment are *equally likely*, the **probability of an event** A from sample space S is given by

   $$P(A) = \frac{n(A)}{n(S)}.$$

   F. An **impossible event** is an event with a probability of 0. An impossible event can never occur.
   G. A **certain event** is an event with a probability of 1. A certain event is sure to happen.

   H. If A is an event and $A \subseteq S$ and S is the sample space, then $0 \leq P(A) \leq 1$.
   I. Two events are **mutually exclusive** if, and only if, exactly one of the events can occur at any given time— that is, if, and only if, the events are disjoint.
   J. The probability of the **complement of an event** is given by $P(\overline{A}) = 1 - P(A)$, where A is the event and $\overline{A}$ is its complement.
   K. **Multiplication rule for probabilities**   For all **multistage experiments**, the probability of the outcome along any path of a tree diagram is equal to the product of all the probabilities along the path.
   L. If A and B are independent events, then $P(A \cup B) = P(A) + P(B) - P(A \cap B)$.
   M. If events E_1 and E_2 are **independent**—that is, the outcome of one does not depend on the outcome of the other—then $P(E_1 \text{ and } E_2) = P(E_1) \cdot P(E_2)$.

N. Simulations can play an important part in probability. Fair coins, dice, spinners, and random-digit tables are useful in performing simulations.

II. Odds, expected value, and conditional probability

A. The **odds in favor** of an event A are given by

$$\frac{P(A)}{P(\overline{A})} = \frac{P(A)}{1 - P(A)}.$$

B. The **odds against** an event A are given by

$$\frac{P(\overline{A})}{P(A)} = \frac{1 - P(A)}{P(A)}.$$

C. If events A and B are events in sample space S and $P(A) \neq 0$, then the **conditional probability** that event B occurs given that event A occurs is

$$P(B|A) = \frac{P(A \cap B)}{P(A)}.$$

D. If, in an experiment, the possible outcomes are numbers $a_1, a_2, \ldots, a_n$, occurring with probabilities $p_1, p_2, \ldots, p_n$, respectively, then the **expected value** (**mathematical expectation**) E is defined as

$$E = a_1 \cdot p_1 + a_2 \cdot p_2 + a_3 \cdot p_3 + \ldots + a_n \cdot p_n.$$

E. A **fair game** is a game in which the expected net winnings or expected value is \$0.

III. Counting principles

A. Fundamental Counting Principle If an event M can occur in m ways and, after it has occurred, event N can occur in n ways, then event M followed by event N can occur in $m \cdot n$ ways.

B. Permutations are arrangements in which order is important. The number of permutations of r elements chosen from n elements is given by:

$$_nP_r - \frac{n!}{(n - r)!}$$

C. The expression $n!$, called n **factorial**, represents the product of all the natural numbers less than or equal to n. 0! is defined as 1.

D. Permutations of like objects If a set contains n elements, of which r_1 are of one kind, r_2 are of another kind, and so on through r_k, then the number of different arrangements of all n elements is equal to

$$\frac{n!}{r_1! \cdot r_2! \cdot r_3! \cdot \ldots \cdot r_k!}.$$

E. Combinations are arrangements in which order is *not* important. To find the number of combinations possible, first use the Fundamental Counting Principle to find the number of permutations and then divide by the number of ways in which each choice can be arranged:

$$_nC_r = \frac{_nP_r}{_rP_r}$$

C H A P T E R   R E V I E W

1. A coin is flipped 3 times and heads (H) or tails (T) are recorded.
   a. List all the elements in the sample space.
   b. List the elements in the event "at least two heads appear."
   c. Find the probability that the event in part (b) occurs.

2. Suppose the names of the days of the week are placed in a box and one name is drawn at random.
   a. List the sample space for this experiment.
   b. List the event consisting of outcomes that the day drawn starts with the letter T.
   c. What is the probability of drawing a day that starts with T?

3. If you have a jar of 1000 jelly beans and you know that $P(\text{Blue}) = \frac{4}{5}$ and $P(\text{Red}) = \frac{1}{8}$, list several things you can say about the beans in the jar.

4. In the 1960 presidential election, John F. Kennedy received 34,226,731 votes and Richard M. Nixon received 34,108,157. If a 1960 voter is chosen at random, answer the following:

   a. What is the probability that the person voted for Kennedy?
   b. What is the probability that the person voted for Nixon?
   c. What are the odds that a person chosen at random did not vote for Nixon?

5. A box contains three red balls, five black balls, and four white balls. Suppose one ball is drawn at random. Find the probability of each of the following events:
   a. A black ball is drawn.
   b. A black or a white ball is drawn.
   c. Neither a red nor a white ball is drawn.
   d. A red ball is not drawn.
   e. A black ball and a white ball are drawn.
   f. A black or white or red ball is drawn.

6. One card is selected at random from an ordinary set of 52 cards. Find the probability of each of the following events:
   a. A club is drawn.
   b. A spade and a 5 are drawn.
   c. A heart or a face card is drawn.
   d. A jack is not drawn.

7. A box contains five colored balls and four white balls. If three balls are drawn one by one, find the probability that they are all white if the draws are made as follows:
   a. With replacement
   b. Without replacement

8. Consider the following two boxes. If a letter is drawn from box 1 and placed into box 2 and then a letter is drawn from box 2, what is the probability that the letter is an *L*?

9. Use the following boxes for a two-stage experiment. First select a box at random and then select a letter at random from the box. What is the probability of drawing an *A*?

10. Consider the following boxes. Draw a ball from box 1 and put it into box 2. Then draw a ball from box 2 and put it into box 3. Finally, draw a ball from box 3. Construct a tree diagram for this experiment and calculate the probability that the last ball chosen is colored.

11. What are the odds in favor of drawing a jack when one card is drawn from an ordinary deck of playing cards?

12. A die is rolled once. What are the odds against rolling a prime number?

13. If the odds in favor of a certain event are 3 to 5, what is the probability that the event will occur?

14. A game consists of rolling two dice. Rolling double ones pays $7.20. Rolling double sixes pays $3.60. Any other roll pays nothing. What is the expected value for this game?

15. A total of 3000 tickets have been sold for a drawing. If one ticket is drawn for a single prize of $1000, what is a fair price for a ticket?

16. In a special raffle, a ticket costs $2. You mark any 4 digits on a card (repetition and 0 are allowed). If you select the winning number, you win $15,000. What is the expected value?

17. How many four-digit numbers can be formed if the first digit cannot be 0 and the last digit must be 2?

18. A club consists of ten members. In how many different ways can a group of three people be selected to go on a European trip?

19. Find the number of ways that four flags can be displayed on a flagpole, one above the other, if ten different flags are available.

20. Five women live together in an apartment. Two have blue eyes. If two of the women are chosen at random, what is the probability that they both have blue eyes?

21. Five horses (Applefarm, Bandy, Cash, Deadbeat, and Egglegs) run in a race.
   a. In how many ways can the first-, second-, and third-place horses be determined?
   b. Find the probability that Deadbeat finishes first and Bandy finishes second in the race.
   c. Find the probability that the first-, second-, and third-place horses are Deadbeat, Egglegs, and Cash, in that order.

22. Al and Ruby each roll an ordinary die once. What is the probability that the number of Ruby's roll is greater than the number of Al's roll?

23. Amy has a quiz on which she is to answer any three of the five questions. If she is equally well versed on all questions and chooses three questions at random, what is the probability that question 1 is not chosen?

24. How many batting lineups are there for the nine players of a baseball team if the center fielder must bat fourth and the pitcher last?

25. For all values of n and r, when $r \leq n$, does $_nC_r = \,_nC_{n-r}$? Explain.

26. On a certain street are three traffic lights. At any given time, the probability that a light is green is 0.3. What is the probability that a person will hit all three lights when they are green?

27. A three-stage rocket has the following probabilities for failure. The probability for failure at stage one is $\frac{1}{6}$; at stage two, $\frac{1}{8}$; and at stage three, $\frac{1}{10}$. What is the probability of a successful flight, given that the first stage was successful?

28. How could each of the following be simulated by using a random-digit table?
   a. Tossing a fair die
   b. Picking three months at random from the 12 months of the year
   c. Spinning the spinner shown

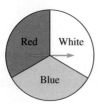

29. If a dart is thrown at the following tangram dart board and we assume the dart lands at random on the board, what is the probability of its landing in each of the following areas?

a. Area *A*   **b.** Area *B*   c. Area *C*

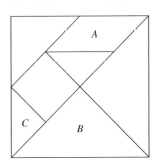

30. The points *M, N, O, P,* and *Q* in the following figure represent exits on a highway (the numbers represent miles). An accident occurs at random between points *M* and *Q*. What is the probability that it has occurred between *N* and *O*?

SELECTED BIBLIOGRAPHY

Aspinwall, L., and K. Shaw. "Enriching Students' Mathematical Intuition with Probability Games and Tree Diagrams." *Mathematics Teaching in the Middle School* 6 (December 2000): 214–220.

Brahier, D. "Genetics as a Context for the Study of Probability." *Mathematics Teaching in the Middle School* 5 (December 1999): 214–221.

Brulag, D. "Choice and Chance in Life: The Game of 'Skunk.'" *Mathematics Teaching in the Middle School* 1 (April 1994): 28–33.

Edwards, T., and S. Hensien. "Using Probability Experiments to Foster Discourse." *Teaching Children Mathematic* 6 (April 2000): 524–529.

English, L. "Problem Solving with Combinations." *Arithmetic Teacher* 40 (October 1992): 72–77.

Ewbank, W., and J. Ginther. "Probability on a Budget." *Mathematics Teaching in the Middle School* 7 (January 2002): 280–283.

Fennell, F. "Implementing the *Standards*: Probability." *Arithmetic Teacher* 38 (December 1990): 18–22.

Freda, A. "Roll the Dice; An Introduction to Probability." *Mathematics Teaching in the Middle School* 4 (October 1998): 85–89.

Hardy, M. "Burgers, Graphs, and Combinations." *Mathematics Teaching in the Middle School* 7 (October 2001): 72–76.

Jardine, D. "Looking at Probability through a Historical Lens." *Mathematics Teaching in the Middle School* 6 (September 2000): 50–54.

Kader, G., and M. Perry. "Push-Penny: What Is Your Expected Score?" *Mathematics Teaching in the Middle School* 3 (February 1998): 370–377.

Kanold, C. "Teaching Probability Theory Modeling Real Problems." *Mathematics Teacher* 85 (April 1994): 232–235.

Lappan, G., et al. "Area Models for Probability." *Mathematics Teacher* 80 (November 1987): 650–654.

Lappan, G., and M. Winter. "Probability Simulation in Middle School." *Mathematics Teacher* 73 (September 1980): 446–449.

Lawrence, A. "From *The Giver* to *The Twenty-One Balloons*: Explorations with Probability." *Mathematics Teaching in the Middle School* 4 (May 1999): 504–509.

Litwiller, B., and D. Duncan. "Combinatorics Connections: Playoff Series and Pascal's Triangle." *Mathematics Teacher* 85 (October 1992): 532–535.

Litwiller, B., and D. Duncan. "Matching Garage Door Openers." *Mathematics Teacher* 85 (March 1992): 217–219.

Martin, H., and J. Zawojewski. "Dealing with Data and Chance: An Illustration from the Middle School Addendum to the Standards." *Arithmetic Teacher* 41 (December 1993): 220–223.

May, E. "Are Seven-Game Baseball Playoffs Fairer?" *Mathematics Teacher* 85 (October 1992): 528–531.

Norton, R. "Determining Probabilities by Examining Underlying Structure." *Mathematics Teaching in the Middle School* 7 (October 2001): 78–82.

Quinn, R. "Using Attribute Blocks to Develop a Conceptual Understanding of Probability." *Mathematics Teaching in the Middle School* 6 (January 2001): 290–294.

Quinn, R. "Having Fun with Baseball Statistics." *Mathematics Teaching in the Middle School* 1 (May 1996): 780–785.

Shaughnessy, M. "Probability and Statistics." *Mathematics Teacher* 86 (March 1993): 244–248.

Shaughnessy, J., and T. Dick. "Monty's Dilemma: Should You Stick or Switch?" *Mathematics Teacher* 84 (April 1991): 252–256.

Tarr, J. "Providing Opportunities to Learn Probability Concepts." *Teaching Children Mathematic* 8 (April 2002): 482–487.

Thompson, D., and R. Austin. "Socrates and the Three Little Pigs: Connecting Patterns, Counting Trees, and Probability." *Mathematics Teaching in the Middle School* 5 (November 1999): 156–161.

Van Zoest, L., and R. Walker. "Racing to Understand Probability." *Mathematics Teaching in the Middle School* 3 (October 1997): 162–170.

Wiest, L., and R. Quinn. "Exploring Probability through an Evens-Odds Dice Game." *Mathematics Teaching in the Middle School* 4 (March 1999): 358–362.

Woodword, E., and M. Woodword. "Expected Value and the Wheel of Fortune Game." *Mathematics Teacher* 87 (January 1994): 13–17.

–8–

Data Analysis/Statistics: An Introduction

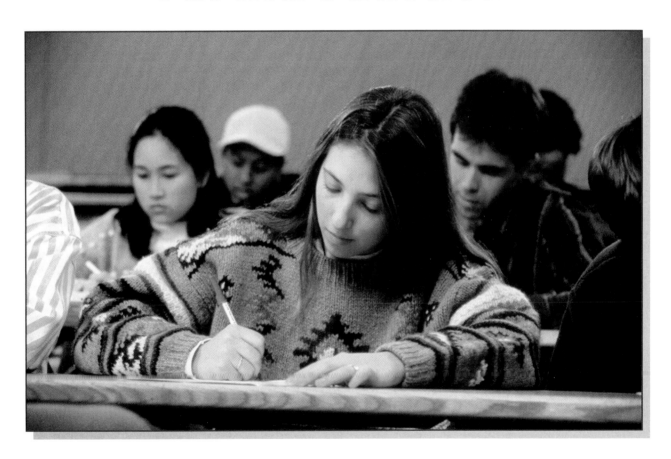

P R E L I M I N A R Y   P R O B L E M

Ouida had test grades of 91, 89, 83, 78, 76, and 75. Her teacher uses the average (mean) of the test scores as the final grade of the class. Ouida has the option of keeping her current test average *or* replacing the highest and lowest scores that she currently has with a single score on a final exam. If Ouida chooses to take the final exam, what is the lowest score she can receive and still maintain at least the average that she currently has?

I n the *Principles and Standards*, we find the following:

Instructional programs from prekindergarten through grade 12 should enable all students to

- *formulate questions that can be addressed with data and collect, organize, and display relevant data to answer them;*
- *select and use appropriate statistical methods to analyze data;*
- *develop and evaluate inferences and predictions that are based on data . . .* (p. 48)

In addition, we find the following:

The amount of data available to help make decisions in business, politics, research, and everyday life is staggering. Consumer surveys guide the development and marketing of products. Polls help determine political-campaign strategies, and experiments are used to evaluate the safety and efficacy of new medical treatments. Statistics are often misused to sway public opinion on issues or to misrepresent the quality and effectiveness of commercial products. Students need to know about data analysis and related aspects of probability in order to reason statistically—skills necessary to becoming informed citizens and intelligent consumers. (p. 48)

Data analysis, which usually refers to a more informal approach to statistics, is a relatively new term in mathematics. However, *statistics* once referred to numerical information about state or political territories. The word itself comes from the Latin *statisticus*, meaning "of the state." In today's world, much of statistics involves making sense of data.

In the early grades, students explore the basic ideas of statistics by collecting data, organizing the data pictorially, and then interpreting information from their displays. The ideas of gathering, representing, and analyzing data are expanded in the later grades. In this chapter we deal with representations of data and also key statistical concepts including measures of central tendency and of variation. We also address some uses and misuses of statistics.

HISTORICAL NOTE

The seventeenth-century work of John Graunt (1620–1674) and the eighteenth-century work of Adolph Quetelet (1796–1874) involved making predictions on the collection of data. Graunt dealt with birth and death records, and Quetelet dealt with crime and mortality rates. Florence Nightingale (1820–1910) worked with mortality tables during the Crimean War to get British hospitals to improve care. Other notables who worked with data collection and analysis include Sir Francis Galton (1822–1911) and Gregor Mendel (1822–1884). In the twentieth century, work continued by Ronald Fisher (1890–1962) in genetics and Andrei Nikolaevich Kolmogorov (1903–1987), who also was chairman of the Commission for Mathematical Education under the Presidium of the Academy of Sciences of the former Soviet Union. Also working in this century have been John Tukey (1915–2000), who developed many of the current graphical representations used to depict statistics, including stem-and-leaf plots, Gertrude Mary Cox (1900–1978), who wrote *Experimental Designs* in 1950, a classic textbook on design and analysis of replicated experiments, and Sir Ronald Fisher (1890–1962), a pioneer of modern statistics.

Statistical Graphs

Visual illustrations are an important part of statistics. Such illustrations or graphs take many forms: pictographs, circle graphs, pie charts, dot plots, line plots, scatterplots, stem-and-leaf plots, box plots, frequency tables, histograms, bar graphs, and frequency polygons or line graphs. A *graph* is a picture that displays **data**. Graphs are used to try to tell a story. In the "Herman" cartoon, we see a graph being used to display some particular data to make a point to an audience. What message do you think the presenter is trying to get across? What labels might appear on the vertical and horizontal axes?

data

"That's the last time I go on vacation."

NOW TRY THIS 8-1

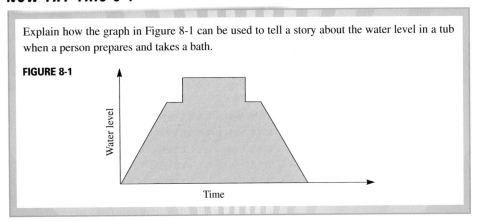

Explain how the graph in Figure 8-1 can be used to tell a story about the water level in a tub when a person prepares and takes a bath.

FIGURE 8-1

In the *Principles and Standards*, we find the following:

A fundamental idea in prekindergarten through grade 2 is that data can be organized or ordered and that this "picture" of the data provides information about the phenomenon or question. In grades 3–5, students should develop skill in representing their data, often using bar graphs, tables, or line plots. . . . Students in grades 6–8 should begin to compare the effectiveness of various types of displays in organizing the data for further analysis or in presenting the data clearly to an audience. As students deal with larger or more complex data sets, they can reorder data and represent data in graphs quickly, using technology so that they can focus on analyzing the data and understanding what they mean. (p. 49)

In particular, we find the following by grade level.

In prekindergarten through grade 2 all students should

- *pose questions and gather data about themselves and their surroundings;*
- *sort and classify objects according to their attributes and organize data about the objects;*
- *represent data using concrete objects, pictures, and graphs;*
- *describe parts of the data and the set of data as a whole to determine what the data show.*

In grades 3–5 all students should

- *design investigations to address a question and consider how data-collection methods affect the nature of the data set;*
- *collect data using observations, surveys, and experiments;*
- *represent data using tables and graphs such as line plots, bar graphs, and line graphs;*
- *recognize the differences in representing categorical and numerical data;*
- *describe the shape and important features of a set of data and compare related data sets, with an emphasis on how the data are distributed;*
- *use measures of center, focusing on the median, and understand what each does and does not indicate about the data set;*
- *compare different representations of the same data and evaluate how well each representation shows important aspects of the data;*
- *propose and justify conclusions and predictions that are based on data and design studies to further investigate the conclusions or predictions.* (p. 400)

In grades 6–8 all students should

- *formulate questions, design studies, and collect data about a characteristic shared by two populations or different characteristics within one population;*
- *select, create, and use appropriate graphical representations of data, including histograms, box plots, and scatterplots;*
- *find, use, and interpret measures of center and spread, including mean and interquartile range;*
- *discuss and understand the correspondence between data sets and their graphical representations, especially histograms, stem-and-leaf plots, box plots, and scatterplots;*
- *use observations about differences between two or more samples to make conjectures about the populations from which the samples were taken;*
- *make conjectures about possible relationships between two characteristics of a sample on the basis of scatterplots of the data and approximate lines of fit;*
- *use conjectures to formulate new questions and plan new studies to answer them.* (p. 401)

Pictographs

pictograph   One type of graph seen in newspapers and magazines is a **pictograph**. In a pictograph, a symbol or an icon is used to represent a quantity of items. A *legend* tells what the symbol represents. Pictographs are used frequently to show comparisons of outputs, as in Figure 8-2. A major disadvantage of pictographs is evident in Figure 8-2(a). The month of September contains a partial bundle of newspapers. It is impossible to tell from the graph the weight of that bundle with any accuracy.

FIGURE 8-2

(a)   Weights of Newspapers

(b)   Students per Class

REMARK   All graphs need titles; if needed, legends should be shown.

Dot Plots/Line Plots

dot plot ◆ line plot   Next we examine a **dot plot** or **line plot**. A dot plot, unlike a pictograph, has no numerical values. Dot plots provide a quick, simple way of organizing numerical data. Typically, we use them when there is only one group of data with fewer than 50 values.

REMARK   Dot plots and line plots are not always synonymous.

Suppose the 30 students in Abel's class received the following test scores:

82 97 70 72 83 75 76 84 76 88 80 81 81 52 82

82 73 98 83 72 84 84 76 85 86 78 97 97 82 77

A dot plot for the class scores consists of a horizontal number line on which each score is denoted by an x above the corresponding number-line value, as shown in Figure 8-3. The number of x's above each score indicates how many times each score occurred.

FIGURE 8-3

Scores on Abel's Class Test

Figure 8-3 yields information about Abel's class exam scores. For example, 3 students scored 76 and 4 scored greater than 90. We also see that the low score was 52, the high score was 98, and the most frequent score was 82. Several features of the data become more obvious when dot plots are used. For example, outliers, clusters, and gaps are appar-

outlier   ent. An **outlier** is a data point whose value is significantly greater or less than other values, such as the score of 52 in Figure 8-3. (Outliers are discussed in greater detail in the next

cluster   section.) A **cluster** is an isolated group of points, such as the one located at the scores 97

gap   and 98. A **gap** is a large space between points, such as the one between 88 and 97.

If a dot plot is constructed on grid paper, then shading in the squares with ×'s and adding a vertical axis depicting the scale allows the formation of a *bar graph*, as in Figure 8-4. (Bar graphs are discussed in more detail later in this section.)

FIGURE 8-4

Scores on Abel's Class Test

REMARK   The break in the horizontal axis is denoted by a squiggle and indicates that a part of the number line is missing.

Stem-and-Leaf Plots

stem-and-leaf plot   The **stem-and-leaf plot** is akin to the dot plot, but the number line is usually vertical, and digits are used rather than ×'s. A stem-and-leaf plot of test scores for Abel's class is shown in Figure 8-5.

FIGURE 8-5

Scores on Abel's Class Test

5	2
6	
7	0223566678
8	011222233444568
9	7778

9 | 7 represents 97

stems

leaves

The numbers on the left side of the vertical line are the **stems**, and the numbers on the right side are the **leaves**. In Figure 8-5, the stems are the tens digits of the scores on the test and the leaves are the units digits. In this case the legend, "9|7 represents 97," shows how to read the plot.

NOW TRY THIS 8-2

Construct a stem-and-leaf plot using the data in Table 8-1, which lists the presidents of the United States and their ages at death.

Table 8-1

President	Age at Death	President	Age at Death	President	Age at Death
George Washington	67	Millard Fillmore	74	Theodore Roosevelt	60
John Adams	90	Franklin Pierce	64	William Taft	72
Thomas Jefferson	83	James Buchanan	77	Woodrow Wilson	67
James Madison	85	Abraham Lincoln	56	Warren Harding	57
James Monroe	73	Andrew Johnson	66	Calvin Coolidge	60
John Q. Adams	80	Ulysses Grant	63	Herbert Hoover	90
Andrew Jackson	78	Rutherford Hayes	70	Franklin Roosevelt	63
Martin Van Buren	79	James Garfield	49	Harry Truman	88
William H. Harrison	68	Chester Arthur	57	Dwight Eisenhower	78
John Tyler	71	Grover Cleveland	71	John Kennedy	46
James K. Polk	53	Benjamin Harrison	67	Lyndon Johnson	64
Zachary Taylor	65	William McKinley	58	Richard Nixon	81

ordered stem-and-leaf plot

The data in a stem-and-leaf plot, as in Figure 8-5, are in order from least to greatest on a given row. This is an **ordered stem-and-leaf plot**. It should be noted that stem-and-leaf plots are sometimes first constructed with data in the order given. To be useful, most users then order data.

There is no unique way to construct stem-and-leaf plots. Smaller numbers are usually placed at the top so that when the plot is turned counterclockwise 90°, it resembles a bar graph or a histogram (discussed later in this section). Important advantages of stem-and-leaf plots are that they can be created by hand rather easily and they do not become unmanageable when the number of values becomes large. Moreover, no original values are lost in a stem-and-leaf plot. For example, in a stem-and-leaf plot of the presidents' ages at death, we could tell that the youngest age at death was 46 and that exactly two presidents died when they were 90. A disadvantage of stem-and-leaf plots is that we do lose some information; for example, we know from such a plot that a president died at age 88, but we do not know which one.

Following is a summary of how to construct a stem-and-leaf plot.

1. Find the high and low values of the data.
2. Decide on the stems.
3. List the stems in a column from least to greatest.
4. Use each piece of data to create leaves to the right of the stems on the appropriate rows.

5. If the plot is to be ordered, list the leaves in order from least to greatest.
6. Add a legend identifying the values represented by the stems and leaves.
7. Add a title explaining what the graph is about.

Back-to-Back Stem-and-Leaf Plots

If two sets of related data with a similar number of data values are to be compared, a *back-to-back stem-and-leaf plot* can be used. In this case, two plots are made: one with leaves to the right, and one with leaves to the left. For example, if Abel gave the same test to two classes, he might prepare a back-to-back stem-and-leaf plot, as shown in Figure 8-6.

FIGURE 8-6

Abel's Test Class Scores

Second-period Class		Fifth-period Class
20	5	2
531	6	24
99987542	7	1257
875420	8	4456999
1	9	2457
	10	0

0 | 5 | represents
a score of 50

| 5 | 2 represents a
score of 52

NOW TRY THIS 8-3

In the stem-and-leaf plots in Figure 8-6, which class do you think did better on the test? Why?

EXAMPLE 8-1

Group the presidents in Table 8-1 into two groups, the first consisting of George Washington to Ulysses Grant and the second consisting of Rutherford Hayes to Richard Nixon.

a. Create a back-to-back stem-and-leaf plot of the two groups and see if there appears to be a difference in ages at death between the two groups.
b. Which group of presidents seems to have lived longer?

Solution **a.** Because the ages at death vary from 46 to 90, the stems vary from 4 to 9. In Figure 8-7, the first 18 presidents are listed on the left and the remaining 18 on the right.

FIGURE 8-7

Ages of Presidents at Death

Early Presidents		Later Presidents
	4	96
63	5	787
364587	6	707034
741983	7	0128
053	8	81
0	9	0

3 | 8 | represents
83 years old

| 6 | 7 represents
67 years old

    b. The early presidents seem, on average, to have lived longer because the ages at the high end, especially in the 70s and 80s, come more often from the early presidents. The ages at the lower end come more often from the later presidents. For the stems in the 50s and 60s, the numbers of leaves are about equal.

A stem-and-leaf plot shows how wide a range of values the data cover, where the values are concentrated, whether the data has any symmetry, where gaps in the data are, and whether any data points are decidedly different from the rest of the data.

Frequency Tables

classes The stem-and-leaf plot in Figure 8-5 naturally groups scores into intervals or **classes**. For the data in Figure 8-5, the following classes are used: 50–59, 60–69, 70–79, 80–89, and 90–99. Each class has interval size 10; that is, 10 different scores can fall within the interval 50 and 59. Students often incorrectly report the interval size as 9 because $59 - 50 = 9$.

grouped frequency table A slightly different way to display data is to use a grouped frequency table. A **grouped frequency table** shows how many times a certain piece of data occurs. For example, consider the data in Table 8-1 for the ages of the presidents at death. These results may be summarized in the grouped frequency table in Table 8-2.

Table 8-2

Ages at Death	Tally	Frequency
40–49	II	2
50–59	IHt	5
60–69	IHt IHt II	12
70–79	IHt IHt	10
80–89	IHt	5
90–99	II	2
	Total	36

Table 8-2 does not show the actual death ages. Although Table 8-2 shows that 12 ages appear in the interval 60 through 69, it does not show the particular ages in the interval. As the interval size increases, more information is lost. Choices of interval size may vary. Classes should be chosen to accommodate all the data and each item should fit into only one class; that is, the classes should not overlap. Data from frequency tables can be graphed, as will be shown below.

Histograms and Bar Graphs

histogram The data in Table 8-2 can be pictured graphically using a **histogram**, a graph closely related to a stem-and-leaf plot. Figure 8-8(a) shows a histogram of the frequencies in Table 8-2. A histogram is made up of adjoining rectangles, or bars. In this case, the death ages are shown on the horizontal axis and the numbers along the vertical axis give the scale for the frequency. The frequencies of the death ages are shown by the bars, which are all the same width. The scale on the vertical axis must be uniform. In addition, all histograms should have the axes labeled and should include a title identifying the graph's content.

FIGURE 8-8

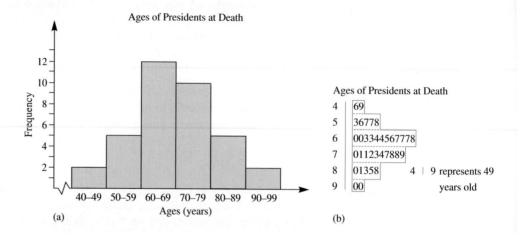

(a)

(b)

Histograms can be made easily from single-sided stem-and-leaf plots. For example, if we take the stem-and-leaf plot in Figure 8-8(b) and enclose each row (set of leaves) in a bar, we will have what looks like a histogram. We can make Figure 8-8(b) resemble Figure 8-8(a) by rotating the graph 90° counterclockwise. Histograms show gaps and clusters just as stem-and-leaf plots do. However, with a histogram we cannot retrieve data as we can in a stem-and-leaf plot. Another disadvantage of a histogram is that it is often necessary to estimate the heights of the bars.

The student page shows a histogram in grade 7. Read the page and try problem 21.

bar graph

A **bar graph** typically has spaces between the bars. A bar graph showing the heights in centimeters of five students is given in Figure 8-9.

FIGURE 8-9

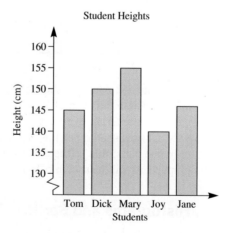

The height of each bar represents the height in centimeters of each student named on the horizontal axis. Each space between bars is usually one half the width of a bar.

double-bar graph

Double-bar graphs can be used to make comparisons in data. For example, the data in the back-to-back stem-and-leaf plot of Figure 8-7 can be pictured as shown in Figure 8-10. The dark-colored bars represent the later presidents, while the light-colored bars represent the earlier presidents.

Sample School Book Page:
HISTOGRAMS

GOAL

LEARN HOW TO...
* interpret histograms

AS YOU...
* examine the results of a 5K race

KEY TERM
* histogram

Exploration 3

Histograms

▷ In Exploration 2, you saw running times displayed with a stem-and-leaf plot. Sometimes another type of data display is more convenient.

The Schoolpower Laguna Beach Classic is run along the Pacific coast and through a scenic canyon. In 1996, runners aged 3–78 helped raise money to aid local schools.

20 Discussion Nearly 1000 people ran in the 5 km, or 5K, race of the 1996 Schoolpower Laguna Beach Classic. Their times ranged from the winning time of 15 min 36 s to times slightly over an hour.

a. Estimate the range of the running times in the 5K race.

b. Suppose you had a list of all the individual running times for the 5K race. Why would it be difficult to use a stem-and-leaf plot to display the data?

▷ The frequency table below shows how many runners finished the 1996 Schoolpower 5K race in each of the time intervals listed. The *histogram* below displays the same data.

1996 Schoolpower Laguna Beach Classic Finishing Times	
Interval (min:s)	Frequency
15:00–24:59	168
25:00–34:59	462
35:00–44:59	218
45:00–54:59	121
55:00–64:59	21

A histogram is a bar graph with no spaces between the bars.

21 a. Why does the first time interval start at 15 rather than at 0?

b. In which time interval did most of the runners finish the race?

c. How many runners finished in the 45:00–54:59 time interval?

Source: Middle Grades MATH Thematics, Book 2, McDougal Littell, 2002 (p. 318).

FIGURE 8-10

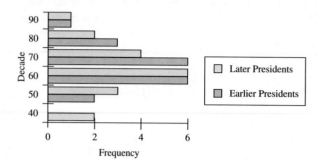

Ages of Presidents at Death

Line Graphs

line graph   Another graphical form used to present data is a line graph. A **line graph** typically shows the trend of a variable over time. Time is usually marked on the horizontal axis with the variable being considered marked on the vertical axis. An example is seen in Figure 8-11, where Sanna's weight over 10 years is depicted. Observe that consecutive data points are connected by line segments.

FIGURE 8-11

Sanna's Weight over Ten Years

Scatterplots

scatterplot   A relationship between two sets of data is sometimes determined by using a **scatterplot**. Figure 8-12(a) shows a scatterplot depicting the relation between the number of hours studied and quiz scores. The highest score is a 10 and the lowest is 1.

   Frequently, not all of the points on a scatterplot fall on a particular line, but on some
trend line   scatterplots the points fall near a **trend line**. A trend line is used to make predictions. If a trend line slopes up from left to right, as in Figure 8-12(b), then we say there is a *positive correlation* between the number of hours studied and the quiz score. From the trend line in Figure 8-12(b), we would predict that students who studied 7 hours might score 6.

   In Figure 8-12, note that the student who studied 4 hours and received a score of 1 did no better than the one who did not study. Although there is a possible correlation between studying and scoring well on a quiz, we cannot deduce cause and effect based on scatterplots and trend lines.

FIGURE 8-12

(a)

(b)

In Chapter 10, we will write equations of trend lines that are considered *lines-of-best fit*; that is, lines that appear to most closely fit the data. If the trend line slopes downward to the right, we can also make predictions; we say there is a *negative correlation*. If the points do not approximately fall about any line, we say there is *no correlation*. Scatterplots also show clusters of points and outliers. Examples of various correlations are given in Figure 8-13.

FIGURE 8-13

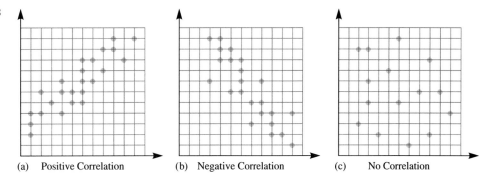

(a)   Positive Correlation   (b)   Negative Correlation   (c)   No Correlation

Circle Graphs (Pie Charts)

circle graph ◆ pie chart

Another type of graph used to represent data is the circle graph. A **circle graph**, or **pie chart**, consists of a circular region partitioned into disjoint sections, with each section representing a part or percentage of the whole. A circle graph shows how parts are related to the whole. An example of a circle graph is given in Figure 8-14.

FIGURE 8-14

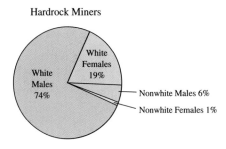

Hardrock Miners

Example 8-2 shows how a circle graph can be constructed from given data.

**EXAMPLE
8-2**

Construct a circle graph for the information in Table 8-3, which is based on information taken from a U.S. Bureau of the Census Report, (2000).

Table 8-3

Age	Number of U.S. People (nearest million)
Under 5	19
5–19	61
20–34	59
35–54	82
55–65	24
Over 65	35
Total	280*

*Rounding makes this total less than the census shows.

Solution The entire circle represents the total 280 million people. The measure of the central angle (an angle whose vertex is at the center of the circle) of each sector of the graph is proportional to the fraction or percent of the population the section represents. For example, the measure of the angle for the sector for the under-5 group is 19/280, or approximately 7% of the circle. Because the entire circle is 360°, then 7% of 360°, which is approximately 25°, should be devoted to the under-5 group. Similarly, we can compute the number of degrees for each age group, as shown in Table 8-4. (What formulas could be used in a spreadsheet to create columns 3 and 4?)

Table 8-4

Age	Ratio	Approximate Percent	Approximate Degrees
Under 5	19/280	7	25
5–19	61/280	22	79
20–34	59/280	21	76
35–54	82/280	29	105
55–65	24/280	9	32
Over 65	35/280	12	43
Total	280/280	100	360

The percents and degrees in Table 8-4 are only approximate. A compass can be used to draw a circle and a protractor can be used to draw the sectors in the circle graph, as shown in Figure 8-15.

FIGURE 8-15

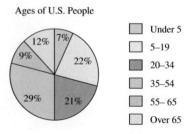

Ages of U.S. People

▨	Under 5
☐	5–19
▨	20–34
☐	35–54
▨	55–65
☐	Over 65

Choosing a Data Display

Choosing an appropriate data display is not always easy. Each type of graph is suitable for presenting certain kinds of data. In this section you have seen pictographs, dot plots, stem-and-leaf plots, histograms, bar graphs, line graphs, scatterplots, and circle graphs (pie charts). Some uses follow:

Bar graph—Used to compare numbers of data items in grouped categories

Histogram—Used to compare numbers of data items grouped in numerical intervals

Box plot—Used to show median, quartile, and extremes of data set

Stem-and-leaf plot—Used to show each value in a data set and to group values into intervals

Scatter plot—Used to show the relationship between two sets of data

Line graph—Used to show how data values change over time

Circle graph—Used to show the division of a whole into parts

NOW TRY THIS 8-4

a. Which graph in Figure 8-16 or 8-17 displays the data more effectively? Why?

FIGURE 8-16

FIGURE 8-17

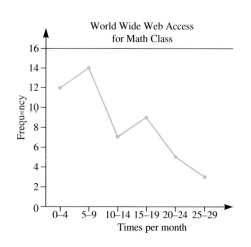

Note: Figure 8-17 could have been formed by connecting the midpoints of the tops of the bars in Figure 8-16.

b. To show each of the following, which graph is the best choice: line graph, bar graph, or circle graph? Why?

(i) The percentage of a college student's budget devoted to housing, clothing, food, tuition and books, taxes

(ii) Showing the change in the cost of living over the past 12 months

1. Make a pictograph to represent the data in the following table. Use 🥤 to represent 10 glasses of lemonade sold.

Glasses of Lemonade Sold

Day	Tally	Frequency
Monday	ЖН ЖН ЖН	15
Tuesday	ЖН ЖН ЖН ЖН	20
Wednesday	ЖН ЖН ЖН ЖН ЖН ЖН	30
Thursday	ЖН	5
Friday	ЖН ЖН	10

2. The following pictograph shows the approximate number of people who speak the six most common languages on Earth.
   a. About how many people speak Spanish?
   b. About how many people speak English?
   c. About how many more people speak Mandarin than Arabic?

Number of People Speaking the Six
Most Common Languages

Arabic	🔴 ◗
English	🔴 🔴 🔴 ◖
Hindi	🔴 🔴 ◗
Mandarin	🔴 🔴 🔴 🔴 🔴 🔴 ◖
Russian	🔴 🔴 ◖
Spanish	🔴 🔴 ◗

Each 🔴 represents 100 million people.

3. Following are the ages of the 30 students from Washington School who participated in the city track meet. Draw a dot plot to represent these data.

10	10	11	10	13	8	10	13	14	9
14	13	10	14	11	9	13	10	11	12
11	12	14	13	12	8	13	14	9	14

4. The following stem-and-leaf plot gives the weight in pounds of all 15 students in the Algebra 1 class at East Junior High:
   a. Write the weights of the 15 students.
   b. What is the weight of the lightest student in the class?
   c. What is the weight of the heaviest student in the class?

Weights of Students in East Junior
High Algebra 1 Class

```
 7 | 24
 8 | 112578
 9 | 2478
10 | 3          10 | 3 represents
11 |                  103 lb
12 | 35
```

5. Draw a histogram based on the stem-and-leaf plot in problem 4.

6. Toss a coin 30 times.
   a. Construct a dot plot for the data.
   b. Draw a histogram for the data.

7. The following figure shows a bar graph of the rainfall in centimeters during the last school year.

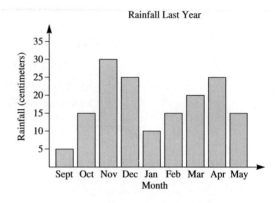

Rainfall Last Year

   a. Which month had the most rainfall, and how much did it have?
   b. How much total rain fell in October, December, and January?

8. HKM Company employs 40 people of the following ages:

34	58	21	63	48	52	24	52	37	23
23	34	45	46	23	26	21	18	41	27
23	45	32	63	20	19	21	23	54	62
41	32	26	41	25	18	23	34	29	26

   a. Draw a stem-and-leaf plot for the data.
   b. Are more employees in their 40s or in their 50s?
   c. How many employees are less than 30 years old?
   d. What percentage of the people are 50 years or older?

9. Given the following bar graph, estimate the length of the following rivers:
   a. Mississippi   **b.** Columbia

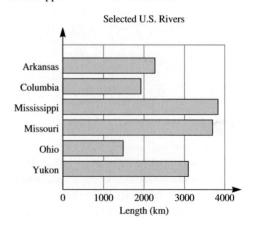

Selected U.S. Rivers

10. Draw a bar graph to represent the data in the following table:

Distances from the Sun

Planet	Distance (millions of miles)
Earth	93
Mars	142
Mercury	36
Venus	67

11. Five coins are tossed 64 times. A distribution for the number of heads obtained is shown in the following table. Draw a histogram for the data.

Number of Heads	0	1	2	3	4	5
Frequency	2	10	20	20	10	2

12. The following table shows the grade distribution for the final examination in the mathematics course for elementary teachers. Draw a circle graph for the data.

Grade	Frequency
A	4
B	10
C	37
D	8
F	1

13. In a circle graph, a sector containing 32° represents what percentage of the data?

14. A single bar graph is sometimes used like a circle graph. If the bar is 8 cm, how long is each piece?

Savings	Rent	Food	Auto Payment	Tuition
10%	30%	12%	27%	x%

15. The following are the amounts (to the nearest dollar) paid by 25 students for textbooks during the fall term:

```
35   42   37   60   50
42   50   16   58   39
33   39   23   53   51
48   41   49   62   40
45   37   62   30   23
```

a. Draw an ordered stem-and-leaf plot to illustrate the data.
b. Construct a grouped frequency table for the data, starting the first class at $15.00 with intervals of $5.00 each.
c. Draw a histogram of the data.

16. The following horizontal bar graph gives the top speeds of several animals:

a. Which is the slowest animal shown?
b. How fast can a chicken run?
c. Which animal can run twice as fast as a rabbit?
d. Can a lion outrun a zebra?

17. The following bar graph shows the life expectancies for men and women:

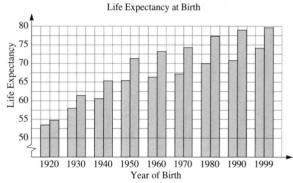

a. Whose life expectancy has changed the most since 1920?
b. In 1920, about how much longer was a woman expected to live than a man?
c. In 1999, about how much longer was a woman expected to live than a man?

18. The following graph shows how the value of a car depreciates each year. This graph allows us to find the trade-in value of a car for each of 5 yr. The percents given in the graph are based on the selling price of the new car.

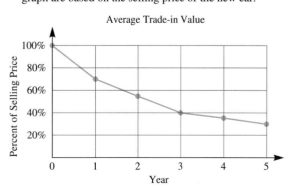

a. What is the approximate trade-in value of a $12,000 car after 1 yr?

b. How much has a $20,000 car depreciated after 5 yr?

c. What is the approximate trade-in value of a $20,000 car after 4 yr?

d. Dani wants to trade in her car before it loses half its value. When should she do this?

19. Use the following circle graph to answer the following questions:

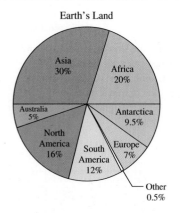

Earth's Land

a. Which is the largest continent?

b. Which continent is about twice the size of Antarctica?

c. How does Africa compare in size to Asia?

d. Which two continents make up about half of Earth's surface?

e. What is the ratio of the size of Australia to North America?

f. If Europe has approximately 4.1 million mi² of land, what is the total area of the land on Earth?

20. A list of presidents, with the number of children for each, follows:

1. Washington, 0	**2.** J. Adams, 5
3. Jefferson, 6	**4.** Madison, 0
5. Monroe, 2	**6.** J. Q. Adams, 4
7. Jackson, 0	**8.** Van Buren, 4
9. W. H. Harrison, 10	**10.** Tyler, 14
11. Polk, 0	**12.** Taylor, 6
13. Fillmore, 2	**14.** Pierce, 3
15. Buchanan, 0	**16.** Lincoln, 4
17. A. Johnson, 5	**18.** Grant, 4
19. Hayes, 8	**20.** Garfield, 7
21. Arthur, 3	**22.** Cleveland, 5
23. B. Harrison, 3	**24.** McKinley, 2
25. T. Roosevelt, 6	**26.** Taft, 3
27. Wilson, 3	**28.** Harding, 0
29. Coolidge, 2	**30.** Hoover, 2
31. F. D. Roosevelt, 6	**32.** Truman, 1

33. Eisenhower, 2	**34.** Kennedy, 4
35. L. B. Johnson, 2	**36.** Nixon, 2
37. Ford, 4	**38.** Carter, 4
39. Reagan, 4	**40.** G. Bush, 5
41. Clinton, 1	**42.** G. W. Bush, 2

a. Construct a dot plot for these data.

b. Make a frequency table for these data.

c. What is the most frequent number of children?

21. Coach Lewis kept track of the basketball team's jumping records for a 10-year period, as follows:

Year	1993	1994	1995	1996	1997	1998
Record (nearest in.)	65	67	67	68	70	74

Year	1999	2000	2001	2002
Record (nearest in.)	77	78	80	81

a. Draw a scatterplot for the data.

b. What kind of correlation is there for these data?

22. Refer to the following scatterplot regarding movie attendance in a certain city.

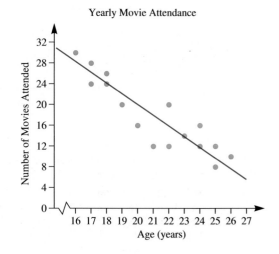

Yearly Movie Attendance

a. What type of correlation exists for these data?

b. About how many movies does an average 25-year-old attend?

c. From the data in the scatterplot, conjecture how old you think a person is who attends 16 movies a year.

23. The following table depicts the number of deaths in males in the United States from Acquired Immunodeficiency Syndrome (AIDS) by age in 1985 and in 1999.

Age (yr)	1985	1999
13–19	28	126
20–29	1503	3973
30–39	3588	14,308
40–49	1633	10,953
50–59	597	3506
60–69	159	1188

  a. Choose and construct a graph to display the data.
  b. Are any patterns of difference evident in the comparison of the two groups of data?

Communication

24. a. Discuss when a pictograph might be more appropriate than a circle graph.
  b. Discuss when a circle graph might be more appropriate than a bar graph or a line graph.
  c. Give an example of a set of data for which a stem-and-leaf plot would be more informative than a histogram.
25. Explain whether a circle graph would change if the number of data in each category were doubled.
26. Explain why the sum of the percents in a circle graph should always be 100. How could it happen that the sum is close to 100%?
27. The federal budget for one year is typically depicted with one type of visual representation. Which one is used and why?
28. Tell whether it is appropriate to use a bar graph for each of the following. If so, draw the appropriate graph.
  a. U.S. Population
  b. Continents of the World

Year	Population
1920	105,710,620
1930	122,775,046
1940	131,669,275
1950	150,697,361
1960	179,323,175
1970	203,302,031
1980	226,542,203
1990	248,765,170
2000	281,421,906

Continent	Area in Square Miles (mi²)
Africa	11,694,000
Antarctica	5,100,000
Asia	16,968,000
Australia	2,966,000
Europe	4,066,000
North America	9,363,000
South America	6,886,000

29. Discuss the trend in U.S. car sales from 1983 to 2000 based on the information in the given circle graphs.

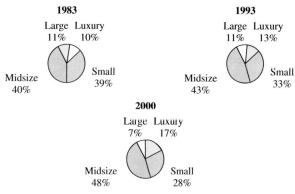

U.S. Car Sales by Vehicle Size and Type

Data taken from *The World Almanac and Book of Facts 2002*, World Almanac Books, 2002.

30. The following graphs give the temperatures for a certain day. Which graph is more helpful for guessing the actual temperature at 10:00 A.M.? Why?

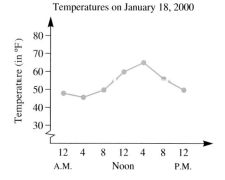

Open-Ended

31. Find six recent examples of different types of visual representations of data in your newspaper. Explain whether you think the representations are appropriate.
32. Choose a topic, describe how you would go about collecting data on the topic, and then explain how you would display your data in a graph. Tell why you chose the particular graph.

33. A graph similar to the one at right was depicted on a package of cigarettes in Canada.
  a. Make a circle graph of the data.
  b. Explain which graph you think is more effective.
  c. Explain whether you would like to see this labeling on cigarette packages in the United States.

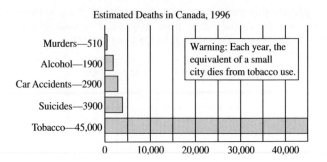

34. The problem below, from *Middle Grades Math Thematics, Book 2*, McDougal Littell, 1999, (page 332) depicts a way of finding a trend line (fitted line). Choose any scatterplot and answer questions 18a–c.

18 a. Place a piece of spaghetti on the scatter plot so that the data points are close to the spaghetti and there are about the same number of points on one side of the spaghetti as on the other side.

b. Draw a line segment along the piece of spaghetti. This is a **fitted line** for the scatter plot.

c. Discussion Do you think every person will draw the same line? Explain.

35. Study the graph below and draw some conclusions about the death rates for the selected causes.

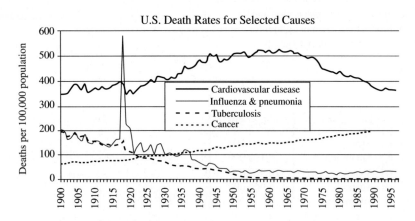

Data taken from *The World Almanac and Book of Facts 1999*, World Almanac Books, 1999.

Cooperative Learning

36. In groups, collect data on head circumference in centimeters of class members. Make a frequency table of all class data, choose an appropriate graph, and display the data. If you were a seller of hats, what is the most common size head for which you would purchase hats?

TECHNOLOGY
C O R N E R

The student page shows how scatterplots may be drawn with a spreadsheet. See how the technology you use allows you to find a trend line or fitted line.

Sample School Book Page:
SCATTER PLOTS

TECHNOLOGY — **Using Technology to Make Scatter Plots**

You can use spreadsheet software or other graphing technology to make your scatter plot for Question 17 on page 332.

Step 1 Enter the data for the graph into the spreadsheet.

Enter the data for the horizontal axis in column A.

| File | Edit | Format | Calculate | Options | View |

NUMBER OF PENNIES VS. DISTANCE

B6   × ✓   1.5

	A	B	C	D	E
1	Number of pennies	Distance (cm)			
2	5	0.5			
3	10	0.8			
4	15	1.2			
5	20	1.4			
6	25	1.5			

Enter the corresponding data for the vertical axis in column B.

Step 2 To make a graph, highlight the data you entered and choose the option that makes a chart. Then select the type of graph you want to make.

Options
Make Chart...
Protect Cells
Unprotect Cells
Add Page Break
Remove Page Break
Lock Title Position
Print Range...
Go To Cell...

Chart Options

Modify: Axis, Series, Labels, General

Gallery: Bar, Line, Scatter, Pie, Stacked Bar, X–Y Line, X–Y Scatter, Pictogram

Step 3 Experiment with the labels, grid lines, and scale until the graph appears the way you want it to. Be sure to include a title.

Number of Pennies vs. Distance

(scatter plot with x-axis "Number of pennies" 0–50 and y-axis "Distance (cm)" 0–4)

Step 4 You can print out the graph and draw a fitted line through your scatter plot as you did in Question 18 on page 332. Some graphing technology will also let you draw a fitted line or it will draw one for you.

Source: Middle Grades Math Thematics, Book 3, MacDougal Littell, 2002 (p. 333).

In the Fox Trot cartoon, Peter describes one situation where a line of best fit might be used. Decide whether you think this is appropriate or not.

8-2 Measures of Central Tendency and Variation

The media present us with a variety of data and statistics. For example, we find in the *World Almanac* that the average person's lifetime includes 6 yr of eating, 4 yr of cleaning, 2 yr of trying to return telephone calls to people who never seem to be in, 6 mo waiting at stop lights, 1 yr looking for misplaced objects, and 8 mo opening junk mail. In the previous section, we examined data by looking at graphs to display the overall distribution of values. In this section, we describe specific aspects of data by using a few carefully chosen numbers. Two important aspects of data are its *center* and its *spread*. The mean, median, and mode are **measures of central tendency** that describe where data are centered. Each of these measures is a single number that describes the data. However, each does it slightly differently. The *range, variance,* and *standard deviation* introduced later in this section describe the spread of data.

measures of central tendency

A word that is often used in statistics is *average*. For example, suppose that, as the "Far Side" cartoon on page 461 suggests, the average number of children in a family is 1.5. What does this mean? How can the average number of children be 1.5?

To explore more about averages, examine the following set of data for three teachers, each of whom claims that his or her class scored better *on the average* than the other two classes did:

Mr. Smith:	62, 94, 95, 98, 98
Mr. Jones:	62, 62, 98, 99, 100
Ms. Rivera:	40, 62, 85, 99, 99

All of these teachers are correct in their assertions because each has used a different number to characterize the scores in his or her class. In the following, we examine how each teacher can justify the claim.

THE FAR SIDE® BY GARY LARSON

© 1988 FarWorks, Inc. All Rights Reserved/Dist. by Creators Syndicate

The Far Side® by Gary Larson © 1988 FarWorks, Inc. All Rights Reserved. Used with permission.

"Bob and Ruth! Come on in. ... Have you met
Russell and Bill, our 1.5 children?"

Computing Means

arithmetic mean
average ◆ mean

The number commonly used to characterize a set of data is the **arithmetic mean**, frequently called the **average**, or the **mean**. To find the mean of scores for each of the teachers given previously, we find the sum of the scores in each case and divide by 5, the number of scores.

$$\text{Mean (Smith):} \qquad \frac{62 + 94 + 95 + 98 + 98}{5} = \frac{447}{5} = 89.4$$

$$\text{Mean (Jones):} \qquad \frac{62 + 62 + 98 + 99 + 100}{5} = \frac{421}{5} = 84.2$$

$$\text{Mean (Rivera):} \qquad \frac{40 + 62 + 85 + 99 + 99}{5} = \frac{385}{5} = 77$$

In terms of the mean, Mr. Smith's class scored better than the others. In general, we define the *arithmetic mean* as follows.

> ## Definition of Mean

The **arithmetic mean** of the numbers $x_1, x_2, \ldots, x_n$, denoted $\bar{x}$ and read "x bar," is given by
$$\bar{x} = \frac{x_1 + x_2 + x_3 + \cdots + x_n}{n}.$$

Understanding the Mean as a Balance Point

Because the mean is the most widely used measure of central tendency, we provide a model for thinking about it. Suppose a student at a rural school reports that the mean number of pets for the six students in a group is 5. Do we know anything about the distribution of these pets? All six students could have exactly five pets, as shown in the line plot in Figure 8-18(a).

FIGURE 8-18

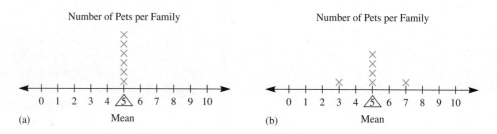

If we change the line plot as shown in Figure 8-18(b), the mean is still 5. Notice that the new line plot could be obtained by moving one value from Figure 8-18(a) 2 units to the right and then balancing this by moving one value 2 units to the left. We can think of the mean as a *balance point*.

Consider Figure 8-19, which shows the number of children for each family in a group. The mean of 5 is the balance point where the sum of the total distances from the mean to the data points above the mean equals the sum of the total distances from the mean to the data points below the mean. The sum of the distances above the mean is 3 + 5, or 8. The sum of the distances below the mean is 1 + 2 + 2 + 3, or 8. In this case, we see that the data are centered about the mean, but the mean does not belong to the set of data.

FIGURE 8-19

NOW TRY THIS 8-5

a. A litter of six puppies was born with a mean average weight of 7 pounds. List two possibilities for the weights of the pups.

b. Could the mean average of a set of scores ever be equal to the greatest score? the least score? Explain your answers.

Computing Medians

median The value exactly in the middle of an ordered set of numbers is the **median**. To find the median for the teachers' scores, we arrange each of their scores in increasing or decreasing order and pick the middle score. Intuitively, we know that half the scores are greater than the median and half are less.

Median (Smith):   62, 94, (95,) 98, 98   median = 95

Median (Jones):   62, 62, (98,) 99, 100   median = 98

Median (Rivera):   40, 62, (85,) 99, 99   median = 85

In terms of the median, Mr. Jones's class scored better than the others.

With an odd number of scores, as in the present example, the median is the middle score. With an even number of scores, however, the median is defined as the mean of the middle two scores. Thus to find the median, we add the middle two scores and divide by 2. For example, the median of the scores

64, 68, | 70, 74 | 82, 90

is given by

$$\frac{70 + 74}{2}, \text{ or } 72.$$

In general, to find the median for a set of n numbers, proceed as follows.

1. Arrange the numbers in order from least to greatest.
2. a. If n is odd, the median is the middle number.
   b. If n is even, the median is the mean of the two middle numbers.

Finding Modes

mode The **mode** of a set of data is the number that appears most frequently, if there is one. In some distributions, no number appears more than once. In other distributions, there may be more than one mode. For example, the set of scores 64, 79, 80, 82, 90 has no mode. (Some would say that this set of data has five modes, but because no one score appears more than another, we prefer to say there is no mode.)

bimodal The set of scores 64, 75, 75, 82, 90, 90, 98 is **bimodal** (two modes) because both 75 and 90 are modes. It is possible for a set of data to have too many modes for this type of number to be useful in describing the data.

For the three classes listed previously, if the mode is used as the criterion, Ms. Rivera's class scored better than the others.

Mode (Smith):   62, 94, 95, 98, 98   mode = 98

Mode (Jones):   62, 62, 98, 99, 100   mode = 62

Mode (Rivera):   40, 62, 85, 99, 99   mode = 99

EXAMPLE 8-3   Find (a) the mean, (b) the median, and (c) the mode for the following collection of data:

60   60   70   95   95   100

Solution   **a.** $\bar{x} = \dfrac{60 + 60 + 70 + 95 + 95 + 100}{6} = \dfrac{480}{6} = 80$

   b. The median is $\dfrac{70 + 95}{2}$, or 82.5.

   c. The set of data is bimodal and has both 60 and 95 as modes.

EXAMPLE 8-4

When the data values are all the same, the mean, median, and mode are all the same. Describe a situation in which not all the data points are the same and the mean, median, and mode are still the same.

Solution   Answers may vary. For example, one set of data is 92, 94, 94, 94, 96, in which the mean, median, and mode are all 94.

NOW TRY THIS 8-6

   a. Suppose the average number of children per family for the employees of the university in a certain city is 2.58. Could this be a mean? median? mode? Explain why.
   b. Answer the questions in (a) if the average number of children was reported to be 2.5.

Choosing the Most Appropriate Average

Although the *mean* is the number most commonly used to describe a set of data, it may not always be the most appropriate choice.

EXAMPLE 8-5

Suppose a company employs 20 people. The president of the company earns $200,000, the vice president earns $75,000, and 18 employees earn $10,000 each. Is the mean the best number to choose to represent the "average" salary for the company?

Solution   The mean salary for this company is

$$\frac{\$200,000 + \$75,000 + 18(\$10,000)}{20} = \frac{\$455,000}{20} = \$22,750.$$

In this case, the mean salary of $22,750 is not representative. Either the median or mode, both of which are $10,000, would describe the typical salary better.

In Example 8–5, notice that *the mean is affected by extreme values.* In most cases, the *median* is not affected by extreme values. The median, however, can also be misleading, as shown in the following example.

EXAMPLE 8-6

Suppose nine students make the following scores on a test:

$$30, 35, 40, 40, 92, 92, 93, 98, 99$$

Is the median the best "average" to represent the set of scores?

Solution The median score is 92. From that score, one might infer that the individuals all scored very well, yet 92 is certainly not a typical score. In this case, the mean of approximately 69 might be more appropriate than the mode. However, with the spread of the scores, neither is very appropriate for this distribution.

The *mode*, too, can be misleading in describing a set of data with very few items that occur frequently, as shown in the following example.

E X A M P L E
8-7

Is the mode an appropriate "average" for the following test scores?

$$40, 42, 50, 62, 63, 65, 98, 98$$

Solution The mode of the set of scores is 98 because this score occurs most frequently. The score of 98 is not representative of the set of data because of the large spread of scores.

The choice of which number to use to represent a particular set of data is not always easy. In the example involving the three teachers, each teacher chose the average that best suited his or her claim. The type of average should always be specified.

PROBLEM SOLVING **The Missing Grades**

Students of Dr. Van Horn were asked to keep track of their own grades. One day, Dr. Van Horn asked the students to report their grades. One student had lost the papers but claims to remember the grades on four of six assignments: 100, 82, 74, and 60. In addition, the student remembered that the mean of all six papers was 69, and the other two papers had identical grades. What were the grades on the other two homework papers?

Understanding the Problem The student had scores of 100, 82, 74, and 60 on four of six papers. The mean of all six papers was 69, and two identical scores were missing. The missing scores must be less than 60; otherwise, from observation, the mean could not be less than three of the four known scores and greater than the fourth one given.

Devising a Plan To find the missing grades, we use the strategy of *writing an equation* for x. The mean is obtained by finding the sum of the scores and then dividing by the number of scores, which is 6. So if we let x stand for each of the two missing grades, we have

$$69 = \frac{100 + 82 + 74 + 60 + x + x}{6}.$$

Carrying Out the Plan We now solve the equation as follows:

$$69 = \frac{100 + 82 + 74 + 60 + x + x}{6}$$

$$69 = \frac{316 + 2x}{6}$$

$$49 = x$$

Since the solution to the equation is $x = 49$, each of the two missing scores was 49.

Looking Back The answer of 49 seems reasonable, since the mean of 69 is less than three of the four given scores. We can check this by computing the mean of the scores 100, 82, 74, 60, 49, 49 and showing that it is 69.

Measures of Dispersion

range

The mean, median, and mode provide limited information about the whole distribution of data. For example, if you sit in a sauna for 30 minutes and then in a refrigerated room for 30 minutes, an average temperature of your surroundings for that hour might sound comfortable. To tell how much the data are scattered, we develop measures of *spread* or *dispersion*. Perhaps the easiest way to measure spread is the **range**, the difference between the greatest and the least values in a data set. For example, the range in the set of data 1, 3, 7, 8, 10 is $10 - 1 = 9$. However, just because the range of two sets of data is the same, the data do not have to have the same dispersion. For example, the data set 1, 10, 10, 10, 10 also has a range of 9 and is spread quite differently from the first collection of data. For this reason we need other measures of dispersion besides the range.

Another measure of dispersion is the *interquartile range (IQR)*. The IQR is the range of the middle half of the data. Consider the following set of thirteen test scores:

$$20 \quad 25 \quad 40 \quad 50 \quad 50 \quad 60 \quad 70 \quad 75 \quad 80 \quad 80 \quad 90 \quad 100 \quad 100$$

The range for this set of scores is $100 - 20 = 80$. The median score for this set of data is 70. We mark this location with a vertical bar between the 7 and the 0 as shown below.

$$20 \quad 25 \quad 40 \quad 50 \quad 50 \quad 60 \quad 7\,|\,0 \quad 75 \quad 80 \quad 80 \quad 90 \quad 100 \quad 100$$

vertical bar

Next, we consider only the data values to the left of the **vertical bar** and draw another vertical bar where the median of those values is located:

$$20 \quad 25 \quad 40\,|\,50 \quad 50 \quad 60$$

lower quartile ◆ first quartile (Q_1)

upper quartile (Q_3)

The score of $45 = (40 + 50)/2$ is the median of the scores less than the median of all scores and is the **lower quartile**. The lower quartile, or the **first quartile**, is denoted Q_1. One quarter, or 25%, of the scores lie at or below Q_1. Similarly, we can find the upper, or third, quartile (Q_3), which is $(80 + 90)/2$, or 85. The **upper quartile (Q_3)** is the median of the scores greater than the median of all scores. Three quarters, or 75%, of the scores lie at or below Q_3. Thus we have divided the scores into four groups of three scores each:

$$20 \quad 25 \quad 40\,|\,50 \quad 50 \quad 60 \quad 7\,|\,0 \quad 75 \quad 80 \quad 80\,|\,90 \quad 100 \quad 100$$

| Lower extreme | Lower quartile | Median | Upper quartile | Upper extreme |

interquartile range (IQR)

The **interquartile range (IQR)** is the difference between the upper quartile and the lower quartile. In this case, $IQR = 85 - 45 = 40$. The IQR is itself another useful measure of variation because it is less influenced by extreme values. The IQR contains the middle 50% of the values.

Box Plots

box plot ◆ box-and-whisker plot

A **box plot**, or **box-and-whisker plot**, is a way to display data visually and draw informal conclusions. Box plots show only certain data. These plots are visual representations of the *five-number summary* of the data. The five numbers are the median, the upper and lower quartiles, and the least and greatest values in the distribution. The center, the spread, and the overall range are immediately evident by looking at the plot.

To construct a box plot, we need data along with its median, upper and lower quartiles, and extremes marked with vertical bars. To construct the box, we connect the vertical bars at the quartiles to form a box. We draw segments from each end of the box to the extreme values to form the whiskers. The box plot can be either vertical or horizontal. A vertical version of the box plot for the given data is shown in Figure 8-20.

FIGURE 8-20

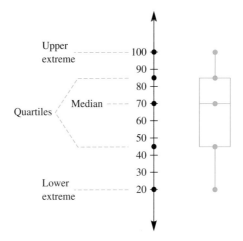

The box plot gives a fairly clear picture of the spread of the data. If we look at the graph in Figure 8-20, we can see that the median is 70, the maximum value is 100, the minimum value is 20, and the upper and lower quartiles are 45 and 85. The median is above the center of the box and so there are more scores above than below it.

EXAMPLE 8-8

What are the minimum and maximum values, the median, and the lower and upper quartiles of the box plot shown in Figure 8-21?

FIGURE 8-21

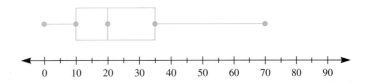

Solution   The minimum value is 0, the maximum value is 70, the median is 20, the lower quartile is 10, and the upper quartile is 35.

Outliers

An *outlier* is a value that is widely separated from the rest of a group of data. For example, in a set of scores such as

$$91 \quad 92 \quad 92 \quad 93 \quad 93 \quad 93 \quad 94$$

all data are grouped close together and no values are widely separated. However, in a set of scores such as

$$21 \quad 92 \quad 92 \quad 93 \quad 93 \quad 93 \quad 95 \quad 150$$

both 21 and 150 are widely separated from the rest of the data. These values are potential outliers. The upper and lower extreme values are not necessarily outliers. In data such as

$$75 \quad 90 \quad 91 \quad 92 \quad 92 \quad 93 \quad 93,$$

outlier   it is not easy to decide, so we develop a convention for determining outliers. *An **outlier** is any value that is more than 1.5 times the interquartile range above the upper quartile or below the lower quartile.* Statisticians sometimes use values different from 1.5 to determine outliers.

   It is common practice to indicate outliers with asterisks. Whiskers are then drawn to the extreme points that are not *outliers.* To investigate how this works, consider Example 8-9.

**EXAMPLE
8-9**

Draw a box plot of the data in Table 8-5 and identify possible outliers.

Table 8-5   Final Medal Standings for Top 20 Countries—2000 Summer Olympics

Country	Medals	
United States	97	
Russia	88	
China	59	
Australia	58	
Germany	57	$Q_3 = 45.5$
France	38	
Italy	34	
Cuba	29	
Britain	28	
South Korea	28	
Romania	26	Median $(Q_2) = 27$
Netherlands	25	
Ukraine	23	
Japan	18	
Hungary	17	$Q_1 = 17$
Belarus	17	
Poland	14	
Canada	14	
Bulgaria	13	
Greece	13	

Data taken from *The World Almanac and Book of Facts 2002*, World Almanac Books, 2002.

Solution The extreme scores are 97 and 13, the median is 27, $Q_1 = 17$, and $Q_3 = 45.5$. The IQR is $45.5 - 17$, or 28.5. Outliers are scores that are greater than $45.5 + 1.5(28.5)$, or 88.25, or less than $17 - 1.5(28.5)$, or $^-25.75$. Therefore, in this data 97 is the only outlier. A box plot is given in Figure 8-22. Notice that the whisker stops at the extreme point 13 on the lower end and at 88 on the upper end. The outlier is indicated with an asterisk.

FIGURE 8-22

Comparing Sets of Data

Box plots are used primarily for large sets of data or for comparing several distributions. The stem-and-leaf plot is usually a much clearer display for a single distribution. Parallel box plots drawn using the same number line give us the easiest comparison of medians, extreme scores, and the quartiles for the sets of data. As an example, we construct parallel box plots comparing the data in Table 8-6.

Table 8-6 Median Earnings of Males and Females, 1960–1992 (full-time workers age 15 and older)

Year	Women	Men
1960	$ 3,257	$ 5,368
1970	5,323	8,966
1980	11,197	18,612
1983	13,915	21,881
1984	14,780	23,218
1985	15,624	24,195
1986	16,232	25,256
1987	16,911	25,946
1988	17,606	26,656
1989	18,769	27,331
1990	19,822	27,678
1991	20,553	29,421
1992	21,440	30,358

Data taken from *Information Please Almanac Atlas and Yearbook 1995*, 48th Edition. Boston: Houghton Mifflin Company, 1995.

Before constructing parallel box plots, we find the five important values for each group of data. These values are given in Table 8-7.

Table 8-7

Value	Women	Men
Maximum	$21,440.00	$30,358.00
Upper quartile	19,295.50	27,504.50
Median	16,232.00	25,256.00
Lower quartile	12,556.00	20,246.50
Minimum	3,257.00	5,368.00

In this example, the IQR for men is $7,258.00. The lower cutoff point for outliers is $20,246.50 − 1.5(7,258.00), or $9,359.50. Two salaries, $5,368.00 and $8,966.00, are less than the cutoff point and thus are outliers. Checking reveals there are no outliers in the women's salaries.

Next we draw the horizontal scale and construct the box plots for the women and men using the data in Table 8-7, as shown in Figure 8-23.

FIGURE 8-23

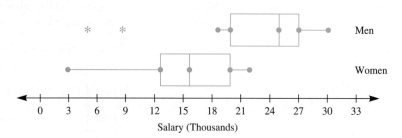

From the box plot in Figure 8-23, we can see that the salaries for men have been higher than those for women, since the extreme values, median, and quartiles for the men are greater than those for women. Also, more than 50% of the median salaries for men are greater than those for the median salaries of women over the time period.

Although we cannot spot clusters or gaps in box plots as we can with stem-and-leaf or line plots, we can more easily compare data from different sets. With box plots, we do not need to have sets of data that are approximately the same size, as we did for stem-and-leaf plots. To compare data from two or more sets using their box plots, we first study the boxes to see if they are located in approximately the same places. Next, we consider the lengths of the boxes to see if the variability of the data is about the same. We also check whether the median, the quartiles, and the extreme values in one set are greater than those in another set. If they are, the data in the first set are greater than those of the other set, no matter how we compare them. If they are not, we can continue to study the data for other similarities and differences.

NOW TRY THIS 8-7

> Using only the data from 1983 through 1992 in Table 8-6, decide whether there are outliers. How do you think the two box plots would compare for this data with the comparison made in Figure 8-23?

 Read carefully the box plots from the student text and complete problem 26.

Variance and Standard Deviation

Suppose Professors Abel and Babel each taught a section of a graduate statistics course and each had six students. Both professors gave the same final exam. The results, along with the means for each group of scores, are given in Table 8-8, with stem-and-leaf plots in Figure 8-24(a) and (b), respectively. As the stem-and-leaf plots show, the sets of data are very different. The first is more spread out, or varies more, than the second. However, each set has 60 as the mean. Each median also equals 60. Although the mean and the median for these two groups are the same, the two distributions of scores are very different.

Table 8-8

Abel's Class Scores	Babel's Class Scores
100	70
80	70
70	60
50	60
50	60
10	40
$\bar{x} = \dfrac{360}{6} = 60$	$\bar{x} = \dfrac{360}{6} = 60$

FIGURE 8-24

Professor Abel's Class Scores

```
 1 | 0
 2 |
 3 |
 4 |
 5 | 00
 6 |
 7 | 0        7 | 0 represents
 8 | 0            a score of 70
 9 |
10 | 0
```
(a)

Professor Babel's Class Scores

```
 4 | 0
 5 |
 6 | 000
 7 | 00      7 | 0 represents
                 a score of 70
```
(b)

As we have seen, there are many ways to measure the spread of data. The simplest way is to find the range. The range for Professor Abel's class is $100 - 10$, or 90. The range for Professor Babel's class is $70 - 40$, or 30. If we use the range as our measure of dispersion, we see that Abel's class is much more spread out than Babel's class. If we use

Sample School Book Page:
BOX PLOTS

▶ **Box-and-whisker plots are useful for comparing two or more sets of data. The box-and-whisker plots below show how two stone-skipping rivals have performed in competition from 1992–1995.**

Numbers of Skips: Mackinac Island Stone Skipping Tournament, 1992–1995

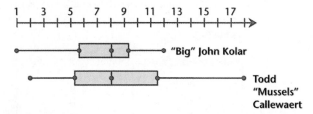

26 ✔ **CHECKPOINT** Use the box-and-whisker plots above.

a. Each year contestants make 6 throws. Each plot above shows 24 throws for the four years of competition. About how many data points are in each box? in each whisker?

b. Who had the most skips in 1992–1995 tournament play? Who had the fewest? How many skips was this for each?

c. Compare the median number of skips made by each stone skipper during the four years of tournament play.

d. The best 25% of Todd Callewaert's throws from 1992–1995 made 11.5 skips or more. How does this compare with John Kolar's throws?

e. Is it possible to tell who won most often in the years 1992–1995? Explain.

✔ **QUESTION 26**

…checks that you can interpret box-and-whisker plots.

Source: Middle School Math Thematics, Book 3, MacDougal Littell, 2002 (p. 335).

the interquartile range, the IQR for Abel's class is 30, and for Babel's class 10. Again these measures of dispersion show more of a spread for Abel's class than for Babel's.

Two other commonly used measures of dispersion are the *variance* and the *standard deviation*. These measures are based on how far the scores are from the mean. To find out how far each value differs from the mean, we subtract each value in the data from the mean to obtain the deviation. Some of these deviations may be positive, and others may be negative. Because the mean is the balance point, the total of the deviations above the mean equals the total of the deviations below the mean. (The mean of the deviations is 0 because the sum of the deviations is 0.) Squaring the deviations makes them all positive. The mean of the squared deviations is the **variance**. Because the variance involves squaring the deviations, it does not have the same units of measurement as the original observations. For example, lengths measured in feet have a variance measured in square feet. To obtain the same units as the original observations, we take the square root of the variance and obtain the **standard deviation**.

variance

standard deviation

The steps involved in calculating the variance v and standard deviation s of n numbers are as follows.

1. Find the mean of the numbers.
2. Subtract the mean from each number.
3. Square each difference found in step 2.
4. Find the sum of the squares in step 3.
5. Divide by n to obtain the variance, v.
6. Find the square root of v to obtain the standard deviation, s.

These six steps can be summarized for the numbers $x_1, x_2, x_3, \ldots, x_n$ as follows, where $\bar{x}$ is the mean of these numbers:

$$s = \sqrt{v} = \sqrt{\frac{(x_1 - \bar{x})^2 + (x_2 - \bar{x})^2 + (x_3 - \bar{x})^2 + \cdots + (x_n - \bar{x})^2}{n}}$$

REMARK In some textbooks, this formula involves division by $n - 1$ instead of by n. Division by $n - 1$ is more useful for advanced work in statistics.

The variances and standard deviations for the final exam data from the classes of Professors Abel and Babel are calculated by using Tables 8-9 and 8-10, respectively.

Table 8-9 *Abel's Scores*

x	$x - \bar{x}$	$(x - \bar{x})^2$
100	40	1600
80	20	400
70	10	100
50	$^-10$	100
50	$^-10$	100
10	$^-50$	2500
Totals 360	0	4800

$\bar{x} = \dfrac{360}{6} = 60$

$v = \dfrac{4800}{6} = 800$

$x = \sqrt{800} \doteq 28.3$

Table 8-10 *Babel's Scores*

x	$x - \bar{x}$	$(x - \bar{x})^2$
70	10	100
70	10	100
60	0	0
60	0	0
60	0	0
40	$^-20$	400
Totals 360	0	600

$\bar{x} = \dfrac{360}{6} = 60$

$v = \dfrac{600}{6} = 100$

$s = \sqrt{100} = 10$

Values far from the mean on either side will have larger positive squared deviations, whereas values close to the mean will have smaller positive squared deviations. Therefore the standard deviation is a greater number when the values from a set of data are widely spread and a lesser number (close to 0) when the data values are close together.

E X A M P L E
8-10

Professor Abel gave two group exams. Exam A had grades of 0, 0, 0, 100, 100, 100, and exam B had grades of 50, 50, 50, 50, 50, 50. Find the following for each exam:

a. Mean   **b.** Median   **c.** Standard deviation

Solution   **a.** The means for exams A and B are each 50.
b. The medians for the exams are each 50.
c. The standard deviations for exams A and B are as follows:

$$S_A = \sqrt{\frac{3(0-50)^2 + 3(100-50)^2}{6}} = 50$$

$$S_B = \sqrt{\frac{6(50-50)^2}{6}} = 0$$

Normal Distributions

To better understand how standard deviations are used as measures of dispersion, we next consider normal distributions. The graphs of normal distributions are the bell-shaped curves called normal curves. These curves often describe distributions such as IQ scores for the population of the United States.

normal curve   A **normal curve** is a smooth, bell-shaped curve that depicts frequency values distributed symmetrically about the mean. (Also, the mean, median, and mode all have the same value.) The normal curve is a theoretical distribution that extends infinitely in both directions. It gets closer and closer to the *x*-axis but never reaches it. On a normal curve, about 68% of the values lie within one standard deviation of the mean, about 95% lie within two standard deviations, and about 99.8% are within three standard deviations. The percentages represent approximations of the total percent of area under the curve. The curve and the percentages are illustrated in Figure 8-25.

FIGURE 8-25

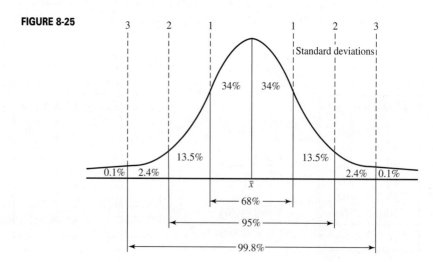

Suppose the area under the curve represents the population of the United States. Psychologists claim that the mean IQ is 100 and the standard deviation is 15. They also claim that an IQ score of over 130 represents a superior score. Because 130 is equal to the mean plus two standard deviations, we see from Figure 8-25 that only 2.5% of the population fall into this category.

E X A M P L E
8-11

When a standardized test was scored, there was a mean of 500 and a standard deviation of 100. Suppose that 10,000 students took the test and their scores had a mound-shaped distribution, making it possible to use a normal curve to approximate the distribution.

a. How many scored between 400 and 600?
b. How many scored between 300 and 700?
c. How many scored between 200 and 800?

Solution   **a.** Since one standard deviation on either side of the mean is from 400 to 600, about 68% of the scores fall in this interval. Thus, 0.68(10,000), or 6800, students scored between 400 and 600.

b. About 95% of 10,000, or 9500, students scored between 300 and 700.

c. About 99.8% of 10,000, or 9980, students scored between 200 and 800.

REMARK   About 0.2%, or 20, students' scores in Example 8-11 fall outside three standard deviations. About 10 of these students did very well on the test, and about 10 students did very poorly.

H I S T O R I C A L
N O T E

Abraham De Moivre (1667–1754), a French Huguenot, was the first to develop and study the normal curve. He was one of the first to study actuarial information, in his book *Annuities upon Lives*. He also worked in trigonometry and complex numbers. There is an interesting fable about the death of De Moivre. It is reported that he noticed that each day he required one-quarter of an hour more sleep than he had on the previous day; when the arithmetic progression for sleep reached 24 hr, he died. De Moivre's work with the normal curve went essentially unnoticed. Later, the normal curve was developed independently by Pierre Laplace (1749–1827) and Karl Friedrich Gauss (1777–1855). Gauss found so many applications for the normal curve that it is sometimes referred to as the *Gaussian curve*.

Suppose that a group of students asked their teacher to grade "on a curve." If the teacher gave a test to 200 students and the mean on the test was 71, with a standard deviation of 7, the graph in Figure 8-26 shows how the grades could be assigned. In Figure 8-26, the teacher has used the normal curve in grading. (The use of the normal curve presupposes that the teacher had a mound-shaped distribution of scores and also that the teacher arbitrarily decided to use the lines marking standard deviations to determine the boundaries of the A's, B's, C's, D's, and F's.) Thus, based on the normal curve in Figure 8-26, Table 8-11 shows the range of grades that the teacher might assign if the grades are rounded. Students who ask their teachers to grade on the curve may wish to reconsider if the normal curve is to be used.

FIGURE 8-26

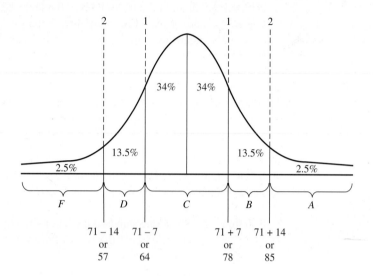

Table 8-11

Test Score	Grade	Number of People per Grade	Percentage Receiving Grade
85 and above	A	5	2.5%
78–84	B	27	13.5%
64–77	C	136	68%
57–63	D	27	13.5%
Below 57	F	5	2.5%

percentiles

When students take a standardized test such as the ACT or SAT, their scores are often reported in **percentiles**. A percentile shows a person's score relative to other scores. For example, if a student's score is at the 82nd percentile, this means that approximately 82% of those taking the test scored lower than the student and approximately 18% had higher scores.

BRAIN
T E A S E R

At a birthday party, the honoree would not tell his age but agreed to give hints. He computed and announced that the mean age of his seven party guests was 21. When 29-year-old Jill arrived at the party, the honoree announced that the mean age of the eight people was now 22. Jack, another 29-year-old, arrived next. The honoree then added his age to the set of ages of the other nine people and announced that the mean was now 27. How old was the honoree?

O N G O I N G   A S S E S S M E N T   8 - 2

1. Calculate the mean, the median, and the mode for each of the following data sets:
   a. 2, 8, 7, 8, 5, 8, 10, 5
   b. 10, 12, 12, 14, 20, 16, 12, 14, 11
   c. 18, 22, 22, 17, 30, 18, 12
   d. 82, 80, 63, 75, 92, 80, 92, 90, 80, 80
   e. 5, 5, 5, 5, 5, 10

2. a. If each of six students scored 80 on a test, find each of the following for the set of six scores:
      i. Mean   ii. Median   iii. Mode
   b. Make up another set of six scores that are not all the same but in which the mean, median, and mode are all 80.

3. The mean score on a set of 20 tests is 75. What is the sum of the 20 test scores?

4. The tram at a ski area has a capacity of 50 people with a load limit of 7500 lb. What is the mean weight of the passengers if the tram is loaded to capacity?

5. The mean for a set of 28 scores is 80. Suppose two more students take the test and score 60 and 50. What is the new mean?

6. The names and ages for each person in a family of five follow:

Name	Dick	Jane	Kirk	Jean	Scott
Age	40	36	8	6	2

   a. What is the mean age?
   b. Find the mean of the ages 5 years from now.
   c. Find the mean 10 years from now.
   d. Describe the relationships among the means found in (a), (b), and (c).

7. Suppose you own a hat shop and decide to order hats in only *one* size for the coming season. To decide which size to order, you look at last year's sales figures, which are itemized according to size. Should you find the mean, median, or mode for the data? Why?

8. A table showing Jon's fall quarter grades follows. Find his grade point average for the term (A = 4, B = 3, C = 2, D = 1, F = 0).

Course	Credits	Grade
Math	5	B
English	3	A
Physics	5	C
German	3	D
Handball	1	A

9. If the mean weight of seven tackles on a team is 230 lb and the mean weight of the four backfield members is 190 lb, what is the mean weight of the 11-person team?

10. If 99 people had a mean income of $12,000, how much is the mean income increased by the addition of a single income of $200,000?

11. The following table gives the annual salaries of the 40 dancers of a certain troupe.
    a. Find the mean annual salary for the troupe.
    b. Find the median annual salary.
    c. Find the mode.

Salary	Number of Dancers
$ 18,000	2
22,000	4
26,000	4
35,000	3
38,000	12
44,000	8
50,000	4
80,000	2
150,000	1

12. Refer to the following chart. In a gymnastics competition, each competitor receives six scores. The highest and lowest scores are eliminated, and the official score is the mean of the four remaining scores.

Gymnast	Scores					
Balance Beam						
Meta	9.2	9.2	9.1	9.3	9.8	9.6
Lisa	9.3	9.1	9.4	9.6	9.9	9.4
Olga	9.4	9.5	9.6	9.6	9.9	9.6
Uneven Bars						
Meta	9.2	9.1	9.3	9.2	9.4	9.5
Lisa	10.0	9.8	9.9	9.7	9.9	9.8
Olga	9.4	9.6	9.5	9.4	9.4	9.4
Floor Exercises						
Meta	9.7	9.8	9.4	9.8	9.8	9.7
Lisa	10.0	9.9	9.8	10.0	9.7	10.0
Olga	9.4	9.3	9.6	9.4	9.5	9.4

    a. If the only events in the competition are the balance beam, the uneven bars, and the floor exercise, find the winner of each event.
    b. Find the overall winner of the competition if the overall winner is the person with the highest combined official scores.

13. Maria needed 8 gal of gas to fill her car's gas tank. The mileage odometer read 42,800 mi. When the odometer read 43,030, Maria filled the tank with 12 gal. At the end of the trip, she filled the tank with 18 gal and the odometer read 43,390 mi. How many miles per gallon did she get for the entire trip?

14. The youngest person in a company is 24 years old. The range of ages is 34 yr. How old is the oldest person in the company?

15. Choose the data set(s) that fit the descriptions given in each of the following:
    a. The mean is 6.
       The range is 6.
       Set *A*: 3, 5, 7, 9
       Set *B*: 2, 4, 6, 8
       Set *C*: 2, 3, 4, 15
    b. The mean is 11.
       The median is 11.
       The mode is 11.
       Set *A*: 9, 10, 10, 11, 12, 12, 13
       Set *B*: 11, 11, 11, 11, 11, 11, 11
       Set *C*: 9, 11, 11, 11, 11, 12, 12
    c. The mean is 3.
       The median is 3.
       It has no mode.

       Set *A*: $0, 2\frac{1}{2}, 6\frac{1}{2}$

       Set *B*: 3, 3, 3, 3
       Set *C*: 1, 2, 4, 5
    d. The box plot shown below.

       Set *A*: 2, 3, 4, 4, 6, 6, 7, 15
       Set *B*: 2, 3, 6, 6, 8, 9, 12, 14, 15
       Set *C*: 2, 4.5, 8, 13, 15
       Set *D*: 2, 3, 6, 6, 8, 9, 10, 11, 15

16. To receive an A in a class, Willie needs at least a mean of 90 on five exams. Willie's grades on the first four exams were 84, 95, 86, and 94. What minimum score does he need on the fifth exam to receive an A in the class?

17. Ginny's median score on three tests was 90. Her mean score was 92 and her range was 6. What were her three test scores?

18. The mean of five numbers is 6. If one of the five numbers is removed, the mean becomes 7. What is the value of the number that was removed?

19. a. Find the mean and the median of the following arithmetic sequences:
       i. 1, 3, 5, 7, 9   ii. 1, 3, 5, 7, 9, . . . , 199
       iii. 7, 10, 13, 16, . . . , 607
    b. Based on your answers in (a), make a conjecture about the mean and the median of any arithmetic sequence.

20. Construct a box plot for the following gas mileages per gallon of various company cars:

    22 18 14 28 30 12 38 22
    30 39 20 18 14 16 10

21. Following are box plots comparing the ticket prices of two performing arts theaters:
    a. What is the median ticket price for each theater?
    b. Which theater has the greatest range of prices?
    c. What is the highest ticket price at either theater?
    d. Make some statements comparing the ticket prices at the two theaters.

22. Construct a box plot for the following set of test scores. Indicate outliers, if any, with asterisks.

    20 95 40 70 90 70 80 80 90 95

23. The following table shows the heights in feet of the tallest 10 buildings in Los Angeles and in Minneapolis:

Los Angeles	Minneapolis
858	950
750	775
735	668
699	579
625	561
620	447
578	440
571	416
534	403
516	366

    a. Draw horizontal box plots to compare the data.
    b. Are there any outliers in this data? If so, which values are they?
    c. Based on your box plots from (a), make some comparisons of the heights of the buildings in the two cities.

24. The following shows box plots for the piano practice times in hours per week for Tom and Dick. Make some comparisons for their practice times.

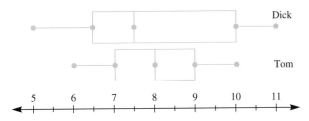

25. What is the standard deviation of the heights of seven trapeze artists if their heights are 175 cm, 182 cm, 190 cm, 180 cm, 192 cm, 172 cm, and 190 cm?

26. a. If all the numbers in a set are equal, what is the standard deviation?

b. If the standard deviation of a set of numbers is zero, must all the numbers in the set be equal?

27. In a Math 131 class at DiPaloma University, the grades on the first exam were as follows:

```
96  71  43  77  75  76  61
83  71  58  97  76  74  91
74  71  77  83  87  93  79
```

a. Find the mean.   **b.** Find the median.
c. Find the mode.   **d.** Find the IQR.
e. Find the variance of the scores.
f. Find the standard deviation of the scores.

28. In a school system, teachers start at a salary of $25,200 and have a top salary of $51,800. The teachers' union is bargaining with the school district for next year's salary increment.

a. If every teacher is given a $1000 raise, what happens to each of the following?

   i. Mean   ii. Median
   iii. Extremes   iv. Quartiles
   v. Standard deviation   vi. IQR

b. If every teacher received a 5% raise, what does this do to the following?

   i. Mean   ii. Standard deviation

29. The mean IQ score for 1500 students is 100, with a standard deviation of 15. Assuming the scores have a normal curve,

a. how many have an IQ between 85 and 115?
b. how many have an IQ between 70 and 130?
c. how many have an IQ over 145?

30. Sugar Plops boxes say they hold 16 oz. To make sure they do, the manufacturer fills the box to a mean weight of 16.1 oz, with a standard deviation of 0.05 oz. If the weights have a normal curve, what percentage of the boxes actually contains 16 oz or more?

31. For certain workers, the mean wage is $5.00/hr, with a standard deviation of $0.50. If a worker is chosen at random,

what is the probability that the worker's wage is between $4.50 and $5.50? Assume a normal distribution of wages.

32. Assume a normal distribution and that the average phone call in a certain town lasted 4 min with a standard deviation of 2 min. What percentage of the calls lasted fewer than 2 min?

33. In a normal distribution, how are the mean and the median related? Why?

34. According to psychologists, IQs are normally distributed with a mean of 100 and a standard deviation of 15.

a. What percentage of the population have IQs between 100 and 130?

b. What percentage of the population have IQs lower than 85?

35. The weights of newborn babies are distributed normally with a mean of approximately 105 oz and a standard deviation of 20 oz. If a newborn is selected at random, what is the probability that the baby weighs less than 125 oz?

36. On a certain exam, the mean is 72 and the standard deviation is 9. If a grade of A is given to any student who scores at least two standard deviations above the mean, what is the lowest score that a person could receive and still get an A?

37. Assume that the heights of American women are approximately normally distributed, with a mean of 65.5 in. and a standard deviation of 2.5 in. Within what range are the heights of 95% of American women?

38. A tire company tests a particular model of tire and found the tires to be normally distributed with respect to wear. The mean was 28,000 mi, and the standard deviation was 2500 mi. If 2000 tires are tested, about how many are likely to wear out before 23,000 mi?

39. A standardized mathematics test was given to 10,000 students, and the scores were normally distributed. The mean was 500, and the standard deviation was 60. If a student scored below 440 points, the student was considered deficient in mathematics. About how many students were rated deficient?

★40. Show that the following formula for variance is equivalent to the one given in the text:

$$v = \frac{x_1^2 + x_2^2 + \cdots + x_n^2}{n} - \bar{x}^2$$

Communication

41. If you were considering ages and wanted one number to represent the age at which a person can get a driver's license, which "average" would you use and why?

42. A movie chain conducts a popcorn poll in which each person entering a theater and buying a box of popcorn is asked a yes-no question. Which "average" do you think is used to report the result and why?

43. When a government agency reports the rainfall for a state for a year, which "average" do you think they use and why?

44. Carl had scores of 90, 95, 85, and 90 on his first four tests.
   a. Find the median, mean, and mode.
   b. Carl scored a 20 on his fifth exam. Which of the three averages would Carl want the instructor to use to compute his grade? Why?
   c. Which measure is affected most by an extreme score?

45. The mean of the five numbers given below is 50:

20   35   50   60   85

   a. Add four numbers to the list so that the mean of the nine numbers is still 50.
   b. Explain how you could choose the four numbers to add to the list so that the mean did not change.
   c. How does the mean of the four numbers you added to the list compare to the original mean of 50? Why?

46. Sue drives 5 mi at 30 mph and then 5 mi at 50 mph. Is the mean speed for the trip 40 mph? Why or why not?

Open-Ended

47. In 1991, students from countries around the world took the International Assessment of Educational Progress test. The table below gives the average mathematics scores for 15 countries along with the number of days that students in each country spend in school each year.

Country	Days of School	Math Score
Canada	188	62
France	174	64
Hungary	177	68
Ireland	173	61
Israel	215	63
Italy	204	64
Jordan	191	40
Korea	222	73
Scotland	191	61
Slovenia	190	57
Soviet Union	198	70
Spain	188	55
Switzerland	207	71
Taiwan	222	73
United States	178	55

(a) Make a conjecture about the relationship between the country's mathematics score and the number of days spent in school.

(b) Test your conjecture by using a box plot to compare students who spend 190 days or fewer in school with those who spend more than 190 days in school.

(c) Explain how your graph supports or disproves your conjecture.

(d) Draw a scatterplot for the data and see if there seems to be a correlation between mathematics scores and days in school. Is this the same message your box plot gave you? Which plot would you use to support your conjecture?

48. Use the data in the following table to compare the number of people living in the United States from 1810 through 1900 and the number living in the United States from 1910 through 2000. Use any form of graphical representation to make the comparison and explain why you chose the representation that you did.

Year	Number (thousands)	Year	Number (thousands)
1810	7,239	1910	92,228
1820	9,638	1920	106,021
1830	12,866	1930	123,202
1840	17,068	1940	132,164
1850	23,191	1950	151,325
1860	31,443	1960	179,323
1870	38,558	1970	203,302
1880	50,189	1980	226,542
1890	62,979	1990	248,765
1900	76,212	2000	281,422

Data taken from *The World Almanac and Book of Facts 2002*, World Almanac Books, 2002.

Cooperative Learning

49. In small groups, determine a method of finding the number and types of graphs and statistical representations used in at least two newspapers in your campus library. Based on your findings, write a report defending which type(s) of representation should be emphasized in a journalistic statistics class.

Review Problems

50. Given the following double-bar graph, make some comparisons of the number of men and women in the labor force over the years.

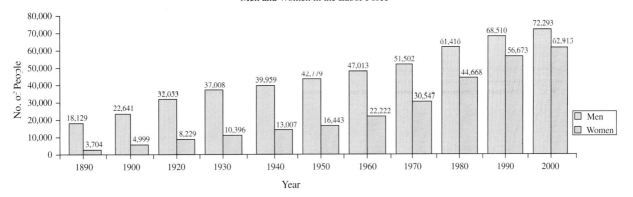

Men and Women in the Labor Force

Data taken from *The World Almanac and Book of Facts 2002,* World Almanac Books, 2002.

51. Consider the following circle graph. What is the number of degrees in each sector of the graph?

U.S. Car Sales by Vehicle Size and Type

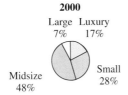

2000
Large Luxury
7%   17%

Midsize   Small
48%   28%

52. Given the following bar graph, answer the following:
    a. Which mountain is the highest? Approximately how high is it?
    b. Which mountains are higher than 6000 m?

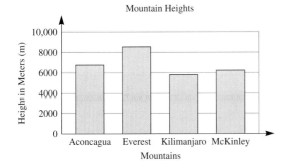

53. Following are raw test scores from a history test:

86	85	87	96	55
90	94	82	68	77
88	89	85	74	90
72	80	76	88	73
64	79	73	85	93

   a. Construct an ordered stem-and-leaf plot for the given data.
   b. Construct a grouped frequency table for these scores with intervals of 5, starting the first class at 55.
   c. Draw a histogram of the data.
   d. If a circle graph of the grouped data in (b) were drawn, how many degrees would be in the section representing the 85 through 89 interval?

LABORATORY
A C T I V I T Y

We can model the mean as a measure of central tendency using a strip of cardboard that is 1 in. wide and 1 ft long with holes 1 in. apart and $\frac{1}{8}$ in. from the edge, as in Figure 8-27.

FIGURE 8-27

51 52 53 54 55 56 57 58 59 60 61 62

(continued)

Use string and tape to suspend the strip from a desk with the string tied through a hole punched between 56 and 57. Then use paper clips of equal size to investigate means, as in Figure 8-28.

FIGURE 8-28

1. **a.** If paper clips are hung in the holes at 51, 53, and 60, where should an additional clip be hung in order to achieve a balance?
   b. If paper clips are hung at 51, 54, and 60, where should two additional paper clips be hung to achieve a balance?
   c. If paper clips are hung at 51, 53, 54, and 55, where should four additional clips be hung to achieve a balance?
2. Find the mean of the data of all the numbers in each part in (1) and compare this answer with the number in the center of the strip.
3. Would any of the means in (2) change if we hung an additional paper clip in the center of the strip?
4. Find the median and mode for 51, 53, 54, 56, 58, 58, and 59.
5. Hang paper clips in each hole in (4). If a number appears more than once, hang that number of paper clips in the hole. Is there a balance around the median? Is there a balance around the mode?
6. Under what conditions do you think there would be a balance around (a) the mean, (b) the median, and (c) the mode? Test your conjecture using the cardboard strip.

TECHNOLOGY
CORNER

Use a graphing calculator or create a spreadsheet to find the variance and standard deviation of the set of scores 32, 41, 47, 53, and 57. If you use a spreadsheet, make column A be the set of scores, column B the scores minus the mean, and column C the squares of the difference of the scores and the mean. Compute the variance and the standard deviation.

8-3   Abuses of Statistics

Statistics are frequently abused. Benjamin Disraeli (1804–1881), an English prime minister, once remarked, "There are three kinds of lies: lies, damned lies, and statistics." People sometimes deliberately use statistics to mislead others. This can be seen in advertising. More often, however, the misuse of statistics is the result of misinterpreting what the statistics mean. For example, if we were told that the "average" depth of water in a lily pond was 2 ft, most of us would presume that a heron could stand up in any part of the pond. This is not necessarily the case, as seen in the following cartoon.

THE FAR SIDE® By GARY LARSON

Consider an advertisement reporting that of the people responding to a recent survey, 98% said that Buffepain is the most effective pain reliever of headaches and arthritis. To certify that the statistics are not being misused, the following information should have been reported:

1. The number of people surveyed
2. The number of people who responded
3. How the people who participated in the survey were chosen
4. The number and type of pain relievers tested

Without the information listed, the following situations are possible, all of which could cause the advertisement to be misleading:

1. Suppose 1,000,000 people nationwide were sent the survey, and only 50 responded. This would mean that there was only a 0.005% response, which would certainly cause us to mistrust the ad.
2. Of the 50 responding in (1), suppose 49 responses were affirmative. The 98% claim is true, but 999,950 people did not respond.
3. Suppose all the people who received the survey were chosen from a town in which the major industry was the manufacture of Buffepain. It is very doubtful that the survey would represent an unbiased sample.
4. Suppose only two "pain relievers" were tested: Buffepain, whose active ingredient is 100% aspirin, and a placebo containing only powdered sugar.

This is not to say that advertisements of this type are all misleading or dishonest, but simply that statistics are only as honest as their users.

A different type of misuse of statistics involves graphs. Among the things to look for in a graph are the following. If they are not there, then the graph may be misleading.

1. Title
2. Labels on both axes of a line or bar chart and on all sections of a pie chart
3. Source of the data
4. Key to a pictograph
5. Uniform size of symbols in a pictograph
6. Scale: Does it start with zero? If not, is there a break shown?
7. Scale: Are the numbers equally spaced?

To see an example of a misleading use of graphs, consider how graphs can be used to distort data or exaggerate certain pieces of information. Graphs using a break in the vertical axis can be used to create different visual impressions, which are sometimes misleading. For example, consider the two graphs in Figure 8-29, which represent the number of girls trying out for basketball at each of three middle schools. As we can see, the graph in Figure 8-29(a) portrays a different picture from the one in Figure 8-29(b).

FIGURE 8-29

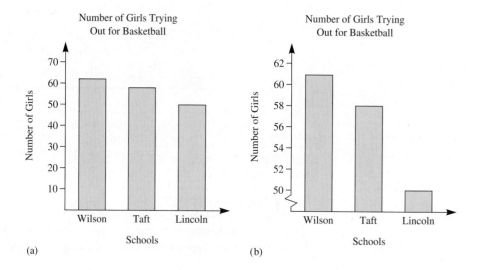

A line graph, histogram, or bar graph can be altered by changing the scale of the graph. For example, consider the data in Table 8-12 for the number of graduates from a community college for the years 1999 through 2003.

Table 8-12

Year	1999	2000	2001	2002	2003
Number of Graduates	140	180	200	210	160

The graphs in Figure 8-30(a) and (b) represent the same data, but different scales are used in each. The statistics presented are the same, but these graphs do not convey the same psychological message. In Figure 8-30(b), the spacing of the years on the horizontal axis of the graph is more spread out and that for the numbers on the vertical axis is more condensed than in Figure 8-30(a). Both of these changes minimize the variability of the data. A college administrator might use a graph like the one in Figure 8-30(b) to convince people that the college was not in serious enrollment trouble.

FIGURE 8-30

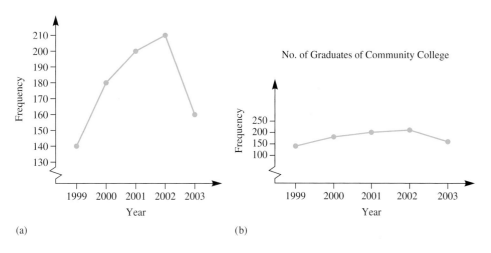

(a)

(b)

Another error that frequently occurs in all arenas is the use of continuous curve graphs, as in Figure 8-30, to depict data that are discrete (a finite number of data values). In Figure 8-31, it may or may not make sense to discuss the enrollment at 1999.5, yet the way in which the graph is constructed leads us to believe that such a value exists.

Other ways to distort graphs include omitting a scale, as in Figure 8-31(a). The scale is given in Figure 8-31(b).

FIGURE 8-31

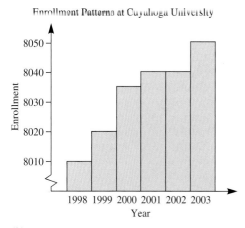

(a)

(b)

Other graphs can also be misleading. Suppose, for example, that the number of boxes of cereal sold by Sugar Plops last year was 2 million and the number of boxes of cereal sold by Korn Krisps was 8 million. The Korn Krisps executives prepared the graph in Figure 8-32 to demonstrate the data. The Sugar Plops people objected. Do you see why?

FIGURE 8-32

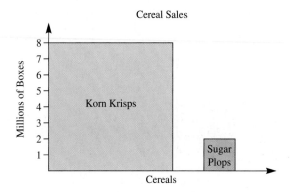

The graph in Figure 8-32 clearly distorts the data, since the figure for Korn Krisps is both four times as high and four times as wide as the bar for Sugar Plops. Thus the area of the box face representing Korn Krisps is 16 times the comparable area representing Sugar Plops, rather than four times the area, as would be justified by the original data.

Figure 8-33 shows how the comparison of Sugar Plops and Korn Krisps cereals might look if the figures were made three-dimensional. The figure for Korn Krisps has a volume 64 times the volume of the Sugar Plops figure.

FIGURE 8-33

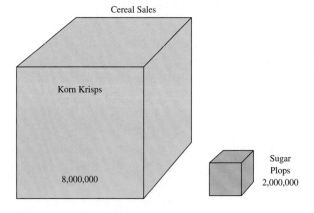

Circle graphs easily become distorted when attempts are made to depict them as three-dimensional. Many graphs of this type do not acknowledge either the variable thickness of the depiction or the distortion due to perspective. Observe that the 27% sector pictured in Figure 8-34 looks far greater than the 23% sector, although they should be very nearly the same size.

FIGURE 8-34

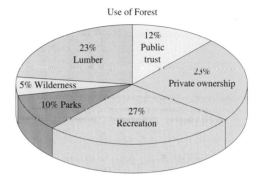

The final examples of the misuses of statistics involve misleading uses of mean, median, and mode. All these are "averages" and can be used to suit a person's purposes. As discussed in Section 8-2 in the example involving the teachers Smith, Jones, and Rivera, each teacher had reported that his or her class had done better than the other two. Each of the teachers used a different number to represent the test scores.

As another example, company administrators wishing to portray to prospective employees a rosy salary picture may find a mean salary of $38,000 for line workers as well as upper management in the schedule of salaries. At the same time, a union that is bargaining for salaries may include part-time employees as well as line workers and will exclude management personnel in order to present a mean salary of $29,000 at the bargaining table. The important thing to watch for when a mean is reported is disparate cases in the reference group. If the sample is small, then a few extremely high or low scores can have a great influence on the mean.

Suppose Figure 8-35 shows the salaries of both management and line workers of the company. If the median is being used as the average, then the median might be $33,500, which is representative of neither major group of employees. The bimodal distribution means the median is nonrepresentative of the distribution.

FIGURE 8-35

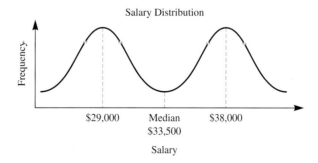

To conclude the comments on the misuse of statistics, consider a quote from Darrell Huff's book *How to Lie with Statistics* (p. 8):

So it is with much that you read and hear. Averages and relationships and trends and graphs are not always what they seem. There may be more in them than meets the eye, and there may be a great deal less.

The secret language of statistics, so appealing in a fact-minded culture, is employed to sensationalize, inflate, confuse, and oversimplify. Statistical methods and statistical terms are necessary in reporting the mass data of social and economic trends, business conditions, "opinion" polls, census. But without writers who use the words with honesty and understanding and readers who know what they mean, the result can be semantic "nonsense."

ONGOING ASSESSMENT 8-3

This entire set of assessment items is appropriate for communication and cooperative learning. Many items are open-ended and several lend themselves to further investigation.

1. Discuss whether the following claims could be misleading. Explain why and how.

    a. A car manufacturer claims its car is quieter than a glider.

    b. A motorcycle manufacturer claims that more than 95% of its cycles that were sold in the United States in the last 15 yr are still on the road.

    c. A company claims its fruit juice has 10% more fruit solids than is required by U.S. government standards. (The government requires 10% fruit solids.)

    d. A brand of bread claims to be 40% fresher.

    e. A used-car dealer claims that a car she is trying to sell will get up to 30 mpg.

    f. Sudso claims that its detergent will leave your clothes brighter.

    g. A sugarless gum company claims that eight of every ten dentists responding to the survey recommend sugarless gum.

    h. Most accidents occur in the home. Therefore, to be safer, you should stay out of your house as much as possible.

    i. More than 95% of the people who fly to a certain city do so on Airline A. Therefore most people prefer Airline A to other airlines.

2. The city of Podunk advertised that its temperature was the ideal temperature in the country because its mean temperature was 25°C. What possible misconceptions could people draw from this advertisement?

3. Jenny averaged 70 on her quizzes during the first part of the quarter and 80 on her quizzes during the second part of the quarter. When she found out that her final average for the quarter was not 75, she went to argue with her teacher. Give a possible explanation for Jenny's misunderstanding.

4. Suppose the following circle graphs are used to illustrate the fact that the number of elementary teaching majors at teachers' colleges has doubled between 1993 and 2003, while the percent of male elementary teaching majors has stayed the same. What is misleading about the way the graphs are constructed?

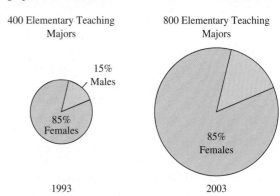

5. What is wrong with the following line graph?

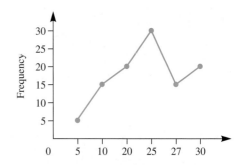

6. Can you draw any valid conclusions about a set of data in which the mean is less than the median?

7. A student read that nine out of ten pickup trucks sold in the last 10 yr are still on the road. She concluded that the average life of a pickup is around 10 yr. Is she correct?

8. General Cooster once asked a person by the side of a river if the river was too deep to ride his horse across. The person responded that the average depth was 2 ft. If General Cooster rode out across the river, what assumptions did he make on the basis of the person's information?

9. Doug's Dog Food Company wanted to impress the public with the magnitude of the company's growth. Sales of Doug's Dog Food had doubled from 2002 to 2003, so the company displayed the following graph, in which the radius of the base and the height of the 2003 can are double those of the 2002 can. What does the graph really show with respect to the growth of the company? (*Hint:* The volume of a cylinder is given by $V = \pi r^2 h$, where r is the radius of the base and h is the height.)

Doug's Dog Food Sales

10. Explain what is wrong with the following graph:

11. Refer to the following pictograph:

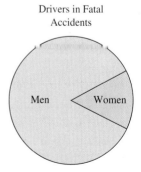

Ms. McNulty claims that on the basis of this information, we can conclude that men are worse drivers than women. Discuss whether you can reach that conclusion from the pictograph or you need more information. If more information is needed, what would you like to know?

12. The following graph was prepared to compare prices of washing machines at three stores:

Which of the following statements is true? Explain why or why not.

a. Prices vary widely at the three stores.

b. The price at Discount House is four times as great as that at J-Mart.

c. The prices at J-Mart and Super Discount differ by less than $10.

13. The following table gives the number of accidents per year on a certain highway for a 5-yr period:

Year	1999	2000	2001	2002	2003
Number of Accidents	24	26	30	32	38

a. Draw a bar graph to convince people that the number of accidents is on the rise and that something should be done about it.

b. Draw a bar graph to show that the rate of accidents is almost constant, and that nothing needs to be done.

14. Write a list of scores for which the mean and median are not representative of the list.

15. The following graph depicts the mean center of population of the United States and shows how the center has shifted from 1790 to 2000. Based solely on this graph, could you conclude that the population of the West Coast has increased since 1790?

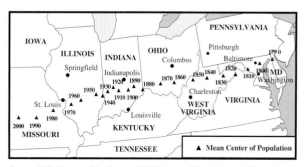

Source: U.S. Bureau of the Census, *2000 Census of Population and Housing, Population and Housing Unit Counts, United States* (2000 CPH-2-1).

16. The data in the graph of problem 15 roughly follows a line. If the mean center of the population continues to move westward in the next 200 years, where would you expect it to be at the end of that period? At the end of 400 years?

17. A prospective homeowner considered the dropping interest rates for house loans in the early 1990s and decided to wait until the year 2000 to buy. Explain what type of statistics might be used in making this decision and whether you consider the prospective homeowner's decision to be wise.

18. A student made 99 on a quiz and was ecstatic over the grade. What other information might you need in order to decide if the student was justified in being happy?

19. A school administrator reports to you, a school board member, that the "average" number of students in a class in a school is 32. What other information might you need in order to predict whether any single classroom was overcrowded?

20. Consider a state such as Montana that has both mountains and prairies. What numbers might you report to depict the "average" height above sea level of such a state? Why?

21. Is it possible for a state or country to have a mean sea level height that is negative? If so, what might such a region look like?

22. Describe how you might pick a random sample of adults that is representative of the members of your town.

23. A very large and successful manufacturer of computer chips released data in the early 1990s stating that approximately 65% of its chips were defective when they came off the assembly line. Give some reasons why this statistic could be accurate and yet the company could still be successful.

Review Problems

24. On the English 100 exam, the scores were as follows:

43	91	73	65
56	77	84	91
82	65	98	65

a. Find the mean.
b. Find the median.
c. Find the mode.
d. Find the variance.
e. Find the standard deviation.

25. If the mean of a set of 36 scores is 27 and two more scores of 40 and 42 are added, what is the new mean?

26. On a certain exam, Tony corrected 10 papers and found the mean for his group to be 70. Alice corrected the remaining 20 papers and found that the mean for her group was 80. What is the mean of the combined group of 30 students?

27. Following are the men's gold-medal times for the 100-m run in the Olympic games from 1896 to 2000 rounded to the nearest tenth. Construct an ordered stem-and-leaf plot for the data.

Year	Time (sec), (rounded)
1896	12.0
1900	11.0
1904	11.0
1908	10.8
1912	10.8
1920	10.8
1924	10.6
1928	10.8
1932	10.3
1936	10.3
1948	10.3
1952	10.4
1956	10.5
1960	10.2
1964	10.0
1968	10.0
1972	10.1
1976	10.1
1980	10.3
1984	10.0
1988	9.9
1992	9.7
1996	9.8
2000	9.9

28. Following are the record swimming times of the women's 100-m freestyle and 100-m butterfly in the Olympics from 1960 to 2000. Draw parallel box plots of the two sets of data to compare them.

Year	Time—100-m Freestyle (sec)	Time—100-m Butterfly (sec)
1960	61.20	69.50
1964	59.50	64.70
1968	60.00	65.50
1972	58.59	63.34
1976	55.65	60.13
1980	54.79	60.42
1984	55.92	59.26
1988	54.93	59.00
1992	54.64	58.62
1996	54.50	59.13
2000	53.83	56.61

Hint for Solving the Preliminary Problem

What is Ouida's mean at the present time? If she drops the highest and lowest scores, what will be her total? Can you find another test score that could be added to the total and then divided by 5 to still result in a mean of at least her current mean?

QUESTIONS FROM THE CLASSROOM

1. A student asks, "If the average income of each of ten people is $10,000 and one person gets a raise of $10,000, is the median, the mean, or the mode changed and, if so, by how much?"

2. Jose asks, why can a median number of children not be 3.8? How do you respond?

3. Andrea asks, does a spaghetti fit line really give a line-of-best-fit? How do you respond?

4. Suppose the class takes a test and the following averages are obtained: mean, 80; median, 90; mode, 70. Tom, who scored 80, would like to know if he did better than half the class. What is your response?

5. A student wants to know the advantages of presenting data in graphical form rather than in tabular form. What is your response? What are the disadvantages?

6. A student asks if it is possible to find the mode for data in a grouped frequency table. What is your response?

7. A student asks if she can draw any conclusions about a set of data if she knows that the mean for the data is less than the median. How do you answer?

8. A student asks if it is possible to have a standard deviation of $^-5$. How do you respond?

9. Mel's mean on ten tests for the quarter was 89. She complained to the teacher that she should be given an A because she missed the cutoff of 90 by only a single point. Explain whether it is clear that she really missed an A by only a single point?

10. A student asks, "Is it always true that in any set of data, there must be at least one data point in the data that is less than or equal to the mean and at least one data point greater than or equal to the mean?"

11. A student asks if the precision with which manufacturers must calibrate their tools is at all related to statistics. How do you respond?

CHAPTER OUTLINE

I. Descriptive statistics
Information can be summarized in each of the following forms:
  1. **Pictographs**
  2. **Dot plots/line plots**
  3. **Stem-and-leaf plots**
  4. **Frequency tables**
  5. **Histograms**
  6. **Bar graphs**
  7. **Line graphs**
  8. **Circle graphs/pie charts**
  9. **Box plots/box-and-whisker plots**
  10. **Scatterplots**

II. Measures of central tendency
  A. The **mean** of n given numbers is the sum of the numbers divided by n.
  B. The **median** of a set of numbers is the middle number if the numbers are arranged in numerical order; if there is no middle number, the median is the mean of the two middle numbers.

  C. The **mode** of a set of numbers is the number or numbers that occur most frequently in the set.

III. Measures of variation
  A. The **range** is the difference between the greatest and least numbers in the data.
  B. The **variance** of a data set is found by subtracting the mean from each value, squaring each of these differences, finding the sum of these squares, and dividing by n, where n is the number of observations.
  C. The **standard deviation** is equal to the square root of the variance.
  D. **Box plots**, or **box-and-whisker plots**, focus attention on the median, the quartiles, and the extremes and invite comparisons among them.
    1. The **lower quartile** is the median of the subset of data less than the median of all the values in the data set.
    2. The **upper quartile** is the median of the subset of data greater than the median of all the values in the data set.

3. The **interquartile range (IQR)** is calculated as the difference between the upper quartile and the lower quartile.
4. An **outlier** is any value more than 1.5 IQR above the upper quartile or more than 1.5 IQR below the lower quartile.

E. **Scatterplots** are graphs of ordered pairs that allow us to examine the relationship (correlation) between two sets of data.

F. A **trend line** or a line-of-best-fit is a line that approximates data in a scatterplot.

G. A **normal curve** is a smooth, bell-shaped curve that depicts frequency values distributed symmetrically about the mean as shown:

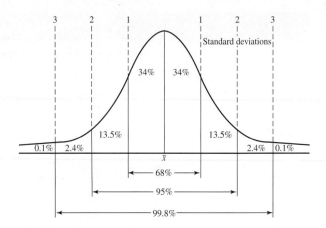

CHAPTER REVIEW

1. Suppose you read that "the average family in Rattlesnake Gulch has 2.41 children." What average is being used to describe the data? Explain your answer. Suppose the sentence had said 2.5? Then what are the possibilities?

2. At Bug's Bar-B-Q restaurant, the average weekly wage for full-time workers is $150. There are ten part-time employees whose average weekly salary is $50 and the total weekly payroll is $3950. How many full-time employees are there?

3. Find the mean, the median, and the mode for each of the following groups of data:
   a. 10, 50, 30, 40, 10, 60, 10
   b. 5, 8, 6, 3, 5, 4, 3, 6, 1, 9

4. Find the range, variance, and standard deviation for each set of scores in problem 3.

5. The mass, in kilograms, of each child in Ms. Rider's class follows:

   40 49 43 48 46 42 49 39 47 49
   42 41 42 39 41 40 45 43 44 42

   a. Make a line plot for the data.
   b. Make an ordered stem-and-leaf plot for the data.
   c. Make a frequency table for the data.
   d. Make a bar graph of the data.

6. The grades on a test for 30 students follow:

   96 73 61   76   77 84
   78 98 98   80   67 82
   61 75 79   90   73 80
   85 63 86 100   94 77
   86 84 91   62   77 64

   a. Make a grouped frequency table for these scores, using four classes and starting the first class at 61.
   b. Draw a histogram of the grouped data.

7. The budget for the Wegetem Crime Co. is $2,000,000. Draw a circle graph to indicate how the company spends its money where $600,000 is spent on bribes, $400,000 for legal fees, $300,000 for bail money, $300,000 for contracts, and $400,000 for public relations. Indicate percentages on your graph.

8. What, if anything, is wrong with the following bar graph?

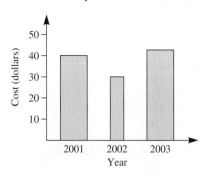

Monthly Health Club Costs

9. The mean salary of 24 people is $9000. How much will one additional salary of $80,000 increase the mean salary?

10. A cheetah can run 70 mph, a lion can run 50 mph, and a human can run 28 mph. Draw a bar graph to represent these data.

11. The life expectancies at birth for males and females are given in the following table:

Year	Male	Female	Year	Male	Female
1970	67.1	74.7	1987	71.5	78.4
1971	67.4	75.0	1988	71.5	78.3
1972	67.4	75.1	1989	71.7	78.5
1973	67.6	75.3	1990	71.8	78.8
1974	68.2	75.9	1991	72.0	78.9
1975	68.8	76.6	1992	72.1	78.9
1976	69.1	76.8	1993	72.1	78.9
1977	69.5	77.2	1994	72.4	79.0
1978	69.6	77.3	1995	72.5	78.9
1979	70.0	77.8	1996	73.1	79.1
1980	70.0	77.5	1997	73.6	79.2
1981	70.4	77.8	1998	73.8	79.5
1982	70.9	78.1	1999	73.9	79.4
1983	71.0	78.1			
1984	71.2	78.2			
1985	71.2	78.2			
1986	71.3	78.3			

Data from *The World Almanac and Book of Facts 2002*, World Almanac Books, 2002.

a. Draw back-to-back ordered stem-and-leaf plots to compare the data.

b. Draw box plots to compare the data.

12. Larry and Marc took the same courses last quarter. Each bet that he would receive the better grades. Their courses and grades are as follows:

Course	Larry's Grades	Marc's Grades
Math (4 credits)	A	C
Chemistry (4 credits)	A	C
English (3 credits)	B	B
Psychology (3 credits)	C	A
Tennis (1 credit)	C	A

Marc claimed that the results constituted a tie, since both received 2 A's, 1 B, and 2 C's. Larry said that he won the bet because he had the higher grade-point average for the quarter. Who is correct? (Allow 4 points for an A, 3 points for a B, 2 points for a C, 1 point for a D, and 0 points for an F.)

13. Following are the lengths in yards of the nine holes of the University Golf Course:

$$160 \quad 360 \quad 330$$
$$350 \quad 180 \quad 460$$
$$480 \quad 450 \quad 380$$

Find each of the following measures with respect to the lengths of the holes:

a. Median

b. Mode

c. Mean

d. Standard deviation

14. The speeds in miles per hour of 30 cars were checked by radar. The data are as follows:

$$62 \quad 67 \quad 69 \quad 72 \quad 75 \quad 60 \quad 58 \quad 86 \quad 74 \quad 68$$
$$56 \quad 67 \quad 82 \quad 88 \quad 90 \quad 54 \quad 67 \quad 65 \quad 64 \quad 68$$
$$74 \quad 65 \quad 58 \quad 75 \quad 67 \quad 65 \quad 66 \quad 64 \quad 45 \quad 64$$

a. Find the median.

b. Find the upper and lower quartiles.

c. Draw a box plot for the data and indicate outliers (if any) with asterisks.

d. What percentage of the scores is in the interquartile range?

e. If every person driving faster than 70 mph received a ticket, what percentage of the drivers received speeding tickets?

f. Is the median in the center of the box? Why or why not?

15. The following scattergram was developed with information obtained from the girls trying out for the high-school basketball team:

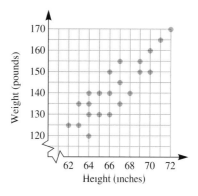

Height and Weights of Girls' Basketball Team Players

a. What kind of correlation exists between the heights and weights that are listed?

b. What is the weight of the girl who is 72 in. tall?

c. How tall is the girl who weighs 145 lb?

d. What is the mode of the heights?

e. What is the range of the weights?

16. The Nielsen Television Index rating of 30 means that an estimated 30% of American televisions are tuned to the show with that rating. The ratings are based on the preferences of a scientifically selected sample of 1200 homes.

a. Discuss possible ways in which viewers could bias this sample.

b. How could networks attempt to bias the results?

17. List and give examples of several ways to misuse statistics graphically.

18. Explain whether you think it is reasonable for a ski resort to advertise excellent skiing because the runs have 64 in. of snow at the top of the hill and 23 in. at the bottom.

19. The following bar graph shows the number of students per computer in the United States from 1983 to 1996.

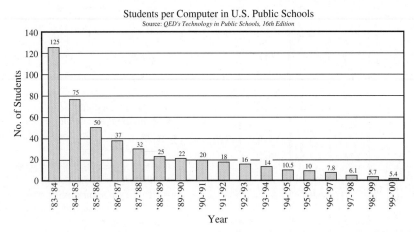

Data taken from *The World Almanac and Book of Facts 1999,* World Almanac Books, 2002.

a. Predict the results for the years 00–01, 01–02, and 02–03.

b. Between what two years did the greatest decrease in the number of students per computer occur?

c. Is a bar graph the most appropriate graph to use for this data? Why?

d. How could you distort this data to make it appear that the change has been very dramatic over the years?

20. The table shows the United States Infant Mortality Rates for males and females from 1980 to 1999.

  a. Draw a back-to-back stem-and-leaf plot for the data.

  b. What can you say about the mortality rates based on your graph?

  c. What other kinds of graphs might you use to show comparisons you made in part (b)? Choose one and graph it.

21. The heights of 1000 girls at East High School were measured, and the mean was found to be 64 in., with a standard deviation of 2 in. If the heights are approximately normally distributed, about how many of the girls are

  a. Over 68 in. tall?

  b. Between 60 and 64 in. tall?

  c. If a girl is selected at random at East High School, what is the probability that she will be over 66 in. tall?

22. A standardized test has a mean of 600 and a standard deviation of 75. If 1000 students took the test and their scores approximated a normal curve, how many scored between 600 and 750?

U.S. Infant Mortality Rates 1980–1999*

Year	Male Deaths	Female Deaths	Year	Male Deaths	Female Deaths
1980	13.9	11.2	1990	10.3	8.1
1981	13.1	10.7	1991	10.0	7.8
1982	12.8	10.2	1992	9.4	7.6
1983	12.3	10.0	1993	9.3	7.4
1984	11.9	9.6	1994	8.8	7.2
1985	11.9	9.3	1995	8.3	6.8
1986	11.5	9.1	1996	8.0	6.6
1987	11.2	8.9	1997	8.0	6.5
1988	11.0	8.9	1998	7.8	6.5
1989	10.8	8.8	1999	7.7	6.4

*The rates are per 1000 live births.

2002 Data taken from *The World Almanac and Book of Facts 2002,* World Almanac Books, 2002.

SELECTED BIBLIOGRAPHY

Basile, C., "Collecting Data Outdoors: Making Connections to the Real World." *Teaching Children Mathematics* 6 (September 1999): 8–12.

Butula, M., and M. Ford. "All About Us: Connecting Statistics with Real Life." *Teaching Children Mathematics* 4 (September 1997): 14–19.

Brosnan, P. "Implementing Data Analysis in a Sixth-Grade Classroom." *Mathematics Teaching in the Middle School* 1 (January–February 1996): 622–628.

Bryan, E. "Exploring Data with Box Plots." *Mathematics Teacher* 81 (November 1988): 658–663.

Dixon, J., and C. Falba. "Graphing in the Information Age: Using Data from the World Wide Web." *Mathematics Teaching in the Middle School* 2 (March–April 1997): 298–304.

Franklin, C. "The Other Life of Florence Nightingale." *Mathematics Teaching in the Middle School* 7 (February 2002): 337–340.

Friel, S., and W. O'Connor. "Sticks to the Roof of Your Mouth?" *Mathematics Teaching in the Middle School* 4 (March 1999): 404–411.

Grummer, D. "Plotting Margo's Party." *Teaching Children Mathematics* 2 (November 1995): 176–179.

Hofstetter, E., and L. Sgroi. "Data with Snap, Crackle, and Pop." *Mathematics Teaching in the Middle School* 1 (March–April 1996): 760–764.

Huff, D. *How to Lie with Statistics.* New York: Norton, 1954.

Isaacs, A., and C. Kelso. "Pictures, Tables, Graphs, and Questions: Statistical Processes." *Teaching Children Mathematics* 2 (February 1996): 340–345.

Jacobs, V. "How Do Students Think about Statistical Sampling?" *Mathematics Teaching in the Middle School* 7 (December 1999): 240–246, 263.

Johnson, A. "Now & Then Community Planning through Data Analysis." *Mathematics Teaching in the Middle School* 7 (March 2000): 458–464.

Kader, G. "Means and MADs." *Mathematics Teaching in the Middle School* 4 (March 1999): 398–403.

Litton, N. "Graphing from A to Z." *Teaching Children Mathematics* 2 (December 1995): 220–223.

McClain, K. "Reflecting on Students' Understanding of Data." *Mathematics Teaching in the Middle School* 4 (March 1999): 374–380.

Morita, J. "Capture and Recapture Your Students' Interest in Statistics." *Mathematics Teaching in the Middle School* 4 (March 1999): 412–418.

O'Keefe, J. "The Human Scatterplot." *Mathematics Teaching in the Middle School* 3 (November–December 1997): 208–212.

Quinn, R. "Having Fun with Baseball Statistics." *Mathematics Teaching in the Middle School* 1 (May 1996): 780–785.

Rubink, W., and S. Taube. "Mathematics Connections from Biology: 'Killer' Bees Come to Life in the Classroom." *Mathematics Teaching in the Middle School* 4 (March 1999): 350–356.

Russell, S., and J. Mokros. "What Do Children Understand about Average?" *Teaching Children Mathematics* 2 (February 1996): 360–364.

Uccellini, J. "Teaching the Mean Meaningfully." *Mathematics Teaching in the Middle School* 2 (November–December 1996): 112–115.

Urso, J. "What Do You Like to Read?" *Teaching Children Mathematics* 6 (September 1999): 34–37.

Wilson, M., and C. Krapfl. "Exploring Mean, Median, and Mode with a Spreadsheet." *Mathematics Teaching in the Middle School* 1 (September–October 1995): 490–495.

Zawojewski, J., and J. Shaughnessy. "Mean and Median: Are They Really So Easy?" *Mathematics Teaching in the Middle School* 7 (March 2000): 436–440.

−9−
Introductory Geometry

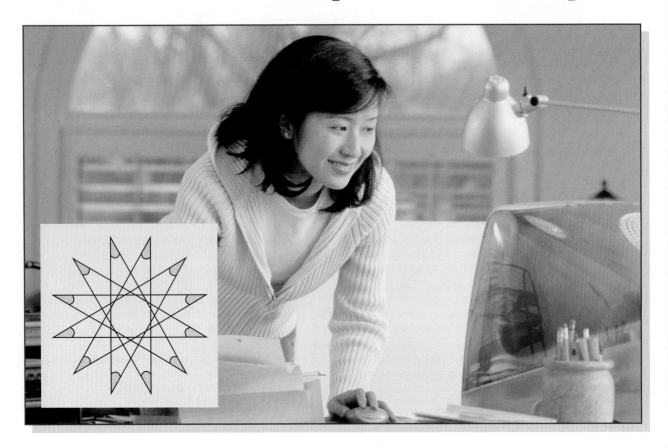

P R E L I M I N A R Y   P R O B L E M

Sylvia, a graphic designer, needs to know the measurement of the shaded angles at the vertices of the 12-pointed star, in which all the sides and all the marked angles are congruent. How can she find the exact measurement of the angles without using a protractor?

eometry has taken on a very different meaning since antiquity when the word it-self came from two Greek words meaning "earth measure." Even in the time of Euclid (ca. 300 B.C.), geometry was developing into a mathematical field that was removed from its physical beginnings. Today, we still consider geometry of the plane but recognize that as only one aspect of the mathematical field known as geometry.

From knowing that the world is not flat, to measurement between planets, to measurement between cells, to Mandelbrot's work with fractals, geometry has changed as our knowledge base has expanded. In schools, too, geometry has changed. We no longer consider geometry as consisting solely of theorems and proofs; we no longer consider geometry in isolation from the rest of mathematics. As a result of these changes, the notion of what constitutes geometry for prospective elementary teachers has changed.

According to the *Principles and Standards*,

The study of geometry in grades 3–5 requires thinking and doing. As students sort, build, draw, model, trace, measure, and construct, the capacity to visualize geometric relationships will develop. At the same time they are learning to reason and to make, test, and justify conjectures about these relationships. This exploration requires access to a variety of tools, such as graph paper, rulers, pattern blocks, geoboards, and geometric solids, and is greatly enhanced by electronic tools that support exploration, such as dynamic geometry software. (p. 165)

The following are some of the expectations from the *Principles and Standards* for different grade levels that will be covered in this chapter.

In grades Pre-K–2, all students should

- *recognize, name, build, draw, compare, and sort two- and three-dimensional shapes;*
- *describe attributes and parts of two- and three-dimensional shapes;*
- *investigate and predict the results of putting together and taking apart two- and three-dimensional shapes.* (p. 96)

In grades 3–5, all students should

- *identify, compare, and analyze attributes of two- and three-dimensional shapes and develop vocabulary to describe the attributes;*
- *classify two- and three-dimensional shapes according to their properties and develop definitions of classes of shapes such as triangles and pyramids;*
- *investigate, describe, and reason about the results of subdividing, combining, and transforming shapes;*
- *make and test conjectures about geometric properties and relationships and develop logical arguments to justify conclusions.* (p. 164)

In grades 6–8, all students should

- *precisely describe, classify, and understand relationships among types of two- and three-dimensional objects using their defining properties;*
- *use visual tools such as networks to represent and solve problems.* (p. 240)

HISTORICAL
N O T E

Little is known of Euclid of Alexandria (ca. 300 B.C.), although legend has it that he studied geometry for its beauty and logic. Euclid is best known for *The Elements*, a work so systematic and encompassing that many earlier mathematical works were simply discarded and lost to all future generations. *The Elements*, composed of 13 books, includes not only geometry but arithmetic and topics in algebra. Euclid set up a *deductive system* by starting with a set of statements that he assumed to be true and showing that geometric discoveries followed logically from these assumptions.

Basic Notions

The fundamental building blocks of geometry are *points, lines,* and *planes.* Ironically, the building blocks are *undefined terms* in order to avoid circular definitions. An example of a circular definition and the frustration involved in starting without some basic undefined notions is given in the following "B.C." cartoon.

Because other geometric concepts are developed from such undefined terms, we present an intuitive notion of these terms in Table 9-1.

Table 9-1

Term/Symbolism	Illustration
Point *A* Point *B* Point *C*	

Table 9-1 *continued*

Term/Symbolism	Illustration
line ℓ	ℓ ⌐ Centerline of road
line m, line AB, $\overleftrightarrow{AB}$, or $\overleftrightarrow{BA}$	m A B
Plane α	α
Plane ABC or Plane γ	A B γ C

Linear Notions

In geometry, a line has no thickness and it extends forever in two directions. *It is determined by two points.* When we discuss situations that involve points and lines, we rely on such undefined relations as "contains," "belongs to," or "is on," and "is between." The meanings of these words are usually understood from the context. For example, Table 9-2 illustrates many common terms and their intuitive meanings.

Table 9-2

Term	Illustration and Symbolism
Collinear points are points on the same line. (Any two points are collinear but not every three points have to be collinear.)	ℓ A B C D Line ℓ contains points A, B, and C. Points A, B, and C belong to line ℓ. Points A, B, and C are collinear. Points A, B, and D are not collinear.
Point B **is between** points A and C on line ℓ.	ℓ A B C
A **line segment**, or **segment**, is a subset of a line that contains two points of the line and all points between those two points.	A B $\overline{AB}$ or $\overline{BA}$
A **ray** is a subset of a line that contains the endpoint and all points on the line on one side of the point.	A B $\overrightarrow{AB}$

Planar Notions

A plane has no thickness and it extends indefinitely in two directions. *A plane is determined by three points that are not all on the same line.* In other words, given three noncollinear points, a unique plane is determined. Table 9-3 illustrates intuitive planar notions.

Table 9-3

Term	Illustration and Symbolism
Points in the same plane are **coplanar**.	Points D, E, and G are coplanar.
Noncoplanar points cannot be placed in a single plane.	Points D, E, F, and G are noncoplanar.
Lines in the same plane are **coplanar lines**.	Lines DE, DF, and FE are coplanar. Lines DE and EG are coplanar.
Skew lines are lines that do not intersect, and there is no plane that contains them.	Lines GF and DE are skew lines.
Intersecting lines are two coplanar lines with exactly one point in common.	Lines DE and GE are intersecting lines; they intersect at point E.
Concurrent lines are lines that contain the same point.	Lines DE, EG, and EF are concurrent.
Two distinct coplanar lines m and n that have no points in common are **parallel lines**.	m is parallel to n, written $m \parallel n$.

NOW TRY THIS 9-1

  a. How many different lines can be drawn through two points?
  b. Can skew lines be parallel? Why?
  c. On a globe, a "line" is a great circle, that is, a circle the same size as the equator. How many different lines can be drawn through two different points?

We assume the following properties of points, lines, and planes:

> **Properties of Points, Lines, and Planes**
>
> 1. There is exactly one line that contains any two distinct points.
> 2. If two points lie in a plane, then the line containing the points lies in the plane.
> 3. If two distinct planes intersect, then their intersection is a line.
> 4. There is exactly one plane that contains any three distinct noncollinear points.
> 5. A line and a point not on the line determine a plane.
> 6. Two parallel lines determine a plane.
> 7. Two intersecting lines determine a plane.

Euclid assumed the first four of the above properties as axioms—statements presumed true—and showed that statements 5, 6, and 7 followed logically from the first four. For example, property 7 can be proved as follows:

> Two intersecting lines have exactly one point in common. Each line contains at least one other point not on the other line. Thus there are at least three noncollinear points on the two intersecting lines. Those points determine a plane containing the lines.

NOW TRY THIS 9-2

Show that statements 5 and 6 follow logically from the first four statements.

PROBLEM SOLVING   **Lines Through Points**

Given 15 points, no three of which are collinear, how many lines can be drawn through the 15 points?

Understanding the Problem   We are asked to find the number of lines that are determined by 15 points, no 3 of which are collinear. Because two points determine exactly one line, we must consider ways to find out how many lines are determined by the 15 points.

Devising a Plan   We use the strategy of *examining related simpler cases* of the problem in order to think through the original problem. Figure 9-1 shows that 3 non-collinear points determine 3 lines, 4 determine 6 lines, 5 determine 10 lines, and 6 determine 15 lines.

FIGURE 9-1

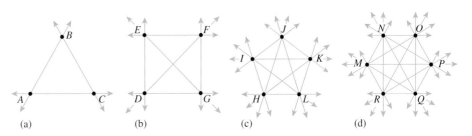

(a)   (b)   (c)   (d)

Examining Figure 9-1(d), we see that through any one of the six points, we can draw only five lines to connect to the other five points. If five lines are drawn through each point, there seems to be 6 times 5, or 30, lines. But in this approach, each line is counted twice; for example, line NO is counted as one of the five lines through N and also as one of the five lines through O. Thus, there are $\dfrac{6 \cdot 5}{2}$, or 15, lines in the figure. We use this information to determine the solution for 15 points.

Carrying Out the Plan   Each of the 15 points can be paired with all points other than itself to determine a line; that is, each point can be paired with the other 14 points to determine 14 lines. If we do this and account for counting each line twice, we see that there should be $\dfrac{15 \cdot 14}{2}$, or 105, lines.

Looking Back   Using this reasoning, we conclude that the number of lines determined by n points, no 3 of which are collinear, is $\dfrac{n(n-1)}{2}$.

An alternative solution to this problem uses the notion of combinations found in Chapter 7. The number of ways that n points, no 3 of which are collinear, can be chosen 2 at a time to form lines is $_nC_2$, or $\dfrac{n(n-1)}{2}$.

A different approach is to use a strategy of *solving a simpler problem*. Two points determine exactly one line. When we add a third point so that the three points are not collinear, as in Figure 9-1(a), we can connect that point to the two existing points and create two new lines, for a total of $1 + 2$ lines. When a fourth point is added (so that no three of the four points are collinear), it can be connected to the three existing points to obtain three additional lines, for a total of $1 + 2 + 3$ lines. Continuing in this way so that no three points are collinear, when the 15th point is added to the existing 14 points, 14 new lines are created for a total of $1 + 2 + 3 + \ldots + 14$ lines. Using what we know about the sum of an arithmetic sequence (see Chapter 1), we get:

$$1 + 2 + 3 + \ldots + 14 = \frac{(14 + 1)14}{2} = \frac{15 \cdot 14}{2}; \text{ that is, 105 lines.}$$

In general, when the nth point is added, we can connect it to the $n - 1$ existing points to obtain $n - 1$ new lines. Thus the number of lines determined by n points, no three of which are collinear, is: $1 + 2 + 3 + \ldots + n - 1 = \dfrac{(1 + n - 1)(n - 1)}{2}$ or $\dfrac{n(n-1)}{2}$.

NOW TRY THIS 9-3

Use a geometric model to find the number of handshakes that take place at a party of 20 people if each person shakes hands with everybody else at the party. (*Hint:* Think about people as points and handshakes as lines.)

Other Planar Notions

Two distinct planes either intersect in a line or are parallel. In Figure 9-2(a), planes α and β are parallel; that is, they have no points in common. Figure 9-2(b) shows planes that intersect in $\overleftrightarrow{AB}$.

FIGURE 9-2

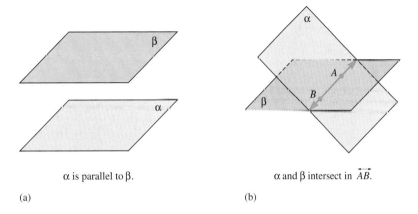

α is parallel to β.

(a)

α and β intersect in $\overleftrightarrow{AB}$.

(b)

A line and a plane can be related in one of three ways. If a line and a plane have no points in common, the line is parallel to the plane, as in Figure 9-3(a). If two points of a line are in the plane, then the entire line containing the points is contained in the plane, as **half-plane** in Figure 9-3(b). In Figure 9-3(b), the line AB separates plane α into two **half-planes,** denoted AB-C and AB-D. Plane α is the union of the three mutually disjoint sets: the two half-planes AB-C and AB-D, and the line AB. If a line intersects a plane but is not contained in the plane, it intersects the plane at only one point, as in Figure 9-3(c).

FIGURE 9-3

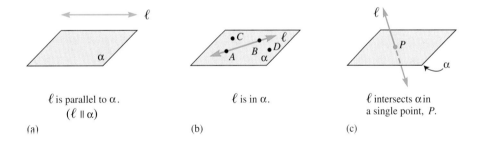

ℓ is parallel to α.
($\ell \parallel \alpha$)

(a)

ℓ is in α.

(b)

ℓ intersects α in
a single point, P.

(c)

Angles

angle   When two rays share an endpoint, an **angle** is formed, as shown in Figure 9-4(a). The
side ◆ vertex   rays of an angle are the **sides** of the angle, and the common endpoint is the **vertex** of the angle. An angle can be named by three different points: the vertex and a point on each ray, with the vertex always listed between the other two points. Thus the angle in Figure 9-4(a) may be named $\angle CBA$ or $\angle ABC$. When there is no risk of confusion, it is customary simply to name an angle by its vertex, by a number, or by a lowercase Greek letter. The angle in Figure 9-4(a) therefore also can be named $\angle B$ or $\angle 1$. In Figure 9-4(b), however, more than one angle has vertex P, namely, $\angle QPR$, $\angle RPS$, and $\angle QPS$. Thus the notation $\angle P$ is inadequate for naming any one of the angles α, β, or $\angle QPS$. Angles, such as $\angle QPR$
adjacent angles   (or α) and $\angle RPS$ (or β) in Figure 9-4(b) are **adjacent angles**, which share a common vertex and a common side and do not have overlapping interiors.

FIGURE 9-4

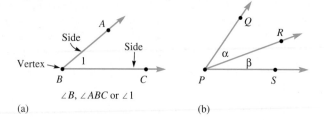

$\angle B, \angle ABC$ or $\angle 1$

(a)   (b)

Angle Measurement

degree   An angle is measured according to the amount of "opening" between its sides. The **degree** is commonly used to measure angles. A complete rotation about a point has a measure of 360 degrees, written 360°. One degree is then $\frac{1}{360}$ of a complete rotation. Figure 9-5 shows that $\angle BAC$ has a measure of 30 degrees, written $m(\angle BAC) = 30°$. The measuring de-

protractor   vice pictured in the figure is a **protractor**. A degree is subdivided into 60 equal parts—

minutes ◆ seconds   **minutes**—and each minute is further divided into 60 equal parts—**seconds**. The measurement 29 degrees, 47 minutes, 13 seconds is written 29°47'13".

FIGURE 9-5

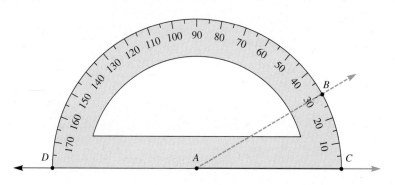

REMARK   The degree is not the only unit to measure angles. In calculus and in

radian   science, a **radian** is used as a unit of angle measurement. One *radian* is approxi-

grad   mately 57.296°. The **grad** is another unit of angle measurement, which is sometimes used in civil engineering. One *grad* is equal to 1/100 of 90°, that is, 0.9°. Most scientific calculators allow measurement of angles to be entered in degree-minute-second format or in radian measure.

NOW TRY THIS 9-4

Convert 8.42° to degrees, minutes, and seconds.

In 1634 Pierre Herigone used a symbol for an angle. It was not until 1923 that the Mathematical Association of America recommended ∠ as the standard symbol for angle in the United States. The use of 360° to measure angles seems to date to the Babylonian culture (4000–3000 B.C.), with minutes and seconds coming from Latin translations of Arabic translations of Babylonian sexagesimal (base 60) fractions.

EXAMPLE
9-1

a. In Figure 9-6, find the measure of $\angle BAC$ if $m(\angle 1) = 47°45'$ and $m(\angle 2) = 29°58'$.
b. Express $47°45'$ as a number of degrees.

FIGURE 9-6

Solution **a.** $m(\angle BAC) = 47°45' - 29°58'$
$= 46°(60 + 45)' - 29°58'$
$= 46°105' - 29°58'$
$= (46 - 29)° + (105 - 58)'$
$= 17°47'$

b. $47°45' = 47\dfrac{45'}{60} = 47.75°$

Types of Angles

We can create different types of angles by paper folding, especially with wax paper. Consider the folds shown in Figure 9-7(a) and (b). A piece of paper is folded in half and then reopened. If any point on the fold line labeled ℓ is chosen as the vertex, then the measure of the angle pictured is 180°. If the paper is refolded and folded once more, as shown in Figure 9-7(c), and then is reopened, as shown in Figure 9-7(d), four angles of the same size are created. Each angle has measure 90° and is a right angle. The symbol ⌐ denotes a right angle. (Why is the measure of each of these angles 90°?)

FIGURE 9-7

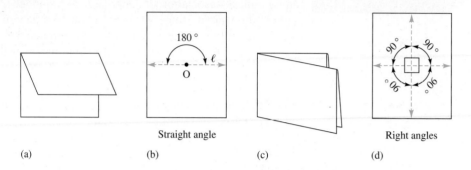

Straight angle   Right angles

(a)   (b)   (c)   (d)

If the paper is folded as shown in Figure 9-8 and reopened, then angles α and β are formed, with measures that are less than 90° and greater than 90°, respectively. (Note that β has measure less than 180°.) Angle α is an *acute* angle while β is an *obtuse* angle.

FIGURE 9-8

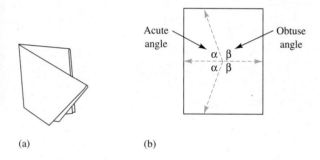

(a)   (b)

The types of planar angles just discovered are shown in Figure 9-9, along with their definitions.

FIGURE 9-9

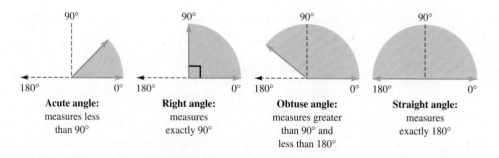

Acute angle: **Right angle:**   **Obtuse angle:**   **Straight angle:**
measures less   measures   measures greater   measures
than 90°   exactly 90°   than 90° and   exactly 180°
                                            less than 180°

On the student page we find a way to use paper folding to create angles of various measures. Answer question 6 on the student page.

Sample School Book Page:
CREATING ANGLES

8-4 Lines and Angles

You'll Learn ...

■ to draw, measure, and identify angles

... How It's Used

Lighting technicians know how to set a dramatic mood by staging lights at various angles.

Vocabulary

angle

vertex

line

line segment

endpoints

ray

straight angle

right angle

acute angle

obtuse angle

complementary

supplementary

congruent

angle bisector

▶ **Lesson Link** You have learned how to use various units of measurement. Now you will learn about lines and angles. ◀

An **angle** is formed when two lines (or line segments, or rays) meet at one point, called the **vertex**. Angles are usually measured in degrees.

There are 360° in a complete circle.

└ Vertex ┘

Explore | Angles

The Angle in Creases

Materials: Sheet of wax paper, Compass, Scissors

1. Use your compass to draw the largest circle possible on the sheet of wax paper. Cut out the circle.

2. Fold the circle in half by lining up the edge of your circle. Fold the circle in half again.

3. Fold the circle in half two more times.

4. Each time you folded the circle, you made an angle. What part of the circle was located at the vertex of each angle?

5. The full circle shows 360°. When you fold the full circle in half, you make a 180° angle. What is the resulting angle measure if you fold this in half?

6. What is the number pattern that results each time an angle is folded in half? Write an algebraic equation for this.

7. If each quarter of the circle is 90°, what is the angle measure of three-quarters of a circle? How did you arrive at your answer?

8. On your circle, label as many creases as you can with the appropriate angle measure.

9. Use your circle as a measuring tool to approximate the measure of angles you can find in your classroom.

410 *Chapter 8 • Geometry and Measurement*

Source: Scott Foresman–Addison Wesley Middle School Math, Course 3, 2002 (p. 471).

REMARK   In higher mathematics and in scientific applications, it is important to view an angle as being created by a ray rotating about its endpoint. If the ray makes one full rotation, we say that it sweeps an angle of 360°. Angles with positive measure are created by a counterclockwise rotation, and angles with negative measure by a clockwise rotation. Angles whose measure is greater than 360° are created when the ray makes more than one full rotation about its endpoint.

Perpendicular Lines

perpendicular lines

When two lines intersect so that the angles formed are right angles, as in Figure 9-10, the lines are **perpendicular lines**. In Figure 9-10, lines m and n are perpendicular, and we write $m \perp n$. Two intersecting segments, two intersecting rays, or one segment and one ray that intersect are perpendicular if they lie on perpendicular lines. For example, in Figure 9-10, $\overline{AB} \perp \overline{BC}$, $\overrightarrow{BA} \perp \overrightarrow{BC}$, and $\overline{AB} \perp \overrightarrow{BC}$.

FIGURE 9-10

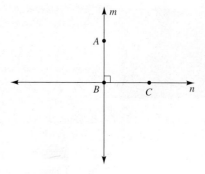

A Line Perpendicular to a Plane

If a line and a plane intersect, they can be perpendicular. For example, consider Figure 9-11, where planes β and γ represent two walls intersecting along $\overleftrightarrow{AB}$. The edge $\overleftrightarrow{AB}$ is perpendicular to the floor. Also, every line in the plane of the floor (plane α) passing through point A is perpendicular to $\overleftrightarrow{AB}$. This discussion should help you understand what we mean by "a line perpendicular to a plane."

FIGURE 9-11

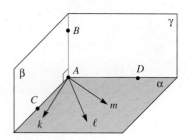

line perpendicular to a plane   A **line perpendicular to a plane** is a line that is perpendicular to every line in the plane through its intersection with the plane.

NOW TRY THIS 9-5

> **a.** Is it possible for a line intersecting a plane to be perpendicular to exactly one line in the plane through its intersection with the plane? Explain by making an appropriate drawing.
>
> **b.** Is it possible for a line intersecting a plane to be perpendicular to two distinct lines in a plane going through its point of intersection with the plane, and yet not be perpendicular to the plane?

After answering the questions in *Now Try This 9-5*, you will likely find the following theorem quite plausible (the proof of the theorem requires concepts from Chapter 10.)

> ### Theorem 9-1
>
> A line perpendicular to two distinct lines in the plane through its intersection with the plane is perpendicular to the plane.

ONGOING ASSESSMENT 9-1

1. **a.** Points *A*, *B*, *C*, and *D* are collinear. In how many ways can the line be named using only these points?
   b. Points *A*, *B*, *C*, *D*, and *E* are coplanar and no three are collinear. In how many ways can the plane be named using only these points?

2. For the following figure, answer the following:
   a. Name two pairs of skew lines.
   b. Are $\overleftrightarrow{BD}$ and $\overleftrightarrow{FH}$ parallel, skew, or intersecting lines?
   c. Are $\overleftrightarrow{BD}$ and $\overleftrightarrow{GH}$ parallel?
   d. Find the intersection of $\overleftrightarrow{BD}$ and plane *EFG*.
   e. Find the intersection of $\overleftrightarrow{BH}$ and plane *DCG*.
   f. Name two pairs of perpendicular planes.
   g. Name two lines that are perpendicular to plane *EFH*.

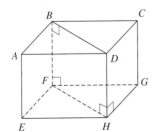

3. A **dihedral angle** is the union of two half-planes and the common line defining the half-planes. In the accompanying figure, the dihedral angle $O - AC - D$ is formed by the intersecting planes α and β. Note that the point O is in

the plane α, $\overleftrightarrow{AC}$ is the edge of the dihedral angle, and point D is in plane β. A dihedral angle is measured by any of the associated planar angles such as $\angle OPD$ in the following figure. (Note that $\overleftrightarrow{PO} \perp \overleftrightarrow{AC}$ and $\overleftrightarrow{PD} \perp \overleftrightarrow{AC}$.)

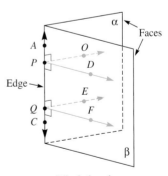

Dihedral angle

Use the figure in problem 2 to answer the following:
   a. Name a planar angle that could be used to measure dihedral angle *E-FG-B*.
   b. What is the measure of dihedral angle *D-HG-F*?
   c. How can the concept of dihedral angle be used to define perpendicular planes?
   d. Explain why planes *BDH* and *FHG* in problem 2 are perpendicular.

4. Use the following drawing of one of the Great Pyramids of Egypt to find the following:
   a. The intersection of $\overline{AD}$ and $\overline{CE}$
   b. The intersection of planes *ABC*, *ACE*, and *BCE*
   c. The intersection of $\overleftrightarrow{AD}$ and $\overleftrightarrow{CA}$
   d. A pair of skew lines
   e. A pair of parallel lines
   f. A plane not determined by one of the triangular faces or by the base

5. Determine how many acute angles are in the following figure:

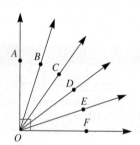

6. Identify a physical model for each of the following:
   a. Perpendicular lines
   b. An acute angle
   c. An obtuse angle

7. Find the measure of each of the following angles:
   a. ∠*EAB*   b. ∠*EAD*
   c. ∠*GAF*   d. ∠*CAF*

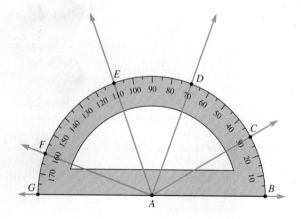

8. Use a protractor to find the measure of each of the following pictured angles:

Paper scissors

(a)

Barber's shears

(b)

9. a. Perform each of the following operations. Leave your answers in simplest form.
   i. 18°35′29″ + 22°55′41″
   ii. 93°38′14″ − 13°49′27″
   b. Express each of the following in degrees, minutes, and seconds, without decimals:
   i. 0.9°
   ii. 15.13°

10. Consider a correctly set clock that starts ticking at noon and answer the following:
    a. Find the measure of the angle swept by the hour hand by the time it reaches
    i. 3 P.M.
    ii. 12:25 P.M.
    iii. 6:50 P.M.
    b. Find the exact angle measure between the minute and the hour hands at 1:15 P.M.
    c. At what time between 12 noon and 1 P.M. will the angle measure between the hands be 180°?

11. Mario was studying right angles and wondered if during his math class the minute and hour hands of the clock formed a right angle. If his class meets from 2:00 P.M. to 2:50 P.M., is a right angle formed? If it is, figure out to the nearest minute when the hands form the right angle.

12. Given three collinear points *A*, *B*, *C*, four different rays can be named using these points: $\overrightarrow{AB}$, $\overrightarrow{BA}$, $\overrightarrow{BC}$, and $\overrightarrow{CB}$. Determine how many different rays can be named given each of the following:
    a. Four collinear points   **b.** Five collinear points
    c. *n* collinear points

13. Refer to the following table.

Number of Intersection Points

	0	1	2	3	4	5
2			Not possible	Not possible	Not possible	Not possible
3					Not possible	Not possible
4						
5						
6						

Number of Lines (vertical axis label)

a. Sketch the possible intersections of the given number of lines. Three sketches are given for you.
    b. Given *n* lines, find a formula for determining the greatest possible number of intersection points.

14. Trace each of the following drawings. In your tracings, use dashed lines for segments that would not be seen and solid lines for segments that would be seen. (Different people may see different perspectives.)

(a)   (b)

(c)

(d)

15. Draw pictures illustrating a real-world example of the following:
    a. Three planes intersecting in a common line
    b. Three planes intersecting in a common point

16. In each of the following pairs, determine whether the symbols name the same geometric figure.
    a. $\overrightarrow{AB}$ and $\overrightarrow{BA}$
    b. $\overline{AB}$ and $\overline{BA}$
    c. $\overleftrightarrow{AB}$ and $\overleftrightarrow{BA}$.

17. a. How many planes are determined by three noncollinear points?
    b. How many planes are determined by four points, no three of which are collinear?
    c. How many planes are determined by *n* points, no three of which are collinear?

Communication

18. Forest rangers use degree measures to identify directions and locate critical spots such as fires. In the following drawing, a forest ranger at tower *A* observes smoke at a bearing of 149° (clockwise from the north), while another forest ranger at tower *B* observes the same source of smoke at a bearing of 250° (clockwise from the north).

a. Choose two locations for *A* and *B* and use a protractor and a straightedge to locate the source of the smoke.
    b. Explain how the forest rangers could find the location of the fire.
    c. Describe other situations in which location can be determined by similar methods.

19. Is it possible to locate four points in a plane such that the number of lines determined by the points is not exactly 1, 4, or 6? Explain.

20. Given *n* lines in the plane, no two of which are parallel and no three of which intersect in a single point, find the number of non-overlapping regions that are created by the *n* lines.

Cooperative Learning

21. Each member of your group should use a protractor to make a triangle out of cardboard that has one angle measuring 30° and another 50°. Answer the following and compare your solutions with other members of your group:

   a. Show how to use the triangle (without a protractor) to draw an angle with measure 40°.

   b. Is there more than one way to draw an angle as in (a) using the triangle? Explain.

   c. What other angles can be drawn with the triangle? Why?

Open-Ended

22. Within the classroom, identify a physical object with the following shapes:
   a. Parallel lines   b. Parallel planes
   c. Skew lines   d. Right angles

23. On a sheet of dot paper or on a geoboard like the one shown, create the following:

   a. Right angle   b. Acute angle
   c. Obtuse angle   d. Adjacent angles
   e. Parallel segments f. Intersecting segments

LABORATORY
A C T I V I T Y

Many geometric ideas can be experienced through paper folding, as in Figure 9-12. Consider the following construction of perpendicular lines and answer the questions that follow:

FIGURE 9-12

Fold one corner of a sheet of paper over and crease it along the fold.

Fold any part of the crease onto itself.

Unfold to reveal the two crease lines forming right angles.

   a. Explain why the two crease lines are perpendicular.

   b. Use a sheet of paper and follow the above instructions to create two pairs of perpendicular lines.

   c. Use paper folding to create angles with the following measures:
      i. 45°   ii. 135°   iii. 22°30′

      (*Mathematics Through Paper Folding* by Olson and *Geometric Exercises in Paper Foldings* by Row are listed in the bibliography as resource books.)

  Polygons

curve

With a pencil, draw a path on a piece of paper without lifting the pencil and without retracing any part of the path except single points. The resulting drawing is restricted to the plane of the paper and not lifting the pencil implies that there are no breaks in the drawing. The drawing is *connected* and is a **curve**.

   In Table 9-4 each curve is in the plane and is connected, but there are some obvious differences among the curves. Table 9-4 shows sample curves and their classifications.

Table 9-4

Simple	Closed	Polygon	Convex	Concave

simple
closed

polygon
convex

concave

A **simple** curve does not cross itself, except that if you draw it with a pencil, the starting and stopping points may be the same. A **closed** curve can be drawn starting and stopping at the same point. A curve can be classified as simple, nonsimple, closed, nonclosed, and so on. **Polygons** are simple and closed and have *sides* that are segments. A point where two sides of a polygon meet is a *vertex*. **Convex** curves are simple, closed, and have no indentations. More precisely, the segment connecting any two points *in the interior of the curve is wholly contained in the interior of the curve.* **Concave** curves are simple, closed, and not convex; that is, they have an indentation.

NOW TRY THIS 9-6

Draw a curve that is neither simple nor closed.

polygonal regions

As in Figure 9-13(a), every simple closed curve separates the plane into three disjoint subsets: the interior of the curve, the exterior of the curve, and the curve itself. Of specific interest to us are polygons and their interiors, together called **polygonal regions**. Figure 9-13(b) shows a polygonal region.

FIGURE 9-13

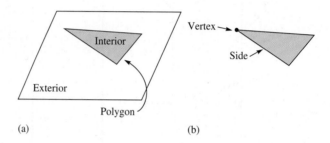

(a)   (b)

Whether a point is inside or outside a curve is not always obvious. This is explored in *Now Try This 9-7.*

NOW TRY THIS 9-7

Determine whether point *X* is inside or outside the simple closed curve of Figure 9-14. Explain your reasoning so that it can be generalized to other simple closed curves.

FIGURE 9-14

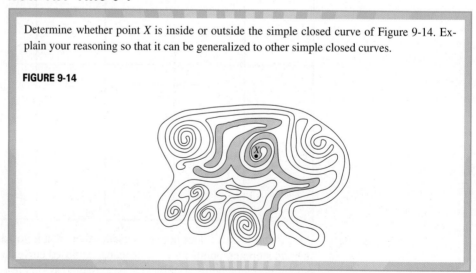

More About Polygons

Polygons are classified according to the number of sides or vertices they have. For example, consider the polygons listed in Table 9-5.

Table 9-5

Polygon	Number of Sides or Vertices
Triangle	3
Quadrilateral	4
Pentagon	5
Hexagon	6
Heptagon	7
Octagon	8
Nonagon	9
Decagon	10
n-gon	n

A polygon is referred to by the capital letters that represent its consecutive vertices, such as *ABCD* or *CDAB* (but not *BCAD*) shown in Figure 9-15(a). Any two sides of a polygon having a common vertex determine an **interior angle**, or **angle of the polygon**, such as ∠1 of polygon *ABCD* in Figure 9-15(a). An **exterior angle of a convex polygon** is determined by a side of the polygon and the extension of a contiguous side of the polygon. An example is ∠2 in Figure 9-15(b). Any line segment connecting nonconsecutive vertices of a polygon such as $\overline{AC}$ in Figure 9-15(a) is a **diagonal** of polygon *ABCD*.

interior angle, or **angle, of a polygon** ◆ **exterior angle of a convex polygon**

diagonal

FIGURE 9-15

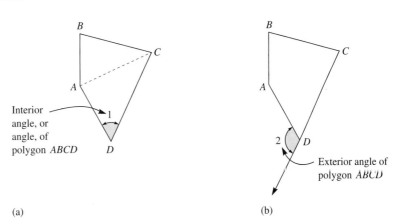

(a) (b)

Congruent Segments and Angles

congruent parts

Most modern industries operate on the notion of creating **congruent parts**, parts that are of the same size and shape. For example, the specifications for all cars of a particular model are the same, and all parts produced for that model are basically the same. Usually congruent figures refer to figures in a plane. For example, two line **segments** are **congruent** (≅) if a tracing of one line segment can be fitted exactly on top of the other line segment. If $\overline{AB}$ is congruent to $\overline{CD}$, we write $\overline{AB} \cong \overline{CD}$. Two **angles** are **congruent** if they have the same measure. Congruent segments and congruent angles are shown in Figure 9-16(a) and (b), respectively.

congruent segments

congruent angles

FIGURE 9-16

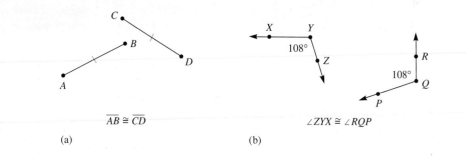

$\overline{AB} \cong \overline{CD}$

(a)

$\angle ZYX \cong \angle RQP$

(b)

Regular Polygons

regular polygons

Polygons in which all the interior angles are congruent and all the sides are congruent are **regular polygons**. A regular polygon is both *equiangular* and *equilateral*. A regular triangle is an equilateral triangle. A regular pentagon and a regular hexagon are illustrated in Figure 9-17. The congruent sides and congruent angles are marked.

FIGURE 9-17

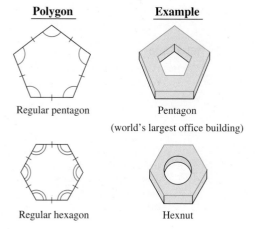

Polygon	**Example**
Regular pentagon	Pentagon (world's largest office building)
Regular hexagon	Hexnut

Triangles and Quadrilaterals

Triangles may be classified according to their angle measures, as shown in Table 9-6. Quadrilaterals may be classified as shown in Table 9-6.

Table 9-6

Definition	Illustration	Example
A triangle containing one right angle is a **right triangle**.		

Table 9-6 *continued*

Definition	Illustration	Example
A triangle in which all the angles are acute is an **acute triangle**.		
A triangle containing one obtuse angle is an **obtuse triangle**.		
A triangle with no congruent sides is a **scalene triangle**.		
A triangle with at least two congruent sides is an **isosceles triangle**.		
A triangle with three congruent sides is an **equilateral triangle**.		
A **trapezoid** is a quadrilateral with at least one pair of parallel sides.		
A **kite** is a quadrilateral with at least two distinct pairs of consecutive congruent sides.		
An **isosceles trapezoid** is a trapezoid with one pair of congruent base angles. (Equivalently, an isosceles trapezoid is a trapezoid with two congruent nonadjacent sides.)		
A **parallelogram** is a quadrilateral in which each pair of opposite sides is parallel.		
A **rectangle** is a parallelogram with a right angle. (Equivalently, a rectangle is a quadrilateral with four right angles.)		
A **rhombus** is a parallelogram with all sides congruent. (Equivalently, a rhombus is a quadrilateral with all sides congruent.)		
A **square** is a rectangle with all sides congruent. (Equivalently, a square is a quadrilateral with four right angles and four congruent sides.)		

Some texts give different definitions for trapezoids and other figures. Many elementary texts define a trapezoid as a quadrilateral with *exactly* one pair of parallel sides. Note the definition of a trapezoid on the following student page.

NOW TRY THIS 9-8

a. Answer the questions on the student page.
b. Which of the quadrilaterals on the student page are defined differently in Table 9-6?
c. Why do you think this text defines some of the quadrilaterals as in Table 9-6 and not as on the student page?

The many names for geometric figures can be overwhelming, as depicted in the following cartoon.

WITH SO MANY GEOMETRIC FIGURES, I'M GONNA RUN OUT OF ALPHABET NAMING THE PARTS!

Hierarchy Among Polygons

Every triangle is a polygon, and every equilateral triangle is also isosceles. However, not every isosceles triangle is equilateral. Using set concepts, we can say that the set of all triangles is a proper subset of the set of all polygons. Also, the set of all equilateral triangles is a proper subset of the set of all isosceles triangles. This hierarchy is shown in Figure 9-18, where more general terms appear above more specific ones. Compare Figure 9-18 with the diagram of the student page. How do they differ?

Sample School Book Page:
QUADRILATERALS

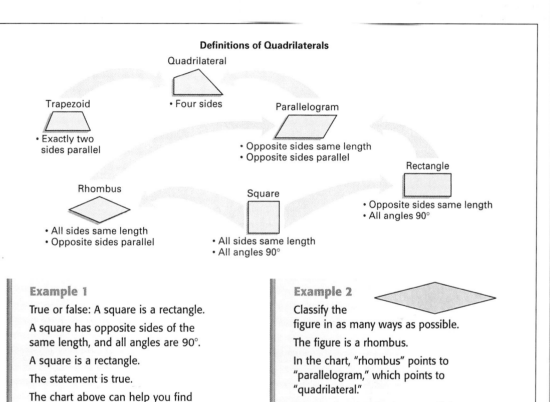

Definitions of Quadrilaterals

Quadrilateral
• Four sides

Trapezoid
• Exactly two sides parallel

Parallelogram
• Opposite sides same length
• Opposite sides parallel

Rectangle
• Opposite sides same length
• All angles 90°

Rhombus
• All sides same length
• Opposite sides parallel

Square
• All sides same length
• All angles 90°

Example 1

True or false: A square is a rectangle.

A square has opposite sides of the same length, and all angles are 90°.

A square is a rectangle.

The statement is true.

The chart above can help you find all the classifications for a figure.

Example 2

Classify the figure in as many ways as possible.

The figure is a rhombus.

In the chart, "rhombus" points to "parallelogram," which points to "quadrilateral."

So, any rhombus is also a parallelogram and also a quadrilateral.

Talk About It

1. A geometry book said that a square is a "rectangular rhombus." Do you agree? Explain your reasoning.

2. How are trapezoids and parallelograms alike? How are they different?

3. Quadrilaterals can be classified based on whether or not their opposite sides are parallel. Can triangles also be classified in this way? Explain.

Source: Scott Foresman–Addison Wesley Math 2002, Grade 6 (p. 429).

FIGURE 9-18

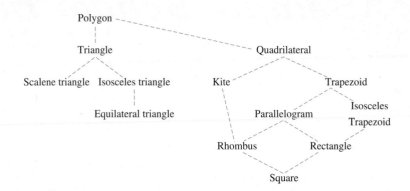

NOW TRY THIS 9-9

Use the definitions in Table 9-6 to experiment with several drawings to decide which of the following are true:

1. An equilateral triangle is isosceles.
2. A square is a regular quadrilateral.
3. If one angle of a rhombus is a right angle, then all the angles of the rhombus are right angles.
4. A square is a rhombus with a right angle.
5. All the angles of a rectangle are right angles.
6. A rectangle is an isosceles trapezoid.
7. Some isosceles trapezoids are kites.
8. If a kite has a right angle, then it must be a square.

ONGOING ASSESSMENT 9-2

1. Determine for each of the following which of the figures labeled (1) through (10) can be classified under the given term:
   a. Simple closed curve   b. Polygon
   c. Convex polygon   d. Concave polygon

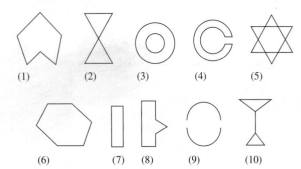

(1)   (2)   (3)   (4)   (5)

(6)   (7) (8)   (9)   (10)

2. What is the maximum number of intersection points between a quadrilateral and a triangle (where no sides of the polygons are on the same line)?
3. What type of polygon must have a diagonal such that part of the diagonal falls outside of the polygon?

4. Which of the following figures are convex, and which are concave? Why?

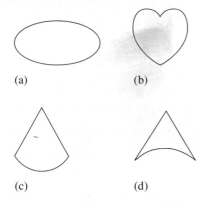

(a)   (b)

(c)   (d)

5. If possible, draw the following triangles. If it is not possible, state why.
   a. An obtuse scalene triangle
   b. An acute scalene triangle
   c. A right scalene triangle

d. An obtuse equilateral triangle

e. A right equilateral triangle

f. An obtuse isosceles triangle

g. An acute isosceles triangle

h. A right isosceles triangle

6. Determine how many diagonals each of the following has:

   a. Decagon

   b. 20-gon

   c. 100-gon

   d. *n*-gon.

   Justify your answer.

7. Identify each of the following triangles as scalene, isosceles, or equilateral:

(a)

(b)

(c)

8. Describe regions (a) and (b) in the following Venn diagram, where the universal set is the set of all parallelograms:

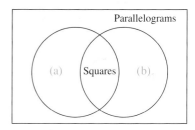

9. Use only the labeled points in the following drawing to answer the questions:

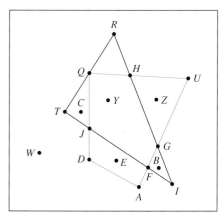

---

a. Which points belong to triangle *TRI*?

b. Which points belong to the interior of the quadrilateral *QUAD*?

c. Which points belong to the exterior of triangle *TRI*?

d. Which points belong to triangle *TRI* and quadrilateral *QUAD*?

e. Which points belong to the intersection of the interiors of triangle *TRI* and quadrilateral *QUAD*?

Communication

10. **a.** Fold a rectangular piece of paper to create a square. Describe your procedure in writing and orally with a classmate. Explain why your approach creates a square.

    b. Crease the square in (a) so that the two diagonals are shown. Use paper folding to show that the diagonals of a square are congruent and perpendicular and bisect each other. Describe your procedure and explain why it works.

Open-Ended

11. On a geoboard or dot paper, construct each of the following:

    a. A scalene triangle   **b.** A square

    c. A trapezoid   **d.** A convex hexagon

    e. A concave quadrilateral

    f. A parallelogram

Cooperative Learning

12. Work with a partner. One of you should construct a figure on a geoboard or draw it on a piece of paper and identify it. Do not show the figure to your partner but tell your partner sufficient properties of the figure to identify it. Have your partner identify the figure you constructed. Your partner earns 1 point if the figure is correctly identified and 2 points if a figure is found that has all the required attributes but is different from the one you drew. Each of you should take the same number of turns. Try this with each of the following types of figure:

    a. Scalene triangle   **b.** Isosceles triangle

    c. Square   **d.** Parallelogram

    e. Trapezoid   **f.** Rectangle

    g. Regular polygon   **h.** Rhombus

    i. Isosceles trapezoid   **j.** A kite that is not a rhombus

13. **a.** Compare the information in the diagram on the student page on page 519 in this section to the quadrilateral hierarchy of Figure 9-18.

    b. Work with partners to create a Venn diagram showing all triangles, isosceles, equilateral, and right triangles.

14. a. Investigate the meaning and uses of Reuleaux triangles.
   b. Explain the similarities and differences between a Reuleaux triangle and an equilateral triangle.
15. a. With partners, decide how you might define a triangle on a globe.
   b. With partners, a globe, string, and a ruler, decide if you think a square can exist on a globe.

Review Problems

16. If three distinct rays with the same vertex are drawn as shown in the following figure, then three angles are formed: $\angle AOB$, $\angle AOC$, and $\angle BOC$:

What is the maximum number of angles (measuring less than 180°) formed by using
   a. 10 distinct noncollinear rays with the same vertex?
   b. *n* distinct noncollinear rays with the same vertex?
17. Determine the possible intersection sets of a line and an angle.
18. Classify the following as true or false. If false, tell why.
   a. A ray has two endpoints.
   b. For any points *M* and *N*, $\overleftrightarrow{MN} = \overleftrightarrow{NM}$.
   c. Skew lines are coplanar.
   d. $\overrightarrow{MN} = \overrightarrow{NM}$
   e. A line segment contains an infinite number of points.
   f. If two distinct planes intersect, their intersection is a line segment.

LABORATORY
A C T I V I T Y

Use paper folding, tape or glue, and any other tools to create a shape larger than, but similar to, that in Figure 9-19.

FIGURE 9-19

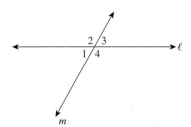

9-3 More About Angles

In Figure 9-20, two lines intersect and form the angles marked 1, 2, 3, and 4.

FIGURE 9-20

vertical angles   **Vertical angles** are pairs of angles such as $\angle 1$ and $\angle 3$ and appear any time two lines intersect. Another pair of vertical angles in Figure 9-20 is $\angle 2$ and $\angle 4$.

You have probably noticed that vertical angles seem to be congruent. Indeed, referring to Figure 9-20, we see that $\angle 1$ and $\angle 2$ are two angles, the sum of whose measure is 180°. This is also true for $\angle 2$ and $\angle 3$. Thus;

$$m(\angle 1) = 180° - m(\angle 2),$$
$$m(\angle 3) = 180° - m(\angle 2).$$

Consequently $m(\angle 1) = m(\angle 3)$. In a similar way we can show that $m(\angle 2) = m(\angle 3)$. We have proved therefore the following:

> **Theorem 9-2**

Vertical angles are congruent.

Other pairs of angles appear frequently enough that it is convenient to refer to them by specific names. Table 9-7 shows several types of angle.

Table 9-7

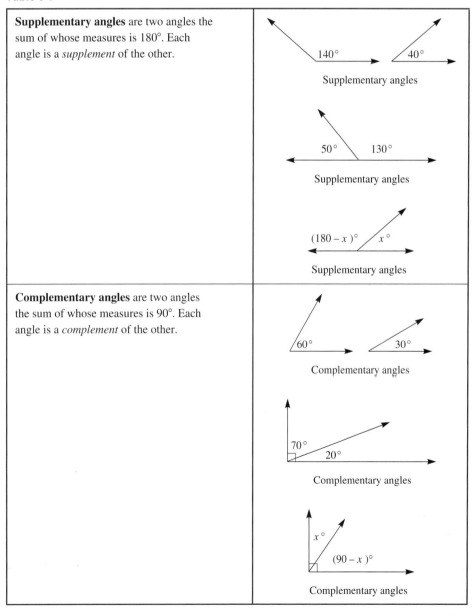

Supplementary angles are two angles the sum of whose measures is 180°. Each angle is a *supplement* of the other.	140° 40° Supplementary angles 50° 130° Supplementary angles $(180 - x)°$ $x°$ Supplementary angles
Complementary angles are two angles the sum of whose measures is 90°. Each angle is a *complement* of the other.	60° 30° Complementary angles 70° 20° Complementary angles $x°$ $(90 - x)°$ Complementary angles

Angles are also formed when a line intersects two distinct lines. Any line that inter-
transversal sects a pair of lines is a **transversal** of those lines. In Figure 9-21(a), line *p* is a transversal
of lines *m* and *n*. Angles formed by these lines are named according to their placement in
relation to the transversal and the two given lines. They are listed in Table 9-8.

FIGURE 9-21

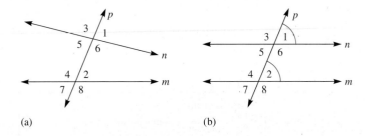

(a)   (b)

Table 9-8

Interior angles	$\angle 2, \angle 4, \angle 5, \angle 6$
Exterior angles	$\angle 3, \angle 1, \angle 7, \angle 8$
Alternate interior angles	$\angle 5$ and $\angle 2$, $\angle 4$ and $\angle 6$
Alternate exterior angles	$\angle 1$ and $\angle 7$, $\angle 3$ and $\angle 8$
Corresponding angles	$\angle 3$ and $\angle 4$, $\angle 5$ and $\angle 7$, $\angle 1$ and $\angle 2$, $\angle 6$ and $\angle 8$

Suppose corresponding angles such as $\angle 1$ and $\angle 2$ in Figure 9-21(b) are congruent.
With this assumption, and because $\angle 1$ and $\angle 5$ are congruent vertical angles, we know that
the pair of alternate interior angles $\angle 2$ and $\angle 5$ are also congruent. Similarly, each pair of
corresponding angles, alternate interior angles, and alternate exterior angles are congruent.

If we examine Figure 9-21(b) further, we see that lines *m* and *n* appear to be parallel
when $\angle 1$ is congruent to $\angle 2$. Conversely, if the lines are parallel, the sets of angles mentioned previously are congruent. This is true and is summarized in the following theorem,
which we state without proof.

> ### Theorem 9-3
>
> If any two distinct coplanar lines are cut by a transversal, then a pair of corresponding angles,
> alternate interior angles, or alternate exterior angles are congruent if, and only if, the lines are
> parallel.

Constructing Parallel Lines

A method commonly used by architects to construct a line ℓ through a given point *P* parallel to a given line *m* is shown in Figure 9-22. Place the side $\overline{AB}$ of triangle *ABC* on line
m, as shown in Figure 9-22(a). Next, place a ruler on side $\overline{AC}$. Keeping the ruler station-

ary, slide triangle *ABC* along the ruler's edge until its side $\overline{AB}$ (marked $\overline{A'B'}$) contains point *P*, as in Figure 9-22(b). Use the side $\overline{A'B'}$ to draw the line ℓ through *P* parallel to *m*.

To show that the construction produces parallel lines, notice that when triangle *ABC* slides, the measures of its angles are unchanged. The angles of triangle *ABC* and triangle *A'B'C'* in Figure 9-22(b) are correspondingly congruent angles. ∠*A* and ∠*A'* are corresponding angles formed by *m* and ℓ and the transversal $\overline{EF}$. Because corresponding angles are congruent, Theorem 9-3 implies that $\ell \parallel m$. In Chapter 10, we show how to construct parallel lines using only a compass and straightedge.

FIGURE 9-22

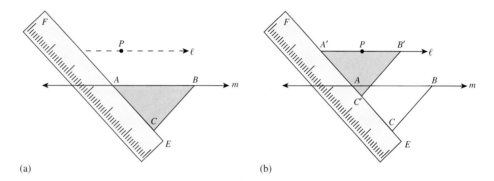

(a)   (b)

The Sum of the Measures of the Angles of a Triangle

The sum of the measures of the angles in a triangle can be shown intuitively to be 180°. We show this by using a torn triangle, as shown in Figure 9-23. Angles 1, 2, and 3 of triangle *ABC* in Figure 9-23(a) are torn as pictured and then replaced as shown in Figure 9-23(b). The three angles seem to lie along a single line ℓ.

FIGURE 9-23

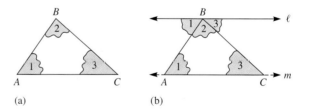

(a)   (b)

The angle measures seem to add up to a straight angle, which measures 180°. This conclusion, which is based on observation, is an example of *inductive reasoning*, discussed in Chapter 1. In contrast, *deductive reasoning* shows that a statement is true by using the given information, previously defined and undefined terms, theorems or statements assumed to be true, and logic. A conclusion based on *deductive reasoning* must be true if the hypothesis is true.

Next, we use deductive reasoning to show that the sum of the measures of the interior angles in every triangle is 180°. In Figure 9-23(b), the line ℓ appears to be parallel to *m*. This suggests drawing a line ℓ parallel to $\overline{AC}$ through vertex *B* of triangle *ABC*, as in Figure 9-24(b), and showing that the angles formed are congruent to the interior angles of the triangle.

FIGURE 9-24

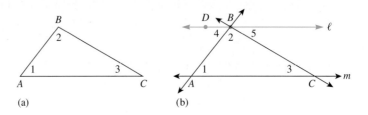

(a)   (b)

In Figure 9-24(b), ℓ and $\overline{AC}$ are parallel, with transversals $\overleftrightarrow{AB}$ and $\overleftrightarrow{BC}$, so it follows that alternate interior angles are congruent. Consequently, $m(\angle 1) = m(\angle 4)$ and $m(\angle 3) = m(\angle 5)$. Thus $m(\angle 1) + m(\angle 2) + m(\angle 3) = m(\angle 4) + m(\angle 2) + m(\angle 5) = 180°$. So, $m(\angle 1) + m(\angle 2) + m(\angle 3) = 180°$. From this, we obtain the following theorem.

> ### Theorem 9-4

The sum of the measures of the interior angles of a triangle is 180°.

NOW TRY THIS 9-10

An alternative way to show that the sum of the measures of the interior angles of a triangle is 180° is suggested in Figure 9-25. We start at vertex A in Figure 9-25(a) facing B, walk all the way around the triangle, and stop at the same position and facing in the same direction as when we started. This trip is shown in Figure 9-25(b).

FIGURE 9-25

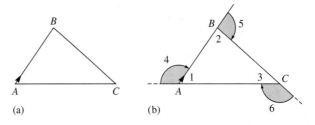

(a)   (b)

a. Write an argument for the sum of the measures of the exterior angles of the triangle to be 360°.
b. Use the fact that the sum of the measures of the exterior angles of a triangle is 360° to write an argument that the sum of the measures of the interior angles of the triangle is 180°.
c. Generalize the sum of the measures of the exterior angles of any convex polygon. Explain your reasoning.

Now Try This 9-10 can be summarized in Theorem 9-5.

> ## Theorem 9-5

The sum of the measures of the exterior angles (one at each vertex) of a convex polygon is 360°.

E X A M P L E
9-2

In the framework for a bridge, shown in Figure 9-26(a), *ABCD* is a parallelogram. If ∠*ADC* of the parallelogram measures 50°, what are the measures of the other angles of the parallelogram?

FIGURE 9-26

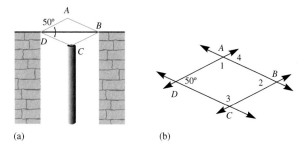

(a)   (b)

Solution   Refer to Figure 9-26(b). We draw the lines containing the sides of parallelogram *ABCD*. ∠*ADC* has a measure of 50°, and ∠4 and ∠*ADC* are corresponding angles formed by parallel lines $\overleftrightarrow{AB}$ and $\overleftrightarrow{CD}$ cut by transversal $\overleftrightarrow{AD}$. So it follows that $m(\angle 4) = 50°$. Because ∠1 and ∠4 are supplementary, $m(\angle 1) = 180° - 50° = 130°$. Using similar reasoning, we find that $m(\angle 2) = 50°$ and $m(\angle 3) = 130°$.

E X A M P L E
9-3

In Figure 9-27, $m \parallel n$ and k is a transversal. Explain why $m(\angle 1) + m(\angle 2) = 180°$.

FIGURE 9-27

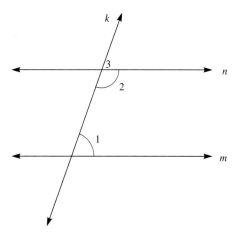

Solution Because ∠1 and ∠3 are corresponding angles and $m \parallel n$, $m(\angle 1) = m(\angle 3)$. Also because ∠2 and ∠3 are supplementary angles, $m(\angle 2) + m(\angle 3) = 180°$. Substituting $m(\angle 1)$ for $m(\angle 3)$, we have $m(\angle 2) + m(\angle 1) = 180°$.

NOW TRY THIS 9-11

When a plane flies directly from New York to London and then to Nairobi and back to New York, it flies along the sides of a spherical triangle, as shown in Figure 9-28(a), approximately following the surface of Earth. On a sphere, the shortest path between two points is along an arc of a great circle. A great circle is obtained when a plane through the center of the sphere intersects the sphere. (An example of a great circle is the equator.) To obtain a great circle through two given points on the sphere, we need consider only a plane through the two points and the center of the sphere. A great circle through points A and B is shown in Figure 9-28(b). A *spherical triangle* consists of three points on the sphere and arcs of great circles (the shortest path) connecting the points.

FIGURE 9-28

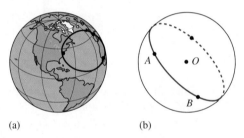

(a)   (b)

a. How many great circles go through the North Pole and the South Pole on the globe?
b. Describe a spherical triangle that has one vertex at the North Pole and the other two vertices on the equator.
c. Is there a spherical triangle with three right angles? If so, find one.

The Sum of the Measures of the Interior Angles of a Convex Polygon with *n* Sides

We can find the sum of the measures of all the interior angles in any convex *n*-gon. We first illustrate the approach for a convex pentagon. Extend each side of the pentagon as shown in Figure 9-29 so that at each vertex, an exterior angle is formed. Because at each vertex an interior angle and the corresponding exterior angle are supplementary, the sum of the measures of all the exterior and interior angles of the pentagon is $5 \cdot 180°$. By Theorem 9-5, the sum of the measures of the exterior angles is $360°$. Thus, the sum of the measures of the interior angles is $5 \cdot 180° - 360°$, or $540°$. The same reasoning applies to any convex *n*-gon. The sum of the measures of an interior angle and the corresponding exterior angle at each vertex is $180°$. Because there are *n* vertices, the sum of the measures of all the interior and exterior angles is $n \cdot 180°$. The sum of the measures of the exterior angles is $360°$, so the sum of the measures of the interior angles is $n \cdot 180° - 360°$, or $(n - 2)180°$.

FIGURE 9-29

In a regular n-gon, all n interior angles are congruent and the sum of their measures is $180n - 360$, so the measure of a single angle is $\dfrac{180n - 360}{n}$, or $\dfrac{(n - 2)180°}{n}$.

The results from this discussion are summarized by the following theorem.

> ### Theorem 9-6
>
> **a.** The sum of the measures of the interior angles of any convex polygon with n sides is $180n - 360$, or $(n - 2)180°$.
> **b.** The measure of a single interior angle of a regular n-gon is $\dfrac{180n - 360}{n}$, or $\dfrac{(n - 2)180°}{n}$.

NOW TRY THIS 9-12

We next consider an alternative way to justify Theorem 9-6.

We can use the fact that the sum of the measures of a triangle's interior angles is 180° to find the sum of the measures of the interior angles of a quadrilateral by dividing the quadrilateral into two triangles. Because the sum of the measures of the interior angles in each triangle is 180°, the sum of the measures of the interior angles in the quadrilateral is $2 \cdot 180°$, or 360°. Use this approach to find the sum of the measures of the interior angles for any convex n-gon. Is your result the same as in Theorem 9-6?

EXAMPLE 9-4

a. Find the measure of each angle of a regular decagon.
b. Find the number of sides of a regular polygon, each of whose interior angles has a measure of 175°.

Solution **a.** Because a decagon has ten sides, the sum of the measures of the angles of a decagon is $10 \cdot 180 - 360$, or 1440°. A regular decagon has ten angles, all of which are congruent, so each one has a measure of $\dfrac{1440°}{10}$, or 144°. As an alternative solution, each exterior angle is $\dfrac{360°}{10}$, or 36°. Hence, each interior angle is $180 - 36$, or 144°.

b. Each interior angle of the regular polygon is 175°. Thus the measure of each exterior angle of the polygon is $180° - 175°$, or 5°. Because the sum of the measures of all exterior angles of a convex polygon is 360°, the number of exterior angles is $\dfrac{360}{5}$, or 72. Hence, the number of sides is 72.

Walks Around Stars and Other Figures

In Now Try This 9-10 and Theorem 9-5, we have seen that the sum of the measures of the exterior angles of any convex polygon is 360°. We can use the same idea of walking around the polygon to generalize Theorem 9-5 to "polygons" that cross themselves. Consider the five-pointed star in Figure 9-30 with congruent angles at the vertices *A, B, C, D,*

FIGURE 9-30

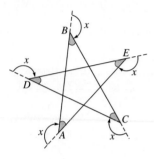

and *E*. We begin a trip on the star at any vertex *A*, walk along the line to *B*, and then turn by the exterior angle whose measure is *x*, walk to *C*, turn by *x* again, walk to *D*, turn by *x*, walk to *E*, turn by *x*, walk back to *A*, and finally turn again by *x*. In this way we not only started at *A* and ended there, but we also face in the same direction as when we started. Our total turning is 5*x*, but because we face in the same direction as we started, we must have turned a multiple of 360°. Thus, $5x = k \cdot 360°$, for some positive integer *k*. If *k* = 1, then *x* = 72°, which is not reasonable because it is clear from the figure that 90° < *x* < 180°. If *k* = 2, then *x* = 144°, and each shaded interior angle of the five-pointed star is 180° − 144°, or 36°. Notice that *k* = 3 results in *x* = 216°, which is greater than 180° and hence impossible. For the same reason, values of *k* greater than 3 will yield impossible values of *x*.

BRAIN TEASER

Jon, a tile designer, was working to come up with convex tiles like some of the ones in Figure 9-31, that had only acute angles. Could he find more than one type of shape for his tiles?

FIGURE 9-31

ONGOING ASSESSMENT 9-3

1. If three lines all meet in a single point, how many pairs of vertical angles are formed?

2. Find the measure of the third angle in each of the following triangles:

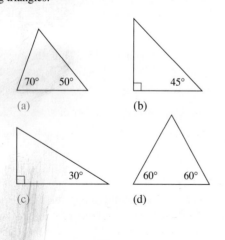

(a)   (b)

(c)   (d)

3. For each of the following figures, determine whether *m* and *n* are parallel lines. Justify your answers.

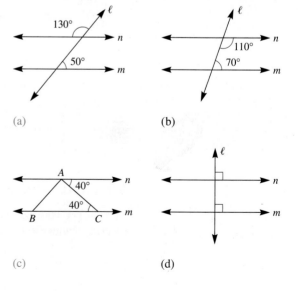

(a)   (b)

(c)   (d)

4. Two angles are complementary and the ratio of their measures is $7:2$. What are the angle measures?

5. a. In a regular polygon, the measure of each angle is $162°$. How many sides does the polygon have?

   b. Find the measure of each of the angles of a regular dodecagon.

6. In the following figure, $\overleftrightarrow{DE} \parallel \overleftrightarrow{BC}$, $\overleftrightarrow{EF} \parallel \overleftrightarrow{AB}$, and $\overleftrightarrow{DF} \parallel \overleftrightarrow{AC}$. Also, $m(\angle 1) = 45°$ and $m(\angle 2) = 65°$. Find each of the following values:

   a. $m(\angle 3)$ b. $m(\angle D)$
   c. $m(\angle E)$ d. $m(\angle F)$

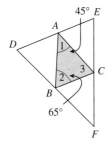

7. Lines a, b, and c are parallel. Find the measures of the numbered angles.

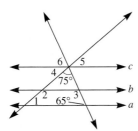

8. For each of the following, determine x if the lines a and b are parallel.

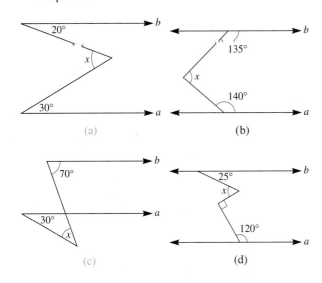

(a)   (b)

(c)   (d)

9. In the following figures, find the measures of the angles marked x and y:

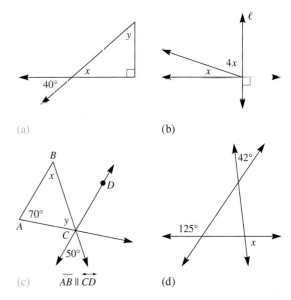

(a)   (b)

(c) $\overleftrightarrow{AB} \parallel \overleftrightarrow{CD}$ (d)

10. a. Determine the measure of an angle whose measure is twice that of its complement.

    b. If two angles of a triangle are complementary, what is the measure of the third angle?

11. Find the sum of the measures of the marked angles in each of the following figures:

(a)   (b)

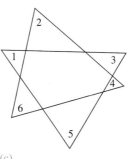

(c)

12. Calculate the measure of each angle of a pentagon, where the measures of the angles form an arithmetic sequence and the least measure is $60°$.

13. Two sides of a regular octagon are extended as shown in the following figure. Find the measure of ∠1.

14. Find the measure of angle *x* in the following figure:

15. Find the measures of angles 1, 2, and 3 given that *TRAP* is a trapezoid with $\overline{TR} \parallel \overline{PA}$.

16. Home plate on a baseball field has three right angles and two other congruent angles. Refer to the following figure and find the measures of each of these two other congruent angles:

17. Refer to the following figure and answer (a) and (b):

  a. Find *m*(∠1).

  b. ∠1 is an exterior angle of △*ABC*. Use your answer in (a) to make a conjecture concerning the measure of an exterior angle of a triangle. Justify your conjecture.

18. Refer to the following figure and answer (a) and (b):

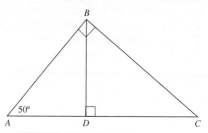

  a. If *m*(∠*ABC*) = 90° and $\overline{BD} \perp \overline{AC}$ and *m*(∠*A*) = 50°, find the measure of all the angles of △*ABC*, △*ADB*, and △*CDB*.

  b. If *m*(∠*A*) = α in (a), find the measures of all the angles of △*ABC*, △*ADB*, and △*CDB* in terms of α.

19. If one interior angle of a parallelogram measures 120°, what are the measures of the other three interior angles?

20. In a quadrilateral the smallest angle has measure 49°30′. If the measures of the four angles form an arithmetic sequence, find the measures of the other angles.

Communication

21. Explain how you might find a measure of an angle of a staircase that will describe the staircase's steepness.

22. a. If one angle of a triangle is obtuse, can another also be obtuse? Why or why not?

  b. If one angle in a triangle is acute, can the other two angles also be acute? Why or why not?

  c. Can a triangle have two right angles? Why or why not?

  d. If a triangle has one acute angle, is the triangle necessarily acute? Why or why not?

23. In the following figure, *A* is a point not on line ℓ. Discuss whether it is possible to have two distinct perpendicular segments from *A* to ℓ in a plane.

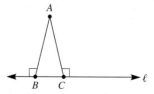

24. a. Explain how to find the sum of the measures of the interior angles of any convex pentagon by choosing any point *P* in the interior and constructing triangles, as shown in the following figure:

b. Using the method suggested by the diagram in (a), explain how to find the sum of the measures of the angles of any convex *n*-gon. Is your answer in (b) the same as the one already obtained in this section, $n \cdot 180 - 360$?

25. In the following figure, the legs of the ladder are congruent. If the ladder makes an angle of 120° with the ground, what is *x*? Explain your reasoning.

26. Explain how, through paper folding, you would show each of the following:
    a. In an isosceles triangle, the angles opposite congruent sides are congruent.
    b. If two angles of a triangle are congruent, the triangle is isosceles.
    c. In an equilateral triangle, all the interior angles are congruent.
    d. An isosceles trapezoid has two pairs of congruent angles.

27. **a.** Explain how to find the sum of the measures of the interior angles of a quadrilateral like the following:

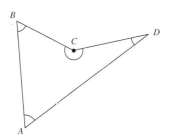

    b. Conjecture whether the formula for the sum of the measures of the angles of a convex polygon is true for nonconvex polygons.
    c. Justify your conjecture in (b) for pentagons and hexagons and explain why you think your conjecture is true in general.

28. Regular hexagons have been used to tile floors. Can a floor be tiled using only regular pentagons? Why or why not?

29. Lines *a* and *b* are cut by a transversal *c*, creating angles 1 and 2. If $m(\angle 1) + m(\angle 2) = 180°$, can you conclude that *a* and *b* are parallel? Justify your answer.

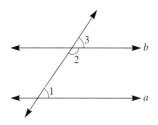

30. Prove that lines *a* and *b* are parallel.

31. A beam of light from *A* hits the surface of a mirror at point *B*, is reflected, and then hits a perpendicular mirror and is reflected again. If $\angle 1 \cong \angle 2$ and $\angle 3 \cong \angle 4$, prove that the reflected beam is parallel to the incoming beam, that is, that the rays $\overrightarrow{AB}$ and $\overrightarrow{CD}$ are parallel.

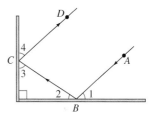

32. *ABCD* is a quadrilateral in which opposite angles have the same measure as indicated in the figure below. What kind of quadrilateral is *ABCD*? Justify your answer.

Open-Ended

33. Draw three different nonconvex polygons. When you walk around a polygon, at each vertex you need to turn either right (clockwise) or left (counter-clockwise). A turn to the left is measured by a positive number of degrees and a turn to the right by a negative number of degrees. Find the sum of the measures of the turn angles of the polygons you drew. Assume you start at a vertex facing in the direction of a side, walk around the polygon, and end up at the same vertex facing in the same direction as when you started.

34. In Now Try This 9-11, you may have found that on a sphere a triangle with three right angles is possible. List other geometric properties of figures on a sphere that are different from corresponding properties in the plane.

Cooperative Learning

35. In $\triangle ABC$, $\overrightarrow{AD}$ and $\overrightarrow{BD}$ are *angle bisectors*, that is, they divide the angles at A and B into congruent angles.
    a. If the measures of $\angle A$ and $\angle B$ are known, then $m(\angle D)$ can be found. How?

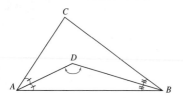

    b. Suppose the measures of $\angle A$ and $\angle B$ are not known but that of $\angle C$ is. Can $m(\angle D)$ be found? To answer this question, assign each member of your group a triangle with different angles but with the same measure for $\angle C$. Each person should compute $m(\angle D)$ for his or her triangle. Use the results to make a conjecture related to the previous question.
    c. Discuss a strategy for answering the question in (b) and write a solution to be distributed to the entire class.
36. Each person in your group is to draw a large triangle like $\triangle ABC$ in the following figure and cut it out. Obtain the crease $\overline{BB'}$ by folding the triangle at B so that A falls on some point A' on $\overline{AC}$. Next, unfold and fold the top B along $\overline{BB'}$ so that B falls on B'. Then fold vertices A and C along $\overline{AC}$ to match point B', as shown in the following figures:

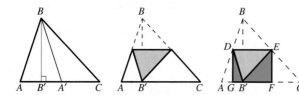

a. Why is $\overline{BB'}$ perpendicular to $\overline{AC}$?
b. What theorem does the folded figure illustrate? Why?
c. The folded figure seems to be a rectangle. Explain why.
d. What is the length of $\overline{GF}$ in terms of the length of the base $\overline{AC}$ of $\triangle ABC$? Why?

Review Problems

37. In each of the following, find the required properties. If this is not possible, explain why.
    a. Two properties that hold true for all rectangles but not for all rhombuses
    b. Two properties that hold true for all squares but not for all isosceles trapezoids
    c. Two properties that hold true for all parallelograms but not for all squares
38. Sort the shapes below according to the following attributes:

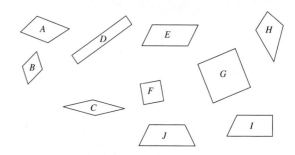

a. Number of parallel sides
b. Number of right angles
c. Number of congruent sides
d. Polygons with congruent diagonals
39. Use the figures in problem 38 to identify properties characteristic of different classes of figures. For example, "Congruent opposite sides describe a parallelogram."

9-4 Geometry in Three Dimensions

Simple Closed Surfaces

A visit to the grocery store exposes us to many three-dimensional objects that have simple closed surfaces. Figure 9-32 shows some examples.

FIGURE 9-32

simple closed surface   A **simple closed surface** has exactly one interior, has no holes, and is hollow. An ex-
sphere   ample is a sphere, as shown in Figure 9-33(c). A **sphere** is defined as the set of all points
center   at a given distance from a given point, the **center**. The set of all points on a simple closed
solid   surface with all interior points is a **solid**. Figures 9-33(a), (b), (c), and (d) are examples of
polyhedron   simple closed surfaces; (e) and (f) are not. A **polyhedron** (polyhedra is the plural) is a
face   simple closed surface made up of polygonal regions, or **faces**. The vertices of the polygo-
vertices   nal regions are the **vertices** of the polyhedron, and the sides of each polygonal region are
edges   the **edges** of the polyhedron. Figures 9-33(a) and (b) are examples of polyhedra, but (c),
(d), (e), and (f) are not.

FIGURE 9-33

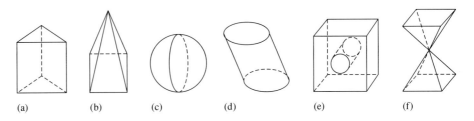

(a)   (b)   (c)   (d)   (e)   (f)

prism   A **prism** is a polyhedron in which two congruent faces lie in parallel planes and the
other faces are bounded by parallelograms. Figure 9-34 shows four different prisms. The
bases   shaded parallel faces of a prism are the **bases** of the prism. A prism usually is named after
its bases, as the figure suggests.

FIGURE 9-34

Triangular   Quadrilateral   Hexagonal   Hexagonal
right prism   right prism   right prism   oblique prism

(a)   (b)   (c)   (d)

lateral face   The faces other than the bases are the **lateral faces** of a prism. If the lateral faces of a
right prism   prism are all bounded by rectangles, the prism is a **right prism**, as in Figure 9-34(a)-(c).
oblique prism   Figure 9-34(d) is an **oblique prism** because some of its lateral faces are *not* bounded by
rectangles.
        Students often have trouble drawing three-dimensional figures. Figure 9-35 gives an
example of how to draw a right pentagonal prism.

FIGURE 9-35

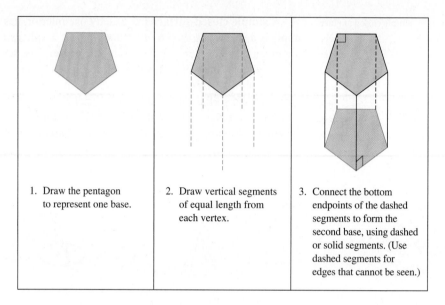

1. Draw the pentagon to represent one base.

2. Draw vertical segments of equal length from each vertex.

3. Connect the bottom endpoints of the dashed segments to form the second base, using dashed or solid segments. (Use dashed segments for edges that cannot be seen.)

pyramid

base ◆ apex

A **pyramid** is a polyhedron determined by a polygon and a point not in the plane of the polygon. The pyramid consists of the triangular regions determined by the point and each pair of consecutive vertices of the polygon and the polygonal region determined by the polygon. The polygonal region is the **base** of the pyramid, and the point is the **apex**. As with a prism, the faces other than the base are **lateral faces**. Pyramids are classified according to their bases, which are shaded in Figure 9-36.

FIGURE 9-36

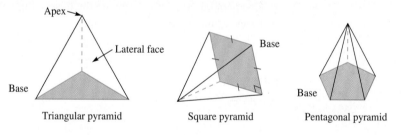

Triangular pyramid   Square pyramid   Pentagonal pyramid

To draw a pyramid, follow the steps in Figure 9-37.

FIGURE 9-37

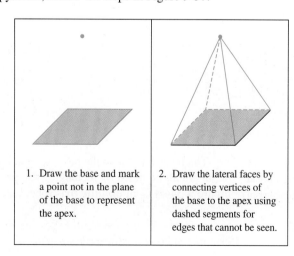

1. Draw the base and mark a point not in the plane of the base to represent the apex.

2. Draw the lateral faces by connecting vertices of the base to the apex using dashed segments for edges that cannot be seen.

Regular Polyhedra

convex polyhedron

A polyhedron is a **convex polyhedron** if, and only if, the segment connecting any two points in the interior of the polyhedron is itself in the interior. Figure 9-38 shows a concave polyhedron (that is, one that is caved in).

regular polyhedron

A **regular polyhedron** is a convex polyhedron whose faces are congruent regular polygonal regions such that the number of edges that meet at each vertex is the same for all the vertices of the polyhedron.

FIGURE 9-38

Concave polyhedron

HISTORICAL NOTE

The regular solid polyhedra are known as the **Platonic solids**, after the Greek philosopher Plato (ca. 350 B.C.). Plato attached a mystical significance to the five regular polyhedra, associating them with what he believed were the four elements (earth, air, fire, water) and the universe. Plato suggested that the smallest particles of earth have the form of a cube, those of air an octahedron, those of fire a tetrahedron, those of water an icosahedron, and those of the universe a dodecahedron.

Regular polyhedra, as in Figure 9-39, have fascinated mathematicians for centuries. At least three of them were identified by the Pythagoreans (ca. 500 B.C.). Two others were

FIGURE 9-39

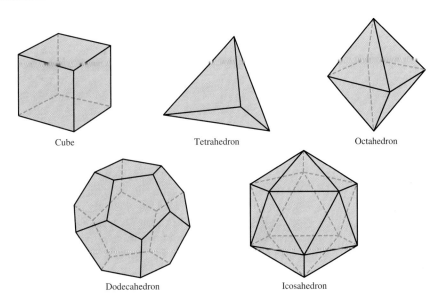

Cube   Tetrahedron   Octahedron

Dodecahedron   Icosahedron

known to the followers of Plato (ca. 350 B.C.). Three of the five polyhedra occur in nature in the form of crystals of sodium sulphantimoniate, sodium chloride (common salt), and chrome alum. The other two do not occur in crystalline form but have been observed as skeletons of microscopic sea animals called *radiolaria*.

PROBLEM SOLVING   **Regular Polyhedra?**

How many regular polyhedra are there?

Understanding the Problem   Each face of a regular polyhedron is congruent to each of the other faces of that polyhedron, and each face is bounded by a regular polygon. We are to find the number of different regular polyhedra.

Devising a Plan   The sum of the measures of all the angles at a vertex of a regular polyhedron must be less than 360°. (Do you see intuitively why this is true?) We next examine the measures of the interior angles of regular polygons to determine which of the polygons could be faces of a regular polyhedron. Then we try to determine how many types of polyhedra there are.

Carrying Out the Plan   We determine the size of an angle of some regular polygons, as shown in Table 9-9. Could a regular heptagon be a face of a regular polyhedron? At least three figures must fit together at a vertex to make a polyhedron. (Why?) If three angles of a regular heptagon were together at one vertex, then the sum of the measures of these angles would be $\dfrac{3 \cdot 900°}{7}$, or $\dfrac{2700°}{7}$, which is greater than 360°. Similarly, more than three angles cannot be used at a vertex. Thus a heptagon cannot be used to make a regular polyhedron.

Table 9-9

Polygon	Measure of an Interior Angle
Triangle	60°
Square	90°
Pentagon	108°
Hexagon	120°
Heptagon	$\left(\dfrac{900}{7}\right)^{\circ}$

The measure of an interior angle of a regular polygon increases as the number of sides of the polygon increases. (Why?) Thus any polygon with more than six sides has an interior angle greater than 120°. So if three angles were to fit together at a vertex, the sum of the measures of the angles would be greater than 360°. This means that the only polygons that might be used to make regular polyhedra are equilateral triangles, squares, regular pentagons, and regular hexagons. Consider the possibilities given in Table 9-10.

Notice that we were not able to use six equilateral triangles to make a polyhedron because 6(60°) = 360° and the triangles would lie in a plane. Similarly, we could not use four squares or any hexagons. We also could not use more than three pentagons because if we did, the sum of the measures of the angles would be more than 360°.

Table 9-10

Polygon	Measure of an Interior Angle	Number of Polygons at a Vertex	Sum of the Angles at the Vertex	Polyhedron Formed	Model
Triangle	60°	3	180°	**Tetrahedron**	
Triangle	60°	4	240°	**Octahedron**	
Triangle	60°	5	300°	**Icosahedron**	
Square	90°	3	270°	**Cube**	
Pentagon	108°	3	324°	**Dodecahedron**	

semiregular polyhedra   **Looking Back**   Interested readers may want to investigate **semiregular polyhedra**. These are also formed by using regular polygons as faces, but the regular polygons used need not have the same number of sides. For example, a semiregular polyhedron might have squares and regular octagons as its faces.

The patterns in Figure 9-40, called *nets*, can be used to construct the five regular polyhedra. It is left as an exercise to determine other patterns for constructing the regular polyhedra

FIGURE 9-40

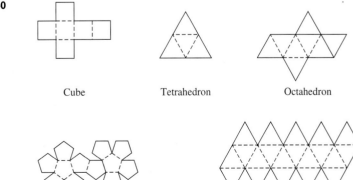

Cube   Tetrahedron   Octahedron

Dodecahedron   Icosahedron

NOW TRY THIS 9-13

A simple relationship among the number of faces, the number of edges, and the number of vertices of any polyhedron was discovered by the French mathematician and philosopher René Descartes (1596–1650) and rediscovered by the Swiss mathematician Leonhard Euler (1707–1783). Table 9-11 suggests a relationship among the numbers of vertices (V), edges (E), and faces (F). This relationship is known as **Euler's formula**.

a. State a relationship suggested by the table.
b. Try your relationship on other polyhedra.

Table 9-11

Name	V	F	E
Tetrahedron	4	4	6
Cube	8	6	12
Octahedron	6	8	12
Dodecahedron	20	12	30
Icosahedron	12	20	30

HISTORICAL NOTE

Leonhard Euler went blind in 1766 and for the remaining 17 years of his life continued to do mathematics by dictating to a secretary and by writing formulas in chalk on a slate for his secretary to copy down. He published 530 papers in his lifetime and left enough work to supply the *Proceedings of the St. Petersburg Academy* for the next 47 years.

Cylinders and Cones

A cylinder is an example of a simple closed surface that is <u>not</u> a polyhedron. Consider line segment $\overline{AB}$ and a line ℓ as shown in Figure 9-41. When $\overline{AB}$ moves so that it always remains parallel to a given line ℓ and points A and B trace simple closed planar curves other than polygons, the surface generated by $\overline{AB}$, along with the simple closed curves and their **cylinder**   interiors, form a **cylinder**. The simple closed curves traced by A and B, along with their **bases**   interiors, are the **bases** of the cylinder and the remaining points constitute the *lateral surface of the cylinder*.

FIGURE 9-41

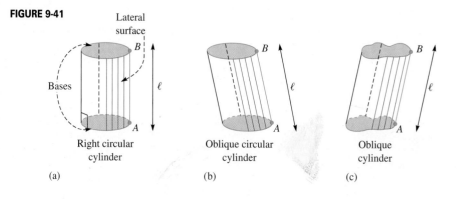

(a) Right circular cylinder

(b) Oblique circular cylinder

(c) Oblique cylinder

circular cylinder

right cylinder ◆

oblique cylinder

If a base of a cylinder is a circular region, as in Figure 9-41(a) and (b), the cylinder is a **circular cylinder**. If the line segment forming a cylinder is perpendicular to a base, the cylinder is a **right cylinder**. Cylinders that are not right cylinders are **oblique cylinders**. The cylinder in Figure 9-41(a) is a right cylinder; those in Figures 9-41(b) and (c) are oblique cylinders.

cone ◆ **vertex**

altitude ◆ **right circular cone**

oblique circular cone

Suppose we have a simple closed curve, other than a polygon, in a plane and a point P not in the plane of the curve. The union of line segments connecting point P to each point of a simple closed curve, the simple closed curve, and the interior of the curve is a **cone**. Cones are pictured in Figure 9-42. Point P is the **vertex** of the cone. The points of the cone not in the base constitute the *lateral surface of the cone*. A line segment from vertex P perpendicular to the plane of the base is the **altitude**. A **right circular cone**, such as the one in Figure 9-42(a), is a cone whose altitude intersects the base (a circular region) at the center of the circle. Figure 9-42(b) illustrates an oblique cone, and Figure 9-42(c) illustrates an **oblique circular cone**.

FIGURE 9-42

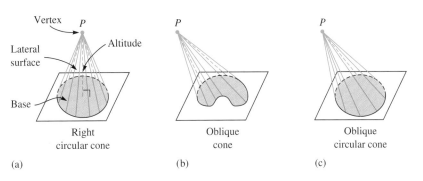

(a)   (b)   (c)

O N G O I N G   A S S E S S M E N T   9 - 4

1. Identify each of the following polyhedra. If a polyhedron can be described in more than one way, give as many names as possible.

(a)   (b)   (c)

2. Given the following tetrahedron, name the following:
   a. Vertices
   b. Edges
   c. Faces
   d. Intersection of face DRW and edge $\overline{RA}$
   e. Intersection of face DRW and face DAW

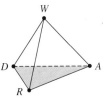

3. Identify five shapes of containers that can be found in a grocery store.

4. Determine for each of the following the minimum number of faces possible:
   a. Prism   b. Pyramid   c. Polyhedron

5. Classify each of the following as true or false:
   a. If the lateral faces of a prism are rectangles, it is a right prism.
   b. Every pyramid is a prism.
   c. Some pyramids are polyhedra.
   d. The bases of a prism lie in perpendicular planes.
   e. The bases of all cones are circles.
   f. A cylinder has only one base.
   g. All lateral faces of an oblique prism are rectangular regions.
   h. All regular polyhedra are convex.

6. If possible, sketch each of the following:
   a. An oblique square prism
   b. An oblique square pyramid
   c. A noncircular right cone
   d. A noncircular cone that is not right

7. For each of the following, draw a prism and a pyramid that have the given region as a base:
   a. Triangle
   b. Pentagon
   c. Regular hexagon

8. Two prisms are sketched on dot paper, as in the following figure. Complete the drawings by using dashed segments for the hidden edges.

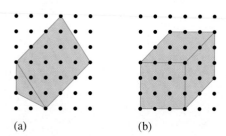

(a)   (b)

9. The following are pictures of stacks of solid cubes. In each case, determine the number of cubes in the stack and the number of faces that are glued together.

(a)   (b)

10. Name each polyhedron that can be constructed using the following flattened polyhedra:

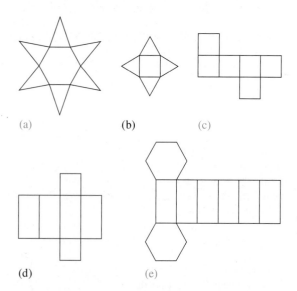

(a)   (b)   (c)

(d)   (e)

11. The following nets along with shaded tabs can be used to construct polyhedra. Copy the nets (or construct similar

ones), fold them, and glue them together using the tabs. What kind of polyhedra do you obtain?

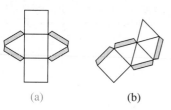

(a)   (b)

12. Draw nets like the ones in problem 11 and as few tabs as possible for each net so that when folded the nets can be glued with the tabs to create polyhedra.

13. The figure on the left in each of the following represents a card attached to a wire as shown. Match each figure on the left with what it would look like if you were to revolve it by spinning the wire between your fingers.

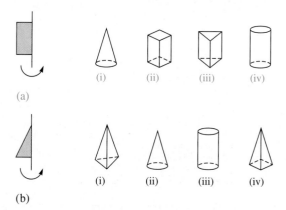

(i)   (ii)   (iii)   (iv)

(a)

(i)   (ii)   (iii)   (iv)

(b)

14. Which of the following three-dimensional figures could be used to make the shadow shown in (a)? in (b)?

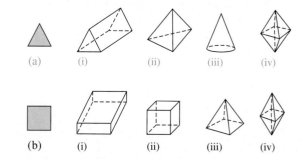

(a)   (i)   (ii)   (iii)   (iv)

(b)   (i)   (ii)   (iii)   (iv)

15. A diagonal of a prism is any segment determined by two vertices that do not lie in the same face, as shown in the following figure.

Complete the following table showing the total number of diagonals for various prisms:

Prism	Vertices per Base	Diagonals per Vertex	Total Number of Diagonals
Quadrilateral	4	1	4
Pentagonal	5		
Hexagonal			
Heptagonal			
Octagonal			
.			
.			
.			
n-gonal			

16. Consider a jar with a lid, as illustrated in the following figure. The jar is half filled with water. In drawings (a) and (b), sketch the water.

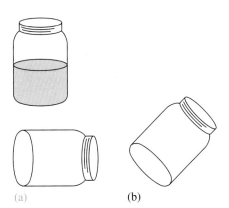

(a)   (b)

17. On the left of each of the following figures is a net for a three-dimensional object. On the right are several objects. Which object will the net fold to make?

(a)

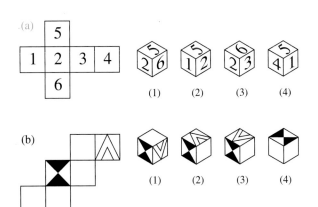

(1)   (2)   (3)   (4)

(b)

(1)   (2)   (3)   (4)

18. Sketch the intersection of each of the following with the plane shown:

Cube

(a)

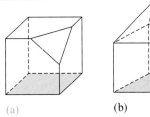

Remainder of unseen figure completes the cube

(b)

Sphere

(c)

Right pentagonal prism

(d)

Right circular cone (plane parallel to base)

(e)

Right circular cylinder (plane not parallel to base)

(f)

19. For each of the following three-dimensional figures, draw all possible cross-sections when the three-dimensional figure is sliced by a plane.
    a. Cube   **b.** Cylinder

20. For each of the following figures, find $V + F - E$, where V, E, and F stand, respectively, for the number of vertices, edges, and faces:

(a)   (b)

21. Complete the following table for each of the polyhedra described in the table:

Polyhedron	Vertices	Faces	Edges
a.		8	12
b.	20	30	
c.	6		15

State the relationship suggested by the table.

22. Answer each of the following questions about a pyramid and a prism, each having an *n*-gon as a base:
    a. How many faces does each have?
    b. How many vertices does each have?
    c. How many edges does each have?
    d. Use your answers to (a), (b), and (c) to verify Euler's formula for all pyramids and all prisms.

Communication

23. How many possible pairs of bases does a rectangular prism have? Explain.
24. A circle can be approximated by a "many-sided" polygon. Use this notion to describe the relationship between each of the following:
    a. A pyramid and a cone   b. A prism and a cylinder
25. Can either or both of the following be drawings of a quadrilateral pyramid? If yes, where would you be standing in each case? Explain why.

     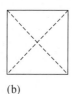

(a)   (b)

Open-Ended

26. When a box in the shape of a right prism, like the one in the following figure, is cut by a plane halfway between the opposite sides and parallel to these sides, that plane is a *plane of symmetry*. If a mirror is placed at the plane of symmetry, the reflection of the front part of the box will look just like the back part. Draw several space figures and find the number of planes of symmetry for each. Summarize your results in a table. Can you identify any figures with infinitely many planes of symmetry?

Cooperative Learning

27. In a two-person game, draw a three-dimensional figure without showing it to your partner. Tell your partner the shape of all possible cross-sections of your figure sufficient to identify the figure. If your partner can identify your figure, 1 point is earned by your partner. If a figure is identified that has all the cross-sections listed but that figure is not your figure, 2 points are earned by your partner. Each of you should take an equal number of turns.
28. Some of the following nets can be folded into a cube. Have each person in your group draw all the nets that can be folded into a cube. Share your findings with the group and decide how many such different nets there are. Dis-

cuss what "different" means in this case. Finally, compare your group's answers with those of other groups.

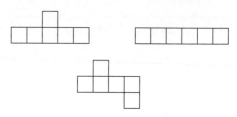

29. Choose different triples of points on the edges of each of the following figures. Then find the cross-section of where a plane through each triple of points intersects the figure. (The following figures show only a few examples. What are the possible figures that can be obtained in this manner?)

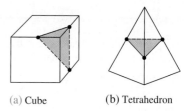

(a) Cube   (b) Tetrahedron

Review Problems

30. If two angles of one triangle are congruent to two angles of another triangle, must the third angles of both be congruent? Why or why not?
31. Triangles *ABC* and *CDE* are equilateral triangles with points *A*, *C*, and *E* collinear. Find the measure of ∠*BCD*.

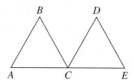

32. What is the measure of each angle in a regular nonagon?
33. Classify the following as true or false. If false, tell why.
    a. Every rhombus is a parallelogram.
    b. Every polygon has at least three sides.
    c. Triangles can have at most two acute angles.
34. Assume that lines ℓ, *m*, and *n* as shown are in the same plane. What can you conclude? Why?

BRAIN
T E A S E R

A rectangular region can be rolled to form the lateral surface of a right circular cylinder. What shape of paper is needed to make an oblique circular cylinder? (See "Making a Better Beer Glass" by A. Hoffer.)

LABORATORY
A C T I V I T Y

Consider a structure made of cubes with the front view, the side view looking from the right, and the top view as in Figure 9-43. Build the structure.

FIGURE 9-43

Top   Front   Right

9-5   *Networks

In the 1700s, the people of Königsberg, Germany (now Kaliningrad in Russia), used to enjoy walking over the bridges of the Pregel River. There were two islands in the river and seven bridges over it, as shown in Figure 9-44. These walks eventually led to the following problem.

Königsberg Bridge Problem

Is it possible to walk across all the bridges so that each bridge is crossed exactly once on the same walk?

FIGURE 9-44

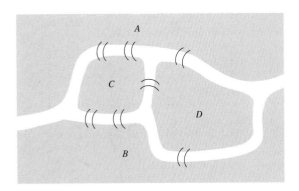

There is no restriction on where to start the walk or where to finish. Leonhard Euler became interested in this problem and solved it in 1736. He made the problem much simpler by representing the land masses, islands, and bridges in a **network**, as shown in the pink portion of Figure 9-45.

network

FIGURE 9-45

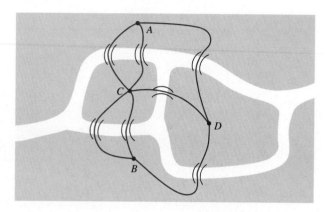

vertices ◆ arcs

traversable

Euler circuit

The points in a network are **vertices**, and the curves are **arcs**. Using a network diagram, we can restate the Königsberg bridge problem as follows: *Is there a path through the network beginning at some vertex and ending at the same or another vertex such that each arc is traversed exactly once?* A network having such a path is **traversable**; that is, each arc is passed through exactly once. A network that is traversable in such a way that the starting point and the stopping point are the same is an **Euler circuit**.

We can walk around an ordinary city block, as illustrated in Figure 9-46(a), and because the starting point is the same as the stopping point, the network is an Euler circuit. We need not start at a particular point, and, in general, we can traverse any simple closed curve. Now consider walking around two city blocks and down the street that runs between them, as in Figure 9-46(b). To traverse this network, it is necessary to start at vertex *B* or *C*. Starting at points other than *B* or *C* might suggest that the figure is not traversable, but this is not the case, as shown in Figure 9-46(b). If we start at *B*, we end at *C* and vice versa. Note that it is permissible to pass through a vertex more than once, but an arc may be traversed only once. Vertices *B* and *C* are endpoints of three arcs, and each of the other vertices are endpoints of two arcs.

FIGURE 9-46

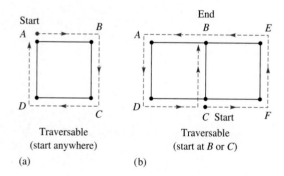

Traversable
(start anywhere)

(a)

Traversable
(start at *B* or *C*)

(b)

A traversable network is the type of network, or route, that a highway inspector would like to have if given the responsibility of checking out all the roads in a highway system. The inspector needs to traverse each road (arc) in the system but would save time by not having to make repeat journeys during an inspection tour. It would be feasible for the inspector to go through any town (vertex) more than once on the route. Consider the networks in Figure 9-47. Is it possible for the highway inspector to do the job with these networks without traversing a road twice?

FIGURE 9-47

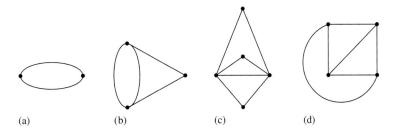

(a)   (b)   (c)   (d)

The first three networks in Figure 9-47 are traversable; the fourth network, (d), is not. Notice that the number of arcs *meeting at each vertex* in networks (a) and (c) is even. Any such vertex is an **even vertex**. If the number of arcs *meeting at a vertex* is odd, it is an **odd vertex**. In network (b), only the odd vertices will work as starting or stopping points. In network (d), which is not traversable, all the vertices are odd. If a network is traversable, each arrival at a vertex other than a starting or a stopping point requires a departure. Thus *each vertex that is not a starting or stopping point must be even*. The starting and stopping vertices in a traversable network may be even or odd, as seen in Figure 9-47(a) and (b), respectively. Which networks, if any, form an Euler circuit?

even vertex
odd vertex

> ## Properties of a Network

In general, networks have the following properties.

1. If a network has all even vertices, it is traversable. Any vertex can be a starting point, and the same vertex must be the stopping point. Thus the network is an Euler circuit.
2. If a network has two odd vertices, it is traversable. One odd vertex must be the starting point, and the other odd vertex must be the stopping point.

NOW TRY THIS 9-14

   a. Is there a traversable network with more than two odd vertices? Why or why not?
   b. Is there a network with exactly one odd vertex?

E X A M P L E
9-5

a. Which of the networks in Figure 9-48 are traversable?
b. Which of the networks in Figure 9-48 are Euler circuits?

FIGURE 9-48

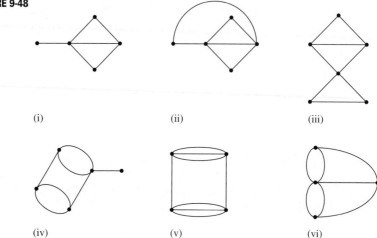

(i)   (ii)   (iii)

(iv)   (v)   (vi)

Solution **a.** Networks in (ii) and (v) have all even vertices and therefore are traversable.
Networks in (i) and (iii) have exactly two odd vertices and are traversable.
Networks in (iv) and (vi) have four odd vertices and are not traversable.
b. Networks (ii) and (v) are Euler circuits.

The network in Figure 9-48(vi) represents the Königsberg bridge problem. It has four odd vertices and consequently is not traversable. Hence, no walk configuration is possible to solve the problem.

A problem similar to the highway inspector problem involves a traveling salesperson. Such a person might have to travel networks comparable to those of the highway inspector. However, the salesperson is interested in visiting each town (vertex) only once, not necessarily in following each road. It is not known for which networks this can be accomplished. Can you find a route for the traveling salesperson for each network in Figure 9-48?

In many applications, *weighted networks* need to be considered. The student page gives an example of such networks. Answer question 29 on the student page.

A different type of application of network problems is discussed in Example 9-6.

E X A M P L E
9-6

Look at the floor plan of the house shown in Figure 9-49. Is it possible for a security guard to go through all the rooms of the house and pass through each door exactly once?

FIGURE 9-49

Sample School Book Page:
WEIGHTED NETWORKS

▶ A driver for a shipping company may deliver as many as 500 packages in a day, so drivers' routes must be efficiently planned. To route their trucks, a shipping company can use **weighted networks** like the one below, where the arcs are labeled with travel times in minutes between delivery points.

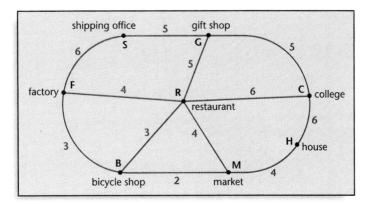

26 How can you tell that the network above is not drawn to scale?

27 **Try This as a Class** Suppose a driver is at the shipping office and must deliver a package to the house. One route the driver could use is to go from S to G to C to H. This route can be written as S–G–C–H.

   a. What is the travel time for this route?

   b. What is another route the driver can use? What is the travel time for this route?

28 ✔ **CHECKPOINT** Suppose a driver must start at the shipping office, deliver packages to each delivery point, and return to the shipping office.

   a. One route the driver can use is S–G–C–H–M–R–B–F–S. Find the travel time for this route.

   b. What is another route the driver can use? What is the travel time for this route?

29 For the situation in Question 28, find the fastest route that starts at the shipping office, goes through each delivery point, and returns to the shipping office. What is its total travel time?

Source: Middle Grades MATH Thematics Book 2, McDougal Littell, 2002 (p. 444).

Solution Represent the floor plan as a network, as in Figure 9-50. Designate the rooms and the outside as vertices and the paths through the doors as arcs. The network has more than two odd vertices, namely, *A, B, D,* and *O.* Thus the network is not traversable, and it is impossible to go through all the rooms and pass through each door exactly once.

FIGURE 9-50

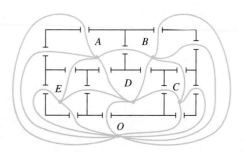

O N G O I N G A S S E S S M E N T 9 - 5

1. Which of the following networks are traversable? If the network is traversable, draw an appropriate path through it, labeling the starting and stopping vertices. Indicate which networks are Euler circuits.

(a)

(b)

(i)   (j)

(c)

(d)

(e)

(f)

(g)

(h)

2. Which of the networks in problem 1 can be traveled efficiently by a traveling salesperson, with no vertex visited more than once?

3. A city contains one river, three islands, and ten bridges, as shown in the following figure. Is it possible to take a walk around the city by starting at any land area, returning after visiting every part of the city, and crossing each bridge exactly once? If so, show such a path both on the original figure and on the corresponding network.

4. Refer to the following floor plans:

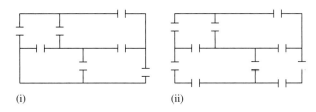

(i)   (ii)

   a. Draw a network that corresponds to each floor plan.

   b. Determine whether a person could pass through each room of each house by passing through each door exactly once. If it is possible, draw the path of such a trip.

5. Refer to the following floor plans:

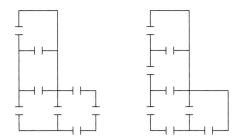

Can a person walk through each door once and only once and also go through both of the houses in a single path? If it is possible, draw the path of such a trip.

6. The following drawing represents the floor plan of an art museum. All tours begin and end at the entry. If possible, design a tour route that will allow a person to see every room but not go through any room twice.

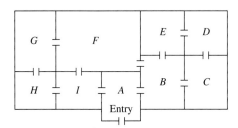

7. Each network in problem 1 separates the plane into several subsets. If R is the number of interior and exterior regions of the plane, V is the number of vertices, and A is the number of arcs, complete the following chart using each of the networks. (The first one is done for you.)

Network	R	V	A	$R + V - A$
(a)	6	6	10	2

8. Molly is making her first trip to the United States and would like to tour the eight states pictured in the following figure. She would like to plan her trip so that she can cross each border between neighboring states exactly once—that is, the Washington-Oregon border, the Washington-Idaho border, and so on.

Is such a trip possible? If so, does it make any difference in which state she starts her trip?

Communication

9. The following network is not an Euler circuit:

   a. Add two arcs to the network so that the resulting network will be an Euler circuit.

   b. Add exactly one arc so that the resulting network will be an Euler circuit.

   c. Explain a real-life application in which the answer in (b) is useful.

10. If you were commissioned to build an eighth bridge to make the Königsberg bridge problem traversable, where would you build your bridge? Is there more than one location where you could build it? Explain why.

11. The formula conjectured in problem 7 connecting the number of regions with the number of vertices and edges of a planar network is similar to Euler's formula for polyhedra. Explain why the formulas are similar by considering a polyhedron made of rubber edges that can be flattened as suggested in the following figure. The upper pentagonal base is flattened onto the plane of the lower base, resulting in the network on the right.

Open-Ended

12. **a.** How would a postal worker's route differ from that of a traveling salesperson or a highway inspector?
    b. Consider a 10-square block area of a city where a postal worker has to cover each side of each street. Design an efficient way to do this route.

13. Using as few vertices and arcs as possible, draw a network that is not traversable.

14. Draw a network that is not an Euler circuit and then add the least number of edges possible so that the new network will be an Euler circuit.

15. One application of Euler circuits is the checking of parking meters. List other real-life applications that could involve the use of Euler circuits. In each case, give a concrete example and describe the corresponding Euler circuit.

Cooperative Learning

16. *Traveler's Dodecahedron* is a puzzle invented in 1857 by the Irish mathematician William Rowen Hamilton. It consists of a wooden dodecahedron (a polyhedron with 12 regular pentagons as faces) with a peg at each vertex of the dodecahedron. The 20 vertices are labeled with the names of different cities around the world. The solver of the puzzle is to find a path that starts at some city, travels along

the edges, goes through each of the remaining cities exactly once, and returns to the starting city. The path traveled is to be marked by a string connecting the pegs.

a. Find a solution to the puzzle, first on the following network and then on the following dodecahedron. Compare your answer with those of other members of your group.

b. Play the following game with a partner. Draw a polyhedron that can be traversed in the way described earlier in this problem. Also draw a two-dimensional network for the polyhedron similar to the one shown in (a). Ask your partner to answer the question posed in (a) for the new polyhedron and the accompanying network. Then switch roles. The person who draws the polyhedron with the greatest number of vertices wins.

LABORATORY
A C T I V I T Y

1. Take a strip of paper like the one in Figure 9-51(i). Give one end a half-twist and join the ends by taping them, as in Figure 9-51(ii). The surface obtained is a Möbius strip.

FIGURE 9-51

a. Use a pencil to shade one side of a Möbius strip. What do you discover?

b. Imagine cutting a Möbius strip all around midway between the edges, as in Figure 9-51(iii). What do you predict will happen? Now do the cutting. What is the result?

c. Imagine cutting a Möbius strip one third of the way from an edge and parallel to the edge all the way through until you return to the starting point. Predict the result. Then do the cutting. Was your prediction correct?

d. Imagine cutting around a Möbius strip one fourth of the way from an edge. Predict the result. Then do the cutting. How does the result compare with the result of the experiment in (c)?

2. a. Take a strip of paper and give it two half-twists (one full twist). Then join the ends together. Answer the questions in part 1.
   b. Repeat the experiment in (a), using three half-twists.
   c. Repeat the experiment in (a), using four half-twists. What do you find for odd-numbered twists? Even-numbered twists?

3. Take two strips of paper and tape each of them in a circular shape. Join them as shown in Figure 9-52.

FIGURE 9-52

   a. What happens if you cut completely around the middle of each strip as shown?
   b. Repeat part (a) if both strips are Möbius strips. Does it make any difference if the half-twists are in opposite directions?
   c. Repeat part (a) if one strip is a Möbius strip and the other is not. What happens when you cut the strips?

BRAIN
T E A S E R

Given three buildings *A, B,* and *C,* as shown in Figure 9-53, and three utility centers for electricity (*E*), gas (*G*), and water (*W*), determine whether it is possible to connect each of the three buildings to each of the three utility centers without crossing lines.

FIGURE 9-53

Hint for Solving the Preliminary Problem

Consider a walk around the star starting at any vertex and coming back to that vertex facing in the same direction as at the beginning of the walk. Then use the total turning to find the measure of each turning angle.

QUESTIONS FROM THE CLASSROOM

1. Henry claims that a line segment has a finite number of points because it has two endpoints. How do you respond?

2. A student claims that if any two planes that do not intersect are parallel, then any two lines that do not intersect should also be parallel. How do you respond?

3. A student says that it is actually impossible to measure an angle, since each angle is the union of two rays that extend infinitely and therefore continue forever. What is your response?

4. Maggie claims that to make the measure of an angle greater, you just extend the rays. How do you respond?

5. A student asks whether a polygon whose sides are congruent is necessarily a regular polygon and whether a polygon with all angles congruent is necessarily a regular polygon. How do you answer?

6. A student thinks that a square is the only regular polygon with all right angles. The student asks if this is true and if so, why. How do you answer?

7. A student says that a line is parallel to itself. How do you reply?

8. A student asks how to find the shortest path between two points *A* and *B* on a right circular cylinder. How do you respond?

9. One student says, "My sister's high-school geometry book talked about equal angles. Why don't we use the term 'equal angles' instead of 'congruent angles'?" How do you reply?

10. A student says there can be only 360 different rays emanating from a point, since there are only 360° in a circle. How do you respond?

11. Jodi identifies the following figure (a) as a rectangle and the figure (b) as a square. She claims that the figure (b) is not a rectangle because it is a square. How do you respond?

(a)   (b)

12. Millie claims that a rhombus is regular because all of its sides are congruent. How do you respond?

13. A student asks what exactly Euclidean geometry is. How do you answer?

14. A student asks if geometry is worth studying if lines have different meaning on a sphere. What do you say?

15. A student claims that when a line ℓ is perpendicular to a plane α, then any plane that contains ℓ is perpendicular to α. How do you respond?

CHAPTER OUTLINE

I. Basic geometric notions
  A. Points, lines, and planes
    1. **Points, lines,** and **planes** are basic, but undefined, terms.
    2. **Collinear points** are points that belong to the same line.
    3. **Segments** and **rays** are important subsets of lines.
    4. **Coplanar points** are points that lie in the same plane. **Coplanar lines** are defined similarly.
    5. Two lines with exactly one point in common are **intersecting lines**.
    6. **Concurrent lines** are lines that contain a common point.
    7. Two distinct coplanar lines with no points in common are **parallel**.
    8. **Skew lines** are lines that cannot be contained in the same plane.

  9. **Parallel planes** are planes with no points in common.
  10. **Space** is the set of all points.
  11. An **angle** is the union of two rays with a common endpoint.
  12. Angles are classified according to size as **acute, obtuse, right,** or **straight**.
  13. Two lines that meet to form a right angle are **perpendicular**.
  14. A **dihedral angle** is the union of two half-planes and the common line defining the half-planes.
  B. Plane figures
    1. A **closed curve** is a curve that, when traced, has the same starting and stopping points and may cross itself at individual points.
    2. A **simple curve** is a curve that does not cross itself when traced, although the starting and stopping points may be the same.

3. A **polygon** is a simple closed curve with segments as sides.

   a. A **diagonal** is any line segment connecting two nonconsecutive vertices of a polygon.

   b. A **convex polygon** is one such that if any two points of the polygonal region are connected by a segment, the segment is a subset of the polygonal region.

   c. A **concave polygon** is a nonconvex polygon.

   d. A **regular polygon** is a polygon in which all the interior angles are congruent and all the sides are congruent.

4. A **polygonal region** is the union of a polygon and its interior.

5. Triangles are classified according to the lengths of their sides as **scalene, isosceles,** or **equilateral** and according to the measures of their angles as **acute, obtuse,** or **right**.

6. Quadrilaterals with special properties are **trapezoids, parallelograms, rectangles, kites, isosceles trapezoids, rhombuses,** and **squares**.

II. Theorems involving angles

   A. Supplements of the same angle, or of congruent angles, are congruent.

   B. Complements of the same angle, or of congruent angles, are congruent.

   C. Vertical angles formed by intersecting lines are congruent.

   D. If any two distinct coplanar lines are cut by a transversal, then a pair of **corresponding angles, alternate interior angles,** or **alternate exterior angles** are congruent if, and only if, the lines are parallel.

   E. The sum of the measures of the interior angles of a triangle is 180°.

F. The sum of the measures of the interior angles of any convex polygon with n sides is $180°n - 360°$, or $180°(n - 2)$. One interior angle of a regular n-gon measures $\dfrac{180°n - 360°}{n}$, or $\dfrac{180°(n - 2)}{n}$.

G. The sum of the measures of the exterior angles of any convex polygon is 360°.

III. Three-dimensional figures

   A. A **polyhedron** is a simple closed surface formed by polygonal regions.

   B. Three-dimensional figures with special properties are **prisms, pyramids, regular polyhedra, cylinders, cones,** and **spheres**.

*IV. Networks

   A. A **network** is a collection of points or **vertices** and a collection of curves or **arcs**.

   B. A vertex of a network is called an **even vertex** if the number of arcs meeting at the vertex is even. A vertex is an **odd vertex** if the number of arcs meeting at the vertex is odd.

   C. A network is called **traversable** if there is a path through the network such that each arc is passed through exactly once.

     1. If all the vertices of a network are even, then the network is traversable. Any vertex can be a starting point, and the same vertex must be the stopping point.

     2. If a network has two odd vertices, it is traversable. One odd vertex must be the starting point, and the other must be the stopping point.

     3. If a network has more than two odd vertices, it is not traversable.

     4. No network has exactly one odd vertex.

   D. A network that is traversable by starting and ending at the same point is an **Euler circuit**.

C H A P T E R   R E V I E W

1. Refer to the following line *m*:

   a. List three names for the line.

   b. Name two rays on *m* that have endpoint *B*.

   c. Find a simpler name for the intersection of rays $\overrightarrow{AB}$ and $\overrightarrow{BA}$.

   d. Find a simpler name for the intersection of rays $\overrightarrow{BA}$ and $\overrightarrow{AC}$.

2. In the figure at right, $\overleftrightarrow{PQ}$ is perpendicular to the plane α. Answer the following:

   a. Name a pair of skew lines.

   b. Using only the letters in the figure, name as many planes as possible that are perpendicular to α.

   c. What is the intersection of planes *APQ* and β?

   d. Is there a single plane containing *A, B, P,* and *Q*? Explain your answer.

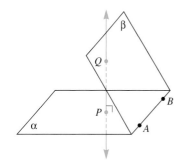

3. Draw each of the following curves:
   a. A simple closed curve
   b. A closed curve that is not simple
   c. A concave hexagon
   d. A convex decagon

4. **a.** Can a triangle have two obtuse angles? Justify your answer.
   b. Can a parallelogram have four acute angles? Justify your answer.

5. In a certain triangle, the measure of one angle is twice the measure of the smallest angle. The measure of the third angle is seven times greater than the measure of the smallest angle. Find the measures of each of the angles in the triangle.

6. **a.** Explain how to derive an expression for the sum of the measures of the interior angles in a convex *n*-gon.
   b. In a certain regular polygon, the measure of each angle is 176°. How many sides does the polygon have?

7. Sketch each of the following:
   a. Three planes that intersect in a point
   b. A plane and a cone that intersect in a circle
   c. A plane and a cylinder that intersect in a segment
   d. Two pyramids that intersect in a triangle

8. Sketch drawings to illustrate different possible intersections of a square pyramid and a plane.

9. In a periscope, a pair of mirrors are parallel. If the dotted line in the following figure represents a path of light and $m(\angle 1) = m(\angle 2) = 45°$, find $m(\angle 3)$ and $m(\angle 4)$:

10. Find $6°48'59'' + 28°19'36''$. Write your answer in simplest terms.

11. In the figure, ℓ is parallel to m, and $m(\angle 1) = 60°$. Find each of the following:
    a. $m(\angle 3)$
    b. $m(\angle 6)$
    c. $m(\angle 8)$

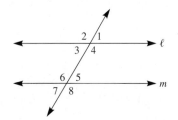

12. Draw a large triangle *ABC* and tear off $\angle B$. Fit the torn-off angle as $\angle BAD$, as shown in the following figure.

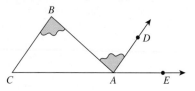

   a. Why is $\overrightarrow{AD} \parallel \overrightarrow{BC}$?
   b. Why is $\angle DAE \cong \angle C$?
   c. Use parts (a) and (b) to show that the sum of the measures of the interior angles of a triangle is 180°.

13. The polygon *ABCDE* contains a point *P* in its interior that can be joined to all the vertices by segments entirely in the interior of the polygon. In this way, the polygon has been "divided" into five triangles. Use such a division into triangles to answer the following.

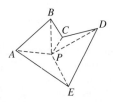

   a. Find the sum of the measures of the interior angles of the polygon *ABCDE*.
   b. If an *n*-gon can be subdivided into triangles in a similar way, explain how to derive the formula for the sum of the measures of the interior angles of the *n*-gon in terms of *n*.
   c. Explain how to find the sum of the measures of the interior angles of the following polygon.

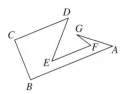

14. In $\triangle ABC$, line *DE* is parallel to line *AB*, and line *DF* is parallel to line *AC*. If $m(\angle C) = 70°$ and $m(\angle B) = 45°$, find the measures of the angles labeled 1, 2, 3, 4, and 5.

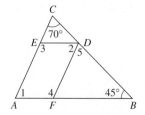

15. If ∠*ACB* is a right angle as shown, and the other angles are as indicated in the figure, find *x*, the measure of ∠*DCB*.

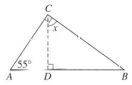

16. In the figure below, ∠1 ≅ ∠2.
   a. Prove that ∠3 ≅ ∠4.
   b. Suppose *m*(∠1) < *m*(∠2). What can you conclude about *m*(∠3) and *m*(∠4)? Justify your answer.

17. In the accompanying figure planes α and β intersect in line *AB*. The dihedral angle *S-AB-Q* measures 90°. The lines *PS* and *PQ* determine a new plane γ.
   a. Why is plane γ perpendicular to α as well as to β?
   b. Why is line *AB* perpendicular to γ?

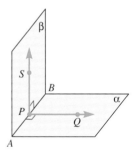

18. If a cube intersects a plane, what possible figures can be obtained by the intersection? Sketch the planes and figures obtained in each case.

19. If a pyramid has an octagon for a base, how many lateral faces does it have?

20. If *ABC* is a right triangle and *m*(∠*A*) = 42°, what is the measure of the other acute angle?

21. In the following, draw in dotted lines for the unseen segments.

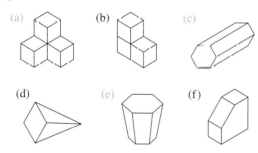

22. If there are *n* points in a plane, no three of which are collinear, how many triangles could be found with those points as vertices?

23. If one is drawing a two-dimensional representation of a large *n* × *n* × *n* cube, will the edges of the square faces appear parallel as they do in a normal square on a piece of paper? Why or why not?

24. Explain whether or not a cylinder has to have a circular base.

25. Draw a curve that is neither simple nor closed.

* **26. a.** Which of the following networks are traversable?
      b. Find a corresponding path for the networks that are traversable.

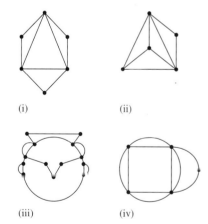

SELECTED BIBLIOGRAPHY

Andrews, A. G. "Solving Geometric Problems by Using Unity Blocks." *Teaching Children Mathematics* 5 (February 1999): 318–323.

Bartels, B. H. "Truss(t)ing Triangles." *Mathematics Teaching in the Middle School* 3 (March–April 1998): 394–396.

Britton, B., and S. Stump. "Unexpected Riches from a Geoboard Quadrilateral Activity." *Mathematics Teaching in the Middle School* 6 (April 2001): 490–493.

Camblin, B. "The Mathematics in Your Note Paper." *Mathematics Teaching in the Middle School* 4 (November–December 1998): 168–169.

Carroll, W. "Middle School Students' Reasoning about Geometric Situations." *Mathematics Teaching in the Middle School* 3 (March–April 1998): 398–403.

Carroll, W. "Polygon Capture: A Geometry Game." *Mathematics Teaching in the Middle School* 4 (October 1998): 90–94.

Clements, D., and J. Sarama. "The Earliest Geometry." *Teaching Children Mathematics* 7 (October 2000): 82–86.

Clements, D., and J. Sarama. "The Role of Technology in Early Childhood Learning." *Teaching Children Mathematics* 8 (February 2002): 340–343.

Greeley, N., and T. R. Offerman. "Now & Then Measuring Angles in Physical Therapy." *Mathematics Teaching in the Middle School* 2 (March–April 1997): 338–344.

Hannibal, M. A. "Young Children's Developing Understanding of Geometric Shapes." *Teaching Children Mathematics* 5 (February 1999): 353–357.

Hoffer, A. "Making a Better Beer Glass." *Mathematics Teacher* 75 (May 1982): 378–379.

Kennedy, J., and E. McDowell. "Geoboard Quadrilaterals." *Mathematics Teacher* 91 (April 1998): 288–290.

Lipka, J., S. Wildfeuer, N. Wahlberg, M. George, and D. Ezran. "Elastic Geometry and Storyknifing: A Yup'ik Eskimo Example." *Teaching Children Mathematics* 7 (February 2001): 337–343.

Long, V. "From Polygons to Poetry." *Mathematics Teaching in the Middle School* 6 (April 2001): 436–438.

"Menu of Problems, Desserts." *Mathematics Teaching in the Middle School* 6 (January 2001): 304.

Oberdorf, C. D., and J. Taylor-Cox. "Shape Up." *Teaching Children Mathematics* 5 (February 1999): 340–345.

Olson, A. T. *Mathematics through Paper Folding.* Washington, D.C.: NCTM (1975).

Olson, J. "What Shapes Can You Make?" *Teaching Children Mathematics* 5 (February 1999): 330–331.

Olson, M. "Coloring Tetras with Two Colors." *Teaching Children Mathematics* 7 (January 2001): 294–295.

Peterson, B. "From Tessellations to Polyhedra: Big Polyhedra." *Mathematics Teaching in the Middle School* 5 (February 2000): 348–356.

Posamentier, A. "Geometry: A Remedy for the Malaise of Middle School Mathematics." *Mathematics Teacher* 82 (December 1989): 678–680.

Rich, W., and J. Joyner. "Using Interactive Web Sites to Enhance Mathematics Learning." *Teaching Children Mathematics* 8 (February 2002): 380–383.

Row, T. S. *Geometric Exercises in Paper Folding.* Dover Publications, Inc. (1966).

Schifter, D. "Learning Geometry: Some Insights Drawn from Teacher Writing." *Teaching Children Mathematics* 5 (February 1999): 360–366.

Sundberg, S. "A Plethora of Polyhedra." *Mathematics Teaching in the Middle School* 3 (March–April 1998): 388–391.

van Hiele, P. M. "Developing Geometric Thinking through Activities That Begin with Play." *Teaching Children Mathematics* 5 (February 1999): 310–316.

Wheatley, G. H., and A. M. Reynolds. "'Image Maker': Developing Spatial Sense." *Teaching Children Mathematics* 5 (February 1999): 374–378.

Williams, C. G. "Sorting Activities for Polygons." *Mathematics Teaching in the Middle School* 3 (March–April 1998): 444–445.

Woodward, E., and Brown, R. "Polydrons and Three-Dimensional Geometry." *Arithmetic Teacher* 41 (April 1994): 451–458.

–10–
Constructions, Congruence, and Similarity

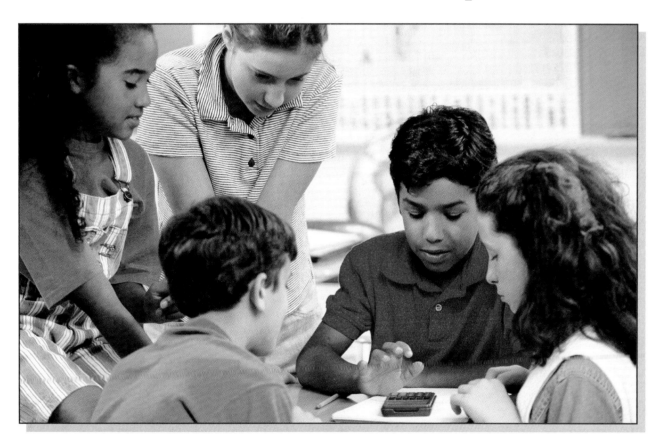

PRELIMINARY PROBLEM

At 9:00 on a sunny morning, Ms. Gonza's class went outside and measured the heights of objects and their accompanying shadows. Back in the class they used the data gathered outside and plotted graphs. If they plotted all points on the same graph with shadow lengths on the horizontal axis and object heights on the vertical axis, what would they see on the graph?

he Principles and Standards *state that students should be able to do the following:*

Pre-K–2

- *relate ideas in geometry to ideas in number and measurement.* (p. 396)

Grades 3–5

- *explore congruence and similarity;*
- *make and use coordinate systems to specify locations and to describe paths;*
- *build and draw geometric objects;*
- *use geometric models to solve problems in other areas of mathematics, such as number and measurement;*
- *recognize geometric ideas and relationships and apply them to other disciplines and to problems that arise in the classroom or in everyday life.* (p. 396)

Grades 6–8

- *use coordinate geometry to represent and examine the properties of geometric shapes;*
- *use coordinate geometry to examine special geometric shapes, such as regular polygons or those with pairs of parallel or perpendicular sides;*
- *draw geometric objects with specified properties, such as side lengths or angle measures.* (p. 397)

In this chapter, we introduce, through constructions and visualization, the concepts of congruence and similarity. We study equations of lines, investigate systems of equations both geometrically and algebraically, and consider basic trigonometry.

Congruence Through Constructions

similar   In mathematics, **similar** ($\sim$) objects have the same shape but not necessarily the same
congruent   size, **congruent** ($\cong$) objects have the same size as well as the same shape. Whenever two figures are congruent, they are also similar. However, the converse is not true (why?). Examples of similar and congruent objects are seen in Figure 10-1.

FIGURE 10-1

Symmetry Work 22

(a)

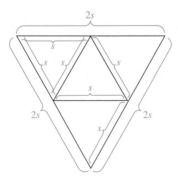

(b)

The Escher print in Figure 10-1(a) shows congruent fish and congruent birds. Figure 10-1(b) contains both congruent and similar equilateral triangles. The smaller triangles are congruent. They also are similar to the large one that contains them. In addition, Figure 10-1(b) is an example of a **rep-tile**, a figure that is used to construct a larger similar figure. In Figure 10–1(b), one of the smaller equilateral triangles is a rep-tile. Figure 10-2 shows two similar circles with the same shape but different sizes. The size of a circle is determined by its radius. In fact, a **circle** is the set of all points in a plane at the same distance (**radius**) from a given point, its **center**. In Figure 10-2, the larger circle (circle *O*) has center *O* and radius *OA*. Note that *radius* is used to describe both the length *OA* and the segment *OA*.

rep-tile

circle

radius ◆ center

FIGURE 10-2

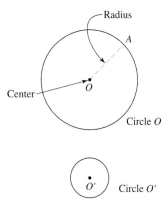

Before studying congruent and similar figures, we first consider some notation and review definitions from Chapter 9. For example, *any two line segments are congruent if they have the same length, while two angles are congruent if they have the same measure.* The length of line segment $\overline{AB}$ is denoted *AB*. Symbolically, we may write the following about congruent segments and angles.

> ## Definition of Congruent Segments and Angles

$\overline{AB} \cong \overline{CD}$ if, and only if, $AB = CD$

$\angle ABC \cong \angle DEF$ if, and only if, $m(\angle ABC) = m(\angle DEF)$

HISTORICAL NOTE

The straight line and circle were considered the basic geometric figures by the Greeks and the straightedge and compass are their physical analogs. It is believed that the Greek philosopher Plato (c. 427–347 B.C.) rejected the use of mechanical devices other than the straightedge and compass for geometric constructions because use of other tools emphasized practicality rather than "ideas," which he regarded as more important.

Geometric Constructions

Ancient Greek mathematicians constructed geometric figures with a straightedge (no markings on it) and a collapsible compass. Figure 10-3 shows a modern compass that can be used to mark off and duplicate lengths and to construct circles or arcs with a radius of a given measure. To draw a circle when given the radius *PQ* of a circle, we follow the steps illustrated in Figure 10-3.

FIGURE 10-3 *Constructing a circle given its radius*

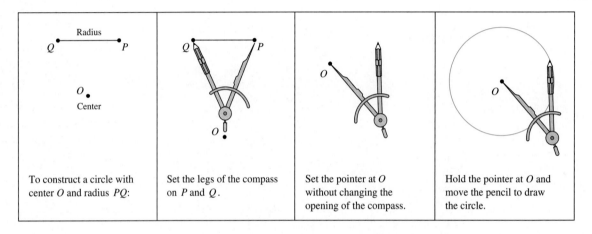

| To construct a circle with center *O* and radius *PQ*: | Set the legs of the compass on *P* and *Q*. | Set the pointer at *O* without changing the opening of the compass. | Hold the pointer at *O* and move the pencil to draw the circle. |

Any circle is similar to any other circle. However, *any circle is congruent to another circle if, and only if, the radii of the two circles are congruent.*

arc   An **arc** of a circle is any part of the circle that can be drawn without lifting a pencil. **center of arc**   (The entire circle could be considered an arc.) The **center of an arc** is the center of the circle containing the arc. If there is no danger of ambiguity in a discussion, the endpoints of the arc are used to name the arc, otherwise three points are used in the naming. In Fig- **minor arc** ◆ **major arc** ure 10-4, $\overset{\frown}{ACB}$ is a **minor arc** and $\overset{\frown}{ADB}$ is a **major arc**. If the major arc and the minor arc **semicircle** of a circle are the same size, each is a **semicircle**. We use the convention that if only two points are used in the arc name, then the minor arc is intended. Thus, in Figure 10-3, $\overset{\frown}{AB}$ is another name for $\overset{\frown}{ACB}$.

FIGURE 10-4

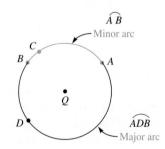

NOW TRY THIS 10-1

In the "Peanuts" cartoon, Sally draws circles in a plane. Describe all the possible ways two circles can intersect.

Constructing Segments

There are many ways to draw a segment congruent to a given segment $\overline{AB}$. A natural approach is to use a ruler, measure $\overline{AB}$, and then draw a congruent segment. A different way is to trace $\overline{AB}$ onto a piece of paper. A third method is to use a straightedge and a compass, as in Figure 10-5.

FIGURE 10-5 *Constructing a line segment congruent to a given segment*

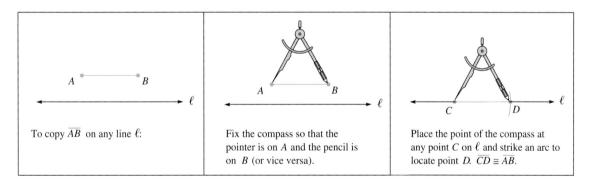

To copy $\overline{AB}$ on any line ℓ:

Fix the compass so that the pointer is on A and the pencil is on B (or vice versa).

Place the point of the compass at any point C on ℓ and strike an arc to locate point D. $\overline{CD} \cong \overline{AB}$.

Triangle Congruence

Informally, two figures are congruent if it is possible to fit one figure onto the other so that all matching parts coincide. In Figure 10-6, $\triangle ABC$ and $\triangle A'B'C'$ have corresponding congruent parts. Tick marks are used to show congruent segments and angles in the triangles. If

FIGURE 10-6

$$\triangle ABC \cong \triangle A'B'C'$$

we were to trace $\triangle ABC$ in Figure 10-6 and put the tracing over $\triangle A'B'C'$ so that the tracing of A is over A', the tracing of B is over B', and the tracing of C is over C', $\triangle ABC$ would coincide with $\triangle A'B'C'$. This suggests the following definition of congruent triangles.

> ### Definition of Congruent Triangles
>
> $\triangle ABC$ is congruent to $\triangle A'B'C'$, written $\triangle ABC \cong \triangle A'B'C'$, if $\angle A \cong \angle A'$, $\angle B \cong \angle B'$, $\angle C \cong \angle C'$, $\overline{AB} \cong \overline{A'B'}$, $\overline{BC} \cong \overline{B'C'}$, and $\overline{AC} \cong \overline{A'C'}$.

In the definition of congruent triangles $\triangle ABC$ and $\triangle A'B'C'$, the order of the vertices is such that the listed congruent angles and congruent sides correspond, leading to the statement: "Corresponding parts of congruent triangles are congruent," abbreviated as CPCTC.

NOW TRY THIS 10-2

In Figure 10-6, $\triangle ABC \cong \triangle A'B'C'$. List all possible ways that the congruence can be symbolized.

**E X A M P L E
10-1**

Write an appropriate symbolic congruence for each of the pairs of congruent triangles in Figure 10-7.

FIGURE 10-7

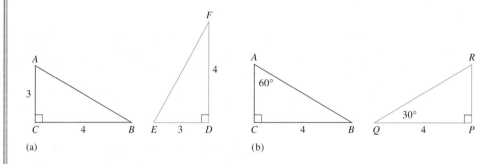

(a)

(b)

Solution **a.** Vertex C corresponds to D because the angles at C and D are right angles. Also, because $\overline{CB} \cong \overline{DF}$ and C corresponds to D, B corresponds to F. Consequently, A corresponds to E. Thus $\triangle ABC \cong \triangle EFD$.

b. $\overline{BC} \cong \overline{QP}$. Vertex C corresponds to P because the angles at C and P are both right angles. To establish the other correspondences, we first find the missing angle measures in the triangles. We see that $m(\angle B) = 90° - 60° = 30°$ and $m(\angle R) = 90° - 30° = 60°$. Consequently, A corresponds to R because $m(\angle A) = m(\angle R) = 60°$, and B corresponds to Q because $m(\angle B) = m(\angle Q) = 30°$. Thus $\triangle ABC \cong \triangle RQP$.

Side, Side, Side Property (SSS)

In an automotive assembly line, the bodies of the same model cars are essentially congruent. Calibration experts work to ensure that car parts are interchangeable so that the same part fits on all basic models of the same car. For the cars to be congruent, the parts must be congruent. In design for automotive production, decisions have to be made about the minimal set of items to consider for eventual congruency. In considering congruence of figures in geometry, we consider the same process.

If three sides and three angles of one triangle are congruent to the corresponding three sides and three angles of another triangle, then the triangles are congruent. However, do we need to know that all six parts of one triangle are congruent to the corresponding parts of the second triangle in order to conclude that the triangles are congruent?

Consider the triangle formed by attaching three segments, as in Figure 10-8. Such a triangle is *rigid*; that is, its size and shape cannot be changed. Because of this property, a manufacturer can make duplicates if the lengths of the sides are known. Note that once the sides are known, all the angles are automatically determined.

FIGURE 10-8

Triangle determined
by its 3 sides

Many bridges and other structures that have exposed frameworks demonstrate the practical use of the rigidity of triangles, as seen in Figure 10-9.

FIGURE 10-9

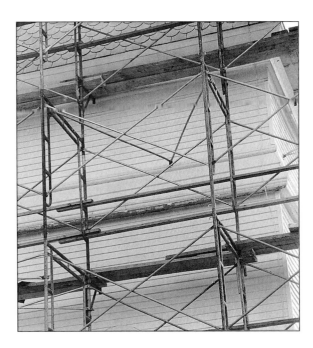

Because a triangle is completely determined by its three sides, we have the following property.

> ### Property
>
> **Side, Side, Side (SSS)**   If the three sides of one triangle are congruent, respectively, to the three sides of a second triangle, then the triangles are congruent.

E X A M P L E
10-2

For each part in Figure 10-10, use SSS to explain why the given triangles are congruent:

FIGURE 10-10

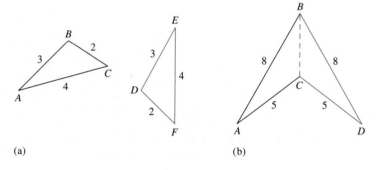

(a)   (b)

Solution   **a.** $\triangle ABC \cong \triangle EDF$ by SSS because $\overline{AB} \cong \overline{ED}, \overline{BC} \cong \overline{DF}$, and $\overline{AC} \cong \overline{EF}$.
b. $\triangle ABC \cong \triangle DBC$ by SSS because $\overline{AB} \cong \overline{DB}, \overline{AC} \cong \overline{DC}$, and $\overline{BC} \cong \overline{BC}$.

Constructing a Triangle Given Three Sides

Using the SSS property, we can construct a triangle $A'B'C'$ congruent to a given triangle ABC if we know the lengths of the three sides. We illustrate this with a compass and straightedge, as in Figure 10-11.

First, we construct a segment congruent to one of the three segments. For example, we may construct $\overline{A'C'}$ so that it is congruent to $\overline{AC}$. To complete the triangle construction, we must locate the other vertex, B'. The distance from A' to B' is AB. All points at a distance AB from A' are on a circle with center at A' and radius of length AB. Similarly, B' must be on a circle with center C' and radius of length BC. The only possible locations for B' are at the points where the two circles intersect. Either point is acceptable. Usually, a picture of the construction shows only one possibility and the construction uses only arcs, as seen in Figure 10-11(c).

FIGURE 10-11

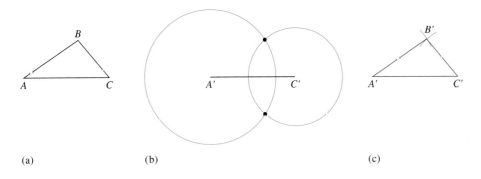

(a)   (b)   (c)

REMARK   Starting the construction with a segment $\overline{A'B'}$ congruent to $\overline{AB}$ or with $\overline{B'C'}$ congruent to $\overline{BC}$ would also result in triangles congruent to $\triangle ABC$.

NOW TRY THIS 10-3

From using the SSS construction as in Figure 10-11, we could think that given any three segments, we could construct a triangle whose sides are congruent to the given segments. To determine if this is true, cut at least ten pieces of straw of different lengths. Make all the possible triangles and answer the following questions:

a. Could a triangle be constructed from each of the three pieces of straws?
b. If three pieces were exactly the same length, what type of triangle could be constructed?
c. If the length of one piece of straw is the exact sum of the lengths of the other two pieces, can a triangle be constructed from the three pieces? Why or why not?
d. If one piece of straw is longer than the two other pieces put together, can a triangle be constructed from the three pieces? Why or why not?

C O R N E R

Work through GSP Lab 4 in Appendix III to investigate congruent triangles.

Both Now Try This 10-3 and the Technology Corner lend credence to the following property.

> ## Property

Triangle inequality   The sum of the measures of any two sides of a triangle must be greater than the measure of the third side.

Constructing Congruent Angles

We use the SSS notion of congruent triangles to construct an angle congruent to a given angle $\angle B$ by making $\angle B$ a part of an isosceles triangle and then reproducing this triangle, as in Figure 10-12.

FIGURE 10-12   *Copying an angle*

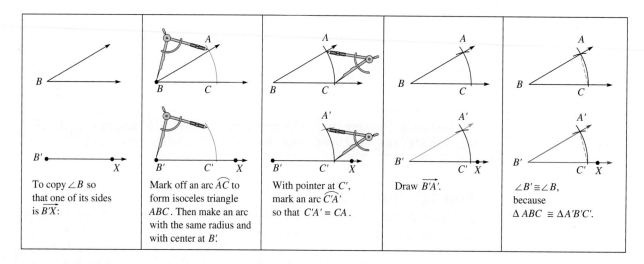

To copy $\angle B$ so that one of its sides is $\overrightarrow{B'X}$:

Mark off an arc $\overset{\frown}{AC}$ to form isoceles triangle ABC. Then make an arc with the same radius and with center at B'.

With pointer at C', mark an arc $\overset{\frown}{C'A'}$ so that $C'A' = CA$.

Draw $\overrightarrow{B'A'}$.

$\angle B' \cong \angle B$, because $\triangle ABC \cong \triangle A'B'C'$.

REMARK   With the compass and straightedge alone, it is impossible in general to construct an angle if given only its measure. For example, an angle of measure $20°$ cannot be constructed with a compass and a straightedge only. Instead, a protractor or some other measuring tool must be used. A geometry drawing utility can also be used to construct angles.

Side, Angle, Side Property (SAS)

included angle

We have seen that, given three segments, no more than one triangle can be constructed. Could more than one triangle be constructed from only two segments? Consider Figure 10-13(b), which shows three different triangles with sides congruent to the segments given in Figure 10-13(a). The length of the third side depends on the measure of the **included angle** between the other two sides.

FIGURE 10-13

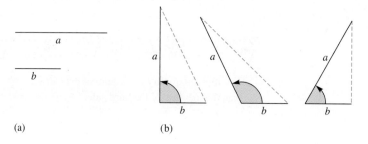

(a)   (b)

Constructions Involving Two Sides and an Included Angle of a Triangle

Figure 10-14 shows how to construct a triangle congruent to $\triangle ABC$ by using two sides $\overline{AB}$ and $\overline{AC}$ and the included angle, $\angle A$, formed by these sides. First, a ray with an arbitrary endpoint A' is drawn, and $\overline{A'C'}$ is constructed congruent to $\overline{AC}$. Then, $\angle A'$ is constructed so that $\angle A' \cong \angle A$ and B' is marked on the side of $\angle A'$ not containing C' so that $\overline{A'B'} \cong \overline{AB}$. Connecting B' and C' completes $\triangle A'B'C'$ so that $\triangle A'B'C'$ appears to be congruent to $\triangle ABC$.

FIGURE 10-14

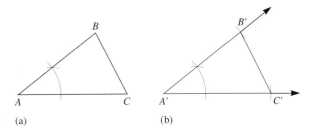

(a)   (b)

It is true that if we knew the lengths of two sides and the measure of the angle included between them, we could construct a unique triangle. We express this fact as the **Side, Angle, Side (SAS)** property.

Side, Angle, Side (SAS)

> ## Property
>
> **Side, Angle, Side (SAS)**   If two sides and the included angle of one triangle are congruent to two sides and the included angle of another triangle, respectively, then the two triangles are congruent.

NOW TRY THIS 10-4

If, in two triangles, two sides and an angle not included between these sides are congruent, respectively, determine whether the triangles must be congruent.

a. If they are congruent, explain why you believe this is true.
b. If they are not congruent, state as few additional conditions as possible that can be placed on the sides or angles to make the triangles congruent.

E X A M P L E
10-3

For each part of Figure 10-15, use SAS to show that the given pair of triangles are congruent.

FIGURE 10-15

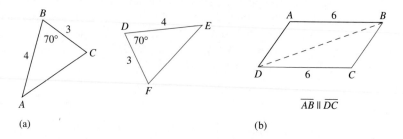

(a)   (b)

$\overline{AB} \parallel \overline{DC}$

Solution   **a.** $\triangle ABC \cong \triangle EDF$ by SAS because $\overline{AB} \cong \overline{ED}$, $\angle B \cong \angle D$ (the included angles), and $\overline{BC} \cong \overline{DF}$.

b. Because $\overline{AB} \cong \overline{CD}$ and $\overline{DB} \cong \overline{BD}$, we need either another side or another angle to show that the triangles are congruent. We know that $\overline{AB} \parallel \overline{DC}$. Since parallel segments $\overline{AB}$ and $\overline{DC}$ are cut by transversal $\overline{BD}$, we have alternate interior angles $\angle ABD$ and $\angle BDC$ congruent. Now $\triangle ABD \cong \triangle CDB$ by SAS.

Selected Triangle Properties

The SAS property of triangle congruence allows us to investigate a number of properties of triangles. For example, in Figure 10-16, consider isosceles triangle ABC with $\overline{AB} \cong \overline{AC}$. We use *paper folding* to construct the angle bisector of $\angle A$. For that purpose we fold a crease through vertex A so that vertex B "falls" on vertex C (this can be done because $\overline{AB} \cong \overline{AC}$). If point D is the intersection of the crease and $\overline{BC}$, then our folding assures that $\angle BAD \cong \angle CAD$. Thus, by SAS, $\triangle ABD \cong \triangle ACD$. Because corresponding parts must be congruent we have: $\angle B \cong \angle C$, $\overline{BD} \cong \overline{CD}$, $\angle BDA \cong \angle CDA$. Because the last pair of angles are supplementary, it follows that each is a right angle. Consequently, $\overline{AD}$ is perpendicular to $\overline{BC}$ and bisects $\overline{BC}$. A line that is perpendicular to a segment and bisects it, is the **perpendicular bisector** of the segment.

perpendicular bisector

FIGURE 10-16

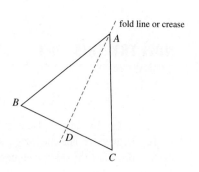

altitude   An **altitude** of a triangle is the perpendicular segment from a vertex of the triangle to the line containing the opposite side of the triangle. These findings are summarized in Theorem 10-1.

> ## Theorem 10-1

The following holds for every isosceles triangle:

a. The angles opposite the congruent sides are congruent. (Base angles of an isosceles triangle are congruent.)

b. The angle bisector of an angle formed by two congruent sides contains an altitude of the triangle and is the perpendicular bisector of the third side of the triangle.

REMARK   Constructions with paper folding are an alternative to constructions with pencil, straightedge, and compass and are especially suitable for elementary and middle school students.

In Figure 10-16, notice that if point A is equidistant from the endpoints B and C, then A is on the perpendicular bisector of $\overline{BC}$. The converse of this statement is also true. The statement and its converse are given in Theorem 10-2.

> ## Theorem 10-2

a. Any point equidistant from the endpoints of a segment is on the perpendicular bisector of the segment.

b. Any point on the perpendicular bisector of a segment is equidistant from the endpoints of the segment.

Construction of the Perpendicular Bisector of a Segment

FIGURE 10-17

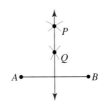

Theorem 10-2 can be used to construct the perpendicular bisector of a segment by constructing any two points equidistant from the endpoints of the segment. Each point is a vertex of an isosceles triangle, and the two points determine the perpendicular bisector of the segment. In Figure 10-17 we have constructed point P equidistant from A and B by drawing intersecting arcs with the same radius—one with center at A, and the other with center at B. Point Q is constructed similarly with two intersecting arcs. By Theorem 10-2 (a), each point is on the perpendicular bisector of $\overline{AB}$. Because two points determine a unique line, $\overleftrightarrow{PQ}$ must be the perpendicular bisector of $\overline{AB}$.

NOW TRY THIS 10-5

In Figure 10-17 we constructed the perpendicular bisector of $\overline{AB}$ by drawing four arcs. An alternative construction of the perpendicular bisector of $\overline{AB}$ can be accomplished by drawing one large enough arc (or circle) with center at A and another one with the same radius and centered at B. The two points where the arcs intersect determine the perpendicular bisector of the segment. Draw any segment and construct its perpendicular bisector using only two arcs.

Construction of a Circle Circumscribed about a Triangle

circumscribed   In Figure 10-18(a), a circle is **circumscribed** about a given $\triangle ABC$; that is, every vertex of the triangle is on the circle. How can such a circle be constructed?

FIGURE 10-18

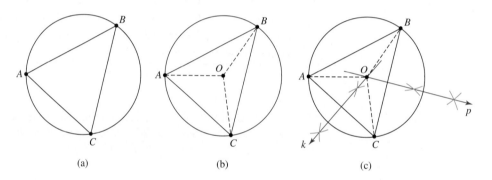

(a)   (b)   (c)

To discover an appropriate construction, imagine that we know the location of center O of the circle, as in Figure 10-18(b). The properties of the center of a circle should enable us to find its location. Because O is the center of the circle circumscribed about $\triangle ABC$, $OA = OC = OB$. The fact that $OA = OC$ implies that O is equidistant from the endpoints of segment $\overline{AC}$. Hence, by Theorem 10-2, O is on the perpendicular bisector, k, of $\overline{AC}$, as shown in Figure 10-18(c). Similarly, because $OC = OB$, O is on the perpendicular bisector, p, of $\overline{BC}$. Because O is on k and on p, it is the point of intersection of the two perpendicular bisectors. Thus, given $\triangle ABC$, we can construct the center of the circumscribed circle by constructing perpendicular bisectors of any two sides of the triangle. The point where the perpendicular bisectors intersect is the center of the required circle. Thus, the required circle is the circle with the center at O and radius OA. The construction is shown in Figure 10-18(c). The center of the circle circumscribed about the triangle is the **circumcenter**   **circumcenter** of the triangle.

PROBLEM SOLVING   Archaeological Find

At the site of an ancient settlement, archaeologists found a fragment of a saucer, as shown in Figure 10-19. To restore the saucer, the archaeologists need to determine the radius of the original saucer. How can they do this?

FIGURE 10-19

Understanding the Problem The border of the shard shown in Figure 10-19 was part of a circle. To reconstruct the saucer, we are to determine the radius of the circle of which the shard is a part.

Devising a Plan We can use a *model* to determine the radius. We trace an outline of the circular edge of the three-dimensional shard on a piece of paper. The result is an arc of a circle, as shown in Figure 10-20. To determine the radius, we must find the center O. We know that by connecting O to points of the circle, we obtain congruent radii. Also, each pair of radii determines an isosceles triangle. Consider points A, B, and O. Triangle ABO is isosceles and O is on the perpendicular bisector of $\overline{AB}$.

FIGURE 10-20

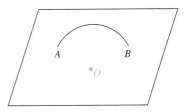

Carrying Out the Plan To find a line containing point O, construct a perpendicular bisector of $\overline{AB}$, as in Figure 10-21(a). Similarly, any other segment (for example, $\overline{AC}$) with end points on $\overparen{AB}$ has a perpendicular bisector containing O, as in Figure 10-21(b). The point of intersection of the two perpendicular bisectors is point O. To complete the problem, measure the length of either $\overline{OB}$ or $\overline{OA}$.

FIGURE 10-21

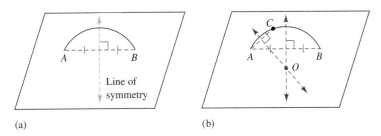

(a)   (b)

Looking Back A related problem is, What would happen if the piece of pottery had been part of a sphere? Would the same ideas still work?

O N G O I N G   A S S E S S M E N T   1 0 - 1

1. In the definition of a circle, why are the points restricted to a plane?

2. If we considered all the points in space that are equidistant from the endpoints of $\overline{AB}$, where would those points lie?

3. **a.** Use any tool to draw triangle *ABC* in which *BC* is greater than *AC*. Measure the angles opposite $\overline{BC}$ and $\overline{AC}$. Compare the angle measures. What did you find?

   b. Based on your finding in (a), make a conjecture concerning the lengths of sides and the measures of angles of a triangle.

4. Use any tools to construct each of the following, if possible:

   a. A segment congruent to $\overline{AB}$ and an angle congruent to $\angle CAB$

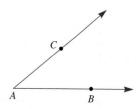

   b. A triangle with sides of lengths 2 cm, 3 cm, and 4 cm

   c. A triangle with sides of lengths 4 cm, 3 cm, and 5 cm (what kind of triangle is it?)

   d. A triangle with sides 4 cm, 5 cm, and 10 cm

   e. An equilateral triangle with sides 5 cm

   f. A triangle with sides 6 cm and 7 cm and an included angle of measure 75°

   g. A triangle with sides 6 cm and 7 cm and a nonincluded angle of measure 40°

   h. A triangle with sides 6 cm and 6 cm and a nonincluded angle of measure 40°

   i. A right triangle with legs 4 cm and 8 cm (the legs include the right angle)

5. For each of the conditions in problem 4(b) through (i), does the given information determine a unique triangle? Explain why or why not.

6. How many different triangles can be constructed with toothpicks by connecting the toothpicks only at their ends if each triangle can contain at most five toothpicks per side?

7. For each of the following, determine whether the given conditions are sufficient to prove that △*PQR* ≅ △*MNO*. Justify your answers.

   a. $\overline{PQ} \cong \overline{MN}$, $\overline{PR} \cong \overline{MO}$, $\angle P \cong \angle M$

   b. $\overline{PQ} \cong \overline{MN}$, $\overline{PR} \cong \overline{MO}$, $\overline{QR} \cong \overline{NO}$

   c. $\overline{PQ} \cong \overline{MN}$, $\overline{PR} \cong \overline{MO}$, $\angle Q \cong \angle N$

8. A rancher designed a wooden gate as illustrated in the following figure. Explain the purpose of the diagonal boards on the gate.

9. A rural homeowner had his television antenna held in place by three guy wires, as shown in the following figure. If the distances to each of the stakes from the base of the antenna are the same, what is true about the lengths of the wires? Why?

10. A group of students on a hiking trip wants to find the distance *AB* across a pond (see the following figure). One student suggests choosing any point *C*, connecting it with *B*, and then finding point *D* such that $\angle DCB \cong \angle ACB$ and $\overline{DC} \cong \overline{AC}$. How and why does this help in finding the distance *AB*?

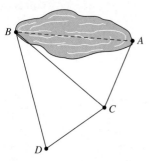

11. Using only a compass and a straightedge, perform each of the following:

   a. Construct an equilateral triangle with the following side $\overline{AB}$.

   b. Construct a 60° angle.

c. Construct an isosceles triangle with ∠A (see the following figure) as the angle included between the two congruent sides:

12. Refer to the following figure and, using only a compass and a straightedge, perform each of the following:

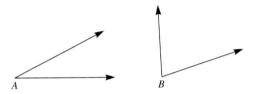

a. Construct ∠C so that $m(\angle C) = m(\angle A) + m(\angle B)$.

b. Using the angles in (a), construct ∠C so that $m(\angle C) = m(\angle B) - m(\angle A)$.

13. An equilateral triangle *ABC* is congruent to itself.

a. Write all possible true correspondences between the triangle and itself.

b. Use one of your answers in (a) to show that an equilateral triangle is also equiangular.

14. a. Draw a circle and use any method to mark off six points that are equally spaced on the circumference of the circle, as shown in the following figure:

b. Connect each of the points to point *O* and connect the points in order around the circle to form a regular hexagon.

c. Explain why all of the triangles are congruent.

d. If the radius of the circle is *r*, what is the length of the side of the hexagon? Justify your answer.

e. Construct any circle, then use your answer to part (d) to inscribe a regular hexagon in the circle; that is, the sides of the hexagon are congruent and all the vertices of the hexagons are on the circle. Describe your construction in words.

f. Construct any circle. Use the construction in part (e) to construct an equilateral triangle inscribed in the circle.

*g. Use the methods of this problem to construct a regular hexagon on Geometer's Sketchpad.

15. Let *ABCD* be a square with diagonals $\overline{AC}$ and $\overline{BD}$ intersecting in point *F*, as shown in this figure:

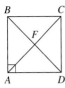

a. What is the relationship between point *F* and the diagonals $\overline{BD}$ and $\overline{AC}$? Why?

b. What are the measures of angles *BFA* and *AFD*? Why?

16. Write a definition for congruent arcs.

17. What minimum amount of information must you know in order to be sure that two cubes are congruent?

18. What is the least number of congruent parts that one must know in order to be sure that square pyramids are congruent?

19. How many different one-to-one correspondences could be listed between the following:

a. Vertices of two triangles

b. Vertices of two quadrilaterals

c. Vertices of two *n*-gons

20. In a pair of right triangles, suppose two legs of one are congruent respectively to two legs of the other. Explain whether the triangles are congruent and why.

21. If two triangles are congruent, what can be said about their perimeters? Why?

22. Construct an obtuse triangle similar to the one shown below. Then, using only a compass and a straightedge, construct the circle that circumscribes the triangle.

23. For which of the following figures is it possible to find a circle that circumscribes the figure? If it is possible to find such a circle, draw the figure and construct the circumscribing circle.

a. A right triangle   **b.** A regular hexagon

24. In the following drawing, a compass is used to draw circle *O*. A point *P* is marked on the circle. Using the compass with the same setting that was used to draw the circle and using point *P* as the center, draw an arc that intersects the original circle in two points *A* and *B*. Repeat the process using points *A* and *B* on the circle. Continue this process.

a. What do you observe?

b. If you connected the points on the circle in order with line segments, starting at *P* and going in a clockwise fashion around the circle, what figure would you draw? Why?

25. Consider a normal stop sign on a highway. Explain whether you think a circle could be circumscribed about this sign.

26. In a circle, consider the lines containing two perpendicular radii. The lines intersect the circle in four points. If the four points are connected,
    a. what type of figure is formed?
    b. Prove your answer in part (a).
27. a. If $\overline{MN}$ is any chord of circle O, what can you say about the perpendicular bisector of $\overline{MN}$?
    b. Prove your answer in part (a).

Communication

28. In circle A with radius AB, let P be a point of $\overline{AB}$ that is not an endpoint. Explain whether P is a part of the circle.
29. Write arguments to convince the class that Theorems 10–1 and 10–2 are true.
30. In the following figure congruent segments are shown with tick marks.

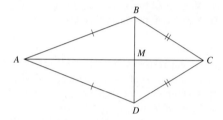

    a. Argue that the diagonal $\overline{AC}$ bisects $\angle A$ and $\angle C$.
    b. Let M be the point on which the diagonals of kite $ABCD$ intersect. Measure $\angle AMD$ and make a conjecture concerning the angle between the diagonals of a kite. Justify your conjecture.
    c. Show that $\overline{BM} \cong \overline{MD}$.

Open-Ended

31. a. Find at least five examples of congruent objects.
    b. Find at least five examples of similar objects that are not congruent.
32. Design a quilt pattern that involves rep-tiles or find a pattern and describe the rep-tiles involved.
33. Use $\triangle AFB$ and $\triangle CED$ shown on the dot paper below to verify $\overline{AB}$ and $\overline{CD}$ are
    a. congruent.
    ★b. perpendicular to each other (consider the angles in $\triangle BGC$).

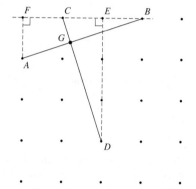

Cooperative Learning

34. Make a set of drawings of congruent figures and write an argument to convince a group of fellow students that the correspondence among vertices is necessary for determining that two triangles are congruent.

Other Congruence Properties

Angle, Side, Angle (ASA)

Triangles can be determined to be congruent by SSS and SAS. Can a triangle be constructed congruent to a given triangle by using two angles and a side? Figure 10-22 shows the construction of a triangle $A'B'C'$ such that $\overline{A'C'} \cong \overline{AC}$, $\angle A' \cong \angle A$, and $\angle C' \cong \angle C$. It

Angle, Side, Angle (ASA)   seems that $\triangle A'B'C' \cong \triangle ABC$. This construction illustrates the **Angle, Side, Angle (ASA)** property of congruence.

FIGURE 10-22

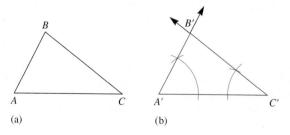

(a)   (b)

> Property

Angle, Side, Angle (ASA)   If two angles and the included side of one triangle are congruent to two angles and the included side of another triangle, respectively, then the triangles are congruent.

EXAMPLE 10-4

In Figure 10-23 $\triangle ABC$ and $\triangle DEF$ have two pairs of angles congruent and a pair of sides congruent. Show that the triangles are congruent.

FIGURE 10-23

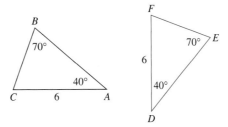

Solution   Notice that $\angle A \cong \angle D$ and $\angle B \cong \angle E$, which implies that $\angle C \cong \angle F$ because the measure of each is $180° - (70 + 40)°$. Then, since $\overline{AC} \cong \overline{DF}$, we have $\triangle ABC \cong \triangle DEF$ by ASA.

Example 10-4 is a special case of the following property.

> Property

Angle, Angle, Side (AAS)   If two angles and a corresponding side of one triangle are congruent to two angles and a corresponding side of another triangle, respectively, then the two triangles are congruent.

EXAMPLE 10-5

Show that the triangles in each part of Figure 10-24 are congruent.

FIGURE 10-24

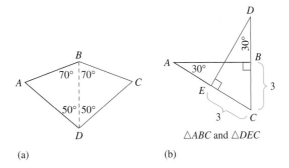

(a)   (b)

Solution   **a.** $\angle ABD \cong \angle CBD$, $\overline{BD} \cong \overline{BD}$, and $\angle ADB \cong \angle CDB$. Consequently, by ASA, $\triangle ABD \cong \triangle CBD$.

b. $\angle A \cong \angle D$, $\angle ABC \cong \angle DEC$, and $\overline{BC} \cong \overline{EC}$. Consequently, by AAS, $\triangle ABC \cong \triangle DEC$.

NOW TRY THIS 10-6

Draw a parallelogram and one of its diagonals. Use the definition of a parallelogram given in Chapter 9 and the ASA congruence property to prove that opposite sides of a parallelogram are congruent.

EXAMPLE 10-6

a. Using the definition of a parallelogram and the property that opposite sides in a parallelogram are congruent (see Now Try This 10-6), prove that the diagonals of a parallelogram bisect each other; that is, in Figure 10-25(a), show that $AO = OC$ and $BO = OD$.

b. Draw a line through the point O where the diagonals of a parallelogram intersect, as in Figure 10-25(b). The line intersects the opposite sides of the parallelogram at points P and Q. Prove that $\overline{OP} \cong \overline{OQ}$.

FIGURE 10-25

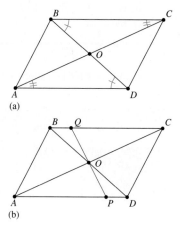

(a)

(b)

Solution   **a.** In Figure 10-25(a) we need to show that $\overline{BO} \cong \overline{DO}$ and $\overline{AO} \cong \overline{CO}$. These segments appear in two pairs of triangles that seem to be congruent. One pair is $\triangle AOD$ and $\triangle COB$. To prove that these triangles are congruent we notice that $\overline{AD} \cong \overline{CB}$ (see Now Try This 10-6). We have no information about the corresponding sides, however we know that $\overline{BC} \parallel \overline{AD}$. Consequently, $\angle CBO \cong \angle DAO$, as these are alternate interior angles formed by the parallel lines and the transversal $\overleftrightarrow{BD}$. Similarly, using the transversal $\overleftrightarrow{AC}$ we have $\angle OAD \cong \angle OCB$ (congruent angles have been similarly marked in Figure 10-25(a)). Now $\triangle AOD \cong \triangle COB$ by ASA. Because corresponding parts in these triangles are congruent, we have $\overline{AO} \cong \overline{OC}$ and $\overline{BO} \cong \overline{OD}$.

b. As in part (a), there are two pairs of triangles that have segments and $\overline{OQ}$ and $\overline{OP}$ as sides; one such pair is $\triangle AOP$ and $\triangle COQ$. In these triangles, $\overline{AO} \cong \overline{OC}$ (as was proved in part (a)). As in part (a) $\angle OAP \cong \angle OCQ$. Also, $\angle AOP \cong \angle COQ$ because these are vertical angles. Thus $\triangle AOP \cong \triangle COQ$ (why?) and $\overline{OP} \cong \overline{OQ}$ because these are corresponding parts in these congruent triangles.

NOW TRY THIS 10-7

If the diagonals of a quadrilateral bisect each other, must the quadrilateral be a parallelogram? Explain why or why not.

Using properties of congruent triangles, we can deduce various properties of quadrilaterals. Table 10-1 summarizes the definitions and lists some properties of six quadrilaterals. These and other properties of quadrilaterals are further investigated in Ongoing Assessment 10-2.

Table 10–1

Quadrilateral and Its Definition	Properties of the Quadrilateral
B *C* *A* *D* *Trapezoid:* A quadrilateral with at least one pair of parallel sides	Consecutive angles between parallel sides are supplementary.
B *D* *A* *C* *Parallelogram:* A quadrilateral in which each pair of opposite sides is parallel	**a.** A parallelogram has all the properties of a trapezoid. **b.** Opposite sides are congruent. **c.** Opposite angles are congruent. **d.** Diagonals bisect each other.
B *D* *A* *C* *Rectangle:* A parallelogram with a right angle	**a.** A rectangle has all the properties of a parallelogram. **b.** All the angles of a rectangle are right angles. **c.** A quadrilateral in which all the angles are right angles is a rectangle. **d.** The diagonals of a rectangle are congruent and bisect each other.

Table 10–1   Continued

Quadrilateral and Its Definition	Properties of the Quadrilateral
  Kite: A quadrilateral with two distinct pairs of congruent adjacent sides.	**a.** Lines containing the diagonals are perpendicular to each other. **b.** A line containing one diagonal is a bisector of the other. **c.** One diagonal bisects nonconsecutive angles.
  Rhombus: A parallelogram with all sides congruent	**a.** A rhombus has all the properties of a parallelogram and a kite. **b.** A quadrilateral in which all the sides are congruent is a rhombus. **c.** The diagonals of a rhombus are perpendicular to and bisect each other. **d.** Each diagonal bisects opposite angles.
  Square: A rectangle with all sides congruent	A square has all the properties of a parallelogram, a rectangle, and a rhombus.

NOW TRY THIS 10-7

> **a.** Define an isosceles trapezoid.
> **b.** Based on your definition in part (a), is a parallelogram an isosceles trapezoid? Explain why.

ONGOING ASSESSMENT 10-2

1. Use any tools to construct each of the following, if possible:
   a. A triangle with angles measuring 60° and 70° and an included side of 8 in.
   b. A triangle with angles measuring 60° and 70° and a nonincluded side of 8 cm on a side of the 60° angle
   c. A right triangle with one acute angle measuring 75° and a leg of 5 cm on a side of the 75° angle
   d. A triangle with angles measuring 30°, 70°, and 80°
2. For each of the conditions in problem 1(a) through (d), is it possible to construct two noncongruent triangles? Explain why or why not.
3. In both the ASA and AAS properties of congruence, if two angles of one triangle are congruent respectively to two angles of another triangle, what must be true about the third angles of the triangles? Justify your answer.
4. **a.** For two right triangles, give a minimal set of conditions based on ASA and AAS to argue that the two triangles are congruent.
   b. Using your answer in (a), write two theorems that can be used to show that right triangles are congruent.
5. For each of the following, determine whether the given conditions are sufficient to prove that $\triangle PQR \cong \triangle MNO$. Justify your answers.
   a. $\angle Q \cong \angle N$, $\angle P \cong \angle M$, $\overline{PQ} \cong \overline{MN}$
   b. $\angle R \cong \angle O$, $\angle P \cong \angle M$, $\overline{QR} \cong \overline{NO}$
   c. $\overline{PQ} \cong \overline{MN}$, $\overline{PR} \cong \overline{MO}$, $\angle N \cong \angle Q$
   d. $\angle P \cong \angle M$, $\angle Q \cong \angle N$, $\angle R \cong \angle O$

6. A parallel ruler, shown as follows, can be used to draw parallel lines. The distance between the parallel segments $\overline{AB}$ and $\overline{DC}$ can vary. The ruler is constructed so that the distance between A and B equals the distance between D and C. The distance between A and C is the same as the distance between B and D. Explain why $\overline{AB}$ and $\overline{DC}$ are always parallel.

7. In each of the following, choose as many of the words *parallelogram, rectangle, rhombus, trapezoid, kite,* or *square* so that the resulting sentence is true. If none of the words makes the sentence true, answer "none" and justify your answer.

  a. A quadrilateral is a _____ if, and only if, its diagonals bisect each other.

  b. A quadrilateral is a _____ if, and only if, its diagonals are congruent.

  c. A quadrilateral is a _____ if, and only if, its diagonals are perpendicular.

  d. A quadrilateral is a _____ if, and only if, its diagonals are congruent and bisect each other.

  e. A quadrilateral is a _____ if, and only if, its diagonals are perpendicular and bisect each other.

  f. A quadrilateral is a _____ if, and only if, its diagonals are congruent and perpendicular and they bisect each other.

  g. A quadrilateral is a _____ if, and only if, a pair of opposite sides is parallel and congruent.

8. Create several trapezoids that have a pair of nonparallel sides congruent. Measure all angles and make a conjecture about the relationships among pairs of angles.

9. Classify each of the following statements as true or false. If the statement is false, provide a counterexample.

  a. The diagonals of a square are perpendicular bisectors of each other.

  b. If all sides of a quadrilateral are congruent, the quadrilateral is a rhombus.

  c. If a rhombus is a square, it must also be a rectangle.

  d. An isosceles trapezoid can be a rectangle.

  e. A square is a trapezoid.

  f. A trapezoid is a parallelogram.

  g. A parallelogram is a trapezoid.

  h. No rectangle is a rhombus.

  i. No trapezoid is a square.

  j. Some squares are trapezoids.

10. **a.** Construct quadrilaterals having exactly one, two, and four right angles.

  b. Can a quadrilateral have exactly three right angles? Why?

  c. Can a parallelogram have exactly two right angles? Why?

11. Explain whether the chevron *ABCD* pictured below is a kite.

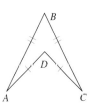

12. Classify each of the figures formed from regular hexagon *ABCDEF*.

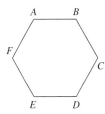

  a. Quadrilateral *ABDE*

  b. Quadrilateral *ABEF*

13. What is the shape that is formed by taking the inner piece of cardboard in a paper towel roll, carefully cutting along the seam, and flattening? How do you know?

14. **a.** What is the maximum number of $3'' \times 5''$ rectangular pieces of paper that can be cut from an $8\ 1/2'' \times 11''$ sheet of paper?

  b. Are all $3'' \times 5''$ rectangular cards congruent? Why or why not?

15. Each fourth grader is given a protractor, two 30-cm sticks, and two 20-cm sticks and is asked to form a quadrilateral with a 75° angle. Sketch all possibilities.

16. The game of Triominoes has equilateral-triangular playing pieces with numbers at each vertex, shown as follows:

If two pieces are placed together as shown in the following figure, explain what type of quadrilateral is formed.

17. A **sector** of a circle is a pie-shaped section bounded by two radii and an arc. What is a minimal set of conditions for determining that two sectors of the same circle are congruent?

18. Draw two quadrilaterals such that two angles and an included side in one quadrilateral are congruent respectively to two angles and an included side in the other quadrilateral. However, the quadrilaterals are not congruent.
19. **a.** In an isosceles trapezoid, make a conjecture concerning the lengths of the sides which are not bases.
    b. Make a conjecture concerning the diagonals of an isosceles trapezoid.
    c. Justify your conjectures in (a) and (b).
20. Two angles of the trapezoid shown below are 45° each. Suppose the lengths of the parallel sides of the trapezoid are *a* cm and *b* cm. Find the height of the trapezoid (the distance between the parallel sides) in terms of *a* and *b*.

21. Using a straightedge and a compass, construct any convex kite. Then construct a second convex kite that is not congruent to the first but whose sides are congruent to the corresponding sides of the first kite.
22. **a.** What type of figure is formed by joining the midpoints of a rectangle (see the following figure)?

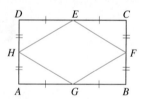

    b. What type of figure is formed by joining the midpoints of the sides of a parallelogram?
    ★**c.** Justify your answer to part (b).
23. What information is needed to determine congruency for each of the following?
    a. Two squares
    b. Two rectangles
    c. Two parallelograms
24. Describe a set of minimal conditions to determine if two regular polygons are congruent.
25. Suppose polygon *ABCD* shown in the following figure is any parallelogram:

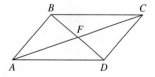

Use congruent triangles to justify each of the following:
    a. $\angle A \cong \angle C$ and $\angle B \cong \angle D$ (opposite angles are congruent).
    b. $\overline{BC} \cong \overline{AD}$ and $\overline{AB} \cong \overline{CD}$ (opposite sides are congruent).
    c. $\overline{BF} \cong \overline{DF}$ and $\overline{AF} \cong \overline{CF}$ (the diagonals bisect each other).
    d. $\angle DAB$ and $\angle ABC$ are supplementary.

Communication

26. Stan is standing on the bank of a river wearing a baseball cap. Standing erect and looking directly at the other bank, he pulls the bill of his cap down until it just obscures his vision of the opposite bank. He then turns around, being careful not to disturb the cap, and picks out a spot that is just obscured by the bill of his cap. He then paces off the distance to this spot and claims that the distance across the river is approximately equal to the distance he paced. Is Stan's claim true? Why?
27. Most ironing boards are collapsible for storage and can be adjusted to fit the height of the person using them. The surface of the board, though, remains parallel to the floor regardless of the height. Explain how to construct the legs of an ironing board to ensure the surface is always parallel to the floor.

Open-Ended

28. **a.** Go to a wallpaper store and examine the pattern books. Determine whether all rolls of a specific pattern of wallpaper are congruent.
    b. On an individual roll of wallpaper, determine the length of wallpaper before a pattern is repeated.
    c. If you were wallpapering a room, explain how congruence or noncongruence could save you money.

Cooperative Learning

29. **a.** Record the definitions of *trapezoid* and *kite* given in different grade 6–8 and secondary-school geometry textbooks.
    b. Compare the definitions found with those in this text and with those other groups found.
    c. Defend the use of one definition over another.

Review Problems

30. In the following regular pentagon, use the existing vertices to find all the triangles congruent to △*ABC*. Show that the triangles actually are congruent.

31. If possible, construct a triangle that has the following three segments *a, b,* and *c* as its sides; if not possible, explain why not.

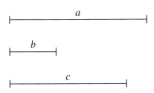

32. Construct an equilateral triangle whose sides are congruent to the following segment:

33. For each of the following pairs of triangles, determine whether the given conditions are sufficient to show that the triangles are congruent. If the triangles are congruent, tell which property can be used to verify this fact.

(a)   (b)

(c)

  Other Constructions

We use the definition of a rhombus and the following properties (also listed in Table 10-1) to accomplish basic compass-and-straightedge constructions:

1. A rhombus is a parallelogram in which all the sides are congruent.
2. A quadrilateral in which all the sides are congruent is a rhombus.
3. Each diagonal of a rhombus bisects the opposite angles.
4. The diagonals of a rhombus are perpendicular.
5. The diagonals of a rhombus bisect each other.

Constructing Parallel Lines

To construct a line parallel to a given line ℓ through a point *P* not on ℓ, as in the leftmost panel of Figure 10-26, our strategy is to construct a rhombus (using property 2 listed above) with one of its vertices at *P* and one of its sides on line ℓ. Because the opposite sides of a rhombus are parallel, one of the sides through *P* will be parallel to ℓ. This construction is shown in Figure 10.26.

FIGURE 10-26 Constructing parallel lines (rhombus method)

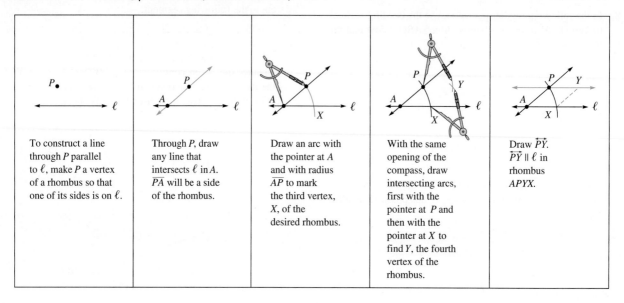

To construct a line through *P* parallel to ℓ, make *P* a vertex of a rhombus so that one of its sides is on ℓ.

Through *P*, draw any line that intersects ℓ in *A*. $\overline{PA}$ will be a side of the rhombus.

Draw an arc with the pointer at *A* and with radius $\overline{AP}$ to mark the third vertex, *X*, of the desired rhombus.

With the same opening of the compass, draw intersecting arcs, first with the pointer at *P* and then with the pointer at *X* to find *Y*, the fourth vertex of the rhombus.

Draw $\overleftrightarrow{PY}$. $\overleftrightarrow{PY} \parallel ℓ$ in rhombus *APYX*.

Figure 10-27 shows another way to do the construction. If congruent corresponding angles are formed by a transversal cutting two lines, then the lines are parallel. Thus the first step is to draw a transversal through *P* that intersects ℓ. The angle marked α is formed by the transversal and line ℓ. By constructing an angle with a vertex at *P* congruent to α, we create congruent corresponding angles; therefore $\overleftrightarrow{PQ} \parallel ℓ$.

FIGURE 10-27 Constructing parallel lines (corresponding angle method)

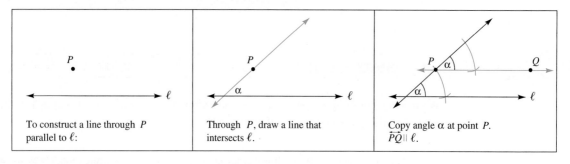

To construct a line through *P* parallel to ℓ:

Through *P*, draw a line that intersects ℓ.

Copy angle α at point *P*. $\overleftrightarrow{PQ} \parallel ℓ$.

NOW TRY THIS 10-8

Parallel lines are frequently constructed using either a ruler and one triangle or two triangles. If a ruler and a triangle are used, the ruler is left fixed and the triangle is slid so that one side of the triangle touches the ruler at all times. In Figure 10-28 the hypotenuses of the right triangles are all parallel (also the legs not on the ruler are all parallel). How can this method be used to construct a line through a given point parallel to a given line?

FIGURE 10-28

Paper folding can be used to construct parallel lines. For example, in Figure 10-29(a) to construct a line *m* parallel to line *p* through point *Q*, we can fold a perpendicular to line *p* so that the fold line does not contain point *Q*, as shown in Figure 10-29(b). Then by marking the image of point *Q* and connecting point *Q* and its image, *Q′*, we have $\overleftrightarrow{QQ'}$ parallel to line *p* (why?).

FIGURE 10-29

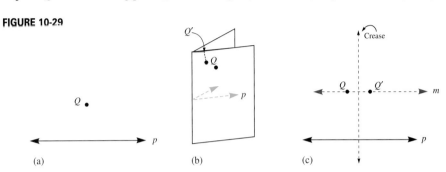

Constructing Angle Bisectors

angle bisector Another construction based on a property of a rhombus is for an **angle bisector**, a ray that separates an angle into two congruent angles. The diagonal of a rhombus with vertex *A* bisects ∠*A*, as shown in Figure 10-30.

FIGURE 10-30 *Bisecting an angle*

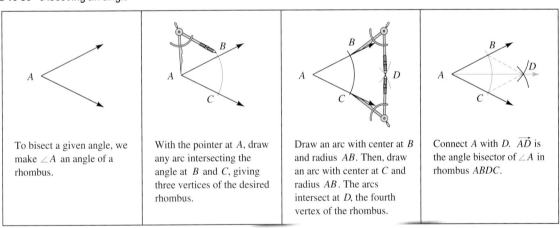

To bisect a given angle, we make ∠*A* an angle of a rhombus.	With the pointer at *A*, draw any arc intersecting the angle at *B* and *C*, giving three vertices of the desired rhombus.	Draw an arc with center at *B* and radius *AB*. Then, draw an arc with center at *C* and radius *AB*. The arcs intersect at *D*, the fourth vertex of the rhombus.	Connect *A* with *D*. $\overrightarrow{AD}$ is the angle bisector of ∠*A* in rhombus *ABDC*.

We can bisect an angle by folding a line through the vertex so that one side of the angle folds onto the other side. For example, in Figure 10-31 we bisect ∠*ABC* by folding and creasing the paper through the vertex *B* so that $\overrightarrow{BC}$ coincides with $\overrightarrow{BA}$. (See also page 570.)

FIGURE 10-31

(a)

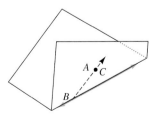

$\overrightarrow{BC}$ superimposed on $\overrightarrow{BA}$

(b)

FIGURE 10-32

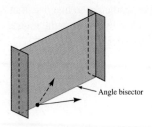

A Mira is a plastic device that acts as a reflector so that the image of an object can be seen behind the Mira. The drawing edge of the Mira acts as a folding line on paper. Any construction demonstrated in this text using paper folding can also be done with a Mira. To construct the bisector of an angle with a Mira, we place the drawing edge of the Mira on the vertex of the angle and reflect one side of the angle onto the other, as shown in Figure 10-32.

Constructing Perpendicular Lines

To construct a line through P perpendicular to line ℓ, where P is not a point on ℓ, as in Figure 10-33, recall that the diagonals of a rhombus are perpendicular to each other. If we construct a rhombus with a vertex at P and a diagonal on ℓ, as in Figure 10-33, the segment connecting the fourth vertex Q to P is perpendicular to ℓ.

FIGURE 10-33 Constructing a perpendicular to a line from a point not on a line

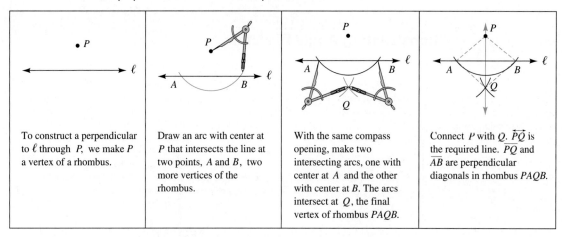

To construct a perpendicular to ℓ through P, we make P a vertex of a rhombus.	Draw an arc with center at P that intersects the line at two points, A and B, two more vertices of the rhombus.	With the same compass opening, make two intersecting arcs, one with center at A and the other with center at B. The arcs intersect at Q, the final vertex of rhombus $PAQB$.	Connect P with Q. $\overleftrightarrow{PQ}$ is the required line. $\overline{PQ}$ and $\overline{AB}$ are perpendicular diagonals in rhombus $PAQB$.

In Section 10-1 we saw how to construct the perpendicular bisector of a segment using a property of a perpendicular bisector stated in Theorem 10-2. Here we show how a property of a rhombus can also be used for constructing the perpendicular bisector of a segment.

To construct the perpendicular bisector of a line segment, as in Figure 10-34, we use the fact that the diagonals of a rhombus are perpendicular bisectors of each other.

FIGURE 10-34 Bisecting a line segment

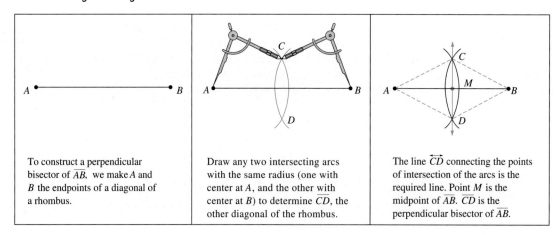

To construct a perpendicular bisector of $\overline{AB}$, we make A and B the endpoints of a diagonal of a rhombus.	Draw any two intersecting arcs with the same radius (one with center at A, and the other with center at B) to determine $\overline{CD}$, the other diagonal of the rhombus.	The line $\overleftrightarrow{CD}$ connecting the points of intersection of the arcs is the required line. Point M is the midpoint of $\overline{AB}$. $\overline{CD}$ is the perpendicular bisector of $\overline{AB}$.

The construction yields a rhombus such that the original segment is one of the diagonals of the rhombus and the other diagonal is the perpendicular bisector, as in Figure 10-34.

Constructing a perpendicular to a line ℓ at a point M on ℓ is based on the fact that the diagonals of a rhombus are perpendicular bisectors of each other. Observe in Figure 10-34 that $\overleftrightarrow{CD}$ is a perpendicular to $\overleftrightarrow{AB}$ through M. Thus we construct a rhombus whose diagonals intersect at point M, as in Figure 10-35.

FIGURE 10-35 Constructing a perpendicular to a line from a point on the line

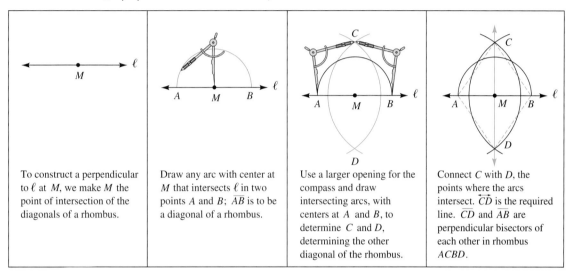

To construct a perpendicular to ℓ at M, we make M the point of intersection of the diagonals of a rhombus.	Draw any arc with center at M that intersects ℓ in two points A and B; $\overline{AB}$ is to be a diagonal of a rhombus.	Use a larger opening for the compass and draw intersecting arcs, with centers at A and B, to determine C and D, determining the other diagonal of the rhombus.	Connect C with D, the points where the arcs intersect. $\overleftrightarrow{CD}$ is the required line. $\overleftrightarrow{CD}$ and $\overline{AB}$ are perpendicular bisectors of each other in rhombus $ACBD$.

Perpendicularity constructions can also be completed by means of paper folding or by using a Mira. To use paper folding to construct a perpendicular to a given line ℓ at a point P on the line, we fold the line onto itself, as shown in Figure 10-36(a). The fold line is perpendicular to ℓ. To perform the construction with a Mira, we place the Mira with the drawing edge on P, as shown in Figure 10-36(b), so that ℓ is reflected onto itself. The line along the drawing edge is the required perpendicular.

FIGURE 10-36

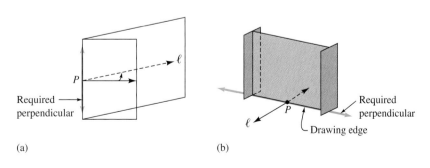

(a)   (b)

Constructing perpendiculars is useful in locating altitudes of a triangle. The construction of altitudes is described in Example 10-7.

E X A M P L E
10-7

Given triangle *ABC*, construct an altitude from vertex *A* in each part of Figure 10-37.

FIGURE 10-37

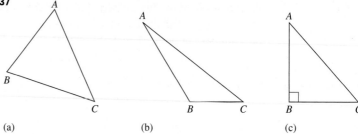

(a)   (b)   (c)

Solution   **a.** An altitude is the perpendicular from a vertex to the line containing the opposite side of a triangle, so we need to construct a perpendicular from point *A* to the line containing $\overline{BC}$. Such a construction is shown in Figure 10-38. $\overline{AD}$ is the required altitude.

FIGURE 10-38

b. The construction of the altitude from vertex *A* is shown in Figure 10-39. Notice that the required altitude $\overline{AD}$ does not intersect the interior of $\triangle ABC$.

FIGURE 10-39

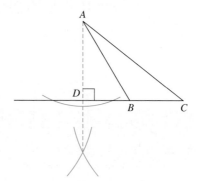

c. Triangle *ABC* is a right triangle. The altitude from vertex *A* is the side $\overline{AB}$. No construction is required.

Use Geometer's Sketchpad to draw all the altitudes of a triangle. Make conjectures about the altitudes of each of the following types of triangles: acute, right, and obtuse.

Properties of Angle Bisectors

Consider the angle bisector in Figure 10-40. It seems that any point P on the angle bisector is equidistant from the sides of the angle; that is, $PD = PE$. (*The distance from a point to a line is the length of the perpendicular from the point to the line.*)

FIGURE 10-40

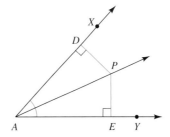

To justify this, we find two congruent triangles that have these segments as corresponding sides. The only triangles pictured are $\triangle ADP$ and $\triangle AEP$. Because $\overrightarrow{AP}$ is the angle bisector, $\angle DAP \cong \angle EAP$. Also, $\angle PDA$ and $\angle PEA$ are right angles and are thus congruent. $\overline{AP}$ is congruent to itself, so $\triangle PDA \cong \triangle PEA$ by AAS. Thus $\overline{PD} \cong \overline{PE}$ because they are corresponding parts of congruent triangles PDA and PEA. Consequently, we have the following theorem.

Theorem 10-3

a. Any point P on an angle bisector is equidistant from the sides of the angle.
b. Any point that is equidistant from the sides of an angle is on the angle bisector of the angle.

Notice that we have proved only Theorem 10-3(a). You are asked to demonstrate part (b) in Now Try This 10-9.

NOW TRY THIS 10-9

Demonstrate that if a point is in the interior of an angle and is equidistant from the sides of the angle, the point must be on the angle bisector of that angle.

E X A M P L E
10-8

In the interior of △*ABC* in Figure 10-41 find the point *P* that is equidistant from the three sides of the triangle and construct the congruent segments through *P* perpendicular to each side.

FIGURE 10-41

Solution To discover an appropriate construction, imagine that we know the location of *P* in Figure 10-41. Then $\overline{PK}$, $\overline{PM}$, and $\overline{PN}$ are perpendicular to the corresponding sides and $PK = PM = PN$. Because *P* is equidistant from the sides of ∠*A* it must be on the angle bisector of *A*. Similarly *P* must be on the angle bisector of ∠*B*. Thus to find the point *P* we construct two angle bisectors of △*ABC*. The intersection of the angle bisectors is the required point. We then construct through *P* perpendiculars to the three lines. The points of intersection of the perpendiculars with the corresponding sides determine the equal distances *PM*, *PK*, and *PN*. The construction is shown in Figure 10-42.

FIGURE 10-42

Notice that if in Figure 10-42 we draw a circle with the center *P* and radius *PM* (or *PK* or *PN*), the circle seems to fit exactly inside the triangle. In fact each line "touches" the circle at one point only. The sides of the triangle are **tangent** to the circle. A line is *tangent to a circle if it intersects the circle in one and only one point and is perpendicular to a radius.* It is possible to show that a line perpendicular to a radius at the endpoint of the radius, which is not the center, is tangent to the circle. Thus the sides of the △*ABC* in Figure 10-41 are tangent to the circle. Such a circle is **inscribed** in the triangle. The center of the inscribed circle is the **incenter** of the triangle.

tangent

inscribed
incenter

NOW TRY THIS 10-10

Use any tools to investigate whether a circle can be inscribed in a square.

ONGOING ASSESSMENT 10-3

1. Refer to the following figure and use a compass and a straightedge to construct a line *m* through *P* parallel to ℓ, using each of the following:
   a. Alternate interior angles
   b. Alternate exterior angles

2. For each of the following items compare these methods of construction: paper folding, Mira, compass and straightedge and Geometer's Sketchpad (if available). Give advantages and disadvantages of each method.
   a. Bisector of $\angle A$
   b. Perpendicular bisector of $\overline{AB}$
   c. Perpendicular from point *P* to line *m*
3. Construction companies avoid vandalism at night by hanging expensive pieces of equipment from the boom of a crane, as show in the following figure:

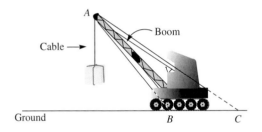

   a. If you consider a triangle with two vertices *A* and *B* as marked in the above figure and the intersection of a line through the cable holding the equipment and the ground as the third vertex, what type of triangle is formed?
   b. If you consider the triangle formed by points *A, B,* and *C,* describe where the altitude containing vertex *A* of the triangle is.
4. Construct the perpendicular bisectors of each of the sides of the following triangles. Use any desired method.

   a. Make a conjecture about the perpendicular bisectors of the sides of an acute triangle.
   b. Make a conjecture about the perpendicular bisectors of the sides of a right triangle.
   c. Make a conjecture about the perpendicular bisectors of the sides of an obtuse triangle.

   d. For each of the three triangles construct the circle that circumscribes the triangle.
5. **a.** Given triangle *ABC,* as in the following figure, construct a point *P* that is equidistant from the three vertices of the triangle. Explain why your construction is correct.

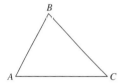

   b. Repeat (a) for the following obtuse triangle:

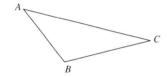

6. Draw an acute triangle and an obtuse triangle and in each case construct the circle inscribed in the triangle.
7. For which of the following figures is it possible to construct a circle that is inscribed in the figure (each side of the figure must be tangent to the circle)? If it is possible to find such a circle, draw the figure and construct the inscribed circle using only a straightedge and a compass; if not, explain how you decided that it is impossible to find an inscribed circle.
   a. A rectangle
   b. A rhombus
   c. A kite that is not a rhombus
   d. A regular hexagon
8. Given $\overline{AB}$ in the following figure, construct a square with $\overline{AB}$ as a side:

9. Suppose you are "charged" 10¢ each time you use your straightedge to draw a line segment and 10¢ each time you use your compass to draw an arc. Using only a compass and a straightedge, determine the cheapest way to construct a square. Explain you reasoning.
10. Given *A, B,* and *C* as vertices, use a compass and a straightedge to construct a parallelogram:

11. In the following concave quadrilateral $APBQ$, $\overline{PQ}$ and $\overline{AB}$ are the diagonals: $\overline{AP} \cong \overline{BP}$, $\overline{AQ} \cong \overline{BQ}$, and $\overline{PQ}$ has been extended until it intersects $\overline{AB}$ at C:

    a. Make a conjecture concerning $\overrightarrow{PQ}$ and $\overline{AB}$.
    b. Justify your conjecture in (a).
    c. Make conjectures concerning the relationships between $\overrightarrow{PQ}$ and $\angle APB$ and between $\overrightarrow{QC}$ and $\angle AQB$.
    d. Justify your conjectures in (c).

12. Some car jacks are constructed like a collapsed rhombus. When used to raise a car, the rhombus is easily seen.

    If the sides of the rhombus are 13″, what is the maximum length of the shaft?

13. If $INTO$ is a rhombus and X is any point on $\overline{NT}$ (except N and T), what type of quadrilateral is $IXTO$? Why?

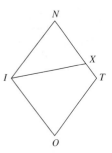

14. If two pieces of tape cross each other, what type of parallelogram is $ABCD$? Why?

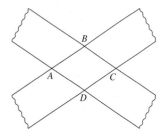

15. Using any tools, construct each of the following, if possible. If the construction is not possible, explain why.
    a. A square, given one side
    b. A square, given one diagonal
    c. A rectangle, given one diagonal
    d. A parallelogram, given two of its adjacent sides
    e. A rhombus, given its diagonals
    f. A triangle with two obtuse angles
    g. A parallelogram with exactly three right angles

16. Using only a compass and a straightedge, construct angles with each of the following measures:
    a. 30°   b. 15°   c. 45°
    d. 75°   e. 105°

17. Given $\overrightarrow{AB}$ in the following figure, use a compass and a straightedge to construct the perpendicular bisector of $\overline{AB}$. You are not allowed to put any marks below $\overline{AB}$.

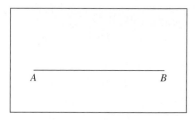

18. a. Explain why the hypotenuses in Figure 10-28 are all parallel.
    b. Use the "sliding triangle" method described in Figure 10-28 to construct a line through a point P parallel to a line ℓ.

19. Draw a line ℓ and a point P not on the line and use the sliding triangle method described in Figure 10-28 to construct a perpendicular to ℓ through P using a straightedge and a right triangle.

20. Draw a convex quadrilateral similar to the one shown below and construct each of the following points, if possible. If it is not possible, explain why. Describe each construction in words and explain why it produces the required point.
    a. The point that is equidistant from $\overline{AB}$ and $\overline{AD}$ and also from points B and C
    b. The point that is equidistant from $\overline{AB}$, $\overline{AD}$, and $\overline{BC}$
    c. The point that is equidistant from A, B, and C
    d. The point that is equidistant from A, B, C, and D

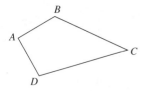

21. Describe how to inscribe a square in any circle. Explain why your construction produces a square.

22. Use problem 21 to describe how to inscribe a regular octagon in a circle.

Communication

23. Given an angle and a roll of tape, describe how you might construct the bisector of the angle.

24. Write a letter from you, a curriculum developer, to parents explaining whether or not the geometry curriculum in grades 5–8 should include construction problems that use only a compass and straightedge.

Open-Ended

25. Explain whether you think there is a single perpendicular from a point to a line on a sphere if a line is defined as a great circle of the sphere (a circle obtained by intersecting the sphere with a plane through its center).

26. Explain whether you think there are parallel lines on a sphere.

27. Explain whether your geometry drawing utility allows the construction of regular polygons.

Cooperative Learning

28. In your group, perform the following paper-folding construction and answer the questions that follow. Let P and Q be two opposite vertices of a rectangular piece of paper, as shown in Figure (i). Fold P onto Q so that a crease is formed. This results in Figure (ii) where A and B are the endpoints of the crease. Next crease again so that point A folds onto point B. This results in Figure (iii). Next, unfold to obtain two creases, as in Figure (iv).

(i)   (ii)

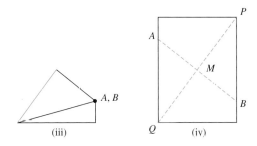

(iii)   (iv)

a. Individually write an explanation of why every point on $\overline{AB}$ is equidistant from the endpoints of $\overline{PQ}$. Compare the explanations in your group and prepare one explanation to be presented to the class.

b. Discuss in your group whether $APBQ$ is a rhombus.

Review Problems

29. In the following figure $\overleftrightarrow{AB} \parallel \overleftrightarrow{ED}$ and $\overline{BC} \cong \overline{CE}$. Explain why $DE = AB$.

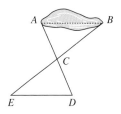

30. Draw $\triangle ABC$. Then construct $\triangle PQR$ congruent to $\triangle ABC$ using each of the following combinations:
   a. Two sides of $\triangle ABC$ and an angle included between these sides
   b. The three sides of $\triangle ABC$
   c. Two angles and a side included between these angles

31. $ABCD$ is a trapezoid with $\overline{AB} \cong \overline{CD}$. Show that
   a. $\angle A \cong \angle D$ (through C draw a line parallel to $\overline{AB}$ and show that the triangle that is created is isosceles).
   b. $\overline{BD} \cong \overline{CA}$.

32. In two right triangles, $\triangle ABC$ and $\triangle DEF$, if $\angle A$ and $\angle D$ are congruent and $\overline{AC}$ and $\overline{DF}$ are congruent, what can you conclude about the two triangles. Why?

BRAIN TEASER

In the grid of squares in Figure 10-43, through how many squares does the diagonal pass?

FIGURE 10-43

Use The Geometer's Sketchpad to do each of the following:

1. a. Draw a circle. Label its center and draw any angle whose vertex is the center and whose sides intersect the circle, as in Figure 10-44. Such an angle is a **central angle** of the circle. The measure of a central angle and its intercepted arc are considered to be the same measure.

central angle

FIGURE 10-44

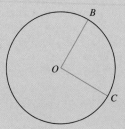

b. Choose any point P on the circumference of the circle that is not B and not C, and not in the interior of $\angle BOC$. Draw $\angle BPC$ and find its measure. $\angle BPC$ is an **inscribed angle** of the circle.

inscribed angle

c. Make a conjecture about the measures of $\angle BOC$ and $\angle BPC$.

2. Draw an inscribed triangle in a circle in such a way that one side of the triangle is a diameter of the circle. Find the measure of the angle that does not have the diameter as a side. Make a conjecture about the measure of any such angle.

Similar Triangles and Similar Figures

When a germ is examined under a microscope or when a slide is projected on a screen, the shapes in each case remain the same, but the sizes are altered. *Two figures that have the same shape but not necessarily the same size are* **similar**. For example, see the student page and do Problem 3. The ratio of the corresponding side lengths is the **scale factor**. On the student page the scale factor in the top figures is $\frac{4}{3}$.

similar

scale factor

It seems that in any enlargement or reduction the resulting figure is similar to the original; that is, the corresponding angle measures remain the same and the corresponding sides are proportional. In general, we have the following definition.

> ### Definition of Similar Triangles
>
> $\triangle ABC$ is similar to $\triangle DEF$, written $\triangle ABC \sim \triangle DEF$, if, and only if, $\angle A \cong \angle D$, $\angle B \cong \angle E$, $\angle C \cong \angle F$, and $\dfrac{AB}{DE} = \dfrac{AC}{DF} = \dfrac{BC}{EF}$.

Sample School Book Page:
SIMILAR FIGURES

GOAL

LEARN HOW TO...
* tell whether triangles are similar
* make indirect measurements

AS YOU...
* estimate the height of a cliff

KEY TERMS
* similar
* corresponding angles
* corresponding sides

Exploration 1

Similar Figures
Similar Figures

SET UP *You will need:* • Labsheet 4A • ruler • protractor

▶ As you'll see in this exploration, Charlotte Lopez uses *similar* figures to estimate the cliff height. Two figures are **similar** if they have the same shape, but not necessarily the same size. The figures below are similar.

∠P and ∠T are *corresponding angles*. **Corresponding angles** have the same measure.

$m\angle P = m\angle T$

Read $m\angle T$ as "the measure of angle *T*."

$\overline{PQ}$ and $\overline{TU}$ are *corresponding sides*. The lengths of **corresponding sides** are in proportion.

$$\frac{PQ}{TU} = \frac{QR}{UV}.$$

Read $\overline{TU}$ as "segment *TU*." Read TU as "the length of segment *TU*."

(figure: quadrilateral PQRS with Q 6 cm R, 5 cm, 4 cm, P 9 cm S)

(figure: quadrilateral TUVW with U 4.5 cm V, 3.75 cm, 3 cm, T 6.75 cm W)

3 **a.** **Try This as a Class** Name all pairs of corresponding angles and corresponding sides in the figures above.

b. Find the ratios $\frac{PQ}{TU}$, $\frac{QR}{UV}$, $\frac{RS}{VW}$, and $\frac{PS}{TW}$. What do you notice?

✓ QUESTION 4

...checks your understanding of the definition of similar figures.

4 **✓ CHECKPOINT** The figures below are similar. Copy and complete each statement.

a. $m\angle C = m\ \underline{\ ?\ }$

b. $\frac{BC}{FG} = \frac{?}{GH}$

c. $\frac{?}{AD} = \frac{EF}{?}$

Source: Math Thematics, Book 3, McDougal Littell, 2002 (p. 202).

E X A M P L E
10-9

Given the pairs of similar triangles in Figure 10-45, find a one-to-one correspondence among the vertices of the triangles such that the corresponding angles are congruent. Then write the proportion for the corresponding sides that follows from the definition.

FIGURE 10-45

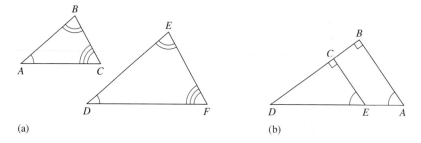

(a)   (b)

Solution   **a.** $\triangle ABC \sim \triangle DEF$

$$\frac{AB}{DE} = \frac{BC}{EF} = \frac{AC}{DF}$$

b. $\triangle ABD \sim \triangle ECD$

$$\frac{AB}{EC} = \frac{BD}{CD} = \frac{AD}{ED}$$

Angle, Angle Property (AA)

As with congruent triangles, minimal conditions may be used to determine when two triangles are similar. For example, suppose two triangles each have angles with measures of 50°, 30°, and 100°, but the side opposite the 100° angle is 5 units long in one of the triangles and 1 unit long in the other.

The triangles appear to have the same shape, as shown in Figure 10-46. The figure suggests that if the angles of the two triangles are congruent, then the triangles are similar. **Angle, Angle, Angle (AAA)** This statement is true in general; it is the **Angle, Angle, Angle** property of similarity for triangles, abbreviated **AAA**. But does it give a minimal set of conditions for similarity of triangles? We know that given the measures of any two angles of a triangle, the measure of the third angle can be found. Hence, if two angles in one triangle are congruent to two angles in another triangle, then the third angles must also be congruent. Consequently, we **Angle, Angle (AA)** have the **Angle, Angle (AA)** property.

FIGURE 10-46

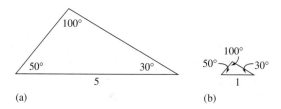

(a)   (b)

> ## Property of Similar Triangles: Angle, Angle (AA)

Angle, Angle (AA)   If two angles of one triangle are congruent, respectively, to two angles of a second triangle, then the triangles are similar.

E X A M P L E
10-10

For each part of Figure 10-47, find a pair of similar triangles.

FIGURE 10-47

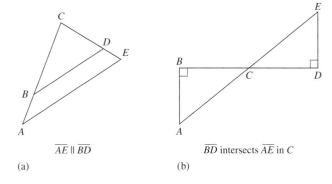

$\overline{AE} \parallel \overline{BD}$

(a)

$\overline{BD}$ intersects $\overline{AE}$ in C

(b)

Solution   **a.** Because $\overline{AE} \parallel \overline{BD}$, congruent corresponding angles are formed by a transversal cutting the parallel segments. Thus $\angle CBD \cong \angle CAE$ and $\angle CDB \cong \angle CEA$. Also, $\angle C \cong \angle C$, so $\triangle CBD \sim \triangle CAE$ by AA.

   b. $\angle B \cong \angle D$ because both are right triangles. Also, $\angle ACB \cong \angle ECD$ because they are vertical angles. Thus $\triangle ACB \sim \triangle ECD$ by AA.

NOW TRY THIS 10-11

Congruency of corresponding angles is sufficient to prove that two triangles are similar. Is the same condition sufficient to prove other polygons are similar to each other? Explain your answer.

E X A M P L E
10-11

In Figure 10-48 solve for x.

FIGURE 10-48

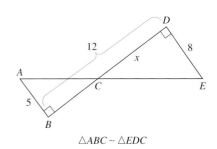

$\triangle ABC \sim \triangle EDC$

Solution $\triangle ABC \sim \triangle EDC$, so

$$\frac{AB}{ED} = \frac{AC}{EC} = \frac{BC}{DC}$$

Now, $AB = 5$, $ED = 8$, and $CD = x$, so $BC = 12 - x$. Thus

$$\frac{5}{8} = \frac{12 - x}{x}$$
$$5x = 8(12 - x)$$
$$5x = 96 - 8x$$
$$13x = 96$$
$$x = \frac{96}{13}$$

PROBLEM SOLVING   **Mysterious Triangles**

Rosa needed a wooden triangle that had one 18-in. side and angle measures of 36°, 84°, and 60°. Rosa had a carpenter make the triangle. Later, she needed another triangle with the same specifications. When the second triangle arrived, it was not congruent to the first one. Explain how this is possible.

Understanding the Problem   We are to explain how two triangles with one 18-in. side and angles of measures 36°, 84°, and 60° could be different sizes. To explain how this is possible, we try to construct two noncongruent triangles with Rosa's specifications.

Devising a Plan   First, we need to construct a triangle with the given side and angles. Then, because the second triangle has the same angles, it must be similar to the first by AAA. Consequently, we try to construct a triangle similar to the first but not congruent to it.

Carrying Out the Plan   In Figure 10-49, $\overline{AB}$ represents the 18-in. side. We then use a protractor to construct $\angle A$ measuring 60° and $\angle B$ measuring 36°. Hence, $m(\angle C) = 84°$ (why?). Next, we are to construct a noncongruent triangle similar to $\triangle ABC$ with one side as long as $\overline{AB}$. Because this may seem difficult, we consider *a simpler but related problem*. We drop the condition that the triangle must have a side of length AB and try to construct a triangle similar to $\triangle ABC$. This can be achieved by using one of the existing vertices of $\triangle ABC$ and drawing a side parallel to the opposite side. For example, in Figure 10-49 $\overline{C_1 B_1} \parallel \overline{CB}$ and $\triangle ACB \sim \triangle AC_1 B_1$ (why?). There are infinitely many such triangles $AC_1 B_1$. We imagine sliding $\overline{BC}$ along $\overrightarrow{AB}$ and $\overrightarrow{AC}$ so that $\overline{B_1 C_1} \parallel \overline{BC}$ and until $AC_1 = AB$. Consequently, $\triangle ACB$ and $\triangle AC_1 B_1$ are two noncongruent similar triangles such that $AC_1 = AB$ and therefore there are two noncongruent triangles with Rosa's specifications.

FIGURE 10-49

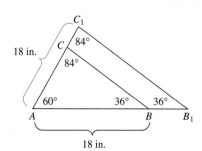

Looking Back If Rosa gave the measurements of two sides of the desired triangles and all the angles, could she then be sure to obtain a unique triangle? If she stated where the 18-in. side should be (for example, between the 36° and 60° angles), would that ensure her new triangle would be congruent to the old one?

Properties of Proportion

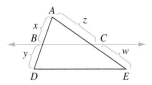

Similar triangles give rise to various properties that involve proportions. For example, in Figure 10-50 if $\overline{BC} \parallel \overline{DE}$, then $\dfrac{AB}{BD} = \dfrac{AC}{CE}$. This can be justified as follows: $\overline{BC} \parallel \overline{DE}$, so $\triangle ADE \sim \triangle ABC$ (why?). Consequently, $\dfrac{AD}{AB} = \dfrac{AE}{AC}$, which may be written as follows:

$$\frac{x+y}{x} = \frac{z+w}{z}$$

$$\frac{x}{x} + \frac{y}{x} = \frac{z}{z} + \frac{w}{z}$$

$$1 + \frac{y}{x} = 1 + \frac{w}{z}$$

$$\frac{y}{x} = \frac{w}{z}$$

$$\frac{x}{y} = \frac{z}{w}$$

This result is summarized in the following theorem.

> ## Theorem 10-4
>
> If a line parallel to one side of a triangle intersects the other sides, then it divides those sides into proportional segments.

The converse of Theorem 10-4 is also true; that is, if in Figure 10-50 we know that $\dfrac{AB}{BD} = \dfrac{AC}{CE}$, then we can conclude that $\overline{BC} \parallel DE$. We summarize this result in the following theorem.

> ## Theorem 10-5
>
> If a line divides two sides of a triangle into proportional segments, then the line is parallel to the third side.

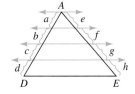

Similarly, if lines parallel to $\overline{DE}$ intersect $\triangle ADE$, as shown in Figure 10-51, so that $a = b = c = d$, it can be shown that $e = f = g = h$. This result is stated in the following theorem.

> ## Theorem 10-6

If parallel lines cut off congruent segments on one transversal, then they cut off congruent segments on any transversal.

NOW TRY THIS 10-12

In Figure 10-52, a graph shows similar triangles used to depict fuel economy standards for automobiles. Explain whether you believe the sides of the triangles are depicted in a way that misleads the reader.

FIGURE 10-52

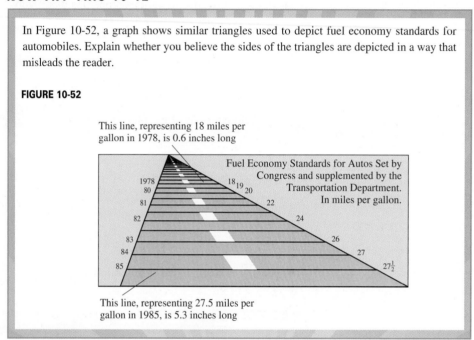

This line, representing 18 miles per gallon in 1978, is 0.6 inches long

Fuel Economy Standards for Autos Set by Congress and supplemented by the Transportation Department. In miles per gallon.

This line, representing 27.5 miles per gallon in 1985, is 5.3 inches long

Theorem 10-6 can be used to divide a given segment into any number of congruent parts. For example, using only a compass and a straightedge, we can divide segment $\overline{AB}$ in Figure 10-53 into three congruent parts by making the construction resemble Figure 10-51.

FIGURE 10-53 Separating a segment into congruent parts

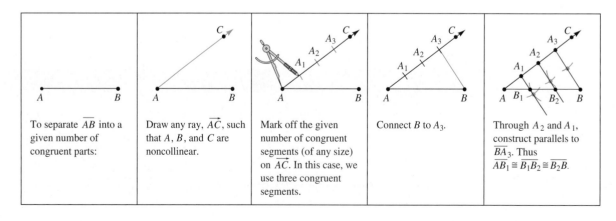

To separate $\overline{AB}$ into a given number of congruent parts:

Draw any ray, $\overrightarrow{AC}$, such that A, B, and C are noncollinear.

Mark off the given number of congruent segments (of any size) on $\overrightarrow{AC}$. In this case, we use three congruent segments.

Connect B to A_3.

Through A_2 and A_1, construct parallels to $\overline{BA_3}$. Thus $\overline{AB_1} \cong \overline{B_1B_2} \cong \overline{B_2B}$.

FIGURE 10-54

REMARK It is necessary to construct only $\overline{A_2B_2}$. We can then use a compass to mark off point B_1, such that $B_1B_2 = BB_2$, as in Figure 10-54.

Midsegments of Triangles and Quadrilaterals

The segment connecting the midpoints of two sides of a triangle or two adjacent sides of a quadrilateral is a **midsegment**. In Figure 10-55, M and N are midpoints of $\overline{AB}$ and $\overline{BC}$, respectively, and $\overline{MN}$ is a midsegment. Because $\dfrac{MB}{MA} = \dfrac{BN}{CN} = 1$ by Theorem 10-5, $\overline{MN} \parallel \overline{AC}$. How is MN related to AC? Notice that $\triangle MBN \sim \triangle ABC$ (why?). Therefore

$$\frac{MN}{AC} = \frac{MB}{AB} = \frac{MB}{2MB} = \frac{1}{2}.$$

midsegment

FIGURE 10-55

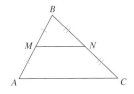

Consequently we have the following theorem.

> ### Theorem 10-7

The Midsegment Theorem The segment connecting the midpoints of two sides of a triangle is parallel to the third side and half as long.

Using Theorem 10-7 and Theorem 10-6, the following theorem follows (why?).

> ### Theorem 10-8

If a line bisects one side of a triangle and is parallel to a second side, then it bisects the third side and therefore is a midsegment.

E X A M P L E
10-12

In the quadrilateral $ABCD$ in Figure 10-56, M, N, P, and Q are the midpoints of the sides. What kind of quadrilateral is $MNPQ$?

FIGURE 10-56

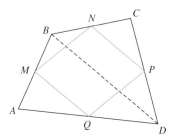

Solution Careful drawings of several quadrilaterals and the corresponding midpoints of their sides suggest that $MNPQ$ is a parallelogram. To prove this conjecture notice that NP is a midsegment in $\triangle BCD$ and consequently $\overline{NP} \parallel \overline{BD}$ and $NP = \frac{1}{2}BD$. Similarly in $\triangle ABD$, $\overline{MQ}$ is a midsegment and therefore $\overline{MQ} \parallel \overline{BD}$. Consequently $\overline{MQ} \parallel \overline{NP}$. In a similar way we could show that $\overline{MN} \parallel \overline{QP}$ (consider midsegments in $\triangle ABC$ and in $\triangle ADC$) and therefore by the definition of a parallelogram, $MNPQ$ is a parallelogram.

Indirect Measurements

Similar triangles have long been used to make indirect measurements. Thales of Miletus (ca. 600 B.C.) is believed to have determined the height of the Great Pyramid of Egypt by using ratios involving shadows, similar to those pictured in Figure 10-57. The sun is so far away that it should make approximately congruent angles at B and B'. Because the angles at C and C' are right angles, $\triangle ABC \sim \triangle A'B'C'$. Hence

$$\frac{AC}{A'C'} = \frac{BC}{B'C'}$$

FIGURE 10-57

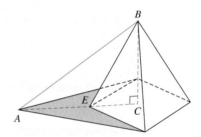

And because $AC = AE + EC$, the following proportion is obtained:

$$\frac{AE + EC}{A'C'} = \frac{BC}{B'C'}$$

The person's height and shadow can be measured. Also, the length AE of the shadow of the pyramid can be measured, and EC can be found because the base of the pyramid is a square. Each term of the proportion except the height of the pyramid is known. Thus the height BC of the pyramid can be found by solving the proportion.

EXAMPLE 10-13

On a sunny day, a tall tree casts a 40-m shadow. At the same time, a meter stick held vertically casts a 2.5-m shadow. How tall is the tree?

FIGURE 10-58

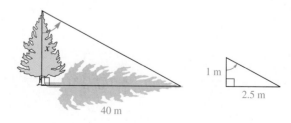

Solution In Figure 10-58 the triangles are similar by AA because the tree and the stick both meet the ground at right angles and the angles formed by the sun's rays are congruent (because the shadows are measured at the same time).

$$\frac{x}{40} = \frac{1}{2.5}$$
$$2.5x = 40$$
$$x = 16$$

The tree is 16 m tall.

BRAIN TEASER

Two neighbors, Smith and Wheeler, plan to erect flagpoles in their yards. Smith wants a 10-ft pole, and Wheeler wants a 15-ft pole. To keep the poles straight while the concrete bases harden, guy wires are to be tied from the tops of the flagpoles to a fence post on the property lines and to the bases of the flagpoles, as shown in Figure 10-59. How high should the fence post be and how far apart should they erect flagpoles for this scheme to work?

FIGURE 10-59

10 ft   15 ft

LABORATORY ACTIVITY

The device pictured in Figure 10-60 is a pantograph. It is used to draw enlarged versions of figures. Well-made adjustable pantographs are available from drafting or art supply stores, but you can make a crude one from wooden lath or other material.

In Figure 10-60 the red dots represent either brads or nuts and bolts. The strips are made of lath or cardboard and are rigid. A pointer at *D* is used to trace along an original figure, which causes the pencil at *F* to draw an enlarged version of the figure. Make or obtain a pantograph and experiment with enlarging figures. Explain how and why this works.

FIGURE 10-60

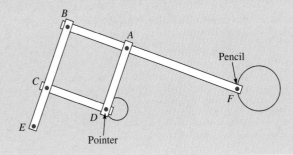

ONGOING ASSESSMENT 10-4

1. In the cartoon below, the human character's size is increased. If we assume that the human figures are similar and the person's height has increased from 5′10″ to 6′11″, what is the scale factor?

2. Which of the following are always similar? Why?
   a. Any two equilateral triangles
   b. Any two squares
   c. Any two rectangles
   d. Any two rhombuses
   e. Any two circles
   f. Any two regular polygons
   g. Any two regular polygons with the same number of sides

3. Use grid paper to draw figures that have sides three times as large as the ones in the following figure and that are colored similarly.

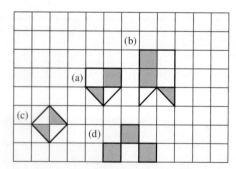

4. a. Construct a triangle with sides of lengths 4 cm, 6 cm, and 8 cm.
   b. Construct another triangle with sides of lengths 2 cm, 3 cm, and 4 cm.
   c. Make a conjecture about the similarity of triangles that have proportional sides only.

5. a. Construct a triangle with sides of lengths 4 cm and 6 cm and an included angle measuring 60°.
   b. Construct a triangle with sides of lengths 2 cm and 3 cm and an included angle measuring 60°.

   c. Make a conjecture about the similarity of triangles that have two sides proportional and congruent included angles.

6. a. Sketch two nonsimilar polygons for which corresponding angles are congruent.
   b. Sketch two nonsimilar polygons for which corresponding sides are proportional.

7. Examine several examples of similar polygons and make a conjecture concerning the ratio of their perimeters.

8. a. Which of the following pairs of triangles are similar? If they are similar, explain why.

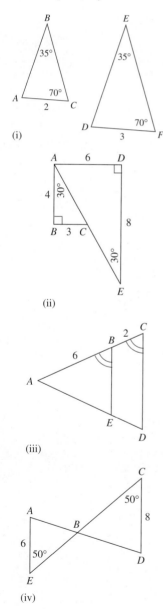

b. For each pair of similar triangles, find the scale factor of the sides of the triangles.

9. Assume that in the following figures the triangles in each part are similar and find the measures of the unknown sides.

(a)   △ABC ~ △ADE

(b)   △ABC ~ △EDF

(c)   △PQT ~ △PRS

(d)   △ABC ~ △FDC

10. Given the following figure, use a compass and a straight-edge to separate $\overline{AB}$ into five congruent pieces.

11. In the following right triangle ABC, $\overline{CD} \perp \overline{AB}$:

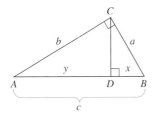

a. Find three pairs of similar triangles. Justify your answers.
b. Write the corresponding proportions for each set of similar triangles.
c. Use part (b) and the above figure to show that $a^2 = xc$. Also argue that $b^2 = yc$.
d. Use part (c) to show that $a^2 + b^2 = c^2$. State this result in words using legs and hypotenuse of a right triangle.

12. In the cartoon below, if a smaller map were obtained and its scale were half the size of the original scale, would the distance to be traveled be different? Why?

13. In the following figure, find the distance *AB* across the pond using the similar triangles shown:

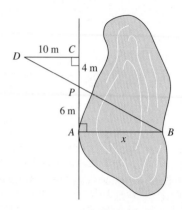

14. To find the height of a tree, a group of Girl Scouts devised the following method. A girl walks toward the tree along its shadow until the shadow of the top of her head coincides with the shadow of the top of the tree. If the girl is 150 cm tall, her distance to the foot of the tree is 15 m, and the length of her shadow is 3 m, how tall is the tree?

15. The angle bisector of one of the angles in an isosceles right triangle is constructed. This angle bisector partitions the original triangle into two isosceles triangles.
    a. What are the angle measures of the original triangle? (There are two possibilities.)
    b. Which, if any, triangles are congruent? similar? Explain your answers.

16. Samantha wants to know how far above the ground the top of a leaning flagpole is. At high noon, when the sun is directly overhead, the shadow cast by the pole is 7 ft long. Samantha holds a plumb bob with a string 3 ft long up to the flagpole and determines that the point of the plumb bob touches the ground 13 in. from the base of the flagpole. How far above the ground is the top of the pole?

17. a. In the accompanying figure, *ABCD* is a trapezoid. *M* is the midpoint of $\overline{AB}$. Through *M*, a line parallel to the bases has been drawn, intersecting $\overline{CD}$ at *N*. (i) Explain why *N* must be the midpoint of $\overline{CD}$ and (ii) express *MN* in terms of *a* and *b*, the lengths of the parallel sides of the trapezoid.

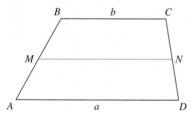

    b. Denote *MN* by *c*. Use your answer to part (a) to show that *b, c, a* form an arithmetic sequence.
    ★c. In the trapezoid *ABCD*, the lengths of the bases are *a* and *b* as shown. Side $\overline{AB}$ has been divided into 9 congruent segments. Through the endpoints of the segments, lines parallel to $\overline{AD}$ have been drawn. In this way, 8 new segments connecting the sides $\overline{AB}$ and $\overline{CD}$ have been created. Show that the sequence of 10 terms, starting with *b*, proceeding with the lengths of the parallel segments, and ending with *a*, is an arithmetic sequence and find the sum of the sequence in terms of *a* and *b*.

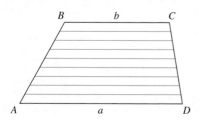

18. The midpoints *M, N, P, Q* of the sides of a quadrilateral *ABCD* have been connected and an interior quadrilateral is obtained. We have shown that *MNPQ* is a parallelogram. What is the most you can say about the kind of parallelogram *MNPQ* is if *ABCD* is
    a. a rhombus?
    b. a kite?
    c. an isosceles trapezoid?
    d. a quadrilateral that is neither a rhombus nor a kite but whose diagonals are perpendicular to each other?

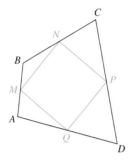

19. Explain why all pairs of regular octagons are similar.
20. If the ratio of corresponding sides of two similar triangles is 1/*k*, what is the ratio of their perimeters? Why?
21. If you took cross-sections of a typical ice cream cone parallel to the circular opening where the ice cream is usually placed, explain whether the cross-sections would be similar.
22. Must all cross-sections of a circular cylinder be similar? Why? Draw a sketch to illustrate your answer.
★23. A carpenter needs to string a wire between two boards $\overline{AB}$ and $\overline{BC}$ so that the colored wire is pictured as shown. How much wire is needed?

Communication

24. Do you think any two cubes are similar? Why or why not?
25. Architects frequently use scale drawings to construct models of projects. Are the models similar to the finished products? Why or why not?
26. Assuming the lines on an ordinary piece of notebook paper are parallel and equidistant, describe a method for using the paper to divide a piece of licorice evenly among 2, 3, 4, or 5 children. Explain why it works.

Open-Ended

27. Build two similar towers out of blocks.
    a. What is the ratio of the heights of the towers?
    b. What is the ratio of the perimeters of the bases of the towers?

Cooperative Learning

28. A building was to be built on a triangular piece of property. The architect was given the approximate measurements of the angles of the triangular lot as 54°, 39°, and 87° and the lengths of two of the sides as 100 m and 80 m. When the architect began the design on drafting paper, she drew a triangle to scale with the corresponding measures and found that the lot was considerably smaller than she had been led to believe. It appeared that the proposed building would not fit. The surveyor was called. He confirmed each of the measurements and could not see a problem with the size. Neither the architect nor surveyor could understand the reason for the other's opinion.
    a. Have one person in your group play the part of the architect and explain why she felt she was correct.
    b. Have one person in the group explain the reason for the miscommunication.
    c. Have the group suggest a way to provide an accurate description of the lot.

Review Problems

29. If a person holds a mirror at arm's length and looks into it, is the image seen congruent to the original? Why or why not?
30. Given the following base of an isosceles triangle and the altitude to that base, construct the triangle:

    _____

    Base

    _____

    Altitude

31. Given the following length of a side of the triangle, construct an altitude of an equilateral triangle.

    _____

32. Write a paragraph describing how you could construct an isosceles right triangle when given the length of the hypotenuse of the 45°-45°-90° triangle.
33. Use a compass and a straightedge to draw a pair of obtuse vertical angles and the angle bisector of one of these angles. Extend the angle bisector. Does the extended angle bisector bisect the other vertical angle? Justify your answer.
34. Describe a minimal set of conditions that can be used to argue that two quadrilaterals are congruent.

<u>TECHNOLOGY</u>
C O R N E R

Work through GSP Lab 6 in Appendix III.

<u>TECHNOLOGY</u>
C O R N E R

In 1975 Benoit Mandelbrot invented the word *fractal* to describe certain irregular and fragmented shapes. These shapes are such that if one looks at a small part of the shape, the small part resembles the larger shape. These shapes are somewhat like rep-tiles, although the smaller structures of fractals are not necessarily identical to the larger structure. (Recall that with rep-tiles, the smaller structures are similar and are identical in all aspects except size.) Fractal geometry was introduced for the purpose of modeling natural phenomena such as irregular coastlines, arteries and veins, the branching structure of plants, the thermal agitation of molecules in a fluid, and sponges. Figure 10-61 shows an example of a fractal—a computer-generated picture of the Mandelbrot set known as the "Tail of the Seahorse."

FIGURE 10-61

Earlier, in 1906, Helge von Koch came up with a curve that has infinite perimeter. To visualize this curve, we construct in Figure 10-62 a sequence of polygons $S_1, S_2, S_3, \ldots$ as follows:

a. S_1 is an equilateral triangle.
b. S_2 is obtained from S_1 by dividing each side of the triangle into 3 congruent parts and constructing on the middle part an equilateral triangle with the base removed.
c. S_3 is obtained from S_2 like S_2 was obtained from S_1.

We continue in a similar way to obtain the other polygons of the sequence in Figure 10-62(d) and (e). These polygons come closer and closer to a curve, called the *snowflake curve*, which is another example of a fractal. Use The Geometer's Sketchpad to construct Figure 10-62(a)–(c).

If S_1 has perimeter 3 units, what is the perimeter of S_2 and S_3? What do you think happens to the perimeter of the snowflakes as the number of sides of the polygons increases?

FIGURE 10-62

Note: GSP's Iterate command, in the Transform menu, is useful for constructing fractals.

BRAIN
T E A S E R

A particular kaleidoscope is a right prism with an equilateral triangle as a base. A beam of light is reflected at a 60° angle from a point *P* on a die of the triangular base, as shown in Figure 10-63. The beam is reflected in the plane of the base to the different mirrored surfaces and continues bouncing off at 60° angles. Find the length of the path of the reflected light when it reaches the point at which it originated.

FIGURE 10-63

*Trigonometry Ratios via Similarity

FIGURE 10-64

trigonometry

Measurements of buildings, structures, and some other objects are frequently required in many occupations. For example, in a tourist brochure advertising California, one region boasts a sequoia tree of great height, such as the one picture in Figure 10-64.

From the previous section, we know how to find the height of the tree by using shadows and similar triangles. Trigonometry might also be used to find the required height of the tree.

Trigonometry developed from a need to compute distances and angle measures, especially in map making, surveying, and range finding for artillery use. Today, trigonometry is an indispensable tool in many applied problems in both science and technology. The word **trigonometry** is derived from the Greek words *trigonom*, which means triangle, and *metron*, which means measurement. In this section, we study the basics of right triangle trigonometry, which has applications to measuring distances and angles.

The definition of trigonometric functions in a right triangle is based on properties of similar triangles. Earlier in this chapter, we saw that corresponding sides of similar triangles are proportional. Consequently, in two similar triangles the ratio of one side to another in one triangle will be the same as the ratio of the corresponding sides in the second triangle. Consider the two similar triangles in Figure 10-65. Both are right triangles, and each has an angle with measure 30°.

FIGURE 10-65

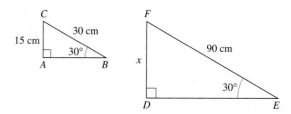

We could find x using the following proportion:

$$\frac{x}{90} = \frac{15}{30},$$

which implies that $x = 45$ cm. If we use this property, it follows that in any right triangle the ratio between the side opposite the angle with measure 30° and the side opposite the right angle, the **hypotenuse**, will be the same as that ratio in the smaller triangle in Figure 10-65, that is, $\frac{15}{30}$, or $\frac{1}{2}$.

hypotenuse

Suppose we use a protractor to construct a right triangle with an angle measuring 37° and measure both the hypotenuse and the side opposite this angle, as shown in Figure 10-66. The ratio between the side opposite the angle with measure 37° and the hypotenuse is $\frac{60}{100}$, or 0.6. Since measurements are approximate, the ratio also is only an approximation. This ratio is the "sine of 37°," or the sin 37. Thus, in a right triangle having an angle with measure 37°,

$$\sin 37 = \frac{\text{length of side opposite the } 37° \text{ angle}}{\text{length of hypotenuse}}.$$

FIGURE 10-66

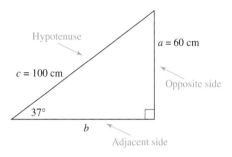

cosine (cos) ◆ **tangent (tan)**   Other ratios such as the **cosine (cos)** and **tangent (tan)** between lengths of sides in a right triangle are also useful and are defined in reference to Figure 10-67 as follows:

FIGURE 10-67

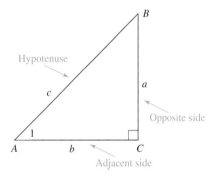

$$\sin(\angle 1) = \frac{a}{c} = \frac{\text{length of opposite side}}{\text{length of hypotenuse}}$$

$$\cos(\angle 1) = \frac{b}{c} = \frac{\text{length of adjacent side}}{\text{length of hypotenuse}}$$

$$\tan(\angle 1) = \frac{a}{b} = \frac{\text{length of opposite side}}{\text{length of adjacent side}}$$

REMARK   Technically, we should write $\sin(m\angle 1)$, but this is typically short-handed to $\sin(\angle 1)$.

Using The Geometer's Sketchpad, draw a right triangle *ABC* with right angle at *C*. Measure each side of the triangle and find the measures of ∠*ABC* and ∠*BAC*. Use The Geometer's Sketchpad to find measures, calculate ratios, and build a table with headings similar to Table 10-2.

Table 10-2

Angle	Angle Meas.	Opp. Side Meas.	Adj. Side Meas.	Hyp. Meas.	Opp. Hypot.	Sine of Angle	Adj. Hypot.	Cosine of Angle	Opp. Adj.	Tangent of Angle
∠*ABC*										
∠*BAC*										

1. What is true about the ratios you found using measurements and the sines, cosines, and tangents found automatically?
2. Explain whether you think it is necessary to find the measures of the sides of a triangle to determine the sine, cosine, and tangent ratios.

Students in upper middle grades use trigonometric ratios to find measures, as seen on the partial student page. Do problem 10(a).

Using Trigonometry Tables

In the seventeenth century, John Napier devised trigonometric tables to 14 decimal places. Today, with the help of a computer, we can find the values of the trigonometric functions to any desired degree of accuracy. Table 10-3 gives rounded trigonometric values for some angle measures.

Table 10-3

Degrees	sin	cos	tan
5	0.0872	0.9962	0.0875
10	0.1736	0.9848	0.1763
15	0.2588	0.9659	0.2679
20	0.3420	0.9397	0.3640
25	0.4226	0.9036	0.4663
30	0.5000	0.8660	0.5774
35	0.5736	0.8192	0.7002
40	0.6428	0.7660	0.8391
45	0.7071	0.7071	1.0000

Sample School Book Page:
THE TANGENT RATIO

GOAL

LEARN HOW TO...
♦ use the tangent ratio to find unknown side lengths in right triangles

AS YOU...
♦ investigate heights of objects

KEY TERM
♦ tangent

Exploration 2

The **Tangent Ratio**

SET UP *Work in a group. You will need:* ◦ *protractor* ◦ *metric ruler* ◦ *scissors* ◦ *calculator*

▶ How can an astrolabe be used to find the heights of objects? In this exploration, you'll study a ratio that will help you answer this question.

10 Adriana uses an astrolabe to sight the top of her school. She finds that the angle of elevation (∠A in the diagram) measures 40°.

a. If Adriana knows only that $m\angle A = 40°$, can she find the height of her school? Explain your thinking.

Source: Math Thematics, Book 3 McDougal Littell, 2002 (p. 360).

FIGURE 10-68

Find the height of the sequoia tree pictured in Figure 10-68.

Solution To find the height of the tree, we use the following trigonometric ratio and Table 10-3:

$$\tan 40 = \frac{h}{190}$$
$$190(\tan 40) = h$$
$$190(0.8391) \doteq h$$
$$159.4 \doteq h$$

Thus the height of the tree is approximately 159.4 ft.

Using Trigonometric Ratios on a Calculator

Tables of trigonometric ratios were essential in all parts of the world until calculators became readily available. Trigonometry in right triangles as we use it today is primarily done using a scientific calculator, graphing calculator, or computer. For example, in a given right triangle with an acute angle of 40°, we can use the $\boxed{\text{SIN}}$, $\boxed{\text{COS}}$, and $\boxed{\text{TAN}}$ buttons to find the respective values of 0.643, 0.766, and 0.839 assigned to a 40° angle.

Each of the trigonometry buttons is a function button that requires an angle measure input either in degrees or radians. Because we use degrees in this text, make sure your calculator is set to use degrees and not radians. One method for telling whether your calculator is in the degree mode is to press $\boxed{\text{SIN}}\boxed{3}\boxed{0}$ to find the sine of 30°. If your answer is 0.5, or .5, then the calculator is in the proper mode. If not, consult a manual to see what you must do to put your calculator in degree mode.

REMARK Check your calculator to determine if you should use $\boxed{\text{SIN}}\boxed{3}\boxed{0}\boxed{)}$ or $\boxed{3}\boxed{0}\boxed{\text{SIN}}$ or $\boxed{\text{SIN}}\boxed{3}\boxed{0}$.

Use a calculator to solve for *x* in Figure 10-69:

FIGURE 10-69

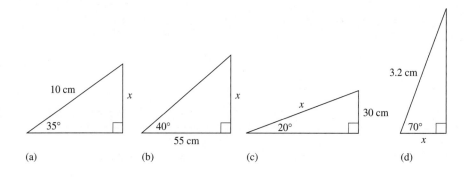

(a) (b) (c) (d)

Solution   **a.** $\dfrac{x}{10} = \sin 35$

$x = 10 \sin 35$

To find the answer on your calculator you may have to press the following keys:

$$\boxed{1}\,\boxed{0}\,\boxed{\times}\,\boxed{\text{SIN}}\,\boxed{3}\,\boxed{5}\,\boxed{)}$$

The resulting display is 5.7357644, or approximately 5.7 cm.

b. $\dfrac{x}{55} = \tan 40$

$x = 55 \tan 40$

$x \doteq 46.1505$, or approximately 46.2, cm

c. $\dfrac{30}{x} = \sin 20$

$x = \dfrac{30}{\sin 20}$

$x \doteq 87.714$, or approximately 87.7, cm

d. $\dfrac{x}{3.2} = \cos 70$

$x = 3.2 \cos 70$

$x \doteq 1.094$, or approximately 1.1, cm

NOW TRY THIS 10-13

In Example 10-15, use Figure 10-69(a) to find x using the cosine function instead of the sine function.

Sometimes the lengths of the sides of a right triangle are given and we need to find the measures of the angles of the triangle. If, for example, a triangle has sides measuring 3 m, 4 m, and 5 m, as shown in Figure 10-70, we can find the measure of angle A by first finding the sin ($\angle A$). We have $\sin(\angle A) = 4/5$. The $\boxed{\text{SIN}^{-1}}$ key on your calculator (or possibly the $\boxed{\text{INV}}$ key used with the $\boxed{\text{SIN}}$ key) can be used to find the measure of the angle as follows:

$$\boxed{\text{SIN}^{-1}}\,\boxed{4}\,\boxed{\div}\,\boxed{5}\,\boxed{)}\,\boxed{=}$$

FIGURE 10-70

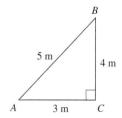

Thus, the angle has measure approximately 53.1°.

EXAMPLE
10-16

If x is an angle measure, solve for x in each part of Figure 10-71:

FIGURE 10-71

(a)   (b)   (c)

Solution   **a.** $\cos x = \dfrac{55}{72}$

$x \doteq 40.191756$, or about $40.2°$

b. $\sin x = \dfrac{41}{63}$

$x \doteq 40.601466$, or approximately $40.6°$

c. $\tan x = \dfrac{3}{4}$

$x \doteq 36.869898$, or approximately $36.9°$

Finding Measurements Using Trigonometric Ratios

Just as the angle of elevation was used to find the height of the sequoia tree, we can use an *angle of depression* to find measures, as demonstrated in Example 10-17.

EXAMPLE
10-17

From the top of Mount Sentinel, the measure of the angle of depression of the Administration Building is 18°, as illustrated in Figure 10-72. If the top of Mount Sentinel is 1575 ft, how far through the air is the top of the mountain from the base of the building?

FIGURE 10-72

Solution   In Figure 10-72, the measure of the angle of elevation must equal the measure of the angle of depression (why?). Using trigonometric ratios, we have the following:

$$\sin 18° = \frac{1575}{d}$$

$$d = \frac{1575}{\sin 18°}, \text{ or approximately 5097 ft}$$

Thus the air distance is approximately 5097 ft.

EXAMPLE 10-18

To measure the height of a flagpole on top of a building, a surveyor measures the distance to the building and the two angles from point *B*, as shown in Figure 10-73. Find the height of the flagpole.

FIGURE 10-73

Solution   We need to find *CD* in Figure 10-73. Because *CD* is not a length of a side of a right triangle, but *y* and *x* whose difference is *CD* are, we must find *x* and *y* first. The solution then is $CD = y - x$. In triangle *BDA*, we have the following:

$$\tan 33 = \frac{x}{12}$$

$$x = 12 \tan 33$$

In triangle *BCA*, we have the following:

$$\tan(14 + 33) = \frac{y}{12}$$

$$y = 12 \tan(14 + 33)$$

Therefore $CD = 12 \tan(14 + 33) - 12 \tan 33$. Using the calculator we find 5.075 on the display. Thus the height of the pole atop the building is about 5.1 m.

NOW TRY THIS 10-14

Find the relationships among the $\sin(\angle A)$, $\cos(\angle A)$, and $\tan(\angle A)$.

ONGOING ASSESSMENT 10-5

1. For each of the following figures, solve for *x* and express each *x* length to the nearest hundredth:

  (a)   (b)   (c)   (d)

2. The angle of elevation of a 15-ft ladder is 70°. Find out how far the base is from the wall.

3. A diagonal is drawn in a 12-in. square floor tile. Find the sine, cosine, and tangent of the angle formed by the diagonal and a side.

4. Determine the height of a tree if it casts a shadow 7 m long on level ground when the angle of elevation of the sun is 50°.

5. Vectors are used in science to depict forces with both magnitudes and directions. If a force of 14 lb is directed at an angle measuring 38° from the horizontal, as depicted in the following figure, determine the vertical and horizontal components as pictured:

6. To find the length of a lake, a person set stakes at point *A* and made the following measurements:

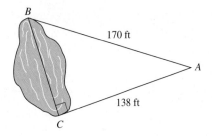

   a. What is the measure of angle *BAC*? (*Hint:* Use estimation skills and your calculator to find out.)
   b. What is the length of the lake?
7. How many feet of cable will it take to anchor a guy wire to a 30-ft vertical pole if the angle of elevation is 28°?
8. As a plane takes off, it flies 1500 ft along a straight path and rises at an angle measuring 22°.
   a. What is the vertical rise when it has flown 1500 ft?
   b. After it has flown 1500 ft, how far has it moved horizontally?
9. A gutter cleaner wants to reach a gutter 40 ft above the ground. Find the length of the shortest ladder that can be used if the steepest angle at which it can be leaned against the house has measure 75°.
10. A jet plane cruising at 450 mph climbs at an angle measuring 13°. Determine how much altitude the jet gains in 5 min.

11. **a.** Complete the following chart.

1	2	3	4	5	6
Angle Measure	Sine	Cosine	Square of Sine	Square of Cosine	Sum of Columns 4 and 5
10°					
20°					
30°					
40°					
50°					
60°					
70°					
80°					

   b. Make a conjecture about the sum of the squares of the sines and cosines of various angles.
12. Find the height of a tree whose horizontal shadow is 120 ft when the angle of elevation of the sun from the tip of the shadow measures 68°.
13. A highway that has a 6% grade rises 6 ft vertically for every 100 ft horizontally. Which trigonometric ratio is being used in reporting the 6% grade? Explain why.
14. The slope of a line in coordinate geometry is described as the rise divided by the run. Which trigonometric ratio does the slope represent? Explain your answer.
15. In navigational terms, a bearing is defined as the number of degrees a direction is from due north. If a plane flying 120 mph has flown 1 hr at a bearing of 32°, how far has it flown in a horizontal direction? In a vertical direction?
16. Find *x* in each of the following:

(a)　　　　　(b)　　　　　(c)

Lines in a Cartesian Coordinate System

The Cartesian coordinate system (named for René Descartes) enables us to study geometry using algebra and to interpret algebraic phenomena geometrically. A Cartesian coordinate system is constructed by placing two number lines perpendicular to each other, as shown in Figure 10-74. The intersection point of the two lines is the **origin**, the horizontal line is the ***x*-axis**, and the vertical line is the ***y*-axis**. The location of any point *P* can be described by an ordered pair of numbers.

origin

***x*-axis** ◆ ***y*-axis**

FIGURE 10-74

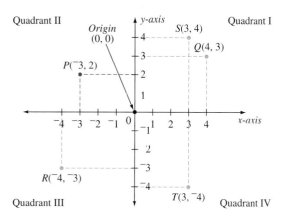

If a perpendicular from *P* to the *x*-axis intersects at a point with coordinate *a* and a perpendicular from *P* to the *y*-axis intersects at a point with coordinate *b*, point *P* has coordinates (*a*, *b*). The first component in the ordered pair (*a*, *b*) is the **abscissa**, or **x-coordinate**, of *P*. The second component is the **ordinate**, or **y-coordinate**, of *P*. To each point in the plane, there corresponds an ordered pair (*a*, *b*) and vice versa. Hence, there is a one-to-one correspondence between all the points in the plane and all the ordered pairs of real numbers.

abscissa ◆ x-coordinate
ordinate ◆ y-coordinate

For example, in Figure 10-74 the *x*-coordinate of *P* is $^-3$ and the *y*-coordinate of *P* is 2, so *P* has coordinate ($^-3$, 2). Similarly, *R* has coordinates ($^-4$, $^-3$), written *R*($^-4$, $^-3$).

Equations of Vertical and Horizontal Lines

Every point on the *x*-axis has a *y*-coordinate of zero. Thus the *x*-axis can be described as the set of all points (*x*, *y*) such that $y = 0$. This set of points on the *x*-axis has equation $y = 0$. Similarly, the *y*-axis can be described as the set of all points (*x*, *y*) such that $x = 0$ and *y* is an arbitrary real number. Thus $x = 0$ is the equation of the *y*-axis. If we plot the set of all points that satisfy a given condition, the resulting picture on the Cartesian coordinate system is the **graph** of the set.

graph

EXAMPLE
10-19

Sketch the graph for each of the following:

a. $x = 2$ **b.** $y = 3$ **c.** $x = 2$ and $y = 3$

Solution   **a.** The equation $x = 2$ represents the set of all points (*x*, *y*) for which $x = 2$ and *y* is any real number. This set is the line perpendicular to the *x*-axis at (2, 0), as in Figure 10-75(a).

FIGURE 10-75

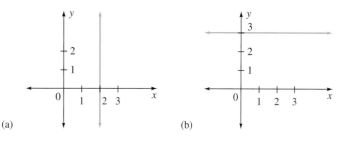

(a)   (b)

b. The equation $y = 3$ represents the set of all points (x, y) for which $y = 3$ and x is any real number. This set is the line perpendicular to the y-axis at $(0, 3)$, as in Figure 10-75(b).

c. The statements in part (c) represents the set of all points (x, y) for which $x < 2$, but y is always 3. The set describes part of a line, as shown in Figure 10-76. Note that the hollow dot at $(2, 3)$ indicates that this point is not included in the solution.

FIGURE 10-76

FIGURE 10-77

In Example 10-19 we found the graphs of the equations $x = 2$ and $y = 3$. In general, the graph of the equation $x = a$, where a is some real number, is a line perpendicular to the x-axis through the point with coordinates $(a, 0)$, as shown in Figure 10-77. Similarly, the graph of the equation $y = b$ is a line perpendicular to the y-axis through the point with coordinates $(0, b)$.

Equations of Lines

Consider the arithmetic sequence 4, 7, 10, 13, . . . in Table 10-4 whose xth term is $3x + 1$. If the number of the term is the x-coordinate and the corresponding term the y-coordinate, the set of points appear to lie on a line that is parallel to neither the x-axis nor the y-axis, as in Figure 10-78.

Table 10-4

Number of Term	Term
1	4
2	7
3	10
4	13
.	.
.	.
.	.
x	$3x + 1$

FIGURE 10-78

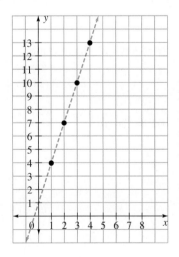

Do all points corresponding to arithmetic sequences lie along lines? To help answer this question, we consider the following sequences in Table 10-5.

Table 10-5

Number of Term x	$1 \cdot x$	$2 \cdot x$	$\frac{1}{2} \cdot x$	$(^-1) \cdot x$	$(^-2) \cdot x$
1	1	2	$\frac{1}{2}$	$^-1$	$^-2$
2	2	4	1	$^-2$	$^-4$
3	3	6	$\frac{3}{2}$	$^-3$	$^-6$
4	4	8	2	$^-4$	$^-8$
5	5	10	$\frac{5}{2}$	$^-5$	$^-10$
6	6	12	3	$^-6$	$^-12$
$\cdot$	$\cdot$	$\cdot$	$\cdot$		
$\cdot$	$\cdot$	$\cdot$	$\cdot$		
$\cdot$	$\cdot$	$\cdot$	$\cdot$		
x	x	$2x$	$\frac{1}{2}x$	^-x	^-2x

In Figure 10-79, the sets of ordered pairs (x, y) are plotted on a graph so that the number of the term is the x-coordinate and the corresponding term appearing in a particular column in Table 10-5, the y-coordinate. The sets of points appear to determine straight lines.

FIGURE 10-79

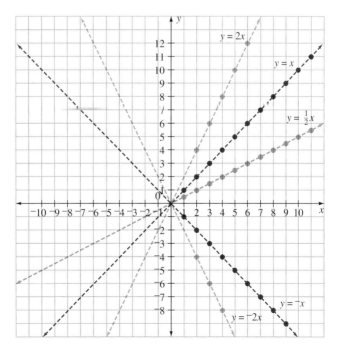

All five lines in Figure 10-79 have equations of the form $y = mx$, where m takes the values $2, 1, \frac{1}{2}, {}^-1,$ and ${}^-2$. If all points along a given dashed line are connected, then all the points on that line satisfy the corresponding equation. The number m is a measure of **slope** steepness and is called the **slope** of the line whose equation is $y = mx$. The graph goes up from left to right (increases) if m is positive, and it goes down from left to right (decreases) if m is negative.

NOW TRY THIS 10-15

a. In the equation $y = mx$, if m is 0, what happens to the line?
b. What happens as m continues to increase?
c. What happens when m continues to decrease?

All lines in Figure 10-79 pass through the origin. This is true for any line whose equation is $y = mx$. If $x = 0$, then $y = m \cdot 0 = 0$ and $(0, 0)$ is a point on the graph of $y = mx$. Conversely, it is possible to show that any nonvertical line passing through the origin has an equation of the form $y = mx$ for some value of m.

EXAMPLE 10-20

Find the equation of the line that contains $(0, 0)$ and $(2, 3)$.

Solution The line goes through the origin; therefore its equation has the form $y = mx$. To find the equation of the line, we must find the value of m. The line contains $(2, 3)$, so we substitute 2 for x and 3 for y in the equation $y = mx$ to obtain $3 = m \cdot 2$, and thus $m = \frac{3}{2}$. Hence, the required equation is $y = \frac{3}{2}x$.

Next, we consider equations of the form $y = mx + b$, where b is a real number. To do this, we examine the graphs of $y = x + 2$ and $y = x$. Given the graph of $y = x$, we can obtain the graph of $y = x + 2$ by "raising" each point on the first graph by 2 units. This is because for a certain value of x, the corresponding y value is 2 units greater. This is shown in Figure 10-80(a). Similarly, to sketch the graph of $y = x - 2$, we first draw the graph of $y = x$ and then lower each point vertically by 2 units, as shown in Figure 10-80(b).

The graphs of $y = x + 2$ and $y = x - 2$ are straight lines. Moreover, the lines whose equations are $y = x, y = x + 2,$ and $y = x - 2$ are parallel. In general, *for a given value of m, the graph of $y = mx + b$ is a straight line through $(0, b)$ and parallel to the line whose equation is $y = mx$.*

Further, the graph of the line $y = mx + b$, where $b > 0$, can be obtained from the graph of $y = mx$ by sliding $y = mx$ up b units, as shown in Figure 10-80. If $b < 0$, $y = mx$ must be slid down $|b|$ units. In general, *any two parallel lines have the same slope, or are vertical lines with no slope.*

FIGURE 10-80

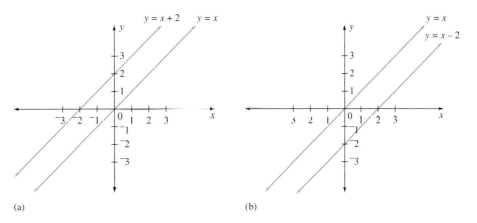

(a)   (b)

The graph of $y = mx + b$ in Figure 10-81 crosses the y-axis at point $P(0, b)$. The value of y at the point of intersection of any line with the y-axis is the **y-intercept**. Thus b is the y-intercept of $y = mx + b$, and this form of the equation of a straight line is the **slope-intercept form**. Similarly, the value of x at the point of intersection of a line with the x-axis is the **x-intercept**.

y-intercept

slope-intercept form
x-intercept

FIGURE 10-81

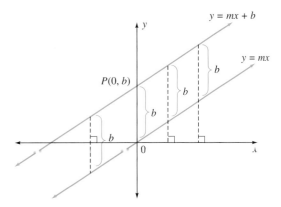

EXAMPLE
10-21

Given the equation $y - 3x = {}^-6$, do the following:

a. Find the slope of the line.
b. Find the y-intercept.
c. Find the x-intercept.
d. Sketch the graph of the equation.

Solution   **a.** To write the equation in the form $y = mx + b$, we add $3x$ to both sides of the given equation to obtain $y = 3x + ({}^-6)$. Hence, the slope is 3.

b. The form $y = 3x + (^-6)$ shows that $b = {}^-6$, which is the y-intercept. (The y-intercept can also be found directly by substituting $x = 0$ in the equation and finding the corresponding value of y.)

c. The x-intercept is the x-coordinate of the point where the graph intersects the x-axis. At that point, $y = 0$. Substituting 0 for y in $y = 3x - 6$ gives 2 as the x-intercept.

d. The y-intercept and the x-intercept are located at $(0, {}^-6)$ and $(2, 0)$, respectively, on the line. We plot these points and draw the line through them to obtain the desired graph in Figure 10-82.

FIGURE 10-82

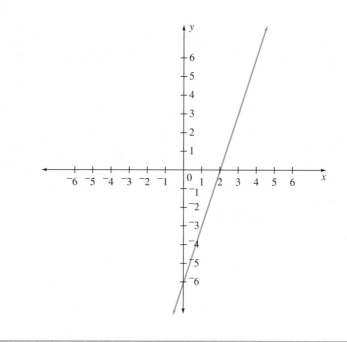

The equation $y = b$ can be written in slope-intercept form as $y = 0 \cdot x + b$. Consequently, its slope is 0 and its y-intercept is b. Because the line is parallel to the x-axis, its steepness, or slope, should be 0. Any vertical line has equation $x = a$ for some real number a. This equation cannot be written in slope-intercept form. In general, *every straight line has an equation of the form either* $y = mx + b$ *or* $x = a$. Any equation that can be put in one of these forms is a **linear equation**.

linear equation

Equation of a Line

Every line has an equation of the form either $y = mx + b$ or $x = a$, where m is the slope and b is the y-intercept.

Using Similar Triangles to Determine Slope

We have defined the slope of a line with equation $y = mx + b$ to be m. The slope is a measure of steepness of a line. A different way to discuss the steepness of a line is to consider how much the line "rises" in relation to how much it "runs." In Figure 10-83, line k is steeper than line ℓ. In other words, line k rises higher than line ℓ for the same horizontal run.

FIGURE 10-83

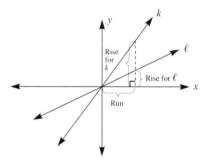

We express the steepness, or slope, as the ratio $\dfrac{\text{rise}}{\text{run}}$. In Figure 10-84, right triangles have been constructed and shaded on several lines. In each triangle, the horizontal side is the run and the vertical side is the rise.

FIGURE 10-84

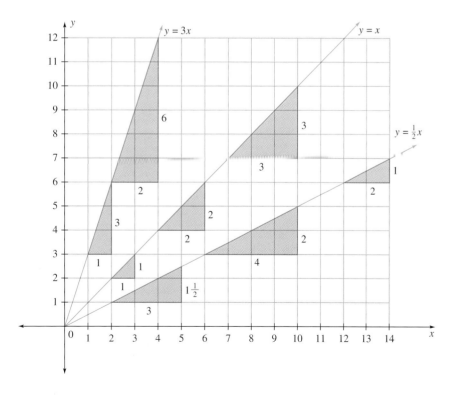

The slope of each line in Figure 10-84 can be calculated as the rise over the run in any of the shaded triangles, with hypotenuse (the side opposite the right angle) along the given line. To test this fact, notice that

$$\text{for } y = \frac{1}{2}x, \quad m = \frac{\text{rise}}{\text{run}} = \frac{1\frac{1}{2}}{3} = \frac{2}{4} = \frac{1}{2}$$

$$\text{for } y = x, \quad m = \frac{\text{rise}}{\text{run}} = \frac{1}{1} = \frac{2}{2} = \frac{3}{3}$$

$$\text{for } y = 3x, \quad m = \frac{3}{1} = \frac{6}{2}.$$

Figure 10-85 illustrates the situation generally when a line is inclined upward from the left to the right.

FIGURE 10-85

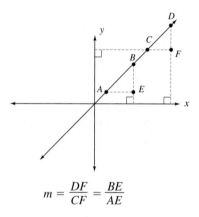

$$m = \frac{DF}{CF} = \frac{BE}{AE}$$

Using the previous notion, we find that the slope of a line $\overleftrightarrow{AB}$ is the change in y-coordinates divided by the corresponding change in x-coordinates of any two points on $\overleftrightarrow{AB}$. The difference $x_2 - x_1$ is the *run*, and the difference $y_2 - y_1$ is the *rise*. Thus the slope is often defined as "rise over run," or $\frac{\text{rise}}{\text{run}}$. The slope formula can be interpreted with coordinates, as shown in Figure 10-86. The ratio $\frac{y_2 - y_1}{x_2 - x_1}$ is always the same, regardless of which two points on a given nonvertical line are chosen.

FIGURE 10-86

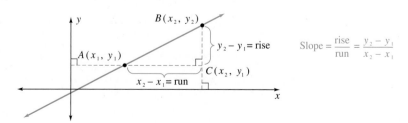

The discussion of slope is summarized in the following formula.

Slope Formula

Given two points $A(x_1, y_1)$ and $B(x_2, y_2)$ with $x_1 \neq x_2$, the slope m of the line $\overleftrightarrow{AB}$ is

$$m = \frac{y_2 - y_1}{x_2 - x_1} = \frac{\text{rise}}{\text{run}}.$$

REMARK By multiplying both the numerator and the denominator on the right side of the slope formula by $^-1$, we obtain

$$m = \frac{y_2 - y_1}{x_2 - x_1} = \frac{(y_2 - y_1)(^-1)}{(x_2 - x_1)(^-1)} = \frac{y_1 - y_2}{x_1 - x_2}.$$

This shows that while it does not matter which point is named (x_1, y_1) and which is named (x_2, y_2), *the order of the coordinates in the subtraction must be the same.*

NOW TRY THIS 10-16

a. Use the slope formula to find the slope of any horizontal line.
b. What happens when we attempt to use the slope formula for a vertical line? What is your conclusion about the slope of a vertical line?

When a line is inclined downward from the left to the right, the slope is negative. This is illustrated in Figure 10-87, where the graph of the line $y = {}^-2x$ is shown. The slope of line $y = {}^-2x$ can be calculated as $\dfrac{\text{rise}}{\text{run}} = \dfrac{{}^-4}{2} = \dfrac{{}^-2}{1}$.

FIGURE 10-87

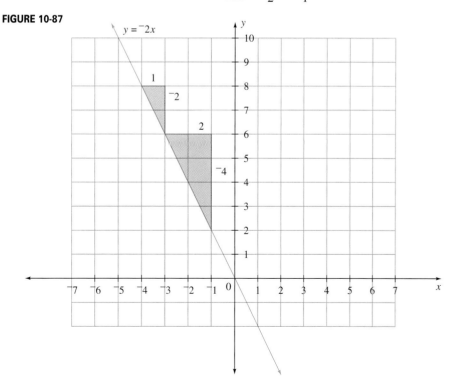

EXAMPLE
10-22

a. Given $A(3, 1)$ and $B(5, 4)$, find the slope of $\overleftrightarrow{AB}$.

b. Find the slope of the line passing through the points $A(^-3, 4)$ and $B(^-1, 0)$.

Solution   **a.** $m = \dfrac{4 - 1}{5 - 3} = \dfrac{3}{2}$,   or $\dfrac{1 - 4}{3 - 5} = \dfrac{^-3}{^-2} = \dfrac{3}{2}$

b. $m = \dfrac{4 - 0}{^-3 - (^-1)} = \dfrac{4}{^-2} = ^-2$,   or $\dfrac{0 - 4}{^-1 - (^-3)} = \dfrac{^-4}{2} = ^-2$

Given two points on a nonvertical line, we can use the slope formula to find the slope of the line and its equation. This is demonstrated in the following example.

EXAMPLE
10-23

In Figure 10-88, the points $(^-4, 0)$ and $(1, 4)$ are on the line ℓ. Find:

a. the slope of the line
b. the equation of the line

FIGURE 10-88

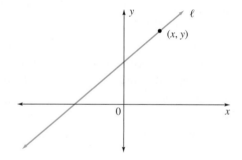

Solution   **a.** $m = \dfrac{4 - 0}{1 - (^-4)} = \dfrac{4}{5}$.

b. Point (x, y) represents any point on the line different from $(^-4, 0)$ if and only if the slope determined by points $(^-4, 0)$ and (x, y) is $\dfrac{4}{5}$, the slope of the line we found in part (a). Thus,

$$\frac{y - 0}{x - (^-4)} = \frac{4}{5},$$

$$y = \frac{4}{5}(x + 4).$$

The slope intercept from the equation of the line is $y = \dfrac{4}{5}x + \dfrac{16}{5}$.

Systems of Linear Equations

The mathematical descriptions of many problems involve more than one equation, each having more than one unknown. To solve such problems, we must find a common solution to the equations, if it exists. An example is given on the following student page. Answer question 21.

Sample School Book Page:

MODELING LINEAR CHANGE

Section ② Key Concepts

Key Concepts

Key Term

linear
equation

Modeling Linear Change (pp. 483–485)

When a quantity changes by the same amount at regular intervals, the quantity shows linear change. You can use a linear equation to model linear change. You can also use a table or a graph.

Example Lynda borrowed $175 from her parents. She pays them back $10 a week. Her sister Maria borrowed $200 and pays back $15 a week. Who will finish paying off her loan first?

Write an equation for each person. Let y = the amount the person owes after x weeks.

Lynda	Maria
$y = 175 - 10x$	$y = 200 - 15x$

Number of weeks	Amount Lynda owes	Amount Maria owes
0	175	200
1	165	185
2	155	170
3	145	155
4	135	140
5	125	125
6	115	110
...	...	...
13	45	5
14	35	0

Lynda's and Maria's Loans

Maria only has to pay $5 in the 14th week.

After five weeks, they owe the same amount of money. After that, Maria is paying more per week than Lynda, so she will pay off her loan first.

21 Key Concepts Question In the Example above, how does the graph show when the sisters owe the same amount of money?

Source: Math Thematics, Book 3, McDougal Littell, 2002 (p. 490).

E X A M P L E
10-24

May Chin ordered lunch for herself and several friends by phone without checking prices. She paid $7.00 for five soyburgers and four orders of fries, and another time she paid $7.00 for four soyburgers and six orders of fries. Set up a system of equations with two unknowns representing the prices of a soyburger and an order of fries, respectively.

Solution Let x be the price in dollars of a soyburger and y be the price of an order of fries. Five soyburgers cost $5x$ dollars, and four orders of fries cost $4y$ dollars. Because May paid $7.00 for the orders, we have $5x + 4y = 7$. Similarly, $4x + 6y = 7$.

An ordered pair satisfying both equations is a point that belongs to each of the lines. Figure 10-89 shows the graphs of $5x + 2y = 6$ and $x - 4y = {}^-1$. The two lines appear to intersect at $\left(1, \dfrac{1}{2}\right)$. Thus $\left(1, \dfrac{1}{2}\right)$ appears to be the solution of the given system of equations. This solution can be checked by substituting 1 for x and $\dfrac{1}{2}$ for y in each equation.

Because two distinct lines intersect in only one point, $\left(1, \dfrac{1}{2}\right)$ is the only solution to the system.

FIGURE 10-89

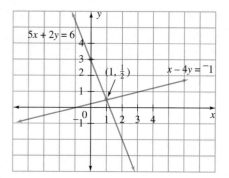

Substitution Method

Drawbacks to estimating graphically a solution to a system of equations include an inability to read noninteger real-number coordinates of points. However, there are algebraic methods for solving systems of linear equations. Consider, for example, the system $y = x + 3$ and $y = 2x - 1$. By substitution, $x + 3 = 2x - 1$, an equation with one unknown. Solving for x gives $3 + 1 = 2x - x$, and, hence, $4 = x$. Substituting 4 for x in either equation gives $y = 7$. Thus $(4, 7)$ is the solution to the given system. As before, this solution can be checked by substituting the obtained values for x and y in the original equation. This method for solving a system of linear equations is the **substitution method**.

substitution method

E X A M P L E
10-25

Solve the following system:

$$3x - 4y = 5$$
$$2x + 5y = 1$$

Solution   First, rewrite each equation, expressing y in terms of x.

$$y = \frac{3x - 5}{4} \qquad \text{and} \qquad y = \frac{1 - 2x}{5}$$

Then equate the expressions for y and solve the resulting equation for x.

$$\frac{3x - 5}{4} = \frac{1 - 2x}{5}$$

$$5(3x - 5) = 4(1 - 2x)$$

$$15x - 25 = 4 - 8x$$

$$23x = 29$$

$$x = \frac{29}{23}$$

Substituting $\frac{29}{23}$ for x in $y = \frac{3x - 5}{4}$ gives $y = \frac{^-7}{23}$. Hence, $x = \frac{29}{23}$ and $y = \frac{^-7}{23}$. This can be checked by substituting the values for x and y in the original equations.

REMARK   Sometimes it is more convenient to solve a system of equations by expressing x in terms of y in one of the equations and substituting the obtained expression for x in the other equation.

Elimination Method

elimination method   The **elimination method** for solving two equations with two unknowns is based on eliminating one of the variables by adding or subtracting the original or equivalent equations. For example, consider the following system:

$$x - y = {}^-3$$
$$x + y = 7$$

By adding the two equations, we can eliminate the variable y. The resulting equation can then be solved for x.

$$
\begin{array}{rcl}
x - y &=& {}^-3 \\
\underline{x + y} &=& \underline{7} \\
2x &=& 4 \\
x &=& 2
\end{array}
$$

Substituting 2 for x in the first equation (either equation may be used) gives $y = 5$. Checking this result shows that $x = 2$ and $y = 5$, or $(2, 5)$, is the solution to the system.

Often, another operation is required before equations are added so that an unknown can be eliminated. For example, consider the following system:

$$3x + 2y = 5$$
$$5x - 4y = 3$$

Adding the equations does not eliminate either unknown. However, if the first equation contained $4y$ rather than $2y$, the variable y could be eliminated by adding. To obtain $4y$ in the first equation, we multiply both sides of the equation by 2 to obtain the equivalent equations $6x + 4y = 10$. Adding the equations in the equivalent system gives the following:

$$
\begin{aligned}
6x + 4y &= 10 \\
\underline{5x - 4y} &= \underline{3} \\
11x &= 13 \\
x &= \frac{13}{11}
\end{aligned}
$$

To find the corresponding value of y, we substitute $\frac{13}{11}$ for x in either of the original equations and solve for y, or we use the elimination method again and solve for y.

An alternative method is to eliminate the x-values from the original system by multiplying the first equation by 5 and the second by $^-3$ (or the first by $^-5$ and the second by 3). Then we add the two equations and solve for y.

$$
\begin{aligned}
15x + 10y &= 25 \\
\underline{^-15x + 12y} &= \underline{^-9} \\
22y &= 16 \\
y &= \frac{16}{22}, \text{ or } \frac{8}{11}
\end{aligned}
$$

Consequently, $\left(\frac{13}{11}, \frac{8}{11}\right)$ is the solution of the original system. This solution, as always, should be checked by substitution in the *original* equations.

Solutions to Systems of Linear Equations

All examples thus far have had unique solutions. However, other situations may arise. Geometrically, a system of two linear equations can be characterized as follows:

1. *The system has a unique solution if, and only if, the graphs of the equations intersect in a single point.*
2. *The system has no solution if, and only if, the equations represent parallel lines.*
3. *The system has infinitely many solutions if, and only if, the equations represent the same line.*

NOW TRY THIS 10-17

Find all the solutions (if any) of each of the following systems by graphing the equations in each system. Then justify your answers by an algebraic approach.

a. $x - y = 1$
  $2x - y = 5$

b. $2x - y = 1$
  $2y - 4x = 3$

c. $2x - 3y = 1$
  $6y - 4x = 2$

Fitting a Line to Data

As noted in Chapter 8, in many practical situations, a relationship between two variables comes from collected data such as from population or business surveys. When the data is graphed, there may not be a single line that goes through all of the points, but the points may appear to approximate, or "follow," a straight line. In such cases, it is useful to find the equation of what seems to be the **best-fitting line**. Knowing the equation of such a line enables us to predict an outcome without actually performing the experiment.

best-fitting line

There are several approaches to define, and hence find, the best-fitting line. We take a graphical approach as follows:

1. Choose a line that seems to follow the given points so that there are about an equal number of points below the line as above the line.
2. Determine two convenient points on the line and approximate the x- and y-coordinates of these points.
3. Use the points in (2) to determine the equation of the line.

**EXAMPLE
10-26**

A shirt manufacturer noticed that the number of units sold depends on the price charged. The data in Table 10-6 shows the number of units sold for a given price per unit.

a. Find the equation of a line that seems to fit the data best.
b. Use the equation in (a) to predict the number of units that will be sold if the price per unit is $60.

Table 10-6

Price per Unit (Dollars)	Number of Units Sold (Thousands)
50	200
44	250
41	300
33	380
31	400
24.5	450
20	500
14.5	550

Solution   a. Figure 10-90(a) shows the graph of the data displayed in Table 10-6. Figure 10-90(b) shows a line that seems to fit the data so that approximately the same number of points are below the line as above the line. We choose the points (50, 200) and (20, 500), which are on the line in Figure 10-90(b).

FIGURE 10-90

(a)   (b)

To find the equation of the line, we need to find m and b in the equation $y = mx + b$ (alternatively, we could use the point-slope form of the line). Substituting the points $(50, 200)$ and $(20, 500)$ into this equation, we obtain the following:

$$200 = 50m + b$$
$$500 = 20m + b$$

One way to solve the equations is to express b in terms of m for each equation:

$$b = 200 - 50m$$
$$b = 500 - 20m$$

We equate the expressions for b and solve for m:

$$200 - 50m = 500 - 20m$$
$$200 - 500 = 50m - 20m$$
$$^-300 = 30m$$
$$m = {}^-10$$

Substituting this value for m, we obtain

$$b = 200 - 50(^-10) = 700.$$

Consequently, the equation of the fitted line is $y = {}^-10x + 700$.

b. Using the equation in (a), substitute $x = 60$ to obtain $y = {}^-10(60) + 700$, or $y = 100$. Thus we predict that 100,000 units will be sold if the price per unit is \$60.

O N G O I N G   A S S E S S M E N T   1 0 - 6

1. The graph of $y = mx$ is given in the following figure. Sketch the graphs for each of the following on the same figure. Explain your answers.

   a. $y = mx + 3$ **b.** $y = mx - 3$

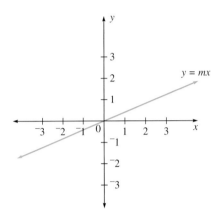

2. Sketch the graphs for each of the following equations:

   a. $y = \dfrac{-3}{4}x + 3$ b. $y = {}^-3$

   c. $y = 15x - 30$ **d.** $x = {}^-2$

   e. $y = 3x - 1$ **f.** $y = \dfrac{1}{20}x$

3. Find the x-intercept and y-intercept for the equations in problem 2, if they exist.

4. In the following figure, part (i) shows a dual scale thermometer and part (ii) shows the corresponding points plotted on a graph.

(i)

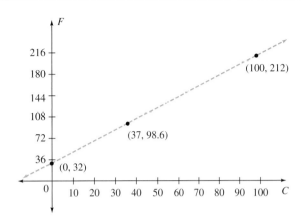

(ii)

   a. Use two of the points on the graph to develop a formula for conversion from degrees Celsius (C) to degrees Fahrenheit (F).

   b. Use your answer in (a) to find a formula for converting from degrees F to degrees C.

5. Write each of the following equations in slope-intercept form and identify the slope and y-intercept:

   a. $3y - x = 0$ **b.** $x + y = 3$

   c. $\dfrac{x}{3} + \dfrac{y}{4} = 1$ **d.** $3x - 4y + 7 = 0$

   e. $x = 3y$ **f.** $x - y = 4(x - y)$

6. For each of the following, write the equation of the line determined by the given pair of points in slope-intercept form or in the form $x = a$:

   a. $({}^-4, 3)$ and $(1, {}^-2)$ **b.** $(0, 0)$ and $(2, 1)$

   c. $(0, 1)$ and $(2, 1)$ **d.** $(2, 1)$ and $(2, {}^-1)$

   e. $\left(0, \dfrac{{}^-1}{2}\right)$ and $\left(\dfrac{1}{2}, 0\right)$ **f.** $({}^-a, 0)$ and $(a, 0)$, $a \neq 0$

7. Find the coordinates of two other points collinear (on the same line) with each of the following pairs of given points:

   a. $P(2, 2), Q(4, 2)$ **b.** $P({}^-1, 0), Q({}^-1, 2)$

   c. $P(0, 0), Q(0, 1)$ **d.** $P(0, 0), Q(1, 1)$

8. For each of the following, give as much information as possible about x and y:

   a. The ordered pairs $({}^-2, 0)$, $({}^-2, 1)$, and (x, y) represent collinear points.

   b. The ordered pairs $({}^-2, 1)$, $(0, 1)$, and (x, y) represent collinear points.

   c. The ordered pair (x, y) is in the fourth quadrant.

9. Consider the lines through $P(2, 4)$ and perpendicular to the x- and y-axes, respectively. Find the area and the perimeter of the rectangle formed by these lines and the axes.

10. Find the equations for each of the following:
    a. The line containing $P(3, 0)$ and perpendicular to the x-axis
    b. The line containing $P(0, {}^-2)$ and parallel to the x-axis
    c. The line containing $P({}^-4, 5)$ and parallel to the x-axis
    d. The line containing $P({}^-4, 5)$ and parallel to the y-axis
11. For each of the following, find the slope, if it exists, of the line determined by the given pair of points:
    a. $(4, 3)$ and $({}^-5, 0)$ **b.** $({}^-4, 1)$ and $(5, 2)$
    c. $(\sqrt{5}, 2)$ and $(1, 2)$ **d.** $({}^-3, 81)$ and $({}^-3, 198)$
    e. $(1.0001, 12)$ and $(1, 10)$ **f.** (a, a) and (b, b)
12. Write the equation of each line in problem 11.
13. Wildlife experts found that the number of chirps a cricket makes in 15-sec intervals is related to the temperature T in degrees Fahrenheit as shown in the following graph:

Number of Chirps as a Function of Temperature

a. If C is the number of chirps in 15 sec, write a formula for C in terms of T (temperature in degrees Fahrenheit) that seems to fit the data best.
b. Use the equation in (a) to predict the number of chirps in 15 sec when the temperature is 90°.
c. If N is the number of chirps per minute, write a formula for N in terms of T.
14. **a.** Graph the following data and find the equation of the best-fitting line.
    b. Use your answer in (a) to predict the value of y when $x = 10$.

x	y
1	8.1
2	9.9
3	12
4	14.1
5	15.9
6	18
7	19.9

15. Solve each of the following systems, if possible. Indicate whether the system has a unique solution, infinitely many solutions, or no solution.
    a. $y = 3x - 1$
    $y = x + 3$
    b. $2x - 6y = 7$
    $3x - 9y = 10$
    c. $3x + 4y = {}^-17$
    $2x + 3y = {}^-13$
    d. $4x - 6y = 1$
    $6x - 9y = 1.5$
16. The vertices of a triangle are given by $(0, 0)$, $(10, 0)$, and $(6, 8)$. Show that the segments connecting $(5, 0)$ and $(6, 8)$, $(10, 0)$ and $(3, 4)$, and $(0, 0)$ and $(8, 4)$ intersect at a common point.
17. The owner of a 5000-gal oil truck loads the truck with gasoline and kerosene. The profit on each gallon of gasoline is 13¢ and on each gallon of kerosene is 12¢. How many gallons of each fuel did the owner load if the profit was $640?
18. At the end of 10 mo, the balance of an account earning simple interest is $2100.
    a. If, at the end of 18 mo, the balance is $2180, how much money was originally in the account?
    b. What is the rate of interest?
19. Josephine's bank contains 27 coins. If all the coins are either dimes or quarters and the value of the coins is $5.25, how many of each kind of coin are there?
20. **a.** Solve each of the following systems of equations. What do you notice about the answers?
    i. $x + 2y = 3$
    $4x + 5y = 6$
    ii. $2x + 3y = 4$
    $5x + 6y = 7$
    iii. $31x + 32y = 33$
    $34x + 35y = 36$
    b. Write another system similar to those in (a). What solution did you expect? Check your guess.
    c. Write a general system similar to those in (a). What solution does this system have? Why?
21. If a triangle has vertices with coordinates $(0, 32)$, $(20, 0)$, and $(100, 212)$ and a similar triangle has vertices $(0, 16)$ and $(10, 0)$, find a possible set of coordinates for the third vertex.
22. An arithmetic sequence having a linear graph was depicted in this chapter. Explain whether a geometric sequence has a linear graph.
23. If a line ℓ forms a 45° angle with the x-axis, what is the slope of
    a. line ℓ? **b.** line m, which is perpendicular to line ℓ?
24. If two sets of data have a negative correlation, what can be said about the slope of the line of best fit for the data?

Communication

25. Dahlia wanted to find what temperature has the same measure when measured in degrees Fahrenheit or degrees Celsius. To do that, she graphed the equation of the conversion formula $C = 5/9(F - 32)$. On the same coordinate system, she also graphed the equation $C = F$ and found the intersection point $(^-40, ^-40)$. Explain why this procedure answers the question Dahlia asked.

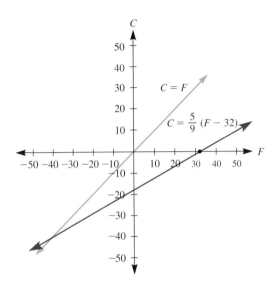

26. Explain in more than one way why two lines with the same slope are parallel.
27. Jonah tried to solve the equation $^-5x + y = 20$ by adding 5 to both sides. He wrote $5 - 5x + y = 5 + 20$ or $0 \cdot x + y = 25$ and finally $y = 25$. How would you help Jonah?
28. Jill would like to know why two lines with an undefined slope are parallel. How would you respond?

Open-Ended

29. Look for data in newspapers, magazines, or books whose graphs appear to be close to linear and find the equations of the lines that you think best fit the data.
30. **a.** Write equations of two lines that intersect but when graphed look parallel.
    b. At what point do those two lines intersect?

Cooperative Learning

31. Play the following game between your group and another group. Each group makes up four linear equations that have a common property and presents the equations to the other group. For example, one group could present the equations $2x - y = 0, 4x - 2y = 3, y - 2x = 3$, and $3y - 6x = 5$. If the second group discovers a common property that the equations share, such as the graphs of the equations are four parallel lines, they get one point. Each group takes a specified number of turns.

Review Problems

32. $ABCD$ is a trapezoid with $\overline{BC} \parallel \overline{AD}$. Solve for x.

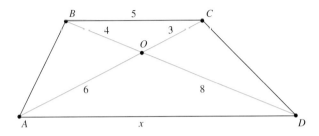

33. Draw an arbitrary triangle ABC. Let $M, N,$ and P be the corresponding midpoints of the sides $\overline{AB}, \overline{BC},$ and $\overline{AC}$. Connect the points $M, N,$ and P. Four triangles are created. Is it true that all of the smaller triangles are congruent and each is similar to $\triangle ABC$? Why or why not?
34. In triangle ABC, a square has been inscribed as shown. The lengths of the sides of $\triangle ABC$ are 3, 4, and 5 as shown. Find the length of a side of the square. (*Hint:* First show that $\triangle AED \approx \triangle ABC$.)

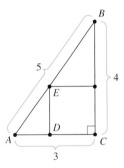

35. In the figure below, find BE.

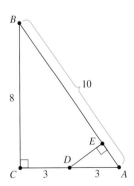

Hint for Solving the Preliminary Problem

What do all the triangles formed by the points at the top of the objects, the points at the base of the objects (straight down from the top), and the points at the ends of the shadows have in common? If each of those points were graphed for each triangle found in the data search, how would they appear on the graph?

QUESTIONS FROM THE CLASSROOM

1. On a test, a student wrote $AB \cong CD$ instead of $\overline{AB} \cong \overline{CD}$. Is this answer correct? Why?

2. A student asks if there are any constructions that cannot be done with a compass and a straightedge. How do you answer?

3. A student asks for a mathematical definition of congruence that holds for all figures. How do you respond? Is your response the same for similarity?

4. One student claims that by trisecting $\overline{AB}$ and drawing $\overrightarrow{CD}$ and $\overrightarrow{CE}$, as shown in the following figure, she has trisected $\angle ACB$:

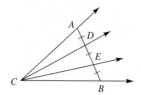

How do you convince her that her construction is wrong?

5. A student claims that polygon $ABCD$ in the following drawing is a parallelogram if $\angle 1 \cong \angle 2$. Is he correct? Why?

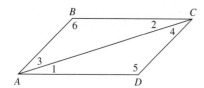

6. A student claims that when the midpoints of the sides of any polygon are connected, a polygon similar to the original results. Is this true? Why?

7. A student asks why "congruent" rather than "equal" is used to discuss triangles that have the same size and shape. What do you say?

8. A student draws the following figure and claims that because every triangle is congruent to itself, we can write $\triangle ABC \cong \triangle BCA$. What is your response?

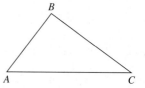

9. A student asks whether there is an AAAA similarity condition for quadrilaterals. How do you respond?

10. A student asks if, for the same n, all regular n-gons are similar. How do you respond?

11. A student says she thinks all circles are similar but would like to know why. How do you answer her?

12. A student says that a vertical line has an infinite slope. How do you respond?

13. A student claims that the lines whose equations are $y = 3x + 5$ and $y = 3x + 4$ are parallel because when she tried to solve the equations, she got the false statement $4 = 5$. How do you respond?

14. A student claims that because one can use slope to move horizontally and then vertically to find other points on a line as well as doing the reverse, then slope could be defined as run/rise. How do you respond?

15. Sue asks if coordinate geometry is "real" geometry. What do you say?

CHAPTER OUTLINE

I. Congruence
  A. Two geometric figures are **congruent** if, and only if, they have the same size and shape.
  B. Two triangles are congruent if they satisfy any of the following properties:
    1. Side, Side, Side (SSS)
    2. Side, Angle, Side (SAS)
    3. Angle, Side, Angle (ASA)
    4. Angle, Angle, Side (AAS)
  C. **Triangle inequality:** The sum of the measure of any two sides of a triangle must be greater than the measure of the third side.
  D. Corresponding parts of congruent figures are congruent.
  E. A **rep-tile** is a figure that is used in the construction of a similar figure.

II. Circles
  A. An **arc** of a circle is part of the circle that can be drawn without lifting a pencil. The **center of an arc** is the center of the circle containing the arc.
  B. A **chord** is a segment whose endpoints lie on a circle.

III. Proportion
  A. If a line parallel to one side of a triangle intersects the other sides, it divides those sides into proportional segments.
  B. If parallel lines cut off congruent segments on one transversal, they cut off congruent segments on any transversal.

IV. Constructions that can be accomplished using a compass and a straightedge
  A. Copy a line segment.
  B. Copy a circle.
  C. Copy an angle.
  D. Bisect a segment.
  E. Bisect an angle.
  F. Construct a perpendicular from a point to a line.
  G. Construct a perpendicular bisector of a segment.
  H. Construct a perpendicular to a line through a point on the line.
  I. Construct a parallel to a line through a point not on the line.
  J. Divide a segment into congruent parts.
  K. Inscribe some regular polygons in a circle.
  L. Circumscribe a circle about a triangle.
  M. Inscribe a circle in a triangle.

V. Similarity and proportion
  A. Two polygons are **similar** if, and only if, their corresponding angles are congruent and their corresponding sides are proportional.
  B. **AA:** If two angles of one triangle are congruent to two angles of a second triangle, respectively, the triangles are similar.
  C. If a line divides two sides of a triangle into proportional segments, then the line is parallel to the third side.

VI. Lines in a Cartesian coordinate system
  A. Every nonvertical line has an equation of the form $y = mx + b$, where m is the slope and b is the y-intercept.
  B. The equation of any vertical line can be written in the form $x = a$ and any horizontal line in the form of $y = b$ or $y = 0 \cdot x + b$.
  C. **Slope formula:** Given two points $A(x_1, y_1)$ and $B(x_2, y_2)$, the slope m of line AB is given by the following:

$$m = \frac{y_2 - y_1}{x_2 - x_1} = \frac{y_1 - y_2}{x_1 - x_2} = \frac{\text{rise}}{\text{run}}$$

  D. The equation of a line with slope m through a given point with coordinates (x_1, y_1) is $y - y_1 = m(x - x_1)$.
  E. Parallel nonvertical lines have the same slope.
  F. If two lines have the same slope they are parallel.
  G. The slope of a horizontal line is 0 and it is impossible to define the slope of a vertical line.
  H. A system of **linear equations** can be solved graphically by drawing the graphs of the equations.
  I. A system of linear equations can be solved algebraically by either the **substitution method** or the **elimination method**.
  J. The **best-fitting line** is a straight line that approximates the data.

*VII. Trigonometric functions
  In a right triangle, as follows, we have the following:

$$\sin(\angle BAC) = \frac{a}{c} = \frac{\text{length of opposite side}}{\text{length of hypotenuse}}$$

$$\cos(\angle BAC) = \frac{b}{c} = \frac{\text{length of adjacent side}}{\text{length of hypotenuse}}$$

$$\tan(\angle BAC) = \frac{a}{b} = \frac{\text{length of opposite side}}{\text{length of adjacent side}}$$

1. Each of the following figures contains at least one pair of congruent triangles. Identify them and tell why they are congruent.

(a)

(b)

(c)

(d)

(e)

(f)

(g)

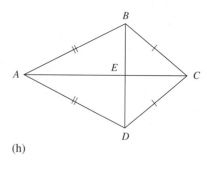

(h)

2. In the following figure, *ABCD* is a square and $\overline{DE} \cong \overline{BF}$. What kind of figure is *AECF*? Justify your answer.

3. Construct each of the following by (1) using a compass and straightedge and (2) paper folding:

(a) Bisector of ∠A

(b) Perpendicular to ℓ at B

(c) Perpendicular to ℓ from B

(d) Parallel to ℓ through P

4. For each of the following pairs of similar triangles, find the missing measures:

(a)

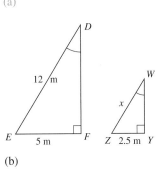

(b)

5. Divide the following segment into five congruent parts:

_____

6. If $ABCD$ is a trapezoid, $\overline{EF} \parallel \overline{AD}$ and $\overline{AC}$ is a diagonal. What is the relationship between $\frac{a}{b}$ and $\frac{c}{d}$? Why?

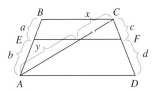

7. Given the following figure, construct a circle that contains A and B and has its center on ℓ:

8. For each of the following figures, show that appropriate triangles are similar and find x and y:

(a)

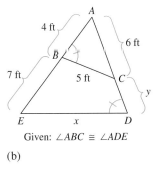

Given: ∠ABC ≅ ∠ADE

(b)

9. Determine if each of the following is true or false. If false, explain why.
   a. A radius of a circle is a chord of the circle.
   b. If a radius bisects a chord of a circle, then it is perpendicular to the chord.

10. A person 2 m tall casts a shadow 1 m long when a building has a 6-m shadow. How high is the building?

11. **a.** Which of the following polygons can be inscribed in a circle? Assume that all sides of each polygon are congruent and that all the angles of polygons (ii) and (iii) are congruent.

(i)   (ii)   (iii)

   b. Based on your answer in (a), make a conjecture about what kinds of polygons can be inscribed in a circle.

12. Determine the vertical height of the playground slide shown in the following figure:

13. Find the distance *d* across the river sketched as follows:

14. Is the following statement always true, always false, or true in some cases and false in others? Explain your answer.
A quadrilateral whose diagonals are congruent and perpendicular is a square.

15. For each of the following, write the equation of the line determined by the given pair of points.
   a. $(2, {}^-3)$ and $({}^-1, 1)$
   b. $({}^-3, 0)$ and $(3, 2)$

16. Use slope to determine if there is a single line through the points with coordinates $(4, 2)$, $(0, {}^-1)$, and $(7, {}^-5)$. Explain your reasoning.

17. Solve each of the following systems, if possible. If the system does not have a unique solution, explain why not.
   a. $x + 2y = 3$
      $2x - y = 9$
   b. $\dfrac{x}{2} + \dfrac{y}{3} = 1$
      $4y - 3x = 2$

   c. $x - 2y = 1$
      $4y - 2x = 0$

18. Prove that two congruent triangles ABC and $A'B'C'$ are similar.

* 19. Prove that $\sin 60 \neq 2 \sin 30°$.

* 20. Solve for x in the following:

(a) x (b)

* 21. **a.** Argue that $\tan 30° = \dfrac{\sin 30°}{\cos 30°}$.

   b. Argue that in general $\tan A = \dfrac{\sin A}{\cos A}$.

SELECTED BIBLIOGRAPHY

Bartels, B. "Truss(t)ing Triangles." *Mathematics Teaching in the Middle School* 3 (March–April 1998): 394–396.

Beckmann, C., and K. Rozanski. "Graphs in Real Time." *Mathematics Teaching in the Middle School* 5 (October 1999): 92–93.

Carrol, W. "Polygon Capture: A Geometry Game." *Mathematics Teaching in the Middle School* 4 (October 1998): 90–94.

Drum, R. "Miniature Toys Introduce Ratio and Proportion with a Real-world Connection." *Mathematics Teaching in the Middle School* 7 (September 2001): 50–54.

Greer, G., and L. Wantuck. "Menu of Problems." *Mathematics Teaching in the Middle School* 1 (March–April 1996): 729.

Kastberg, S. "Euclidean Tools and the Creation of Euclidean Geometry." *Mathematics Teaching in the Middle School* 7 (January 2002): 294–296.

Kennedy, J., and E. McDowell. "Geoboard Quadrilaterals." *Mathematics Teacher* 91 (April 1998): 288–290.

Manouchehri, A., M. Enderson, and L. Pagnucco. "Exploring Geometry with Technology." *Mathematics Teaching in the Middle School* 3 (March–April 1998): 436–442.

Maupin. S. "Middle-Grades Geometry Activities." *Mathematics Teaching in the Middle School* 1 (May 1996): 790–796.

Sanders, C. "Geometric Constructions: Visualizing and Understanding Geometry." *Mathematics Teacher* 91 (October 1998): 554–556.

Sharp, J., and K. Hoiberg. "And Then There Was Luke: The Geometric Thinking of a Young Mathematician." *Teaching Children Mathematics* 7 (March 2001): 432–439.

Slavit, D. "Above and beyond AAA: The Similarity and Congruence of Polygons." *Mathematics Teaching in the Middle School* 3 (January 1998): 276–280.

Slovin, H. "Moving to Proportional Reasoning." *Mathematics Teaching in the Middle School* 6 (September 2000): 58–60.

Vennebush, P. "Menu of Problems." *Mathematics Teaching in the Middle School* 3 (February 1998): 352–353.

Welchman, R., and J. Urso. "Midpoint Shapes." *Teaching Children Mathematics* 6 (April 2000): 506–509

–11–
Concepts of Measurement

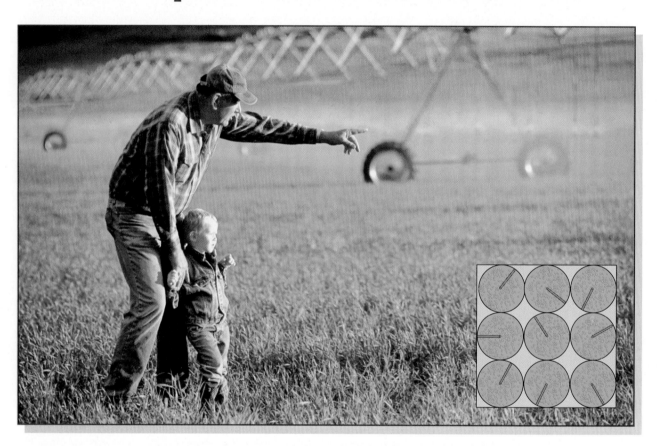

P R E L I M I N A R Y   P R O B L E M

A farmer has a square plot of land. An irrigation system can be installed with the option of one large circular sprinkler or nine small sprinklers, as shown in the accompanying figure. The farmer wants to know which plan will provide water to the greatest percentage of land in the field, regardless of the cost and the watering pattern.

P*rinciples and Standards* discusses the measurable attributes of objects as follows:

A measurable attribute is a characteristic of an object that can be quantified. Line segments have length, plane regions have area, and physical objects have mass. As students progress through the curriculum from preschool through high school, the set of attributes they can measure should expand. Recognizing that objects have attributes that are measurable is the first step in the study of measurement. Children in prekindergarten through grade 2 begin by comparing and ordering objects using language such as longer and shorter. Length should be the focus in this grade band, but weight, time, area, and volume should also be explored. In grades 3–5, students should learn about area more thoroughly, as well as perimeter, volume, temperature, and angle measure. In these grades, they learn that measurements can be computed using formulas and need not always be taken directly with a measuring tool. Middle-grade students build on these earlier measurement experiences by continuing their study of perimeter, area, and volume and by beginning to explore derived measurements, such as speed. (p. 44)

In the United States, two measurement systems are used regularly: the English system and the metric system. In *Principles and Standards*, we find the following concerning the use of the two measurement systems:

Since the customary English system of measurement is still prevalent in the United States, students should learn both customary and metric systems and should know some rough equivalences between the metric and customary systems—for example, that a two-liter bottle of soda is a little more than half a gallon. The study of these systems begins in elementary school, and students at this level should be able to carry out simple conversions within both systems. Students should develop proficiency in these conversions in the middle grades and should learn some useful benchmarks for converting between the two systems. (pp. 45–46)

Objects have measurable attributes such as length, area, volume, and mass. Many concepts of measurement are more confusing for children than for adults because students lack everyday measurement experiences. In this chapter, we use both systems of measurement for length, area, volume, mass, and temperature with the philosophy that students should learn to think within a system. We also develop formulas for the area of plane figures and for surface areas and volumes of solids. We use the concept of area in discussing the Pythagorean Theorem.

Linear Measure

To measure a segment, we must decide on a unit of measure. Early attempts at measurement lacked a standard unit and used fingers, hands, arms, and feet as units of measure. "Hands" are still used to measure the heights of horses. These early crude measurements were refined eventually and standardized by the English.

NOW TRY THIS 11-1

The *Standards* state that in grades Pre-K–2, students should begin their study of measurement using nonstandard units such as paper clips (p. 45).

  a. Estimate the length of this textbook page in terms of paper clips.
  b. Measure the textbook in paper clips.
  c. How close was your estimate to the measure?
  d. Repeat parts a–c using *hands*.

The English System

Originally, in the English system, a yard was the distance from the tip of the nose to the end of an outstretched arm of an adult person and a foot was the length of a human foot. In 1893 the United States defined the yard and other units in terms of metric units. Some units of length in the English system and relationships among them are summarized in Table 11-1.

Table 11-1

Unit	Equivalent in Other Units
yard (yd)	3 ft
foot (ft)	12 in.
mile (mi)	1760 yd, or 5280 ft

Dimensional Analysis (Unit Analysis)

dimensional analysis

To convert from one unit of measure to another, the process known as **dimensional analysis** can be used. This process works with *unit ratios* (ratios equivalent to 1). For example, $\dfrac{1 \text{ yd}}{3 \text{ ft}}$ and $\dfrac{5280 \text{ ft}}{1 \text{ mi}}$ are unit ratios. Therefore to convert 5.25 mi to yards, we have the following.

$$5.25 \text{ mi} = \frac{5.25 \text{ mi}}{1} \times \frac{5280 \text{ ft}}{1 \text{ mi}} \times \frac{1 \text{ yd}}{3 \text{ ft}} = 9240 \text{ yd}$$

EXAMPLE 11-1

If a cheetah is clocked at 60 miles per hour (mph), what is its speed in feet per second?

Solution
$$60 \, \frac{\text{mi}}{\text{hr}} = 60 \, \frac{\text{mi}}{\text{hr}} \times \frac{5280 \text{ ft}}{1 \text{ mi}} \times \frac{1 \text{ hr}}{60 \text{ min}} \times \frac{1 \text{ min}}{60 \text{ sec}} = 88 \, \frac{\text{ft}}{\text{sec}}$$

REMARK The use of *dimensional analysis* will be seen in the solution to many parts of the examples in this text that involve conversions. It will not be the only technique used.

EXAMPLE 11-2

Convert each of the following:

a. 219 ft = ____ yd
b. 8432 yd = ____ mi
c. 0.2 mi = ____ ft
d. 64 in. = ____ yd

Solution

a. Because 1 ft = $\frac{1}{3}$ yd, 219 ft = $219 \cdot \frac{1}{3}$ yd = 73 yd. Alternatively, 219 ft = $219 \text{ ft} \cdot \frac{1 \text{ yd}}{3 \text{ ft}} = 73$ yd.

b. Because 1 yd = $\frac{1}{1760}$ mi, 8432 yd = $8432 \cdot \frac{1}{1760}$ mi $\doteq 4.79$ mi. Alternatively, 8432 yd = $8432 \text{ yd} \cdot \frac{3 \text{ ft}}{1 \text{ yd}} \cdot \frac{1 \text{ mi}}{5280 \text{ ft}} \doteq 4.79$ mi.

c. 1 mi = 5280 ft. Hence, 0.2 mi = $0.2 \cdot 5280$ ft = 1056 ft. Alternatively, 0.2 mi = $0.2 \text{ mi} \cdot \frac{5280 \text{ ft}}{1 \text{ mi}} = 1056$ ft.

d. We first find a connection between yards and inches. We have 1 yd = 3 ft and 1 ft = 12 in. Hence, 1 yd = 3 ft = $3 \cdot 12$ in. = 36 in. Hence, 1 in. = $\frac{1}{36}$ yd; therefore 64 in. = $64 \cdot \frac{1}{36}$ yd $\doteq 1.78$ yd. Alternatively, 64 in. = $64 \text{ in.} \cdot \frac{1 \text{ ft}}{12 \text{ in.}} \cdot \frac{1 \text{ yd}}{3 \text{ ft}} \doteq 1.78$ yd.

The Metric System

metric system

At this time, the United States is the only major industrial nation in the world that continues to use the English system. However, the use of the **metric system** in the United States has been increasing, particularly in the scientific community and in industry. The *2002 World Almanac* points out:

The Trade Act of 1988 and other legislation declare the metric system the preferred system of weights and measures of U.S. trade and commerce, call for the federal government to adopt metric specifications, and mandate the Commerce Department to oversee the program. The conversion process is currently under way; however, the metric system has not become the system of choice for most Americans' daily use.

HISTORICAL NOTE

meter

The metric system, a decimal system, was proposed in France in 1670 by Gabriel Mouton. However, not until the French Revolution in 1790 did the French Academy of Sciences bring various groups together to develop the system. The Academy recognized the need for a standard base unit of linear measurement. The members chose $\frac{1}{10,000,000}$ of the distance from the equator to the North Pole on a meridian through Paris as the base unit of length and called it the **meter** (**m**). In 1960 the meter was redefined in terms of krypton 86 wavelengths and still later as the distance traveled by light in a vacuum during $\frac{1}{299,792,458}$ sec. Since 1893 the yard in the United States has been defined as $\frac{3600}{3937}$ of a meter, whatever the definition of a meter.

Different units of length in the metric system are obtained by multiplying a power of 10 times the base unit. Table 11-2 gives the prefixes for these units, the multiplication factors, and their symbols.

Table 11-2

Prefix	Symbol	Factor	
kilo	k	1000	(one thousand)
*hecto	h	100	(one hundred)
*deka	da	10	(ten)
*deci	d	0.1	(one tenth)
centi	c	0.01	(one hundredth)
milli	m	0.001	(one thousandth)

*Not commonly used

The metric prefixes, combined with the base unit meter, name the different units of length. Table 11-3 gives these units, their relationship to the meter, and the symbol for each.

Table 11-3

Unit	Symbol	Relationship to Base Unit
kilometer	km	1000 m
*hectometer	hm	100 m
*dekameter	dam	10 m
meter	**m**	**base unit**
*decimeter	dm	0.1 m
centimeter	cm	0.01 m
millimeter	mm	0.001 m

*Not commonly used

REMARK   Two other prefixes, mega (1,000,000) and micro (0.000001), are used for very large and very small units, respectively.

Benchmarks that can be used for estimations for a meter, a decimeter, a centimeter, and a millimeter are shown in Figure 11-1. The kilometer is commonly used for measuring longer distances. Because "kilo" stands for 1000, 1 km = 1000 m. Nine football fields, including end zones, laid end to end are approximately 1 km long.

FIGURE 11-1

1 m   1 dm   1 cm   1 mm

Conversions among metric lengths are accomplished by multiplying or dividing by powers of ten. As with money, we simply move the decimal point to the left or right, depending on the units. For example,

0.123 km = 1.23 hm = 12.3 dam = 123 m = 1230 dm = 12,300 cm = 123,000 mm.

It is possible to convert units by using the chart in Figure 11-2. We count the number of steps from one unit to the other and move the decimal point that many steps in the same direction.

FIGURE 11-2

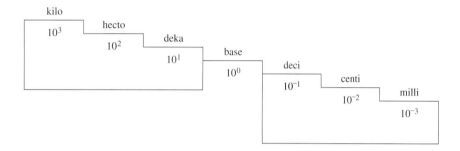

NOW TRY THIS 11-2

If our money system used metric prefixes and the base unit was a dollar, give metric names to each of the following.

a. dime   **b.** penny   **c.** $10 bill   **d.** $100 bill   **e.** $1000 bill

EXAMPLE
11-3

Convert each of the following:

a. 1.4 km = ____ m   **b.** 285 mm = ____ m   **c.** 0.03 km = ____ cm

Solution   **a.** Because 1 km = 1000 m, to change kilometers to meters, we multiply by 1000. Hence, 1.4 km = 1.4 (1000 m) = 1400 m. Altlernatively, 1.4 km = 1.4 km $\cdot \dfrac{1000 \text{ m}}{1 \text{ km}}$ = 1400 m.

b. Because 1 mm = 0.001 m, to change from millimeters to meters, we multiply by 0.001. Thus 285 mm = 285 (0.001 m) = 0.285 m. Alternatively, 285 mm = 285 mm $\cdot \dfrac{1 \text{ m}}{1000 \text{ mm}}$ = 0.285 m.

c. To change kilometers to centimeters, we first multiply by 1000 to convert kilometers to meters and then multiply by 100 to convert meters to centimeters. Therefore we move the decimal five places to the right to obtain 0.03 km = 3000 cm. An alternative approach is to use Figure 11-2. To go from kilo to centi on the steps, we move five places to the right, so we need to move the decimal point in 0.03 five places to the right, which is 3000.

Linear units of length are commonly measured with rulers. Figure 11-3 shows part of a centimeter ruler. Rulers can be used to measure distance.

FIGURE 11-3

Measuring distances in the real world frequently results in errors. Because of this, many industrial plants using parts from a variety of sources rely on portable calibration units that are taken from plant to plant to test measuring instruments used in constructing the parts. This is done so that the final assembly plant can fit all the parts together to make the product. To calibrate the measuring instruments, technicians must establish the greatest possible error (GPE) allowable in order to obtain the final fit. The **greatest possible error (GPE)** of a measurement is one-half the unit used. For example, if the width of a piece of board was measured 5 cm to the nearest centimeter, the actual width must be between 4.5 cm and 5.5 cm. Therefore, the GPE for this measurement is 0.5 cm. If the width of a button is measured as 1.2 cm, then the actual width is between 1.15 cm and 1.25 cm and so the GPE is 0.05 cm or 0.5 mm.

When drawings are given, we assume that the listed measurements are accurate. When actually measuring objects in the real world, we find that such accuracy is usually impossible.

Distance Properties

A person using the expression "the shortest distance between two points is a straight line" may have good intentions, but the expression is actually false. (Why?) The shortest among all the polygonal paths connecting two points A and B is the segment $\overline{AB}$. (The length of $\overline{AB}$ is denoted by AB.) This fact is one of the basic properties of distance listed next.

> ## Properties
>
> 1. The distance between any two points A and B is greater than or equal to 0, written $AB \geq 0$.
> 2. The distance between any two points A and B is the same as the distance between B and A, written $AB = BA$.
> 3. For any three points A, B, and C, the distance between A and B plus the distance between B and C is greater than or equal to the distance between A and C, written $AB + BC \geq AC$.

In the special case where A, B, and C are collinear and B is between A and C, as in Figure 11-4(a), we have $AB + BC = AC$. Otherwise, if A, B, and C are not collinear, as in Figure 11-4(b), then they form the vertices of a triangle and $AB + BC > AC$. This inequality, $AB + BC > AC$, is the **Triangle Inequality**. In general, the Triangle Inequality states that *the sum of the lengths of any two sides of a triangle is greater than the length of the third side.*

FIGURE 11-4

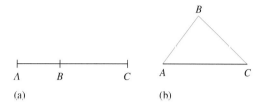

(a)   (b)

NOW TRY THIS 11-3

If two sides of a triangle are 31 cm and 85 cm long and the measure of the third side must be a whole number of centimeters,

a. what is the longest the third side can be?
b. what is the shortest the third side can be?

REMARK Notice the difference between AB, $\overline{AB}$, and $\overleftrightarrow{AB}$. AB is the distance between two points A and B and therefore a nonnegative real number, $\overline{AB}$ is the segment connecting points A and B and therefore a set of points. $\overleftrightarrow{AB}$ is the line through points A and B.

Distance Around a Plane Figure

perimeter

The **perimeter** of a simple closed curve is the length of the curve. If a figure is a polygon, its perimeter is the sum of the lengths of the sides. A perimeter has linear measure.

EXAMPLE 11-4

Find the perimeter of each of the shapes in Figure 11-5.

FIGURE 11-5

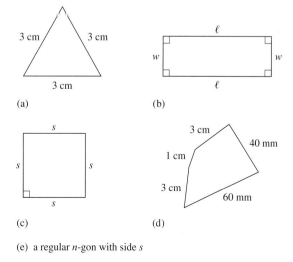

(e) a regular *n*-gon with side *s*

Solution   **a.** The perimeter is 3(3) = 9 cm.

b. The perimeter is $2w + 2l$.

c. The perimeter is $4s$.

d. Because 40 mm = 4 cm and 60 mm = 6 cm, the perimeter is 1 + 3 + 4 + 6 + 3 = 17 cm.

e. Because all sides of a regular *n*-gon with side length *s* are congruent, the perimeter is *ns*.

REMARK   When letters are used for distances, as in Example 11-4(b) and (c), we do not usually attach dimensions to an answer. In this case if the perimeter is $4s$, we actually mean that it is $4s$ units of length.

FIGURE 11-6

PROBLEM SOLVING   <u>Roping a Square</u>

Given a square of any size, stretch a rope tightly around it. Now take the rope off, add 100 ft to it and put the extended rope back around the square so that the new rope makes a square around the original square, as in Figure 11-6. Find *d*, the distance between the squares.

Understanding the Problem   We are to determine the distance between a square and a new square formed by adding 100 ft of rope to a rope that was stretched around the original square. Figure 11-6 shows the situation if the length of the side of the original square is *s* and the unknown distance is *d*.

Devising a Plan   If we use variables to represent the unknowns, we can *write an equation* to model the problem. The perimeter of the new square is $4s + 100$. Another way to represent this perimeter is $4(s + 2d)$. Therefore, we have $4s + 100 = 4(s + 2d)$. We must solve this equation for *d*.

Carrying Out the Plan   We solve the equation as shown below.

$$4s + 100 = 4(s + 2d)$$
$$4s + 100 = 4s + 8d$$
$$100 = 8d$$
$$12.5 = d$$

Therefore the distance between the squares is 12.5 ft.

Looking Back   Try some lengths of different squares to convince yourself that this solution is correct. This problem can be extended to figures other than squares. Try the Brainteaser at the end of this section.

Circumference of a Circle

circle   A **circle**, as shown in Figure 11-7, is defined as the set of all points in a plane that are the

center ◆ circumference   same distance from a given point, the **center**. The perimeter of a circle is its **circumference**. The ancient Greeks discovered that if they divided the circumference of any circle by the length of its diameter, they always obtained approximately the same number.

pi   The ratio of circumference *C* to diameter *d* is symbolized π (**pi**). In the late eighteenth century, mathematicians proved that the ratio $\frac{C}{d}$, or π, is not a terminating or repeating decimal. Rather, it is an irrational number. For most practical purposes, π is approximated by $\frac{22}{7}$, $3\frac{1}{7}$, or 3.14. These values are not exact values of π.

FIGURE 11-7

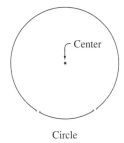

Center

Circle

The relationship $\dfrac{C}{d} = \pi$ is used for finding the circumference of a circle and normally is written $C = \pi d$ or $C = 2\pi r$ because the length of the diameter d is twice the radius (r) of the circle. The exact circumference of a circle with diameter 6 cm is 6π cm, while an approximation might be $6(3.14) = 18.84$ cm.

HISTORICAL
N O T E

$\pi = 3.14159\ 26535\ 89793\ 23846\ 26433\ 83279\ 50288\ 41971\ 69399\ 37510\ 58209 \ldots$

Archimedes (b. 287 B.C.) found an approximation for π given by the inequality $3\dfrac{10}{71} < \pi < 3\dfrac{10}{70}$. A Chinese astronomer thought that $\pi = \dfrac{355}{113}$. Ludolph van Ceulen (1540–1610), a German mathematician, calculated π to 35 decimal places. The approximation was engraved on his tombstone. Leonhard Euler adopted the symbol π in 1737 and caused its wide usage. In 1761 Johann Lambert, an Alsatian mathematician, proved that π is an irrational number. In 1989 Columbia University mathematicians and Soviet émigré brothers, David and Gregory Chudnovsky, used computers to establish 480 million digits of π. If these digits were printed along a line, the line would extend 600 miles. Since 1989 better approximations have been obtained.

NOW TRY THIS 11-4

Explain the cartoon below.

Arc Length

semicircle

The length of an arc depends on the radius of the circle and the central angle determining the arc. If the central angle has a measure of 180°, as in Figure 11-8(a), the arc is a **semicircle**. The length of a semicircle is $\frac{1}{2} \cdot 2\pi r$, or πr. The length of an arc whose central angle is $\theta°$ can be developed as in Figure 11-8(b) by using proportional reasoning. Since a circle has 360°, an angle of $\theta°$ determines $\theta/360$ of a circle. Because the circumference of a circle is $2\pi r$, an arc of $\theta°$ has length $\frac{\theta}{360} \cdot 2\pi r$, or $\frac{\pi r \theta}{180}$.

FIGURE 11-8

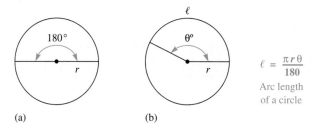

$\ell = \dfrac{\pi r \theta}{180}$

Arc length
of a circle

(a)   (b)

E X A M P L E
11-5

Find each of the following:

a. The circumference of a circle if the radius is 2 m.
b. The radius of a circle if the circumference is 15π m.
c. The length of a 25° arc of a circle of radius 10 cm.
d. The radius of an arc whose central angle is 87° and whose length is 154 cm.

Solution   **a.** $C = 2\pi(2) = 4\pi$; thus the circumference is 4π m.

b. $C = 2\pi r$ implies $15\pi = 2\pi r$. Hence, $r = \dfrac{15}{2}$ and the radius is 7.5 m.

c. The arc length is $\dfrac{\pi r \theta}{180} = \dfrac{\pi \cdot 10 \cdot 25}{180}$ cm, or $\dfrac{25\pi}{18}$ cm, or approximately 4.36 cm.

d. The arc length ℓ is $\dfrac{\pi r \theta}{180}$, so that $154 = \dfrac{\pi r \cdot 87}{180}$.

Thus, $r \doteq 101.4$ cm.

LABORATORY
A C T I V I T Y

To approximate the value of π, you need string, a marked ruler, and several different-sized round tin cans or jars. Pick a can and wrap the string tightly around the can. Use a pen to mark a point on the string where the beginning of the string meets the string again. Unwrap the string and measure its length. Next, determine the diameter of the can by tracing the bottom of the can on a piece of paper. Fold the circle onto itself to find a line of symmetry. The chord determined by the line is a diameter of the circle. Measure the diameter and determine the ratio of the circumference to the diameter. (Use the same units in all of your measurements.) Repeat the experiment with at least three cans and find the average of the corresponding ratios.

O N G O I N G   A S S E S S M E N T   1 1 - 1

1. Use the following picture of a ruler to find each of the lengths in centimeters:

    a. *AB* b. *DE* c. *CJ* d. *EF*
    e. *IJ* f. *AF* g. *IC* h. *GB*

2. Estimate and then measure each of the following in terms of the units listed:
    a. The length of your desktop in cubits (elbow to outstretched fingers)
    b. The length of this page in pencil lengths
    c. The width of this book in pencil widths
3. The United Kingdom used the following money system: 1 pound = 20 shillings, 1 shilling = 12 pence, 1 penny = 2 half-pence, 1 pence = 4 farthings (pence is the plural of penny). Use dimensional analysis to convert each of the following:
    a. 1 pound = _____ farthings
    b. 30 shillings = _____ pound
    c. 12 pounds = _____ pence
4. Convert each of the following:
    a. 100 in. = _____ yd
    b. 400 yd = _____ in.
    c. 300 ft = _____ yd
    d. 372 in. = _____ ft
5. Draw segments that you estimate to be of the following lengths. Use a metric ruler to check the estimates.
    a. 10 mm
    b. 100 mm
    c. 1 cm
    d. 10 cm
    e. 0.01 m
    f. 15 cm
6. Estimate the length of the following segment and then measure it:

    Express the measurement in each of the following units:
    a. Millimeters
    b. Centimeters
7. Choose an appropriate metric unit and estimate each of the following measures (check your estimates):
    a. The length of a pencil

    b. The diameter of a nickel
    c. The width of the top of a desk
    d. The thickness of the top of a desk
    e. The length of this sheet of paper
    f. The height of a door
8. Redo problem 7 using English measures.
9. Complete the following table:

Item	m	cm	mm
a. Length of a piece of paper		35	
b. Height of a woman	1.63		
c. Width of a filmstrip			35
d. Length of a cigarette			100
e. Length of two meter sticks laid end to end	2		

10. For each of the following, place a decimal point in the number to make the sentence reasonable:
    a. A stack of 10 dimes is 1000 mm high.
    b. The desk is 770 m high.
    c. The distance from one side of a street to the other is 100 m.
    d. A dollar bill is 155 cm long.
    e. The basketball player is 1950 cm tall.
    f. A new piece of chalk is about 8100 cm long.
    g. The speed limit in town is 400 km/hr.
11. List the following in decreasing order: 8 cm, 5218 mm, 245 cm, 91 mm, 6 m, 700 mm.
12. Draw each of the following as accurately as possible:
    a. A regular polygon whose perimeter is 12 cm
    b. A circle whose circumference is 4 in.
    c. A triangle whose perimeter is 4 in.
    d. A nonconvex quadrilateral whose perimeter is 8 cm

13. Guess the perimeter in centimeters of each of the following figures and then check the estimates using a ruler:

(a)   (b)

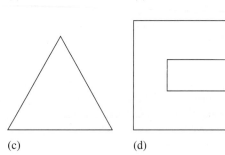

(c)   (d)

14. Complete each of the following:

   a. 10 mm = _____ cm   b. 262 m = _____ km
   c. 3 km = _____ m   d. 30 mm = _____ m
   e. 35 m = _____ cm   f. 359 mm = _____ m
   g. 647 mm = _____ cm   h. 0.1 cm = _____ mm

15. Draw a triangle *ABC*. Measure the length of each of its sides in millimeters. For each of the following, tell which is greater and by how much:

   a. *AB + BC* or *AC*
   b. *BC + CA* or *AB*
   c. *AB + CA* or *BC*

16. Can the following be the lengths of the sides of a triangle? Why or why not?

   a. 23 cm, 50 cm, 60 cm
   b. 10 cm, 40 cm, 50 cm
   c. 410 mm, 260 mm, 14 cm

17. a. How do the ratios of the perimeters of similar triangles compare to the ratios of the corresponding sides? Why?

   b. Does relationship in part (a) hold for all similar polygons?

18. Take an $8\frac{1}{2}$-×-11-in. piece of typing paper, fold it as shown in the following figure, and then cut the folded paper along the diagonal as shown.

a. Rearrange the two smaller pieces to find a triangle with the minimum perimeter.

b. Arrange the two smaller pieces to form a triangle with the maximum perimeter.

19. The following figure made of 6 unit squares has a perimeter of 12 units. The figure is made in such a way that each square must share at least one complete side with another square.

a. Add more squares to the figure above so that the perimeter of the new figure is 18.

b. What is the minimum number of squares required to make a new figure of perimeter 18?

c. What is the maximum number of squares that can be used to make a new figure of perimeter 18?

20. For each of the following circumferences, find the radius of the circle:

   a. 12π cm
   b. 6 m
   c. 0.67 m
   d. 92π cm

21. For each of the following, if a circle has the dimensions given, determine its circumference:

   a. 6 cm diameter
   b. 3 cm radius
   c. $\frac{2}{\pi}$ cm radius
   d. 6π cm diameter

22. What happens to the circumference of a circle if the length of the radius is doubled?

23. The following figure is a circle whose radius is *r* units. The diameters of the two semicircular regions inside the large circle are also *r* units long. Compute the length of the curve that separates the shaded and white regions.

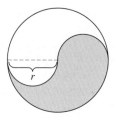

24. Astronomers use a light year to measure distance. A light year is the distance light travels in 1 yr. The speed of light is 300,000 km/sec.

a. How long is 1 light year in kilometers?

b. The nearest star (other than the sun) is Alpha Centauri. It is 4.34 light years from Earth. How far is that in kilometers?

c. How long will it take a rocket traveling 60,000 km/hr to reach Alpha Centauri?

d. How long will it take the rocket in (c) to travel to the sun if it takes approximately 8 min 19 sec for light from the sun to reach Earth?

25. Jet planes can exceed the speed of sound, so a new measurement called *Mach number* was invented to measure the speed of such planes. Mach 2 is twice the speed of sound. (Mach number is a number that indicates the ratio of the speed of an object through a medium to the speed of sound in the medium.) The speed of sound in air is approximately 344 m/sec.

a. Express Mach 2.5 in kilometers per hour.

b. Express Mach 3 in meters per second.

c. Express the speed of 5000 km/hr as a Mach number.

26. Refer to the following figure and determine the perimeter of the paint lane (shaded area) and the semicircle determined by the free-throw line on a basketball court:

27. Find the length of the side of a square that has the same perimeter as a rectangle that is 66 cm by 32 cm.

28. Give the greatest possible error for each of the following measurements:

a. 23 m

b. 3.6 cm

c. 3.12 m

29. On a circular merry-go-round, one horse is 3 m from the center and another is 6 m from the center. The merry-go-round makes 3 revolutions per minute. Are the bases of the merry-go-round that the two horses are standing on traveling at the same speed? If not, how fast is each traveling?

Communication

30. There has been considerable debate about whether the United States should change to the metric system. (a) Based on your experiences with linear measure, what do you see as the advantages of changing? (b) Which system do you think would be easier for children to learn? Why? (c) What things will probably not change if the United States adopts the metric system?

31. A student has a tennis ball can with a flat top and bottom containing three tennis balls. To the student's surprise, the perimeter of the top of the can is longer than the height of the can. The student wants to know if this fact can be explained without performing any measurements. Can you help?

32. In track, the second lane from the inside of the track is longer than the inside lane. Use this information to explain why, in running events that require a complete lap of the track, runners are lined up at the starting blocks as shown in the following figure:

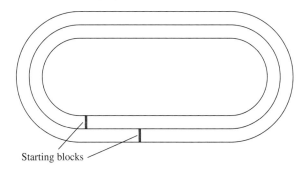

Starting blocks

Open-Ended

33. Observe that it is possible to build a triangle with toothpicks that has sides of 3, 4, and 5 toothpicks, as shown, and answer the questions that follow.

a. Find two other triples of toothpicks that can be used as sides of a triangle and two other triples that cannot be used to create a triangle.

b. Describe how to tell whether a given triple of numbers *a, b, c* can be used to construct a triangle with sides of *a, b,* and *c* toothpicks. Explain why your rule is valid.

Cooperative Learning

34. a. Help each person in the group find his or her height in centimeters.

b. Help each person in the group find the length of his or her outstretched arms (horizontal) from fingertip to fingertip.

c. Compare the difference between the two measurements in parts (a) and (b). Compare the results of the group members and make a conjecture about the lengths of the two measurements.

d. Compare your group's results with other groups to determine if they have similar findings.

35. Jerry wants to design a gold chain 60 cm long made of thin gold wire circles, each of which is the same size. He wants to use the least amount of wire and wonders what the radius of each circle should be.

— 60 cm —

a. Each member of the group should choose a specific number of circles and find the length of wire needed to make a 60-cm chain with the chosen number of circles.
b. Compare your results and make a conjecture based on the results.
c. Justify your conjecture.

BRAIN
T E A S E R

Suppose a wire is stretched tightly around Earth. (The radius of Earth is approximately 6400 km.) Then suppose the wire is cut and its length is increased by 20 m. It is then placed back around the planet so that it is the same distance from Earth at every point. Could you walk under the wire?

11-2   Areas of Polygons and Circles

Area is measured using square units and the area of a region is the number of nonoverlapping square units that cover the region. A square measuring 1 ft on a side has an area of one square foot, denoted 1 ft^2. A square measuring 1 cm on a side has an area of one square centimeter, denoted 1 cm^2.

Areas on a Geoboard

In teaching the concept of area, intuitive activities should precede the development of formulas. Many such activities can be accomplished using a *geoboard* or *dot paper*. Notice that the square unit is defined in the upper left corner of the dot paper in Figure 11-9(a). The area of the pentagon can be found by finding the sum of the areas of smaller pieces. Finding the area in this way, is the *addition method*. The region in Figure 11-9(b) has been divided into smaller pieces in Figure 11-9(c), what is the area of this shape?

FIGURE 11-9

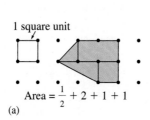

1 square unit

$\text{Area} = \dfrac{1}{2} + 2 + 1 + 1$

(a)

(b)

(c)

FIGURE 11-10

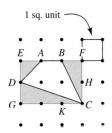

1 sq. unit

Another method of finding the area of shapes on the dot paper is the *rectangle method*. To find the area of quadrilateral *ABCD* in Figure 11-10, we construct the rectangle *EFCG* around the quadrilateral and then subtract the areas of the shaded triangles *EAD*, *BFC*, and *DGC*. The area of the rectangle *EFCG* can be counted to be 6 square units. The area of $\triangle EAD$ is $\frac{1}{2}$ square unit, and the area of $\triangle BFC$ is half the area of rectangle *BFCK*, or $\frac{1}{2}$ of 2, or 1 square unit. Similarly, the area of $\triangle DGC$ is half the area of rectangle *DHCG*, that is, $\frac{1}{2} \cdot 3$, or $\frac{3}{2}$ square units. Consequently, the area of *ABCD* is $6 - \left(\frac{1}{2} + 1 + \frac{3}{2}\right)$, or 3 square units.

EXAMPLE 11-6

Using a geoboard, find the area of each of the shaded parts of Figure 11-11.

FIGURE 11-11

(a)

(b)

Solution **a.** We construct a rectangle around the hexagon and then subtract the areas of regions *a*, *b*, *c*, *d*, and *e* from the area of this rectangle, as shown in Figure 11-12. Therefore the area of the hexagon is $16 - (3 + 1 + 1 + 1 + 1)$, or 9 square units. The addition method could also be used in this problem.

FIGURE 11-12

b. The area of the hexagon equals the area of the surrounding rectangle shown in Figure 11-13 minus the sum of the areas of figures *a*, *b*, *c*, *d*, *e*, *f*, and *g*. Thus the area of the hexagon is $12 - (3 + 1 + \frac{1}{2} + \frac{1}{2} + 1 + 1 + 1)$, or 4 square units.

FIGURE 11-13

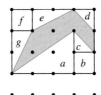

NOW TRY THIS 11-5

Instead of using a square for the unit of area, find how many of each of the following non-standard shapes are contained in Figure 11-14:

FIGURE 11-14

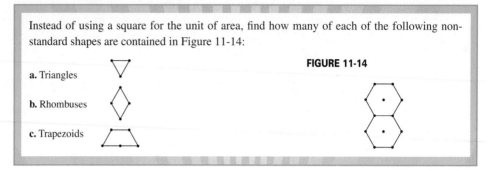

a. Triangles

b. Rhombuses

c. Trapezoids

Converting Units of Area

The price of new carpet for a house is quoted in terms of dollars per square yard, for example, $12.50/yd^2. The most commonly used units of area in the English system are the square inch (in.^{2}), the square foot (ft^2), the square yard (yd^2), the square mile (mi^2), and, for land measure, the acre (A). In the metric system, the most commonly used units are the square millimeter (mm^2), the square centimeter (cm^2), the square meter (m^2), the square kilometer (km^2), and, for land measure, the hectare (ha). It is often necessary to convert from one area measure to another within a system.

To determine how many 1-cm squares are in a square meter, look at Figure 11-15(a). There are 100 cm in 1 m, so each side of the square meter has a measure of 100 cm. Thus it takes 100 rows of 100 1-cm squares each to fill a square meter, that is, $100 \cdot 100$, or 10,000 1-cm squares. Because the area of each centimeter square is 1 cm $\cdot$ 1 cm, or 1 cm^2, there are 10,000 cm^2 in 1 m^2. In general, the area A of a square that is s units on a side is s^2, as shown in Figure 11-15(b).

FIGURE 11-15

1 m = 100 cm   1 m^2 = 10,000 cm^2

$A = s^2$
Square

s

(b)

1 cm^2 →

(a)   1 m = 100 cm

Other metric conversions of area measure can be developed similarly. For example, Figure 11-16(a) shows that 1 m^2 = 10,000 cm^2 = 1,000,000 mm^2. Likewise, Figure 11-16(b) shows that 1 m^2 = 0.000001 km^2. Similarly, 1 cm^2 = 100 mm^2 and 1 km^2 = 1,000,000 m^2.

FIGURE 11-16

(a)   (b)

Table 11-4 shows the symbols for metric units of area and their relationship to the square meter.

Table 11-4

Unit	Symbol	Relationship to Square Meter
square kilometer	km^2	1,000,000 m^2
*square hectometer	hm^2	10,000 m^2
*square dekameter	dam^2	100 m^2
square meter	$\mathbf{m^2}$	**1** $\mathbf{m^2}$
*square decimeter	dm^2	0.01 m^2
square centimeter	cm^2	0.0001 m^2
square millimeter	mm^2	0.000001 m^2

*Not commonly used

EXAMPLE 11-7

Convert each of the following:

a. 5 cm^2 = _____ mm^2
b. 124,000,000 m^2 = _____ km^2

Solution   **a.** 1 cm^2 = 100 mm^2 implies 5 cm^2 = 5 · 1 cm^2 = 5 · 100 mm^2 = 500 mm^2.
 b. 1 m^2 = 0.000001 km^2 implies 124,000,000 m^2 = 124,000,000 · 1 m^2 = 124,000,000 · 0.000001 km^2 = 124 km^2

REMARK   Students sometimes confuse the area of 5 cm^2 with the area of a square 5 cm on each side. The area of a square 5 cm on each side is $(5 \text{ cm})^2$, or 25 cm^2. Five squares each 1 cm by 1 cm have the area of 5 cm^2. Thus 5 $cm^2 \neq (5 \text{ cm})^2$.

Based on the relationship among units of length in the English system, it is possible to convert among English units of area. For example, because 1 yd = 3 ft, it follows that $(1 \text{ yd})^2$ = 1 yd · 1 yd = 3 ft · 3 ft = 9 ft^2. Similarly, because 1 ft = 12 in., $(1 \text{ ft})^2$ = 1 ft · 1 ft = 12 in. · 12 in. = 144 $in.^2$ Table 11-5 summarizes various relationships among units of area in the English system.

Table 11-5

Unit of Area	Equivalent of Other Units
1 ft^2	$\frac{1}{9}$ yd^2, or 144 in.^{2}
1 yd^2	9 ft^2
1 mi^2	3,097,600 yd^2, or 27,878,400 ft^2

Land Measure

One application of area today is in land measure. The common unit of land measure in the

acre   English system is the **acre**. Historically, an acre was the amount of land a man with one horse could plow in one day. There are 4840 yd^2 in 1 acre. For very large land measures

square mile   in the English system, the **square mile** (mi^2), or 640 acres, is used.

In the metric system, small land areas are measured in terms of a square unit 10 m on a

are   side, called an **are** (pronounced "air") and denoted by **a**. Thus 1 a = 10 m · 10 m, or 100 m^2.

hectare   Larger land areas are measured in **hectares**. A hectare is 100 a. A hectare, denoted by **ha**, is the amount of land whose area is 10,000 m^2. It follows that 1 ha is the area of a square that is

square kilometer   100 m on a side. Therefore, 1 ha = hm^2. For very large land measures, the **square kilometer**, denoted by km^2, is used. One square kilometer is the area of a square with a side 1 km, or 1000 m, long. Land area measures are summarized in Table 11-6.

Table 11-6

Unit of Area	Equivalent of Other Units
1 a	100 m^2
1 ha	100 a, or 10,000 m^2, or 1 hm^2
1 km^2	1,000,000 m^2
1 acre	4840 yd^2
1 mi^2	640 acres

EXAMPLE
11-8

a. A square field has a side of 400 m. Find the area of the field in hectares.
b. A square field has a side of 400 yd. Find the area of the field in acres.

Solution   **a.** $A = (400 \text{ m})^2 = 160,000 \text{ m}^2 = \dfrac{160,000}{10,000} \text{ ha} = 16 \text{ ha}$

b. $A = (400 \text{ yd})^2 = 160,000 \text{ yd}^2 = \dfrac{160,000}{4840} \text{ acre} \doteq 33.1 \text{ acre}$

TECHNOLOGY
C O R N E R

GSP Lab 8 in Appendix III can be used at this point to motivate the formulas for finding the areas of a rectangle, parallelogram, and trapezoid.

Area of a Rectangle

To measure area, we may count the number of units of area contained in any given region. For example, suppose the square in Figure 11-17(a) represents 1 square unit. Then, the rectangle $ABCD$ in Figure 11-17(b) contains $3 \cdot 4$, or 12 square units.

FIGURE 11-17

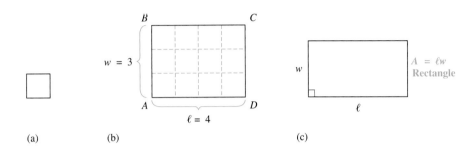

(a)   (b)   (c)

If the unit in Figure 11-17(a) is 1 cm^2, then the area of rectangle $ABCD$ is 12 cm^2. In general, the area A of any rectangle can be found by multiplying the lengths of two adjacent sides ℓ and w, or $A = \ell w$, as given in Figure 11-17(c).

EXAMPLE 11-9

Find the area of each rectangle in Figure 11-18.

FIGURE 11-18

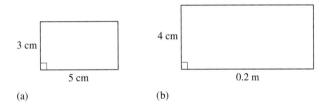

(a)   (b)

Solution   **a.** $A = (3 \text{ cm})(5 \text{ cm}) = 15 \text{ cm}^2$

b. First, write the lengths of the sides in the same unit of length. Because 0.2 m = 20 cm, $A = (4 \text{ cm})(20 \text{ cm}) = 80 \text{ cm}^2$. Alternatively, 4 cm = 0.04 m, so $A = (0.04 \text{ m})(0.2 \text{ m}) = 0.008 \text{ m}^2$.

NOW TRY THIS 11-6

Estimate the area in square centimeters of a dollar bill. Measure and calculate how close your estimate is to the actual area.

Area of a Parallelogram

The area of a parallelogram can be found by *reducing the problem to one that we already know how to solve*, in this case, finding the area of a rectangle. To develop the area formula for a parallelogram, complete Now Try This 11-7.

NOW TRY THIS 11-7

Cut out a parallelogram *ABCD* similar to the one in Figure 11-19(a). Now cut off a shaded triangle as shown and move it to the right to obtain a rectangle.

FIGURE 11-19

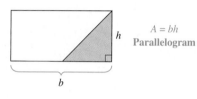

(a)   (b)

a. How do the areas of the parallelogram and the rectangle compare? Why?
b. How does this experiment lead to the formula for finding the area of a parallelogram?

base ◆ height

FIGURE 11-20

In general, any side of a parallelogram can be designated as a **base**. The **height** (*h*) is the distance between the bases and is always the length of a segment perpendicular to the lines containing the bases. Now Try This 11-6 shows that the area of parallelogram *ABCD* is given by $A = bh$, that is, the length of the base times the corresponding height. Similarly, in Figure 11-20, *EB*, or *g*, is the height that corresponds to the bases $\overline{AD}$ and $\overline{BC}$, each of which has measure *a*. Consequently, the area of the parallelogram *ABCD* is *ag*. Similarly, its area can be expressed as *bh*. Therefore $A = ag = bh$.

Area of a Triangle

The formula for the area of a triangle can be derived from the formula for the area of a parallelogram. To explore this, suppose $\triangle BAC$ in Figure 11-21(a) has base of length *b* and height *h*. Let $\triangle BAC'$ be the image of $\triangle BAC$ when $\triangle BAC$ is rotated 180° about *M*, the midpoint of $\overline{AB}$, as in Figure 11-21(b). Proving that quadrilateral *BCAC'* is a parallelogram

FIGURE 11-21

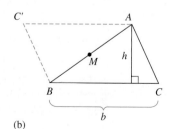

(a)   (b)

is left as an exercise. Parallelogram $BCAC'$ has area bh and is constructed of congruent triangles BAC and BAC'. So the area of $\triangle ABC$ is $\frac{1}{2}bh$. In general, the area of a triangle is equal to half the product of the length of a side and the altitude to that side.

In Figure 11-22, $\overline{BC}$ is a base of $\triangle ABC$, and the corresponding height h_1, or AE, is the distance from the opposite vertex A to the line containing $\overline{BC}$. Similarly, $\overline{AC}$ can be chosen as a base. Then h_2, or BG, the distance from the opposite vertex B to the line containing $\overline{AC}$, is the corresponding height. If $\overline{AB}$ is chosen as a base, then the corresponding height is h_3, or FC. Thus the area of $\triangle ABC$ is

$$\text{Area}\,(\triangle ABC) = \frac{bh_1}{2} = \frac{ah_2}{2} = \frac{ch_3}{2}.$$

FIGURE 11-22

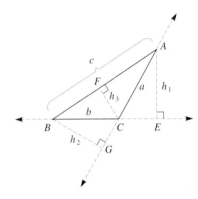

NOW TRY THIS 11-8

To see how the formula for the area of a triangle can be derived from the formula for the area of a rectangle, cut out any triangle as in Figure 11-23(a) and fold the altitude in half as shown in Figure 11-23(b). Next fold along the colored segments in the trapezoid in Figure 11-23(c) to obtain the rectangle in Figure 11-23(d).

FIGURE 11-23

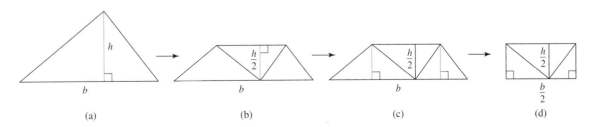

a. What is the area of the rectangle in Figure 11-23(d)?

b. How can the formula for the area of a triangle be developed from your answer in part (a)?

E X A M P L E
11-10

Find the areas in Figure 11-24. Assume the quadrilaterals *ABCD* in (a) and (b) are parallelograms.

FIGURE 11-24

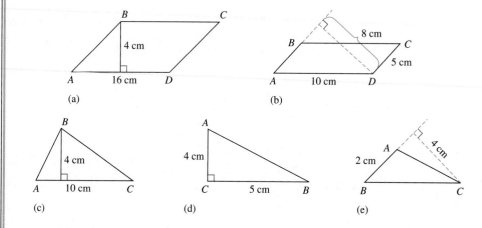

(a)

(b)

(c)

(d)

(e)

Solution   **a.** $A = bh = (16 \text{ cm})(4 \text{ cm}) = 64 \text{ cm}^2$

b. $A = bh = (5 \text{ cm})(8 \text{ cm}) = 40 \text{ cm}^2$

c. $A = \frac{1}{2}bh = \frac{1}{2}(10 \text{ cm})(4 \text{ cm}) = 20 \text{ cm}^2$

d. $A = \frac{1}{2}bh = \frac{1}{2}(5 \text{ cm})(4 \text{ cm}) = 10 \text{ cm}^2$

e. $A = \frac{1}{2}bh = \frac{1}{2}(2 \text{ cm})(4 \text{ cm}) = 4 \text{ cm}^2$

Area of a Trapezoid

The formula for the area of a trapezoid can be developed using the formula for the area of a parallelogram, as shown in Now Try This 11-9.

NOW TRY THIS 11-9

Cut out a trapezoid *ABCD* as shown in Figure 11-25. Copy and place as shown. Use the figure obtained to derive the formula for the area of a trapezoid.

FIGURE 11-25

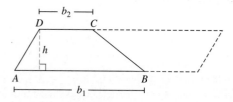

Areas of general polygons can also be found by partitioning the polygons into triangles, finding the areas of the triangles, and summing those areas. In Figure 11-26(a), trapezoid $ABCD$ has bases b_1 and b_2 and height h. By connecting points B and D, as in Figure 11-26(b), we create two triangles: one with base of length $\underline{AB}$ and height DE and the other with base length of CD and height BF. Because $\overline{DE} \cong \overline{BF}$, each has length h. Thus the areas of triangles ADB and DCB are $\frac{1}{2}(b_1 h)$ and $\frac{1}{2}(b_2 h)$, respectively. Hence, the area of trapezoid $ABCD$ is $\frac{1}{2}(b_1 h) + \frac{1}{2}(b_2 h), = \frac{1}{2}h(b_1 + b_2)$. That is, the area of a trapezoid is equal to half the height times the sum of the lengths of the bases, which should be the same as the formula you derived in Now Try This 11-8.

FIGURE 11-26

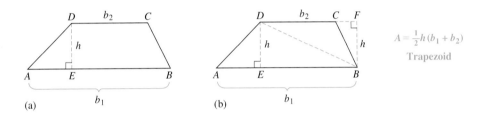

(a)   (b) $A = \frac{1}{2}h(b_1 + b_2)$
                          Trapezoid

EXAMPLE 11-11

Find the areas of the trapezoids in Figure 11-27.

FIGURE 11-27

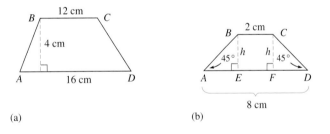

(a)   (b)

Solution   **a.** $A = \frac{1}{2}h(b_1 + b_2) = \frac{1}{2}(4 \text{ cm})(12 \text{ cm} + 16 \text{ cm}) = 56 \text{ cm}^2$

b. To find the area of trapezoid $ABCD$, we *use the strategy of determining a subgoal* of finding the height, h. In Figure 11-27(b), $BE = CF = h$. Also, $\overline{BE}$ is a side of $\triangle ABE$, which has angles with measures of 45° and 90°. Consequently, the third angle in triangle ABE is $180 - (45 + 90)$, or 45°. Therefore $\triangle ABE$ is isosceles and $AE = BE = h$. Similarly, it follows that $FD = h$. Because $AD = 8 \text{ cm} = h + EF + h$, we could find h if we knew the value of EF. From Figure 11-27(b), $EF = BC = 2 \text{ cm}$ because $BCFE$ is a rectangle (why?) and opposite sides of a rectangle are congruent. Now $h + EF + h = h + 2 + h = 8 \text{ cm}$.

Thus $h = 3 \text{ cm}$ and the area of the trapezoid is $A = \frac{1}{2}(3 \text{ cm})(2 \text{ cm} + 8 \text{ cm})$, or 15 cm^2.

PROBLEM SOLVING   <u>**Equal Areas Problem**</u>

Larry purchased a plot of land surrounded by a fence. The former owner had subdivided the land into 13 equal-sized square plots, as shown in Figure 11-28. To reapportion the property into two plots of equal area, Larry wishes to build a single, straight fence beginning at the far left corner (point *P* on the drawing). Is such a fence possible? If so, where should the other end be?

FIGURE 11-28

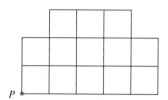

Understanding the Problem   We want to divide the land in Figure 11-28 into two plots of equal area by means of a straight fence starting at point *P*. A *subgoal* is to find the other endpoint. Because the area of the entire plot is 13 square units, the area of each part formed by the fence must be $\frac{1}{2} \cdot 13$, or $6\frac{1}{2}$ square units.

Devising a Plan   To find an approximate location for the fence, consider a fence connecting *P* with point *A*, as shown in Figure 11-29. The area of the land below fence *PA* is the sum of the areas of $\triangle APD$ and the rectangle *DAFE*. The area of $\triangle APD$ is 4 and the area of rectangle *DAFE* is 2, so the area below the fence $\overline{PA}$ is 4 + 2, or 6, square units. We want an area of $6\frac{1}{2}$ square units. Consequently, the other end of the fence should be above point *A*.

FIGURE 11-29

A similar argument shows that the area below $\overline{PB}$ is 8 square units and hence the end of the fence should be below *B*. Thus the other end of the fence should be at a point *C* between *A* and *B*. To find the exact location of point *C*, we designate *CA* by *x*. We then *write an equation* for *x* by finding the area below $\overline{PC}$ in terms of *x*, make the area equal to $6\frac{1}{2}$, and solve for *x*.

Carrying Out the Plan   The area below $\overline{PC}$ equals the area of $\triangle PCD$ plus the area of the rectangle *DAFE*. The area of $\triangle PCD$ is

$$\frac{PD \cdot DC}{2} = \frac{4(2 + x)}{2} = 2(2 + x) = 4 + 2x.$$

The area of rectangle *DAFE* is 2, so $(4 + 2x) + 2$ should equal half the area of the plot. Consequently, we have the following:

$$4 + 2x + 2 = \frac{13}{2}$$
$$2x = \frac{1}{2}$$
$$x = \frac{1}{4}$$

Therefore the fence should be built along the line connecting point *P* to the point *C*, which is $\frac{1}{4}$ unit directly above point *A*. Point *C* can be found by dividing $\overline{AB}$ into four congruent parts.

Looking Back   We check that the solution is correct by finding the area above $\overline{PC}$. The problem can be varied by changing the shape of the plot. Another variation is to ask if Larry could divide the plot into thirds, fourths, and so on. We could also approach the problem as if Larry wanted to subdivide the land but wanted to use the existing lines that mark the squares.

Area of a Regular Polygon

The area of a triangle can be used to find the area of any regular polygon, as illustrated *using a simpler case strategy* involving a regular hexagon in Figure 11-30(a). The hexagon can be separated into six congruent triangles, each with a vertex at the center (the center of the circle containing each vertex), with side *s* and height *a*. The height of such a triangle of a regular polygon is the *apothem* and is denoted *a*. The area of each triangle is $\frac{1}{2}as$. Because six triangles make up the hexagon, the area of the hexagon is $6(\frac{1}{2}as)$, or $\frac{1}{2}a(6s)$. However, 6*s* is the perimeter *p* of the hexagon, so the area of the hexagon is $\frac{1}{2}ap$. The same process can be used to develop the formula for the area of any regular polygon. That is, the area of any regular polygon is $\frac{1}{2}ap$, where *a* is the height of one of the triangles involved and *p* is the perimeter of the polygon, as shown in Figure 11-30(b).

FIGURE 11-30

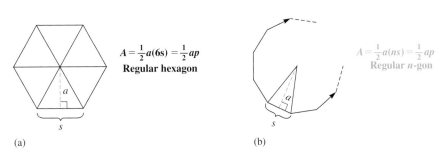

$A = \frac{1}{2}a(6s) = \frac{1}{2}ap$
Regular hexagon

$A = \frac{1}{2}a(ns) = \frac{1}{2}ap$
Regular *n*-gon

(a)

(b)

Area of a Circle

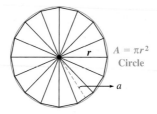

FIGURE 11-31

We use the strategy of *examining a related problem* to find the area of a circle. The area of a regular polygon inscribed in a circle, as in Figure 11-31, approximates the area of the circle, and we know that the area of any regular n-gon is $\frac{1}{2}ap$, where a is the height of a triangle of the n-gon and p is the perimeter. If the number of sides n is made very large, then the perimeter and the area of the n-gon are close to those of the circle.

Also, the apothem a is approximately equal to the radius r of the circle, and the perimeter p approximates the circumference $2\pi r$. Because the area of the circle is approximately equal to the area of the n-gon, $\frac{1}{2}ap \doteq \frac{1}{2}r \cdot 2\pi r = \pi r^2$. In fact, the area of the circle is precisely πr^2.

Another approach for leading students to discover the formula for finding the area of a circle is given in Now Try This 11-10.

NOW TRY THIS 11-10

> **a.** Draw a circle of radius 4 cm and divide it into eight equal-sized sections.
> **b.** Using the circle you constructed, answer question 24–28 on the student page.
> **c.** How can you obtain the formula for the area of a circle by following the instructions in question 28 on the student page?

Area of a Sector

sector
central angle

A **sector** of a circle is a pie-shaped region of the circle determined by an angle whose vertex is the center of the circle. This angle is a **central angle**. The area of a sector depends on the radius of the circle and the measure of the central angle determining the sector. If the angle has a measure of 90°, as in Figure 11-32(a), the area of the sector is one-fourth the area of the circle, or $\frac{90}{360}\pi r^2$. The area of a sector with central angle of 1° is $\frac{1}{360}$ of the area of a circle and a sector with central angle $\theta°$ has area $\frac{\theta}{360}$ of the area of the circle or $\frac{\theta}{360}(\pi r^2)$, as shown in Figure 11-32(b).

FIGURE 11-32

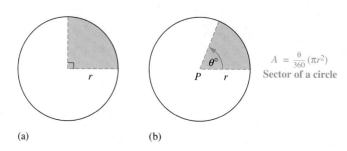

(a)   (b)

Sample School Book Page:

AREA OF A CIRCLE

24 **Use Labsheet 2A.** Follow the directions below.

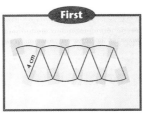

First

Cut out the *Circle*. Then cut apart the eight sectors and arrange them to form the figure shown. Tape the figure to a sheet of paper.

Then

Use a ruler to draw segments across the top and bottom of your figure. Extend the sides of the figure to meet the bottom segment.

25 What kind of polygon is the new figure you drew in Question 24?

26 **Try This as a Class** Use the figure you made in Question 24.

a. Estimation Explain how you could use the new figure you drew to estimate the area of the circle. Then estimate the area. Do you think this is a good estimate? Why or why not?

b. How is the length of the base of the figure related to the circumference of the circle?

c. How is the height of the figure related to the radius of the circle?

27 **Discussion** Examine the drawings shown.

a. As a circle is cut into more and more sectors and put back together as shown, what begins to happen to its shape?

b. The area *A* of a parallelogram is found by multiplying the length of its base *b* by the height *h*, or $A = bh$. Use your figure to explain why this formula can be written as $A = \frac{1}{2}Cr$ to find the area of a circle, where *C* is the circumference and *r* is the length of the radius of the circle.

28 The circumference *C* of a circle is equal to $2\pi r$, where *r* is the length of the radius. Rewrite the formula $A = \frac{1}{2}Cr$ by substituting $2\pi r$ for *C*.

Source: McDougal Littell, Middle Grades MATH Thematics, Book 2, 2002 (p. 402).

ONGOING ASSESSMENT 11-2

1. As an example of measuring area with a nonstandard measure, estimate the area of your desktop in terms of a piece of notebook paper as your unit of area. Then measure the area of your desktop with the paper and compare it to your estimate.

2. Choose the most appropriate metric units (cm², m², or km²) and English units (in.², yd², mi²) for measuring each of the following:
   a. Area of a sheet of notebook paper
   b. Area of a quarter
   c. Area of a desktop
   d. Area of a classroom floor
   e. Area of a parallel parking space
   f. Area of an airport runway

3. Estimate and then measure each of the following using cm², m², or km².
   a. Area of a door b. Area of a chair seat
   c. Area of a desktop d. Area of a chalkboard

4. Complete the following conversion table:

Item	m²	cm²	mm²
a. Area of a sheet of paper		588	
b. Area of a cross-section of a crayon			192
c. Area of a desktop	1.5		
d. Area of a dollar bill		100	
e. Area of a postage stamp		5	

5. Using a calculator, complete the following conversions:
   a. 4000 ft² = _____ yd² b. 10^6 yd² = _____ mi²
   c. 10 mi² = _____ acre d. 3 acres = _____ ft²

6. Complete each of the following:
   a. A football field is about 49 m × 100 m or _____ m².
   b. About _____ a are in two football fields.
   c. About _____ ha are in two football fields.

7. Find the areas of each of the following figures if the distance between two adjacent dots in a row or a column is one unit:

(a)

(b)

(c)

(d)

(e)

(f)

8. If all vertices of a polygon are points on square-dot paper, the polygon is a **lattice polygon**. In 1899, G. Pick discovered a surprising theorem involving I, the number of dots *inside* the polygon, and B, the number of dots that lie *on* the polygon. The theorem states that the area of any lattice polygon is $I + \frac{1}{2}B - 1$. Check that this is true for the polygons in problem 7.

9. Find the area of $\triangle ABC$ in each of the following triangles:

1 acre = 4840 yd²
1 mi² = 640 acre

(a)

(b)

(c)

(d)

10. Find the area of each of the following quadrilaterals:

Square
(a)

Rectangle
(b)

Parallelogram
(c)

Trapezoid
(d)

Trapezoid
(e)

11. a. A rectangular piece of land is 1300 m × 1500 m.
    i. What is the area in square kilometers?
    ii. What is the area in hectares?
    b. A rectangular piece of land is 1300 yd × 1500 yd.
    i. What is the area in square miles?
    ii. What is the area in acres?
    c. Explain which measuring system you would rather use to solve problems like those in (a) and (b).

12. For a parallelogram whose sides are 6 cm and 10 cm, which of the following is true?
    a. The data are insufficient to enable us to determine the area.
    b. The area equals 60 cm².
    c. The area is greater than 60 cm².
    d. The area is less than 60 cm².

13. If the diagonals of a rhombus are *a* and *b* units long, find the area of the rhombus in terms of *a* and *b*.

14. Find the cost of carpeting the following rectangular rooms:
    a. Dimensions: 6.5 m × 4.5 m; cost = $13.85/m²
    b. Dimensions: 15 ft × 11 ft; cost = $30/yd²

15. Find the area of each of the following. Leave your answers in terms of π.

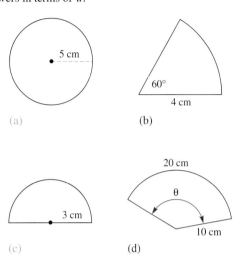

(a)

(b)

(c)

(d)

16. Joe uses stick-on square carpet tiles to cover his 3 m × 4 m bathroom. If each tile is 10 cm on a side, how many tiles does he need?

17. A rectangular plot of land is to be seeded with grass. If the plot is 22 m × 28 m and a 1-kg bag of seed is needed for 85 m² of land, how many bags of seed are needed?

18. Find the area of each of the following regular polygons:

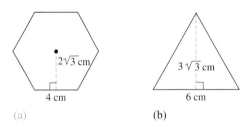

(a)

(b)

19. Suppose the largest square peg possible is placed in a circular hole as shown in the following figure and that the largest circular peg possible is placed in a square hole. In which case is there a smaller percentage of space wasted?

20. a. If a circle has a circumference of 8π cm, what is its area?
    b. If a circle of radius *r* and a square with a side of length *s* have equal areas, express *r* in terms of *s*.

21. Find the area of each of the following shaded parts. Assume all arcs are circular.

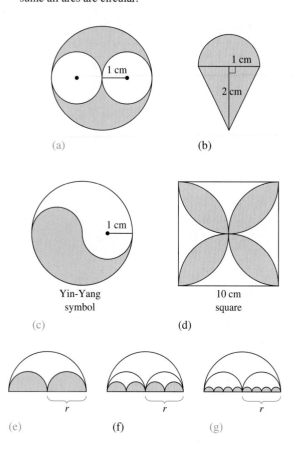

Yin-Yang symbol
(c)

10 cm square
(d)

(a)

(b)

(e)

(f)

(g)

22. A circular flower bed is 6 m in diameter and has a circular sidewalk around it 1 m wide. Find the area of the sidewalk in square meters.

23. a. If the area of a square is 144 cm², what is its perimeter?
   b. If the perimeter of a square is 32 cm, what is its area?

24. a. What happens to the area of a square when the length of each side is doubled?
   b. If the ratio of the sides of two squares is 1 to 5, what is the ratio of their areas?

25. a. What happens to the area of a circle if its diameter is doubled?
   b. What happens to the area of a circle if its radius is increased by 10%?
   c. What happens to the area of a circle if its circumference is tripled?

26. A rectangular field is 64 m × 25 m. Shawn wants to fence a square field that has the same area as the rectangular field. How long are the sides of the square field?

27. A store has wrapping paper on sale. One package is 3 rolls of $2\frac{1}{2}$ ft × 8 ft for $6.00. Another package is 5 rolls of $2\frac{1}{2}$ ft × 6 ft for $8.00. Which is the better buy?

28. Find the shaded area enclosed by two semicircles as shown in the following figure:

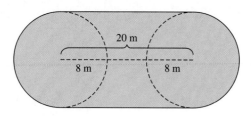

29. An aircraft company starts with a square piece of metal measuring 10 in. × 10 in. and wants to remove a strip x in. wide from all sides to form another square with an area of 64 in.² Find x.

30. The following figure consists of five congruent squares. Find a segment through point P that divides the figure into two parts of equal area.

31. a. Sketch a graph showing the relationship between the length and width of all rectangles with perimeters of 12 cm.
   b. Sketch a graph showing the relationship between the length and width of all rectangles with areas of 12 cm².

32. For a dartboard (see the following figure), Joan is trying to determine how the area of the outside shaded region compares with the area of the inside shaded region so that she can determine payoffs. How do they compare?

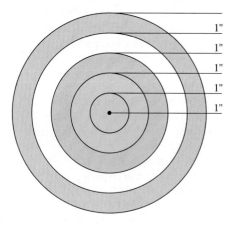

33. Quadrilateral *MATH* has been dissected into squares. The area of the red square is 64 square units and the area of the blue square is 81 square units. Determine the dimensions and the area of quadrilateral *MATH*.

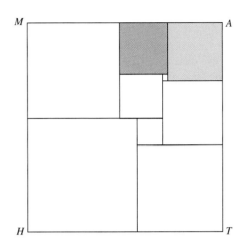

34. Complete and explain how to use geometric shapes to find an equivalent algebraic expression not involving parentheses for each of the following:

a. $a(b + c)$

b. $(a + b)(c + d)$

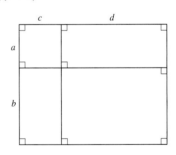

35. Draw 2 rectangles that have the same perimeter but different areas.

36. a. If the area of a rectangle remains constant but its perimeter has increased, how has the shape of the rectangle changed?

b. If the perimeter of a rectangle remains constant but its area has increased, how has the shape of the rectangle changed?

37. In the following figure, $\ell \parallel \overleftrightarrow{AB}$. If the area of $\triangle ABP$ is 10 cm^2, what are the areas of $\triangle ABQ$, $\triangle ABR$, $\triangle ABS$, $\triangle ABT$, and $\triangle ABU$? Explain your answers.

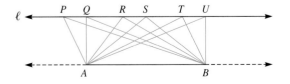

38. Hero's (or Heron's) formula can be used to find the area of a triangle if the lengths of the three sides are known. If the lengths of the three sides are *a, b,* and *c* units and the semiperimeter $s = \dfrac{a + b + c}{2}$, then the area of the triangle is given by $\sqrt{s(s - a)(s - b)(s - c)}$. Use Hero's formula to find the areas of the right triangles with sides given below.

a. 3 cm, 4 cm, 5 cm

b. 5 cm, 12 cm, 13 cm

39. Given $\triangle ABC$ with parallel lines dividing $\overline{AB}$ into three congruent segments as shown, how does the area of $\triangle BDE$ compare with the area of $\triangle ABC$?

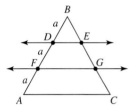

40. In the following figure, quadrilateral $ABCD$ is a parallelogram and P is any point on $\overline{AC}$. Prove that the area of $\triangle BCP$ is equal to the area of $\triangle DPC$.

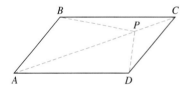

Communication

41. On a field trip, Glenda, a sixth-grade student was looking at a huge dinosaur footprint and wondering about its area. Glenda said all you have to do is place a string around the border of the print and then take the string off and form it into a square and compute the area of the square. How would you help her?

42. John claimed he had a garden twice as large as Al's rectangular-shaped garden that measured 15 ft by 30 ft. When they visited John's rectangular-shaped garden they found it measured 18 ft by 50 ft. Al claimed that it could not be twice as large since neither the length nor the width were twice as large. Who was correct and why?

43. a. If a 10-in. (diameter) pizza costs $10, how much should a 20-in. pizza cost? Explain the assumptions you made in your answer.

b. If the ratio between the diameters of two pizzas is $1 : k$, what should the ratio be between the prices? Explain the assumptions you made in your answer.

44. **a.** Explain how the following drawing can be used to determine a formula for the area of $\triangle ABC$:

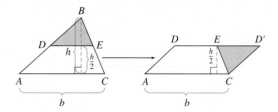

b. Use paper cutting to reassemble $\triangle ABC$ in (a) into parallelogram $ADD'C$.

45. The area of a parallelogram can be found by using the concept of a half-turn (a turn by 180°). Consider the parallelogram $ABCD$ and let M and N be the midpoints of $\overline{AB}$ and $\overline{CD}$, respectively. Rotate the shaded triangle with vertex M about M by 180° clockwise and rotate the shaded triangle with vertex N about N by 180° counterclockwise. What kind of figure do you obtain? Now complete the argument to find the area of the parallelogram.

Open-Ended

46. **a.** Estimate the area in square centimeters that your handprint will cover.

b. Trace the outline of your hand on square-centimeter grid paper and use the outline to obtain an estimate for the area. Explain how you arrived at your estimate.

47. **a.** Give dimensions of a square and a rectangle that have the same perimeter but the square has the greater area.

b. Give dimensions of a square and a rectangle that have equal area but the rectangle has greater perimeter.

Cooperative Learning

48. Use five squares to build the following cross shape and discuss the questions that follow:

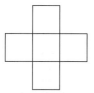

a. What is the area of this shape?

b. What is the perimeter of this shape?

c. Add squares to the shape so that each square added touches a complete edge with at least one other square.

  i. What is the minimum number of squares that can be added so that the shape has a perimeter of 18?

  ii. What is the maximum number?

  iii. What is the maximum area the new shape could have and still have a perimeter of 18?

d. Using the five squares, have members of the group start with shapes different from the original cross shape and answer the questions in (c). Discuss your results.

e. Explore shapes that are made up of more than five squares.

TECHNOLOGY
C O R N E R

Use The Geometer's Sketchpad (GSP) to explore some area concepts:

1. Complete each of the following:

  a. Construct a segment and label the endpoints A and B.

  b. Choose a point not on $\overline{AB}$ and label it C.

  c. Select $\overline{AB}$ and the point C and construct a line through C parallel to $\overline{AB}$.

  d. Choose a point on the new line and label it D.

  e. Select points A and D and construct a segment connecting points A and D.

  f. Select $\overline{AD}$ and point B and construct a line through B parallel to $\overline{AD}$.

  g. Select the two constructed lines. Construct the point at their intersection and label it E.

  h. Select the vertices (E, D, A, B) and construct the interior of the polygon.

  i. Measure the area of the polygon.

  j. Select $\angle DAB$ and measure the angle.

  k. Move point D along $\overleftrightarrow{DC}$ and find the area of all the new parallelograms formed by D, C, B, and A. How are the areas related?

  l. How does this activity lead to the formula for finding the area of a parallelogram if you know how to find the area of a rectangle?

2. Complete each of the following:
  a. Repeat steps (a) through (d) from part 1.
  b. Select points *A, B,* and *D* and construct segments connecting these points to form a triangle.
  c. Select the vertices *A, D,* and *B* and construct the interior of the polygon.
  d. Measure the area of △*ADB*.
  e. Move point *D* along $\overleftrightarrow{DC}$ and find the area of all the triangles that are formed by *A, D,* and *B*.
  f. How do these areas compare with the area of the original triangle?
  g. How can this activity be used to motivate the formula for finding the area of a triangle?
3. Take your triangle and line in 2(b) and add a line through *B* parallel to $\overline{AD}$ to form a parallelogram. Find the area of the parallelogram and compare it to the area of the triangle. How can this activity be used to motivate the formula for finding the area of a triangle?
4. Devise a way to motivate the formula for finding the area of a trapezoid using the geometry utility.

LABORATORY
A C T I V I T Y

1. On a 5 × 5 geoboard, make △*DEF* as shown in Figure 11-33. Keep the rubber band around *D* and *E* fixed and move the vertex *F* to all the possible locations so that the triangles formed will have the same area as the area of △*DEF*. How do the locations for the third vertex relate to *D* and *E*?

FIGURE 11-33

2. On a 5 × 5 geoboard, construct, if possible, squares of areas 1, 2, 3, 4, 5, 6, and 7 square units.

3. On a 5 × 5 geoboard, construct triangles that have areas $\frac{1}{2}$, 1, $1\frac{1}{2}$, 2, . . . , until the maximum-sized triangle is reached.

BRAIN
T E A S E R

The rectangle in Figure 11-34(b) was apparently formed by cutting the square in Figure 11-34(a) along the dotted lines and reassembling the pieces as pictured.

FIGURE 11-34

   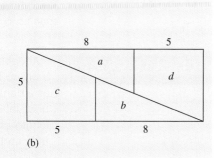

(a)   (b)

1. What is the area of the square in (a)?
2. What is the area of the rectangle in (b)?
3. How do you explain the discrepancy between the areas?

The Pythagorean Theorem and the Distance Formula

Surveyors often have to calculate distances that cannot be measured directly such as distances across water, as illustrated in Figure 11-35.

FIGURE 11-35

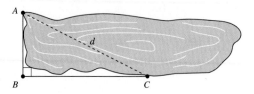

To measure the distance from point *A* to point *C*, they could use one of the most remarkable and useful theorems in geometry: the Pythagorean Theorem. This theorem was illustrated on a Greek stamp in 1955, as shown in Figure 11-36, to honor the 2500th anniversary of the founding of the Pythagorean School.

FIGURE 11-36

hypotenuse ◆ legs

In the triangle on the stamp and in triangle *ABC* in Figure 11-35, the side opposite the right angle is the **hypotenuse**. The other two sides are **legs**. Interpreted in terms of area, the Pythagorean Theorem states that the area of a square with the hypotenuse of a right triangle as a side is equal to the sum of the areas of the squares with the legs as sides.

Pythagoras (ca. 582–507 B.C.), a Greek philosopher and mathematician, was head of a group known as the Pythagoreans. Members of the group regarded Pythagoras as a demigod and attributed all their discoveries to him. One of Pythagoras's most unusual discoveries was the dependence of the musical intervals on the ratio of the length of strings at the same tension, with the ratio 2:1 giving the octave, 3:2 the fifth, and 4:3 the fourth.

Because the Pythagoreans affirmed geometric results on the basis of special cases, mathematical historians believe it is possible they may have discovered the theorem by looking at a floor tiling like the one illustrated in Figure 11-37.

FIGURE 11-37

FIGURE 11-38

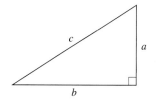

Each square can be divided by its diagonal into two congruent isosceles right triangles, so we see that the shaded square constructed with $\overline{AB}$ as a side consists of four triangles, each congruent to $\triangle ABC$. Similarly, each of the shaded squares with legs $\overline{BC}$ and $\overline{AC}$ as sides consists of two triangles congruent to $\triangle ABC$. Thus the area of the larger square is equal to the sum of the areas of the two smaller squares. The theorem is true in general and is stated as follows using Figure 11-38.

> **Theorem 11-1**

Pythagorean Theorem   If a right triangle has legs of lengths a and b and hypotenuse of length c, then $c^2 = a^2 + b^2$.

TECHNOLOGY
C O R N E R

THE GEOMETER'S
SKETCHPAD

GSP Lab 9 in Appendix III can be used at this point to investigate the Pythagorean Theorem.

There are hundreds of known proofs for the Pythagorean Theorem. The classic book *The Pythagorean Proposition*, by E. Loomis, contains many of these proofs. Some proofs involve the strategy of *drawing diagrams* with a square area c^2 equal to the sum of the areas a^2 and b^2 of two other squares. One such proof is given in Figure 11-39; others are discussed in Ongoing Assessment 11-3. In Figure 11-39(a), the measures of the legs of a right triangle *ABC* are a and b and the measure of the hypotenuse is c. We draw a square with sides of length $a + b$ and subdivide it, as shown in Figure 11-39(b). In Figure 11-39(c), another square with side of length $a + b$ is drawn and each of its sides is divided into two segments of length a and b, as shown.

FIGURE 11-39

(a)   (b)

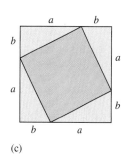

(c)

Each yellow triangle is congruent to $\triangle ABC$ (why?). Consequently, each triangle has hypotenuse c and the same area, $\frac{1}{2}ab$. Thus the length of each side of the inside blue quadrilateral in Figure 11-39(c) is c and so the figure is a rhombus. In fact, it is possible to show that the figure is a square whose area is c^2. To complete the proof, we consider the four triangles in Figure 11-39(b) and (c). Because the areas of the sets of four triangles in both Figure 11-39(b) and (c) are equal, the sum of the areas of the two shaded squares in Figure 11-39(b) equals the area of the shaded square in Figure 11-39(c), that is, $a^2 + b^2 = c^2$.

NOW TRY THIS 11-11

Henry Perigal, a London stockbroker, discovered what has been called the "paper and scissors" proof of the Pythagorean Theorem. It is illustrated in Figure 11-40. Explain how this figure could be used to justify the theorem.

FIGURE 11-40

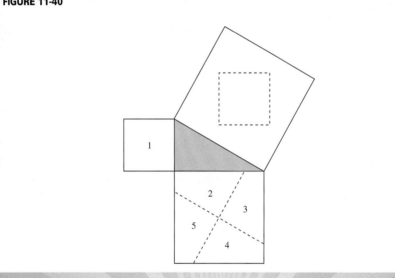

EXAMPLE 11-12

a. For the drawing in Figure 11-41, find the value of x.

FIGURE 11-41

Rectangle

b. The size of a rectangular television screen is given as the length of the diagonal of the screen. If the length of the screen is 24 cm and the width is 18 cm, as shown in Figure 11-42, what is the diagonal length?

FIGURE 11-42

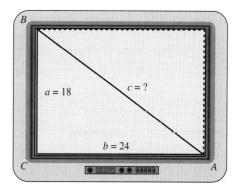

Solution   **a.** In the rectangle, the diagonal partitions the rectangle into two right triangles, each with lengths 5 units and width x units. Thus we have the following:

$$5^2 + x^2 = 7^2$$
$$25 + x^2 = 49$$
$$x^2 = 24$$
$$x = \sqrt{24}, \text{ or approximately 4.9 units.}$$

b. A right triangle is formed with the diagonal as the hypotenuse and the legs of measure 24 cm and 18 cm. The Pythagorean Theorem can be used to find the length of the diagonal.

$$c^2 = 18^2 + 24^2$$
$$c^2 = 324 + 576$$
$$c^2 = 900$$
$$c = 30$$

Because all the measurements are in centimeters, the diagonal has length 30 cm.

E X A M P L E 11-13

A pole $\overline{BD}$, 28 ft high, is perpendicular to the ground. Two wires $\overline{BC}$ and $\overline{BA}$, each 35 ft long, are attached to the top of the pole and to stakes A and C on the ground, as shown in Figure 11-43. If points A, D, and C are collinear, how far are the stakes A and C from each other?

FIGURE 11-43

Solution $\overline{AC}$ is not a side in any known right triangle, but we want to find AC. Because a point equidistant from the endpoints of a segment must be on a perpendicular bisector of the segment, then $AD = DC$. Therefore AC is twice as long as DC. Our *subgoal* is to find DC. We may find DC by applying the Pythagorean Theorem in triangle BDC. This results in the following:

$$28^2 + (DC)^2 = 35^2$$
$$(DC)^2 = 35^2 - 28^2$$
$$DC = \sqrt{441}, \text{ or 21 ft}$$
$$AC = 2 \cdot DC = 42 \text{ ft}$$

EXAMPLE 11-14

FIGURE 11-44

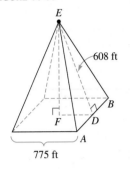

How tall is the Great Pyramid of Cheops, a right regular square pyramid, if the base has a side 775 ft and the slant height is 608 ft?

Solution In Figure 11-44, $\overline{EF}$ is a leg of a right triangle formed by $\overline{FD}$, $\overline{EF}$, and $\overline{ED}$. Because the pyramid is a right regular pyramid, $\overline{EF}$ intersects the base at its center. Thus $DF = \left(\frac{1}{2}\right)AB$, or $\left(\frac{1}{2}\right)775$, or 387.5 ft. Now ED, the slant height, has length 608 ft, and we can apply the Pythagorean Theorem as follows:

$$(EF)^2 + (DF)^2 = (ED)^2$$
$$(EF)^2 + (387.5)^2 = (608)^2$$
$$(EF)^2 = 219,507.75$$
$$EF \doteq 468.5 \text{ ft}$$

Thus the Great Pyramid is approximately 468.5 ft tall.

NOW TRY THIS 11-12

In the cartoon below, Jason runs a different pattern than he was told. Explain how he arrived at this pattern.

Special Right Triangles

45°-45°-90° right triangle

An isosceles right triangle has two legs of equal length and two 45° angles. Any such triangle is a **45°-45°-90° right triangle**. Drawing a diagonal of a square forms two of these triangles, as shown in Figure 11-45.

In Figure 11-46, we see several 45°-45°-90° triangles. Each side of the shaded square is a hypotenuse of a 45°-45°-90° triangle. The area of the shaded square is 2 square units (why?). Therefore $c^2 = 2$ and $c = \sqrt{2}$. Another way to see that $c = \sqrt{2}$ is to apply the Pythagorean Theorem to one of the nonshaded triangles. Because $c^2 = 1^2 + 1^2 = 2$, then $c = \sqrt{2}$.

FIGURE 11-45

FIGURE 11-46

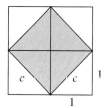

In the isosceles right triangle in Figure 11-46, each leg is 1 unit long and the hypotenuse is $\sqrt{2}$ units long. This property is generalized when the isosceles right triangle has a leg of length a, as follows.

> **Property**

Property of 45°-45°-90° triangle   In an isosceles right triangle, if the length of each leg is a, then the hypotenuse has length $a\sqrt{2}$.

Similarly, Figure 11-47(a), shows that a 30°-60°-90° triangle is half of an equilateral triangle. When the equilateral triangle has side 2 units long, then in the 30°-60°-90° triangle, the leg opposite the 30° angle is 1 unit long and the leg opposite the 60° angle has a length of $\sqrt{3}$ units.

FIGURE 11-47

(a)   (b)

This example may also be generalized using the triangle in Figure 11-47(b). When the side of the equilateral triangle ABC is $2s$, then in triangle ABD, the side opposite the 30° angle, $\overline{BD}$, is s units long, and AD may be found using the Pythagorean Theorem to have a length of $s\sqrt{3}$ units. This discussion is summarized in the following property.

> **Property**

Property of 30°-60°-90° triangle   In a 30°-60°-90° triangle, the length of the hypotenuse is two times as long as the leg opposite the 30° angle and the leg opposite the 60° angle is $\sqrt{3}$ times the shorter leg.

Converse of the Pythagorean Theorem

The converse of the Pythagorean Theorem is also true. It provided a useful way for early surveyors in particular, the Egyptian rope stretchers, to determine right angles. Figure 11-48(a) shows a knotted rope with 12 equally spaced knots. Figure 11-48(b) shows how the rope might be held to form a triangle with sides of lengths 3, 4, and 5. The triangle formed is a right triangle and contains a 90° angle.

FIGURE 11-48

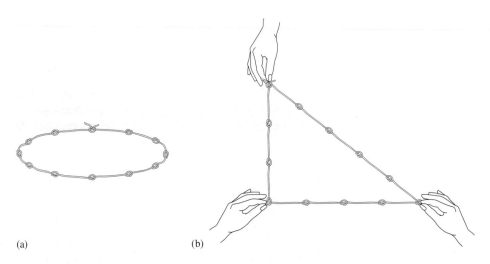

(a)   (b)

Given a triangle with sides of lengths a, b, and c such that $a^2 + b^2 = c^2$, must the triangle be a right triangle? The answer is yes, and we state the following theorem without proof.

> ### Theorem 11-2

Converse of the Pythagorean Theorem   If $\triangle ABC$ is a triangle with sides of lengths a, b, and c such that $a^2 + b^2 = c^2$, then $\triangle ABC$ is a right triangle with the right angle opposite the side of length c.

EXAMPLE 11-15

Determine if the following can be the lengths of the sides of a right triangle:

a. 51, 68, 85
b. 2, 3, $\sqrt{13}$
c. 3, 4, 7

Solution   **a.** $51^2 + 68^2 = 7225 = 85^2$, so 51, 68, and 85 can be the lengths of the sides of a right triangle.
b. $2^2 + 3^2 = 4 + 9 = 13 = (\sqrt{13})^2$, so 2, 3, and $\sqrt{13}$ can be the lengths of the sides of a right triangle.
c. $3^2 + 4^2 \neq 7^2$, so the measures cannot be the lengths of the sides of a right triangle. In fact, since $3 + 4 = 7$, these segments do not form a triangle.

NOW TRY THIS 11-13

a. Draw three segments that could be used to form the sides of a right triangle and discuss how you would show that these three lengths determine a right triangle.

b. Multiply the lengths of the three segments in (a) by a fixed number and determine if the resulting three lengths could be sides of a right triangle.

c. Using three new numbers, repeat the experiment in (a) and (b). Form a conjecture based on your experiments.

The Distance Formula: An Application of the Pythagorean Theorem

Given the coordinates of two points A and B, we can find the distance AB. We first consider the special case in which the two points are on one of the axes. For example, in Figure 11-49(a), $A(2, 0)$ and $B(5, 0)$ are on the x-axis. The distance between these two points is 3 units:

$$AB = OB - OA = 5 - 2 = 3$$

FIGURE 11-49

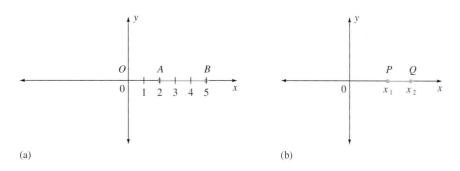

(a)   (b)

In general, if two points P and Q are on the x-axis, as in Figure 11-49(b), with x-coordinates x_1 and x_2, respectively, and $x_2 > x_1$, then $PQ = x_2 - x_1$. In fact, *the distance between two points on the x-axis is always the absolute value of the difference between the x-coordinates of the points* (why?). A similar result holds for any two points on the y-axis.

Figure 11-50 shows two points in the plane: $C(2, 5)$ and $D(6, 8)$. The distance between C and D can be found by using the strategy of *looking at a related problem*. We know how to find the length of a segment if the segment is a side or the hypotenuse of a right triangle. We obtain a right triangle by drawing perpendiculars from the points to the x-axis and to the y-axis, as shown in Figure 11-50, thus defining triangle CDE. The lengths of the legs of triangle CDE are found by using horizontal and vertical distances and properties of rectangles.

$$CE = |6 - 2| = 4$$

$$DE = |8 - 5| = 3$$

FIGURE 11-50

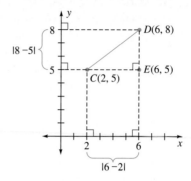

The distance between C and D can be found by applying the Pythagorean Theorem to the triangle.

$$CD^2 = DE^2 + CE^2$$
$$= 3^2 + 4^2$$
$$= 25$$
$$CD = \sqrt{25}, \text{ or } 5$$

The method can be generalized to find a formula for the distance between any two points $A(x_1, y_1)$ and $B(x_2, y_2)$. Construct a right triangle with $\overline{AB}$ as one of its sides by drawing a segment through A parallel to the x-axis and a segment through B parallel to the y-axis, as shown in Figure 11-51. The lines containing the segments intersect at point C, forming right triangle ABC. Now, apply the Pythagorean Theorem.

FIGURE 11-51

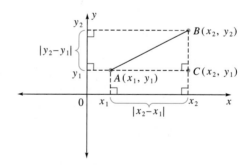

In Figure 11-51, we see that $AC = |x_2 - x_1|$ and $BC = |y_2 - y_1|$. By the Pythagorean Theorem, $(AB)^2 = |x_2 - x_1|^2 + |y_2 - y_1|^2$, and consequently $AB = \sqrt{|x_2 - x_1|^2 + |y_2 - y_1|^2}$. Because $|x_2 - x_1|^2 = (x_2 - x_1)^2$ and $|y_2 - y_1|^2 = (y_2 - y_1)^2$, $AB = \sqrt{(x_2 - x_1)^2 + (y_2 - y_1)^2}$.

distance formula   This result is known as the **distance formula**.

Distance Formula

The distance between the points $A(x_1, y_1)$ and $B(x_2, y_2)$ is given by

$$AB = \sqrt{(x_2 - x_1)^2 + (y_2 - y_1)^2}.$$

NOW TRY THIS 11-14

Investigate whether it makes any difference in the distance formula if $(x_1 - x_2)$ and $(y_1 - y_2)$ are used instead of $(x_2 - x_1)$ and $(y_2 - y_1)$, respectively.

EXAMPLE 11-16

a. Show that $A(7, 4)$, $B(^-2, 1)$, and $C(10, ^-5)$ are the vertices of an isosceles triangle.
b. Show that $\triangle ABC$ in (a) is a right triangle.

Solution **a.** Using the distance formula, we find the lengths of the sides.

$$AB = \sqrt{(^-2 - 7)^2 + (1 - 4)^2} = \sqrt{(^-9)^2 + (^-3)^2} = \sqrt{90}$$
$$BC = \sqrt{[10 - (^-2)]^2 + (^-5 - 1)^2} = \sqrt{12^2 + (^-6)^2} = \sqrt{180}$$
$$AC = \sqrt{(10 - 7)^2 + (^-5 - 4)^2} = \sqrt{3^2 + (^-9)^2} = \sqrt{90}$$

Thus $AB = AC$, and so the triangle is isosceles.
b. Because $(\sqrt{90})^2 + (\sqrt{90})^2 = (\sqrt{180})^2$, $\triangle ABC$ is a right triangle with $\overline{BC}$ as hypotenuse and $\overline{AB}$ and $\overline{AC}$ as legs.

EXAMPLE 11-17

Determine whether the points $A(0, 5)$, $B(1, 2)$, and $C(2, -1)$ are collinear.

Solution It is hard to tell by graphing the points whether they are collinear (on the same line). If they are not collinear, they would be the vertices of a triangle, and hence $AB + BC$ would be greater than AB. (triangle inequality). If $AB + BC = AC$, a triangle could not be formed and the points would be collinear. Using the distance formula, we find the lengths of the sides:

$$AB = \sqrt{(0 - 1)^2 + (5 - 2)^2} = \sqrt{1 + 9} = \sqrt{10}$$
$$BC = \sqrt{(2 - 1)^2 + (-1 - 2)^2} = \sqrt{1 + 9} = \sqrt{10}$$
$$AC = \sqrt{(0 - 2)^2 + (5 - (-1))^2} = \sqrt{4 + 36} = \sqrt{40}$$

Thus, $AB + BC = 2\sqrt{10}$. Is this sum equal to $\sqrt{40}$? Because $\sqrt{40} = \sqrt{4 \cdot 10} = \sqrt{4} \cdot \sqrt{10} = 2\sqrt{10}$, we have $AB + BC = AC$, and consequently, A, B, and C are collinear.

ONGOING ASSESSMENT 11-3

1. Find the length of the following segments. Assume that the horizontal and vertical distances between neighboring dots is 1 unit.

(a) (b)

2. Use the Pythagorean Theorem to find *x* in each of the following:

(a)

(b)

(c)

Equilateral triangle
(d)

(e)

Right rectangular prism
(f)

Right square
pyramid
(g)

Right circular
cone
(h)

Cube
(i)

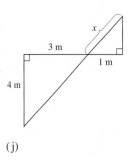

(j)

3. On a geoboard, construct segments of the following lengths.
   a. $\sqrt{13}$ **b.** $\sqrt{5}$ **c.** $\sqrt{10}$

4. If the hypotenuse of a right triangle is 30 cm long and one leg is twice as long as the other, how long are the legs of the triangle?

5. For each of the following, determine whether the given numbers represent lengths of sides of a right triangle:
   a. 10, 24, 16   **b.** 16, 34, 30
   c. $\sqrt{2}, \sqrt{2}, 2$ **d.** $\dfrac{3}{2}, \dfrac{4}{2}, \dfrac{5}{2}$

6. What is the longest line segment that can be drawn in a right rectangular prism that is 12 cm wide, 15 cm long, and 9 cm high?

7. Two airplanes depart from the same place at 2:00 P.M. One plane flies south at a speed of 376 km/hr, and the other flies west at a speed of 648 km/hr. How far apart are the airplanes at 5:30 P.M.?

8. Starting from point *A*, a boat sails due south for 6 mi, then due east for 5 mi, and then due south for 4 mi. How far is the boat from *A*?

9. a. In the cartoon on page 689, is Hobbes's square really a square? Why?
   b. If Hobbes's figure in the second panel is a rectangle that is 6 units by 3 units, how long is *y*?
   c. If Hobbes draws a rectangle with each dimension doubled, how does the length of the diagonal change?
   d. Was Calvin's measure of the diagonal correct?

10. A 15-ft ladder is leaning against a wall. The base of the ladder is 3 ft from the wall. How high above the ground is the top of the ladder?

11. In the following figure, two poles are 25 m and 15 m high. A cable 14 m long joins the tops of the poles. Find the distance between the poles.

12. Find the area of each of the following:

(a)

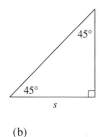

(b)

Calvin and Hobbes
by Bill Watterson

13. For each of the following, solve for the unknowns:

(a)

(b)

14. A builder needs to calculate the dimensions of a regular hexagonal window. Assuming the height CD of the window is 1.3 m, find the width AB (O is the midpoint of $\overline{AB}$) in the following figure:

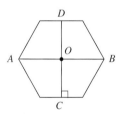

15. The following two rhombuses have perimeters that are equal. Use the properties of a rhombus to find the area of each rhombus.

(a)

(b)

16. The length of the diagonal $\overline{AC}$ of a rhombus $ABCD$ is 20 cm. The distance between $\overline{AB}$ and $\overline{DC}$ is 12 cm. Find the length of the sides of the rhombus and the length of the other diagonal.

17. If $\overline{AB}$, a diameter of circle O, has length 10 cm, point C is on circle O, and AC is 6 cm, how long is $\overline{BC}$?

18. Georgette wants to put a diagonal brace on a rectangular gate that is 3 ft wide and 5 ft high. If she uses a board that is 6 in. wide and 8 ft long for the diagonal, how much will she have left?

19. If a third baseman on the base throws to first base, how far is the ball thrown? (*Hint:* The distance from home plate to first base is 90 ft.)

20. What is the longest piece of straight spaghetti that will fit in a cylindrical can that has a radius of 2 in. and height of 10 in.?

21. If possible, draw a square with the given number of square units on a geoboard grid. (You will have to draw your own geoboard grid.)
    a. 5 **b.** 7 **c.** 8 **d.** 14 **e.** 15

22. Use the following drawing to prove the Pythagorean Theorem by using corresponding parts of similar triangles $\triangle ACD$, $\triangle CBD$, and $\triangle ABC$. Lengths of sides are indicated by a, b, c, x, and y. (*Hint:* Show that $b^2 = cx$ and $a^2 = cy$.)

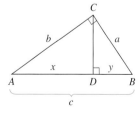

23. An access ramp enters a building 1 m above ground level and starts 3 m from the building. How long is the ramp?

24. To make a homeplate for a neighborhood baseball park, we can cut the plate from a square, as shown in the following figure. If *A, B,* and *C* are midpoints of the sides of the square, what are the dimensions of the square to the nearest tenth of an inch?

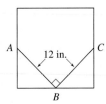

25. A company wants to lay cable across a lake. To find the length of the lake, they made the following measurements. What is the length of the lake?

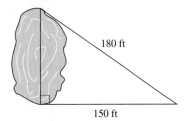

26. A CB radio station *C* is located 3 mi from the interstate highway *h*. The station has a range of 6.1 mi in all directions from the station. If the interstate is along a straight line, how many miles of highway are in the range of this station?

27. Before James Garfield was elected President of the United States, he discovered a proof of the Pythagorean Theorem. He formed a trapezoid like the one that follows and found the area of the trapezoid in two ways. Can you discover his proof?

28. Use the following figure to prove the Pythagorean Theorem by first proving that the quadrilateral with side *c* is a square. Then, compute the area of the square with side *a* + *b* in two ways: (a) as $(a + b)^2$ and (b) as the sum of the areas of the 4 triangles and the square with side *c*.

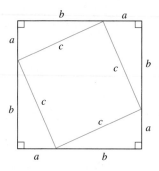

29. Show how the following figure could be used to prove the Pythagorean Theorem.

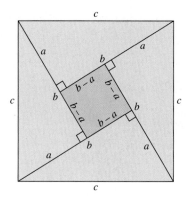

30. Construct semicircles on right triangle *ABC* with $\overline{AB}$, $\overline{BC}$, and $\overline{AC}$ as diameters. Is the area of the semicircle on the hypotenuse equal to the sum of the areas of the semicircles on the legs? Why?

31. On each side of a right triangle, construct an equilateral triangle. Is the area of the triangle constructed on the hypotenuse always equal to the sum of the areas of the triangles constructed on the legs? Why?

32. For each of the following, find the length of $\overline{AB}$:
   a. $A(0, 3), B(0, 7)$
   b. $A(0, 3), B(4, 0)$
   c. $A(^-1, 2), B(3, ^-4)$
   d. $A(4, ^-5), B\left(\dfrac{1}{2}, \dfrac{^-7}{4}\right)$

33. Find the perimeter of the triangle with vertices at $A(0, 0)$, $B(^-4, ^-3)$, and $C(^-5, 0)$.

34. Show that $(0, 6)$, $(^-3, 0)$, and $(9, ^-6)$ are the vertices of a right triangle.

35. Show that the triangle whose vertices are $A(^-2, ^-5)$, $B(1, ^-1)$, and $C(5, 2)$ is isosceles.

36. Find x if the distance between $P(1, 3)$ and $Q(x, 9)$ is 10 units.
37. If the hypotenuse in a 30°-60°-90° triangle is $c/2$ units, what is the length of the side opposite the 60° angle? Explain your answer.

Communication

38. Given the following square, describe how to use a compass and a straightedge to construct a square whose area is as follows:
    a. Twice the area of the given square
    b. Half the area of the given square

39. If the hypotenuse and a leg of one right triangle are congruent to the hypotenuse and a leg of another right triangle, respectively, must the triangles be congruent? Explain.
40. Gail tried the Egyptian method of using a knotted rope to determine a right angle so that she could build a shed. She placed her knots so that each was 1 ft from the next. She stretched out her rope in the form of a triangle whose sides were of lengths 5, 12, and 13 ft. Did she have a right angle? Explain why or why not.

Open-Ended

41. Draw several kinds of triangles including a right triangle. Draw a square on each of the sides of the triangles. Compute the areas of the squares and use this information to investigate whether the Pythagorean Theorem works for only right triangles. Use a geometry utility if available.
42. Find an application from real life in which knowing the Pythagorean Theorem would be useful. Write a problem about the application to share with the class.
43. **Pythagorean triples** are three natural numbers a, b, and c that satisfy the relationship $a^2 + b^2 = c^2$. The least three numbers that are Pythagorean triples are 3-4-5. Another triple is 5-12-13 because $5^2 + 12^2 = 13^2$.
    a. Find two other Pythagorean triples.
    b. Does doubling each number in a Pythagorean triple result in a new Pythagorean triple? Why or why not?
    c. Does adding a fixed number to each number in a Pythagorean triple result in a new Pythagorean triple? Why or why not?
    d. Suppose $a = 2uv$, $b = u^2 - v^2$, and $c = u^2 + v^2$, where u and v are whole numbers. Determine whether a-b-c is a Pythagorean triple.

Cooperative Learning

44. Have each person in the group use a 1-m string to make a different right triangle. Measure each side to the nearest centimeter. Use these measurements to see if the Pythagorean Theorem holds for your measurements.

Review Problems

45. Arrange the following in decreasing order: 3.2 m, 322 cm, 0.032 km, 3.020 mm.
46. Find the area of each of the following figures:

(a)

(b)

Trapezoid

(c)

47. Complete the following table, which concerns circles:

	Radius	Diameter	Circumference	Area
a.	5 cm			
b.		24 cm		
c.				$17\pi\,\text{m}^2$
d.			20π cm	

48. A 10-m wire is wrapped around a circular region. If the wire fits exactly, what is the area of the region?

BRAIN

A spider is sitting at *A*, the midpoint of the edge of the ceiling in the room shown in Figure 11-52. It spies a fly on the floor at *C*, the midpoint of the edge of the floor. If the spider must walk along the wall, ceiling, or floor, what is the length of the shortest path the spider can travel to reach the fly?

FIGURE 11-52

TECHNOLOGY

Use GSP to determine the relationship between the length of the hypotenuse of a 45°-45°-90° triangle and the length of a leg.

a. Construct a 45°-45°-90° triangle, label the vertices as in Figure 11-53, and measure the lengths of the sides. Record the data for triangle 1 in the following table and compute the ratio.

FIGURE 11-53

	AC	*CB*	*AB*	*AB/CB*
Triangle 1				
Triangle 2				
Triangle 3				
Triangle 4				

b. Repeat (a) for three other triangles.
c. Make a conjecture about the relationship between the length of the hypotenuse and the length of a leg for these triangles.
d. Given a 30°-60°-90° triangle, determine the relationship between the lengths of the hypotenuse and the shorter leg and the relationships between the lengths of the longer and shorter legs.

11-4   Surface Areas

Painting houses, buying roofing, seal-coating driveways, and buying carpet are among the common applications that involve computing areas. In many real-world problems, we must find the surface areas of such three-dimensional figures as prisms, cylinders, pyramids, cones, and spheres. Formulas for finding these areas are usually based on finding the area of two-dimensional pieces of the three-dimensional figures.

Surface Area of Right Prisms

Consider the cereal box shown in Figure 11-54(a). If we ignore the flaps for gluing the box together, to find the amount of cardboard necessary to make the box, we cut the box along the edges and make it lie flat, as shown in Figure 11-54(b). When we do this we obtain a *net* for the box. The box is composed of a series of rectangles. We find the area of each rectangle and sum those areas to find the surface area of the box.

FIGURE 11-54

(a)

(b)

NOW TRY THIS 11-15

    a. Find the surface area of the box in Figure 11-54.

    b. Could the box be made from a rectangular piece of cardboard 21 in. by 15 in.? If not, what size rectangle could you use and how would you do it?

    A similar process can be used for many three-dimensional figures. For example, the surface area of the cube in Figure 11-55(a) is the sum of the areas of the faces of the cube. A net for the cube is shown in Figure 11-55(c). Because each of the six faces is a square of area 16 cm^2, the surface area is $6 \cdot (16 \text{ cm}^2)$, or 96 cm^2, or in general, for a cube whose edge is *e* units as in Figure 11-55(b), the surface area is $6e^2$.

FIGURE 11-55

(a)   4 cm

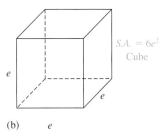

$S.A. = 6e^2$
Cube

(b)   *e*

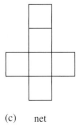

(c)   net

To find the surface area of a right prism, like the cereal box in Figure 11-54(a), we find the sum of the areas of the rectangles that make up the lateral faces and the areas of the top and bottom. The sum of the areas of the lateral faces is the **lateral surface area**. The **surface area** (*S.A.*) is the sum of the lateral surface area and the area of the bases.

lateral surface area

surface area

NOW TRY THIS 11-16

Figure 11-56 shows a right pentagonal prism with a net for the prism. If B stands for the area of each of the prism's bases, show that the surface area of the prism could be computed as $S.A. = ph + 2B$, where p is the perimeter of the base of the prism and h is the height. Does this formula hold for all right prisms? Why or why not?

FIGURE 11-56

(a)   (b)

**EXAMPLE
11-18**

Find the surface area of each of the right prisms in Figure 11-57.

FIGURE 11-57

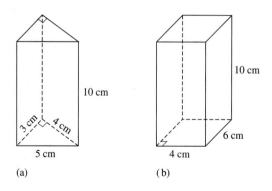

(a)   (b)

Solution **a.** Each base is a right triangle. The area of the bases is $2(1/2 \cdot 3 \cdot 4)$, or 12 cm^2. The area of the three lateral faces is $4 \cdot 10 + 3 \cdot 10 + 5 \cdot 10$, or 120 cm^2. Thus the surface area is $12 \text{ cm}^2 + 120 \text{ cm}^2$, or 132 cm^2.

b. The area of the bases is $2(4 \cdot 6)$, or 48 cm^2. The lateral surface area is $2 \cdot (10 \cdot 6) + 2 \cdot (4 \cdot 10)$, or 200 cm^2. Thus the surface area is 248 cm^2.

Surface Area of a Cylinder

If the number of sides of a right regular prism is increasing, as shown in Figure 11-58, then the figure approaches the shape of a right regular cylinder.

FIGURE 11-58

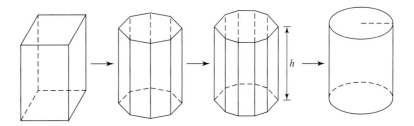

To find the surface area of the right circular cylinder shown in Figure 11-59, we cut off the bases and slice the lateral surface open by cutting along any line perpendicular to the bases. Such a slice is shown as a dotted segment in Figure 11-59(a). Then we unroll the cylinder to form a rectangle, as shown in Figure 11-59(b). To find the total surface area, we find the area of the rectangle and the areas of the top and bottom circles. The length of the rectangle is the circumference of the circular base $2\pi r$, and its width is the height of the cylinder h. Hence, the area of the rectangle is $2\pi rh$. The area of each base is πr^2. Because the surface area is the sum of the areas of the two circular bases and the lateral surface area, we have $S.A. = 2\pi r^2 + 2\pi rh$.

FIGURE 11-59

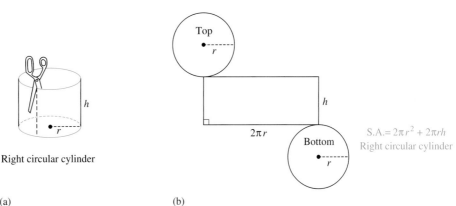

Right circular cylinder

(a)   (b)

$S.A. = 2\pi r^2 + 2\pi rh$
Right circular cylinder

Surface Area of a Pyramid

The surface area of a pyramid is the sum of the lateral surface area of the pyramid and the area of the base. A right regular pyramid is a pyramid such that the segments connecting the apex to each vertex of the base are congruent and the base is a regular polygon. The lateral faces of the right regular pyramid pictured in Figure 11-60 are congruent triangles. Each triangle has an altitude of length ℓ, called the *slant height*. Because the pyramid is right regular, each side of the base has the same length b. To find the lateral surface area of a right regular pyramid, we need to find the area of one face $\frac{1}{2}b\ell$ and multiply it by n, the number of faces. Adding the lateral surface area $n\left(\frac{1}{2}b\ell\right)$ to the area of the base B gives the surface area.

FIGURE 11-60

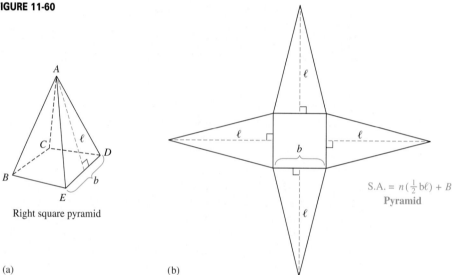

Right square pyramid

$$\text{S.A.} = n\left(\tfrac{1}{2}\,b\ell\right) + B$$
Pyramid

(a)   (b)

Find the surface area of the right regular pyramid in Figure 11-61.

FIGURE 11-61

5 cm

4 cm

4 cm

Solution   The surface area consists of the area of the square base plus the area of the four triangular faces. Hence, the surface area is

$$4 \text{ cm} \cdot 4 \text{ cm} + 4 \cdot \left(\frac{1}{2} \cdot 4 \text{ cm} \cdot 5 \text{ cm}\right) = 16 \text{ cm}^2 + 40 \text{ cm}^2$$

$$= 56 \text{ cm}^2.$$

E X A M P L E
11-20

The Great Pyramid of Cheops is a right square pyramid with a height of 148 m and a square base with perimeter of 930 m. The altitude of each triangular face is 188 m. The basic shape of the Transamerica Building in San Francisco is a right square pyramid that has a height of 260 m and a square base with a perimeter of 140 m. The altitude of each triangular face is 261 m. How do the lateral surface areas of the two structures compare?

Solution The length of one side of the square base of the Great Pyramid is $\frac{930}{4}$, or 232.5, m. Likewise the length of one side of the square base of the Transamerica Building is 35 m. The lateral surface area (*L.S.A.*) of the two are computed below.

$$\text{(Great Pyramid) } L.S.A. = 4 \cdot (1/2 \cdot 232.5 \cdot 188) = 87{,}420 \text{ m}^2$$
$$\text{(Transamerica) } L.S.A. = 4 \cdot (1/2 \cdot 35 \cdot 261) = 18{,}270 \text{ m}^2$$

Therefore the lateral surface area of the Great Pyramid is approximately 4.8 times greater than that of the Transamerica Building.

Surface Area of a Cone

If the number of sides of a right regular pyramid is increasing, as shown in Figure 11-62, then the figure approaches the shape of a right circular cone.

FIGURE 11-62

It is possible to find a formula for the surface area of a right circular cone by approximating the cone with a pyramid with many sides. As shown in Figure 11-63, we inscribe in the circular base of the cone a regular polygon with many sides. The polygon can be used as the base of a regular right pyramid. The lateral surface area of the pyramid is close to the lateral surface area of the cone. The greater the number of faces of the pyramid, the closer the surface area of the pyramid is to that of the cone. The lateral surface of the pyramid is $\frac{1}{2}p \cdot h$, where p is the perimeter of the base and h is the height of each triangle.

With many sides in the pyramid, the perimeter of its base is close to the perimeter of the circle, $2\pi r$. The height of each triangle of the pyramid is close to the slant height ℓ, a segment that connects the vertex of the cone with a point on the circular base, as shown in Figure 11-63(b). Consequently, it is reasonable that the lateral surface of the cone becomes $\frac{1}{2} \cdot 2\pi r \cdot \ell$, or $\pi r \ell$. To find the total surface area of the cone, we add πr^2, the area of the base. Thus $S.A. = \pi r^2 + \pi r \ell$.

FIGURE 11-63

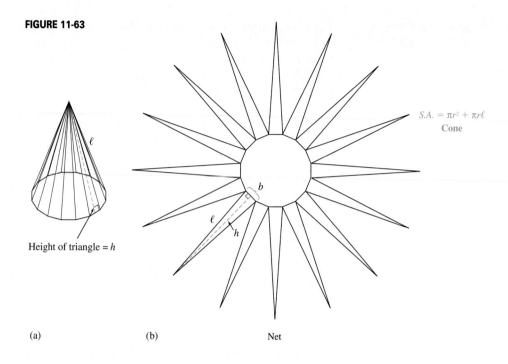

$S.A. = \pi r^2 + \pi r\ell$
Cone

Height of triangle = h

(a)   (b)   Net

Given the cone in Figure 11-64, find the surface area of that cone.

5 cm
4 cm
3 cm

Right circular cone

FIGURE 11-64

Solution   The base of the cone is a circle with radius 3 cm and area $\pi(3\text{ cm})^2$, or $9\pi\text{ cm}^2$. The lateral surface has area $\pi(3\text{ cm})(5\text{ cm})$, or $15\pi\text{ cm}^2$. Thus we have the following surface area:

$$\begin{aligned} S.A. &= \pi(3\text{ cm})^2 + \pi(3\text{ cm})(5\text{ cm}) \\ &= 9\pi\text{ cm}^2 + 15\pi\text{ cm}^2 \\ &= 24\pi\text{ cm}^2 \end{aligned}$$

Surface Area of a Sphere

great circle   A **great circle** of a sphere is a circle on the sphere whose radius is equal to the radius of the sphere. A great circle is obtained whenever a plane through the center of the sphere intersects the sphere. There are infinitely many great circles on a sphere. However, they are all congruent. Finding a formula for the surface area of a sphere is a simple task using calculus, but it is not easy in elementary mathematics. The surface area of a sphere is four times the area of a great circle of the sphere. Therefore the formula is $S.A. = 4\pi r^2$, as pictured in Figure 11-65.

FIGURE 11-65

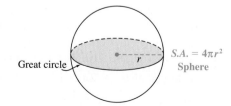

Great circle

$S.A. = 4\pi r^2$
Sphere

LABORATORY
A C T I V I T Y

Create different cones from sectors of a circle. Use a compass to draw a sector of a circle whose diameter is almost as large as the width of a page of paper. Draw two such sectors that have the same radii but different central angles. In one sector, make the central angle measure smaller than 180°, and in the other, make it measure greater than 180°. Then make a cone from each sector by gluing the edges of each sector together. Can you predict which cone will be taller? Without performing the experiment, can you explain why that cone will be taller?

O N G O I N G   A S S E S S M E N T   1 1 - 4

1. Find the surface area of each of the following:

Cube

(a)

Right circular cylinder

(b)

(g)

(h)

Right rectangular prism

(c)

Sphere

(d)

Right circular cone

(e)

Right square pyramid

(f)

2. How many liters of paint are needed to paint the walls of a rectangular prism-shaped room that is 6 m × 4 m × 2.5 m if 1 L of paint covers 20 m²? (Assume there are no doors or windows.)

3. The napkin ring pictured in the following figure is to be re-silvered. How many square millimeters must be covered?

4. Assume the radius of Earth is 6370 km and Earth is a sphere. What is its surface area?

5. Two cubes have sides of length 4 cm and 6 cm, respectively. What is the ratio of their surface areas?

6. Suppose one right circular cylinder has radius 2 m and height 6 m and another has radius 6 m and height 2 m.
   a. Which cylinder has the greater lateral surface area?
   b. Which cylinder has the greater total surface area?

7. The base of a right pyramid is a regular hexagon with sides of length 12 m. The altitude of the pyramid is 9 m. Find the total surface area of the pyramid.

8. A soup can has a $2\frac{5}{8}$-in. diameter and is 4 in. tall. What is the area of the paper that will be used to make the label for the can if the paper covers the entire lateral surface area?

9. A square piece of paper 10 cm on a side is rolled to form the lateral surface area of a right circular cylinder and then a top and bottom are added. What is the surface area of the cylinder?

10. Approximately how much material is needed to make the tent illustrated in the following figure (both ends and the bottom should be included)?

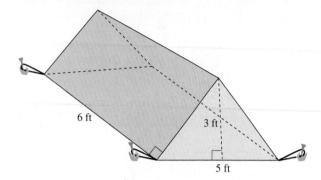

6 ft 3 ft 5 ft

11. The top of a rectangular box has an area of 88 cm². The sides have areas 32 cm² and 44 cm². What are the dimensions of the box?

12. How does the surface area of a box (including top and bottom) change if
    a. each dimension is doubled?
    b. each dimension is tripled?
    c. each dimension is multiplied by a factor of k?

13. How does the lateral surface area of a cone change if
    a. the slant height is tripled but the radius of the base remains the same?
    b. the radius of the base is tripled but the slant height remains the same?
    c. the slant height and the radius of the base are tripled?

14. What happens to the surface area of a sphere if the radius is
    a. doubled?   b. tripled?

15. Find the surface area of a square pyramid if the area of the base is 100 cm² and the height of the pyramid is 20 cm.

16. Suppose a structure is composed of unit cubes with at least one face of each cube connected to the face of another cube, as shown in the following figure:

    a. If one cube is added, what is the maximum surface area the structure can have?
    b. If one cube is added, what is the minimum surface area the structure can have?
    c. Is it possible to design a structure so that one can add a cube and yet add nothing to the surface area of the structure? (*Hint:* Cubes might have to be glued together.) Explain your answer.

17. The sector shown in the following figure is rolled into a cone so that the dotted edges just touch. Find the following:

1.5 m 240°

    a. The lateral surface area of the cone
    b. The total surface area of the cone

18. Each region in the following figure revolves about the indicated axis. For each case, sketch the three-dimensional figure obtained and find its surface area.

10 cm 20 cm (a)   30 cm 15 cm (b)

35 cm 15 cm 25 cm ★ (c)

19. The total surface area of a cube is 10,648 cm². What is the length of each of the following?
    a. One of the sides
    b. A diagonal that is not a diagonal of a face

20. A square pyramid and a right circular cone are inscribed in a cube as shown. Find each of the following:
    a. Surface area of the pyramid
    b. Surface area of the cone

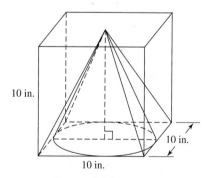

10 in. 10 in. 10 in.

★ 21. Find the total surface area of the following stand, which was cut from a right circular cone:

60 cm 40 cm 100 cm

★ 22. In the following figure, a right circular cylinder is inscribed in a right circular cone. Find the lateral surface area of the cylinder if the height of the cone is 40 cm, the height of the cylinder 30 cm, and the radius of the base of the cone is 25 cm.

Communication

23. Which do you think would melt faster in an ice chest: a block of ice made from a gallon of water or ice cubes made from a gallon of water? Explain why.

24. A student wonders if she doubles each measurement of a cereal box, will she need twice as much cardboard to make the new box. How would you help her decide?

25. Tennis balls are packed tightly three to a can that is shaped like a cylinder.
    a. Estimate how the surface area of the balls compares to the lateral surface area of the can. Explain how you arrived at your estimate.
    b. See how close your estimate in (a) was by actually computing the surface area of the balls and the lateral surface area of the can.

Open-Ended

26. One method of estimating body surface area in burn victims uses the fact that 100 handprints will approximately cover the whole body.
    a. What percentage of the body surface area is the surface area of two handprints?
    b. Estimate the percentage of the body surface area of one arm. Explain how you arrived at your estimate.
    c. Estimate your body surface area in square centimeters. Explain how you arrived at your estimate.
    d. Find the area of the flat part of your desk. How does the area of the desk compare with the surface area of your body?

27. Design a net for a polyhedron in such a way that the surface area of the polyhedron is 10 cm². Explain what polyhedron the net will form and why its surface area is 10 cm².

Cooperative Learning

28. a. Shawn used small cubes to build a bigger cube that was solid and was three cubes long on each side. He then painted all the sides of the new, large cube red. He dropped the newly painted cube and all the little cubes came apart. He noticed that some cubes had only one side painted, some had two sides painted, and so on. Describe the number of cubes with 0, 1, 2, 3, 4, 5, or 6 sides painted. Have each member of the group choose a different number of sides and then combine your data to see if it makes sense. Look for any patterns that occur.
    b. What would the answers be if the large cube was four small cubes long on a side?
    c. Make a conjecture about how to count the cubes if the large cube were *n* small cubes long on a side.

29. In groups, work through the Package Design Contest as described on the student page on page 702.

Review Problems

30. Complete each of the following:
    a. $10 \text{ m}^2 = $ _____ cm^2 b. $13,680 \text{ cm}^2 = $ _____ m^2
    c. $5 \text{ cm}^2 = $ _____ mm^2 d. $2 \text{ km}^2 = $ _____ m^2
    e. $10^6 \text{ m}^2 = $ _____ km^2 f. $10^{12} \text{ mm}^2 = $ _____ m^2

31. The sides of a rectangle are 10 cm and 20 cm long. Find the length of a diagonal of the rectangle.

32. The length of the side of a rhombus is 30 cm. If the length of one diagonal is 40 cm, find the length of the other diagonal.

33. Find the perimeters and the areas of the following figures:

(a)

Trapezoid

(b)

34. In the following, the length of the diagonal $\overline{AC}$ of rhombus *ABCD* is 40 cm; AE = 24 cm. Find the length of a side of the rhombus and the length of the diagonal $\overline{BD}$.

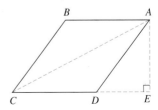

Sample School Book Page:

Package Design Contest

The Worldwide Sporting Company wants new package designs for its table-tennis balls (Ping-Pong balls). The company's table-tennis balls are about 3.8 cm in diameter. There are three main requirements for the packages:

- The board of directors wants to have three different size packages: small, medium, and large.
- The president of the company wants the cost of the packages to be a primary consideration.
- The sales manager wants the packages to be appealing to customers, to stack easily, and to look good on store shelves.

The company holds a package design contest, and you decide to enter.

- You must design three different packages for the table-tennis balls.
- You must submit your designs and a written proposal to WSC.
- You must try, in your written proposal, to convince WSC to use your designs.

Include the following things in your proposal:

1. A description of the shape or shapes of the packages and an explanation for why you selected these shapes.
2. Patterns for each package that, when they are cut out, folded, and taped together, will make models of your packages. Use centimeter grid paper to make your patterns.
3. Cost estimates to construct your designs. The packaging material costs $0.005 per square centimeter.
4. An explanation of how you have addressed WSC's requirements.

Remember, you are trying to convince WSC that your designs are the best and that they meet the requirements. Your written proposal should be neat, well organized, and easy to read so that the company officials can follow your work and ideas easily.

Source: Prentice Hall, Connected Mathematics: Filling and Wrapping, 2002 (p. 73).

TECHNOLOGY
C O R N E R

Find various-shaped cardboard containers and cut them apart to form nets. Make sure the nets are smaller than your computer screen.

a. Estimate the surface area of the nets.

b. Trace the perimeter of each net on a transparency sheet and hang the sheet on the monitor of your computer. Use GSP to trace the outline from the transparency and compute the area.

c. Compare your estimate in (a) with the answer in (b).

BRAIN
T E A S E R

A manufacturer of paper cups wants to produce paper cups in the form of truncated cones 16 cm high, with one circular base of radius 11 cm and the other of radius 7 cm, as shown in Figure 11-66. When the base of such a cup is removed and the cup is slit and flattened, the flattened region looks like a part of a circular ring. To design a pattern to make the cup, the manufacturer needs the data required to construct the flattened region. Find these data.

FIGURE 11-66

11-5 Volume, Mass, and Temperature

In Section 11-4, we investigated surface areas of various-shaped containers. In this section, we explore how much the containers will hold. This distinction is sometimes confused by elementary-school students. Whereas the surface area is the number of square units covering a three-dimensional figure, volume describes how much space a three-dimensional figure will hold. The unit of measure for volume must be a shape that tessellates space. Cubes tessellate space; that is, they can be stacked so that they leave no gaps and fill space. Standard units of volume are based on cubes and are *cubic units*. A cubic unit is the amount of space enclosed within a cube that measures 1 unit on a side. The distinction between surface area and volume is demonstrated in Figure 11-67.

FIGURE 11-67

To find the surface area, count squares:

To find volume, count cubes: .

The surface area is 18 square units.

The volume is 4 cubic units.

NOW TRY THIS 11-17

In Figure 11-68, the purple block is moved from one position to another.

FIGURE 11-68

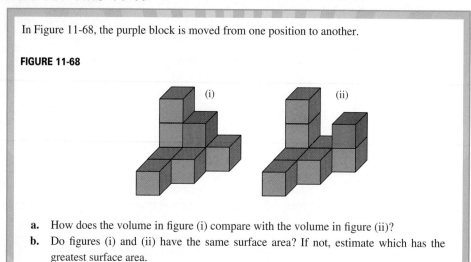

a. How does the volume in figure (i) compare with the volume in figure (ii)?

b. Do figures (i) and (ii) have the same surface area? If not, estimate which has the greatest surface area.

c. Find the surface area of each figure.

Volume of Right Rectangular Prisms

The volume of a right rectangular prism can be measured by determining how many cubes are needed to build it. To find the volume, count how many cubes cover the base and then how many layers of these cubes are used to fill the prism. As shown in Figure 11-69(a), there are $8 \cdot 4$, or 32, cubes required to cover the base and there are five such layers. The volume of the rectangular prism is $(8 \cdot 4) \cdot 5$, or 160 cubic units. For any right rectangular prism with dimensions ℓ, w, and h measured in the same linear units, the volume of the prism is given by the area of the base, ℓw, times the height, h, or $V = \ell w h$, as shown in Figure 11-69(b).

FIGURE 11-69

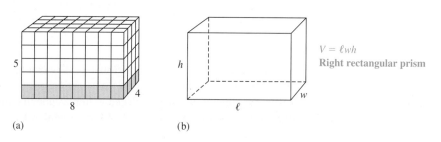

$V = \ell w h$
Right rectangular prism

(a)   (b)

Converting Metric Measures of Volume

cubic centimeter
cubic meter

The most commonly used metric units of volume are the **cubic centimeter** and the **cubic meter**. A cubic centimeter is the volume of a cube whose length, width, and height are each 1 cm. One cubic centimeter is denoted 1 cm^3. Similarly, a cubic meter is the volume of a cube whose length, width, and height are each 1 m. One cubic meter is denoted 1 m³. Other metric units of volume are symbolized similarly.

Figure 11-70 shows that since 1 dm = 10 cm, 1 dm³ = (10 cm) · (10 cm) · (10 cm) = 1000 cm³.

FIGURE 11-70

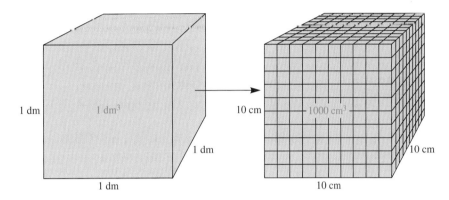

Figure 11-71 shows that 1 m³ = 1,000,000 cm³ and that 1 dm³ = 0.001 m³.

FIGURE 11-71

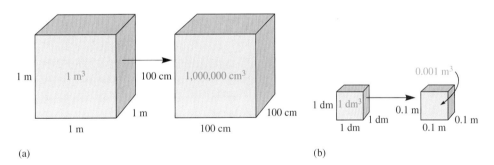

(a)   (b)

Each metric unit of length is 10 *times as great as the next smaller unit. Each metric unit of area is* 100 *times as great as the next smaller unit. Each metric unit of volume is* 1000 *times as great as the next smaller unit.* For example:

$$1 \text{ cm} = 10 \text{ mm}$$
$$1 \text{ cm}^2 = 100 \text{ mm}^2$$
$$1 \text{ cm}^3 = 1000 \text{ mm}^3$$

Because 1 cm = 0.01 m, then 1 cm³ = (0.01 · 0.01 · 0.01) m³, or 0.000001 m³. To convert from cubic centimeters to cubic meters, we move the decimal point six places to the left.

NOW TRY THIS 11-18

a. Describe how to determine how many places to move the decimal point in a metric area conversion if you know how many places and the direction to move in the corresponding length conversion.

b. Describe how to determine how many places to move the decimal point in a metric volume conversion if you know how many places and the direction to move in the corresponding length conversion.

EXAMPLE
11-22

Convert each of the following:

a. $5 \text{ m}^3 = \underline{\hspace{1cm}} \text{ cm}^3$ **b.** $12{,}300 \text{ mm}^3 = \underline{\hspace{1cm}} \text{ cm}^3$

Solution **a.** $1 \text{ m} = 100 \text{ cm}$, so $1 \text{ m}^3 = (100 \text{ cm})(100 \text{ cm})(100 \text{ cm})$, or $1{,}000{,}000 \text{ cm}^3$. Thus $5 \text{ m}^3 = (5)(1{,}000{,}000 \text{ cm}^3) = 5{,}000{,}000 \text{ cm}^3$.

b. $1 \text{ mm} = 0.1 \text{ cm}$, so $1 \text{ mm}^3 = (0.1 \text{ cm})(0.1 \text{ cm})(0.1 \text{ cm})$, or 0.001 cm^3. Thus $12{,}300 \text{ mm}^3 = 12{,}300(0.001 \text{ cm}^3) = 12.3 \text{ cm}^3$.

In the metric system, cubic units may be used for either dry or liquid measure, although units such as liters and milliliters are usually used for liquid measures. By defini-
liter tion, a **liter**, symbolized L, equals, or is the capacity of, a cubic decimeter; that is, $1 \text{ L} = 1 \text{ dm}^3$. (In the United States, L is the symbol for liter, but this is not universally accepted.)

Because $1 \text{ L} = 1 \text{ dm}^3$ and $1 \text{ dm}^3 = 1000 \text{ cm}^3$, it follows that $1 \text{ L} = 1000 \text{ cm}^3$ and $1 \text{ cm}^3 = 0.001 \text{ L}$. Also, $0.001 \text{ L} = 1 \text{ milliliter} = 1 \text{ mL}$. Hence, $1 \text{ cm}^3 = 1 \text{ mL}$. These relationships are summarized in Figure 11-72 and Table 11-7.

FIGURE 11-72

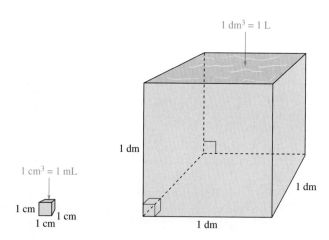

Table 11-7

Unit	Symbol	Relation to Liter
kiloliter	KL	1000 L
*hectoliter	hL	100 L
*dekaliter	daL	10 L
liter	**L**	**1 L**
*deciliter	dL	0.1 L
centiliter	cL	0.01 L
mililiter	mL	0.001 L

*Not commonly used

EXAMPLE 11-23

Convert each of the following as indicated:

a. $27 \text{ L} = \underline{\hspace{1cm}} \text{ mL}$

b. $362 \text{ mL} = \underline{\hspace{1cm}} \text{ L}$

c. $3 \text{ mL} = \underline{\hspace{1cm}} \text{ cm}^3$

d. $3 \text{ m}^3 = \underline{\hspace{1cm}} \text{ L}$

Solution   **a.** $1 \text{ L} = 1000 \text{ mL}$, so $27 \text{ L} = 27 \cdot 1000 \text{ mL} = 27{,}000 \text{ mL}$. Alternatively, $27\text{L} = 27\text{L} \cdot \dfrac{1000 \text{ mL}}{1 \text{ L}} = 27{,}000 \text{ mL}$.

b. $1 \text{ mL} = 0.001 \text{ L}$, so $362 \text{ mL} = 362(0.001 \text{ L}) = 0.362 \text{ L}$.

c. $1 \text{ mL} = 1 \text{ cm}^3$, so $3 \text{ mL} = 3 \text{ cm}^3$.

d. $1 \text{ m}^3 = 1000 \text{ dm}^3$ and $1 \text{ dm}^3 = 1 \text{ L}$, so $1 \text{ m}^3 = 1000 \text{ L}$ and $3 \text{ m}^3 = 3000 \text{ L}$. Alternatively, $3 \text{ m}^3 = 3 \text{ m}^3 \cdot \dfrac{1000 \text{ dm}^3}{1 \text{ m}^3} \cdot \dfrac{1 \text{ L}}{1 \text{ dm}^3} = 3000 \text{ L}$.

Converting English Measures of Volume

Basic units of volume in the English system are the cubic foot (1 ft^3), the cubic yard (1 yd^3), and the cubic inch (1 in.^3). In the United States, $1 \text{ gal} = 231 \text{ in.}^3$, which is about 3.8 L, and $1 \text{ qt} = \dfrac{1}{4} \text{ gal}$, or about 58 in.^3

Relationships among the one-dimensional units enable us to convert from one unit of volume to another, as shown in the following example.

EXAMPLE 11-24

Convert each of the following, as indicated:

a. $45 \text{ yd}^3 = \underline{\hspace{1cm}} \text{ ft}^3$

b. $4320 \text{ in.}^3 = \underline{\hspace{1cm}} \text{ yd}^3$

c. $10 \text{ gal} = \underline{\hspace{1cm}} \text{ ft}^3$

d. $3 \text{ ft}^3 = \underline{\hspace{1cm}} \text{ yd}^3$

Solution   **a.** Because $1 \text{ yd}^3 = (3 \text{ ft})^3 = 27 \text{ ft}^3$, $45 \text{ yd}^3 = 45 \cdot 27 \text{ ft}^3$, or 1215 ft^3.

b. Because $1 \text{ in.} = \dfrac{1}{36} \text{ yd}$, $1 \text{ in.}^3 = \left(\dfrac{1}{36}\right)^3 \text{ yd}^3$. Consequently, $4320 \text{ in.}^3 = 4320 \cdot \left(\dfrac{1}{36}\right)^3 \text{ yd}^3 \doteq 0.0926 \text{ yd}^3$, or approximately 0.1 yd^3.

c. Because 1 gal $= 231$ in.^{3} and 1 in.$^3 = \left(\dfrac{1}{12}\right)^3$ ft^3, 10 gal $= 2310$ in.$^3 =$

$2310\left(\dfrac{1}{12}\right)^3$ ft$^3 \doteq 1.337$ ft^3, or approximately 1.3 ft^3.

Alternatively, 10 gal $= 10$ gal $\cdot \dfrac{231 \text{ in.}^3}{1 \text{ gal}} \cdot \dfrac{\left(\dfrac{1}{12}\right)^3 \text{ ft}^3}{1 \text{ in.}^3} \doteq 1.3$ ft^3

d. As seen in (a), 1 ft$^3 = \dfrac{1}{27}$ yd^3. Hence 3 ft$^3 = 3 \cdot \dfrac{1}{27}$ yd$^3 = \dfrac{1}{9}$ yd^3.

Volumes of Prisms and Cylinders

We have shown that the volume of a right rectangular prism, as shown in Figure 11-73, involves multiplying the area of the base times the height. If we denote the area of the base by B and the height by h, then $V = Bh$.

FIGURE 11-73

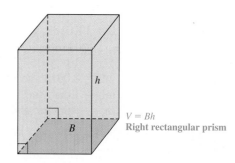

$V = Bh$
Right rectangular prism

Formulas for the volumes of many three-dimensional figures can be derived using the volume of a right prism. In Figure 11-74(a), a rectangular solid box has been sliced into thin layers. If the layers are shifted to form the solids in Figure 11-74(b) and (c), the volume of each of the three solids is the same as the volume of the original solid. This idea is the basis for **Cavalieri's principle**.

Cavalieri's principle

Cavalieri's Principle

Two solids each with a base in the same plane have equal volumes if every plane parallel to the bases intersects the solids in cross-sections of equal area.

FIGURE 11-74

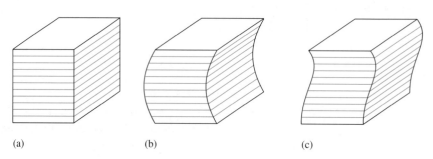

(a)   (b)   (c)

Bonaventura Cavalieri (1598–1647), an Italian mathematician and disciple of Galileo, contributed to the development of geometry, trigonometry, and algebra in the Renaissance. He became a Jesuit at an early age and later, after reading Euclid's *Elements*, was inspired to study mathematics. In 1629, Cavalieri became a professor at Bologna and held that post until his death. Cavalieri is best known for his principle concerning the volumes of solids.

NOW TRY THIS 11-19

a. The two right prisms in Figure 11-75 have the same height. How do their volumes compare? Explain why.

FIGURE 11-75

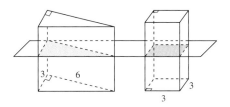

b. Consider the right prism and right cylinder in Figure 11-76(a) and (c) as stacks of papers. If the papers are shifted as shown in Figure 11-76(b) and (d), an oblique prism and an oblique cylinder, respectively, are formed.
  (i) Explain how the volume of the oblique prism is related to the volume of the right prism.
  (ii) Explain how the volume of the oblique cylinder is related to the volume of the right cylinder.

FIGURE 11-76

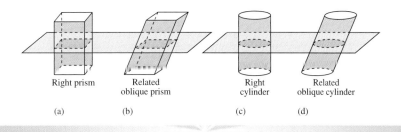

Right prism	Related oblique prism	Right cylinder	Related oblique cylinder
(a)	(b)	(c)	(d)

The volume of a cylinder can be approximated using prisms with increasing numbers of sides in their bases. The volume of each prism is the product of the area of the base and the height. Similarly, the **volume *V* of a cylinder** is the product of the area of the base *B* and the height *h*; that is, $V = Bh = \pi r^2 h$.

volume of a cylinder

Another way to conceptualize the fact that the volume of a cylinder is equal to the area of the base times the height is shown on the student page on page 710. Answer the questions in the Problem 4.1 Follow-Up.

Sample School Book Page:
VOLUME OF A CYLINDER

4.1 Filling a Cylinder

The *volume* of a container is the number of unit cubes it will hold. In the last investigation, you saw that you could find the volume of a prism-shaped box by figuring out how many unit cubes will fit in a single layer at the bottom of the box and then multiplying by the total number of layers needed to fill the box. In this problem, you will develop a method for determining how many cubes will fit inside a cylinder.

Problem 4.1

Make a cylinder by taping together the ends of a sheet of paper. Use the same size paper you used to make the prism shapes in Problem 3.3.

A. Set the cylinder on its base on a sheet of centimeter grid paper. Trace the cylinder's base. Look at the centimeter squares inside your tracing. How many cubes would fit in one layer at the bottom of the cylinder? Consider whole cubes and parts of cubes.

B. How many layers of cubes would it take to fill the cylinder?

| Trace the base. | How many cubes would fit in one layer? | How many layers would it take to fill the cylinder? |

C. What is the volume of the cylinder?

■ **Problem 4.1 Follow-Up**

1. How can you use the dimensions of the cylinder to help you estimate its volume more accurately? Explain.

2. How does the volume of the cylinder compare to the volumes of the prisms you made in Problem 3.3?

Source: Prentice Hall, Connected Mathematics: Filling and Wrapping, 2002 (p. 38).

EXAMPLE 11-25

Find the volume of each figure in Figure 11-77.

FIGURE 11-77

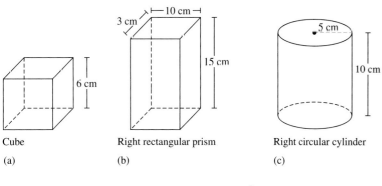

Cube
(a)

Right rectangular prism
(b)

Right circular cylinder
(c)

Solution   **a.** $V = Bh = (6 \text{ cm} \cdot 6 \text{ cm}) \cdot 6 \text{ cm} = 216 \text{ cm}^3$
  b. $V = Bh = (10 \text{ cm} \cdot 3 \text{ cm}) \cdot 15 \text{ cm} = 450 \text{ cm}^3$
  c. $V = \pi r^2 h = \pi (5 \text{ cm})^2 \cdot 10 \text{ cm} = 250\pi \text{ cm}^3$

Volumes of Pyramids and Cones

Figure 11-78(a) shows a right prism and a right pyramid with congruent bases and equal heights.

FIGURE 11-78

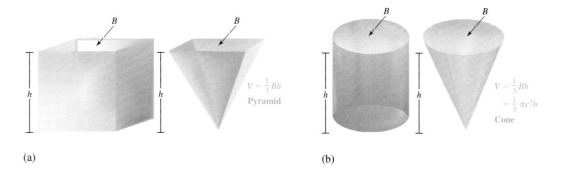

(a)   (b)

How are the volumes of these containers related? Students may explore the relationship by filling the pyramid with water, sand, or rice and pouring the contents into the prism. They should find that it takes three full pyramids to fill the prism. Therefore the volume of the pyramid is equal to one-third the volume of the prism. This relationship between prisms and pyramids with congruent bases and heights, respectively, is true in general; that is, for a pyramid $V = (1/3)Bh$, where B is the area of the base and h is the height. The same relationship holds between the volume of a cone and the volume of a cylinder, where they have congruent bases and equal heights, as shown in Figure 11-78(b). Therefore the volume of a cone is given by $V = (1/3)Bh$, or $V = (1/3)\pi r^2 h$.

This relationship between the volume of a cone and the volume of a cylinder is explored in Problem 5.2 on the partial student page on page 712.

Sample School Book Page:
CONES AND CYLINDERS

Problem 5.2

- Roll a piece of stiff paper into a cone shape so that the tip touches the bottom of your cylinder.

Trim around lip of cylinder.

Tape seam of cone.

- Tape the cone shape along the seam and trim it to form a cone with the same height as the cylinder.

- Fill the cone to the top with sand or rice, and empty the contents into the cylinder. Repeat this as many times as needed to completely fill the cylinder.

What is the relationship between the volume of the cone and the volume of the cylinder?

Source: Prentice Hall, Connected Mathematics: Filling and Wrapping, 2002 (p. 49).

Another way to determine the area of a pyramid in terms of a prism is to start with a cube and three diagonals from one vertex drawn to other vertices of the "opposite face," as shown in Figure 11-79(a). We can see that there are three pyramids formed inside the cube, as shown in Figure 11-79(b), (c), and (d).

FIGURE 11-79

   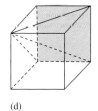

(a)   (b)   (c)   (d)

The three pyramids are identical in size and shape, do not overlap, and their union is the whole cube. Therefore, each pyramid has volume one-third that of the cube. This result is true in general, and once again we see that for a pyramid $V = (1/3)Bh$, where B is the area of the base and h is the height. This can be demonstrated by building three paper models of the pyramids and fitting them together into a prism. A net that can be enlarged and used for the construction is given in Figure 11-80.

FIGURE 11-80

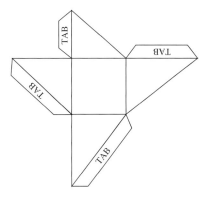

EXAMPLE 11-26

Find the volume of each figure in Figure 11-81.

FIGURE 11-81

Right square pyramid

(a)

Right circular cone

(b)

Solution
a. The figure is a pyramid with a square base whose area is 4 cm · 4 cm and whose height is 5 cm. Hence, $V = \frac{1}{3}Bh = \frac{1}{3}(4 \text{ cm} \cdot 4 \text{ cm})(5 \text{ cm}) = \frac{80}{3}\text{cm}^3$.

b. The base of the cone is a circle of radius 6 cm. Because the volume of the cone is given by $V = \frac{1}{3}\pi r^2 h$, we need to know the height. In the right triangle OAB, $OA = h$ and by the Pythagorean Theorem, $h^2 + 6^2 = 10^2$. Hence, $h^2 = 100 - 36$, or 64, and $h = 8$ cm. Thus $V = \frac{1}{3}\pi r^2 h = \frac{1}{3}\pi(6 \text{ cm})^2(8 \text{ cm}) = 96\pi \text{ cm}^3$.

E X A M P L E
11-27

Figure 11-82 is a net for a pyramid. If each triangle is equilateral, find the volume of the pyramid.

FIGURE 11-82

10 cm

Solution The pyramid obtained from the folded model is shown in Figure 11-83. The volume of the pyramid is $V = \frac{1}{3}Bh = \frac{1}{3} \cdot 10^2 h$. We must find h. Notice that h is a leg in the right triangle EOF, where F is the midpoint of $\overline{CB}$. We know that $OF = 5$ cm. If we knew EF, we could find h by applying the Pythagorean Theorem to $\triangle EOF$. To find the length of $\overline{EF}$, notice that $\overline{EF}$ is a leg in the right triangle EBF. ($\overline{EF}$ is the perpendicular bisector of $\overline{BC}$ in the equilateral triangle BEC.) In the right triangle EBF, we have $(EB)^2 = (BF)^2 + (EF)^2$. Because $EB = 10$ cm and $BF = 5$ cm, it follows that $10^2 = 5^2 + (EF)^2$, or $EF = \sqrt{75}$ cm $\doteq 8.66$ cm. In $\triangle EOF$, we have $h^2 + 5^2 = (EF)^2$, or $h^2 + 25 = 75$. Thus, $h = \sqrt{50}$ cm $\doteq 7.07$ cm, and $V \doteq \frac{1}{3} \cdot 10^2 \cdot 7.07 \doteq 235.7$ cm^3.

FIGURE 11-83

Volume of a Sphere

To find the volume of a sphere, imagine that a sphere is composed of a great number of congruent pyramids with apexes at the center of the sphere and that the vertices of the base touch the sphere, as shown in Figure 11-84. If the pyramids have very small bases, then the height of each pyramid is nearly the radius r. Hence, the volume of each pyramid is $\frac{1}{3}Bh$ or $\frac{1}{3}Br$, where B is the area of the base. If there are n pyramids each with base area B, then the total volume of the pyramids is $V = \frac{1}{3}nBr$. Because nB is the total surface area of all the bases of the pyramids and because the sum of the areas of all the bases of the pyramids is very close to the surface area of the sphere, $4\pi r^2$, the volume of the sphere is given by $V = \frac{1}{3}(4\pi r^2)r = \frac{4}{3}\pi r^3$.

FIGURE 11-84

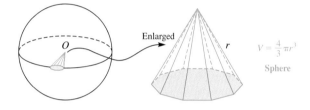

EXAMPLE 11-28

Find the volume of a sphere whose radius is 6 cm.

Solution $V = \frac{4}{3}\pi(6 \text{ cm})^3 = \frac{4}{3}\pi(216 \text{ cm}^3) = 288\pi \text{ cm}^3$

NOW TRY THIS 11-20

A cone, a cylinder, and sphere have the same radius and same height, as shown in Figure 11-85.

FIGURE 11-85

a. Find the volume of each figure in terms of r.
b. Use your answer to part (a) to show that the volumes are in the ratio $3:1:2$.

| PROBLEM SOLVING | **Volume Comparisons: Cylinders and Boxes** |

A metal can manufacturer has a large quantity of rectangular metal sheets 20 cm × 30 cm. Without cutting the sheets, the manufacturer wants to make cylindrical pipes with circular cross-sections from some of the sheets and box-shaped pipes with square cross-sections from the other sheets. The volume of the box-shaped pipes is to be greater than the volume of the cylindrical pipes. Is this possible? If so, how would the pipes be made and what are their volumes?

Understanding the Problem   We are to use 20 cm × 30 cm rectangular sheets of metal to make some cylindrical pipes as well as some box-shaped pipes with square cross-sections that have a greater volume than do the cylindrical pipes. Is this possible, and if so, how should the pipes be designed and what are their volumes?

Figure 11-86 shows a sheet of metal and two sections of pipe made from it, one cylindrical and the other box-shaped. A model for such pipes can be designed from a piece of paper by bending it into a cylinder or by folding it into a right rectangular prism, as shown in the figure.

FIGURE 11-86

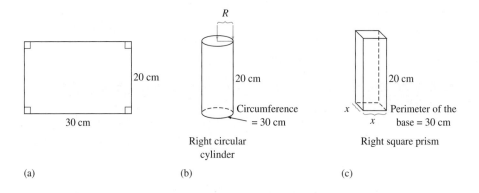

(a)

(b)

Right circular
cylinder

(c)

Right square prism

Devising a Plan   If we compute the volume of the cylinder in Figure 11-86(b) and the volume of the prism in Figure 11-86(c), we can determine which is greater. If the prism has a greater volume, the solution of the problem will be complete. Otherwise, we look for other ways to design the pipes before concluding that a solution is impossible.

To compute the volume of the cylinder, we find the area of the base. The area of the circular base is πr^2. To find r, we note that the circumference of the circle $2\pi r$ is 30 cm. Thus $r = \dfrac{30}{2\pi} \doteq 4.77$ cm, and the area of the circle is $\pi r^2 \doteq \pi(4.77)^2 \doteq 71.48$ cm^2.

With the given information, we can also find the area of the base of the rectangular box. Because the perimeter of the base of the prism is $4x$, we have $4x = 30$, or $x = 7.5$ cm. Thus the area of the square base is $x^2 = (7.5)^2$, or 56.25 cm^2.

Carrying Out the Plan   Denoting the volume of the cylindrical pipe by V_1 and the volume of the box-shaped pipe by V_2, we have $V_1 \doteq 71.48 \cdot 20$, or approximately 1429.6 cm^3. For the volume of the box-shaped pipe, we have $V_2 \doteq 56.25 \cdot 20$, or 1125 cm^3. We see that in the first design for the pipes, the volume of the cylindrical pipe is greater than the volume of the box-shaped pipe. This is not the required outcome.

Rather than bend the rectangular sheet of metal along the 30-cm side, we could bend it along the 20-cm side to obtain either pipe, as shown in Figure 11-87. Denoting the radius of the cylindrical pipe by r, the side of the box-shaped pipe by y, and their volumes by V_3 and V_4, respectively, we have $V_3 = \pi r^2 \cdot 30 = \pi(20/2\pi)^2 \cdot 30 = (10^2 \cdot 30)/\pi$, or approximately 954.9 cm^3. Also, $V_4 = y^2 \cdot 30 = \left(\dfrac{20}{4}\right)^2 \cdot 30 = 25 \cdot 30$, or 750 cm^3. Because $V_2 = 1125$ cm^3 and $V_3 = 945.9$ cm^3, we see that the volume of the box-shaped pipe with an altitude of 20 cm is greater than the volume of the cylindrical pipe with an altitude of 30 cm. Determine the order of volumes from greatest to least for the four shapes.

FIGURE 11-87

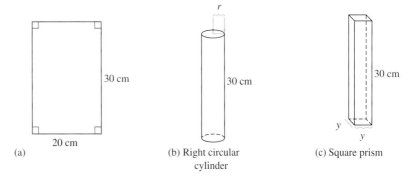

(a)   (b) Right circular cylinder   (c) Square prism

Looking Back   We could ask for the volumes of other three-dimensional objects that can be obtained by bending the rectangular sheets of metal. Also, because the lateral surface areas of the four types of pipes were the same but their volumes were different, we might want to investigate whether there are other cylinders and prisms that have the same lateral surface area and the same volume. Is it possible to find a circular cylinder with lateral surface area of 600 cm^2 and smallest possible volume? Similarly, is there a circular cylinder with the given surface area and greatest possible volume?

Mass

Three centuries ago, Isaac Newton pointed out that in everyday life the word *weight* is used for what is really mass. *Mass* is a quantity of matter as opposed to *weight*, which is a force excited by gravitational pull. When astronauts are in orbit above Earth, their weights have changed even though their masses remain the same. In common parlance on Earth, *weight* and *mass* are still used interchangeably. In the English system, weight is measured in avoirdupois units such as tons, pounds, and ounces. One pound (lb) equals 16 ounces (oz) and 2000 lb equals 1 English ton.

gram   In the metric system, the unit for mass that prefixes are used with is the **gram**, denoted g. An ordinary paper clip or a thumbtack each has a mass of about 1 g. As with other base metric units, prefixes are added to *gram* to obtain other units. For example, a kilogram (kg) is 1000 g. Two standard loaves of bread have a mass of about 1 kg. A person's mass also is measured in kilograms. A newborn baby has a mass of about 4 kg. Another unit of mass is the metric ton (t), which is equal to 1000 kg. The metric ton is used to record the masses of objects such as cars and trucks. A small foreign car has a mass of about 1 t. Mega (1,000,000) and micro (0.000001) are other prefixes used with the base unit.

Table 11-8 lists metric units of mass. Conversions that involve metric units of mass are handled in the same way as conversions that involve metric units of length.

Table 11-8

Unit	Symbol	Relationship to Gram
ton (metric)	t	1,000,000 g
kilogram	kg	1000 g
*hectogram	hg	100 g
*dekagram	dag	10 g
gram	**g**	**1 g**
*decigram	dg	0.1 g
*centigram	cg	0.01 g
milligram	mg	0.001 g

*Not commonly used

EXAMPLE 11-29

Complete each of the following:

a. 34 g = ___ kg

b. 6836 kg = ___ t

Solution　**a.** 34 g = 34(0.001 kg) = 0.034 kg
　　　　　　b. 6836 kg = 6836(0.001 t) = 6.836 t

Relationships Among Metric Units of Volume, Capacity, and Mass

The relationships among the units of volume, capacity, and mass in the metric system is illustrated in Figure 11-88. Does the English system have any relationships among units that are easy to remember?

FIGURE 11-88

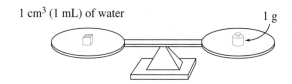

1 cm³ (1 mL) of water　　　　　　1 g

1 dm³ (1 L) of water　　　　　　1 kg

NOW TRY THIS 11-21

Find the following relationships:

a. 1 cm³ of water has a mass of 1 _____.
b. 1 dm³ of water has a mass of 1 _____.
c. 1 L of water has a volume of 1 _____ .
d. 1 cm³ of water has a capacity of 1 _____.
e. 1 mL of water has a mass of 1 _____.
f. 1 m³ of water has a capacity of 1 _____.
g. 1 m³ of water has a mass of 1 _____.

EXAMPLE
11-30

A waterbed measures 180 cm × 210 cm × 20 cm.

a. Approximately how many liters of water can it hold?
b. What is its mass in kilograms when it is full of water?

Solution **a.** The volume of the waterbed is approximated by multiplying the length ℓ times the width w times the height h.

$$V = \ell w h$$
$$= 180 \text{ cm} \cdot 210 \text{ cm} \cdot 20 \text{ cm}$$
$$= 756{,}000 \text{ cm}^3, \text{ or } 756{,}000 \text{ mL}$$

Because 1 mL = 0.001 L, the volume is 756 L.

b. Because 1 L of water has a mass of 1 kg, 756 L of water has a mass of 756 kg, which is 0.756 t.

REMARK To see one advantage of the metric system, suppose the bed in Example 11-30 is 6 ft × 7 ft × 9 in. Try to approximate the volume in gallons and the weight of the water in pounds.

Temperature

degree Kelvin

The base unit of temperature for the metric system, the **degree Kelvin**, is used only for scientific measurements and is an absolute temperature. The freezing point of water is 273° on this scale. For normal temperature measurements in the metric system, the base

degree Celsius

unit is the **degree Celsius**, named for Anders Celsius, the Swedish scientist who invented the system. The Celsius scale has 100 equal divisions between 0 degrees Celsius (0°C), the freezing point of water, and 100 degrees Celsius (100°C), the boiling point of water, as seen in Figure 11-89. In the English system, the Fahrenheit scale has 180 equal divisions between 32°F, the freezing point of water, and 212°F, the boiling point of water.

FIGURE 11-89

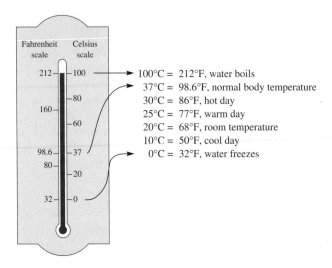

Figure 11-89 gives other temperature comparisons of the two scales and further illustrates the relationship between them. Because the Celsius scale has 100 divisions between the freezing point and the boiling point of water, whereas the Fahrenheit scale has 180 divisions, the relationship between the two scales is 100 to 180, or 5 to 9. For every 5 degrees on the Celsius scale, there are 9 degrees on the Fahrenheit scale, and for each degree on the Fahrenheit scale, there is $\frac{5}{9}$ degree on the Celsius scale. Because the ratio between the number of degrees above freezing on the Celsius scale and the number of degrees above freezing on the Fahrenheit scale remains the same and equals $\frac{5}{9}$, we may convert temperature from one system to the other.

For example, suppose we want to convert 50° on the Fahrenheit scale to the corresponding number on the Celsius scale. On the Fahrenheit scale, 50° is $50 - 32$, or 18°, above freezing, but on the Celsius scale, it is $\frac{5}{9} \cdot 18$, or 10°, above freezing. Because the freezing temperature on the Celsius scale is 0°, 10° above freezing is 10° Celsius. Thus 50°F = 10°C. In general, F degrees is $F - 32$ above freezing on the Fahrenheit scale, but only $\frac{5}{9}(F - 32)$ above freezing on the Celsius scale. Thus we have the relation $C = \frac{5}{9}(F - 32)$. If we solve the equation for F, we obtain $F = \frac{9}{5}C + 32$.

NOW TRY THIS 11-22

Does it ever happen that the temperature measured in Celsius degrees is the same if it is measured in Fahrenheit degrees? If so, when?

ONGOING ASSESSMENT 11-5

1. Complete each of the following:
   a. $8 \text{ m}^3 = \underline{\hspace{1cm}} \text{ dm}^3$
   b. $500 \text{ cm}^3 = \underline{\hspace{1cm}} \text{ m}^3$
   c. $675{,}000 \text{ m}^3 = \underline{\hspace{1cm}} \text{ km}^3$
   d. $3 \text{ m}^3 - \underline{\hspace{1cm}} \text{ cm}^3$
   e. $7000 \text{ mm}^3 = \underline{\hspace{1cm}} \text{ cm}^3$
   f. $0.002 \text{ m}^3 = \underline{\hspace{1cm}} \text{ cm}^3$
   g. $400 \text{ in.}^3 = \underline{\hspace{1cm}} \text{ yd}^3$
   h. $25 \text{ yd}^3 = \underline{\hspace{1cm}} \text{ ft}^3$
   i. $0.2 \text{ ft}^3 = \underline{\hspace{1cm}} \text{ in.}^3$
   j. $1200 \text{ in.}^3 = \underline{\hspace{1cm}} \text{ ft}^3$

2. If a faucet is dripping at the rate of 15 drops/min and there are 20 drops/mL, how many liters of water are wasted in a 30-day month?

3. Jeremy has a fish tank that has a 40-cm by 70-cm rectangular base. The water is 25 cm deep. When he drops rocks into the tank, the water goes up by 2 cm. What is the volume in liters of the rocks?

4. Maggie is planning to build a new one-story house with floor area of 2000 ft². She is thinking about putting in a 9-ft ceiling instead of an 8-ft ceiling. If she does this, how many more cubic feet of space will she have to heat and cool?

5. Find the volume of each of the following:

(a)

(b) Right rectangular prism

(c) Right triangular prism

(d) Square pyramid

(e) Right circular cone

(f) Right circular cylinder

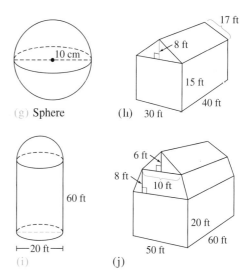

(g) Sphere   (h)   30 ft

(i)   (j)

6. Complete the following chart:

	a.	b.	c.	d.	e.	f.
cm³		500			750	4800
dm³	2					
L			1.5			
mL				5000		

7. Place a decimal point in each of the following to make it an accurate sentence:
   a. A paper cup holds about 2000 mL.
   b. A regular soft drink bottle holds about 320 L.
   c. A quart milk container holds about 10 L.
   d. A teaspoonful of cough syrup is about 500 mL.

8. Determine the volume of silver needed to make the napkin ring in the following figure out of solid silver. Give your answer in cubic millimeters.

9. Two cubes have sides of lengths 4 cm and 6 cm, respectively. What is the ratio of their volumes?

10. What happens to the volume of a sphere if the radius is doubled?

11. Complete the following chart for right rectangular prisms with the given dimensions:

	a.	b.	c.	d.
Length	20 cm	10 cm	2 dm	15 cm
Width	10 cm	2 dm	1 dm	2 dm
Height	10 cm	3 dm		
Volume (cm³)				
Volume (dm³)				7.5 dm³
Volume (L)			4 L	

12. Determine how many liters a right cylindrical tank holds if it is 6 m long and 13 m in diameter.
13. Earth's diameter is approximately four times the moon's and both bodies are spheres. What is the ratio of their volumes?
14. An Olympic-sized pool in the shape of a right rectangular prism is 50 m × 25 m. If it is 2 m deep throughout, how many liters of water does it hold?
15. A standard straw is 25 cm long and 4 mm in diameter. How much liquid can be held in the straw at one time?
16. a. What happens to the volume of an aquarium that is in the shape of a rectangular prism if the length, width, and height are all doubled?
    b. From your answer to (a), conjecture what happens to the volume of the aquarium if all the measurements are tripled.
    c. When you multiply each linear dimension of an aquarium by a positive value n, what happens to the volume?
17. The Great Pyramid of Cheops is a right square pyramid with height of 148 m and a square base with a perimeter of 930 m. The Transamerica Building in San Francisco has the basic shape of a right square pyramid that has a square base with a perimeter of 140 m and a height of 260 m. Which one has the greater volume and by how many times greater?
18. The Great Pyramid of Cheops has a square base of 756 ft on a side and a height of 481 ft. How many apartments 35 ft × 20 ft × 8 ft would be needed to have a volume equivalent to that of the Great Pyramid's?
19. A rectangular swimming pool with dimensions 10 m × 25 m is being built. The pool has a shallow end that is uniform in depth and a deep end that drops off as shown in the following figure. What is the volume of this pool in cubic meters?

20. If 50 steel marbles that are 1 cm in diameter are melted down, will enough steel result to build a marble that is 4 cm in diameter? Explain.
21. A heavy metal sphere with radius 10 cm is dropped into a right circular cylinder with base radius of 10 cm. If the original cylinder has water in it that is 20 cm high, how high is the water after the sphere is placed in it?
22. A cone-shaped paper water cup has a height of 8 cm and a radius of 4 cm. If the cup is filled with water to half its height, what portion of the volume of the cup is filled with water?
23. If each edge of a cube is increased by 30%, by what percent does the volume increase?
24. One freezer measures 1.5 ft × 1.5 ft × 5 ft and sells for $350. Another freezer measures 2 ft × 2 ft × 4 ft and sells for $400. Which freezer is the better buy in terms of dollars per cubic foot?
25. A tennis ball can in the shape of a cylinder holds three tennis balls snugly. If the radius of a tennis ball is 3.5 cm, what percentage of the tennis ball can is occupied by air?
26. A box is packed with six soda cans, as in the following figure. What percentage of the volume of the interior of the box is not occupied by the cans?

27. A right rectangular prism with base *ABCD* as the bottom is shown in the following figure.

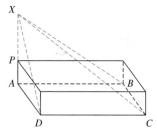

Suppose X is drawn so that $AX = 3 \cdot AP$, where AP is the height of the prism and X is connected to A, B, C, and D to form a pyramid. How do the volumes of the pyramid and the prism compare?
28. A right cylindrical can is to hold approximately 1 L of water. What should be the height of the can if the radius is 12 cm?
29. A theater decides to change the shape of its popcorn container from a regular box to a right regular pyramid and charge only half as much as shown in the following figure.

If the containers are the same height and the tops are the same size, is this a bargain for the customer? Explain.

30. Which is the better buy: a grapefruit 5 cm in radius that costs 22¢ or a grapefruit 6 cm in radius that costs 31¢? Explain.

31. Two spherical cantaloupes of the same kind are sold at a fruit and vegetable stand. The circumference of one is 60 cm and that of the other is 50 cm. The larger melon is $1\frac{1}{2}$ times as expensive as the smaller. Which melon is the better buy and why?

32. An engineer is to design a square-based pyramid whose volume is to be 100 m³.
   a. Find the dimensions (the length of a side of the square and the altitude) of one such pyramid.
   b. How many (noncongruent) such pyramids are possible? Why?

33. A square sheet of cardboard measuring y cm on a side is to be used to produce an open-top box when the maker cuts off a small square x cm $\times$ x cm from each corner and bends up the sides. Find the volume of the box if $y = 200$ cm and $x = 20$ cm.

34 a. Suppose a scoop of ice cream that is a sphere with radius 5 cm fits exactly along one of its great circles in a sugar cone, as shown in the following figure.

5 cm

10 cm

Suppose the ice cream melts and the cone does not absorb any of it. If the cone is 10 cm tall, will it hold the melted ice cream? If not, how tall would the cone have to be to hold the melted ice cream?
   b. Suppose the scoop of ice cream in part (a) fits exactly along the top of a right circular cylinder of height 10 cm. Will the cylinder hold the melted ice cream? If yes, what height of the cylinder will be reached?

★**35.** Half of the air is let out of a spherical balloon. If the balloon remains in the shape of a sphere, how does the radius of the smaller balloon compare to the original radius?

36. For each of the following, select the appropriate metric unit of measure (gram, kilogram, or metric ton):
   a. Car   **b.** Adult
   c. Can of frozen orange juice   **d.** Elephant
   e. Jar of mustard   **f.** Bag of peanuts
   g. Army tank   **h.** Cat

37. For each of the following, choose the correct unit (milligram, gram, or kilogram) to make each sentence reasonable:
   a. A staple has a mass of about 340 ____.
   b. A professional football player has a mass of about 110 ____.
   c. A vitamin tablet has a mass of about 1100 ____.
   d. A dime has a mass of 2 ____.
   e. The recipe said to add 4 ____ of salt.
   f. One strand of hair has a mass of 2 ____.

38. Complete each of the following:
   a. 15,000 g = ____ kg   **b.** 8000 kg = ____ t
   c. 0.036 kg = ____ g   **d.** 72 g = ____ kg
   e. 4320 mg = ____ g   **f.** 5 kg 750 g = ____ g
   g. 0.03 t = ____ kg   **h.** 2.6 lb = ____ oz
   i. 25 oz = ____ lb   **j.** 3.8 lb = ____ oz

39. A paper dollar has a mass of approximately 1 g. Is it possible to lift $1,000,000 in the following denominations:
   a. $1 bills   **b.** $10 bills
   c. $100 bills   **d.** $1000 bills
   e. $10,000 bills

40. A fish tank, which is a right rectangular prism, is 40 cm $\times$ 20 cm $\times$ 20 cm. If it is filled with water, what is the mass of the water?

41. Convert each of the following from degrees Fahrenheit to the nearest integer degree Celsius:
   a. 10°F   **b.** 0°F
   c. 30°F   **d.** 100°F
   e. 212°F   **f.** ⁻40°F

42. Answer each of the following:
   a. The thermometer reads 20°C. Can you go snow skiing?
   b. The thermometer reads 26°C. Will the outdoor ice rink be open?
   c. Your body temperature is 39°C. Are you ill?
   d. It is 40°C. Will you need a sweater at the outdoor concert?
   e. The temperature reads 35°C. Should you go water skiing?
   f. Your bath water is 16°C. Will you have a hot, warm, or chilly bath?
   g. It's 30°C in the room. Are you comfortable, hot, or cold?

43. a. Rainfall is usually measured in linear measure. Suppose St. Louis received 2 cm of rain on a given day. If a certain lot in St. Louis has measure 1 ha, how many liters of rainfall fell on the lot?
   b. What is the mass of the water that fell on the lot?

Communication

44. a. Which will increase the volume of a circular cylinder more: doubling its height or doubling its radius? Explain.
   b. Is your answer the same for a circular cone? Why?

45. Write a one-page paper to a sixth-grade student explaining the difference between surface area and volume.

46. Explain how you would find the volume of an irregular shape.
47. Read the following problems (i) and (ii):
    i. A tank in the shape of a cube 5 ft 3 in. on a side is filled with water. Find the volume in cubic feet, the capacity in gallons, and the weight of the water in pounds.
    ii. A tank in the shape of a cube 2 m on a side is filled with water. Find the volume in cubic meters, the capacity in liters, and the mass of the water in kilograms.
    Discuss which problem is easier to work and why.

Open-Ended

48. A right circular cylinder has a 4-in. diameter, is 6 in. high, and is completely full of water. Design a right rectangular prism that will hold the water as exactly as possible.
49. Circular-shaped cookies are to be packaged 48 to a box. Each cookie is approximately 1 cm thick and has a diameter of 6 cm. Design a box that will hold this volume of cookies and has the least amount of surface area.
50. Design a cylinder that will hold 1 L of juice. Give the dimensions of your cylinder and tell why you designed the shape as you did.

Cooperative Learning

51. **a.** Find many different types of cans that are in the shape of a cylinder. Measure the height and diameter of each can.
    b. Find the surface area of each can.
    c. Find the volume of each can.
    d. Compute the ratio of surface area to volume for each can.
    e. Compare your results with those of other groups.
    f. Based on the information collected, write recommendations to the manufacturers of the cans about an ideal surface-area-to-volume ratio.

Review Problems

52. Find the perimeter and the area of the following figures:

(a)   (b) The shaded portion only

53. Complete the following:
    a. 350 mm = ____ cm   **b.** 1600 cm^2 = ____ m^2
    c. 0.4 m^2 = ____ mm^2 **d.** 5.2 cm^2 = ____ m^2
54. Determine whether each of the following is a right triangle:

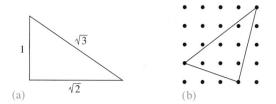

(a)   (b)

55. Find the surface area of each of the following:

(a) Right circular cone   (b) Right prism in which the faces are either rectangles or right triangles

---

LABORATORY
A C T I V I T Y

Record the mass of each U.S. coin. Which coin has the greatest mass? Which of the following have the same mass?

a. A half-dollar vs. two quarters
b. A quarter vs. two dimes and a nickel
c. A dime vs. two nickels
d. A dime vs. ten pennies
e. A nickel vs. five pennies

Hint for Solving the Preliminary Problem

We can compute the area of the large circular area in terms of the side *s* of the square, the radius of the circle or the radius of the smaller circles and calculate the percentage of the square covered by the larger sprinkler. Next, we can compute the area of one of the small circles in terms of the same variable, multiply this by nine, and then compute the percentage of the square covered by the nine smaller sprinklers. We can then compare the percents and make a decision on the two systems.

QUESTIONS FROM THE CLASSROOM

1. A student asks if the units of measure must be the same for each term in order to use the formulas for volumes. How do you respond?

2. As part of the discussion of the Pythagorean Theorem, squares were constructed on each side of a right triangle. A student asks, "If different similar figures are constructed on each side of the triangle, does the same type of relationship still hold?" How do you reply?

3. A student asks, "Can I find the area of an angle?" How do you respond?

4. A student argues that a square has no area because its interior can be thought of as the union of infinitely many points, each of which has no area. How do you react?

5. A student asks whether the volume of a prism can ever be the same number as its surface area. How do you answer?

6. A student asks, "Should the United States switch to the metric system?" How do you reply?

7. A student claims that in a triangle with 20° and 40° angles, the side opposite the 40° angle is twice as long as the side opposite the 20° angle. How do you reply?

8. A student interpreted 5 cm³ as shown in Figure 11-90. What is wrong with this interpretation?

9. A student claims that because *are* and *hectare* are measures of area, we should say "square are" and "square hectare." How do you respond?

10. A student claims that the area of his hand does not exist because it cannot be found by any formula. How do you respond?

11. A student claims that since a circular cylinder has a curved surface, its lateral surface area should not be expressed in square units. How do you respond?

12. A student claims that it does not make any difference if his temperature is 2 degrees above normal Fahrenheit or 2 degrees above normal Celsius because in either case he is only 2 degrees above normal. How do you respond?

13. Larry and Gary are discussing whose garden has the most area to plant flowers. Larry claims that all they have to do is walk around the two gardens to get the perimeter and the one with the greatest perimeter has the greatest area. How would you help these students?

14. Andrea claims that if she doubles the length and width of the base of a rectangular prism and triples the height, she has increased the volume by a factor 2 · 2 · 3 = 12. What would you tell her?

15. Jimmy claims that to find the area of a parallelogram he just has to multiply length times width. In Figure 11-91 he multiplies 25 × 20 = 500 in.². What would you tell him?

FIGURE 11-90

5 cm
5 cm
5 cm

FIGURE 11-91

25 in.
20 in.

CHAPTER OUTLINE

I. The English system of measure

  A. Linear measure

  1 ft = 12 in.

  1 yd = 3 ft

  1 mi = 5280 ft = 1760 yd

  B. Area measure

  1. Units commonly used are the **square inch** (in.^{2}), **square yard** (yd^2), and **square foot** (ft^2).

  2. Land can be measured in **acres**.

  C. Volume measure

  Units commonly used are the **cubic inch** (in.^{3}), **cubic foot** (ft^3), **cubic yard** (yd^3), and **gallon**.

  D. Mass

  Units of mass commonly used are **pound** (lb), **ounce** (oz) (1 oz = $\frac{1}{16}$ lb), and **ton** (t) (1 ton = 2000 lb).

II. The metric system of measure

  A. A summary of relationships among prefixes and the base unit of linear measure follows:

Prefix	Unit	Relationship to Base Unit	Symbol
kilo	kilometer	1000 m	km
*hecto	hectometer	100 m	hm
*deka	dekameter	10 m	dam
meter		**1 m**	**m**
*deci	decimeter	0.1 m	dm
centi	centimeter	0.01 m	cm
milli	millimeter	0.001 m	mm

  *Not commonly used

  B. Area measure

  1. Units commonly used are the **square kilometer** (km^2), **square meter** (m^2), **square centimeter** (cm^2), and **square millimeter** (mm^2).

  2. Land can be measured using the **are** (a) (100 m^2) and the **hectare** (ha) (10,000 m^2).

  C. Volume measure

  1. Units commonly used are the **cubic meter** (m^3), **cubic decimeter** (dm^3), and **cubic centimeter** (cm^3).

  2. 1 dm^3 = 1 L and cm^3 = 1 mL.

  D. Mass

  1. Units of mass commonly used are the **milligram** (mg), **gram** (g), **kilogram** (kg), and **metric ton** (t).

  2. 1 L and 1 mL of water have masses of approximately 1 kg and 1 g, respectively.

  E. Temperature

  1. In the metric system the unit commonly used is the **degree Celsius** (°C). In the English system, the unit of temperature is the **degree Fahrenheit** (°F).

  2. Basic temperature reference points are the following:

  100°C—boiling point of water

  37°C—normal body temperature

  20°C—comfortable room temperature

  0°C—freezing point of water

  3. $C = \frac{5}{9}(F - 32)$ and $F = \frac{9}{5}C + 32$

III. Distance

  A. **Distance properties.** Given points A, B, and C,

  a. $AB \geq O$

  b. $AB = BA$

  c. $AB + BC \geq AC$

  B. The distance around a two-dimensional figure is the **perimeter**. The distance C around a circle is the **circumference**. $C = 2\pi r = \pi d$, where r is the radius of the circle and d is the **diameter**.

  C. **Distance formula.** The distance between the points A (x_1, y_1) and B (x_2, y_2) is given by

  $$AB = \sqrt{(x_2 - x_1)^2 + (y_2 - y_1)^2}$$

IV. Areas

  A. Formulas for areas

  1. **Square:** $A = s^2$, where s is the length of a side.

  2. **Rectangle:** $A = \ell w$, where ℓ is the length and w is the width.

  3. **Parallelogram:** $A = bh$, where b is the length of the base and h is the height.

  4. **Triangle:** $A = \frac{1}{2}bh$, where b is the length of the base and h is the altitude to that base.

  5. **Trapezoid:** $A = \frac{1}{2}h(b_1 + b_2)$, where b_1 and b_2 are the lengths of the bases and h is the height.

  6. **Regular polygon:** $A = \frac{1}{2}ap$, where a is the apothem and p is the perimeter.

  7. **Circle:** $A = \pi r^2$, where r is the radius.

  8. **Sector:** $A = \theta\pi r^2/360$, where θ is the measure of the central angle forming the sector and r is the radius of the circle containing the sector.

  B. **The Pythagorean Theorem:** In any right triangle, the square of the length of the hypotenuse is equal to the sum of the squares of the lengths of the legs.

  C. Triangle relations

  1. **Property of 30°-60°-90° triangle:** The length of the hypotenuse in a 30°-60°-90° triangle is 2 times the length of the leg opposite the 30° angle, and the length of the leg opposite the 60° angle is $\sqrt{3}$ times the length of the short leg.

  2. **Property of 45°-45°-90° triangle:** The length of the hypotenuse of a 45°-45°-90° triangle is $\sqrt{2}$ times the length of a leg.

D. Converse of the Pythagorean Theorem: In any triangle *ABC* with sides of lengths *a, b,* and *c* such that
$a^2 + b^2 = c^2$, $\triangle ABC$ is a right triangle with the right
angle opposite the side of length *c*.

V. Surface areas and volumes

  A. Formulas for areas

    1. Right prism: $S.A. = 2B + ph$, where *B* is the area
of a base, *p* is the perimeter of the base, and *h* is
the height of the prism.

    2. Right circular cylinder: $S.A. = 2\pi r^2 + 2\pi rh$,
where *r* is the radius of the circular base and *h* is
the height of the cylinder.

    3. Right circular cone: $S.A. = \pi r^2 + \pi r\ell$, where *r*
is the radius of the circular base and ℓ is the slant
height.

    4. Right regular pyramid: $S.A. = B + \frac{1}{2}p\ell$, where
B is the area of the base, *p* is the perimeter of the
base, and ℓ is the slant height.

    5. Sphere: $S.A. = 4\pi r^2$, where *r* is the radius of the
sphere.

  B. Formulas for volumes

    1. Right prism: $V = Bh$, where *B* is the area of the
base and *h* is the height.

      a. Right rectangular prism: $V = \ell wh$, where ℓ
is the length, *w* is the width, and *h* is the height.

      b. Cube: $V = e^3$, where *e* is an edge.

    2. Right circular cylinder: $V = \pi r^2 h$, where *r* is the
radius of the base and *h* is the height of the cylinder.

    3. Pyramid: $V = \frac{1}{3}Bh$, where *B* is the area of the
base and *h* is the height of the pyramid.

    4. Circular cone: $V = \frac{1}{3}\pi r^2 h$, where *r* is the radius
of the circular base and *h* is the height.

    5. Sphere: $V = \frac{4}{3}\pi r^3$, where *r* is the radius of the
sphere.

CHAPTER REVIEW

1. Complete the following.

  a. 50 ft = _____ yd   **b.** 947 yd = _____ mi

  c. 0.75 mi = _____ ft   **d.** 349 in. = _____ yd

  e. 5 km = _____ m   **f.** 165 cm = _____ m

  g. 52 cm = _____ mm   **h.** 125 m = _____ km

2. Given three segments of length *p, q,* and *r,* where $p > q$,
determine if it is possible to construct a triangle with sides
of length *p, q,* and *r* in each of the following cases. Justify
your answers.

  a. $p - q > r$ **b.** $p - q = r$

3. Determine the area of the shaded region on each of the following geoboards if the unit of measure is 1 cm²:

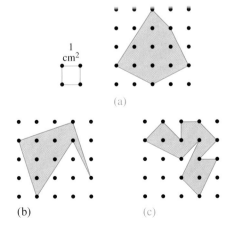

  (a)

  (b)   (c)

4. Explain how the formula for the area of a trapezoid can be
found by using the following figures:

5. Lines *a, b,* and *c* are parallel to the line containing side *AB*
of the triangles shown below.

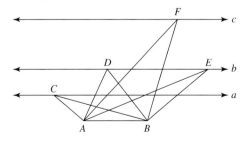

List the triangles in order of size of their areas from least
to greatest. Explain why your order is correct.

6. Use the following figure to find each of the following areas:
   a. The area of the regular hexagon
   b. The area of the circle

7. Find the area of each shaded region in the following figures:

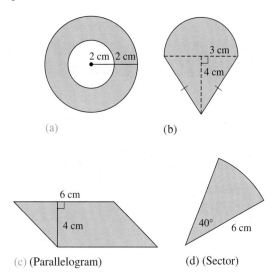

(a)

(b)

(c) (Parallelogram)

(d) (Sector)

(e)

(f)

8. Find the surface area of the following box (include the bottom).

9. A baseball diamond is actually a square 90 ft on a side. What is the distance a catcher must throw from home plate to second base?

10. Find the length of segment *AG* in the spiral shown below.

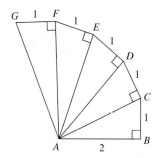

11. For each of the following, determine whether the measures represent sides of a right triangle. Explain your answers.
    a. 5 cm, 12 cm, 13 cm   b. 40 cm, 60 cm, 104 cm

12. Find the surface area and volume of each of the following figures:

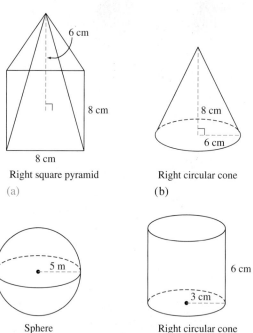

Right square pyramid
(a)

Right circular cone
(b)

Sphere
(c)

Right circular cone
(d)

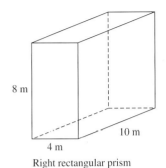

8 m

10 m

4 m

Right rectangular prism

(e)

13. Find the lateral surface area of the following right circular cone:

12 m

5 m

14. Doug's Dog Food Company wants to impress the public with the magnitude of the company's growth. Sales of Doug's Dog Food doubled from 2000 to 2003, so the company is displaying the following graph, which shows the radius of the base and the height of the 2003 can to be double those of the 2000 dog food can. What does the graph really show with respect to the company's growth? Explain your answer.

2003

2000

15. Find the area of the kite shown in the following figure:

20 cm

13 cm

5 cm

12 cm

16. The diagonal of a rectangle has measure 1.3 m, and a side of the rectangle has measure 120 cm. Find the following:
  a. Perimeter of the rectangle
  b. Area of the rectangle
17. Find the area of a triangle that has sides of 3 m, 3 m, and 2 m.

18. A poster is to contain 0.25 m^2 of printed matter, with margins of 12 cm at top and bottom and 6 cm at each side. Find the width of the poster if its height is 74 cm.
19. A right circular cylinder and a right circular cone share a circular base and have the same volume. What is the height of the cone?

10 cm

20. Complete each of the following:
  a. A very heavy object has mass that is measured in _____.
  b. A cube whose length, width, and height are each 1 cm has a volume of _____.
  c. If the cube in (b) is filled with water, the mass of the water is _____.
  d. Which has a larger volume: 1 L or 1 dm^3?
  e. If a car uses 1 L of gas to go 12 km, the amount of gas needed to go 300 km is _____ L.
  f. 20 ha = _____ a
  g. 51.8 L = _____ cm^3
  h. 10 km^2 = _____ m^2
  i. 50 L = _____ mL
  j. 5830 mL = _____ L
  k. 25 m^3 = _____ dm^3
  l. 75 dm^3 = _____ mL
  m. 52,813 g = _____ kg
  n. 4800 kg = _____ t
21. Two cones are defined to be similar if the ratio between their heights equals the ratio between their radii. If two similar cones have heights h_1 and h_2, find the ratio between their volumes in terms of h_1 and h_2.
22. a. A tank that is a right rectangular prism is 1 m × 2 m × 3 m. If the tank is filled with water, what is the mass of the water?
  b. Suppose the tank is exactly half full of water and then a heavy metal sphere of radius 30 cm is put into the tank. How high is the water now if the height of the tank is 3 m?
23. For each of the following, fill in the correct unit to make the sentence reasonable:
  a. Anna filled the gas tank with 80 _____.
  b. A man has a mass of about 82 _____.
  c. The textbook has a mass of 978 _____.
  d. A nickel has a mass of 5 _____.
  e. A typical adult cat has a mass of about 4 _____.
  f. A compact car has a mass of about 1.5 _____.
  g. The amount of coffee in the cup is 180 _____.

24. For each of the following, decide if the situation is likely or unlikely:

a. Carrie's bath water has a temperature of 15°C.

b. Anne found 26°C too warm and so lowered the thermostat to 21°C.

c. Jim is drinking water that has a temperature of ⁻5°C.

d. The water in the teakettle has a temperature of 120°C.

e. The outside temperature dropped to 5°C, and ice appeared on the lake.

25. Complete each of the following:

a. 2 dm^3 of water has a mass of ____ g.

b. 1 L of water has a mass of ____ g.

c. 3 cm^3 of water has a mass of ____ g.

d. 4.2 mL of water has a mass of ____ kg.

e. 0.2 L of water has a volume of ____ m^3.

SELECTED BIBLIOGRAPHY

Ameis, J. "Developing an Area Formula for a Circle with Goldilocks and the Three Bears." *Mathematics Teaching in the Middle School* 7 (November 2001): 140–142.

Andrews, A. "Solving Geometric Problems by Using Unit Blocks." *Teaching Children Mathematics* 5 (February 1999): 318–323.

Battista, M. "How Many Blocks?" *Mathematics Teaching in the Middle School* 3 (March–April 1998): 404–411.

Battista, M., and D. Clements. "Finding the Number of Cubes in Rectangular Cube Buildings." *Teaching Children Mathematics* 4 (January 1998): 258–264.

Bellasanta, B., B. Hunter, K. Irwin, M. Sheldon, C. Thompson, and C. Vistro-Yu. "By the Unit or Square Unit." *Mathematics Teaching in the Middle School* 7 (November 2001): 132–137.

Berry, R., and J. Wiggins. "Measurement in the Middle Grades." *Mathematics Teaching in the Middle School* 7 (November 2001): 154–156.

Chappell, M. "Geometry in the Middle Grades: From Past to the Present." *Mathematics Teaching in the Middle School* 9 (May 2001): 516–519.

Collier, P., and T. Pateracki. "Geometry in the Middle School: An Exchange of Ideas and Experiences. *Mathematics Teaching in the Middle School* 3 (March–April 1998): 412–415.

Hayes, N. "Cardboard Tubes Bring Geometry from Home." *Mathematics Teaching in the Middle School* 4 (October 1998): 120–122.

Lamphere, P. "Geoboard Patterns and Figures." *Teaching Children Mathematics* 1 (January 1995): 282–287.

LaSaracina, B., and S. White. "The Restless Rectangle and the Transforming Trapezoid." *Teaching Children Mathematics* 5 (February 1999): 336–337, 366.

Loomis, E. *The Pythagorean Proposition.* National Council of Teachers of Mathematics. Reston, Va.: NCTM, 1976.

Manouchehri, A., M. Enderson, and L. Pagnucco. "Exploring Geometry with Technology." *Mathematics Teaching in the Middle School* 3 (March–April 1998): 436–442.

Miller, W., and L. Wagner. "Pythagorean Dissection Puzzles." *Mathematics Teacher* 86 (April 1993): 302–308, 313–314.

Moore, D. "Some Like It Hot: Promoting Measurement and Graphical Thinking by Using Temperature." *Teaching Children Mathematics* 5 (May 1999): 538–543.

Naraine, B. "If Pythagoras Had a Geoboard." *Mathematics Teacher* 86 (February 1993): 137–140, 145–148.

Nitabach, E., and R. Lehrer. "Developing Spatial Sense through Area Measurement." *Teaching Children Mathematics* 2 (April 1996): 473–476.

Robertson, S. "Getting Students Actively Involved in Geometry." *Teaching Children Mathematics* 5 (May 1999): 526–529.

Shultz, J. "Area Models: Spanning the Mathematics of Grades 1–9." *Arithmetic Teacher* 39 (October 1991): 42–46.

Smith, L. "Areas and Perimeters of Geoboard Polygons." *Mathematics Teacher* 83 (May 1990): 392–398.

Smith, L. "Using Dragon Curves to Learn about Length and Area." *Mathematics Teaching in the Middle School* 5 (December 1999): 222–223.

Spangler, D. "A Case of the Smash Hit." *Mathematics Teaching in the Middle School* 3 (March–April 1998): 424–427.

Stone, M. "Teaching Relationships between Area and Perimeter with the Geometer's Sketchpad." *Mathematics Teacher* 87 (November 1994): 590–594.

Taylor, L. "Exploring Geometry with the Geometer's Sketchpad." *Arithmetic Teacher* 40 (November 1992): 187–191.

Taylor, M. "Do Your Students Measure Up Metrically?" *Teaching Children Mathematics* 7 (January 2001): 282–287.

Tent, M. "Circles and the Number Π." *Mathematics Teaching in the Middle School* 6 (April 2001): 452–457.

Weinberg, S. "How Big Is Your Foot?" *Mathematics Teaching in the Middle School* 6 (April 2001): 476–481.

–12–
Motion Geometry and Tessellations

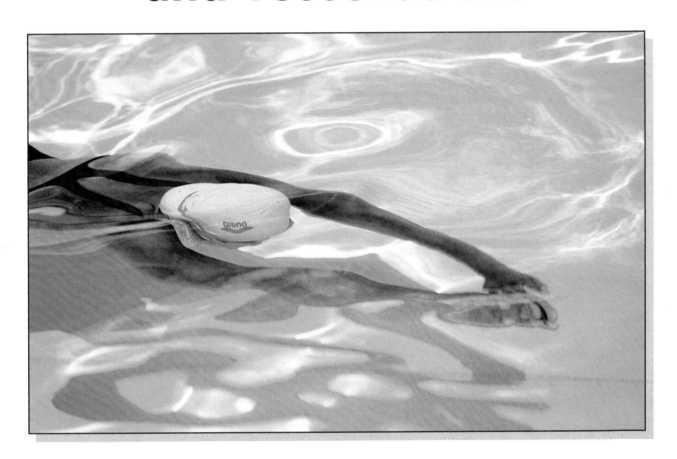

PRELIMINARY PROBLEM

Eva is in a rectangular swimming pool *ABCD* at point *P*, which is 6 meters from both side $\overline{AB}$ and side $\overline{BC}$. She wants to swim to side $\overline{BC}$, put down her goggles, then swim to point *Q*, which is 14 m from side $\overline{AB}$ and 9 m from side $\overline{BC}$. Toward which point on the side $\overline{BC}$ should she swim if her total swimming path is to be as short as possible? How long will her path be?

E uclid envisioned moving one geometric figure in a plane and placing it on top of another to determine if the two figures were congruent. Intuitively, we know this can be done by making a tracing of one figure, then sliding, turning, or flipping the tracing, and finally placing it back down atop the other figure.

Symmetries are fundamental in the study of geometry, nature, and shapes. Many symmetries are the results of sliding, flipping, and turning shapes. A study of these "motions" and symmetries leads to tessellations of the plane or space. A **tessellation** is the filling of a plane or space with repetitions of a figure (or figures) in such a way that none overlap and there are no gaps. This chapter contains sections on motions, symmetries, and tessellations.

tessellation

In the *Principles and Standards*, we find the following:

 Young children come to school with intuitions about how shapes can be moved. Students can explore motions such as slides, flips, and turns by using mirrors, paper folding, and tracing. Later, their knowledge about transformations should become more formal and systematic. In grades 3–5 students can investigate the effects of transformations and begin to describe them in mathematical terms. Using dynamic geometry software, they can begin to learn the attributes needed to define a transformation. For example, to transform a figure using a rotation, students need to define the center of rotation, the direction of the rotation, and the angle of rotation, as illustrated in figure 3.3. In the middle grades, students should learn to understand what it means for a transformation to preserve distance, as translations, rotations, and reflections do. . . . At all grade levels, appropriate consideration of symmetry provides insights into mathematics and into art and aesthetics. (p. 43)

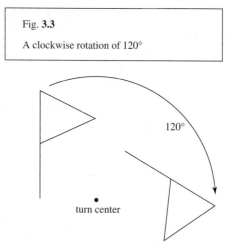

Fig. **3.3**

A clockwise rotation of 120°

120°

turn center

The *Principles and Standards* also lists the following expectations for different grade levels.

In prekindergarten through grade 2 all students should

- *recognize and apply slides, flips, and turns;*
- *recognize and create shapes that have symmetry.* (p. 96)

In grades 3–5 all students should

- *predict and describe the results of sliding, flipping, and turning two-dimensional shapes;*
- *describe a motion or a series of motions that will show that two shapes are congruent;*

- *identify and describe line and rotational symmetry in two- and three-dimensional shapes and designs.* (p. 164)

In grades 6–8 all students should

- *describe sizes, positions, and orientations of shapes under informal transformations such as flips, turns, slides, and scaling;*
- *examine the congruence, similarity, and line or rotational symmetry of objects using transformations.* (p. 232)

HISTORICAL NOTE

In 1872, at age 23, Felix Klein (1849–1925) was appointed to a chair at the University of Erlangen, Germany. His inaugural address, referred to as the *Erlanger Programm*, described geometry as the study of properties of figures that do not change under a particular set of transformations. Specifically, Euclidean geometry was described as the study of such properties of figures as area and length, which remain unchanged under a set of transformations called *isometries*.

One of the first attempts to introduce geometric transformations into the elementary school in the United States was by the University of Illinois Committee on School Mathematics (UICSM). UICSM published *Motion Geometry* in four volumes in 1969.

12-1   Translations and Rotations

Translations

translation/slide

Figure 12-1 shows a two-dimensional representation of a child moving down a slide without twisting or turning. This type of motion is a **translation**, or **slide**.

FIGURE 12-1

preimage
slide line ◆ image

In Figure 12-1, the child (**preimage**) at the top of the slide moves a certain distance in a certain direction along a **slide line** to obtain the **image** at the bottom of the slide.

slide arrow ◆ vector

Figure 12-1 shows a translation that takes the preimage to its image. The translation is determined by the **slide arrow**, or **vector**, from *M* to *N*. The vector determines the image of any point in a plane in the following way: The image of a point *A* in the plane is the point *A′* obtained by sliding *A* along a line parallel to $\overleftrightarrow{MN}$ in the direction from *M* to *N* by the distance *MN*. ($\overleftrightarrow{MN}$ is also denoted by *d* in Figure 12-1.) Notice that *AA′* = *MN* = *d* and $\overleftrightarrow{MN}$ is parallel to $\overleftrightarrow{AA}$ ′. It appears that under the translation, figures change neither their shapes nor their sizes. In fact, a translation preserves both length and angle size, and thus congruence of figures.

isometry
rigid motion

Any motion that preserves length or distance is an **isometry** (derived from Greek and meaning "equal measure"), or **rigid motion**. For example, a translation is an isometry. Notice that a translation is a function whose domain is the plane; that is, the set of all the points in the plane.

> Definition of a Translation

A **translation** is a motion of a plane that moves every point of the plane a specified distance in a specified direction along a straight line.

TECHNOLOGY
C O R N E R

GSP Lab 10 activities 6–8 can be used to investigate properties of translations.

NOW TRY THIS 12-1

A translation is a function whose domain is the plane. What is the range of this function?

Notice that a translation of a plane is a one-to-one correspondence between the plane and itself. Any function from a plane to itself that is a one-to-one correspondence between a plane and itself is a **transformation** of the plane.

transformation

We assume the following properties of a translation from a plane to a plane.

> Properties of Translations

- A figure and its image are congruent.
- The image of a line is a line parallel to it.

Constructions of Translations

The image of a figure under a translation can be constructed easily with tracing paper or by using only a compass and straightedge. Using tracing paper may be the more natural way to construct a "motion." However, since traditionally most constructions in geometry are accomplished with a compass and a straightedge, we consider first how that might be done and then leave the actual construction as an activity in "Now Try This 12-2."

To construct the image of an object under a translation, we first need to know how to construct the image A' of a single point A. In Figure 12-1, by definition of translation $MN = AA'$ and $\overleftrightarrow{MN}$ is parallel to $\overleftrightarrow{AA}'$. Thus, $MAA'N$ will be a parallelogram. (Why?) Consequently, to construct the image A' of a point A with a compass and straightedge, we need only to construct a parallelogram $MAA'N$ so that $\overrightarrow{AA}'$ is in the same direction as $\overrightarrow{MN}$.

NOW TRY THIS 12-2

In Figure 12-2 use a compass and straightedge to construct the following:

a. The image of A under a translation that takes M to N.

b. The image of A under a translation that takes N to M.

FIGURE 12-2

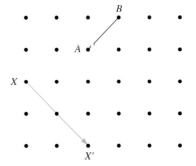

The properties of a translation tell us that to find the image of a triangle under a translation, it suffices to find the images of the three vertices of the triangle by using a process similar to that used in Figure 12-1 or Figure 12-2 and connect these images with segments to form the triangle's image.

It is possible to use a geoboard or a grid to find an image of a segment, as the following example shows.

EXAMPLE 12-1

Find the image of $\overline{AB}$ under the translation from X to X' pictured on the dot paper in Figure 12-3.

FIGURE 12-3

Solution X' is the image of X under the translation. X' could be obtained from X by shifting X two units vertically down and then two units horizontally to the right, as shown in Figure 12-4. This shifting determines the slide arrow from X to X'. The image of each point on the dot paper can be obtained by first shifting it 2 units down and then 2 units to the right. The image of $\overline{AB}$ is found in this way in Figure 12-4.

FIGURE 12-4

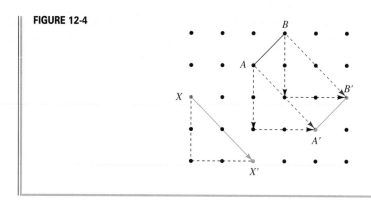

Coordinate Representation of Translations

In many applications of mathematics, such as computer graphics, it is necessary to use translations in a coordinate system. In Figure 12-5, $\triangle A'B'C'$ is the image of $\triangle ABC$ under the translation defined by the slide arrow from O to O', where O is the origin and O' has coordinates $(5, {}^-2)$. Point O' is the image of point O under the given translation. The point $O'(5, {}^-2)$ can be obtained by moving O horizontally to the right 5 units and then 2 units down. As each point in the triangle is translated in the direction from O to O' by the distance OO', we can obtain the image of any point by moving horizontally to the right 5 units and then vertically 2 units down. This is shown in Figure 12-5 for points A, B, C and their corresponding images A', B', and C'.

FIGURE 12-5

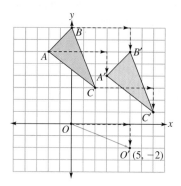

Table 12-1 shows how the coordinates of the image vertices A', B', and C' in Figure 12-5 are obtained from the coordinates of A, B, and C.

Table 12-1

Point (x, y)	Image Point $(x + 5, y - 2)$
$A\,({}^-2, 6)$	$A'\,(3, 4)$
$B\,(0, 8)$	$B'\,(5, 6)$
$C\,(2, 3)$	$C'\,(7, 1)$

This discussion suggests that we could describe a translation by showing how the coordinates of any point (x, y) are changed. The translation described in Table 12-1 can be written symbolically as $(x, y) \rightarrow (x + 5, y - 2)$ where "$\rightarrow$" denotes "moves to." In this notation $(x + 5, y - 2)$ is the image of (x, y).

> ### Definition of a Translation in a Coordinate System

A translation is a function from the plane to the plane such that to every point (x, y) corresponds the point $(x + a, y + b)$ where a and b are real numbers.

In general, a translation is symbolized as $(x, y) \rightarrow (x + a, y + b)$ where the point $(x + a, y + b)$ is the image of the point (x, y). Similarly, the same translation could be determined by the slide arrow from $(0, 0)$ to (a, b) or other comparable slide arrows involving a movement of a units horizontally and b units vertically.

E X A M P L E
12-2

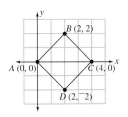

FIGURE 12-6

Find the coordinates of the image of quadrilateral *ABCD* in Figure 12-6 under the translations in parts (a) through (c). Draw the image in each case.

a. $(x, y) \rightarrow (x - 2, y + 4)$
b. A translation determined by the slide arrow from $A(0, 0)$ to $A'(-2, 4)$
c. A translation determined by the slide arrow from $S(4, {}^-3)$ to $S'(2, 1)$

Solution   **a.** Because $(x, y) \rightarrow (x - 2, y + 4)$, the images $A', B', C',$ and D' of the corresponding points $A, B, C,$ and D can be found as follows:

$$A(0, 0) \rightarrow A'(0 - 2, 0 + 4), \text{ or } A'({}^-2, 4)$$
$$B(2, 2) \rightarrow B'(2 - 2, 2 + 4), \text{ or } B'(0, 6)$$
$$C(4, 0) \rightarrow C'(4 - 2, 0 + 4), \text{ or } C'(2, 4)$$
$$D(2, {}^-2) \rightarrow D'(2 - 2, {}^-2 + 4), \text{ or } D'(0, 2)$$

The square *ABCD* and its image $A'B'C'D'$ are shown in Figure 12-7.

FIGURE 12-7

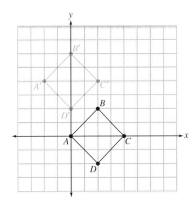

b. This is the same translation as in (a) and hence the image of *ABCD* is the same as that in (a).

c. We could move from $S(4, {}^-3)$ to $S'(2, 1)$ by moving a certain number of units horizontally and then a certain number of units vertically. Because $4 + ({}^-2) = 2$ and ${}^-3 + 4 = 1$, moving 2 units to the left and then 4 units up will take us from S to S'. The image of any point (x, y) under the translation from S to S' can be obtained in the same way; that is, the image of any point (x, y) is $(x - 2, y + 4)$. Thus the image of $ABCD$ also is the same as that obtained in (a).

Translations are useful in determining frieze patterns such as those appearing in wallpaper designs. Such patterns are explored in problem 18 of the Ongoing Assessment 12-4.

Rotations

rotation/turn   A **rotation**, or **turn**, is another kind of isometry. Figure 12-8 illustrates congruent figures that resulted from a rotation about point O. The image of the letter **F** is shown in green.

FIGURE 12-8

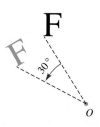

A rotation can be constructed by using tracing paper, as in Figure 12-9. In Figure 12-9(a), $\triangle ABC$ and point O are traced on tracing paper. Holding point O fixed, we turn the tracing paper to obtain the image, $\triangle A'B'C'$, as shown in Figure 12-9(b). Point O is the **turn center**, and $\angle COC'$ is the **turn angle**.

turn center ◆ turn angle

FIGURE 12-9   *Construction of a rotation using tracing paper*

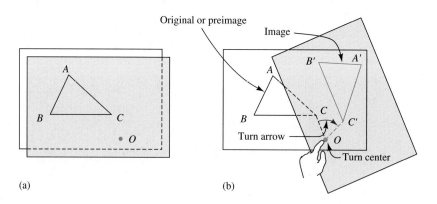

To determine a rotation, we must know three pieces of data: the turn center; the direction of the turn, either clockwise or counterclockwise; and the amount of the turn. The amount and the direction of the turn can be illustrated by a **turn arrow**, or they can be specified in numbers of degrees.

turn arrow

This discussion leads to the following definition.

> ### Definition of Rotation

A **rotation** is a transformation of the plane determined by holding one point—the center—fixed and rotating the plane about this point by a certain amount in a certain direction.

REMARK In higher mathematics and its applications it is customary to assign a positive measure to a counterclockwise turn and a negative measure to a clockwise turn.

To construct an image of a figure under a rotation, observe that every point on the tracing-paper construction moves along a circle. Also the angle formed by any point, the center of the rotation O, and the image of the point is the angle of the turn. (Why?) With this in mind, we construct the image of a point under a rotation in the following "Now Try This" activity.

NOW TRY THIS 12-3

Use a compass and a straightedge to construct the image of point P under a rotation with center O through the angle and in the direction given in Figure 12-10. (*Hint:* Construct an isosceles triangle BAC with B on one side of the given angle and C on the other side so that $AB = AC = OP$. Then construct $\triangle POP'$ congruent to $\triangle BAC$.)

FIGURE 12-10

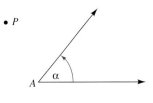

TECHNOLOGY
C O R N E R

THE GEOMETER'S
SKETCHPAD

GSP Lab 10 activities 9–11 can be used to investigate properties of rotations.

Because a rotation is an isometry, the image of a figure under a rotation is congruent to the original figure. It can be shown that *under any isometry, the image of a line is a line, the image of a circle is a circle, and the images of parallel lines are parallel lines.*

For certain angles like 90°, rotations may be constructed on a geoboard or dot paper, as demonstrated in Example 12-3.

E X A M P L E
12-3

In Figure 12-11 find the image of △*ABC* under the rotation with center *O*.

FIGURE 12-11

Solution △*A′B′C′*, the image of △*ABC*, is shown in Figure 12-12. The image of *A* is *A′* because ∠*A′OA* is a right angle (why?) and *OA* = *OA′*. Similarly *B′* is the image of *B*. To find the location of *C′*, we use the fact that rotation is an isometry and hence △*A′B′C′* ≅ △*ABC*. Thus ∠*B* ≅ ∠*B′*. The location of point *C′* shown makes ∠*B* ≅ ∠*B′*, *C′B′* = *CB* (why?), and the direction of the rotation is counterclockwise as specified.

FIGURE 12-12

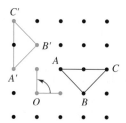

identity transformation

half-turn

A rotation of 360° about a point will move any point and hence any figure onto itself. Such a transformation is an **identity transformation**. It plays an important role in more advanced studies of transformations. A rotation of 180° about a point is also of particular interest. Such a rotation is a **half-turn**. Because a half-turn is a rotation, it has all the properties of rotations. Figure 12-13 shows some shapes and their images under a half-turn about point *O*.

FIGURE 12-13

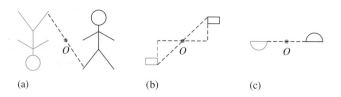

(a)   (b)   (c)

Rotations are useful in determining turn symmetries, which we investigate later. A different application of rotations appears when we consider the slopes of perpendicular lines, as seen in the following.

Slopes of Perpendicular Lines

Transformations can be used to investigate various mathematical relationships. For example, they can be used to determine the relationship between the slopes of two perpendicular lines, neither of which is vertical.

We first consider a special case in which the lines go through the origin. Suppose the slopes of the lines ℓ_1 and ℓ_2, shown in Figure 12-14, are m_1 and m_2, respectively. Because the slope of a line is equal to rise over run, the slope of ℓ_1 can also be determined from $\triangle OBA$, in which we choose $OA = 1$. We have $m_1 = \dfrac{\text{rise}}{\text{run}} = \dfrac{BA}{1} = BA$.

FIGURE 12-14

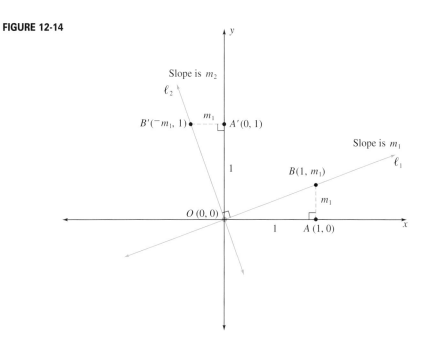

We then rotate the plane $90°$ counterclockwise about center O. The image of ℓ_1 is ℓ_2. To determine the image of $\triangle OBA$, we need only determine the images of each of the vertices of the triangle. The image of O is O itself. The image of A is A' on the y-axis (why?), and the image of B is B' on ℓ_2 (why?). Because rotation preserves congruence, $\triangle OB'A' \cong \triangle OBA$; consequently, $\angle B'A'O$ is a right angle, $A'B' = m_1$, and $OA' = 1$. Thus, as shown in Figure 12-14, point B' is at $(^-m_1, 1)$. We can use the slope formula to find the slope of ℓ_2 as follows:

$$m_2 = \frac{1 - 0}{^-m_1 - 0} = \frac{1}{^-m_1} = \frac{^-1}{m_1}.$$

Thus $m_2 = {^-1}/m_1$, or $m_1 m_2 = {^-1}$.

The relationship between the slopes m_1 and m_2 of two perpendicular lines (neither of which is vertical) that do not intersect at the origin can always be found using two lines parallel to the original lines but that pass through the origin. Because parallel lines have equal slopes, the relationship between the slopes of the perpendicular lines is the same as the relationship between the slopes of the perpendicular lines through the origin; that is, $m_1 m_2 = {^-1}$.

It is also possible to prove the converse statement; that is, if the slopes of two lines satisfy the condition $m_1 m_2 = {}^-1$, then the lines are perpendicular. We summarize these results in the following property.

> ### Property of Slopes of Perpendicular Lines
>
> Two lines, neither of which is vertical, are perpendicular if, and only if, their slopes m_1 and m_2 satisfy the condition $m_1 m_2 = {}^-1$. Any vertical line is perpendicular to a line with slope 0.

EXAMPLE 12-4

Find the equation of line ℓ through point $({}^-1, 2)$ and perpendicular to the line $y = 3x + 5$.

Solution   If m is the slope of ℓ as in Figure 12-15, then ℓ can be written as $y = mx + b$.

FIGURE 12-15

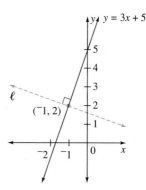

Because the line $y = 3x + 5$ has slope 3 and is perpendicular to ℓ, we have $m \cdot 3 = {}^-1$; therefore $m = -\dfrac{1}{3}$. Consequently, the equation of ℓ is

$$y = -\frac{1}{3}x + b.$$

Because the point $({}^-1, 2)$ is on ℓ, we can substitute $x = {}^-1$, $y = 2$ in $y = -\dfrac{1}{3}x + b$ and solve for b as follows:

$$2 = -\frac{1}{3} \cdot ({}^-1) + b$$

$$\frac{5}{3} = b.$$

Consequently, the equation of ℓ is

$$y = -\frac{1}{3}x + \frac{5}{3}.$$

O N G O I N G   A S S E S S M E N T   1 2 - 1

1. For each of the following, find the image of the given quadrilateral under a translation from A to B:

(a)   (b)

2. Find the figure whose image is given in each of the following under a translation from X to X′:

(a)   (b)

3. Construct the image of $\overline{BC}$ under the translation pictured in the following figure by using the following:
   a. Tracing paper
   b. Compass and straightedge

4. Find the coordinates of the image for each of the following points under the translation defined by $(x, y) \rightarrow (x + 3, y - 4)$:
   a. $(0, 0)$ **b.** $(^-3, 4)$ c. $(^-6, ^-9)$
   d. $(7, 14)$ e. (h, k)

5. Find the coordinates of the points whose images under the translation $(x, y) \rightarrow (x - 3, y + 4)$ are the following:
   a. $(0, 0)$ **b.** $(^-3, 4)$ c. $(^-6, ^-9)$
   d. $(7, 14)$ e. (h, k)

6. Consider the translation $(x, y) \rightarrow (x + 3, y - 4)$. In each of the following, draw the image of the figure under the trans-

lation and find the coordinates of the images of the labeled points.

(a)

(b)

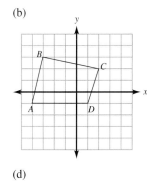

(c)   (d)

7. Consider the translation $(x, y) \rightarrow (x + 3, y - 4)$. In each of the following, draw the figure whose image is shown:

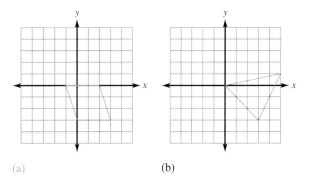

(a)   (b)

8. Find the image of the following quadrilateral in a 90° counterclockwise rotation about O:

9. If ℓ is a line whose equation is $y = 2x - 1$, find the equation of the image of ℓ under each of the following translations.
   a. $(x, y) \rightarrow (x, y - 2)$
   b. $(x, y) \rightarrow (x + 3, y)$
   c. $(x, y) \rightarrow (x - 3, y + 2)$

10. If $y = {}^{-}2x + 3$ is the image of line k under the translation $(x, y) \rightarrow (x + 3, y - 2)$, find the equation of k.

11. If P' is the image of point P under a half-turn about its center O, what can be said about points P', P, and O? Why?

12. Use a compass and a straightedge to find the image of line ℓ under a half-turn about point O as shown.

13. The images of $\overline{AB}$ under various rotations are given in the following figures. Find $\overline{AB}$ in each case.

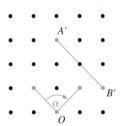

A rotation with center O through α

(a)

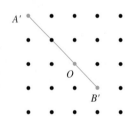

A half-turn through O

(b)

14. The image of NOON is still NOON after a special half-turn. List some other words that have the same property. What letters can such words contain?

15. a. Refer to the following figure and use paper folding or any other method to show that if P' is the image of P under rotation about point O by a given angle, then O is on the perpendicular bisector of $\overline{PP'}$.

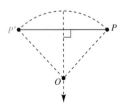

   b. $\triangle A'B'C'$ shown in the following figure was obtained by rotating $\triangle ABC$ about a certain point O. Explain how to find the point O and the angle of rotation.

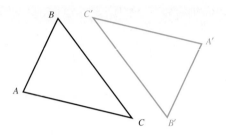

   c. Triangles ABC and $A'B'C'$ shown below are congruent. Trace them and explain how to show that it is impossible to find a rotation under which $\triangle A'B'C'$ is the image of $\triangle ABC$.

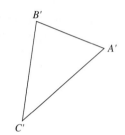

16. The images of any point under a rotation by certain angles can be found with only a compass and straightedge (without the use of a protractor). Construct P', the image of P when it is rotated about O, as shown in the following figure, for angles with the following measures and direction:
    a. 45° counterclockwise
    b. 60° clockwise
    c. 30° counterclockwise

• P

• O

17. For each of the following points, find the coordinates of the image point under a half-turn about the origin:
    a. $(4, 0)$
    b. $(0, 3)$
    c. $(2, 4)$
    d. $({}^{-}2, 5)$
    e. $({}^{-}2, {}^{-}4)$
    f. (a, b)
    g. $({}^{-}a, {}^{-}b)$

18. In each of the following figures, find the image of the figure under a half-turn about O:

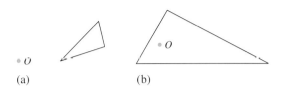

(a)   (b)

19. Draw any line and label it ℓ. Use tracing paper to find ℓ', the image of ℓ under each of the following rotations. In each case, describe in words how ℓ' is related to ℓ.
   a. Half-turn about point O on ℓ
   b. Half-turn about point O, not on ℓ
   c. A 90° turn counterclockwise about point O, not on ℓ
   d. A 60° turn counterclockwise about point O, not on ℓ

20. a. Find the final image of $\triangle ABC$ by performing two rotations in succession each with center O, one by angle α and one by angle β in the directions shown in the figure.

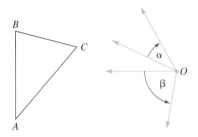

   b. Is the order of the rotations important?
   c. Could the result have been accomplished in one rotation?

21. When $\triangle ABC$ in the following figure is rotated about a point O by 360°, each of the vertices traces a path.

   a. What geometric figure does each vertex trace?
   b. Identify all points O for which two vertices trace an identical path. Justify your answer.
   c. Given any $\triangle ABC$, is there a point O such that the three vertices trace an identical path? If so, describe how to find such a point.

22. a. A translation from A to B is followed by a translation from B to C, as shown. Show that the same result can be accomplished by a single translation. What is that translation?
   b. Find a single translation equivalent to a translation from A to B followed by a translation from D to E.

c. Suppose the order of the translations in part (b) is reversed; that is, a translation from D to E is followed by a translation from A to B. Is the result different from the one in part (b)?

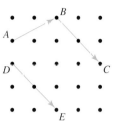

Communication

23. If we are given two congruent nonparallel segments, is it always possible to find a rotation so that the image of one segment will be the other segment? Explain why or why not.

24. a. If you rotate an object 180° clockwise or counterclockwise, using the same center, is the image the same in both cases? Explain.
   b. Answer part (a) if you rotate the object 360°.

25. For each of the following figures, trace the figure on tracing paper, rotate the tracing by 180° about the given point O, sketch the image, and then make a conjecture about the kind of figure that is formed by the union of the original figure and its image. In each case, explain why you think your conjecture is true.

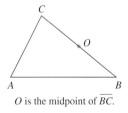

O is the midpoint of $\overline{BC}$.

(a)

 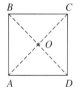

$ABCD$ is a trapezoid and $ABCD$ is a square and
O is the midpoint of $\overline{CD}$. O is the intersection
                           of its diagonals.

(b)   (c)

26. If $\overline{AB}$ is rotated about point O by 90° clockwise, explain whether its image is perpendicular to $\overline{AB}$, regardless of the location of point O.

Open-Ended

27. A drawing of a cube, shown in the following figure, can be created by drawing a square *ABCD*, finding its image under translation defined by the slide arrow from *A* to *A′* so that *AA′* = *AB*, and connecting the points *A, B, C,* and *D* with their corresponding images.

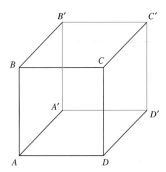

Draw several other perspective geometric figures using translations. In each case, name the figures and indicate the slide arrow that defines the translation.

28. Wall stenciling has been used to obtain an effect similar to that of wallpapering. The stencil pattern in the following figure can be used to create a border on a wall.

Measure the length of a wall of a room and design your own stencil pattern to create a border. Cut the pattern from a sheet of plastic or cardboard. Define the translation that will accomplish creating an appropriate border for the wall.

29. The following pattern can be created by rotating figure *A* about *O* by the indicated angle, then rotating the image *B* about *O* by the same angle, and then rotating the image *C* about *O* by the same angle, and so on until one of the images coincides with the original figure *A*.

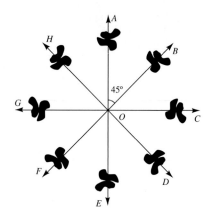

Make several designs with different numbers of congruent figures around a circle in which the image of each figure under the same rotation is the next figure and so that one of the images coincides with the original figure.

Cooperative Learning

30. Mark a point *A* on a sheet of paper and set a straightedge through *A* as shown in the following figure. Find a circular shape (a jar lid is a good choice) and mark point *P* on the edge of the shape. Place the shape on the straightedge so that *P* coincides with *A*. Consider the path traced by *P* as the circle rolls so that its edge stays in contact with the straightedge all the time and until *P* comes in contact with the straightedge again at point *B*.

a. Have one member of your group roll the circular shape and another draw the path traced by *P* as accurately as possible.

b. Discuss how to check if the path traced by point *P* is an arc of a circle.

c. Find the length of *AB*.

TECHNOLOGY
C O R N E R

Use GSP to draw an equilateral triangle and two altitudes of the triangle. Let *O* be the point at which the altitudes intersect. Rotate the triangle by 120° about *O* in any direction. Make a conjecture based on this experiment. Do you think your conjecture may be true for some triangles that are not equilateral? Why?

In Figure 12-16, a coin is shown above and touching another coin. Suppose the top coin is rotated around the circumference of the bottom coin until it rests directly below the bottom coin. Will the head be straight up or upside down?

FIGURE 12-16

  Reflections and Glide Reflections

Reflections

reflection ◆ flip

Another isometry is a **reflection**, or **flip**. One example of a reflection often encountered in our daily lives is a mirror image. Figure 12-17 shows a figure with its mirror image.

FIGURE 12-17

Mirror

Another reflection is shown in the following "B.C." cartoon.

B.C.   **by johnny hart**

12-15

reflecting line
mirror image

We can obtain reflections in a line in various ways. Consider the half tree shown in Figure 12-18(a). Folding the paper along the **reflecting line** and drawing the image gives the **mirror image**, or *image*, of the half tree. In Figure 12-18(b), the paper is shown unfolded. Another way to simulate a reflection in a line involves using a Mira, as illustrated in Figure 12-18(c).

FIGURE 12-18

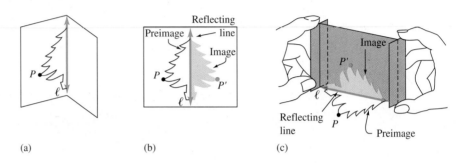

(a)   (b)   (c)

In Figure 12-19(a), the image of P under a reflection in line ℓ is P'. $\overline{PP'}$ is both perpendicular to and bisected by ℓ, or equivalently, ℓ is the perpendicular bisector of $\overline{PP'}$.

FIGURE 12-19

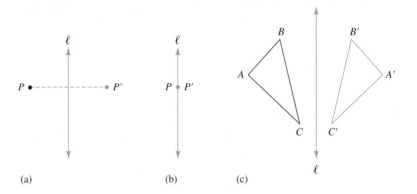

(a)   (b)   (c)

In Figure 12-19(b), P is its own image under the reflection in line ℓ. If ℓ were a mirror, then P' would be the mirror image of P. This leads us to the following definition of a reflection.

> Definition of Reflection

A **reflection** in a line ℓ is a transformation of a plane that pairs each point P of the plane with a point P' in such a way that ℓ is the perpendicular bisector of $\overline{PP'}$, as long as P is not on ℓ. If P is on ℓ, then $P = P'$.

In Figure 12-19(c), we see another property of a reflection. In the original triangle *ABC*, if we walk clockwise around the vertices, starting at vertex *A*, we see the vertices in the order *A-B-C*. However, in the reflection image of triangle *ABC*, if we start at *A'* (the image of *A*) and walk clockwise, we see the vertices in the following order: *A'-C'-B'*. Thus a reflection does something that neither a translation nor a rotation does; it reverses

orientation

the **orientation** of the original figure.

There are many methods of constructing a reflection image. We already illustrated such constructions with paper folding and a Mira. Next, we illustrate the construction of the image of a figure under a reflection in a line with tracing paper.

Constructing a Reflection by Using Tracing Paper

Figure 12-20(a) shows the use of tracing paper. We trace the original figure, the *reflecting line*, and a point on the reflecting line, which we use as a *reference point*. When we flip the tracing paper over to perform the reflection, we align the reflecting line and the reference point, as in Figure 12-20(b). Aligning the reference point ensures that no translating occurs along the reflecting line when the reflection is performed. If we wish the image to be on the paper with the original, we may indent the tracing paper or acetate sheet to mark the images of the original vertices.

FIGURE 12-20

(a)

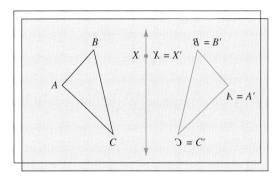

(b)

NOW TRY THIS 12-4

Use the definition of a reflection in a line and properties of a rhombus to construct the image P' of point P in Figure 12-21 under reflection in line m using only a compass and straightedge.

FIGURE 12-21

    Reflections, rotations, and translations appear early in the elementary curriculum, as shown in the following student page. Work through questions 1–8 on the page.

E X A M P L E
12-5

Describe how to construct the image of $\overleftrightarrow{AB}$ under a reflection in line m in Figure 12-22.

FIGURE 12-22

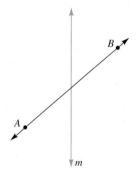

Solution   Under a reflection, the image of a line is a line. Thus, to find the image of $\overleftrightarrow{AB}$, it is sufficient to choose any two points on the line and find their images. The images determine the line that is the image of $\overleftrightarrow{AB}$. We choose two points whose images are easy to find. Point X, the intersection of $\overleftrightarrow{AB}$ and m, is its own image. If we choose point A and use a compass and straightedge, we produce the construction shown in Figure 12-23.

FIGURE 12-23

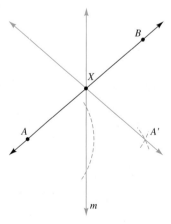

Sample School Book Page:
FLIP, TURN, AND SLIDE

Connect ·

Two figures that have the same size and shape are **congruent**.

Congruent   **Not congruent**

You can **flip** (or reflect), **turn** (or rotate), and **slide** (or translate) a figure to test if two figures are congruent.

| **a flip** | **a turn** | **a slide** |
| (a reflection) | (a rotation) | (a translation) |

Each pair of triangles fit on top of each other exactly.

Practice ·

Write whether each picture shows a translation, reflection, or rotation.

4. **Reasoning** Brian says that a square looks the same whether he translates it, reflects it, or rotates it 90°. Is he right? Explain.

5. **Fine Arts** Draw a part of the design in the tile that shows·

Mexican tile makers are known for the beauty of their designs.

   a. a translation.

   b. a reflection.

   c. a rotation.

6. Do two triangles drawn side by side always show a slide? Explain.

7. **Language Arts** If you turn a lower-case b, you get a q. Find letters that look like other letters after they are flipped or turned. (Don't forget capital letters.)

8. **Journal** How can you use slides, flips, and turns to decide whether two figures are congruent?

Source: Scott Foresman–Addison Wesley MATH, Grade 4, 2002 (p. 353).

Constructing a Reflection on Dot Paper or a Geoboard

On dot paper or a geoboard, the images of figures under a reflection can sometimes be found by inspection, as seen in Example 12–6.

EXAMPLE
12-6

Find the image of $\triangle ABC$ under a reflection in line m, as in Figure 12-24.

FIGURE 12-24

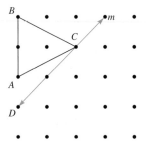

Solution The image $A'B'C'$ is given in Figure 12-25. Note that C is the image of itself and the images of the vertices A and B are A' and B' such that m is the perpendicular bisector of $\overline{AA'}$ and $\overline{BB'}$.

FIGURE 12-25

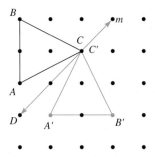

It is possible to find the reflecting line, if we are given an original figure and its reflection image. This is left as an exercise.

NOW TRY THIS 12-5

Trace $\triangle ABC$ and $\triangle A'B'C'$ from Figure 12-25 on a sheet of paper (without tracing line m). Find the line of reflection using paper folding.

Reflections in a Coordinate System

For some reflection lines like the x-axis and y-axis and the line $y = x$, it is quite easy to find the coordinates of the image, given the coordinates of the point. In Figure 12-26, the line $y = x$ bisects the angle between the x-axis and y-axis. The image of $A(1, 4)$ is the point $A'(4, 1)$. Also the image of $B(^-3, 0)$ is $B'(0, \ ^-3)$. It is left as an exercise to show that in general the image of $P(a, b)$ is the point $P'(b, a)$. Consequently, the reflection in the line $y = x$ exchanges the coordinates of the point. Is this still true if the point is not above line $y = x$?

FIGURE 12-26

Glide Reflections

glide reflection   Another basic isometry is a **glide reflection**. An example of a glide reflection is shown in the footprints of Figure 12-27. We consider the footprint labeled F_1 to have been translated to footprint F_2 and then reflected over line m (parallel to $\overline{F_1F_2}$) to yield F_3, the image of F_2. F_3 is the final image of F_1.

FIGURE 12-27

Note that point A is translated to find point A' and then point A' is reflected over line m (parallel to $\overline{F_1F_2}$) to obtain point A''. Thus, A'' is the image of A in the glide reflection.

The illustration in Figure 12-27 leads us to the following definition.

> ### Definition of Glide Reflection
>
> A **glide reflection** is a transformation consisting of a translation followed by a reflection in a line parallel to the slide arrow.

Because constructing a glide reflection involves constructing a translation and a reflection, the task of constructing a glide reflection is not a new problem. Exercises involving the construction of images of figures under glide reflections are given in the Ongoing Assessment 12-2.

Congruence Via Isometries

We have seen that under an isometry, the image of a figure is a congruent figure. Also, given two congruent polygons, it is possible to show that one can be transformed to the other by isometries. In fact, we can define two figures as *congruent* if one is an image of the other under an isometry or under a composition of isometries. The following example shows one illustration of this approach to congruence.

**EXAMPLE
12-7**

ABCD in Figure 12-28 is a rectangle. Describe a sequence of isometries to show

a. $\triangle ADC \cong \triangle CBA$;
b. $\triangle ADC \cong \triangle BCD$; and
c. $\triangle ADC \cong \triangle DAB$.

FIGURE 12-28

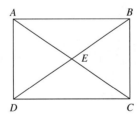

Solution **a.** A half-turn of $\triangle ADC$ with center E is one such transformation.
b. A reflection in a line passing through E and parallel to $\overline{AD}$ is one such transformation.
c. A reflection of $\triangle ADC$ in a line passing through E and parallel to $\overline{DC}$ is one such transformation.

Light Reflecting from a Surface

When a ray of light bounces off a mirror or when a billiard ball bounces off the rail of a billiards table, the **angle of incidence**, the angle formed by the incoming ray in Figure 12-29 and a line perpendicular to the mirror, is congruent to the **angle of reflection**, the angle between the reflected ray and the line perpendicular to the mirror.

angle of incidence
angle of reflection

FIGURE 12-29

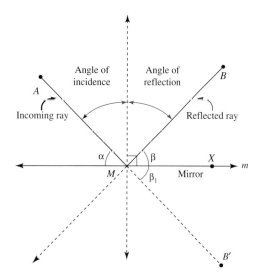

Because the angle of incidence is congruent to the angle of reflection, the respective complements of these angles must be congruent. If the measures of these complements are α and β, as indicated in Figure 12-29, then $\alpha = \beta$. Figure 12-29 shows B', the image of B under reflection in m, and hence $\angle XMB'$ is the image of $\angle XMB$. Notice that β, the measure of $\angle XMB$ must equal β_1, the measure of $\angle XMB'$ because reflection preserves angle measurement. Because $\alpha = \beta$ and $\beta = \beta_1$ we get $\alpha = \beta_1$. For that reason points A, M, B' are collinear (why?). We can show that these facts imply *Fermat's Principal: Light follows the path of shortest distance*; that is, the path *A-M-B* that light travels is the shortest among all the paths connecting A with a point in the mirror to B. The proof is explored in Now Try This 12-6.

NOW TRY THIS 12-6

Trace Figure 12-29 and mark on the mirror m a point P other than M. Prove that $AM + MB <$ $AP + PB$ by showing that $MB = MB'$ and $BP = B'P$, and then using the triangular inequality applied to $\triangle APB'$ and the fact that A, M, B' are collinear.

ONGOING ASSESSMENT 12-2

1. For each of the following figures, find the image of the given quadrilateral under a reflection in ℓ.

(a)

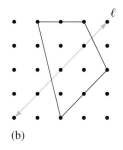

(b)

2. In the following figure, find the image of $\triangle ABC$ under a reflection in line ℓ.

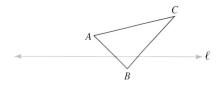

3. Draw a line and then draw a circle whose center is not on the line. Find the image of the circle under a reflection in the line.

4. Determine which of the following figures have a reflecting line such that the image of the figure under the reflecting line is the figure itself. In each case, find as many such reflecting lines as possible, sketching appropriate drawings.

   a. Circle
   b. Segment
   c. Ray
   d. Line
   e. Square
   f. Rectangle
   g. Scalene triangle
   h. Isosceles triangle
   i. Equilateral triangle
   j. Trapezoid whose base angles are not congruent
   k. Isosceles trapezoid
   l. Arc
   m. Kite
   n. Rhombus
   o. Regular hexagon
   p. Regular *n*-gon

5. Determine the final result when △*ABC* is reflected in line ℓ and then its image is reflected again in ℓ.

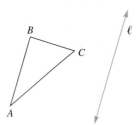

6. a. Refer to the following figure and suppose lines ℓ and *m* are parallel and △*ABC* is reflected in ℓ to obtain △*A′B′C′* and then △*A′B′C′* is reflected in *m* to obtain △*A″B″C″*. Determine whether the same final image is obtained if △*ABC* is reflected first in *m* and then its image is reflected in ℓ.

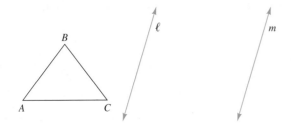

   b. Conjecture what single transformation will take △*ABC* directly to △*A″B″C″*. Check your conjecture using tracing paper.

7. a. For the following figure, use any construction method to find the image of △*ABC* if △*ABC* is reflected in ℓ to obtain △*A′B′C′* and then △*A′B′C′* is reflected in *m* to obtain △*A″B″C″* (ℓ and *m* intersect at *O*).

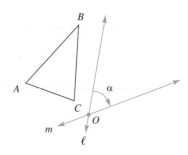

   b. Conjecture what single transformation will take △*ABC* directly to △*A″B″C″*. Check your conjecture using tracing paper.
   c. Answer the questions in (a) and in (b) for the case in which ℓ and *m* are perpendicular.

8. Use a Mira if available to investigate problems 6 and 7.

9. Given △*ABC* and its reflection image △*A′B′C′*, find the line of reflection.

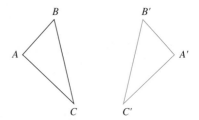

10. a. The word TOT is its own image when it is reflected through a vertical line through O, as shown in the following figure. List some other words that are their own images when reflected similarly.

   b. The image of BOOK is still BOOK when it is reflected through a horizontal line. List some other words that have the same property. Which uppercase letters can you use?

c. With an appropriate font, the image of 1881 is 1881 after reflection in either a horizontal or vertical line, as shown in the following figure. What other natural numbers less than 2000 have this property?

11. A glide reflection is determined by a translation parallel to a given line followed by a reflection in that line.
    a. Determine whether the same final image is obtained if the reflection is followed by the translation.
    b. Use your answer in (a) to determine whether the reflection and translation involved in the glide reflection are commutative.

12. For the following figure numbered 1, decide whether a reflection, a translation, a rotation, or a glide reflection will transform the figure into each of the other numbered figures. (There may be more than one answer.)

13. Given points $A(3, 4)$, $B(2, {}^-6)$, and $C({}^-2, 5)$, find the coordinates of the images of these points under each of the following transformations.
    a. Reflection in the x-axis
    b. Reflection in the y-axis
    c. Reflection in the line $y = x$
    d. Reflection in the line $y = {}^-x$

14. a. Conjecture what the image of a point with coordinates (x, y) will be under each of the transformations in problem 13.
    b. Suppose a point P with coordinates (x, y) is reflected in the x-axis and then its image P' is reflected in the y-axis to obtain P''. What are the coordinates of P'' in terms of x and y? Justify your answer.

15. Two farm houses are located away from a road, as shown. A telephone company wants to construct a telephone pole at the edge of the road so that the telephone cable connecting the houses to the pole is as short as possible. Where should the pole be located?

Telephone Pole

16. A *fixed point* of a transformation is a point whose image is the point itself. List all the fixed points of any of the following isometries.
    a. Reflection in line ℓ
    b. Rotations by a given angle and direction about point O
    c. Translation with slide arrow from A to B
    d. Glide reflection determined by a translation with slide arrow $\overrightarrow{AB}$ followed by a reflection in line ℓ parallel to line AB

Communication

17. If you look into a hinged mirror (as depicted below) and see a polygon with six sides, what is the minimum number of sides that the original could have? Explain your reasoning.

18. When a billiard ball bounces off a side of a pool table, the angle of incidence is usually congruent to the angle of reflection. In the following figure showing a scale drawing of a pool table, a cue ball is at point A. Show how a player should aim to hit two sides of the table and then the ball at B. Justify your solution.

19. a. Draw an isosceles triangle ABC and then construct a line such that the image of $\triangle ABC$ when reflected in the line is $\triangle ABC$ though every point is not necessarily its own image. Explain why the line you constructed has the required property.

b. For what kind of triangles is it possible to find more than one line with the property in (a)? Justify your answer.

c. Given a scalene triangle *ABC*, is it possible to find a line ℓ such that when △*ABC* is reflected in ℓ, its image is itself? Explain your answer.

d. Draw a circle with center *O* and a line with the property that the image of the circle, when reflected in the line, is the original circle. Identify all such lines. Justify your answer.

20. Use the following drawing to explain how a periscope works.

Open-Ended

21. In the following figure representing a miniature golf course, explain and justify the procedure showing how to aim the ball so that it gets in the hole if it is to bounce off
    a. one wall only.
    b. two walls.

22. Design several wall stencil patterns using a reflection. In each case, explain how you would use the stencil in practice.

23. Design wall stencil patterns using a glide reflection.

24. If a right triangle △*ABC* is reflected in one of its legs as shown in the following triangle, the triangle and its image form an isosceles triangle △*ABA'*.

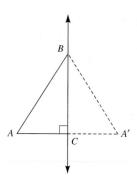

From the properties of reflection, we can deduce that the base angles in an isosceles triangle are congruent and that the altitude to the base bisects ∠*ABA'* as well as $\overline{AA'}$.

Apply the concept of reflection to deduce properties of other geometric figures by reflecting (a) a scalene triangle in one of its sides, (b) a right angle trapezoid in one of its sides, and (c) other figures. In each case, define the reflection, list the geometric properties of the figure obtained from the union of your original figure and its image, and justify the properties.

Cooperative Learning

25. In the following figure representing a pool table, ball *B* is sent on a path that makes a 45° angle with the table wall, as shown. It bounces off the wall five times and returns to its original position.

a. Have each member of your group use graph paper to construct rectangular models of different-sized pool tables. Simulate the experiment using any tools (such as a straightedge, compass, and protractor) by choosing different positions for ball *B*.

b. Share the results of your experiments with the rest of the group and together conjecture for which dimensions of the pool table and for what positions of *B* the experiment described in the problem will work.

Review Exercises

26. Which single digits are their own images under a rotation by an angle whose measure is less than 360°?

27. What is the image of a point (*a, b*) under a half-turn in the origin?

28. a. Find all possible rotations that transform a circle into itself.

    b. By what other kinds of transformations can a circle be transformed onto itself?

29. Explain how a translation can be used to construct a rectangle whose area is equal to that of the parallelogram *ABCD* in the following figure.

BRAIN
T E A S E R

Two cities are on opposite sides of a river, as shown in Figure 12-30.

FIGURE 12-30

The cities' engineers want to build a bridge across the river that is perpendicular to the banks of the river and access roads to the bridge so that the distance between the cities is as short as possible. Where should the bridge and the roads be built?

Size Transformations

Isometries preserve distance. Consequently, the image of a figure under an isometry is a figure congruent to the original. A different type of transformation happens when a slide is projected on a screen. All objects on the slide are often enlarged on the screen by the same factor. Figure 12-31 is another example of such a transformation.

The point *O* is the *center* of the *size transformation* and 2 is the *scale factor*. Points *O, A,* and *A'* are collinear and $OA' = 2 \cdot OA$; also, *O, C,* and *C'* are collinear and $OC' = 2 \cdot OC$. Similarly, *O, B,* and *B'* are collinear and $OB' = 2 \cdot OB$. It can be shown that $\triangle A'B'C'$ is similar to $\triangle ABC$ and hence that each side of $\triangle A'B'C'$ is twice as long as the corresponding sides of $\triangle ABC$.

FIGURE 12-31

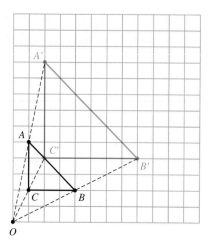

In general, we have the following definition.

> ## Definition of Size Transformation

A size transformation from the plane to the plane with center O and scale factor r ($r > 0$) is a transformation that assigns to each point A in the plane a point A', such that O, A, and A' are collinear and $OA' = r \cdot OA$ and so that O is not between A and A'.

Notice that a size transformation is a function from the plane to the plane. What is the range of this function?

REMARK It is possible to define a size transformation when the scale factor is negative in the same way as in the above definition for positive scale factor, except that O *must be between A and A'*.

E X A M P L E
12-8

a. In Figure 12-32(a), find the image of point P under a size transformation with center O and scale factor $\frac{2}{3}$.

FIGURE 12-32

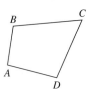

$\bullet$
P

$\bullet$
O

$\bullet$
O

(a)   (b)

b. Find the image of the quadrilateral *ABCD* in Figure 12-32(b) under the size transformation with center *O* and scale factor $\frac{2}{3}$.

Solution **a.** In Figure 12-33(a), we connect *O* with *P* and divide $\overline{OP}$ into three congruent parts. The point *P'* is the image of *P* because $OP' = \frac{2}{3}OP$.

b. We find the image of each of the vertices and connect the images to obtain the quadrilateral *A'B'C'D'* shown in Figure 12-33(b).

FIGURE 12-33

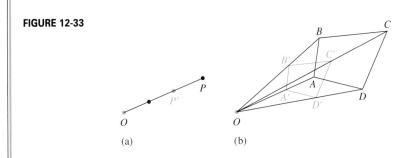

(a)   (b)

In Figure 12-33(b), the sides of the quadrilateral *A'B'C'D'* are all parallel to the corresponding sides of the original quadrilateral and the angles of the quadrilateral *A'B'C'D'* are congruent to the corresponding angles of quadrilateral *ABCD*. Also, each side in the quadrilateral *A'B'C'D'* is $\frac{2}{3}$ as long as the corresponding side of quadrilateral *ABCD*.

These properties are true for any size transformation and are summarized in the following theorem.

Theorem 12-1

A size transformation with center *O* and scale factor *r* (*r* > 0) has the following properties:

1. The image of a line segment is a line segment parallel to the original segment and *r* times as long.
2. The image of an angle is an angle congruent to the original angle.

From Theorem 12-1, it follows that the image of a polygon under a size transformation is a similar polygon (why?). However, for any two similar polygons it is not always possible to find a size transformation so that the image of one polygon under the transformation is the other polygon. But, given two similar polygons, we can "move" one polygon to a place so that it will be the image of the other under a size transformation. The following examples show such instances.

EXAMPLE
12-9

Show that $\triangle ABC$ in Figure 12-34 is the image of $\triangle ADE$ under a size transformation. Identify the center of the size transformation and the scale factor.

FIGURE 12-34

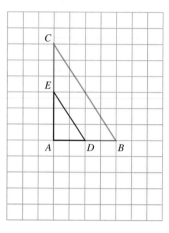

Solution   Because $\dfrac{AB}{AD} = \dfrac{AC}{AE} = 2$, we choose A as the center of the size transformation and 2 as the scale factor. Notice that under this transformation, the image of A is A itself. The image of D is B, and the image of E is C.

EXAMPLE
12-10

Show that $\triangle ABC$ in Figure 12-35 is the image of $\triangle APQ$ under a succession of isometries with a size transformation.

FIGURE 12-35

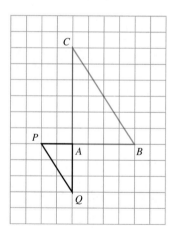

Solution   We use the strategy of *looking at a related problem*. In Example 12–9, the common vertex served as the center of the size transformation. This was possible because the corresponding sides of the triangles were parallel. To achieve a similar situation, we first transform $\triangle APQ$ by a half-turn in A and obtain $\triangle AP'Q'$, as shown in Figure 12-36.

FIGURE 12-36

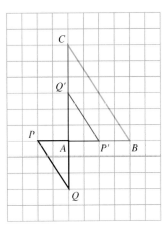

Now C is the image of Q' under a size transformation with center at A and scale factor 2. B is the image of P', and A is the image of itself under this transformation. Thus $\triangle ABC$ can be obtained from $\triangle APQ$ by first finding the image of $\triangle APQ$ under a half-turn in A and then applying a size transformation with center A and a scale factor 2 to that image.

Examples 12-9 and 12-10 are a basis for an alternative definition of similar figures.

> ### Definition of Similar Figures

Two figures are similar if it is possible to transform one onto the other by a sequence of isometries followed by a size transformation.

 Size transformations and similarity in the coordinate plane are discussed on the following student page. Answer the questions on the student page. Conjecture the coordinates of the image of the point (x, y) under a size transformation with center at the origin and scale factor r.

Applications of Size Transformations

perspective drawing One way to make an object appear three-dimensional is to use a **perspective drawing**. For example, to make a letter appear three-dimensional we can use a size transformation with an appropriate center O and a scale factor, as shown in Figure 12-37 for the letter L.

FIGURE 12-37

(a)   (b)   (c)

Sample School Book Page:
TRANSFORMATIONS AND SIMILARITY

15. You can use an algorithm to model a change that involves stretching. The transformation shown is modeled by the algorithm below.

Step 1 Multiply the *x*- and *y*-coordinates of each point by 2.

Step 2 Translate each point up 1 unit.

a. Draw *OBCD* with coordinates *O*(0, 0), *B*(0, 2), *C*(2, 2) and *D*(2, 0). Translate the figure up 1 unit. Then multiply each coordinate by 2. Draw the final image.

b. Compare your results from part (a) with the transformation shown. Does the order in which you perform the steps matter?

16. Copy the figure below. Then use the algorithm to transform the figure.

Step 1 Multiply the *x*- and *y*-coordinates of each point by 3.

Step 2 Reflect each point over the *x*-axis.

Step 3 Translate each point up 12 units.

17. You already know how to stretch a figure using multiplication. You can also use multiplication to shrink a figure. Draw the figure below. Then use the algorithm to transform the figure.

Step 1 Multiply the *x*- and *y*-coordinates of each point by $\frac{1}{2}$.

Step 2 Translate each point to the left 1 unit.

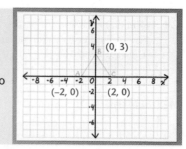

Source: McDougal Littell, Middle Grades MATH Thematics, 2002, Book 3 (p. 517).

When a picture of an object is taken, the object appears upside down on the negative. The picture of the object on the negative can be interpreted as an image under composition of a half-turn and a size transformation. Figure 12-38(a) illustrates the image of an arrow from A to B under a composition of a half-turn followed by a size transformation with scale factor $\frac{1}{2}$.

FIGURE 12-38

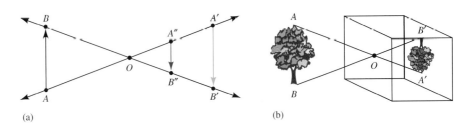

(a)   (b)

The image A' of A under the half-turn with center O is found on the ray opposite $\overrightarrow{OA}$ so that $OA' = OA$. The point B', the image of B under the half-turn, is found similarly on the ray opposite $\overrightarrow{OB}$. The images of A' and B' under the size transformation are A'' and B'', respectively. Consequently, the image of the arrow from A to B under the composition of the half-turn followed by the size transformation is the arrow from A'' to B''. Figure 12-38(b) illustrates another composition of a half-turn and a size transformation in a simple box camera.

O N G O I N G   A S S E S S M E N T   1 2 - 3

1. In the following figures, describe a sequence of isometries followed by a size transformation so that the larger triangle is the final image of the smaller one.

(a)

(b)

(c)

2. In the following drawing, find the image of $\triangle ABC$ under the size transformation with center O and scale factor $\frac{1}{2}$:

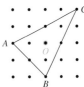

3. In each of the following drawings, find transformations that will take $\triangle ABC$ to its image, $\triangle A'B'C'$, which is similar:

(a)

(b)

(c)

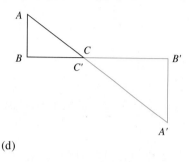

(d)

4. In each of the following figures, the smaller one is the image of the larger under a size transformation. In each case, find the scale factor and the length of *x* and *y* as pictured.

(a)

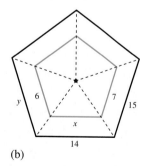

(b)

5. $\overline{A'B'}$ is the image of a candle $\overline{BA}$ produced by a box camera. Given the measurement of the figure, find the height of the candle.

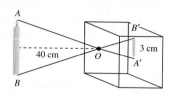

6. Each of the following figures describes a size transformation with center *O* and images in blue. Find the scale factor and the lengths designated by *x* and *y*.

(a)

(b)

7. Find the coordinates of the images of $A(2, 3)$, and $B(^-2, 3)$ under the following transformations. Assume that all size transformations are centered at the origin.
   a. A size transformation with a scale factor 3 followed by a size transformation with a scale factor 2
   b. A size transformation with scale factor 2 followed by a size transformation with a scale factor 3
   c. A size transformation with scale factor 2 followed by a translation with a slide arrow from (2, 1) to (3, 4)
   d. A translation with a slide arrow from (2, 1) to (3, 4) followed by a size transformation with scale factor 2
   e. What can you conclude from your answers to parts (c) and (d) concerning the order in which the transformations are performed?
8. If a size transformation with center *O* and scale factor *r* takes a quadrilateral *ABCD* to *A'B'C'D'*, what size transformation will take *A'B'C'D'* back to *ABCD*?

Communication

9. Which of the following properties do not change under a size transformation? Explain how you can be sure of your answers.

a. Distance between points
b. Angle measure
c. Parallelism; that is, if two lines are parallel to each other, then their images are parallel to each other.

10. Given two similar figures, explain how to tell if there is a size transformation that transforms one of the figures onto the other.

11. a. Consider two consecutive size transformations, each with center O and corresponding scale factors $\frac{1}{2}$ and $\frac{1}{3}$, respectively. Suppose the image of figure Γ under the first transformation is F' and the image of F' under the second transformation is F''. What single transformation will map F directly onto F''? Explain why.
    b. What would be the answer to (a) if the scale factors were r_1 and r_2?

12. Copy the following figure onto grid paper and determine the center and the scale factor of the size transformation. Explain why there is only one possibility for the center.

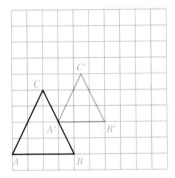

13. a. Is the image of a circle with center O under a size transformation with center O always a circle? Explain why or why not.
    b. Assume that under a size transformation with scale factor r, the image of a segment of length a is a segment of length ra and answer part (a) of this question in case the center of the circle is not at the origin.

Open-Ended

14. Describe several real-life situations other than the ones discussed in this section in which size transformations occur.

15. Use a sheet of graph paper with a coordinate system. Locate the origin as the center of a transformation with a scale factor of $^-1$ and find the image of some triangle located in the first quadrant. What other transformation that you've studied has the same image as this transformation?

Cooperative Learning

16. Have members of your group draw several figures and find their images under a size transformation with a scale factor of 3 and center of your choice.
    a. How does the perimeter of each image compare to the perimeter of the original figure? Compare your answers.
    b. How does the area of each image compare to the area of the original figure? Compare your answers.
    c. Make a conjecture concerning the relationship between the perimeter of each image and the perimeter of the original figure under a size transformation with a scale factor r.
    d. Repeat (c) for the area of each figure.
    e. Discuss your findings and come up with a group conjecture.

Review Problems

17. Describe a transformation that would "undo" each of the following:
    a. A translation determined by slide arrow from M to N
    b. A rotation of 75° with center O in a clockwise direction
    c. A rotation of 45° with center A in a counterclockwise direction
    d. A glide reflection that is the composition of a reflection in line m and a translation that takes A to B
    e. A reflection in line n

18. In the following coordinate plane, find the images of each of the given points in the transformation that is the composition of a reflection in line m followed by a reflection in line n.
    a. $(4, 3)$
    b. $(0, 1)$
    c. $(^-1, 0)$
    d. $(0, 0)$

TECHNOLOGY
CORNER

Use GSP to draw △*ABC* and three lines *m, n,* and *p* that intersect in a single point as shown in Figure 12-39. Reflect △*ABC* in line *m* to obtain its image △*A'B'C'*. Then reflect △*A'B'C'* in line *n* to obtain △*A"B"C"*. Finally reflect △*A"B"C"* in line *p* to obtain the final image △*A'''B'''C'''*.

FIGURE 12-39

Find a single line *q* that could be used to reflect the original △*ABC* onto the final image.

Symmetries

Line Symmetries

The concept of a reflection can be used to identify line symmetries of a figure. All the drawings in Figure 12-40 have symmetries about the dashed lines.

FIGURE 12-40

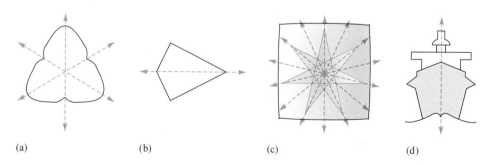

(a)   (b)   (c)   (d)

line of symmetry   Mathematically, a geometric figure has a **line of symmetry** ℓ if it is its own image under a reflection in ℓ. A method of creating a symmetrical figure is seen in Example 12-11.

EXAMPLE
12-11

In Figure 12-41, we are given a figure and a line *m*. Do the minimum amount of drawing to create a figure from the given figure so that the result has line *m* as its line of symmetry.

FIGURE 12-41

Solution   For the resulting figure both to be symmetric about line *m* and to incorporate the existing figure, we need to reflect the existing figure about line *m*. The desired result of doing that is the combination of the original figure and the image. The resulting figure is shown in Figure 12-42.

FIGURE 12-42

EXAMPLE
12-12

How many lines of symmetry does each drawing in Figure 12-43 have?

FIGURE 12-43

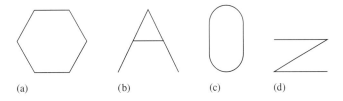

(a)   (b)   (c)   (d)

Solution   **a.** 6   **b.** 1   **c.** 2   **d.** 0

EXAMPLE

12-13

Given an arc *AB* in Figure 12-44 use symmetry and paper folding to find the center and the radius of the circle to which the arc belongs.

FIGURE 12-44

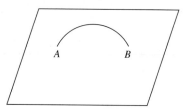

Solution The arc is part of a circle. The center of the circle is equidistant from the end-points of any chord of the circle, and hence is on the perpendicular bisector of the chord. That perpendicular bisector is a line of symmetry of the circle. A circle has infinitely many lines of symmetry and each line passes through the center of the circle, where all the lines of symmetry intersect. To find a line of symmetry, fold the paper containing $\widehat{AB}$ so that a portion of the arc is folded onto itself. Then unfold the paper and draw the line of symmetry on the fold mark, as shown in Figure 12-45(a). By refolding the paper in Figure 12-45(a) so that a different portion of the arc $\widehat{AB}$ is folded onto itself, we can determine a second line of symmetry, as shown in Figure 12-45(b). The two dotted lines of symmetry intersect at *O*, the center of the circle of which $\widehat{AB}$ is an arc. Either $\overline{OB}$, $\overline{OA}$, or any segment connecting *O* to a point on the arc represent a radius of the circle.

FIGURE 12-45

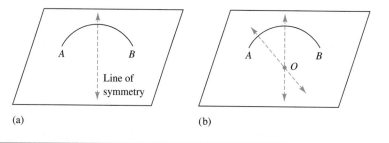

(a)   (b)

Rotational (Turn) Symmetries

rotational symmetry ◆
turn symmetry

A figure has **rotational symmetry**, or **turn symmetry**, when the traced figure can be rotated less than 360° about some point so that it matches the original figure. Note that the condition "less than 360°" is necessary because any figure will coincide with itself if it is rotated 360° about any point. In Figure 12-46, the equilateral triangle coincides with itself after a rotation of 120° about point *O*. Hence, we say that the triangle has 120° rotational symmetry. Also in Figure 12-46, if we were to rotate the triangle another 120°, we would find again that it matches the original. So we can say that the triangle also has 240° rotational symmetry.

FIGURE 12-46

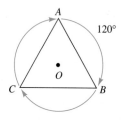

In general, if a figure has $\alpha°$ rotational symmetry, it also will coincide with itself when rotated by $n\alpha°$ for any nonzero integer *n*. For this reason, in rotational symmetry it is sufficient to report the smallest possible positive angle measure that turns the figure onto itself. Notice that a circle has a rotational symmetry by any turn around its center. Thus a circle has infinitely many rotational symmetries.

Other examples of figures that have rotational symmetry are shown in Figure 12-47. Figures 12-47(a), (b), (c), and (d) have 72°, 90°, 180°, and 180° rotational symmetries, respectively [(a) and (b) also have other rotational symmetries].

FIGURE 12-47

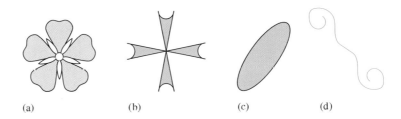

(a)   (b)   (c)   (d)

In general, we can determine whether a figure has rotational symmetry by tracing it and turning the tracing about a point (the center of the figure) to see if it aligns on the figure before the tracing has turned in a complete circle, or 360°. The amount of the rotation can be determined by measuring the angle $\angle POP'$ through which a point P is rotated around a point O to match another point P' when the figures align. Such an angle, $\angle POP'$, is labeled with points $P, O,$ and P' in Figure 12-48 and has measure 120°. Point O, the point held fixed when the tracing is turned, is the *turn center*.

FIGURE 12-48

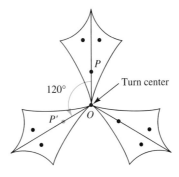

EXAMPLE 12-14

Determine the amount of the turn for the rotational symmetries of each part of Figure 12-49.

FIGURE 12-49

(a)   (b)   (c)

Solution   **a.** The amounts of the turns are $\dfrac{360°}{5}$ or 72°, 144°, 216°, and 288°.

         b. The amount of the turn is 180°.

         c. The amounts of the turns are 60°, 120°, 180°, 240°, and 300°.

The rotations in Figure 12-49(b) and (c) exemplify yet another type of symmetry, namely, point symmetry.

Point Symmetry

point symmetry

Any figure that has 180° rotational symmetry is said to have **point symmetry** about the turn center. Some figures with point symmetry are shown in Figure 12-50.

FIGURE 12-50

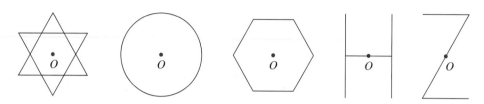

As illustrated in Figure 12-50, any figure with point symmetry is its own image under a half-turn. This makes the center of the half-turn the midpoint of a segment connecting a point and its image.

Tracing and paper folding are commonly used in elementary school to investigate symmetries of figures, as shown in the following student page. Determine which figures on the student page have point symmetry.

Classification of Figures by Their Symmetries

Geometric figures in a plane can be classified according to the number of symmetries they have. Consider a triangle described as having exactly one line of symmetry and no turn symmetries. What could the triangle look like? The only possibility is a triangle in which two sides are congruent; that is, an isosceles triangle that is not equilateral. The line of symmetry passes through a vertex, as shown in Figure 12-51.

FIGURE 12-51

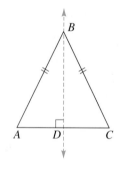

We can describe equilateral and scalene triangles in terms of the number of lines of symmetry they have. This is left as an exercise.

A square, as in Figure 12-52, can be described as a four-sided polygon with four lines of symmetry—d_1, d_2, h, and v—and three turn symmetries about point O. In fact, we can use lines of symmetry and turn symmetries to define various types of quadrilaterals normally used in geometry. It is left as an exercise to see how these definitions differ from those in Chapter 9.

FIGURE 12-52

Sample School Book Page:
INVESTIGATING SYMMETRY

Connect •

How many lines of symmetry does this figure have?

You can check by tracing the outline.

Fold the figure along the possible lines of symmetry.

If the two sides match exactly, your fold line is a line of symmetry.

This figure has two lines of symmetry.

Practice •

Trace the figure. Draw all lines of symmetry.

1.

2.

3.

Trace the figure. Use the line of symmetry to complete the figure.

4.

5.

6.

Use flips, turns, or slides. Is each pair of figures congruent? Explain.

7.

8.

9.

10. These figures are called hexominoes.
    How many lines of symmetry does each hexomino have?

11. Draw three hexominoes that have no lines of symmetry.

12. Describe how you could use a mirror to see if a figure has a line of symmetry.

13. **Journal** Explain how you know whether a figure is symmetric.

Source: Scott Foresman–Addison Wesley MATH, Grade 5, 2002 (p. 289).

Symmetries of Three-Dimensional Figures

plane of symmetry

A three-dimensional figure has a **plane of symmetry** when every point of the figure on one side of the plane has a mirror image on the other side of the plane. Examples of figures with plane symmetry are shown in Figure 12-53. Solids can also have point symmetry, line symmetry, and turn symmetry. Notice that the right circular cylinder in Figure 12-53(a) has turn symmetries about the line n which goes through the centers of the upper and lower bases and is perpendicular to them. The line n is the **axis of rotation**. If the cylinder is rotated by any number of degrees about its axis of rotation, its image is the cylinder itself. Hence, the cylinder has infinitely many rotational symmetries. The cube in Figure 12-53(b) also has rotational symmetries. For the cube, if n is a line connecting the centers of two opposite square faces, then a rotation of 90° in any direction will result in an image that coincides with the original cube. Because we can create an axis of rotation by connecting the centers of any two opposite faces, the cube has 3 axes of rotation, each with a 90° rotational symmetry. These three-dimensional symmetries are analogous to the two-dimensional symmetries and are further investigated in Ongoing Assessment 12-4.

axis of rotation

FIGURE 12-53

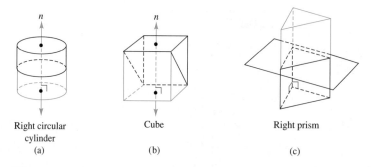

Right circular
cylinder
(a)

Cube
(b)

Right prism
(c)

NOW TRY THIS 12-7

a. If we connect two opposite vertices of a cube which are farthest apart, like the pair in Figure 12-54, we obtain an axis of rotation. (i) What is the smallest angle by which the cube needs to be rotated about this axis so that its image will coincide with the original cube? (ii) How many such axes are there?

b. Figure 12-54(b) shows another axis of rotation for the cube. (i) By what angle does the cube need to be rotated about this axis for the image to be the same as the original cube? (ii) How many such axes of rotation are there for a cube?

FIGURE 12-54

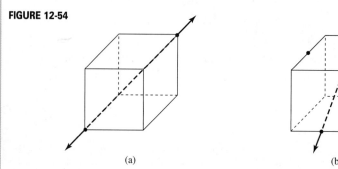

(a)

(b)

ONGOING ASSESSMENT 12-4

1. What geometric properties make "SOS" a good choice for the international distress symbol?

2. Various international signs have symmetries. Determine which of the following have (i) line symmetry, (ii) rotational symmetry, and/or (iii) point symmetry.

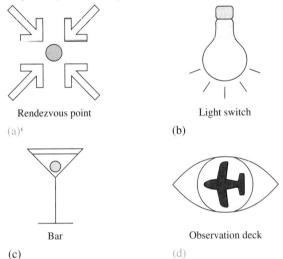

Rendezvous point

(a)'

Light switch

(b)

Bar

(c)

Observation deck

(d)

3. Design symbols that have each of the following symmetries, if possible:
  a. Line symmetry but not rotational symmetry
  b. Rotational symmetry but not point symmetry
  c. Rotational symmetry but not line symmetry

4. In each of the following figures, complete the sketches so that they have line symmetry about ℓ.

(a) Line symmetry about ℓ

(b) Line symmetry about ℓ

5. a. Determine the number of lines of symmetry in each of the following flags.
  b. Sketch the lines of symmetry for each.

Switzerland

(i)

South Korea

(ii)

Israel

(iii)

Barbados

(iv)

6. a. Determine how many lines of symmetry the following figure has.

b. Does the figure have rotational symmetry?

7. Find the lines of symmetry, if any, for each of the following trademarks.

Volkswagen of America

(a)

The Yellow Pages

(b)

Chevrolet

(c)

Chrysler Corporation

(d)

8. In each of the following figures, complete the sketches so that they have the indicated symmetry.

Point symmetry about *O*

(a)

60° rotational symmetry about *O*

(b)

9. Determine how many planes of symmetry, if any, each of the following three-dimensional vehicle controls has.

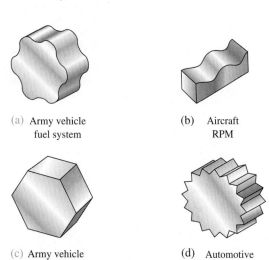

(a) Army vehicle fuel system

(b) Aircraft RPM

(c) Army vehicle special-purpose equipment

(d) Automotive finger-operated continuous multiturn

10. The following figures were drawn using the computer language Logo. Determine what kinds of symmetries each figure has.

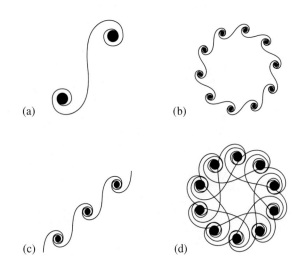

(a)

(b)

(c)

(d)

Communication

11. Answer each of the following. If your answer is no, provide a counterexample.
    a. If a figure has point symmetry, must it have rotational symmetry? Why?
    b. If a figure has rotational symmetry, must it have point symmetry? Why?
    c. Can a figure have point, line, and rotational symmetry? If so, sketch a figure that has these properties.
    d. If a figure has point symmetry, must it have line symmetry? Is the converse true? Why?
    e. If a figure has both point and line symmetry, must it have rotational symmetry? Why?

Open-Ended

12. If possible, sketch a triangle that satisfies each of the following:
    a. It has no lines of symmetry.
    b. It has exactly one line of symmetry.
    c. It has exactly two lines of symmetry.
    d. It has exactly three lines of symmetry.
13. Sketch a figure that has point symmetry but no line symmetry.
14. a. In the following figure, *ABCD* is a rectangular sheet of paper. Fold the paper so that the opposite edges $\overline{AB}$ and $\overline{DC}$ coincide (the crease $\overline{EF}$ is created). Then fold the resulting rectangle *ABEF* so that $\overline{BE}$ and $\overline{AF}$ coincide (the crease $\overline{HG}$ is created). The rectangle *AFGH* is obtained. Now cut a curved piece of paper out of the corner *G* as shown and unfold the paper. Describe all the symmetries that the unfolded figure has.

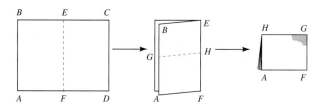

b. Repeat the experiment in (a) by successively folding a new sheet of paper three times and cutting out a curved piece containing a corner that resulted from the three folds. Predict all the symmetries of the unfolded figure. Check your answer by unfolding the paper.
15. For each of the following, use paper folding or any other method to create, if possible, two nonsimilar figures that have the specified symmetries:
    a. Point symmetry but no other symmetries
    b. Exactly one line of symmetry
    c. Exactly two lines of symmetry but no rotational symmetry
    d. 45° rotational symmetry

Cooperative Learning

16. With a partner, design a three-mirror kaleidoscope by fastening three mirrors together, each perpendicular to a flat surface so that they form an equilateral triangular prism. Place colored paper with a pattern (or design your own pattern) in the base of the kaleidoscope. Peer over the edge of the kaleidoscope to view the generated figure. Repeat the experiment for different patterns.

17. With another person or group, play the following game several times. First, draw a polygon that has different kinds of symmetries. Without revealing your polygon to your partner, tell your partner all you know about the symmetries of the figure. Next, from this information, your opponent attempts to draw the type of figure you drew. If your opponent produces a figure of the type you drew, he or she earns two points. If your opponent produces a different figure having the symmetries that you reported or if you failed to reveal some of the symmetries of your polygon, your opponent gets three points. Alternate roles several times.

18. A *frieze pattern* is a pattern that extends indefinitely in both directions and the image of the pattern under a translation is the original pattern. Pictured below are seven frieze patterns, each of which is the image of itself under a translation and also by the other isometries indicated. Every frieze pattern can be classified into one of these seven categories.

   a. Have each member of your group draw one or two of the patterns (depending on the size of the group) on tracing paper or a transparency with a corresponding label using the letters *T, R, H, V,* or *G,* as in the figure. Exchange the drawings so that each member of your group checks how each of the patterns can be transformed onto itself by each of the isometries. Compare your answers with those of your group members.

   b. Create other more elaborate patterns for each of the seven categories and present each pattern to a partner for identification. (Label the patterns with numbers 1 through 7, keeping to yourself the corresponding *T, R, H, V, G* labeling.) Compare your partner's answers with yours.

Label	Description
T	Translation
TR	Translation and rotation by 180°
TV	Translation and vertical line reflection
TG	Translation and glide reflection
THG	Translation, horizontal line reflection, and glide reflection
TRVG	Translation, rotation by 180°, vertical line reflection, and glide reflection
TRHVG	Translation, rotation by 180°, horizontal line reflection, vertical line reflection, and glide reflection

Review Problems

19. For each of the following cases, find the image of the given figure using paper folding:

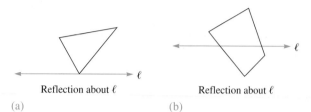

Reflection about ℓ

(a)

Reflection about ℓ

(b)

A translation from *A* to *B*

(c)

20. Construct each image in problem 19 using a compass and a straightedge.

BRAIN TEASER

Suppose you are looking in a mirror hung flat on a wall and your image goes from the top of the mirror to the bottom. How does the length of the part of your body that you see compare with the length of the mirror?

*Tessellations of the Plane

tessellation

In this section we use concepts from motion geometry to study *tessellations* of the plane. A **tessellation** of a plane is the filling of the plane with repetitions of figures in such a way that no figures overlap and there are no gaps. (Similarly, one can tessellate space.) The tiling of a floor and various mosaics are examples of tessellations. Maurits C. Escher, born in the Netherlands in 1902, was a master of tessellations. Many of his drawings have fascinated mathematicians for decades. An example of his work, *Study of Regular Division of the Plane with Reptiles* (pen, ink, and watercolor), 1939, contains an exhibit of a tessellation of the plane by a lizardlike shape, as shown in Figure 12-55.

FIGURE 12-55

At the heart of the tessellation in the figure, we see a regular hexagon. But perhaps the simplest tessellation of the plane can be achieved with squares. Figure 12-56 shows two different tessellations of the plane with squares.

FIGURE 12-56

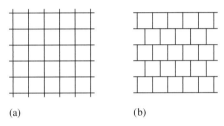

(a)   (b)

Regular Tessellations

Tessellations with regular polygons are appealing and interesting because of their simplicity. Figure 12-57 shows portions of tessellations with equilateral triangles (a) and with regular hexagons (b).

FIGURE 12-57

(a)   (b)

To determine other regular polygons that tessellate the plane, we investigate the possible size of the interior angle of a tessellating polygon. If n is the number of sides of a regular polygon, then because the sum of the measures of the exterior angles of the regular polygon is $360°$, the measure of a single exterior angle of the polygon is $360°/n$. Hence, the measure of an interior angle is $180° - 360°/n$. Table 12-2 gives some values of n, the type of regular polygon related to each, and the angle measure of an interior angle found by using the expression $180° - 360°/n$.

Table 12-2

Number of Sides (*n*)	Regular Polygon	Measure of Interior Angle
3	Triangle	60°
4	Square	90°
5	Pentagon	108°
6	Hexagon	120°
7	Heptagon	900/7°
8	Octagon	135°
9	Nonagon	140°
10	Decagon	144°

If a regular polygon tessellates the plane, the sum of the congruent angles of the polygons around every vertex must be 360°. Thus 360 divided by the angle measure gives the number of angles around a vertex and hence must be an integer. If we divide 360° by each of the angle measures in the table, we find that of these measures only 60°, 90°, and 120° divide 360°; hence of the listed polygons, only an equilateral triangle, a square, and a regular hexagon can tessellate the plane.

Can other regular polygons tessellate the plane? Notice that $\frac{360}{120} = 3$. Hence, 360 divided by a number greater than 120 also is smaller than 3. However, the number of sides of a polygon cannot be less than 3. Because a polygon with more than six sides has an interior angle greater than 120°, it actually is not necessary to consider polygons with more than six sides.

Semiregular Tessellations

When more than one type of regular polygon is used and the arrangement of the polygons at each vertex is the same, the tessellation is *semiregular*. The following partial student page shows an example of a semiregular tessellation and one that is not semiregular.

NOW TRY THIS 12-8

Create a semiregular tessellation consisting only of squares and equilateral triangles.

Tessellating with Other Shapes

Next, we consider tessellating the plane with arbitrary convex quadrilaterals. Before reading on, you may wish to investigate the problem yourself, with the help of cardboard quadrilaterals. Figure 12-58 shows an arbitrary convex quadrilateral and a way to tessellate the plane with the quadrilateral. Successive 180° turns of the quadrilateral about the midpoints *P, Q, R,* and *S* of its sides will produce four congruent quadrilaterals around a common vertex. Notice that the sum of the measures of the angles around vertex *A* is *a* + *b* + *c* + *d*. This is the sum of the measures of the interior angles of the quadrilateral, or 360°.

FIGURE 12-58

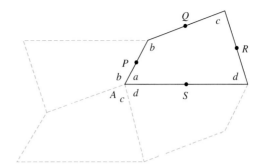

Sample School Book Page:
SEMIREGULAR TESSELLATIONS

Extension ▶ ▶

Semi-Regular Tessellations

In Exercise 6 on page 573, you saw that one regular polygon can be used to create a tessellation. You can also create tessellations using more than one regular polygon. For example, an equilateral triangle and a regular hexagon were used to create the tessellation below.

17. **a.** Which pattern blocks are regular polygons?

　　b. Create two or three different tessellations that include more than one type of the pattern blocks you identified in part (a).

A *semi-regular tessellation* uses more than one kind of regular polygon, and has the same arrangement of polygons at every vertex. The tessellation shown above is an example of a semi-regular tessellation.

18. Two different arrangements of regular polygons appear in the tessellation below, so it is not a semi-regular tessellation.

　　a. Identify which of your tessellations from Exercise 17(b) are semi-regular tessellations.

　　b. Is the tessellation shown on page 565 a semi-regular tessellation? Explain.

Source: McDougal Littell, Middle Grades MATH Thematics, Book 2, 2002 (p. 575).

As we saw earlier in this section, a regular pentagon does not tessellate the plane. However, some nonregular pentagons do. One is shown in Figure 12-59, along with a tessellation of the plane by the pentagon.

FIGURE 12-59

HISTORICAL NOTE

Determining which irregular pentagons tessellate is a surprisingly rich problem. Mathematicians thought they had solved it when they had classified eight types of pentagons that would tessellate. They believed they had all of them. But then in 1975, Marjorie Rice, a woman with no formal training in mathematics, discovered a ninth type of tessellating pentagon. She went on to discover four more by 1977. Her interest was piqued by reading an article in *Scientific American* by Martin Gardner. Two of the pentagons she found are shown in Figure 12-60. The problem of how many types of pentagons tessellate remains unsolved.

FIGURE 12-60

Type 9 discovered in February 1976

Type 13 discovered in December 1977

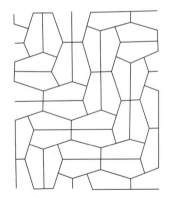

What other types of designs can be made that tessellate a plane? The plane geometry and motions studied earlier give some clues on how to design shapes that work. Consider one of the methods used in Chapter 10 to determine the area of a parallelogram. In Figure 12-61(a), triangle *ABE* was removed from the left of parallelogram *ABCD* and slid to the right forming the rectangle *BB'E'E* of Figure 12-61(b). This same notion can be used to create a tessellating shape.

FIGURE 12-61

(a)   (b)

Consider any polygon known to tessellate a plane, such as rectangle *ABCD* in Figure 12-62(a). On the left side of the figure draw any shape in the interior of the rectangle, as in Figure 12-62(b). Cut this shape from the rectangle and slide it to the right by the slide that takes *A* to *B*, as shown in Figure 12-62(c). The resulting shape will tessellate the plane. (Why?)

FIGURE 12-62

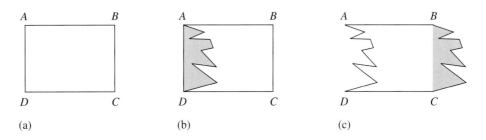

(a)   (b)   (c)

A second method of forming a tessellation involves a series of rotations of parts of a figure. In Figure 12-63(a), we start with an equilateral triangle *ABC*, choose the midpoint *O* of one side of the triangle and cut out a shape, as in Figure 12-63(b), being careful not to cut away more than half of angle *B* and then rotate the shape 180° clockwise around point *O*.

FIGURE 12-63

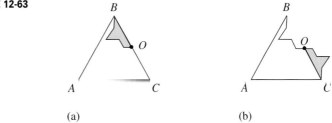

(a)   (b)

If we continue this process on the other two sides, then we obtain a shape that can be rotated around point *A* to tessellate the plane. Complete the tessellating shape and tessellate the plane with it in the following "Now Try This" activity.

NOW TRY THIS 12-9

Continue the drawing of the tessellating shape in Figure 12-63. Cut out the shape and use it to draw a tessellation of the plane.

O N G O I N G   A S S E S S M E N T   1 2 - 5

1. On dot paper, draw a tessellation of the plane using the following figures.

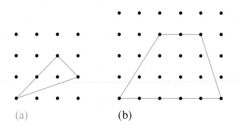

  (a)   (b)

2. **a.** Tessellate the plane with the following quadrilateral.

   b. Is it possible to tessellate the plane with any quadrilateral? Why or why not?

3. On square-dot paper, use each of the following four pentominoes, one at a time, to make a tessellation of the plane, if possible. (A *pentomino* is a polygon composed of five congruent, nonoverlapping squares.) Which of the pentominoes tessellate the plane?

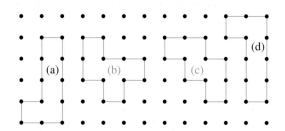

4. We have seen that equilateral triangles, squares, and regular hexagons are the only regular polygons that will tessellate the plane by themselves. However, there are many ways to tessellate the plane by using combinations of these and other regular polygons, as shown in the following figure.

Try to produce other such tessellations by using the following.
   a. Only equilateral triangles, squares, and regular hexagons
   b. Regular octagons (8-gons) and squares

5. To determine if a shape created using a glide reflection will tessellate the plane, complete the following:
   a. Start with a rectangle. Determine some shape that you might use with a slide to form a tessellating shape. Slide it as shown below. Determine the horizontal line of symmetry of the rectangle, and reflect as shown below.

   b. Explain why the described series of motions is a glide reflection.
   c. Determine whether the final shape will tessellate the plane.

6. The **dual of a tessellation** is the tessellation obtained by connecting the centers of the polygons in the original tessellation that share a common side. The dual of the tessellation of equilateral triangles is the tessellation of regular hexagons, shown in color in the following figure.

Describe and show the dual of each of the following:
   a. The regular tessellation of squares shown in Figure 12-56(a)
   b. The tessellation of squares in Figure 12-56(b)
   c. A tessellation of regular hexagons

7. A sidewalk is made of tiles of the type shown in the following figure:

Each tile is made of three regular hexagons from which three sides have been removed. Draw a partial tessellation composed of seven such figures.

8. Which of the following tessellations are semiregular and which are not? Justify your answers.

(a)

(b)

(c)

(d)

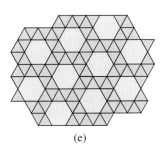

(e)

Communication

9. The following figure is a partial tessellation of the plane with the trapezoid *ABCD*:

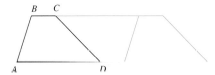

a. Explain how the tessellation can be used to find a formula for the area of the trapezoid.
b. Tessellate the plane with a triangle and show how the tessellation can be used to find the relationship between the length of the segment connecting the midpoints of the two sides of a triangle and the length of the third side.

10. Explain in your own words why only three types of regular polygons tessellate the plane.

Open-Ended

11. There are endless numbers of figures that tessellate a plane. In the following drawing, the shaded figure is shown to tessellate the plane.

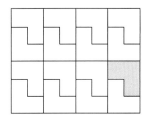

Design several different polygons and show how each can tessellate the plane. What transformations are used in each of your designs? Explain how they are used to tessellate the plane.

12. Examine different quilt patterns or floor coverings and make a sketch of those you found that tessellate a plane.

13. A cube will tessellate space but a sphere will not. List several other solids that will tessellate space and several that will not.

Cooperative Learning

14. Each member of a small group is to find a drawing by M. C. Escher that does not appear in this text and in which the concept of tessellation is used. Each then shows the other members of the group, in detail, how he or she thinks Escher created the tessellation in his or her drawing.

15. a. Convince the members of your group that the following figure containing six equilateral triangles tessellates the plane:

   b. As a group, find different figures that contain six equilateral triangles. How many such figures can you find? Discuss the meaning of "different."
   c. Find some of the figures in (b) that are *rep-tiles*. (A rep-tile is a figure whose copies can be used to form a larger figure similar to itself.) Convince other members of your group that your figures are rep-tiles and that they tessellate the plane.
16. Trace each of the following shapes and cut out several copies of each. Each member of a small group should pick a shape, decide if it tessellates the plane, and convince

other members of the group if it does or does not tessellate. The group should report the answers with figures or an argument why a shape does not tessellate.

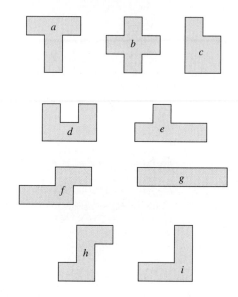

LABORATORY

A C T I V I T Y

Use pattern blocks to construct tessellations using each of the following types of pieces:

1. Squares
2. Equilateral triangles
3. Octagons and squares
4. Rhombuses

Hint for Solving the Preliminary Problem

Reflect point *P* or point *Q* in side $\overline{BC}$. Use the *Pythagorean Theorem* or the *distance formula* to find the length of the path.

QUESTIONS FROM THE CLASSROOM

1. A student asks, "If I have a point and its image, is that enough to determine whether the image was found using a translation, reflection, rotation, or glide reflection?" How do you respond?
2. Another student asks a question similar to question 1 but is concerned about a segment and its image. How do you respond to this student?
3. A student claims that a kite has no lines of symmetry. How do you respond?
4. A student says that every three-dimensional figure that has plane symmetry automatically has line symmetry. Do you agree? Why or why not?

5. A student says that in a size transformation with the scale factor 0, we do not have a transformation. Is that true?
6. A student asks if every translation on a grid can be accomplished by a translation along a vertical direction followed by a translation along a horizontal direction. How do you respond?
7. A student asks why the images of two perpendicular lines will also be perpendicular under a size transformation. How do you respond?
8. When asked if symmetries are used in occupations other than mathematics, how do you respond?

9. A student asks why some wheel covers have symmetry. How do you respond?

10. A student asks, "If I have two triangles that are not similar, is it possible to transform one onto the other by a sequence of isometries followed by a size transformation?" How do you respond?

C H A P T E R   O U T L I N E

I. Motions of the plane
   A. A **transformation** of the plane is a function from the plane to itself which is a one-to-one correspondence. **Isometries** are transformations that preserve distance.
      1. A **translation** is a transformation of the plane that moves every point a specified distance in a specified direction along a straight line.
         In terms of coordinates, a translation of the plane is a transformation of the plane such that to every point (x, y) corresponds the point $(x + a, y + b)$ for real numbers a and b.
      2. A **rotation** is a transformation of the plane determined by holding one point (the center) fixed and rotating the plane about this point by a certain amount in a certain direction.
      3. A **half-turn** is a rotation of $180°$.
      4. Properties of a rotation can be used to show that two lines, neither of which is vertical, are perpendicular if, and only if, their slopes m_1 and m_2 satisfy the condition $m_1 m_2 = {}^-1$.
      5. A **reflection** in a line m is a transformation among points of the plane that pairs each point P of the plane with a point P' in such a way that m is the perpendicular bisector of $\overline{PP'}$, as long as P is not on m. If P is on m, then $P = P'$.
      6. A **glide reflection** is the composition of a translation and a reflection in a line parallel to the slide arrow of the translation.
   B. A **size transformation** S from the plane to the plane is defined as follows: Some point O, the center of the size transformation, is its own image. For any other point Q of the plane, its image Q' is such that $OQ'/OQ = r$, where r is a positive real number and O, Q, and Q' are collinear.
   C. Two figures are **similar** if it is possible to transform one onto the other by a sequence of isometries followed by a size transformation.

II. Symmetries
   A. A figure has **line symmetry** if it is its own image under a reflection.
   B. A figure has **rotational symmetry** if it is its own image under a rotation of less than $360°$ about a turn center.
   C. A figure has **point symmetry** if it has $180°$ rotational symmetry.
   D. A three-dimensional figure has a **plane of symmetry** when every point of the figure on one side of the plane has a mirror image on the other side of the plane.
   E. A three-dimensional figure has **rotational symmetry** if when rotated about an axis of rotation it coincides with itself.

*III. Tessellations
   A **tessellation** of a plane is the filling of the plane with repetitions of figures in such a way that no figures overlap and there are no gaps.

C H A P T E R   R E V I E W

1. Complete each of the following motions.

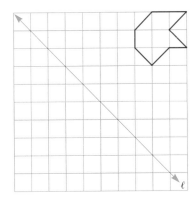

A reflection in ℓ

(a)

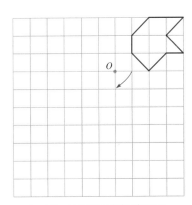

A rotation in O through the given arc

(b)

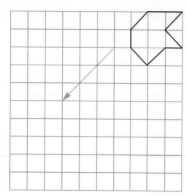

A translation, as pictured

(c)

2. For each of the following figures, construct the image of △*ABC*.

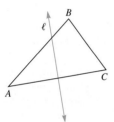

Through a reflection in ℓ

(a)

Through the given rotation in *O*

(b)

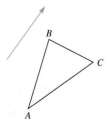

Through the translation arrow pictured

(c)

3. Determine how many lines of symmetry, if any, each of the following figures has.

(a)

(b)

(c)

(d)

(e)

(f)

4. For each of the following figures, identify the types of symmetry (line, rotational, or point) it possesses.

(a)   (b)

(c)

5. Determine how many planes of symmetry each of the following has.
   a. A ball
   b. A right cylindrical water pipe
   c. A box that is a right rectangular prism but not a cube
   d. A cube

6. What type of symmetry (line, rotational, or point) does each of the lowercase letters of the printed English alphabet have?

7. In the following figure, △*A′B′C′* is the image of △*ABC* under a size transformation.

Locate points *A, B,* and *C* such that *A′* is the center of the size transformation and $BC = \frac{1}{2}B'C'$.

8. Given that *STAR* in the following figure is a parallelogram, describe a sequence of isometries to show the following:
a. △*STA* ≅ △*ARS*
b. △*TSR* ≅ △*RAT*

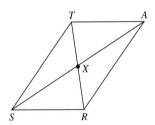

9. Given that *BEAUTY* in the following figure is a regular hexagon, describe a sequence of isometries that will transform the following:
a. *BEAU* into *AUTY*
b. *BEAU* into *YTUA*

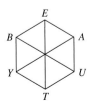

10. Given that △*SNO* ≅ △*SWO* in the following figure, describe one or more isometries that will transform △*SNO* into △*SWO*.

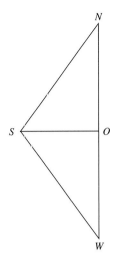

11. Show that △*SER* in the following figure is the image of △*HOR* under a succession of isometries with a size transformation.

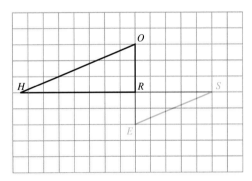

12. Show that △*TAB* in the following figure is the image of △*PIG* under a succession of isometries with a size transformation:

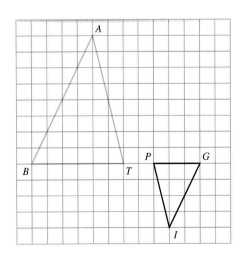

13. The triangle $A'B'C'$ with $A'(0, 7.91)$, $B'(^-5, ^-4.93)$, $C'(4.83, 0)$ is the image of triangle ABC under the translation $(x, y) \rightarrow (x + 3, y - 5)$.
    a. Find the coordinates of A, B, and C.
    b. Under what translation will the image of $\triangle A'B'C'$ be $\triangle ABC$?

14. If a translation is determined by $(x, y) \rightarrow (x + 3, y - 2)$ is followed by another translation determined by $(x, y) \rightarrow (x - 3, y + 2)$, describe a transformation that would achieve the same thing.

15. Suppose $\triangle A''B''C''$ with $A''(0, 0)$, $B''(1, 5)$, $C''(^-2, 7)$ is the image of $\triangle ABC$ under the translation $(x, y) \rightarrow (x + 2, y - 1)$ followed by the translation $(x, y) \rightarrow (x + 1, y + 3)$.
    a. Find the coordinates of A, B, and C.
    b. Under what single transformation will the image of $\triangle ABC$ be $\triangle A''B''C''$?

16. Write each of the following as a single transformation.
    a. (i) A translation from A to B followed by a translation from B to C.
    (ii) A translation from B to C followed by a translation from A to B.
    b. A rotation about O by 90° counterclockwise, followed by a rotation about O by 30° clockwise.
    c. (i) A size transformation with center O and scale factor 3 followed by a size transformation with center O and scale factor 2.
    (ii) The size transformations in part (i) in reverse order.

17. Which of the following figures has more symmetries? Justify your answer.
    a. A rhombus or a square?
    b. An isosceles trapezoid or a parallelogram?
    c. A cube or a box; that is, a rectangular right prism?

*18. Explain why a regular octagon cannot tessellate the plane.

*19. A square will tessellate a plane; can we always find a square that will tessellate a rectangle?

*20. Can any tessellating shape be used as a unit for measuring area? If so, explain why.

SELECTED BIBLIOGRAPHY

Clason, R., D. Ericksen, and C. Ericksen. "Cross-and-Turn Tile Patterns." *Mathematics Teaching in the Middle Schools* 2 (May 1997): 430–437.

Clements, D., and J. Sarama. "The Earliest Geometry." *Teaching Children Mathematics* 7 (October 2000): 82–86.

Dayoub, I., and J. Lott. *Geometry: Constructions and Transformations.* White Plains, NY: Dale Seymour Publishing Company, 1977.

Fossnaugh, L., and M. Harrell. "Covering the Plane with Rep-Tiles." *Mathematics Teaching in the Middle Schools* 1 (January-February 1996): 666–670.

Harrell, M., and L. Fossnaugh. "Allium to Zircon: Mathematics & Nature." *Mathematics Teaching in the Middle Schools* 2 (May 1997): 380–389.

Harris, J. "Using Literature to Investigate Transformations." *Teaching Children Mathematics* 4 (May 1998): 510–513.

Peterson, B. "From Tessellations to Polyhedra." *Mathematics Teaching in the Middle Schools* 5 (February 2000): 348–356.

Phillips, J. M., and R. E. Zwoyer. *Motion Geometry Book 2: Congruence.* New York: Harper & Row, Publishers, 1969.

——— *Motion Geometry Book 1: Slides, Flips, and Turns.* New York: Harper & Row, Publishers, 1969.

——— *Motion Geometry Book 3: Symmetry.* New York: Harper & Row, Publishers, 1969.

——— *Motion Geometry Book 4: Area, Similarity, and Constructions.* New York: Harper & Row, Publishers, 1969.

Sakshaug, L. "Patterns in Squares." *Teaching Children Mathematics* 7 (November 2000): 172–173.

Seidel, J. "Symmetry in Season." *Teaching Children Mathematics* 4 (January 1998): 244–249.

Sellke, D. "Geometric Flips via the Arts." *Teaching Children Mathematics* 4 (February 1999): 379–383.

Speer, W., and J. Dixon. "Reflections of Mathematics." *Teaching Children Mathematics* 2 (May 1996): 537–543.

Walter, M. *The Mirror Puzzle Book.* New York: Parkwest Publications (1985).

White, D. "Kenta, Kilts, and Kiminos: Exploring Cultures and Mathematics through Fabrics." *Teaching Children Mathematics* 7 (February 2001): 354–359.

Zaslavsky, C. "Symmetry in American Folk Art." *Arithmetic Teacher* 37 (January 1990): 6–12.

Zilliox, J., and S. Lowrey. "Many Faces Have I." *Mathematics Teaching in the Middle Schools* 3 (November–December 1997): 180–183.

Appendix I:
Using a Spreadsheet

Introduction

spreadsheet

An electronic **spreadsheet** is a table of rows and columns in which each cell may contain a value that can be operated on and changed at any time. A spreadsheet has the capacity to allow a change in one cell to be reflected in any other cell that relies on the data in that original cell.

Table AI-1 depicts certain values for the function $f(x) = x^2$. In Table AI-1, each item in the $f(x)$ column depends on the value in the x column. A spreadsheet, as it might appear on a computer, is shown in Figure AI-1, depicting the information in Table AI-1. (The labels x and $f(x) = x^2$ are for headings only.)

Table AI-1

x	f(x)
1	1
2	4
3	9
4	16
5	25

FIGURE AI-1

	A	B	C	D	E	F
1	x	f(x)=x^2				
2	1	1				
3	2	4				
4	3	9				
5	4	16				
0	5	25				
7						

Workbook1

In Figure AI-1, an index column down the left side numbers the rows of the table. Across the top, an index row of letters identifies the columns. In the body of the table, the value 3 is in column A and row 4. As a result, the value 3 could be identified by label A4, where A is the column heading and 4 is the row number. The labels can be used to write formulas for the values of column B in terms of column A. For example, the value in B2 could be found by multiplying the A2 value times itself, or in computer language as A2^2, depicting $(A_2)^2$. Similarly, the value in B5 could be written = A5^2. In Figure AI-1, the items in row 1 are used as headings to indicate what the table is depicting.

The user bars on an opening of the *Microsoft Excel* spreadsheet are shown in Figure AI-2.

FIGURE AI-2

Menu bar

Toolbars

Formula bar

Figure AI-2 depicts the **Menu** bar, the **Standard** toolbars, and a **Formula** bar. The **Menu** bar offers such options as **File, Edit, Format,** and so on. For example, as a beginning user you might choose to click **File** and choose *New* to obtain a new worksheet on the screen. The standard toolbars show different options available to the user, including file folder, disk, and printing options on the left along with other types of options, such as **B** for bold type and the *I* for italics. The **Formula** bar is for entry of items in a worksheet and is discussed later in this appendix.

Developing a Spreadsheet

To create the spreadsheet in Figure AI-1, we first open a new worksheet and then type the entries in cells A1 and B1 by typing x and $f(x) = x^2$, respectively, in the entry line (also known as the **Formula** bar) and pressing ⎡RETURN⎤ after each. These are simply headings for our reference.

1. To create the column of values listed under x in the A column, we enter the first item as 1 in A2 and press ⎡RETURN⎤. Then we use a formula to create the value for A3 by assigning the values for A3 using a formula. We tell the spreadsheet that a formula is being used by highlighting the cell to be filled and typing = in the entry line followed by the formula we wish to use. In this case, we want A3 to have the value A2 + 1. We signal this by highlighting cell A3, typing = A2 + 1 and pressing ⎡RETURN⎤. That done, the value 2 appears in A3, as shown in Figure AI-3. (Near the **Formula** bar are two boxes, one containing an × and one containing a tick mark. The × is used to cancel any changes you have made in a formula. The tick is used in the same way as the ⎡RETURN⎤ key.)

FIGURE AI-3

	A	B	C	D	E	F
1	x	f(x)=x^2				
2	1					
3	2					
4						

Workbook1

2. To complete the column under A, we use the *Fill Down* command by first highlighting A3 and all the cells to be filled and then using the *Fill Down* command in the **Menu** bar normally found under the **Edit** menu. The *Fill Down* command fills successive cells in column A by adapting the created formula to accommodate the cell number. For example, the entry in A4 is automatically created as the value of A3 + 1, and so on. The *Fill Down* command will fill all highlighted cells. If the cells A3 through A6 are highlighted, the result is seen in Figure AI-4. (If there is no data in a cell to create other cells the program assumes that the value in the cell is 0.)

FIGURE AI-4

	A	B	C	D	E	F
1	x	f(x)=x^2				
2	1					
3	2					
4	3					
5	4					
6	5					

Workbook1

3. To complete the column under the heading B and $f(x) = x$^2, we highlight cell B2, type = A2^2, and press ⃞RETURN⃞. This should cause a 1 to be placed in cell B2. We then highlight cell B2 and the rest of the column through row 6 and use the *Fill Down* command to complete column B.

REMARK   Most spreadsheets also have a *Fill Right* command to fill in cells in rows as well as columns.

To clear a table or a set of values in *Excel*, highlight the desired values to be deleted and pull down the **Edit** menu. If we choose *Clear*, then we are asked about clearing *All, Formats, Formulas, or Notes*. To clear all highlighted values, choose *All* and press ⃞RETURN⃞.

Most spreadsheets allow the use of various functions, including $+$, $-$, $\div$, $\cdot$, $\wedge$, trigonometric functions, square roots, and absolute values. To determine what your spreadsheet can do, consult the software manual or the **Help** menu. (Note that many graphing calculators have the capability of acting like a spreadsheet.)

Graphing with a Spreadsheet

In addition to allowing the use of arithmetic operations, most spreadsheets can create graphs of the data presented in a table. For example, to create a graph of the data in Figure AI-1, we follow these steps:

1. Highlight the information to be graphed. In the graph in Figure AI-5, the data from rows A2 through A6 and columns B2 through B6 were highlighted. After the data is highlighted, then we choose the *Graph* icon from the **Toolbar**. (On some spreadsheets, when you choose the *Graph* icon, you can size the graph as you want; other spreadsheets will do this automatically.) In *Excel*, clicking the icon once causes the highlighted information to be placed in a flashing dashed rectangle. If we move the mouse pointer on the worksheet, we see a + symbol. Click the mouse, and drag it while holding down the mouse button to size the graph. Once the graph is sized, most spreadsheets ask for a variety of information, such as what you want for the *x*-values, what you want for the *y*-values, what legends you want, and what maximum and minimum values you want. Because each spreadsheet is different, we suggest that you consult your user's manual to see what features are available. For example, in *Excel* the first question is about the range of data. With the data we are graphing, the range is written $A$2:$B$6 automatically. We can change or accept this range. The $A$2 indicates that the first values from our table to be used in the graph start at A2 and this will not change in the graph; $B$6 tells the computer that cell B6 contains the last value of the graph.

FIGURE AI-5

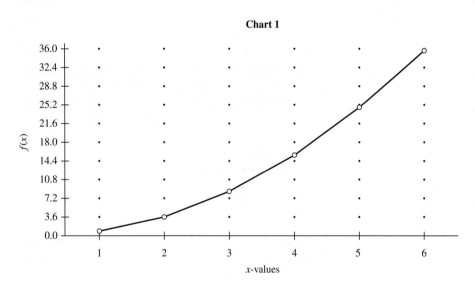

2. Because the range from A2 through B6 contains the values we intend to graph, we move to the next screen, where we must select a chart type, usually from several options. *Excel* presents these options in icon form. Figure AI-5 was created as a scatter-

---

REMARK The $ is used before and after a variable to indicate that the variable is fixed and does not change in this application. This feature is useful particularly when we want to use a specific value of a variable over and over in an application. An example is seen in Ongoing Assessment problem 4, where we use the calculated mean of a set of data over and over to find the standard deviation of the set of data.

---

plot. Once we choose the scatterplot style, by double-clicking an icon, the next screen asks about the type of scatterplot desired. Again, in *Excel*, the choices are presented as icons. We chose the connected scatterplot (option 2), after which a graph is drawn. But there are other options to consider. To use the data as ordered pairs with the x data as the first column, we are using the data series in columns. Finally, we are asked if we want to use the first row as a legend or as data. Because we started with A2, we want this as the first value of x data. Next, we are asked if we want to add a legend to the graph. Figure AI-5 shows the data from Figure AI-1 as a connected scatterplot. Using a title of Chart 1, we see a finished product with the $f(x)$ values and x-values labeled along the axes.

The same information could be depicted as a bar graph, as shown in Figure AI-6, by using other graph icons.

FIGURE AI-6

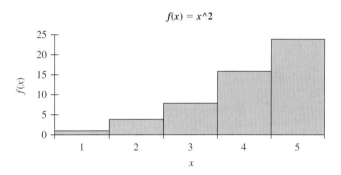

Many spreadsheets allow the options of using scatterplots, line plots, bar graphs, stem and leaf plots, and three-dimensional plots. Again, check the user's manual to see what is available for your spreadsheet.

Explicit and Recursive Formulas

recursive formula

When using a spreadsheet as in the previous paragraphs, most users discover they need to know the difference between explicit and recursive formulas. In Figure AI-4, a **recursive formula** was used—a value in a cell was determined by the value in the cell immediately above it. For example, the value in cell A5 is 1 plus the value in cell A4. Whenever a value in any cell is expressed in terms of a value in a previous cell (or cells), we say that the expression is a *recursive expression* or *formula*. Recursive formulas are typically used by most young students to describe patterns. For example, most students would describe the following pattern as adding 3, meaning that to find the next item, a person would add 3 to the previous term:

$$3, 6, 9, 12, 15, 18, 21, 24, \ldots$$

On a spreadsheet, the pattern could be depicted using two columns. Row A may serve to count the numbers of the terms, as seen in Figure AI-7. (Note that column A serves the same purpose as the index column, but we can use the numbers in the A cells to create the terms in the B column.)

FIGURE AI-7

	A	B
1	1	3
2	2	6
3	3	9
4	4	12
5	5	
6	6	

To fill in additional rows, we can highlight cell B5 and type $= B4 + 3$ in the entry line and then use the *Fill Down* command by highlighting the number of entries needed. Clearly, the value of a cell is determined by the cell immediately above it.

In this example, the values in column B are multiples of 3. If n is the term number, then the corresponding value is $3n$. The expression $3n$ is an *explicit formula* for finding the value of an expression as a function of the number of the term n.

To use the explicit formula $3n$ to create the entries in column B, we use the formula $= 3*A:A$ to fill in the entry in B1 and then use the *Fill Down* command to fill all highlighted cells of column B where there is a corresponding A entry. The use of :A at the end of the formula tells the spreadsheet to use column A to fill column B entries.

Other Features of a Spreadsheet

Spreadsheets can act as simple calculators. For example, determine the number of handshakes at a party that 25 people attended. Each person shook hands with everyone else, and no one shook hands with himself or herself. This problem can be solved using a spreadsheet. We consider a *simpler case* whereby there is first only one person in the room, in which case there are no handshakes. Then another person enters for a total of two persons, and so one handshake occurs. When a third person enters the room, two more handshakes take place, and so on. This could be recorded as in Figure AI-8, in which column A records the number of people in the room and is developed by using the *Fill Down* command and the formula $= A2 + 1$. Column B depicts the number of additional handshakes when another person enters the room. Column B is 1 less than the number in column A and can be set up using the formula $= A2 - 1$.

FIGURE AI-8

	A	B
1	No. People	No. of Additional Handshakes
2	1	0
3	2	1
4	3	2
5	4	3
...	...	...
26	25	24
27	Total	300

To find the total number of handshakes at the party, we need to find the total number of handshakes in column B. The spreadsheet does this when we highlight the cell in which we want the total, in this case B27, and then click the $\boxed{\Sigma}$ button. (On some spreadsheets, you may need to use the *SUM* feature.) When we click $\boxed{\Sigma}$, the spreadsheet surrounds the numbers immediately above the highlighted cell with a flashing rectangle to show what will be added. (In some cases, we may have to click and drag a rectangle around the numbers that are to be added. This is true especially if there is an empty cell among the other cells to be added.) When the $\boxed{\text{RETURN}}$ or $\boxed{\text{ENTER}}$ key is pressed, the total appears in the highlighted cell. As Figure AI-8 shows, the total is 300 handshakes for the 25 people.

Many other features available on most spreadsheets are not discussed here. We suggest that you consult the user's manual that comes with your spreadsheet program and try the following problems.

ONGOING ASSESSMENT A·I

1. a. Write any arithmetic sequence.
   b. In column A of your spreadsheet, list the number of the term of the arithmetic sequence.
   c. What formula did you use to fill down the column?
   d. List the first 25 terms of the arithmetic sequence in column B.
   e. What formula could be used to fill in the terms in column B?
   f. Find the sum of the first 25 terms in the arithmetic sequence. Describe how that was done with a spreadsheet.
   g. Plot the number of the terms of the arithmetic sequence versus the actual terms using the graphing or chart option of your spreadsheet. Describe the graph of the arithmetic sequence.

2. a. Write any geometric sequence.
   b. In column A of your spreadsheet, list the number of the term of the geometric sequence.
   c. List the first 25 terms of the geometric sequence in column B.
   d. What formula could be used to fill in the terms of column B?
   e. Find the sum of the first 25 terms of the geometric sequence. Describe how that was done by using a spreadsheet.
   f. Plot the number of the terms of the geometric sequence versus the actual terms using the graphing or chart option of your spreadsheet. Describe the graph of the geometric sequence.

3. Given the following set of data, use a spreadsheet to find the arithmetic mean:

   23, 45, 67, 78, 98, 54, 36, 76, 75, 24, 43, 54, 100, 99

4. Use the data in problem 3 to develop a spreadsheet to find the standard deviation of the data. Use the columns of the spreadsheet to represent the number of the term, the term, and the difference of the mean and the term. Then find the square of each of the differences, the sum of those squares, and the quotient of the sum and n, where n is the number of terms. Finally, find the square root of the quotient.

5. Businesspeople use spreadsheets for the calculation of interest on loans or outstanding bills. Consider a debt of $1000 with payments of $40 per month, which includes 1.5% interest per month on the unpaid balance. Develop a spreadsheet that shows the number of the month the payment was made, the amount of payment in each month, and the outstanding balance. If no other debts accrue, how many months will it take to pay off the debt?

6. Use a spreadsheet to show the first 100 multiples of 13. Explain all steps in developing this spreadsheet.

7. Develop a spreadsheet for finding your college grade-point average. Explain all steps used in developing the spreadsheet.

8. The sequence of Fibonacci numbers is 1, 1, 2, 3, 5, 8, . . . , where each successive term after the first two is the sum of the two preceding terms.
   a. Develop a spreadsheet to find the first 25 Fibonacci numbers.
   b. Extend your spreadsheet to find the square of each term of the Fibonacci sequence and the sum of those squares. Make a conjecture about the sum of the squares of the first n terms of the sequence.
   c. To examine the updating feature of your spreadsheet, change the first two terms of the Fibonacci sequence and observe how each cell that was written based on these terms is changed. Does the conjecture in (b) still hold?

9. Develop a spreadsheet for finding $n!$. Explain the steps used to develop the spreadsheet.

Appendix II: Graphing Calculators

Introduction

A graphing calculator can be a useful tool in problem solving. By working through problems we show how a graphing calculator might be used. One advantage of the graphing calculator is the display, not only of graphs but also of text. With this feature, computations and answers can be viewed, various methods can be compared, and changes can be made easily.

In this appendix, we assume your calculator has at least the capabilities of the Texas Instruments TI-73 middle-school graphing calculator. If you use other calculators, you will have to determine whether the discussed features are available on them.

PROBLEM SOLVING   <u>Molly's CD Problem</u>

Molly belongs to a club that sells CDs by mail. The CDs sell for $12.95 each, and she can order as many as she wants each month. Each order has a shipping charge of $5.00 no matter how many CDs are ordered. She would like to develop a table that tells her how much money she owes when she orders from 1 to 10 CDs. Develop such a table.

This problem is worked using a variety of techniques to show some of the capabilities of the graphing calculator.

Using the Replay Feature

Suppose we want to solve Molly's CD Problem using paper and pencil to build a table and using the calculator only to perform the computations. First, we must realize that the cost for any number of CDs is given by multiplying the number of CDs by $12.95 and adding $5.00. To find the cost of one CD using this process, enter the following:

$$\boxed{1}\boxed{\times}\boxed{1}\boxed{2}\boxed{.}\boxed{9}\boxed{5}\boxed{+}\boxed{5}$$

and press $\boxed{\text{ENTER}}$. The answer, 17.95, is displayed. This number can then be recorded in a table. It is important for elementary school students to see the whole problem as well as the answer. This allows students to check visually whether they have entered their numbers and operations correctly.

To find the cost for other quantities of CDs, we use the **replay feature** of the calculator. To activate this feature, press $\boxed{\text{2nd}}$ $\boxed{\text{ENTRY}}$; the previous entry is displayed. We then use the left arrow to move the cursor over the first 1 and replace it with a 2. When $\boxed{\text{ENTER}}$ is pressed, the next answer, 30.90, is displayed. We could shorten the left

replay feature

arrow strokes even further by pressing 2nd followed by the left arrow; the cursor will go to the beginning of the line. If we continue in this manner, as shown in Figure AII-1, we could find the cost of any number of CDs and enter these costs into a table.

FIGURE AII-1

```
1*12.95+5
          17.95
2*12.95+5
          30.9
3*12.95+5
          43.85
4*12.95+5
```

Using Data Lists

CLRLIST

Many graphing calculators can display sequences of numbers as *lists*. To clear existing lists, press STAT and choose the **CLRLIST** (under OPS on the TI-73) feature with the name of the list as input. For example, to clear list 1 (2nd L1), we enter CLRLIST L1 and press ENTER . A message is displayed telling us that the list is cleared. Other lists are cleared in the same way.

EDIT

We use L1 to represent the number of CDs and then use L2 to represent the total cost for the CDs. To enter the values for L1, we press STAT and choose the **EDIT** feature. We then press ENTER , and the lists are shown in columns as in Figure AII-2(a). (On a TI-73 press LIST .) On the bottom edit line where L1(1) = is displayed, type the numeral 1 followed by ENTER . A 1 will appear as the first entry in L1, as shown in Figure AII-2(a).

FIGURE AII-2

(a)

(b)

```
L1      L2      L3
1       17.95   ------
2       30.9
3       43.85
4       56.8
5       69.75
------
L2(6)=
```

(c)

By pressing the right arrow, we move to list L2. The first entry in L2 can be entered directly or it can be computed by entering the expression L2(1) = 12.95 × 1 + 5 in the edit line at the bottom of the screen, as shown in Figure AII-2(b). When ENTER is pressed, 17.95 appears as the first entry in L2. We next use the left and down arrows to return to the second entry in L1 and enter 2. The remainder of the table as shown in Figure AII-2(c) can be completed.

An easier method for finding the various costs is to define a general pattern and have the calculator do all the computations at once. To do this, enter the numbers 1 through 10 in L1. Move the cursor to the top of L3 so that L3 is highlighted. When L3 is highlighted, anything that is done in the edit line on the bottom will happen to every element in L3. In the edit line, enter L3 = 12.95L1 + 5, as shown in Figure AII-3(a), and press ENTER. The entire list in L3 is then computed based on the entries in L1 and the rule given in the edit line (see Figure AII-3b). Lists L2 and L3 should be the same even though they were obtained in two different ways.

FIGURE AII-3

(a)   (b)

Using Lists on the Home Screen

Computations involving lists can be done on the home screen using the braces { and } located above the parentheses keys (or in the TEXT editor on a TI-73). A list can be entered by using a left brace, followed by the list, with each element separated by a comma. Figure AII-4(a) shows a list representing the number of possible CDs ordered: {1, 2, 3, 4, 5, 6, 7, 8, 9, 10}. We then multiply each element in this list by 12.95 and add 5 to the result; the answers are given on the screens by pressing ENTER. To see the entire list of answers, scroll to the right using the right arrow key.

FIGURE AII-4

 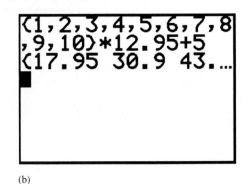

(a)   (b)

You can store the list of answers in one of the list memories by using STO and the list number you choose. By pressing STO L4 ENTER, the answers are stored in L4.

The list of answers still appears on the home screen, as shown in Figure AII-4(b), even though the answers are stored in L4. If we press $\boxed{\text{STAT}}$, select EDIT, and use the right arrow to move to the L4 column, we can see that the list of answers has been stored in L4. (On a TI-73, press $\boxed{\text{LIST}}$.) Notice that this list matches the ones in L2 and L3.

Using STAT Plot Graphing Capabilities

Next we investigate how Molly's CD Problem could be solved using a graphical representation. First, we need to set an appropriate size graphing window. If we plot the number of CDs ordered on the x-axis and the total costs on the y axis, we need only look at our lists to determine appropriate values. The number of CDs ranges from 1 to 10, and the cost ranges from $12.95 to $134.50. We have several choices. If we press $\boxed{\text{WINDOW}}$, then the choices can be entered, as shown in Figure AII-5(a). After selecting $\boxed{\text{WINDOW}}$, we can enter the minimum and maximum values for the x- and y-axes and the scale that gives the distance between the marks on each axis. (On certain calculators you can have the calculator choose the appropriate window.)

FIGURE AII-5

(a)

(b)

We can plot these points by using $\boxed{\text{2nd}}$ to choose $\boxed{\text{STAT PLOT}}$ (or $\boxed{\text{PLOT}}$) and then select Plot1, as shown in Figure AII-5(b). We see in Figure AII-5(b) that Plot1 is on, the first choice of a scatterplot is chosen, the x-values come from L1, and the y-values come from L2. We can choose 5 plots and each plot can be a scatterplot, a line graph, a box-and-whisker plot, or a histogram.

By pressing $\boxed{\text{GRAPH}}$, we obtain the graph shown in Figure AII-6(a). If we then press $\boxed{\text{TRACE}}$ and use the right and left arrow keys, we can see the trace cursor move along the dots, displaying the x- and y-values at each point, as shown in Figure AII-6(b).

FIGURE AII-6

(a)

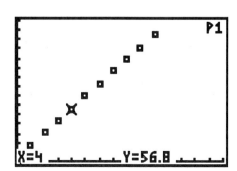

(b)

NOW TRY THIS AII-1

a. How are the values that are displayed using the |TRACE| feature related to L1 and L2?

b. Why are just the points shown rather than a line containing the points?

c. What pattern is shown in the graphical representation that is not shown when working with only numbers or lists?

d. Use the graph to approximate the cost of 12 CDs.

Connecting Graphing and Algebra

Earlier in this appendix, we generated a mathematical rule for computing the total cost for any number of CDs in Molly's CD Problem. The rule was to multiply the number of CDs by 12.95 and add 5. We can enter this rule as a function by pressing $\boxed{Y =}$. We can enter the rule for Y_1 using x to represent the number of calculators. The variable x has a separate key—$\boxed{X}$, $\boxed{X, T}$, or $\boxed{X, T, \theta}$. Figure AII-7(a) shows the entered function, and Figure AII-7(b) shows the graph obtained when $\boxed{GRAPH}$ is pressed.

FIGURE AII-7

(a)

(b)

Press $\boxed{TRACE}$ and a P1 (Plot1) appears in an upper corner. The P1 indicates that the STAT PLOT (P1) is being traced. The values that appear are the same as those we generated earlier when we built the cost tables. If we press the up arrow, a 1 appears in the corner. This indicates that the line Y_1 from the $\boxed{Y =}$ menu is being traced. We can toggle back and forth between the two graphs by pressing the up arrow.

When the line Y_1 is being traced, the x-values can be nonintegers. The graph of the line Y_1 is not really an appropriate graph for this problem because the data in this case are not continuous; that is, the y-values exist only for nonnegative integer values of x. There is no such thing as a cost for 1.5 CDs as implied by the graph. However, the graph can be used to find values of y (costs) when x is a nonnegative integer.

Using Tables

We can build a table based on the algebraic rule developed for Molly's CD Problem. To do this, we press $\boxed{2nd}$ to choose $\boxed{TBLSET}$ and set the table menu, as shown in Figure AII-8(a). The TblMin, or TblStart on some calculators, set at 1 starts the table at 1 and the $\triangle$Tbl setting of 1 sets the increment between x-values at 1. If we next press $\boxed{2nd}$ to select $\boxed{TABLE}$, we see the table of values generated by the rule $y = 12.95x + 5$. Notice that the x-values are incremented by 1 in each case because this is what we selected in the TblSet menu. Also notice that if we use the up and down arrow keys, we can continue to obtain *y*-values for any integer *x*-value, as shown in Figure AII-8(b). From the result in Figure AII-8(b), we see that the cost of 15 CDs is 199.25. Use the down arrow to determine the cost of 17 CDs.

FIGURE AII-8

(a)

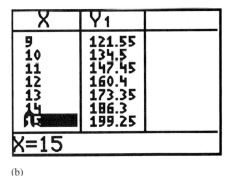

(b)

PROBLEM SOLVING   <u>Choosing a CD Company</u>

Another company is advertising CDs for $7.95 per CD with no shipping charge. However, the company charges a processing fee of $20 for each order. Molly is considering switching companies. Compare the prices of the two companies and find which one has the better price.

The rule for computing the cost under the second plan is $Y = 7.95x + 20$. If we enter this rule as Y_2 in the $\boxed{Y =}$ menu, as shown in Figure AII-9(a), we can compare the two plans using tables. If we keep the same table setup as in the earlier problem, then Figure AII-9(b) shows a comparison of the two rules. It follows that the first plan is better if we order either one or two CDs. If we order three CDs, it makes no difference which plan we use. If we order more than three CDs, then the second plan is better.

FIGURE AII-9

(a)

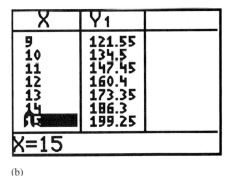

(b)

We can compare the two plans graphically by pressing $\boxed{\text{GRAPH}}$. The two graphs are shown in Figure AII-10(a). The same comments that were made about continuous data are also true in this case. If $\boxed{\text{TRACE}}$ and the arrow keys are used, then we see in Figure AII-10(b) that the two lines appear to intersect at point (3, 43.85), which is the point at which the two plans match. After $x = 3$, we see that the second line illustrates the less expensive cost.

FIGURE AII-10

(a)

(b)

Using ZOOM

Various zoom features can be used to adjust the viewing window to see more of the features of the graph. Press ZOOM to see the menu shown in Figure AII-11(a). The first item on the menu, ZBox, allows the cursor to select opposite corners of a box to define a new viewing window. To use this feature, we move the zoom cursor to any point on the screen on which we want to locate a corner of the box and then press ENTER. As we move the cursor away from the selected point, we see a small square dot indicating the selected corner. We can then move the cursor to the diagonal corner of the box that we want to define. As we use the arrow keys to move the cursor, we see the box change on the screen. When we get the box located where we want it, as shown in Figure AII-11(b), we press ENTER to replot the graph as shown in Figure AII-11(c). The TRACE feature can now be used to find values of various points. We can cancel ZBox at any time by pressing CLEAR before pressing ENTER.

FIGURE AII-11

(a)

(b)

(c)

There are other zoom features in the ZOOM menu. For example, we can select ZOOM IN from the menu and then press ENTER . We then can move the cursor to the point on which we want the center of the new viewing window to be and press ENTER . The graph will be replotted. We can also select ZOOM OUT in a similar manner.

These are only a few of the features available on a graphing calculator. Many other important features are contained in menus under keys such as MATH . Consult your user's manual to see how you can use these other tools to solve mathematical problems.

ONGOING ASSESSMENT A-II

In the following problems, the section in the book dealing with this topic is listed in parentheses.

1. Use trial and error to determine when $1000 invested at 6% annual compounded interest will double in value. (*Hint:* The value after 10 yr is given by $1000 \times 1.06^\wedge 10$.) (Section 6-5)

2. Given the sequence 3, 6, 9, 12, 15, 18, ... , use the TABLE feature to find the 32nd term by entering the appropriate equation using the Y = menu. (Section 1-1)

3. Enter $y = 3x^2 + 5x + 7$ in the Y = menu and use the TABLE feature to evaluate the function at 10 and $^-10$. (Section 4-2)

4. Set the WINDOW to graph on each axis from $^-10$ to 10 with increments of 1 unit, then graph each of the following, and answer the questions that follow:
   i. $y = x + 3$
   ii. $y = 2x + 3$
   iii. $y = 3x + 3$
   iv. $y = 4x + 3$
   a. What do the graphs have in common?
   b. How do they differ?
   c. How does changing the slope, m, change the shape of the graph in the equation $y = mx + b$? (Section 10-5)

5. Leave the WINDOW the same as it was in problem 4, graph each of the following, and answer the questions that follow:
   i. $y = x + 3$
   ii. $y = x + 4$
   iii. $y = x + 5$
   iv. $y = x + 6$
   a. What do the graphs have in common?
   b. How do they differ?

c. How does changing the value, b, in the equation $y = mx + b$ change the shape of the graph? (Section 10-5)

6. Graph the following system. Make sure to choose an appropriate window. Use ZOOM and TRACE features to find the point of intersection to two decimal places. (Section 10-5)

$$y = 2x - 3$$
$$y = {}^-7x + 8$$

7. The distance from Missoula to Billings is 350 mi. To investigate how long it takes to drive this distance, Joan entered the following equations for Y = . (Section 10-5)

$$y_1 = 50X, y_2 = 60X, y_3 = 70X, y_4 = 350.$$

She set the window for Xmin = 0, Xmax = 10, Xscl = 1, Ymin = $^-100$, Ymax = 600, and Yscl = 20 and then graphed the functions.
   a. How could she tell the time it takes to make the trip traveling at 50, 60, and 70 mph?
   b. How much time is saved traveling at 70 mph rather than 50 mph? (Section 6-6)

8. a. Evaluate the function $y = x^2 - 5x + 4$ at each integer value between $^-10$ and 10. How many sign changes are there in this range, and where do they occur?
   b. Set the window from $^-10$ to 10 on the x-axis and $^-10$ to 10 on the y-axis with increments of 1 and graph the equation.
   c. Use the TRACE feature to examine where the function crosses the x-axis.

9. Linda has 33 coins in dimes and quarters. The value of the coins is $5.55. Determine how many of each coin she has. (Section 1-3 or 10-5)

Appendix III:
Using a Geometry
Drawing Utility

(a)

(b)

Introduction

In the time of Plato, a compass and straightedge were the norm for constructions. Today's world demands that we consider other tools. In this appendix, we present a series of labs appropriate for a computer geometry utility. Most geometry utilities allow both drawing and construction. Some educators have noted the difference between the two methods. In a drawing, an "eyeballing" approach is used to draw a figure to look as it should, but the figure may not be constrained by elements of its geometric properties. For example, a segment may be drawn in a circle to look like a diameter, as in Figure AIII-1(a). However, if it is not constructed to pass through the center of the circle and one moves the circle as in Figure AIII-1(b), the segment may no longer move with the circle and may not appear to be a diameter.

The constraint of having the diameter pass through the center was not used. If the segment is constructed as a chord to contain the center as a part of the construction, then when the circle is moved, the segment moves accordingly (as a diameter should). For most purposes in this appendix, we are using constructions with all the geometric constraints applied.

The Lab Activities in this appendix are arranged in the order they might be used with the geometry chapters of the book. The activities may be used independently if the teacher provides the language and definitions as needed. The materials in this appendix are based on the work of Jim Williamson and Terry Souhrada at the University of Montana.

About a Geometry Utility

Figure AIII-2 is an example of a drawing window with the Toolbox and Menu Bar shown from *The Geometer's Sketchpad (GSP)*. Other utilities have different windows, but we use *GSP* for illustrations in this appendix.

The Menu bar of Figure AIII-2 shows the following menu options:

- **File**, for opening, closing, saving, and printing documents
- **Edit**, for selecting objects, editing object properties, and setting preferences
- **Display**, for changing the appearance of drawings
- **Construct**, for constructing figures

- **Transform**, for translating, rotating, dilating, reflecting and iterating [optimal] figures
- **Measure**, for displaying measurements and making calculations
- **Graph**, for options with coordinate axes and function plots
- **Help**, for accessing Sketchpad's help system

The Laboratory Activities that follow contain a reference to a section in the book where they are appropriate to use. In many cases, the mathematical content of a section can be explored by working through the appropriate activity. GSP Lab 1 provides an introduction to GSP and can be used to acquaint users with the main features of the program. Additional features will be introduced as needed. More activities and problems are given in Ongoing Assessment A-III. Many of the Technology Corners in Chapters 9–12 also contain GSP activities or problems.

FIGURE AIII-2

Translate, Rotate, and Dilate Tools

Press and hold to open pop-up **Selection Arrow** palette. Drag right to choose **Translate, Rotate,** or **Dilate** tool. Select and drag objects with **Rotate** tool to rotate them around marked center. **Dilate** tool dilates selected objects toward or away from marked center.

Segment, Ray, and Line Tools

Press and hold to open pop-up Straightedge tool palette. Drag right to choose **Segment, Ray,** or **Line** tool. Construct segments, rays, and lines by clicking twice in sketch.

The Geometer's Sketchpad

GSP Lab 1 (Section 9-1)

What Is GSP?

The Geometer's Sketchpad (GSP) is a graphics program that allows us to:

- simulate straightedge and compass constructions;
- save the steps in a construction so we can do them over and over again;
- explore and discover mathematical, especially geometric, properties.

Accessing GSP

Double-click on the GSP icon. In a second, the GSP title box appears on the screen. Then the GSP window appears in the background. Click anywhere inside the title box to activate the GSP window. (See Figure AIII-3)

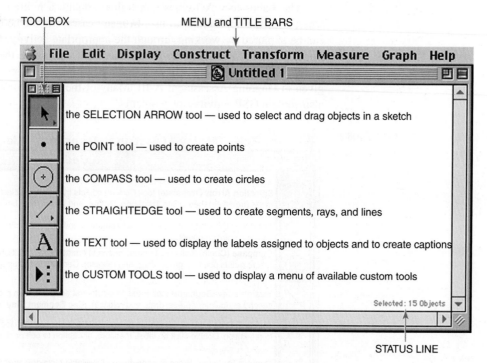

FIGURE AIII-3   TOOLBOX   MENU and TITLE BARS

STATUS LINE

Think of the window as a "blank sheet of paper" on which we can draw a sketch. On the left side of the window is the **Toolbox**. Each icon stands for a different tool. In this lab, we will experiment with some of these tools to learn how GSP operates.

Working with GSP

As we work through the exercises, keep an eye on the **Status Line** in the lower left (Windows) or lower right (Mac) corner of the sketch. This box explains exactly what GSP is doing. It can be a real help if we are unsure about what is going on!

1. **a.** Click on the **POINT** tool. How does GSP indicate that the **POINT** tool is active?
   b. Notice how the cursor changes when we move it onto the sketch. Click to create several points.
   c. Choose the **TEXT** tool. How does the cursor change?
   d. Click on each point created. What happens?

GSP automatically labels points with capital letters, starting with A, then B, and so on. We can change a label using the **TEXT** tool; just double-click on the label. A box will appear that allows us to type any label wanted. Try it!

2. With the **TEXT** tool active, double click in an empty part of the sketch. A text box is created that can be used to type captions in the sketch. After typing a caption, use the **ARROW** tool to "grab" the caption (point with the mouse and hold the button down) and move it around the sketch ("drop" it by releasing the mouse button). Go back to the **TEXT** tool to edit the caption.

3. Place several points in the sketch. Then choose the **ARROW** tool. Notice the cursor is now an arrow. Click on a point. How does GSP tell that the point has been selected? Click anywhere else in the sketch to deselect it.

With the **ARROW** tool active, we can select several points at once by dragging a selection rectangle around them. Start in one corner and hold the button on the mouse down while the cursor is dragged down and over. A dashed box is drawn. When the button is released, everything inside the box is selected. Notice that if we click the mouse button in blank space, everything gets de-selected.

Another way to select several objects at the same time is simply by selecting them with the **ARROW** tool one by one. Click on an unselected object to select it, click on a selected object to deselect it; click in blank space to deselect all objects. Experiment with it.

We can get rid of created objects by selecting them and pressing the $\boxed{\text{DELETE}}$ or $\boxed{\text{BACKSPACE}}$ key. Experiment with that key.

Finally, all the objects on the screen can be selected by using the **Select All** command found in the **Edit** menu at the top of the screen while the **ARROW** tool is active. Select the remaining points and delete them. *Note:* If the **POINT** is active, only points will be selected using this method. Likewise, if the **COMPASS** tool, one of the **STRAIGHT-EDGE** tools, or the **TEXT** tool is active, only objects of that type will be selected.

4. Choose the **COMPASS** tool.
  a. To create circles in a sketch, click the mouse button once to create the center point, then click elsewhere to create the radius point (or click, drag, and release).
  b. Use the **TEXT** tool to label the two points.
  c. Choose the **ARROW** tool. Drag either of the points. What happens?
  d. Point at the circle and select it. How does GSP indicate that the circle has been selected?
5. Clear any objects from the sketch.
  a. Choose the **SEGMENT** tool. (If the **SEGMENT** tool isn't showing, press and hold down the button on the current **STRAIGHTEDGE** tool to see the three available options: SEGMENT, RAY, and LINE.)
  b. To create a segment in the sketch, click at two locations where you'd like the two endpoints to be. The segment is selected. Use the **TEXT** tool to see what kinds of labels are assigned to segments.
  c. Go back to the **Toolbox** and choose the **LINE** option of the **STRAIGHTEDGE** tool. Return to the sketch and see how lines are drawn and labeled. Do the same with the **RAY** option.

The Construct Menu

The **Construct** menu on the menu bar across the top of the sketch contains some very powerful tools. A key idea for GSP success is:

Whenever possible, use a command from the **Construct** menu to define objects.

6. Here is an example of how to use the **Construct** menu.
  a. Use the **POINT** tool to create two points. Use the **SELECT ARROW** tool to select both points. (If you hold down the **SHIFT** key while creating the points, they remain selected.)
  b. Choose **Segment** from the **Construct** menu.
7. a. Clear the objects and then use the **POINT** tool to create three points. Select the three points; then use the segment construction. What happens?
  b. Can we move the points around after the construction?
  c. Can we move the segments around?

8. **a.** What happens when we use the segment construction with four points?
    b. Does the order in which we select the four points matter?
9. There are two ways to find the point(s) where two objects intersect.
    a. Clear any objects from the screen. Draw two circles that intersect. Then draw a ray and a segment that intersect.
    b. Method 1: Select the two circles, then choose **Intersections** from the **Construct** menu. What happens?
    c. Method 2: Choose the **ARROW** or **POINT** tool from the **Toolbox**. Move the cursor so that it points at the intersection of the segment and the ray. Be careful—look at the status line to be sure that GSP recognizes that the intersection point is desired. Then click the mouse button once.

If we want a new window, we choose **New Sketch** from the **File** menu. You can have several sketches available at one time. *Note:* There is a Window menu in Windows GSP, but not in all versions of Mac GSP.

The Measure Menu

10. **a.** In a new sketch, draw a segment and select it. Choose **Point On Segment** from the **Construct** menu. What happens?
    b. Select the segment. Pull down the **Measure** menu and choose **Length**. What happens? (*Note:* We can select the unit of measurement, inches, centimeters, or pixels, by going to **Preferences** in the **Edit** menu.)
    c. Select an endpoint of the segment and the point on the segment. Choose **Distance** from the **Measure** menu. What happens?
11. We can use **Calculate** in the **Measure** menu to do calculations with numbers, measurements, and functions.
    a. Choose **Calculate** from the **Measure** menu. A calculator should appear. Click on one of the measurements on the screen. Next, click on the minus sign $(-)$ on the key pad. Finally, click on the second measurement. Click on **OK** and the difference of the measurements should appear on the screen.
    b. Select the point on the segment and move it back and forth. What happens to the measurements and the difference?
    c. Change the length and position of the segment by dragging one of the endpoints. What happens to the measurements and the difference?

GSP Lab 2: Measuring Angles of Polygons (Sections 9-2 and 9-3)

1. **a.** Open a new sketch.
    b. Construct a triangle using 3 points from the **POINT** tool and **Segment** from the **Construct** menu and label its vertices.
    c. Measure each interior angle of the triangle.

Measuring an Angle

To measure an angle:
- Select three points that determine the angle. Be sure the vertex is the second point selected.
- From the **Measure** menu, choose **Angle**. The measure of the angle will appear on the sketch.

Calculating a Sum

d. Calculate the sum of the interior angles of the triangle.

To calculate a sum:

- Open the Calculator by choosing **Calculate** from the **Measure** menu.
- Enter a measurement to be added by clicking on the desired measurement. *Note:* It is possible to enter numbers on the calculator keypad as well, but these numbers will not be updated when the sketch is changed.
- Click on the desired operation on the calculator keypad.
- Continue to alternate between selecting measurements from the sketch and operations on the calculator until all measurements and operations needed are entered. When you are done click on **OK**. The operation and result will appear on the sketch.

e. Move the vertices of the triangle to change its size and shape. What happens to the sum of the measures of the interior angles?

Making a Conjecture

f. Repeat Part (e) several times, then make a *conjecture* (i.e., an educated guess based on your observations) about the sum of the measures of the interior angles of a triangle.

2. a. Repeat Exercise 1(b–f) for the following convex polygons: a quadrilateral, a pentagon, and a hexagon. Use the results to make a conjecture about the sum of the interior angles of a convex *n*-gon (a polygon with *n* sides).

Testing Your Conjecture

b. Test the conjecture by repeating Exercise 1(b–f) for a convex octagon.

3. a. Open a new sketch.

b. Construct a triangle. Moving clockwise, label the vertices *A, B,* and *C*. Form the exterior angles of the triangle by selecting two points and then choosing **Ray** from the **Construct** menu. Construct rays $\overrightarrow{AB}$, $\overrightarrow{BC}$, and $\overrightarrow{CA}$. Place a point on each ray so that you can measure each angle. Calculate the sum of the measures of the exterior angles.

c. Change the size and shape of the triangle several times. What happens to the sum of the measures of the exterior angles?

d. What seems to be true about the sum of the measures of the exterior angles of a triangle? Record your conjecture in a caption in the sketch.

e. Repeat Parts (b–d) for the following convex polygons: a quadrilateral, a pentagon, and a hexagon. Use the results to make a conjecture about the sum of the measures of the exterior angles of a convex *n*-gon.

f. Test the conjecture in Part (e) by repeating Parts (b–d) for a convex octagon.

GSP Lab 3: Regular Polygons (Section 9-2)

In this section, we construct regular polygons by using the **Rotate** command from the **Transform** menu. Transformations are discussed in detail in Chapter 12.

The Transform Menu

1. a. In a new sketch, draw a segment $\overline{AB}$ and select point *A*.

b. Go to the **Transform** menu and choose **Mark Center**.

FIGURE AIII-4

(a)

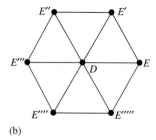

(b)

c. Select segment $\overline{AB}$ and point B. Go back to the **Transform** menu and choose **Rotate** . . . A dialog box allows us to tell GSP how many degrees to rotate the selected objects. Because the central angle of a regular pentagon is 72°, put that number in the box and click on OK. What happens?

d. Continue to rotate the segment and point around point A until there are five segments, each making a 72° angle with the next one at the center A. What are the labels on the points? (Depending on the Preferences setting, labels may not be showing.)

e. Now connect the vertices to make a regular pentagon as in Figure AIII-4(a). Why does a rotation of 72° result in the vertices of a pentagon?

2. a. In a new sketch, create a regular hexagon as in Figure AIII-4(b) using the method in Exercise 1 but adjusting the angle measure.

b. By how many degrees did you rotate the segment around the center each time to create a regular hexagon?

c. By how many degrees would you rotate the segment each time to create a regular *n*-gon?

There are two ways to create a circle using the **Construct** menu.

3. The first way is to use a center point and a radius.

a. Create a segment and a point not on the segment. Select them both.

b. From the **Construct** menu, choose **Circle By Center+Radius** Notice that the segment (the radius) does not have to have the center of the circle as one of its endpoints.

c. What happens to the circle if the center is moved?

d. What happens if the length controlling the radius is changed?

4. The second way is to use two points.

a. In a new sketch, create and select two points.

b. From the **Construct** menu, choose **Circle By Center+Point**. Select the points in the opposite order. Does the order of selecting points matter?

5. a. In a new sketch, draw a segment.

b. Use two circles to create an equilateral triangle that has the segment in Part (a) as one of its sides. The size and position of the triangle can be changed by dragging a vertex, but it should always remain an equilateral triangle.

c. Hide everything except the triangle and its vertices.

Hiding Objects

To hide objects:
- Select all the objects to be hidden.
- From the **Display** menu, select **Hide Objects** (or **Points, Lines,** etc.).

GSP Lab 4: Congruent or Not Congruent? (Section 10-1)

Side-Side-Side

1. In a new sketch, draw $\triangle ABC$. Measure its sides and angles.

In part 2 below, we construct a triangle, $\triangle XYZ$, whose sides are congruent to the sides of $\triangle ABC$.

2. a. Create a point X. Next, we construct $\overline{XY}$, a copy of $\overline{AB}$. Select X and $\overline{AB}$. Use the **Circle By Center+Radius** command from the **Construct** menu to construct a circle.

What is the center of the circle? What is the radius of the circle? What does the circle represent?

b. Select the circle and use **Point On Circle** to construct a point on the circle; label it Y. Construct $\overline{XY}$. What is true about the measures of segments $\overline{XY}$ and $\overline{AB}$? Hide the circle.

c. Side $\overline{XZ}$ in $\triangle XYZ$ will be congruent to side $\overline{AC}$ in $\triangle ABC$. To create $\overline{XZ}$ we first find the possible locations of point Z from X. Use the **Circle By Center+Radius** command to construct a circle with radius $\overline{AC}$ and center X. What does this circle represent?

d. Side $\overline{YZ}$ in $\triangle XYZ$ will be congruent to $\overline{BC}$. To create $\overline{YZ}$ we find the possible locations of point Z from Y. Use the **Circle By Center+Radius** command to construct a circle with radius $\overline{BC}$ and center Y.

e. There are two possible locations for point Z. Construct one of the points and label it Z. Construct $\overline{XZ}$ and $\overline{YZ}$ to complete $\triangle XYZ$. Then hide the two circles.

3. a. Measure the sides and angles of $\triangle XYZ$. How are $\triangle ABC$ and $\triangle XYZ$ related? Support your answer.

b. Change the shape and size of $\triangle ABC$. Does the relationship between the triangles change?

c. When the sides of one triangle are congruent respectively to the sides of another triangle (SSS) what appears to be true about the triangles?

Side-Angle-Side

4. Draw a new triangle, $\triangle PQR$. Measure its sides and angles.

In Exercise 5, we construct a triangle, $\triangle LMN$, that has two sides and the angle between them congruent, respectively, to two sides and the included angle in $\triangle PQR$.

5. a. Use the method from Exercises 2a and 2b to construct $\overline{LM}$ with the same measure as $\overline{PQ}$. Use the **Line** command from the **Construct** menu to construct ray LM as well. Hide the circle. Locate and label point M.

b. Next construct a copy of $\angle QPR$ with its vertex at L. To do this, first select $\angle QPR$ by selecting points Q, P, and R in that order. Then, choose **Mark Angle** under the **Transform** menu. What happens?

Select point L. Choose **Mark Center** from the **Transform** menu. Create a copy of $\angle QPR$ by selecting $\overleftrightarrow{LM}$ and rotating it using the **Rotate** command from the **Transform** menu. When the dialogue box appears, choose **By Marked Angle**. What happens?

Move point R to help identify which angle is congruent to $\angle QPR$. Place a point U on the rotated line to create $\angle MLU$ so it appears to be congruent to $\angle QPR$. Measure $\angle MLU$ and $\angle QPR$ to be sure they are congruent.

c. Construct $\overline{LN}$ congruent to side $\overline{PR}$ in $\triangle PQR$ by constructing a circle with center L and side $\overline{PR}$ as a radius. Locate and label point N so that $\triangle LMN$ contains $\angle MLU$. Construct point N at the intersection of the circle and the rotated line so that $\angle MLN \cong \angle QPR$. (If it's not clear which intersection to use, try dragging point R.)

d. Complete the triangle by constructing segments $\overline{LN}$ and $\overline{MN}$. Hide the two lines and the circle.

6. a. How are $\triangle LMN$ and $\triangle PQR$ related? Justify your answer.

b. Change the shape and size of $\triangle PQR$ Does the relationship between the triangles change? Drag $\triangle LMN$ on top of $\triangle PQR$ so that corresponding parts of $\triangle LMN$ fall on top of $\triangle PQR$ How do they compare?

c. When two sides and the included angle in one triangle are congruent to two sides and the included angle in another triangle (SAS), what appears to be true about the triangles?

Side-Side-Angle

7. a. In a new window, draw a new scalene triangle, $\triangle TUV$. Measure its sides and angles. We will attempt to construct a triangle, $\triangle DEF$, that is congruent to $\triangle TUV$ using two sides and a non-included angle. Adjust the triangle so that $TU > UV$.

   b. Construct $\overline{DE}$ with the same length as side $\overline{TU}$. Use points D and E to construct ray DE.

   c. Construct the set of possible locations for F so that $\overline{EF}$ will have the same length as side $\overline{UV}$.

   d. Construct a copy of $\angle UTV$ with its vertex at D. Remember to first select $\angle UTV$. Then, under the **Transform** menu, choose **Mark Angle**.

      Select point D. Under the **Transform** menu, choose **Mark Center**. Finally, create the copy of $\angle UTV$ by selecting $\overleftrightarrow{DE}$ and rotating it using the **Rotate** command.

   e. There should be two possible places where F could be located. Label one of them F and the other one G. Draw $\overline{EF}$ and $\overline{EG}$. Hide any remaining circles.

      Are $\triangle DEF$ and $\triangle TUV$ congruent? Explain.

      Are $\triangle DEG$ and $\triangle TUV$ congruent? Explain

      Are $\triangle DEF$ and $\triangle DEG$ congruent? Explain.

   f. If we know that two sides and a non-included angle in one triangle are congruent to two sides and a non-included angle in another triangle (SSA), is that enough information to determine that the triangles are congruent? Explain.

GSP Lab 5: Circles and Chords (Section 10-1)

Drawing and Bisecting Chords

In this lab we explore some relationships among circles, radii, and chords.

1. a. Construct a large circle by drawing a segment and a point, then using the **Circle By Center+Radius** command. Then place two points on the circle by selecting the circle and using **Point On Circle** from the **Construct** menu.

   b. Construct the segment joining the two points. A segment joining two points on a circle is a **chord** of the circle. Move one end of the chord so the chord is clearly visible.

   c. Construct a **perpendicular bisector** of the chord; that is, a line that bisects the chord and is perpendicular to it, by performing the following steps.
- Select the segment. Choose **Midpoint** from the **Construct** menu.
- Select the segment and the midpoint. Choose **Perpendicular Line** from the **Construct** menu. What happens?

   d. What happens if you move one of the points on the circle? What happens if you change the radius of the circle?

   e. Create another chord on the circle and construct its perpendicular bisector. What do you notice about the intersection of the two perpendicular bisectors?

   f. Change the location of the chords and the size of the circle. How does this affect the intersection of the two perpendicular bisectors?

Constructing a Circle Circumscribed about a Triangle

2. a. Draw a triangle. Construct the perpendicular bisectors of two sides of the triangle.

   b. Construct a point at the intersection of the two perpendicular bisectors.

   c. Draw a segment from the intersection point to one of the vertices of the triangle.

FIGURE AIII-5

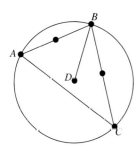

d. Construct a circle that has the point of intersection of the perpendicular bisectors as its center and the segment created in Part (c) as a radius as shown in Figure AIII-5.

e. Describe the relationship between the triangle and the circle.

f. Move the vertices of the triangle to change its shape and size. How does this affect the relationship between the circle and the triangle?

g. If we were to construct the perpendicular bisector of the third side of the triangle, would it intersect the other two? If so, where? If not, why not?

3. a. Create three noncollinear points. Construct a single circle that contains them.

   b. Describe how the circle was found and how this relates to Exercise 2.

GSP Lab 6: Split the Sides (Section 10-4)

1. a. Start with a new sketch. Draw $\triangle ABC$. Construct a point M on $\overline{AB}$.

   b. Construct a segment $\overline{MN}$ such that $\overline{MN}$ is parallel to $\overline{AC}$ and N is on $\overline{BC}$, as in Figure AIII-6.

FIGURE AIII-6

c. Measure $\overline{BM}$, $\overline{BN}$, $\overline{BA}$, and $\overline{BC}$ What is true about the ratios $\dfrac{BM}{BA}$ and $\dfrac{BN}{BC}$?

d. Drag point M to a new position. What is true about the ratios $\dfrac{BM}{BA}$ and $\dfrac{BN}{BC}$?

2. What are the ratios $\dfrac{BM}{BA}$ and $\dfrac{BN}{BC}$ when M is the midpoint of $\overline{AB}$?

3. a. Drag B to form a new triangle. What is true about the ratios $\dfrac{BM}{BA}$ and $\dfrac{BN}{BC}$?

   b. Drag point M to a new position. What is true about the ratios?

4. a. Measure $\overline{MN}$ and $\overline{AC}$. How does the ratio $\dfrac{MN}{AC}$ compare to the ratios $\dfrac{BM}{BA}$ and $\dfrac{BN}{BC}$?

   b. Drag B to form a new triangle. Now how do the ratios in Part (a) compare?

5. What seems to be true when a segment intersects two sides of a triangle and is parallel to the third side?

FIGURE AIII-7

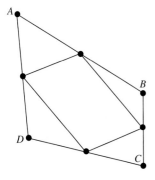

6. What can you conclude about $\triangle ABC$ and $\triangle MBN$? Justify your answer.

GSP Lab 7: Mysterious Midpoints (Section 10-4)

1. a. Start with four points that will form the vertices of a convex quadrilateral. Draw the quadrilateral.

   b. Construct the midpoints of the sides of the quadrilateral and connect the midpoints to form a new polygon as shown in Figure AIII-7.

   c. What kind of quadrilateral is the new polygon? Why?

   d. What happens when you change the shape of the original quadrilateral?

Repeat Exercise 1 starting with four points that are the vertices of

2. a rectangle.
3. a square.
4. a rhombus.
5. a kite.

GSP Lab 8: Areas of Polygons (Section 11-2)

REMEMBER Whenever possible, use a command from the **Construct** menu to define objects.

1. Start with a new sketch. Choose **Preferences** from the **Edit** menu and make sure that the *Distance Unit* is cm and the *Precision* is set to hundredths for both distance and scalars.
2. Complete the following steps to construct a rectangle with a line containing one side shown in Figure AIII-8.

FIGURE AIII-8

   a. Draw a horizontal segment $\overline{AB}$.
   b. Construct lines through A and B perpendicular to $\overline{AB}$.
   c. Construct a point C on the line through A and construct a line through C parallel to $\overline{AB}$. Construct the point of intersection of this line and the vertical line through B. Label the point D.
   d. Hide the two vertical lines and complete the rectangle by constructing segments $\overline{AC}$, $\overline{BD}$, and $\overline{CD}$.
   e. Show the label for $\overline{AB}$ and change it to b for *base*. Show the label for $\overline{AC}$ and change it to h for *height*. Measure the lengths of b and h.
3. In this exercise, we review how to find the area of a rectangle.
   a. Choose **Show Grid** from the **Graph** menu. Hide the two axes and two new points. Choose **Snap Points** from the **Graph** menu. Drag A and B so that they snap to points on the grid, making $\overline{AB}$ horizontal. The length b should be a whole number.
   b. Drag C so that $\overleftrightarrow{CD}$ passes through grid points. C won't snap to the grid, but h should be very close to a whole number.
   c. Count the number of squares in the rectangle. How does the number of squares appear to be related to b and h?
   d. Use **Calculate** from the **Measure** menu to create an algebraic expression in terms of b and h that gives the area of the rectangle. Check that the expression works by dragging A, B, and C to form a rectangle with a different height and base and counting the number of square units as in Part (c).
4. Now we investigate the area of a parallelogram using the sketch from part (3).
   a. Use **Point On Parallel Line** from the **Construct** menu to place a point G on $\overleftrightarrow{CD}$. Then construct $\overline{AG}$.
   b. Construct a line through B parallel to $\overline{AG}$. Construct the point where this line intersects $\overleftrightarrow{CD}$ and label it H. Hide $\overleftrightarrow{BH}$ and construct $\overline{BH}$. Measure AG and BH.

    c. Construct the polygon interior *AGHB* by selecting the vertices of the parallelogram in order and then choosing **Quadrilateral Interior** from the **Construct** menu.

    d. As you move point *G*, what measures in the sketch change? What measures stay the same?

    e. How are the heights of the parallelogram and the rectangle related? How are the lengths of their bases related?

    f. Measure the area of the parallelogram by selecting its interior and then choosing **Area** from the **Measure** menu.

    g. How does the area of the parallelogram change as we drag *G*? How does the area of the parallelogram compare to the area of the rectangle?

    h. Write a rule for finding the area of a parallelogram. Move points *A* and *C* to check that the rule works for parallelograms with different heights and bases.

5. Now we investigate the area of a triangle.

    a. In a new sketch, draw two segments $\overline{IJ}$ and $\overline{JK}$. Construct a line through points *I* and *K*. Construct the altitude $\overline{JL}$ from *J* to $\overleftrightarrow{IK}$ as shown in Figure AIII-9(a).

    b. Construct $\overline{IK}$. Show the label for $\overline{IK}$ and change it to *base*. Show the label for $\overline{JL}$ and change it to *height*. Measure the height and base of △*IJK*.

    c. Construct the midpoint *M* of $\overline{JK}$. Select *M* and choose **Mark Center** from the **Transform** menu.

    d. Select *I*, $\overline{IJ}$, and $\overline{IK}$. Then choose **Rotate** from the **Transform** menu and rotate the selected objects by a fixed angle of 180° to obtain a figure as in Figure AIII-9(b).

    e. What kind of quadrilateral is *IJI′K*? Does the shape change when we drag the vertices of △*IJK*?

    f. How are the heights of △*IJK* and quadrilateral *IJI′K* related? How are the lengths of their bases related?

    g. What is the formula for the area of quadrilateral *IJI′K*?

    h. How does the area of △*IJK* compare to the area of quadrilateral *IJI′K* as shown in Figure AIII-9(c) Check the answer by constructing their interiors and measuring their areas.

    i. Use the results from Parts (f–h) to write a rule for finding the area of a triangle. Record the rule in a caption.

FIGURE AIII-9

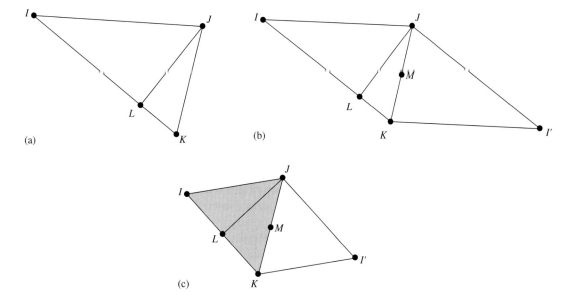

(a)   (b)   (c)

6. Next, we investigate the area of a trapezoid.
   a. In a new sketch, construct a trapezoid with exactly one pair of parallel sides. Label the parallel sides b_1 and b_2 by typing "b[1]" and "b[2]" for the labels.
   b. Construct a segment that is perpendicular to the parallel sides and has its endpoints on them. This is an altitude of the trapezoid. Label it a for *altitude*.
   c. Construct the midpoint of one of the nonparallel sides and rotate the trapezoid 180° about this point. What kind of shape is formed?
   d. What is the length of a base of this doubled trapezoid?
   e. Based on the observations, write a formula for the area A of a trapezoid using b_1 for the length of one base, b_2 for the length of the other base, and a for the altitude.

GSP Lab 9: Right on Pythagoras (Section 11-3)

In this lab, we explore the relationships among the sides and angles in a triangle. To make your work easier we create a **custom tool**.

1. When we plan to repeat a complex procedure several times, *Sketchpad* allows us to record steps in a **custom tool**. Once the tool has been recorded, we can use it to repeat the procedure when we need it. In this exercise, we create a custom tool for constructing a square with a given side.
   a. Draw a segment $\overline{AB}$.
   b. Select one endpoint of $\overline{AB}$. Then choose **Mark Center** from the **Transform** menu.
   c. Select $\overline{AB}$ and the other endpoint of the segment. From the **Transform** menu, choose **Rotate** . . . Enter 90 in the dialogue box.
   d. Select the new endpoint of the newest segment and mark this point as the center.
   e. Select the newest segment and its other endpoint. Rotate them 90 degrees.
   f. Construct the remaining side of the square.
   g. Select the entire figure (four segments and four points). Press and hold the **Custom Tools** tool (the bottom tool in the Toolbox) and choose **Create New Tool** from the menu that appears. Name the tool "Square."
   h. Press and hold the **Custom Tools** tool. You should see the new tool, **Square**, listed in the menu that appears. We'll use the tool later in the activity.

FIGURE AIII-10

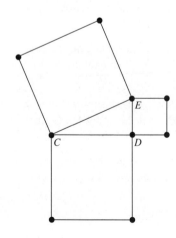

2. Construct a right triangle, $\triangle CDE$, with the right angle at D. (*Note:* We should be able to change the size and shape of $\triangle CDE$ by dragging its vertices, but $\angle D$ should always be a right angle.)
   a. The longest side of a right triangle is the **hypotenuse**. Which side of $\triangle CDE$ is the hypotenuse?
   b. The other two sides are the **legs** of the right triangle. Name the legs of $\triangle CDE$.

In the next exercise, we use the tool you created in Exercise 1 to construct a square on each side of $\triangle CDE$, as shown in Figure AIII-10. The sides of each square should be congruent to the side of the triangle on which it is constructed.

3. a. Choose the **Custom Tools** tool by clicking its icon in the Toolbox. This activates the most recently created or used tool—in this case, **Square**.
   b. Click on points C and E in the sketch. A square is constructed on $\overline{CE}$. (If the square is constructed toward the inside of $\triangle CDE$, rather than outside, choose **Undo Square** from the **Edit** menu, then redo this step, clicking on C and E in the reverse order as before.)

   c. To see what's going on under the hood, choose **Show Script View** from the **Custom Tools** menu. Notice that two points are listed as Givens, meaning that the entire construction is derived from two initial points. With the Script View still open deselect everything in the sketch, then select points E and D. Two buttons appear at the bottom of the script: Next Step and All Steps. Click Next Step repeatedly to see the construction played out step-by-step.

   d. Use the **Square** tool to construct a square on the remaining side of $\triangle CDE$.

   e. Move the vertices of the triangle. What happens to the constructed squares?

4. a. Create the interior of each square and measure its area. How is the area of each square related to the length of the side of the triangle on which it is constructed?

   b. Drag the vertices of $\triangle CDE$ and look for a relationship among the areas of the three squares. Use a calculator to confirm your conjecture.

   c. Complete the following statement

     In a right triangle, if a and b are the lengths of the legs and c is the length of the hypotenuse, then . . .

     This is the **Pythagorean Theorem**.

5. a. Next we explore how the angle measure affects the length of the side opposite the angle. Create a non-right triangle, $\triangle FGH$. Measure each of its angles and the length of each of its sides.

   b. Drag the vertices of $\triangle FGH$ to create several other triangles. How does the length of the side opposite the angle with the greatest measure compare to the length of the other sides?

   c. How does the length of the side opposite the angle with the least measure compare to the length of the other sides?

6. a. Adjust the triangle so that $\overline{FG}$ has the greatest length. Construct squares on the sides of $\triangle FGH$ as in Exercise 3.

   b. Create the interior of each square and measure its area. Then compute the sum of the areas of the two smaller squares.

   c. Examine several triangles in which $\overline{FG}$ is the longest side and the area of the square on $\overline{FG}$ is less than the sum of the areas of the two smaller squares. What type of triangle is formed?

   d. Repeat Part (c) for several triangles in which $\overline{FG}$ is the longest side and the area of the square on $\overline{FG}$ is greater than the sum of the areas of the two smaller squares.

   e. Repeat Part (c) for several triangles in which $\overline{FG}$ is the longest side and the area of the square on $\overline{FG}$ is equal to the sum of the areas of the two smaller squares.

   f. Use the results from Parts (c–e). Complete the following statements.

     *If the square of the length of the longest side of a triangle is **greater than** the sum of the squares of the lengths of the two shorter sides, then the triangle is a(n) _____ triangle.*

     *If the square of the length of the longest side of a triangle is **less than** the sum of the squares of the lengths of the two shorter sides, then the triangle is a(n) _____ triangle.*

     *If the square of the length of the longest side of a triangle is **equal to** to the sum of the squares of the lengths of the two shorter sides, then the triangle is a(n) _____ triangle.*

   This last statement is the **converse** of the Pythagorean Theorem.

7. a. Construct a right triangle, $\triangle XYZ$.
   b. Construct a regular hexagon on each side of $\triangle XYZ$. The sides of each hexagon should be congruent to the side of the triangle on which it is constructed.
   c. Create the interior of each hexagon and measure its area. Then compute the sum of the areas of the two smaller hexagons. Drag the vertices of $\triangle XYZ$ and compare the sum to the area of the hexagon on the hypotenuse. What do you observe? How is this related to the Pythagorean Theorem?

GSP Lab 10: Slides, Flips, and Turns (Sections 12-1 and 12-2)

In this lab, we study transformational or "motion" geometry. A *transformation* is a function that changes a figure's size, shape, or position.

Reflections

One such transformation is a *reflection*. A reflection moves a figure by flipping it over a line. This *reflecting line* represents a mirror over which objects are reflected.

1. a. Choose **Preferences** from the **Edit** menu. On the Text panel, choose **For All New Points** so that points are labeled when they're created.
   b. Draw $\triangle ABC$ and measure its sides and angles.
   c. Draw a line m anywhere on the sketch and select it. Choose **Mark Mirror** from the **Transform** menu.
   d. Select $\triangle ABC$. Then choose **Reflect** from the **Transform** menu to reflect $\triangle ABC$ in line m. $\triangle A'B'C'$ is the image of $\triangle ABC$ under the reflection. The images of points of A, B, and C are A', B', and C', respectively.
2. a. Measure the angles and sides of $\triangle A'B'C'$. How are $\triangle ABC$ and $\triangle A'B'C'$ related?
   b. Change the shape of $\triangle ABC$. Does the relationship still hold?
   c. Change the location of the reflecting line m. Does the relationship still hold?
3. a. Imagine tracing $\triangle ABC$ from A to B to C and back to A. In what direction—clockwise or counterclockwise—would we move?
   b. Now imagine tracing $\triangle A'B'C'$ from A' to B' to C' and back to A'. In what direction would we move?
   c. In Parts (a) and (b), we examined the *orientations* of $\triangle ABC$ and $\triangle A'B'C'$. Are the orientations of the two triangles the same?
4. a. Construct the segments joining each vertex of $\triangle ABC$ to is image. How does the reflecting line seem to be related to each of these segments? (The segments can be colored using the **Color** command from the **Display** menu.)
   b. Find the appropriate measurements to verify the conjecture from Part (a).
5. Use the results from Exercises 1–4 to answer the following questions.
   a. How are the measure of an angle and the measure of its reflection related?
   b. How are the length of a segment and the length of its reflection related?
   c. How are a polygon and its reflection related?
   d. How are the orientations of an object and its image under a reflection related?
   e. How is the reflecting line related to the segment joining a point and its reflection?

Translations

Another transformation is a *translation*. A translation moves every point the same distance in the same direction. The distance and direction are often indicated by a vector.

6. a. Draw a quadrilateral *HIJK* and measure its sides and angles.

   b. Draw $\overline{XY}$ to represent the vector. Select the endpoints of the segment in the order *X, Y*. The order indicates the direction an object is to be moved—in this case, from *X* to *Y*. Choose **Mark Vector** under the **Transform** menu.

   c. To translate quadrilateral *HIJK* the distance and direction indicated by vector *XY*, select quadrilateral *HIJK* and choose **Translate** from the **Transform** menu. A dialogue box will appear. Choose **Marked**. The quadrilateral *H′I′J′K′* that results is the translated image of quadrilateral *HIJK*.

7. a. Measure the sides and angles of quadrilateral *H′I′J′K′*. How are quadrilaterals *HIJK* and *H′I′J′K′* related?

   b. Change the size and shape of quadrilateral *HIJK*. Does the relationship still seem to hold?

   c. Change the length and direction of the translation vector *XY*. Does the relationship change?

8. a. Construct the segments joining each vertex of quadrilateral *HIJK* to its image in quadrilateral *H′I′J′K′*. What appears to be true about these segments?

   b. Find the appropriate measurements to verify the conjecture in Part (a).

   c. Do an object and its translation image have the same orientation?

Rotations

A *rotation* moves a figure by turning it clockwise or counterclockwise about a fixed point. The fixed point is the *center of rotation*. An angle is often used to indicate the amount of rotation that is to take place.

9. a. Draw a triangle $\triangle PQR$ and measure its sides and angles.

   b. Create a point *O* to represent the center of rotation. With point *O* selected, choose **Mark Center** from the **Transform** menu.

   c. Create $\angle STU$ to indicate the amount of rotation. Select the points of the angle in the same order it could be measured. Choose **Mark Angle** from the **Transform** menu.

   d. To rotate $\triangle PQR$ around *O*, select $\triangle PQR$ and choose **Rotate** from the **Transform** menu. A dialogue box will appear. Choose **Marked Angle**. The triangle $\triangle P′Q′R′$ that results is the image of $\triangle PQR$ under the rotation.

10. a. Measure the angles and sides of $\triangle P′Q′R′$. How are $\triangle PQR$ and $\triangle P′Q′R′$ related?

   b. Does the relationship still hold when the shape of $\triangle PQR$ is changed? When the size of $\angle STU$ is changed?

11. a. Construct the segments joining each vertex of $\triangle PQR$ to the center of rotation, *O*. Now construct the segments joining each vertex of the image $\triangle P′Q′R′$ to the center of rotation.

   b. Three angles are formed. Each has its vertex at *O*, the center of rotation, one side passing through a vertex of $\triangle PQR$ and its other side passing through the corresponding vertex of $\triangle P′Q′R′$. What seems to be true about these three angles?

   c. How do these angles appear to compare to $\angle STU$?

   d. Find the appropriate measurements to verify the conjectures.

   e. Do an object and its image under a rotation seem to have the same orientation? Explain.

GSP Lab 11: Other Transformations (Sections 12-2 and 12-3)

If we combine a translation with a reflection, the result is a glide reflection.

Glide Reflections

1. **a.** Choose **Preferences** from the **Edit** menu. On the Text panel, choose **For All New Points**.
   b. Draw $\triangle ABC$ and a translation vector $\overline{DE}$.
   c. Select the endpoints of the segment in the order *D, E* and choose **Mark Vector** from the **Transform** menu.
   d. Construct a line *n* parallel to $\overline{DE}$, select it, and choose **Mark Mirror** from the **Transform** menu.
   e. Translate $\triangle ABC$ by the marked vector $\overline{DE}$ and then reflect its translation image over line *n*. Hide the intermediate triangle, $\triangle A'B'C'$, so that only the first and last triangles are showing. The last triangle, $\triangle A''B''C''$, is the image of $\triangle ABC$ under the **glide reflection**. The images of points *A, B,* and *C* are *A'', B'', C''*, respectively.
   f. Change the length and direction of $\overline{DE}$ and the position of line *n*. How do these changes affect the transformation?
   g. Now we'll create a custom tool to quickly perform the glide reflection. Select, in order, line *n* and points *D, E, A,* and *A''*. Choose **Create New Tool** from the **Custom Tools** menu. Call the tool "Glide Reflect." Check **Show Script View** before clicking OK. In the script, double-click the first *Given*. Check **Automatically Match Sketch Object**, and click **OK**. (This saves you from having to click on this particular given each time.) Do the same for the next two givens, leaving only the *pre-image* as a **Given**. Close the script.
   h. Choose the **Custom Tools** tool to activate the **Glide Reflect** tool. Click on the three sides of $\triangle A''B''C''$ to apply the glide reflection to them.
   i. Repeat the transformation on the newest image triangle two more times. Why does it make sense to call this transformation a glide reflection?
   j. Construct segments $\overline{AB''}$, $\overline{BB''}$, and $\overline{CC''}$ and find their midpoints. What appears to be true about the midpoints?

In the next exercise, we investigate a *dilation*. A dilation uses a fixed point and a scale factor to transform a figure. The fixed point is the *center of dilation*. The scale factor is a ratio that indicates the amount of dilation.

Dilations or Size Transformations (Section 12-3)

2. **a.** Draw $\triangle FGH$ and measure its sides and angles.
   b. Create a point *O* to represent the center of dilation. Then choose **Mark Center** from the **Transform** menu.
   c. Select $\triangle FGH$ and choose **Dilate** from the **Transform** menu. A dialogue box will appear. Choose **By Fixed Ratio**. Enter 2.5 to 1 for the scale factor. $\triangle F'G'H'$ is the image of $\triangle FGH$ under the dilation. The images of points of *F, G,* and *H* are *F', G',* and *H'*, respectively.
   d. Measure the sides and angles of $\triangle F'G'H'$. How are $\triangle FGH$ and $\triangle F'G'H'$ related? Why?
   e. Change the shape of $\triangle FGH$. Does the relationships still hold?
   f. Change the location of point *O*. Does the relationship change?

g. Find the ratio of the length of each side of $\triangle FGH$ to the length of the corresponding side in $\triangle F'G'H'$. How do the ratios compare to the scale factor of the dilation?

h. Do an object and its image under a dilation have the same orientation? Explain.

i. Construct rays $\overrightarrow{OF}$, $\overrightarrow{OG}$, and $\overrightarrow{OH}$. What other point does each ray appear to pass through?

j. How are the distances OF and OF' related? OG and OG'? OH and OH'?

3. Repeat Exercise 2 (a–c, g, i, and j) using a different scale factor than 2.5 to 1.

ONGOING ASSESSMENT A-III

The following problems are suggested for further investigation using GSP. Problems 1–4 are step-by-step activities, and Problems 5–10 are open-ended problems.

1. Inscribing a Circle in a Triangle (Section 10-3)

Steps to Proceed

a. Construct any triangle.

b. Construct a bisector of one angle of the triangle using **Angle Bisector** from the **Construct** menu.

c. Construct a point on the angle bisector with the **Construct** menu command **Point On Bisector**. Construct perpendicular segments from the point to the sides of the angle using the **Perpendicular Line** and **Intersection** commands from the **Construct** menu. (You may need to move the point toward the bisector vertex to do this.)

d. Measure the lengths of the perpendicular segments using the **Measure** menu.

e. Move the point along the angle bisector by clicking the mouse pointer on it and dragging it along the bisector. As the point is dragged, observe the measures shown.

f. Make a conjecture about any observed results.

incircle of the triangle   **g.** Construct the **incircle of the triangle**. The incircle is the circle that is inside the triangular region and is tangent to each of the sides of the triangle. The point at which the three angle bisectors intersect is the center of the incircle. The radius is the length of the perpendicular segment from the center to one of the sides.

2. Angles in Circles (Section 11-2)

Some angles with vertices on a circle may be related to angles with vertices at the circle's center. This investigation explores such a relationship.

Steps to Proceed

a. Draw a circle. Use the **Segment** tool to construct two segments connecting the center to points on the circle (in other words, construct two radii). The angle between these segments is called a *central angle*.

b. Measure the central angle using the **Angle** command from the **Measure** menu.

c. Construct the arc between the two circle points by selecting them and the circle, then choosing **Arc On Circle** from the **Construct** menu. With the arc selected, choose **Thick** from the **Line Width** submenu of the **Display** menu to distinguish the arc from rest of the circle. (If necessary, drag an arc endpoint until the arc is a minor arc in other words, less than half the circumference.) With the arc still selected, choose **Arc Angle** from the **Measure** menu. How does this value compare to the earlier measure?

d. Construct a third point on the circle, but not on the arc. Construct two chords, each connecting the new point with an arc endpoint. The angle between the two chords is an *inscribed angle*.

e. Measure the inscribed angle using the **Angle** command.

f. Move the vertex of the inscribed angle and make a conjecture about the relationship between the measure of an inscribed angle and the central angle that intercepts the same arc.

Extension: If the arc is a semicircle, what is the measure of the inscribed angle?

3. Ratios and Slopes (Section 10-5)
This investigation explores the relationship between slopes and the tangent ratio.

Steps to Proceed

a. Choose **Define Coordinate System** from the **Graph** menu to construct a coordinate system.

b. Construct line *OA*, where *O* is the origin and *A* is somewhere in the first quadrant.

c. Construct point *P* on the line. Construct the line through *P* and perpendicular to the *x*-axis, then construct point *X* where the new line and the *x*-axis intersect.

d. Construct $\overline{OX}$, $\overline{PX}$, and $\overline{OP}$, then measure their lengths.

e. Measure the following ratios using the **Ratio** command from the **Measure** menu:
$$\frac{OX}{OP} \quad \frac{PX}{OP} \quad \frac{PX}{OX}.$$

f. Move point *P* up and down the line. What happens to the ratios?

g. Select $\overleftrightarrow{OA}$ and choose **Slope** from the **Measure** menu. Describe the ratios in terms of slope.

Extension: Drag point *A* while continuing to observe the ratios. What are the maximum and minimum values, if any, for the ratios?

4. Symmetry (Section 12-4)
GSP can be used to design a logo for a company or for fun.

Steps to Proceed

a. Draw a line on the screen.

b. Use the **Transform** menu command **Mark Mirror** to mark the line as a mirror (reflecting line).

c. Use any GSP construction tools to design half of a logo on one side of the line.

d. Select the object (the half of the design created) to be reflected.

e. Choose the **Reflect** command from the **Transform** menu, and GSP will construct the reflected image to complete the design.

Extension: Try other features of the **Transform** menu to design a logo with three-turn or rotational symmetries. Construct one-third of the design and use the **Rotate** command to create the rest of the design.

5. a. Construct any regular polygon inscribed in a circle.

b. Connect vertices to the center.

c. Construct the height of one of the triangles formed, then measure its length.

d. Find the area of each triangle formed.

e. Find the area of the regular polygon.

    f. Find the perimeter of the regular polygon.

    g. What is the ratio of the area in (e) to the height in (c)?

6. a. Draw any circle.

    b. Inscribe a regular polygon in the circle.

    c. Find the measure of the diameter of the circle and the perimeter of the polygon. Find the ratio of the perimeter to the length of the diameter.

    d. Repeat the process using a polygon with twice as many sides.

    e. Find the ratio again.

    f. Repeat the process in (d) two more times. What do you expect the ratio to be? Why?

7. a. Inscribe a circle in a square. Find the percentage of the area in the square not covered by the circular region.

    b. Inscribe a square in a circle. Find the percentage of the area of the circle not covered by the square region.

    c. Use the answers from (a) and (b) to determine whether a square peg might fit better into a round hole or a round peg might fit better in a square hole.

8. a. Draw a rectangle with two circles inside, pictured as follows:

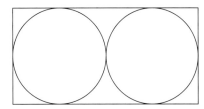

The circles are tangent to each other (touch in only 1 point) and are tangent to the sides of the rectangle. Find the percentage of the area of the rectangle not covered by the circular regions.

    b. Repeat the process in (a) using four circles.

    c. Make a conjecture about the percentage of the area of any rectangle not covered by circular regions when constructed in this manner.

9. a. Draw any polygon.

    b. Draw any line and move the line through the shape.

    c. Stop moving the line when you estimate the shape is divided into two equal areas.

    d. Find the areas of the two subshapes to check the estimate.

    e. Repeat (a) through (d) to practice your area estimation skills.

10. a. Draw any rectangle and a segment, shown as follows:

    b. Move the segment across the rectangle and estimate when 60% of the area is to the right of the segment.

    c. Measure the areas to check.

    d. Repeat steps (a) through (c) to practice area estimation skills with other percents.

—Answers to Problems—

Chapter 1

Ongoing Assessment 1-1

1. (a) **(b)**

(c) **(d)**

(e) **(f)**

2. (a) 11, 13, 15 arithmetic **(b)** 250, 300, 350 arithmetic
(c) 96, 192, 384 geometric **(d)** $10^6, 10^7, 10^8$, geometric
(e) 33, 37, 41 arithmetic **(f)** $6^3, 7^3, 8^3$ neither
3. (a) 199; $2n - 1$ **(b)** 4950; $50(n - 1)$
(c) $3 \cdot 2^{99}; 3 \cdot 2^{n-1}$ **(d)** $10^{100}; 10^n$
(e) 405; $5 + 4n$ or $9 + 4(n - 1)$ **(f)** $100^3 = 1,000,000; n^3$
4. 2, 7, 12
5. (a) Answers vary; for example, one possibility is to notice that the sum of the first n odd numbers is given by n^2; that is, $1 + 3 + 5 + 7 = 4^2 = 16$. **(b)** 324
6. 10 open and 55 black
7. (a) 30, 42, 56 **(b)** 10, 100 **(c)** $n(n + 1)$ or $n^2 + n$
8. (a) 51 **(b)** $6 + (n - 1)5$, or $5n + 1$
9. (a) 41 **(b)** $4n + 1$, or $5 + (n - 1)4$
10. (a) 10,000 **(b)** n^2
11. (a) 42 **(b)** $4n + 2$ or $6 + (n - 1)4$
12. 1200 students
13. 15 liters
14. 23rd year
15. (a) 3, 5, 9, 15, 23, 33 **(b)** 4, 6, 10, 16, 24, 34
(c) 15, 17, 21, 27, 35, 45
16. (a) 299, 447, 644 **(b)** 56, 72, 90
17. (a) 101 **(b)** 61 **(c)** 200 **(d)** 87 **(e)** 11
18. (a) 3, 6, 11, 18, 27 **(b)** 4, 9, 14, 19, 24
(c) 9, 99, 999, 9999, 99999 **(d)** 5, 8, 11, 14, 17
19. (a) 1, 1, 2, 3, 5, 8, 13, 21, 34, 55, 89, 144 **(b)** Yes; the sum of the first four terms equals the sixth term minus 1. The sum of the first five term equals the seventh term minus 1. The sum of the first six terms equals the eighth term minus 1.

(c) 143 **(d)** The sum of the first n terms equals the $(n + 2)$nd term minus 1.
20. (a) 2, 4, 6, 10, 16, 26, 42, 68, 110, 178, 288, 466
(c) 462
21. The second sequence becomes greater than the first sequence on the 12th term.
22. (a) 1, 5, 9, 13, 17, 21, ... **(b)** $4n - 3$ or $1 + (n - 1)4$
23. Two solutions are possible: 64, 128, 256, or $-64, 128, -256$.
24. 6, 5, 4, 6, 5, 4, 6, 5, 4, 6, 5

Communication

25. (a) You must produce at least one rectangle that does not have diagonals that are perpendicular. Any nonsquare rectangle will do. **(b)** You must produce two even numbers whose sum is not divisible by 4. For example $2 + 4 = 6$, and 6 is not divisible by 4.
26. You must produce at least one Montana university student who does not wear cowboy boots.
27. Answers vary; for example, if the sky has dark clouds, then you expect it to rain. This expectation is based on observations you have made.

No. A conclusion based on inductive reasoning is not certain. The conclusion is based on observation or experimentation and is not necessarily true, as can be seen in the example above. It may happen that dark clouds form and it does not rain.
28. (a) Yes. The difference between terms in the new sequence is the same as in the old sequence because a fixed number was added to each number in the sequence.
(b) Yes. If the fixed number is k, the difference between terms of the second sequence is k times the difference between terms of the first sequence. **(c)** Yes. The difference of the new sequence is the sum of the original differences.

Open-Ended

29. Answers vary; for example, two more patterns follow.

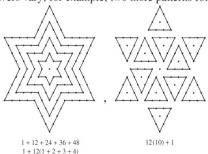

$1 + 12 + 24 + 36 + 48$
$1 + 12(1 + 2 + 3 + 4)$

$12(10) + 1$

30. Answers vary; for example, the following is an array of pentagonal numbers.

The pattern for the number of dots is 1, 5, 12, 22, 35, 51, ... The number of additional dots for each pentagon forms an arithmetic sequence with 1st term 1 and difference 3. For the 100th pentagonal number we would have $1 + 4 + 7 + 10 + 13 + 16 + . . . + 298$ additional dots, where $298 = 1 + (100 - 1)3$. Therefore, the 100th pentagonal number is $(100/2)(1 + 298) = 14,950$.

Cooperative Learning

31. **(a)** No matter what numbers are chosen, the result is always 2.
(b) Answers vary depending on whether only results from the group were used or it was proved to be true for all numbers.
(c) Answers vary; for example: *Explanation*

Pick a number.	n
Multiply by 3.	$3n$
Add 51.	$3n + 51$
Divide by 3.	$(3n + 51)/3$
	$= n + 17.$
Subtract your	$(n + 17) - n = 17.$
original number.	
The answer is 17.	

(d) Answers vary.
32. (a) 81 (b) 40 **(c)** 3^{n-1} **(d)** $1 + 3 + 3^2 + 3^3 + . . . + 3^{n-2}$

Ongoing Assessment 1-2

1. (a) 4950 **(b)** $n(n + 1)/2$ (c) 251,001
2. **(a)** 4 (b) 5 **(c)** $n - 1$
3. 12
4. 12
5. 160 miles
6. Dandy, Cory, Alabama, Bubba
7. 45
8. 18
9. $1.19
10. 275,000,000
11. (a) (i) 541×72 (ii) divide 754 by 12
(b) **(i)** 257×14 **(ii)** divide 124 by 75
12. 17 terms
13. $5,256,000
14. (a) $2^6 - 1$ **(b)** $2^n - 1$ **(c)** Answers check.
15. 12
16. $2.45

17. **(a)** 42, 55, 68, 81, 94, 107, 120, 133, 146, 159, 172, 185, 198 **(b)** 13
18. (a) 10,500 squares **(b)** $n^2 + 5n$ squares
19. **(a)** 11 **(b)** 63
20. width = 230 ft; length = 310 ft
21.

17	7	9
3	11	19
13	15	5

22. **(a)** 100,701 (b) 20,503
23. (a) Answers vary; for example, we could weigh 4 marbles against 4 marbles and then pick the heavier side. We could then weigh 2 marbles against 2 marbles and pick the heavier side. Finally we could weigh 1 marble against 1 marble and the heavier one is the one we are looking for.
(b) We could divide the marbles into groups of 3, 3, and 2 and weigh 3 marbles against 3 marbles. If they balance, only one more weighing is necessary to determine the heavier of the two that were not weighed. If they do not balance, select any two from the heavier side and weigh one against one. If they balance, the heavy one is the one that was not weighed. If they do not balance the heavy one is the one that goes down.
24. **(a)** 25,502,500 **(b)** $\dfrac{n^2(1 + n)^2}{4}$
25. (a) If both numbers were less than or equal to 9, then their product would be less than or equal to $9 \cdot 9 = 81$, which is not greater than 82. **(b)** Follow the same argument as in (a): 81 is not greater than 81.
26. (a) 204 squares **(b)** The number of squares is more than doubled. It is now 1496.

Communication

27. Answers vary, but the discussion should point out that the two methods give the same answer and that the advantage of this method is that it works with an even or odd number of terms.
28. Answers vary; for example, if these nine numbers are to be used in a magic square, then the sum in each of the three columns must be the same and must be a natural number. The natural number must be 1/3 of the sum of all nine numbers. However $1 + 3 + 4 + 5 + 6 + 7 + 8 + 9 + 10 = 53$ and $53/3 = 17 \, 2/3$, which is not a natural number. Therefore these numbers cannot be used for a magic square.

Open-Ended

29. The answers will vary but should include some way to measure the number of breaths in a minute and then multiply the number by 60, then by 24, and then by 365.
30. Answers vary; for example, any of the investigation problems in this section are examples of problems that could be approached with the discussed strategy.

31. Answers may vary from when students have no idea to the point that they are getting closer to an answer by guessing closer and closer.

Cooperative Learning

32. Answers vary; for example, if the average reach of people in your group was 1.8 m, then it would take $40,000,000/1.8 = 22,222,222$ people.
33. (a) Play second and make sure that the sum showing when you hand the calculator to your opponent is a multiple of 3. (b) Play first and press 4. After that, make sure that each time you hand the calculator to your opponent it displays 1 less than a multiple of 5. (c) Play first and press 3. After that, make sure that each time you hand the calculator to your opponent it displays 3 more than a multiple of 10. (d) Play second. Make sure the calculator displays a multiple of 3 each time you hand it to your opponent. (e) Play second. Make sure the calculator displays a multiple of 4 each time you hand it to your opponent. (f) Play first and subtract 3. Then make sure the calculator displays a multiple of 10 each time.

Review Problems

34. (a) 21, 24, 27 (b) 243, 2, 729
35. $22 + (n - 1)10$, or $10n + 12$
36. 21 terms
37. 903
38. (a) The digits in the product always sum to 9. The tens digit in the answer is always one less than the number that is multiplied by 9. This pattern works with the other exercises presented. (b) The pattern can be used to check if you remembered the product of a digit and 9 correctly.

Ongoing Assessment 1-3

1. (a) $20 + 25h$ (b) $175d$ (c) $3x + 3$
(d) $q \cdot 2^n$ (e) $40 - 3t$ (f) $4s + 15,000$
(g) $3x + 6$ (h) $3m$
2. (a) $P = 0.04E$ (b) $E = 25P$ (c) 5.4 lb (d) 2500 lb
3. $d \cong 0.607165g$ or approximately $0.61g$
4. (a) 220 (b) $n(2n + 2)$, or $2n(n + 1)$
5. $89.6°$
6. (a) $K = 273.15 + C$ (b) $C = K - 273.15$
7. (a) $P = 8t$ (b) $P = 15 + 10(t - 1)$ (c) $P = 20 + 10t$
(d) $C = 300 + 4n$ (e) $C = 30 + 0.35m$
8. (a) $x = 18$ (b) $x = {}^-18$
9. If x is any number, then the teacher's instructions were
$\left(\dfrac{3x + 49}{7} - 7\right) \div 3$. This expression is equivalent to
$\left(\dfrac{3x + 49}{7} - 7\right) \div 3 = \dfrac{3x}{7} \cdot \dfrac{1}{3} = \dfrac{x}{7}$. Thus to tell the value of x,
the teacher multiplies the answer $\dfrac{x}{7}$ by 7.
10. Rick has \$100 and David has \$300.

11. Method will vary depending on student; 2
12. Method will vary depending on student; a butterfly costs \$7 and a rose costs \$4.
13. 524 student tickets
14. Eldest \$30,000; middle, \$24,000; youngest, \$10,000

Communication

15. Both are correct. For the first student, x is the first of the three consecutive integers. The second chose x to be the second of the three consecutive integers.
16. (a) $5x$ (b) The sum of any five consecutive natural numbers if 5 times the middle number.

Open-Ended

17. Answers vary. For example:
(a) Take any number, subtract 3, multiply by 4, add 8, and divide by 4. (b) Take any number, subtract 20, divide by 6, add 3, multiply by 3, and add 1. (c) Take any positive number and divide it by its square root.

Cooperative Learning

18. Answers vary.

Review Problems

19. (a) 35, 42, 49 (b) 1, 16, 1
20. $20n - 8$
21. 21 terms
22. 9 ways

Ongoing Assessment 1-4

1. (a) False statement (b) Not a statement (c) False statement (d) Not a statement (e) Not a statement (f) Not a statement (g) True statement (h) Not a statement (i) Not a statement (j) Not a statement
2. (a) There exists a natural number x such that $x + 8 = 11$. (b) For all x, $x + 0 = x$. (c) There exists a natural number x such that $x^2 = 4$. (d) No natural number x exists such that $x + 1 = x + 2$. (e) For all natural numbers x, $x + 3 = 3 + x$. (f) There exists a natural number x such that $3(x + 2) = 12$. (g) For all natural numbers x, $5x + 4x = 9x$.
3. (a) For every natural number, x, $x + 8 = 11$. (b) No natural number x satisfies $x + 0 = x$. (c) Every natural number x satisfies $x^2 = 4$. (d) There exists a natural number x such that $x + 1 = x + 2$. (e) There is no natural number x such that $x + 3 = 3 + x$. (f) For every natural number x, $3(x + 2) = 12$. (g) There is no natural number x such that $5x + 4x = 9x$.
4. (a) This book does not have 500 pages.
(b) Six is greater than or equal to 8, or 6 is not less than 8.
(c) $3 \cdot 5 \neq 15$. (d) No people have blond hair.
(e) Some dogs do not have four legs. (f) All cats have nine lives. (g) Not all squares are rectangles, or some squares are not rectangles. (h) All rectangles are squares.

5. (a)

p	$\sim p$	$\sim(\sim p)$
T	F	T
F	T	F

(b)

p	$\sim p$	$p \vee \sim p$	$p \wedge \sim p$
T	F	T	F
F	T	T	F

(c) Yes   **(d)** No

6. (a) $q \wedge r$ **(b)** $r \vee \sim q$ **(c)** $\sim(q \wedge r)$ **(d)** $\sim q$

7. (a) False   **(b)** True   **(c)** True   **(d)** False
(e) False   **(f)** True   **(g)** False   **(h)** False   **(i)** False
(j) False

8. (a) False   **(b)** False   **(c)** True   **(d)** True
(e) False   **(f)** True   **(g)** False   **(h)** True
(i) True   **(j)** True

9. (a) No   **(b)** Yes   **(c)** No   **(d)** Yes

10.

p	q	$\sim p$	$\sim q$	$\sim p \vee \sim q$
T	T	F	F	F
T	F	F	T	T
F	T	T	F	T
F	F	T	T	T

11. (a) Either today is not Wednesday, or the month is not June.   **(b)** Yesterday I either did not eat breakfast or did not watch television.   **(c)** It is not true that it is both raining and the month is July.

12. (a) $p \to q$ **(b)** $\sim p \to q$ **(c)** $p \to \sim q$
(d) $p \to q$ **(e)** $\sim q \to \sim p$ **(f)** $q \leftrightarrow p$

13. (a) Converse: If $2x = 10$, then $x = 5$. Inverse: If $x \neq 5$, then $2x \neq 10$. Contrapositive: If $2x \neq 10$, then $x \neq 5$.
(b) Converse: If you do not like mathematics, then you do not like this book. Inverse: If you like this book, then you like mathematics. Contrapositive: If you like mathematics, then you like this book.   **(c)** Converse: If you have cavities, then you do not use Ultra Brush toothpaste. Inverse: If you use Ultra Brush toothpaste, then you do not have cavities. Contrapositive: If you do not have cavities, then you use Ultra Brush toothpaste.   **(d)** Converse: If your grades are high, then you are good at logic. Inverse: If you are not good at logic, then your grades are not high. Contrapositive: If your grades are not high, then you are not good at logic.
14. No
15. (a) No   **(b)** Yes   **(c)** No
16. If a number is not a multiple of 4, then it is not a multiple of 8. (Contrapositive)
17. (a) Valid   **(b)** Valid   **(c)** Valid   **(d)** Invalid
18. (a) Helen is poor.   **(b)** Some freshmen are intelligent.
(c) If I study for the final, then I will look for a teaching job.
(d) There exist triangles that are isosceles.
19. (a) If a figure is a square, then it is a rectangle.
(b) If a number is an integer, then it is a rational number.

(c) If a polygon has exactly three sides, then it is a triangle.
(d) If it rains, then it is cloudy.
20. $\sim(p \vee q)$ is equivalent to $\sim p \wedge \sim q$, and $\sim(p \wedge q)$ is equivalent to $\sim p \vee \sim q$.

Communication

21. (a) p: Mary's little lamb follows her to school.
q: The lamb's appearance in school breaks the rules.
r: Mary will be sent home.
Then $p \to (r \wedge q)$.
(b) p: Jack is nimble.
q: Jack is quick.
r: Jack jumps over the candlestick.
Then $\sim(p \wedge q) \to \sim r$.
(c) p: The apple hit Isaac Newton.
q: The laws of gravity would have been discovered.
Then $\sim p \to \sim q$.

Open-Ended

22. Answers vary.

Cooperative Learning

23. Answers vary.
24. "Textbook" is a variable. However, statement (c) causes the most problems. Consider what would happen if each statement is true while the others are false. Can that happen?

Chapter Review

1. (a) 15, 21, 28   **(b)** 32, 27, 22   **(c)** 400, 200, 100
(d) 21, 34, 55   **(e)** 17, 20, 23   **(f)** 256, 1024, 4096
(g) 16, 20, 24   **(h)** 125, 216, 343
2. (a) neither   **(b)** arithmetic   **(c)** geometric
(d) neither   **(e)** arithmetic   **(f)** geometric
(g) arithmetic   **(h)** neither
3. (a) $3n + 2$ **(b)** $n^3 - 1$ **(c)** 3^n
4. (a) 1, 4, 7, 10, 13   **(b)** 2, 6, 12, 20, 30   **(c)** 3, 7, 11, 15, 19
5. (a) 10,100   **(b)** 10,201
6. (a) 123456, 1234567, 12345678, . . .
(b) 1234567890. The last digit of the nth term in the sequence matches the last digit of the number n.

7.

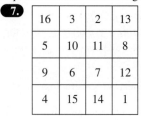

16	3	2	13
5	10	11	8
9	6	7	12
4	15	14	1

8. 26
9. $2.00
10. 21 posts
11. 128 matches
12. $19{,}305 = 3 \cdot 5 \cdot 9 \cdot 11 \cdot 13$.

13. 44,000,000 turns

14. 20 students

15. 39 boxes

16. 48 triangles

17. 9 hours

18. Width is 10 ft, length is 24 ft.

19. There will be 96,000 ants on the seventh day and 192,000 ants on the eighth day, so it will certainly be full by then.

20. 4 questions

21. Select the basket labeled APPLES AND ORANGES and reach in and select a piece of fruit. If the fruit is an orange, move the ORANGES label here, move the APPLES label to where the ORANGES label was, and put the APPLES AND ORANGES label in the remaining slot. If the fruit drawn is an apple, move the APPLES sign to this basket, move the ORANGES sign to where the APPLES sign was, and place the APPLES AND ORANGES label in the remaining slot.

22. (a) 4 (b) 2 (c) Impossible

23. (a) Yes (b) Yes (c) No (d) Yes

24. (a) No women smoke. (b) $3 + 5 \neq 8$. (c) Some heavy-metal rock is not loud, or not all heavy-metal rock is loud. (d) Beethoven wrote some music that is not classical.

25. Converse: If someone will faint, we will have a rock concert. Inverse: If we do not have a rock concert, then no one will faint. Contrapositive: If no one will faint, then we will not have a rock concert.

26. (a) Joe Czernyu loves Mom and apple pie. (b) The Statue of Liberty will eventually rust. (c) Albertina passed Math 100.

27. Let the following letters represent the given sentences.

p: You are fair-skinned.

q: You will sunburn.

r: You do not go to the dance.

s: Your parents want to know why you didn't go to the dance. Symbolically, $p \to q, q \to r, r \to s$. The argument given is valid: $\sim s \to \sim r, \sim r \to \sim q, \sim q \to \sim p$. By the chain rule, $\sim s \to \sim p$; that is, if your parents do not want to know why you didn't go to the dance, then you are not fair-skinned.

Chapter 2

Ongoing Assessment 2-1

1. (a) $\{m, a, t, h, e, i, c, s\}$ (b) $\{x \mid x$ is a state in the United States, but x is not Alaska or Hawaii$\}$ (c) $\{x \mid x$ is a natural number, and $x > 20\}$, or $\{21, 22, 23, \ldots \}$ (d) {Oregon, California, Washington, Hawaii, Alaska}

2. (a) $P = \{a, b, c, d\}$.

(b) $\{1, 2\} \subset \{1, 2, 3, 4\}$

(c) $\{0, 1\} \not\subseteq \{1, 2, 3, 4\}$

(d) $0 \notin \{ \ \}$.

(e) $\{0\} \neq \{ \ \}$.

3. (a) Yes (b) No (c) Yes (d) No (e) No

4. (a) 120 (b) 720 (c) $n(n-1)(n-2) \cdot \ldots \cdot 3 \cdot 2 \cdot 1$

5. (a) 24 (b) 6 (c) 12

6. $A = C, E = H, I = J$

7. (a) $1100 - 100$, or 1000 (b) 501 (c) 11 (d) $\overline{100}$ (e) 3 (f) 5

8. $\overline{A}$ is the set of all college students with at least one grade that is not an A, i.e., those college students who do not have a straight-A average.

9. (a) 7 (b) $\cup$

10. (a) $n(D) = 5$ (b) $C = D$

11. (a) $\notin$ (b) $\notin$ (c) $\notin$ (d) $\notin$ (e) $\in$ (f) $\in$

12. (a) $\not\subseteq$ (b) $\subseteq$ (c) $\subset$ (d) $\subseteq$ (e) $\not\subseteq$ (f) $\not\subseteq$

13. (a) Yes. (b) No. A may equal B. (c) Yes. (d) No. Consider $A = \{1\}$ and $B = \{1, 2\}$.

14. (a) Let $A = \{a, b\}$ and $B = \{a, b, c, d\}$. Then $n(A) = 2$ and $n(B) = 4$. Since $A \subset B$, $n(A)$ is less than $n(B)$, i.e., 2 is less than 4. (b) Let $A = \{1, 2, 3\}$ and $B = \{1, 2, 3, 4, \ldots, 100\}$. Since $A \subset B$, $n(A)$ is less than $n(B)$. So $3 < 100$. (c) Let $A = \emptyset$ and $B = \{1, 2, 3\}$. Since $A \subset B$, $n(A) = 0$ is less than $n(B) = 3$, so $0 < 3$.

15. 35

Communication

16. (a) This set is not well defined, since we do not know what is meant by "wealthy." (b) This set is not well defined, since we do not know what is meant by "great." (c) This set is well defined. Given a number, we can easily tell if it is a natural number greater than 100. (d) This set is well defined. We could just list them all. (e) This set is well defined; it is the empty set.

17. Yes, $\emptyset \subset A$ for all sets A since $A \neq \emptyset$.

18. If A and B are finite subsets, we say $n(A) \leq n(B)$ in case A is a subset (not necessarily proper) of B.

19. (a) Answers vary. For example:

$A = \{1, 2, 3, 4, 5\}, B = \{1, 2, 3, 4, 5, 6, 7, 8, 9\}$, and $U = \{1, 2, 3, \ldots, 20\}$. $\overline{A} = \{6, 7, 8, \ldots, 20\}$, and $\overline{B} = \{10, 11, 12, \ldots, 20\}$.

(b) $\overline{B} \subset \overline{A}$

(c)

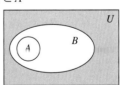

$\overline{B}$ contains only the shaded region. $\overline{A}$ contains all the area outside the circle labeled A.

Open-Ended

20. (a) Answers vary. For example: You are a member of the set of all humans, the set of all college (or university) students, and the set of all males or the set of all females (among many others that are probably more interesting).

(b) Answers vary. For example: The set of all atheists who believe in God, the set of all people who have been to Mars, and the set of all elementary school teachers who are less than 8 years old.

21. (a) Let A be the set of all natural numbers not equal to 1. Then $\bar{A} = \{1\}$ is finite. **(b)** Let A be the set of even natural numbers. Its complement, $\bar{A}$, is the set of odd natural numbers and so is infinite. (Here U is the set of natural numbers.)

22. (i) Let A be the set of all human beings, and B the set of all female humans. (ii) Let A be the set of all nonvacant houses in the United States and B the set of all people in the United States.

Cooperative Learning

23. (a) There are $2^{64} \doteq 1.84 \times 10^{19}$ subsets of $\{1, 2, 3, \ldots, 64\}$. If a computer can list one every millionth of a second, then it would take $1.84 \times 10^{19} \times 0.000001$ sec $\times \dfrac{1 \text{ yr}}{31,536,000 \text{ sec}}$ $\doteq 580,000$ yr to list all the subsets. **(b)** There are $64 \cdot 63 \cdot 62 \cdot \ldots \cdot 2 \cdot 1 \doteq 1.27 \times 10^{89}$ one-to-one correspondences between the 2 sets. So it would take $1.27 \times 10^{89} \times 0.000001$ sec $\times \dfrac{1 \text{ year}}{31,536,000 \text{ sec}} \doteq 4 \times 10^{75}$ yr to list all the one-to-one correspondences between the sets.

Ongoing Assessment 2-2

1. (a) A or C **(b)** A or C **(c)** N **(d)** $\varnothing$
2. (a) Yes **(b)** Yes **(c)** Yes **(d)** Yes
(e) Yes **(f)** No, since $A \cap A = A$ and $A \cap \varnothing = \varnothing$.
3. (a) True. **(b)** False. Let $A = \{a, b, c\}$ and $B = \{a, b\}$. Then $A - B = \{c\}$, but $B - A = \varnothing$. **(c)** True.
(d) False. **(e)** True. **(f)** False. Let $A = \{1, 2, 3\}$, $B = \{3, 4, 5\}$, and $U = \{1, 2, 3, \ldots, 10\}$. Then $\{A \cup B\} - A = \{1, 2, 3, 4, 5\} - \{1, 2, 3\} = \{4, 5\} \neq B$.
(g) False. Let $A, B,$ and U be as in the solution to (f). Then $(A - B) \cup A = A = \{1, 2, 3\}$, but $(A - B) \cup (B - A) = \{1, 2\} \cup \{4, 5\} = \{1, 2, 4, 5\}$.
4. (a) $A \cap B = B$. **(b)** $A \cup B = A$. **(c)** $\varnothing$ **(d)** $\varnothing$
5. (a)

(b)
(c) **(d)**

(e) **(f)**

(g) **(h)**

6. (a) $S \cup \bar{S} = U$ **(b)** $\varnothing \cup S = S$ **(c)** $\bar{U} = \varnothing$
(d) $\bar{\varnothing} = U$ **(e)** $S \cap \bar{S} = \varnothing$ **(f)** $\varnothing \cap S = \varnothing$
7. (a) $A - B = A$ **(b)** $A - B = \varnothing$ **(c)** $A - B = \varnothing$
(d) $A - B = \varnothing$
8. (a) Example 1: $A = \{1, 2, 3, 4\}$ and $B = \{1, 2, 3, 4, 5\}$ and $A \subseteq B$. Example 2: $A = \{2, 4, 6, 8\}$ and $B = \{1, 2, 3, 4, 5, 6, 7, 8\}$ and $A \subseteq B$. **(b)** By definition $A - B$ is the set of all elements in A that are not in B. If $A - B$ is the empty set, then this means that there are no elements in A that are not in B, which makes it a subset of B. A more formal justification is as follows: Suppose $A \nsubseteq B$, then there must be an element in A that is not in B, which implies that it is in $A - B$. This implies that $A - B$ is not empty; a contradiction. Hence $A \subseteq B$.
9. (a) $B - A$ or $B \cap \bar{A}$ **(b)** $\bar{A} \cap \bar{B}$ or $\overline{A \cup B}$
(c) $(A \cap B) - C$ **(d)** $A \cap C$ **(e)** $(A \cup B) \cap C$, or $C - \overline{(A \cup B)}$ **(f)** $((B \cup C) \cap \bar{A}) \cup (A \cap B \cap C)$
10. (a) **(b)**
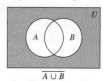
$A \cap B$ $\overline{A \cup B}$
(c) **(d)**
 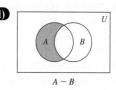
$(A \cap B) \cup \bar{A}$ $A - B$

11. (a) False

$A \cup (B \cap C)$ $(A \cup B) \cap C$

(b) False
 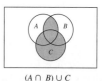
$A \cap (B \cup C)$ $(A \cap B) \cup C$

(c) False

$A - (B - C)$ $(A - B) - C$

12. (a) $A \cap B \cap C \subseteq A \cap B$ **(b)** $A \cup B \subseteq A \cup B \cup C$

(c) $(A \cup B) \cap C \subseteq A \cup B$ **(d)** Neither is, in general, a subset of the other. For example, if A and B are disjoint, then $A - B = A$ and $B - A = B$ and these are disjoint.
13. (a) (i) 5; (ii) 2; (iii) 2; (iv) 3 **(b)** (i) $n + m$; (ii) The smaller of the two numbers m and n; (iii) m; (iv) n
14. (a) Greatest is 15, least is 6. **(b)** Greatest is 4, least is 0.
15. (a)

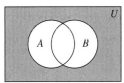

(b) The equation is $\overline{A \cap B} = \overline{A} \cup \overline{B}$ **(c)** Let $U = \{a, b, c, d\}$, $A = \{a, b\}$, and $B = \{b, c\}$. Then $\overline{A} \cap \overline{B} = \{c, d\} \cap \{a, d\} = \{d\} = \overline{A \cup B}$. Also, $\overline{A} \cup \overline{B} = \{c, d\} \cup \{a, d\} = \{a, c, d\} = \overline{A \cap B}$.
16. (a) The set of college basketball players more than 200 cm tall **(b)** The set of humans who are not college students or who are college students less than or equal to 200 cm tall **(c)** The set of humans who are college basketball players or who are college students taller than 200 cm **(d)** The set of all humans who are not college basketball players and who are not college students taller than 200 cm **(e)** The set of all college students taller than 200 cm who are not basketball players **(f)** The set of all college basketball players less than or equal to 200 cm tall
17. (a) The set of all Paxson eighth graders who are members of the band but not the choir **(b)** The set of all Paxson eighth graders who are members of both the band and the choir **(c)** The set of all Paxson eighth graders who are members of the choir but not the band **(d)** The set of all Paxson eighth graders who are members of neither the band nor the choir
18. 18
19. 4
20.

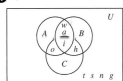

21. Answers vary. The following are possible answers:
The elements that are only in A; $A - (B \cup C)$
The elements that are only in B; $B - (A \cup C)$
The elements that are only in C; $C - (A \cup B)$
The elements in A and in C but not in B; $(A \cap C) - B$
The elements in B and C but not in A; $(B \cap C) - A$
The elements in A and B but not in C; $(A \cap B) - C$
The elements that are in all three sets; $A \cap B \cap C$
The elements that are not in any of the three sets; $\overline{A \cup B \cup C}$
22. (a) 20 **(b)** 10 **(c)** 10

23. The following Venn diagram indicates that only 490 cardholders are accounted for:

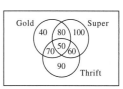

So either there is some other type of credit card the remaining 10 people could have, or else the editor was right.
24. 3. Using the following Venn diagram and the fact that the set of people who are O negative is $100 - n(A \cup B \cup C)$, we see that the answer is 3.

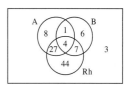

25. (a) False. Let $A = \{a, b, c\}$ and $B = \{1, 2, 3\}$ **(b)** False. Let $A = B$ **(c)** False. Let $A = \{1, 2, 3\}$ and $B = \{1, 2, 3, 4\}$ **(d)** True. **(e)** True. **(f)** False. Let $A = \{1, 2, 3\}$ and $B = \{a, b, c, d\}$
26. Steelers versus Jets, Vikings versus Packers, Bills versus Redskins, Cowboys versus Giants
27. (a) $A \times B = \{(x, a), (x, b), (x, c), (y, a), (y, b), (y, c)\}$. **(b)** $B \times A = \{(a, x), (a, y), (b, x), (b, y), (c, x), (c, y)\}$. **(c)** $B \times \emptyset = \emptyset$. **(d)** $(A \cup B) \times C = \{(x, 0), (y, 0), (a, 0), (b, 0), (c, 0)\}$. **(e)** $A \cup (B \times C) = \{x, y, (a, 0), (b, 0), (c, 0)\}$.
28. (a) $C = \{a\}$, $D = \{b, c, d, e\}$. **(b)** $C = \{1, 2\}$, $D = \{1, 2, 3\}$. **(c)** $C = D = \{0, 1\}$.
29. (a) $4 \cdot 5 = 20$. **(b)** $m \cdot n$ **(c)** $m \cdot n \cdot p$
30. 30
31. 60

Communication

32. (a) Yes. $A \cap B \subseteq A \subseteq A \cup B$ **(b)** No. For example, let $A = \{1, 2, 3\}$, and $B = \{4\}$. Then $2 \in A \cup B$, but $2 \notin A \cap B$.
33. (a) red (b) purple (c) blue (d) orange (e) brown (f) green (g) yellow
34. No. Let $A = \{1\}$, and $B = \{a\}$. Then $A \times B = \{(1, a)\}$, but $B \times A = \{(a, 1)\}$. These are not equal.

Open-Ended

35.–**36.** Answers vary.

Cooperative Learning

37. Answers vary.

Review Problems

38. (a) 6 **(b)** 6
39. (a) These are all the subsets of $\{2, 3, 4\}$. There are
$2^3 = 8$ such subsets. **(b)** There are 8 subsets that contain the
number 1. Every subset either contains 1 or it does not. So
exactly half of the $2^4 = 16$ subsets contain 1. **(c)** Twelve
subsets contain 1 or 2 (or both). There are 4 subsets of $\{3, 4\}$.
We can form subsets that contain 1 or 2 or both by adding 1 to
each, 2 to each, or 1 and 2 to each. By the fundamental
counting principle then, there are $3 \cdot 4 = 12$ possibilities.
(It's also not hard to list them.) **(d)** Four subsets contain
neither 1 nor 2, since 12 subsets do contain 1 or 2.
(e) B has $2^5 = 32$ subsets. Half contain 5 and half do not.
(f) Every subset of A is a subset of B. The others can be listed
by adding the element 5 to each subset of A. So there
are twice as many subsets of B as subsets of A. A has 16 subsets
and B has 32 subsets.
40. (a) A and B are equal. **(b)** C is a proper subset
of A and a proper subset of B, since $C = \{4, 8, 12, 16, \ldots\}$.
41. Answers vary.

Ongoing Assessment 2-3

1. For example, let $A = \{1, 2\}$, $B = \{2, 3\}$, then $A \cup B = \{1, 2, 3\}$. Thus $n(A) = 2$, $n(B) = 2$, $n(A \cup B) = 3$, but $n(A) + n(B) = 2 + 2 = 4 \neq n(A \cup B)$.
2. (a) Yes **(b)** Yes **(c)** Yes **(d)** No, $3 + 5 \notin V$
(e) Yes
3. Answers may vary. For example,

4. (a) $x + 7 = 21$. **(b)** $x = 213 + 119$.
(c) $213 = 119 + x$. **(d)** $213 = x + 119$.
5. (a) Commutative property of addition
(b) Associative property of addition **(c)** Commutative
property of addition
6. No. If $k = 0$, we would have $k = 0 + k$, implying $k < k$.
7. (a) (i) For any whole numbers a and b, $a < b$ if and only if
there exists a natural number k such that $b - k = a$, or
equivalently if and only if $b - a$ is a natural number.
(ii) For any whole numbers a and b, $a > b$ if and only if there
exists a natural number k such that $a - k = b$, or equivalently
$a - b$ is a natural number. **(b)** $a \geq b$ if and only if $a - b$ is
a whole number.
8. (a) 33, 38, 43 **(b)** 56, 49, 42
9. (a) 9 **(b)** 8 **(c)** 3 **(d)** 6 or 8
(e) 5 **(f)** 4 or 8 **(g)** 9
10. (a) 1 **(b)** No, because C = 1 **(c)** 8 or 9 **(d)** 2
11. 0

12. (a)

8	1	6
3	5	7
4	9	2

(b)

17	10	15
12	14	16
13	18	11

13. (a)

8	3
4	12

(b) Examples are not always possible. For example, there is
no solution if we put 14 instead of 15 in part (a).
14. (a) 28 **(b)** If the domino is laying horizontally and
one knows the sum of the dots in the right square plus the sum
of the dots in the left square, that sum is the same if the
domino were turned 180°.
15. Depends on the calculator
16. (a) Kent is the shortest and Vera is the tallest.
(b) Kent 140 cm, Mischa 142 cm, Sally 143 cm, Vera 144 cm
17. Depends on the calculator
18. 26

Communication

19. An arrow starting at 0 and ending at 3 represents the
same number as an arrow starting at 4 and ending at 7. One
way to explain this to students is to make physical models of
each and show that the lengths are the same by matching.
20. (a) $a + b = (a - c) + (b + c)$ where a, b, and c are
natural numbers and $a > c$.
(b) Answers vary. For example, suppose two classes have
a and b students, respectively. The total number of students is
$a + b$. If c students leave the first class and join the second,
the total number of students does not change and it is now
$(a - c) + (b + c)$.
21. (a) $63 - 27 = (63 + 3) - (27 + 3) = 66 - 30 = 36$
(b) $a - b = (a + c) - (b + c)$ **(c)** Answers vary.
22. (a) Suppose we have a blocks, and we want to take
away b blocks and then take away c more blocks. This is the
same as starting with a blocks, taking away c, and then taking
away b. **(b)** Suppose you have a dollars in your checking
account and you spent b dollars in one grocery store and c
dollars in another grocery store. Then your balance can be
calculated as $a - b - c$ or by finding how much was spent on
groceries altogether and subtracting that amount from a, that is
$a - (b + c)$.
23. The authors believe that it is important for both students
and teachers to know names of properties and their uses. One
consideration for students is that if the properties are known,
then barely more than one-half of the addition facts must be
learned.
24. It is very useful to have students learn more than one
method of addition and subtraction if the methods are to
generalize to sets of numbers other than whole numbers. The
missing-addend approach is useful for all sets of numbers in
solving subtraction problems. The method of counting to
compute additions is not effective with sets of fractions or real
numbers.

25. Answers may vary. For example, you can do estimations or mental math to tell if a calculator is correct.

26. (a) When you put 9 and 4 together, it is equal to the same length as 13.   **(b)** If you put 9 and 4 together on top of 4 and 9 together, they both equal 13.   **(c)** Take the length 9 away from 13 and the length left is equal to 4.   **(d)** Take the length 4 away from 13 and the length left is equal to 9.

Open-Ended

27. Colored rods may be used to teach addition to students using a principle of counting on. Choose the rod representing the greatest number and make a train of rods using unit rods until the second number is added. The total train represents the sum.
28. Answers will vary depending upon the calculator.
29. Answers may vary; for example, let $A = \{a, b\}$, $B = \{a, b, c, d\}$. Then $4 - 2 = n(B - A) = n(\{c, d\}) = 2$.

Cooperative Learning

30. The properties can be illustrated with groupings of people. For example, the commutative property can be illustrated by showing that 2 people plus 3 people is the same as 3 people plus 2 people.
31. Students may use number-line models to illustrate how the addition facts for base five can be found. The facts are shown in the table below.

+	0	1	2	3	4
0	0	1	2	3	4
1	1	2	3	4	10
2	2	3	4	10	11
3	3	4	10	11	12
4	4	10	11	12	13

Review Problems

32. (a) Yes, because there are 1000/2 elements in the first one and 1500/3 elements in the second one, so each has 500 elements.   **(b)** Yes, because each has 1000 elements.
(c) Yes, to each element n in the first set corresponds the element $n + 1$ in the second set.   **(d)** Yes, to each element x in the first set corresponds the element $2x$ in the second set.
33. (a) True, can be shown with Venn diagrams
(b) True. $A \subseteq A \cup B = B$.   **(c)** True.
$\overline{A \cup B} = \overline{A} \cap \overline{B} = \varnothing = U$.   **(d)** False, let $A = \{1, 2, 3\}$ and $B = \{a, b, c\}$ and $C = \{1, 2, 3, 4\}$, then A is not a subset of B, B is not a subset of C, but A is a subset of C.
34. (a) 6   **(b)** 9
35. (a) False, let $A = \{a, b, c, d\}$, and $B = \{c\}$, and $C = \{b, d\}$, then $A \cup B = A \cup C$ but B does not equal C.
(b) False, let $A = \{a, b, c, d\}$, $B = \{x, a, y\}$, and $C = \{z, a\}$, then $A \cap B = A \cap C$ but B does not equal C.   **(c)** False, let $A = \{a, b, d\}$, $B = \{x, y, z\}$, and $C = \{c, d, e\}$, then $A \cap B = \varnothing$, $B \cap C = \varnothing$, but $A \cap C = \{d\}$.
36. 15

37. (a) 2200 people, because if all those people saw *Minority Report* as well, then they saw both, but 3100 saw *Minority Report*, and not all of them saw *Gosford Park*.
(b) The least number of people that could have seen both movies is 500. Let x be the number of people who saw both movies. Then $3100 + 2200 - x$, or $5300 - x$, is the number of people who saw one or the other movie (or both). This number cannot exceed 4800, the total number of people in town. Thus the smallest value of x is $5300 - 4800$, or 500. (Any value smaller than 500 will make $5300 - x$ greater than 4800.)
38. (a) $\{a, b, c, d\}$ **(b)** $\{a, d\}$ **(c)** $\varnothing$
(d) $\varnothing$ **(e)** $\varnothing$

Ongoing Assessment 2-4

1. (a) 5   **(b)** 4   **(c)** Any whole number
2. Each possible pairing of two of the sets is disjoint.
3. (a) Yes   **(b)** Yes   **(c)** Yes   **(d)** Yes
(e) Yes   **(f)** No, because $2 \cdot 2 = 4$, which is not in the set.
4. (a) No, $2 + 3 = 5$ **(b)** Yes   **(c)** Not closed for either, $2 + 4 = 6$ and $2 \cdot 3 = 6$.
5. (a) $ac + ad + bc + bd$ **(b)** $3x + 3y + 15$
(c) $\square \triangle + \square \bigcirc$ **(d)** $x^2 + 2xy + xz + y^2 + yz$
(e) ab **(f)** xy
6. (a) $(4 + 3) \times 2 = 14$ **(b)** No parentheses needed
(c) $(5 + 4 + 9) \div 3 = 6$ **(d)** No parentheses needed
7. $a(b + c + d) = a[(b + c) + d] = a(b + c) + ad = ab + ac + ad$
8. (a) $y(x + y)$
(b) $47 \cdot (99 + 1)$ or $47 \cdot 100$
(c) $x(y + 1)$
(d) $(x + 1)(y + 1)$
(e) $ab(a + b)$
9. (a) 6   **(b)** 0   **(c)** 4
10. (a) $40 = 8 \cdot 5$ **(b)** $326 = 2 \cdot x$
(c) $48 = x \cdot 16$ **(d)** $x = 5 \cdot 17$
11. The number is always equal to the original number. It works all the time as seen in the following: Let n be the original number. $(2n + 2)/2 - 1 = 2(n + 1)/2 - 1 = n + 1 - 1 = n$
12. (a) $(8 \div 4) \div 2 \neq 8 \div (4 \div 2)$
(b) $8 \div (2 + 2) \neq (8 \div 2) + (8 \div 2)$
13. (a) $(a + b)^2 = (a + b)(a + b) = (a + b)a + (a + b)b = a^2 + ba + ab + b^2 = a^2 + 2ab + b^2$ **(b)** The area of the square with side $a + b$ can be expressed as $(a + b) \cdot (a + b)$ and also as the sum of areas of four regions: two squares, a^2 b^2, and two rectangles ab and ba. Hence
$$(a + b)^2 = a^2 + b^2 + ab + ba = a^2 + 2ab + b^2.$$

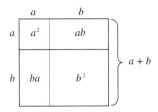

14. **(a)** The area of the shaded region is $a(b - c)$, but it can also be expressed as the area of the large square minus the area of the small rectangle, so $a(b - c) = ab - ac$.
(b) Let $b - c = x$, then $b = x + c$, therefore
$ab = a(c + x)$
$ab = ac + ax$
$ab - ac = ax$. We know $x = b - c$, so
$ab - ac = a(b - c)$.
(c) The distributive property of multiplication over subtraction
15. (a) $y(x - y)$
   (b) $y(x - 1)$
   (c) $47(101 - 1)$ or $47 \cdot 100$
   (d) $(x + 1)(y - 1)$
   (e) $ab(b - a)$
16. (a) Suppose we have two bags of marbles, in one bag a marbles and in the other b marbles. We want to distribute the marbles equally among c students. Then the number of marbles that each student gets can be found in two ways as follows: Putting all the marbles in one bag,
we have $a + b$ marbles and each student gets $(a + b) \div c$ marbles. We could also divide the marbles in the first bag first, and then divide the marbles in the second bag. In this way each student would get $(a \div c) + (b \div c)$ marbles.
   (b) Let $a \div c = x$ and $b \div c = y$. Then $a = xc$ and $b = yc$. Consequently,
$$a + b = xc + yc$$
$$= (x + y) \cdot c.$$
Now by definition of division, $x + y = (a + b) \div c$. When you substitute for x and y, the property follows.
17. After 5 months Samantha will have $10 more than Millie.
18. The first string makes 0 intersections, the second makes one, the third makes two, and so on, so there are $0 + 1 + 2 + \ldots + 8 + 9 = 45$ intersections.
19. 2; 3 left
20. (a) (1,36), (2,18), (3,12), (4,9), (6,6), (9,4), (12,3), (18,2), (36,1)

(b)

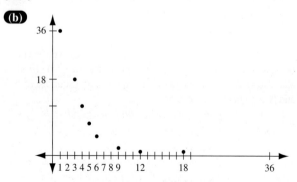

(c) The points in part (b) lie along a curve while the points from the addition lie along a line.

21. A possible answer is given, resulting in $4 \cdot 3$, or 12, color schemes.

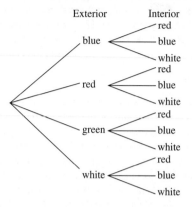

22. 12
23. (a) 3 **(b)** 2 **(c)** 2 **(d)** 6 **(e)** 4
24. 8
25. Yes; 64
26. The remainder is 1. The number can be written as $10q + 6$ where q is a whole number. $10q$ is divisible by 5. When 6 is divided by 5, the remainder is 1.
27. The answers depend upon the keys available on your calculator.
(a) $3 = 1 + 9 - 7.$ $12 = 19 - 7.$
   $4 = 1^7 + \sqrt{9}.$ $13 = 91 \div 7.$
   $5 = 7 - \sqrt{9} + 1.$ $14 = 7(\sqrt{9} - 1).$
   $6 = 7 - 1^9.$ $15 = 7 + 9 - 1.$
   $7 = 7 \cdot 1^9.$ $16 = (7 + 9) \cdot 1.$
   $8 = 7 + 1^9.$ $17 = 7 + 9 + 1.$
   $9 = 1^7 \cdot 9.$ $18 = \sqrt{9}(7 - 1).$
   $10 = 1^7 + 9.$ $19 = ?$
   $11 = 7 + 1 + \sqrt{9}.$ $20 = 7\sqrt{9} - 1.$
(b) For example $4 \cdot 4 - 4 + 4 \div 4$ **(c)** For example, $22 + 2.$ **(d)** For example, $111 - 11$
28. (a) Subtract 18. **(b)** Divide 54 by 9.
(c) Add 11 and 48. **(d)** Add 8.
29. This is not the case when $x = 0$.
30. This is the case when x is either 0 or 1.
31. Let x and y be the whole numbers. Then $x = 0$ and $y = 0$ or $x = 2$ and $y = 2$.
32. (a) A/l **(b)** $f/3$ **(c)** $60h$ **(d)** $d/7$
33. $\{5k + 3 \mid k \in W\} = \{3, 8, 13, 18, 23, \ldots \}$.
34. (a) Yes **(b)** Yes **(c)** Yes, a **(d)** Yes

Communication

35. The argument is not valid. By definition of division $0 \div 0 = x$ if and only if $0 = 0 \cdot x$ has a unique solution. But the last equation is true for all whole numbers x. Because the equation has no unique solution, $0 \div 0$ is not meaningful.

36. The distributive property works with two operations. Only one operation is used in this example. Multiplication is not distributive over multiplication.

37. 0 is not the identity for multiplication because if it were, then any number times 0 must be that number. The result in every case is 0, not the number multiplied by 0.

Open-Ended

38. Answers may vary here.

39. A taxi driver charges $5 for entering a cab and $6 per minute for 8 minutes. (The prices here are unrealistic, but this is the type of problem students may suggest.)

40. Answers vary. One possible explanation is as follows. A whole number that can be divided by 2 without a remainder is an even number. Thus 0, 2, 4, 6, 8, 10, 12, . . . are even numbers. Each of these numbers is a multiple of 2 because $0 = 2 \cdot 0, 2 = 2 \cdot 1, 4 = 2 \cdot 2, 6 = 2 \cdot 3, 10 = 2 \cdot 5,$ $12 = 2 \cdot 6, \ldots$. If we add 1 to an even number, the result is an odd number. Thus all the odd numbers are numbers that can be written as a multiple of 2 plus 1.

Cooperative Learning

41. Answers vary.

Review Problems

42. For example, $\{0, 1\}$
43. No. For example, $5 - 2 \neq 2 - 5$.
44.

45. Because $a < b$, we have $a + k = b$ for some nonzero whole number k. Multiply both sides of the equation by $c(c \neq 0)$ to obtain:
$$(a + k)c = bc,$$
$$ac + kc = bc.$$
Because $k \neq 0$ and $c \neq 0$, $kc \neq 0$. Consequently $ac > bc$.

Ongoing Assessment 2-5

1. (a) Double the input number. **(b)** Subtract 2 from the input number. **(c)** Add 6 to the input number. **(d)** Square the input number and add 1.

2. (a) This is not a function, since the input 1 is paired with 2 outputs (*a* and *d*). **(b)** This is not a function from $\{1, 2, 3\}$ to $\{a, b, c, d\}$, since 2 is not paired with any letter. **(c)** This is a function. **(d)** This is not a function, since the input 1 is paired with several outputs.

3. (a) Answers vary. For example:

(b) 32
4. (a)

(b) $\{(0, 1), (1, 3), (2, 5), (3, 7), (4, 9)\}$

(c)

x	$f(x)$
0	1
1	3
2	5
3	7
4	9

(d)

5. (a) This is a function. **(b)** This is a function. **(c)** This is a function. **(d)** This is not a function, since, for example, $f(3) = 0$ because 3 is in W and $f(3) = 1$ because 3 is in $\{3, 4, 5, 6 \ldots\}$ **(e)** This is a function.
6. Assuming 37¢ for the first ounce and 23¢ for each additional ounce up to 8 ounces, we have:
(a) $C = 37 + 23(n - 1)$, where n is the number of ounces and C is the cost in cents. **(b)** 83¢ **(c)** For each input n (number of ounces), there is only one output. The range is $\{37 + 23 \cdot (n - 1) \mid n = 1, 2, 3, \ldots, 8\}$. **(d)** The graph consists of 8 points that lie on a straight line.

7.

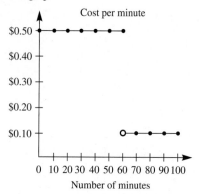

Dosage as a Function of Weight

(y-axis: mg — 125, 110, 95, 80, 65, 50)
(x-axis: lb — 20, 30, 40)

8. (a) 2 chirps per second   **(b)** 50° Fahrenheit
9. (a) 8 dollars   **(b)** $3n + 2$ dollars
10. (a) $L(n) = 2n + (n - 1)$, or $3n - 1$.
   (b) $L(n) = n^2 + 1$.   **(c)** $L(n) = n(n + 1)$.
11. (a) 7   **(b)** 55   **(c)** 2
12. (a) Cost per minute in the first and the total cost for a
      6-minute call in the second.
   (b) That the cost per minute is always the same regardless
      of the length of the conversation and that the company
      charges for each fraction of a minute.
   (c) $c = 0.30$ for the first graph and $c = 0.30t$ for the
      second graph.

13. (a)

Cost per minute

($0.50, $0.40, $0.30, $0.20, $0.10)
(0 10 20 30 40 50 60 70 80 90 100)
Number of minutes

Total cost for calls

($40.00, $30.00, $20.00, $10.00)
(0 10 20 30 40 50 60 70 80 90 100)
Number of minutes

   (b) That the company charges for each part of a minute at
      the rate of $0.50 per minute.
   (c) The two segments represent different charges per
      minute. The one representing the higher cost is steeper.

(d) If $C(t) = 0.50t$ if $O \le t \le 60$, $C(t) = 30 + 0.10(t - 60)$
   if $t > 60$.
14. (a) $5n - 2$ **(b)** 3^n **(c)** $2n$
15. (a) 30   **(b)** 16   **(c)** 65
16. (a) $1, 385, 389$ **(b)** $1, 4, 9, 900$
(c) $2, 12, 2550$
17. (a) $2 \cdot 1 + 2 \cdot 7 = 16; 2 \cdot 2 + 2 \cdot 6 = 16$;
$2 \cdot 6 + 2 \cdot 2 = 16; 2 \cdot 5 + 2 \cdot 5 = 20$ **(b)** $(1, 9), (2, 8),$
$(3, 7), (4, 6), (5, 5), (6, 4), (7, 3), (8, 2), (9, 1)$ **(c)** The
domain is $N \times N$, and the range is the set of all even numbers
greater than or equal to 4.
18. (a) 1 cm   **(b)** The same each month
(c) Her height on her birthday
19. (a) 50 cars   **(b)** Between 6:00 A.M. and 6:30 A.M.
(c) 0   **(d)** Between 8:30 A.M. and 9 A.M., by 100 cars
20. (a) $C(x) = 100 + 40x$.
   (b) and **(c)**:

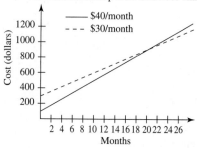

Cost of Membership as a Function of Time

— $40/month
--- $30/month

(y-axis: Cost (dollars) — 1200, 1000, 800, 600, 400, 200)
(x-axis: Months — 2 4 6 8 10 12 14 16 18 20 22 24 26)

(d) 20 months
21. (a) $H(2) = 192$. $H(6) = 192$. $H(3) = 240$. $H(5) = 240$.
Some of the heights correspond to the ball going up, some to
the ball coming down.
   (b)

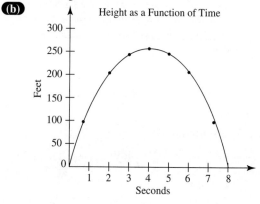

Height as a Function of Time

(y-axis: Feet — 300, 250, 200, 150, 100, 50, 0)
(x-axis: Seconds — 1 2 3 4 5 6 7 8)

At $t = 4$ seconds, the ball's height is $H(4) = 256$ feet above
the ground.
(c) 8 seconds   **(d)** $0 \le t \le 8$.   **(e)** $0 \le H(t) \le 256$.
22. (a) $A(x) = x \cdot \frac{1}{2} (900 - x)$.

(b)

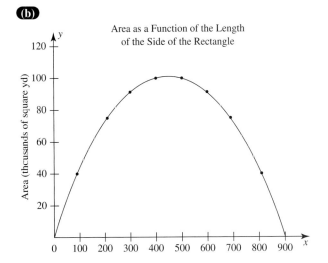

Area as a Function of the Length
of the Side of the Rectangle

(c) Length = 450, width = 225.
23. (a) **(i)** 40
      (ii) 38
      (iii) 22
  (b) **(i)** $S(n) = 2n(n + 1)$
      (ii) $S(1) = 4$, $S(n) = 2n(n + 1) - 2$ when $n \geq 2$
      (iii) $S(n) = 6n - 2$
24. (a) $1 + 2 + 3 + \ldots + n$, or $\dfrac{n(n + 1)}{2}$
  (b) $n(n + 1)$
  (c) $n + 2 + 2n$, or $3n + 2$
  (d) 4^{n-1}
25. The converse is false. For example, the set of ordered pairs $\{(1, 2), (1, 3)\}$ does not represent a function, since the element 1 is paired with two different second components.
26. (a) Boys: *B, J*; Girls: *A, C, D, F, G, I*
  (b) $\{(A, B), (A, C), (A, D), (C, A), (C, B), (C, D), (D, A),$
$(D, B), (D, C), (F, G), (G, F), (I, J)\}$ **(c)** No
27. (a) Function **(b)** Relation, but not a function
(c) Relation, but not a function (assuming there is a mother in Birmingham who has more than one child) **(d)** Function
(e) Relation, but not a function.
28. (a) Yes **(b)** No
29. (a) None **(b)** Reflexive, symmetric, and transitive (and so an equivalence relation) **(c)** Reflexive, symmetric, and transitive (and so an equivalence relation)
(d) Reflexive, symmetric, and transitive (and so an equivalence relation) **(e)** Symmetric **(f)** Reflexive and symmetric **(g)** Transitive
30. (a) Reflexive, symmetric, and transitive; equivalence relation **(b)** Transitive **(c)** Symmetric **(d)** Reflexive, symmetric, and transitive; equivalence relation

Communication

31. Yes, since each element of *A* is paired with exactly one element of *B*.
32. Yes. Answers vary.

33. (a) This is not a function, since a faculty member may teach more than one class. **(b)** This is a function (assuming only one teacher per class). **(c)** This is not a function, since not every senator is paired with a committee. (Not every senator is the chairperson of a committee.)
34. (a)

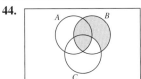

Freeboard as a Function of Draft

It is meaningful. Answers vary.
(b) $f(d) = 50 - d$.

Open-Ended

35. – **39.** Answers vary.

Cooperative Learning

40. – **41.** Answers vary.

Review Problems

42. (a) $109 = 98 + 11$ **(b)** $x = z + y$
(c) $60 = 4 \cdot 15$ **(d)** $x = y \cdot 3$ **(e)** $x = 10 \cdot 5 + 3$
43. No, because if $A \cap B \neq \varnothing$ then we would be counting those elements twice.
44.

Chapter Review

1. $\varnothing$, $\{m\}$, $\{a\}$, $\{t\}$, $\{h\}$, $\{m, a\}$, $\{m, t\}$, $\{m, h\}$, $\{a, t\}$, $\{a, h\}$, $\{t, h\}$, $\{m, a, t\}$, $\{m, a, h\}$, $\{m, t, h\}$, $\{a, t, h\}$, $\{m, a, t, h\}$
2. (a) $A \cup B = A$. **(b)** $C \cap D = \{l, e\}$.
(c) $\overline{D} = \{u, n, i, v, r\}$. **(d)** $A \cap \overline{D} = \{r, v\}$.
(e) $\overline{B} \cup C = \{s, v, u\}$.
(f) $(B \cup C) \cap D = \{l, e, a\}$. **(g)** $\{i, n\}$ **(h)** $\{e\}$
(i) 5 **(j)** 16
3.

(a) $A \cap (B \cup C)$ **(b)** $(\overline{A \cup B}) \cap C$
4. Assuming all seven letters are different, 5040.

5. (a) $t \rightarrow e$ **(b)** 6
$h \rightarrow n$
$e \rightarrow d$

6. It is not true that $A \cap (B \cup C) = (A \cap B) \cup C$ for all A, B, and C as shown in the following diagrams.

 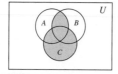

(a) $A \cap (B \cup C)$ **(b)** $(A \cap B) \cup C$

7.

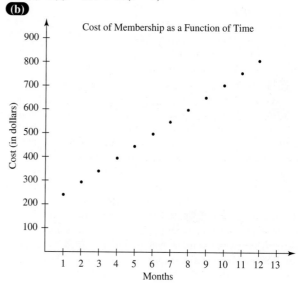

(a) 36 **(b)** 6 **(c)** 5

8. Answers vary. **(a)** $B \cup (C \cap A)$ **(b)** $B - C$

9. (a) False. Consider the sets $\{a\}$ and $\{2\}$. **(b)** False. It is not a proper subset of itself. **(c)** False. Consider the sets $\{t, h, e\}$ and $\{e, n, d\}$. They have the same number of elements, but they are not equal. **(d)** False. This is in one-to-one correspondence with the set of natural numbers. **(e)** False. The set $\{5, 10, 15, 20, \ldots\}$ is a proper subset of the natural numbers, and is equivalent to the natural numbers, since there is a one-to-one correspondence between the 2 sets. **(f)** False. Let $B = \{1, 2, 3\}$ and A be the set of natural numbers. **(g)** True **(h)** False. Let $A = \{1, 2, 3\}$ and $B = \{a, b, c\}$.

10. (a) Because $A \cup B$ is the union of disjoint sets, $A - B$, $B - A$, and $A \cap B$, the equation is true. **(b)** True, because $A - B$ and $B - A$ are disjoint as well as $B - A$ and A. Also, $A \cup B = (A - B) \cup B = (B - A) \cup A$.

11. (a) 17 **(b)** 34 **(c)** 0 **(d)** 17

12. 7

13. The first question might be, "Is the state or province one of the 48 contiguous states in the United States?" If the answer is yes, the second question could be, "Does it begin with a vowel?" The third question can then be, "Is it _____?" If the answer to the first question is no, the second question could be, "Is it in Canada?", and the third question could be the same as above.

14. (a) Distributive property of multiplication over addition **(b)** Commutative property of addition **(c)** Identity property of multiplication for whole numbers **(d)** Distributive property of multiplication over addition **(e)** Commutative property of multiplication **(f)** Associative property of multiplication

15. (a) Let $A = \{1, 2, 3, \ldots, 13\}$ and $B = \{1, 2, 3\}$ then B is a proper subset of A. Therefore B has fewer elements than A so $n(B)$ is less then $n(A)$. Thus $3 < 13$. **(b)** Let $A = \{1, 2, 3, \ldots, 12\}$ and $B = \{1, 2, 3, \ldots, 9\}$, B is a proper subset of A, so A has more elements than B, thus $n(A)$ is greater than $n(B)$, $12 > 9$.

16. (a) 15, 14, 13, 12, 11, or 10 **(b)** 10 **(c)** Any whole number **(d)** Whole numbers from 0 through 26

17. (a) $15a$ **(b)** $5x^2$ **(c)** $xa + xb + xy$ **(d)** $3x + 15 + xy + 5y$

18. 40 cans

19. 12 outfits

20. $w = 26$.

21. $6000 for 80 people is cheaper

22. $214

23. $400

24. (a) Function **(b)** Not a function **(c)** Function

25. (a) Range $= \{3, 4, 5, 6\}$. **(b)** Range $= \{14, 29, 44, 59\}$. **(c)** Range $= \{0, 1, 4, 9, 16\}$. **(d)** Range $= \{5, 9, 15\}$.

26. (a) This is not a function, since one student can have two majors. **(b)** This is a function. The range is the subset of the natural numbers that includes the number of pages in each book in the library. **(c)** This is a function. The range is $\{6, 8, 10, 12, \ldots\}$. **(d)** This is a function. The range is $\{0, 1\}$. **(e)** This is a function. The range is N.

27. (a) $C(x) = 200 + 55(x - 1)$.

(b)

Cost of Membership as a Function of Time

[Scatter plot: Cost (in dollars) on vertical axis from 100 to 900; Months on horizontal axis from 1 to 13]

(c) After the ninth month, the cost exceeds $600.

(d) After the 107th month.

Chapter 3

Ongoing Assessment 3-1

1. (a) $\overline{\overline{\text{MCDXXIV}}}$; The double bar over M represents $1000 \cdot 1000 \cdot 1000$. **(b)** 46,032; The 4 in 46,032 represents 40,000 while the 4 in 4632 represents only 4000. **(c)** < ▼▼; the space in the latter number indicates < is multiplied by $10 \cdot 60$ rather than by 10. **(d)** The 𝔩 represents 1000 while 9 represents only 100. **(e)** ☺ represents three groups of 20 plus zero 1s while ≣ represents three 5s and three 1s.

2. (a) MCML; MCMXLVIII **(b)** $\overline{\text{MII}}$; $\overline{\text{M}}$
(c) M; CMXCVIII **(d)** << <▼▼ ; << <
(e) $\mathcal{L}$991; $\mathcal{L}$9∩∩∩∩∩∩∩∩∩IIIIIIIII **(f)** ⠇⠇ ⠒
3. 1922
4. (a) CXXI **(b)** XLII **(c)** LXXXIX,
(d) VCCLXXXII
5. (a) ∩∩∩∩∩II **(b)** 9III **(c)** ◁III
(d) ∩∩∩IIIIIIII

6. (a) ▼ <▼▼ ; ∩∩∩∩∩∩∩II; LXXII; ⠒
(b) 602; 999II ; DCII; ⠰ **(c)** 1223; << <<▼▼▼;
MCCXXIII; ⠒
7. (a) Hundreds **(b)** Tens **(c)** Thousands
(d) Hundred thousands
8. (a) 3,004,005 **(b)** 20,001 **(c)** 3560 **(d)** 9,000,099
9. 811 or 910
10. (a) 86 **(b)** 11
11. 2112_{four}
12. (a) $(1, 10, 11, 100, 101, 110, 111, 1000, 1001, 1010,$
$1011, 1100, 1101, 1110, 1111)_{\text{two}}$ **(b)** $(1, 2, 10, 11, 12, 20,$
$21, 22, 100, 101, 102, 110, 111, 112, 120)_{\text{three}}$ **(c)** $(1, 2, 3, 10,$
$11, 12, 13, 20, 21, 22, 23, 30, 31, 32, 33)_{\text{four}}$ **(d)** $(1, 2, 3, 4,$
$5, 6, 7, 10, 11, 12, 13, 14, 15, 16, 17)_{\text{eight}}$
13. 20
14. $2032_{\text{four}} = (2 \cdot 10^3 + 0 \cdot 10^2 + 3 \cdot 10^1 + 2 \cdot 1)_{\text{four}}$
15. (a) 111_{two} **(b)** 555_{six} **(c)** 999_{ten} **(d)** $\text{EEE}_{\text{twelve}}$
16. (a) $\text{ETE}_{\text{twelve}}$; $\text{EEl}_{\text{twelve}}$ **(b)** 11111_{two}; 100001_{two}
(c) 554_{six}; 1000_{six} **(d)** 66_{seven}; 101_{seven} **(e)** 444_{five}; 1001_{five}
(f) 101_{two}; 111_{two}
17. (a) There is no numeral 4 in base four. **(b)** There are
no numerals 6 or 7 in base 5. **(c)** There is no numeral T in
base three.
18. 3 blocks, 1 flat, 1 long, 2 units
19.
(a)

(b)

20. (a) 1000_{two} **(b)** 1000_{five} **(c)** $\text{TTE}_{\text{twelve}}$
(d) 1000_{twelve}
(e) When each place value slot is occupied by the greatest digit
for that base and 1 is added, it forces each existing place value to
go to 0 and a new place value slot is created with 1 as the entry.
21. (a) 3212_{five} **(b)** 1177_{twelve} **(c)** 12110_{four}
(d) 100101_{two}
22. 100010_{two}
23. (a) 117 **(b)** 45 **(c)** 1331 **(d)** 1451 **(e)** 157
(f) 181

24. 72¢; 242_{five}¢
25. 1 prize of $625, 2 prizes of $125, and 1 of $25
26. 3 quarters, 4 nickels, and 2 pennies
27. (a) 8 weeks, 2 days **(b)** 4 years, 6 months
(c) 1 day, 5 hours **(d)** 5 feet, 8 inches
28. $\text{E66}_{\text{twelve}}$; 1662
29. (a) 6 **(b)** 1 **(c)** nine **(d)** 3
30. $31001\text{E}_{\text{twelve}}$
31. Above the bar are depicted 5s, 50s, 500s, and 5000s.
Below the bar are 1s, 10s, 100s, and 1000s. Thus there are
$1 \cdot 5000, 1 \cdot 500, 3 \cdot 100, 1 \cdot 50, 1 \cdot 5,$ and $2 \cdot 1$ depicted for a
total of 5857. The number 4869 could be depicted as follows:

32. Assume an eight-digit display without scientific notation.
(a) 98,765,432 **(b)** 12,345,678 **(c)** 99,999,999
(d) 11,111,111
33. (a) Answers vary, e.g., subtract 2020.
(b) Answers vary, e.g., subtract 50.

Communication

34. Answers will vary. Ben is incorrect. Zero is a place holder
in the Hindu-Arabic system. It is used to differentiate between
numbers like 54 and 504. If zero were nothing, then we could
eliminate it without changing our number system. Zero is the
cardinal number of the empty set.
35. (a) The Egyptian system has no zero symbol and no
place value. It is cumbersome to compute with this system and
hard to work with large numbers. **(b)** The Babylonian
system has too few symbols to be useful. Also the use of the
spacing to indicate place value makes the system unusable
unless the numbers can be read in context. **(c)** The Roman
system is fairly complicated. It has no place value except for
some subtractions. It has no zero symbol. Large numbers are
difficult to write. Computation is not easy.
36. (a) This is primarily for readability. It has been proposed
with the metric system to drop the commas and simply use
spaces instead. **(b)** Answers vary.
37. Answers vary.
38. (a) Pennies can be used for units, a nickel represents
10_{five}, and a quarter represents 100_{five}. You can trade 5 pennies
(units) for 1 nickel (10_{five}), and you can trade 5 nickels (10_{five})
for 1 quarter (10^2_{five}).
(b) 88 pennies = 3 quarters and 13 pennies
= 3 quarters, 2 nickels, 3 pennies
Therefore, $88_{\text{ten}} = (3 \cdot 10^2 + 2 \cdot 10^1 + 3 \cdot 1)_{\text{five}} = 323_{\text{five}}$

Open-Ended

39. 4; 1, 2, 4, 8; 1, 2, 4, 8, 16

Cooperative Learning

40. The answers to this problem are totally dependent on students and the properties that they select for the system. Most will probably emulate one of the systems studied in the section.

Ongoing Assessment 3-2

1. (a)
$$\begin{array}{r} 981 \\ + \ 421 \\ \hline 1402 \end{array}$$
(b)
$$\begin{array}{r} 2025 \\ 1196 \\ + \ 3148 \\ \hline 6369 \end{array}$$

2. (a)
$$\begin{array}{r} 383 \\ - \ 159 \\ \hline 224 \end{array}$$
(b)
$$\begin{array}{r} 13296 \\ - \ 8309 \\ \hline 4987 \end{array}$$

3. (a) One possibility:
$$\begin{array}{r} 863 \\ + \ 752 \\ \hline 1615 \end{array}$$
(b) One possibility:
$$\begin{array}{r} 368 \\ + \ 257 \\ \hline 625 \end{array}$$

4. Only if positive numbers are used:

(a)
$$\begin{array}{r} 876 \\ - \ 235 \\ \hline 641 \end{array}$$
(b)
$$\begin{array}{r} 623 \\ - \ 587 \\ \hline 36 \end{array}$$

5. No, not all at dinner. He can have either the steak or the salad.

6. Yes, $124

7.
$$\begin{array}{r} 3428 \\ + \ 5631 \\ \hline 9059 \end{array}$$

8. (a)
$$\begin{array}{r} 93 \\ - \ 37 \\ \hline \end{array} \rightarrow \begin{array}{r} 93 + 3 \\ - \ 37 + 3 \\ \hline \end{array} \rightarrow \begin{array}{r} 96 \\ - \ 40 \\ \hline 56 \end{array}$$

(b)
$$\begin{array}{r} 321 \\ - \ 38 \\ \hline \end{array} \rightarrow \begin{array}{r} 321 + 2 \\ - \ 38 + 2 \\ \hline \end{array} \rightarrow \begin{array}{r} 323 \\ - \ 40 \\ \hline \end{array} \rightarrow \begin{array}{r} 323 + 60 \\ - \ 40 + 60 \\ \hline \end{array} \rightarrow \begin{array}{r} 383 \\ - \ 100 \\ \hline 283 \end{array}$$

9. (a) (i) 1,236 (ii) 1,032 **(b)** The algorithm works because the placement of partial sums still accounts for place value. It is fairly easy in the example because only two digits are added at a time. This process would become more confusing or have to be adapted if more than two numbers were added.

10. Answers may vary; for example, **(a)** The student did not regroup from the ones place to the tens place. **(b)** Partial sums are not in the correct place value position. **(c)** The units minuend is subtracted from the subtrahend. **(d)** After regrouping, you would have four tens minus three tens. The student did not change the 5 to a 4.

11. 1 hour 34 minutes 15 seconds

12. Step 1 - Expanded form

Step 2 - Commutative and associative properties of addition

Step 3 - Distributive property of multiplication over addition

Step 4 - Single-digit addition facts

Step 5 - Place value

13. (a) 121_{five} **(b)** 20_{five} **(c)** 1010_{five} **(d)** 14_{five} **(e)** 1001_{two} **(f)** 1010_{two}

14.

+	0	1	2	3	4	5	6	7
0	0	1	2	3	4	5	6	7
1	1	2	3	4	5	6	7	10
2	2	3	4	5	6	7	10	11
3	3	4	5	6	7	10	11	12
4	4	5	6	7	10	11	12	13
5	5	6	7	10	11	12	13	14
6	6	7	10	11	12	13	14	15
7	7	10	11	12	13	14	15	16

Base eight

15. (a) 9 hours 33 minutes 25 seconds **(b)** 1 hour 39 minutes 40 seconds

16. (a) 2 quarts, 1 pint, 0 cups, or 1 half-gallon, 0 quarts, 1 pint, 0 cups **(b)** 1 pint, 0 cups **(c)** 2 quarts, 1 pint, 1 cup

17. (a) The method produces a palindrome in each case: (i) 363 (ii) 9339 (iii) 5005. **(b)** For example, 89 or 97.

18. (a)

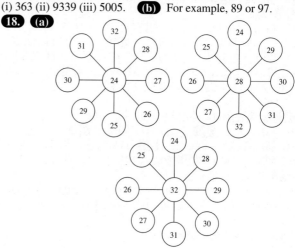

(b) 3 (24, 28, 32)

19. It is doubling the second number in the operation.

20. (a) 34; 34; 34 **(b)** 34 **(c)** 34 **(d)** Yes **(e)** Yes

21. (a)
$$\begin{array}{r} {}^{1}4^{1}32 \text{ ten} \\ {}_{1}9_{4}7_{1}6 \text{ ten} \\ + \ 1418_{6} \text{ ten} \\ \hline 2826 \end{array}$$
(b)
$$\begin{array}{r} {}^{3}3_{1}2 \\ 1\,3_{0} \\ 2\,2 \\ 4_{3}3_{0} \\ 2_{0}3 \\ 1\,2_{0} \\ \hline 3\,1\,0_{\text{five}} \end{array}$$

22. (a) 3 gross 10 dozen 9 ones **(b)** 6 gross 3 dozen 4 ones

23. There is no numeral 5 in base five; $2_{\text{five}} + 3_{\text{five}} = 10_{\text{five}}$.

24. (a)
$$\begin{array}{r} 230_{\text{five}} \\ - \ 22_{\text{five}} \\ \hline 203_{\text{five}} \end{array}$$
(b)
$$\begin{array}{r} 20010_{\text{three}} \\ - \ 2022_{\text{three}} \\ \hline 10211_{\text{three}} \end{array}$$

25.

Hawks	15	32	40	33	120
Elks	20	25	47	39	131

Communication

26. Answers vary. For example, you could talk about how adding 1 and subtracting 1 has the effect of adding 0 to the problem which produces an equivalent problem. The reason for changing the original problem to the new problem is that the numbers are easier to work with. I would tell her that her technique works well and discuss how it works.

27. For example, you might ask her to explain her algorithm with different problems making sure to choose computations where regrouping is necessary. She should understand that what she is really doing is the following:
$97 - 28 = (90 + 7) - (20 + 8) = (90 - 20) + (7 - 8) = 70 + (-1) = 69.$

28. For example, the words *regroup* and *trade* more accurately reflect the actions that are taken when performing an addition or subtraction problem. The words *borrow* and *carry* seem to reflect mechanics and not the mathematical ideas used in the algorithm.

29. Answers vary; for example, the topic of constructivism might be discussed along with whether a student will understand and remember better an algorithm that he or she has developed. There is also merit in finally developing an algorithm that is efficient and students will welcome it more after they have struggled developing their own.

30. For example, the "scratch marks" represent the normal "carries" and is just a way to keep track of them.

31. (a) Answers vary. (b) In the example if 10 is added to the 4 ones to get 14 ones and nothing else is done, this changes the problem. So 10 must be taken away so that the net result is just adding 0, which does not change the original problem. When 1 ten is added to the 8 tens being subtracted on the bottom, this balances the 1 ten that was added in the minuend. Similarly, the algorithm is continued by adding values in the minuend and then adding a corresponding value in the proper place value position in the subtrahend to neutralize the addition on the top.

32. Students are encouraged to use the bibliographies at the end of the chapters to seek mathematics education research to answer this question.

Cooperative Learning

33. The U.S. monetary system is not a true base-ten system because of the coins and bills involved. A true base-ten system would have only pennies, dimes, dollars, ten dollars, 100 dollars, and so on. The system would not have nickels, quarters, half-dollars, five-dollar bills, and so on. Money in other countries varies.

Review Problems

34. This will be studied in detail in later chapters. However with the meter as a basic unit of length, we have 10 meters = 1 decameter, 10 decameters = 1 hectometer, 10 hectometers = 1 kilometer.

35. $5280 = 5 \cdot 10^3 + 2 \cdot 10^2 + 8 \cdot 10^1 + 0 \cdot 1$

36. 1410

37. (a) 1594   (b) 11   (c) 23

38. (a) About 121 weeks   (b) About 3 years   (c) Answers vary; for example, if you are 20 years old, you have lived 630,720,000 seconds.   (d) Answers vary; for example, if your pulse is 72 beats per minute, your heart will beat 37,843,200 times per year.

Ongoing Assessment 3-3

1. (a)
$$\begin{array}{r} 426 \\ \times 783 \\ \hline 1278 \\ 3408 \\ 2982 \\ \hline 333558 \end{array}$$
(b)
$$\begin{array}{r} 327 \\ \times 941 \\ \hline 327 \\ 1308 \\ 2943 \\ \hline 307707 \end{array}$$

2. (a)   **(b)**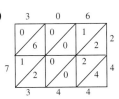

3. Diagonals separate place value as placement does in the traditional algorithm.

4. Answers may vary.   (c) 58,000,000,000 L/day

5. (a) 5^{19} **(b)** 6^{15} (c) 10^{313} **(d)** 10^{12} or $2^{12} \cdot 5^{12}$

6. (a) 2^{100} because $2^{80} + 2^{80} = 2^{80}(1 + 1) = 2^{80} \cdot 2 = 2^{81}$.
(b) 2^{102} because $2^{101} = 2^{100} \cdot 2$ and $2^{102} = 2^{100} \cdot 4$.

7. The following partial products, which are obtained through the distributive property of multiplication over addition, are shown in the model.

(a)
$$\begin{array}{r} 22 \\ \times 13 \\ \hline 6 \\ 60 \\ 20 \\ 200 \\ \hline 286 \end{array}$$
(3×2)
(3×20)
(10×2)
(10×20)

(b)
$$\begin{array}{r} 15 \\ \times 21 \\ \hline 5 \\ 10 \\ 100 \\ 200 \\ \hline 315 \end{array}$$
(1×5)
(1×10)
(20×5)
(20×10)

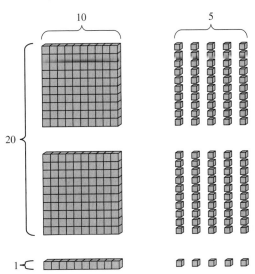

8. (a) $293 \cdot 476 = 139,468$ **(b)** Placement indicates place value.
(c)
$$
\begin{array}{r}
363 \\
\times\ 84 \\
\hline
2904 \\
1452 \\
\hline
30492
\end{array}
$$
$\quad(8 \times 363)$
$\quad(4 \times 363)$

9. $\rightarrow$
17 $\times$		63
8		126
4		252
2		504
$\rightarrow$ 1		1008

and $63 + 1008 = 1071$

10.

a	b	$a \cdot b$	$a + b$
67	56	3752	123
32	78	2496	110
15	18	270	33

Note: In the 3rd row $a = 18$, $b = 15$ is also a possibility.

11. (a) 1332 calories **(b)** Jane, 330 more calories
(c) Maurice, 96 more calories

12. No, only 2352 calories, so he gained less than 1 lb.

13. $60

14. (a) 77 remainder 7 **(b)** 8 remainder 10
(c) 10 remainder 91

15. (a) $3\overline{)876}$ **(b)** $8\overline{)367}$

16. 3

17. 8 cars (remember the match)

18.

2	11
4	15
0	7
6	19
12	31

19. (f) Yes, suppose the 3 numbers are a, b, and c. The 6 different numbers are

ab
ac
bc
ba
cb
$+ ca$ The sum is $2(a + b + c) \cdot 10 + 2 \cdot (a + b + c) =$

$(a + b + c) \cdot 22$. Now if we divide by $(a + b + c)$, we always obtain 22.

20. (a) Answers vary; for example, $12 \cdot 42$.
(b) $(10a + b) \cdot (10c + d) = (10b + a) \cdot (10d + c)$ implies $100ac + 10bc + 10ad + bd = 100bd + 10ad + 10bc + ac$ or $99ac = 99bd$, which implies that $ac = bd$.

21. 3 hr

22. (a) Regrouping was not used; place value was not observed. **(b)** 5 was multiplied by 6 to obtain 30; the 3 was carried; then 3 was multiplied by 2 to obtain 6; the "carry" was added to obtain 9 which was recorded. **(c)** 4 was multiplied by 6 and 2 was "carried;" then 6 and 3 were added instead of multiplied and the 2 was added to obtain the 11. **(d)** When 1 was brought down, the quotient of 0 was not recorded.

23. (a) Expanded form; distributive property of multiplication over addition; associative property of multiplication; definition of a^n; additive identity; place value

(b) $34 \cdot 10^2 = (3 \cdot 10 + 4) \cdot 10^2$ — expanded form
$= (3 \cdot 10) \cdot 10^2 + 4 \cdot 10^2$ — distributive property of multiplication over addition
$= 3 \cdot (10 \cdot 10^2) + 4 \cdot 10^2$ — associative property of multiplication
$= 3 \cdot 10^3 + 4 \cdot 10^2$ — definition of a^n
$= 3 \cdot 10^3 + 4 \cdot 10^2 + 0 \cdot 10$ — additive identity
$\quad + 0 \cdot 1$
$= 3400$ — place value

24. 58 buses needed, not all full

25. (a) Because $a = 131 \cdot 4789 + 200$, then $a = 131 \cdot (4789 + 1) + 69$. Therefore the quotient is 4790 and the remainder is 69. **(b)** $a = 131 \cdot 4790 + 69$.

26. Answers vary. For example, if the number is $10a + b$, the product is $1000a + 100b + 10a + b$, or $abab$.

27. (a) 233_{five} **(b)** $4_{\text{five}}\ \text{R}1_{\text{five}}$ **(c)** 2144_{five} **(d)** 31_{five}
(e) 110_{two} **(f)** 1101110_{two}

28. (a) Nine **(b)** Four **(c)** Six **(d)** Any base greater than or equal to two.

29. (a) 30221_{five} **(b)** $a = 5; b = 7$

30. (a)
$$
\begin{array}{r}
763 \\
\times\ 8 \\
\hline
6104
\end{array}
$$
(b)
$$
\begin{array}{r}
678 \\
\times\ 3 \\
\hline
2034
\end{array}
$$

31. (a)
$$
\begin{array}{r}
762 \\
\times\ 83 \\
\hline
63,246
\end{array}
$$
(b)
$$
\begin{array}{r}
378 \\
\times\ 26 \\
\hline
9828
\end{array}
$$

32. (a)
$$
\begin{array}{r}
37 \\
\times\ 43 \\
\hline
111 \\
1480 \\
\hline
1591
\end{array}
$$
(b)
$$
\begin{array}{r}
93 \\
\times\ 36 \\
\hline
558 \\
2790 \\
\hline
3348
\end{array}
$$
(c)
$$
\begin{array}{r}
13 \\
9\overline{)123} \\
-9 \\
\hline
33 \\
-27 \\
\hline
6
\end{array}
$$

33. (a) 1; 121; 12,321; 1,234,321. For n 1s in each of the two factors, the product "counts up" to n, then back down to 1. The next product should be 123,454,321. **(b)** 9801; 998001; 99980001. For n 9s in each of the two factors, the product appears in order as $(n - 1)$ 9s, one 8, $(n - 1)$ 0s, and one 1. The next product should be 9,999,800,001. **(c)** The pattern continues for (b) but not for (a), which fails when there are 10 1s in each factor.

Communication

34. Any vary; for example, some student may find one algorithm easier to understand or to use than others and therefore it will be easier for him or her to remember or to reproduce.

35. Answers will vary depending upon students' choices. Many students may favor the lattice multiplication algorithm because only single digits are multiplied and addition is accomplished later.

36. NCTM's *Principles and Standards* suggests that the traditional algorithm for division be considered towards the end of grades 3–5 as one efficient way to calculate. Students should be able to justify the procedure. However, NCTM recommends that students consolidate and practice a small number of strategies for division and be able to use them fluently. Long division can be practiced by working on context problems and not necessarily just drill problems. If a student can demonstrate that he or she can handle division problems, there is no need to continue to practice them in excess. Division can then receive less emphasis.

37. The result is always 4. Let the original number be x. The operation appears as follows:

$$[(2x)3 + 24]/6 - x = 4.$$

Open-Ended

38. The recommendation should be to try to complete a proof that the algorithm would work on a general set of numbers. If the student does not have the capacity to complete that task, one method of trial and error is to try a great number of cases. This is not a proof, and that should be emphasized, but it might produce a counterexample.

Cooperative Learning

39. Arguments will vary depending upon groups. Some will argue that addition should be followed by subtraction because they are inverses of each other. Others will argue that addition should be followed by multiplication because multiplication is repeated addition. This would also postpone subtraction until students are more ready for it.

Review Problems

40. 999999∩∩∩∩∩∩∩|||||

41. 300,260

42. For example, $3 + 0 = 3 = 0 + 3$.

43. (a) $x(a + b + 2)$ (b) $(3 + x)(a + b)$

44. 6979 miles

Ongoing Assessment 3-4

1. **(a)** 160 **(b)** 120

2. **(a)** $(9 \cdot 6) \cdot (2 \cdot 5) = 54 \cdot 10 = 540.$

(b) $(8 \cdot 7) \cdot (25 \cdot 4) = 56 \cdot 100 = 5600.$

(c) $(11 \cdot 3) \cdot (5 \cdot 20) = 33 \cdot 100 = 3300.$

(d) $(82 + 18) + (37 + 13) = 100 + 50 = 150.$

3. Associative property of addition; commutative property of addition; associative property of addition; addition algorithm; addition algorithm.

4. (a) 605 **(b)** 963 **(c)** 965 **(d)** 1680

5. (a) 36 **(b)** 120 (c) 114 **(d)** 97

6. 496 mi.

7. **(a)** $28 + 2 = 30$; $30 + 20 = 50$; $50 + 3 = 53$. So the answer is $2 + 20 + 3 = 25$. **(b)** $47 + 3 = 50$; $50 + 10 = 60$; $60 + 3 = 63$. So the answer is $3 + 10 + 3 = 16$.

8. (a) 5300 **(b)** 100,000 (c) 120,000 **(d)** 2,330 (rounding rules may vary when the value to the right is located at the midpoint.)

9. Answers will vary; for example, **(a)** $900/30 = 30$. **(b)** $25,000 - 20,000 = 5000$. **(c)** $30 \cdot 30 = 900$. **(d)** $2000 + 3000 + 6000 + 1000 = 12,000$.

10. Answers vary; for example, (a) $2 + 3 + 5 = 10$, so 10,000 is an initial estimate. $10,000 + 2000$ (adjustment) $= 12,000$ for the final estimate. **(b)** The sum of the front digits is 22, so $2200 + 270$ adjustment gives 2470.

11. (a) The first set of numbers is not clustered. The second set is clustered about 500 so an estimate is 2500. **(b)** Estimates will vary.

12. (a) The range is 600 ($20 \cdot 30$) to 1200 ($30 \cdot 40$). **(b)** The range is 700 ($100 + 600$) to 900 ($200 + 700$). (c) The range is 230 ($200 + 30$) to 340 ($300 + 40$).

13. $30 \cdot 180$ because they are closer to the original numbers than the other two choices.

14. About $3600 \cdot 6 = 21,600$ calories must be burned.

15. Answers vary, for example, $3300 - 100 - 300 - 400 - 500 = 2000$. The estimate is high because the amounts that were taken away were rounded up and resulted in more being taken away than the $13 that was added to the $3287.

16. For example, $40 \cdot 20 = 800$ seats or $40 \cdot 25 = 1000$ seats. 800 will be low and 1000 high.

17. (a) Different answers since the estimates of 800 and 220 are way off. **(b)** Same answers because 22 was divided by 2 to obtain 11 while 32 was multiplied by 2 to obtain 64. The result is multiplying the original computation by 2/2, or 1, which does not change it. **(c)** Same answers because the first number was multiplied by 3 and the second number was divided by 3, which results in just multiplying the original computation by 1, which does not change it.

18. **(a)** False **(b)** False **(c)** False **(d)** True

19. The clustering strategy gives $6 \cdot 70,000$ or 420,000.

20. One possibility is that to find $x5^2$ we could write $x(x + 1)$ and append the digits 25. For example, in 65^2, we take $6 \cdot 7 = 42$ and append 25 to obtain 4225.

21. One possibility to find $xy \cdot 99$ mentally is to write $(xy - 1)$ as the first two digits and then append the digits obtained from $100 - xy$. For example, in $12 \cdot 99$ the first two digits are $12 - 1 = 11$ and the second two digits are $100 - 12$, or 88. Thus $12 \cdot 99 = 1188$.

Communication

22. Mental mathematics is the process of producing an exact answer to a computation without using external aids. Computational estimation is the process of forming an approximate answer to a numerical problem.

23. The front-end estimation is almost always less than the exact sum because an adjustment is usually needed. The only case where this is not true is when each of the front-end numbers that is used is followed by zeroes. In this case the estimate could equal the exact sum.

24. Answers vary; for example, students might suggest that mental mathematics and estimation are necessary every day in order to determine quickly whether their bills at various businesses are being computed correctly. Mental math and estimation help students to know whether the answers that appear on the calculator are reasonable. NCTM makes several important points about the importance of mental math and estimation in the recent edition of their *Principles and Standards* and these *Principles and Standards* should be referred to for convincing arguments.

25. The estimate is always too high. For example, if we increase x by an amount p and decrease y by an amount q, then the estimate is $(x + p) - (y - q)$. This can be rewritten as $(x - y) + (p + q)$. This shows that the estimate is always $(p + q)$ greater than the difference $(x - y)$.

Open-Ended

26. Answers vary; for example, when you are determining the amount of a tip for a waiter in a restaurant.

27. Answers vary; for example, an estimate for $230 + 520 + 640 + 170 + 140$ using front-end estimation is $1500 + 200$ (adjustment) $= 1700$. This is the same result as the one obtained by rounding and adding. An estimate for $210 + 520 + 640 + 130 + 100$ is 1600 using front-end estimation and 1500 using rounding.

Cooperative Learning

28. Answers vary depending upon the grade level and textbook chosen.

29. Answers vary; for example, $19{,}875 \cdot 44$ is greater because the number that is increased is a number that is used to compute each partial product.

Chapter Review

1. (a) tens
   (b) thousands
   (c) hundreds
2. (a) 400,044 **(b)** 117 **(c)** 1704 **(d)** 11 **(e)** 1448
3. (a) CMXCIX **(b)** ∩∩∩∩∩∩∩II **(c)** $\stackrel{\bullet}{\bullet\bullet\bullet}$
   (d) 2341_{fiiv} **(e)** 11011_{two}
4. (a) 3^{17} **(b)** 2^{21} **(c)** 3^5 **(d)** 2^{82} **(e)** 2^{101}
5. 2020_{three}
6. 1 block, 2 flats, 2 longs, 0 units

7. (a)

(b)

8. 1119
9. 60,074
10. (a) 5 remainder 243 **(b)** 91 remainder 10
   (c) 120_{fiiv} remainder 2_{fiiv} **(d)** 11_{two} remainder 10_{two}
11. (a) $5 \cdot 912 + 243 = 4803$.
   (b) $91 \cdot 11 + 10 = 1011$.
   (c) $23_{\text{fiiv}} \cdot 120_{\text{fiiv}} + 2_{\text{fiiv}} = 3312_{\text{fiiv}}$.
   (d) $11_{\text{two}} \cdot 11_{\text{two}} + 10_{\text{two}} = 1011_{\text{two}}$.
12. $395
13. $4380
14. 2600 cases
15. $3842
16. 40 cans
17. 26
18. $2.16
19. $6000
20. There are 36 bikes and 18 trikes.
21. $214
22. $400
23. Selling pencils by the units, dozens, and gross is an example of the use of base 12.
24. (a) The Egyptian system had seven symbols. It was a *tally* system, a *grouping* system, and it used the *additive property*. It did not have a symbol for zero but this was not very important because they did not use place value. **(b)** The Babylonian system used only two symbols. It was a place value system (base 60), and was additive within the positions. It lacked a symbol for zero until around 300 B.C. **(c)** The Roman system used 7 symbols. It was additive, subtractive, and multiplicative. It did not have a symbol for 0. **(d)** The Hindu-Arabic system uses 10 digits. It uses place value and it has a symbol for 0.
25. (a) 1003_{fiiv} **(b)** 10000000_{two} **(c)** $T8_{\text{twelve}}$
26. (a) 212_{fiiv} **(b)** 101_{two} **(c)** 1442_{fiiv} **(d)** 101101_{two}
27. (a) For example, $(26 + 24) + (37 - 7) = 50 + 30 = 80$.
   (b) For example, $(7 \cdot 9)(4 \cdot 25) = 63 \cdot 100 = 6300$.
28. Methods vary. **(a)** 441 **(b)** 36 **(c)** 180
   (d) 406
29. Answers vary. For example, (a) $2300 + 300$ (adjustment) $= 2600$. (b) 2600
30. $2400 \cdot 4 = 9600$.
31. Answers vary; for example, we first estimate how many 14s are contained in 322. There are at least 20, so using place value we record a 2 above the 2 in 32 to indicate that we are

removing 20 sets of 14. If we remove 20 sets of 14, or 280, 42 is left. We next estimate how many 14s are contained in 42. The answer is 3 so we write 3 next to the 2 in the quotient to indicate we are removing another 3 sets of 14. This leaves 0 so there are no more 14s to remove and nothing left over. The 23 indicates that 322 contains 23 sets of 14 and the 0 indicates that there is nothing left over.

32. Answers vary, for example, a system has place value if the value of a digit depends on its placement in a numeral. If a system has only a finite number of digits and they can be used to represent an infinite set of numbers, then the system has place value.

33. Answers vary; for example, lattice multiplication has the advantage that you have to know only basic multiplication facts and record them in a lattice. A disadvantage is that it takes much longer to work a problem than it does using the traditional algorithm.

Chapter 4

Ongoing Assessment 4-1

1. (a) $^-2$ **(b)** 5 **(c)** ^-m **(d)** 0 **(e)** m
(f) $^-a + {}^-b$ or $^-(a + b)$
2. (a) 2 **(b)** m **(c)** 0
3. (a) 5 **(b)** 10 **(c)** $^-5$ **(d)** $^-5$
4. (a)

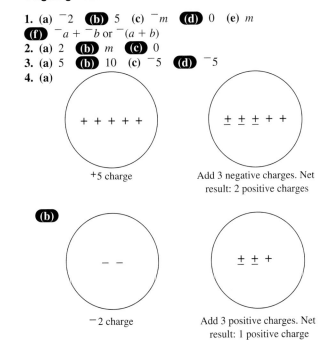

+5 charge

Add 3 negative charges. Net result: 2 positive charges

(b)

$^-2$ charge

Add 3 positive charges. Net result: 1 positive charge

(c)

$^-3$ charge

Add 2 positive charges. Net result: 1 negative charge

(d)

 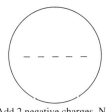

$^-3$ charge on the field

Add 2 negative charges. Net result: 5 negative charges

5. (a) $3 + {}^-({}^-2) = 5$ **(b)** $^-3 + {}^-2 = {}^-5$
(c) $^-3 + {}^-({}^-2) = {}^-1$

6. (a)

(b)

(c)

(d)

7. (a) $^-7$ points **(b)** $^-2°C$ **(c)** 4900 feet
(d) $^-\$150$ **(e)** $^-3$ yards
8. (a) $(^-45) + (^-55) + (^-165) + (^-35) + (^-100) + 75 + 25 + 400$ **(b)** \$400
9. (a)

(b)

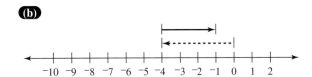

10. (a) $^-4 - 2 = {}^-6; {}^-4 - 1 = {}^-5; {}^-4 - 0 = {}^-4; {}^-4 - {}^-1 = {}^-3$ **(b)** $3 - 1 = 2; 2 - 1 = 1; 1 - 1 = 0;$
$0 - 1 = {}^-1; {}^-1 - 1 = {}^-2; {}^-2 - 1 = {}^-3$
11. (a) $^-9$ **(b)** 3 **(c)** 1 **(d)** $^-19$ **(e)** $^-13$ **(f)** $^-6$

12. (a) (i) $55 - 60$ (ii) $55 + (^-60)$ (iii) $^-5$
(b) (i) $200 - 220$ (ii) $200 + (^-220)$ (iii) $^-20$
13. (a) 59 **(b)** $^-269°C$ **(c)** 192°F
14. (a) 10W–40 or 10W–30 **(b)** 5W–30
(c) 10W–40, 5W–30 or 10W–30 **(d)** none
(e) 10W–30 or 10W–40
15. (a) $1 + 4x$ **(b)** $2x + y$ **(c)** $x - 2$
(d) $4x - (2 - 3x) = 4x + {}^-[2 + {}^-(3x)]$
$$\begin{aligned}&= 4x + {}^-2 + {}^-({}^-3x)\\&= 4x + 3x + {}^-2\\&= 7x + {}^-2\\&= 7x - 2\end{aligned}$$
16. The equation holds if and only if $c = 0$ (a and b can be any integers). Justification: It can be shown that $a - (b - c) = a - b + c$ for all integers $a, b,$ and c. Thus, the original equation holds if, and only if, $(a - b) + {}^-c = (a - b) + c$, which in turn holds if, and only if, ${}^-c = c$. This last equation is true if, and only if, $c = 0$.
17. (a) I **(b)** W **(c)** $I - \{0\}$ **(d)** ∅ **(e)** ∅
(f) I^- **(g)** $\{0\}$ **(h)** W **(i)** I
18.

2	$^-13$	8
5	$^-1$	$^-7$
$^-10$	11	$^-4$

Other answers are possible.

19. (a) 0 **(b)** $^-101$ **(c)** 1 **(d)** $a - 1$ **(e)** $^-4$
20. (a) All negative integers **(b)** All positive integers
(c) All integers less than $^-1$ **(d)** 2 or $^-2$ **(e)** There are none. **(f)** All integers except 0 **(g)** There are none.
21. (a) 9 **(b)** 2 **(c)** 0 or 2 **(d)** The set of all integers greater than or equal to 0
22. (a) x **(b)** If $f(x)$ become an input, the result is the original input x. **(c)** $^-x + k$ for all integers k.
23. (a) 89 **(b)** 19 **(c)** 19 **(d)** $y - x - 1$ or $y - (x + 1)$
24. Greatest possible value: $a - (b - c) - d$, or 8. Least possible value: $a - b - (c - d)$, or $^-6$
25. (a) $d = {}^-3$, next terms: $^-12, ^-15$ **(b)** $d = {}^-4$, next terms: $^-9, ^-13$ **(c)** $d = {}^-y$, next terms: $x - 2y, x - 3y$
(d) $d = 2x$, next terms: $1 + 3x, 1 + 5x$
26. (a) 0 **(b)** 3775 **(c)** 2538
27. $^-1$
28. (a) True **(b)** True **(c)** True **(d)** True
(e) False; let $x = {}^-1$ **(f)** True
29. The smaller gear rotates 28 times in the opposite direction of the larger gear.
30. (a) $^-18$ **(b)** $^-6$ **(c)** 22 **(d)** $^-18$ **(e)** 23
31. (a) $^-101$ **(b)** 516 **(c)** 10,894 **(d)** 5,995

Communication

32. He could have driven 12 mi in either direction from milepost 68. Therefore his location could be either at the $68 - 12 = 56$ milepost or at the $68 + 12 = 80$ milepost.

33. (a) By definition of subtraction $(a - b) + b = a$. Also, using the associative property for addition and the definition of an additive inverse:
$$\begin{aligned}[a + (^-b)] + b &= a + [(^-b) + b]\\&= a + 0\\&= a\end{aligned}$$
Hence, $(a - b) + b = [a + (^-b)] + b$. Adding ^-b to both sides of the last equation, we get the required result.
(b) "Best way" is not well defined; different people may have different opinions. A similar approach, which may appeal more to some, is to show that each expression is a solution of the equation $a = b + x$. Since the equation has only one solution, the expressions are the same.
34. One way is to find the difference of the greater absolute value and the lesser absolute value. The sum has the same sign as the integer with the greater absolute value.
35. Two numbers are opposite if, and only if, their sum is 0. We have:
$$\begin{aligned}(b - a) + (a - b) &= b + (^-a) + a + (^-b)\\&= b + 0 + {}^-b\\&= b + {}^-b\\&= 0\end{aligned}$$
36. No; if $x < 0$, then ^-x is positive.

Open-Ended

37. Answers vary; for example, suppose Alice was figuring how much money she spent yesterday. She had one bill for $50, another bill for $85 arrived in the mail, and then she returned some books for a $30 credit.
38. Answers vary; for example, the floors above ground could be numbered as usual 1, 2, 3, 4, . . . , n, the zero or ground floor could be called G, and the floors below ground could be called 1B, 2B, 3B, 4B, . . . , nB. The system could be modeled on a vertical number line with G replacing 0, and 1B, 2B, 3B, . . . , nB replacing the negative integers. We could have computations like $3 + G = 3$, or $5B + 3B = 8B$.

Cooperative Learning

39. Answers vary.

Ongoing Assessment 4-2

1. $3(^-1) = {}^-3; 2(^-1) = {}^-2; 1(^-1) = {}^-1; 0(^-1) = 0; (^-1)(^-1) = 1$, by continuing the pattern of an arithmetic sequence with fixed difference 1.
2.

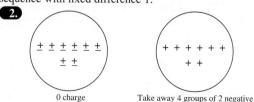

0 charge   Take away 4 groups of 2 negative
                  charges; net result is 8 positive charges.

3.

$$^-8\ ^-7\ ^-6\ ^-5\ ^-4\ ^-3\ ^-2\ ^-1\ 0\ 1\ 2\ 3\ 4\ 5\ 6\ 7\ 8$$

4. (a) $^-20 \cdot 4$ **(b)** $20 \cdot 4$ **(c)** ^-20n **(d)** $20n$
5. (a) 5 **(b)** $^-13$ **(c)** $^-11$ **(d)** 0
(e) Impossible; division by 0 is not defined.
(f) Impossible; division by 0 is not defined.
6. (a) $^-10$ **(b)** a; if a/b is defined **(c)** $^-10$
(d) a; If $b \neq 0$ **(e)** Not defined **(f)** 0 **(g)** Not defined
(h) $^-4$ **(i)** $-\dfrac{1}{2}$
7. (a) $^-30, ^-30 \div ^-6 = 5, ^-30 \div 5 = ^-6$.
(b) $20, 20 \div ^-5 = ^-4, 20 \div ^-4 = ^-5$.
(c) $0, 0 \div ^-3 = 0$; division by 0 is not defined.
(d) 0, division by 0 is not defined.
8. (a) $32°C - 30 \cdot (3°C)$ **(b)** $0°C + 25 \cdot (4°C)$
(c) $^-20°C + 30 \cdot (4°C)$ **(d)** $25°C - 20 \cdot (3°C)$
(e) $^-5 + md$ degrees C **(f)** md degrees C
(g) $20 - md$ degrees C
9. (a) $4(^-11) = ^-44$. Thus 44 yards were lost.
(b) $^-66$ divided by $11 = ^-6$; He lost 6 yards.
10. 84,000 acres if 2003 is not counted
11. (a) $^-1(^-5 + ^-2) = ^-1(^-7) = 7$;
$(^-1)(^-5) + (^-1)(^-2) = 5 + 2 = 7$
(b) $^-3(^-3 + 2) = ^-3(^-1) = 3$;
$(^-3)(^-3) + (^-3)(2) = 9 + ^-6 = 3$
(c) $^-5(2 + ^-6) = ^-5(^-4) = 20$;
$(^-5)(2) + (^-5)(^-6) = ^-10 + 30 = 20$
12. (a) $^-8$ **(b)** 16 **(c)** $^-1000$ **(d)** 81 **(e)** 1
(f) $^-1$ **(g)** 12 **(h)** 0 **(i)** $^-5$ **(j)** 19 **(k)** 9
(l) $^-9$ **(m)** $^-13$ **(n)** $^-8$ **(o)** $^-32$ **(p)** $^-16$
13. (b), (c), (g), (h) are always positive; (a), (f) are always negative.
14. (b) = (c); (d) = (e); (g) = (h)
15. (a) Commutative property of multiplication
(b) Closure property of addition **(c)** Associative property of multiplication **(d)** Distributive property of multiplication over addition
16. (a) xy **(b)** $2xy$ **(c)** $2y$ **(d)** ^-x **(e)** $x + 2y$
(f) b **(g)** x **(h)** y
17. (a) $^-2x + 2y$ **(b)** $^-x^2 - xy$
(c) $^-x^2 + xy$ **(d)** $^-2x - 2y + 2z$ **(e)** $^-x^2 + xy + 3x$
(f) $^-25 - 10x - x^2$ **(g)** $x^2 - y^2 - 1 - 2y$
(h) $^-x^4 + 3x^2 - 2$
18. (a) $^-2$ **(b)** 2 **(c)** 0 **(d)** $^-6$ **(e)** $^-36$
(f) 6 **(g)** All integers except 0 **(h)** All integers except 0 **(i)** No solution is possible. **(j)** 3 or $^-3$
(k) No solution is possible. **(l)** All integers except 0
(m) All integers except 0 **(n)** All integers **(o)** All integers
19. (a) $(50 + 2)(50 - 2) = 50^2 - 2^2 = 2500 - 4 = 2496$
(b) $25 - 10,000 = ^-9975$ **(c)** $x^2 - y^2$ **(d)** $4 - 9x^2$
(e) $x^2 - 1$ **(f)** $(213 + 13)(213 - 13) = 226 \cdot 200 = 45,200$

20. (a) $8x$ **(b)** $(a + 2)x$ **(c)** $x(y + 1)$
(d) $(a - 2)x$ **(e)** $x(x + y)$ **(f)** $6x$
(g) $x(3y + 2 - z)$ **(h)** $x(3x + y - 1)$
(i) $a(b(c + 1) - 1)$ **(j)** $(a + b)c$ **(k)** $(4 + a)(4 - a)$
(l) $(x + 3y)(x - 3y)$ **(m)** $(2x + 5y)(2x - 5y)$
(n) $(x + y)(x - y) + x + y = (x + y)(x - y + 1)$
21. (a)
$(a - b)^2 = (a + ^-b)(a + ^-b) = a(a + ^-b) + ^-b(a + ^-b)$
$\qquad = a^2 + a(^-b) + (^-b)a + (^-b)(^-b)$
$\qquad = a^2 - 2ab + b^2$.
(b) (i) $98^2 = (100 - 2)^2 = 100^2 - 2(200) + 2^2 = 10,000 - 400 + 4 = 9604$ **(ii)** $99^2 = (100 - 1)^2 = 100^2 - 2(100) + 1^2 = 10,000 - 200 + 1 = 9801$ **(iii)** $997^2 = (1000 - 3)^2 = 1000^2 - 2(3000) + 3^2 = 1,000,000 - 6000 + 9 = 994,009$
22. (a) False. Let $x = 3, y = ^-5$, then $|x + y| = 2$ but $|x| + |y| = 8$. **(b)** True. If $x \geq 0$ and $y \geq 0$, then $xy \geq 0$ and hence $|xy| = xy$ and $|x| \cdot |y| = x \cdot y$. If $x \leq 0$ and $y \geq 0$, then $xy \leq 0$ and $|xy| = ^-(xy)$, also $|x| |y| = ^-x \cdot y = ^-(xy)$. Similarly, for $x \geq 0$ and $y \leq 0$. Finally, if $x \leq 0$ and $y \leq 0$, then $xy \geq 0$ and hence $|xy| = xy$, also $|x| \cdot |y| = (^-x)(^-y) = xy$.
(c) True. Because $x^2 \geq 0$, $|x^2| = x^2$. **(d)** True. By parts (b) and (c); $|x|^2 = |x| \cdot |x| = |x \cdot x| = |x^2| = x^2$.
23. (a) The sums are 9 times the middle number.
(b) Let a be the middle number. Then we have the following 9 numbers:

$a - 8$	$a - 7$	$a - 6$
$a - 1$	a	$a + 1$
$a + 6$	$a + 7$	$a + 8$

The sum of these numbers is $9a$, which is 9 times the middle number.
24. (a) $8, 11, d = 3$, nth term is $3n - 13$ **(b)** $^-8, ^-11$, $d = ^-3$, nth term is $^-3n + 13$ **(c)** $^-128, ^-256, r = 2$, nth term $^-(2)^n$ **(d)** $^-128, 256, r = ^-2$, nth term is $(^-2)^n$ **(e)** $2^7, ^-2^8, r = ^-2$, nth term is $2 \cdot (^-2)^{n-1}$ or $^-(^-2)^n$
25. (a) 13,850 **(b)** $^-13,850$
26. (a) $^-9, ^-6, ^-1, 6, 15$ **(b)** $^-2, ^-7, ^-12, ^-17, ^-22$
(c) $^-3, 3, ^-9, 15, ^-33$ **(d)** $0, 8, 0, 32, 0$
(e) $^-1, 4, ^-9, 16, ^-25$ **(f)** $9, 6, 1, 6, 15$
27. 7, 2
28. After 17 minutes. The temperature was $^-108°C$.
29. (a) Sometimes true. If $x \geq 0$ and $y \leq 0$, then $^-|x| \cdot |y| = ^-x \cdot (^-y) = xy$.
Similarly, the statement is true for $x \leq 0$ and $y \geq 0$.
(b) Always true. $(^-x)^3 = (^-x)^2(^-x) = x^2(^-x) = ^-(x^2 \cdot x) = ^-x^3$ **(c)** Sometimes true. True if, and only if, $x = 0$. If $x > 0$, $^-x^2$ is negative and x^2 is positive and hence the expressions cannot be equal. **(d)** Always true. For all x, $|x|$ is nonnegative and hence greater than $^-1$. **(e)** Sometimes true. If x and y are positive or zero, the statement is true. It can be shown that the statement is true if, and only if, $x + y > 0$.

Communication

30. No; it is not of the form $(a - b)(a + b)$.

31. $a^2 + 2a(^-b) + (^-b)^2$
$= a^2 + (^-2ab) + (^-b)^2$ since $2a(^-b) = ^-2ab$
$= a^2 - 2ab + (^-b)^2$
$= a^2 - 2ab + b^2$ since $(^-b)^2 = b^2$

32. (a) $(^-1) \cdot a + a = (^-1)a + 1 \cdot a$
$= (^-1 + 1)a$
$= 0 \cdot a$
$= 0$

(b) Part (a) implies that $(^-1) \cdot a$ is the additive inverse of a. Because ^-a is also the additive inverse of a, it follows that $(^-1)a = ^-a$.

33. $(^-a)b = [(^-1)a]b$
$= ^-1(ab)$ By the associative property of multiplication
$= ^-(ab)$ Problem 32(b)

34. $^-(a + b) = (^-1)(a + b)$ Problem 32(b)
$= (^-1)a + (^-1)b$ By distributive property
$= ^-a + ^-b$ Problem 32(b)

35. (a) The argument is logical if we assume that $(^-1)(^-1)$ is either 1 or $^-1$. That assumption, however, has a flaw; $(^-1)(^-1)$ could be an integer other than 1 or $^-1$.
(b) Yes. For example, if we assume that $(^-a)(^-b)$ is either $^-(ab)$ or ab, we could show in a similar way that $^-(ab)$ causes a contradiction.

36. Answers vary; for example, a student might reason that the 0 represents the border between the B.C. dates and the A.D. dates. The numbers that are negative represent years that are B.C., for example, $^-1000$ represents 1000 B.C. while 2000 represents A.D. 2000.

Open-Ended

37. Answers vary; for example, if the student answered only one problem and missed it, he or she would score $^-1$. If the student answered five correct and missed more than 20, he or she would receive a negative score. Any coordinate falling above the line $4x - y = 0$ would result in a negative score where x is the number of correct and y is the number of incorrect answers.

38. Answers vary depending on grade level and publisher of book selected.

Cooperative Learning

39. (a) Answers vary. For example, use negative quality points for an F. We could use 3 for A, 2 for B, 1 for C, 0 for D, and $^-1$ for F. **(b)** Answers vary.

40. Answers may vary.

Review Problems

41.

42. (a) 5 **(b)** $^-7$ **(c)** 0
43. (a) 14 **(b)** 21 **(c)** $^-4$ **(d)** 22
44. 400 lb

Ongoing Assessment 4-3

1. (a) True **(b)** True **(c)** True **(d)** True
(e) True **(f)** False, 6 is a factor of 30 not a multiple of 30.
2. (a) Yes **(b)** No **(c)** Yes **(d)** No **(e)** Yes
3. (a) 2, 3, 4, 6, 11 **(b)** 2, 3, 6, 9 **(c)** 2, 3, 5, 6, 10
(d) 2, 4 **(e)** 11 **(f)** none of them
4. (a) No, $17|34{,}000$ and $17 \nmid 15$, so $17 \nmid 34{,}015$.
(b) Yes, $17|34{,}000$ and $17|51$, so $17|34{,}051$. **(c)** No, $19|19{,}000$ and $19 \nmid 31$, so $19 \nmid 19{,}031$. **(d)** Yes, 5 is a factor of $2 \cdot 3 \cdot 5 \cdot 7$. **(e)** No, $5|2 \cdot 3 \cdot 5 \cdot 7$ and $5 \nmid 1$, so $5 \nmid (2 \cdot 3 \cdot 5 \cdot 7) + 1$.
5. (a) True by Theorem 4-1 **(b)** True by Theorem 4-2(b)
(c) None **(d)** True by Theorem 4-2(b) **(e)** True by Theorem 4-1
6. (a) True **(b)** False **(c)** False **(d)** True
(e) True **(f)** False **(g)** True
7. (a) Always **(b)** Sometimes **(c)** Never
(d) Always **(e)** Always **(f)** Sometimes
(g) Always
8. (a) A number is divisible by 16 if and only if the last four digits form a number divisible by 16. **(b)** A number is divisible by 25 if, and only if, the number formed by the last two digits is divisible by 25.
9. 85,041
10. (a) 7 **(b)** 7 **(c)** 6
11. (a) Any digit 0 through 9 **(b)** 1, 4, 7
(c) 1, 3, 5, 7, 9 **(d)** 7 **(e)** 7
12. 17
13. Each bar costs 19¢.
14. (a) Yes **(b)** No **(c)** Yes **(d)** Yes
15. (a) 1, 2, 4, 5, 8, 11 **(b)** 4 TD's with extra points and 4 field goals or 1 TD and 11 field goals **(c)** 5 field goals
16.

(a)	4	4	4
(b)	8	8	8
(c)	3	12	3
(d)	8	26	8
(e)	2	20	2

(f) The remainder when n is divided by 9 is equal to the remainder when the sum of the digits of n is divided by 9.
17. (a) $12{,}343 + 4546 + 56 = 16{,}945$; $4 + 1 + 2 = 7$ has a remainder of 7 when divided by 9, as does $1 + 6 + 9 + 4 + 5$.
(b) $987 + 456 + 8765 = 10{,}208$; $6 + 6 + 8 = 20$ has a remainder of 2 when divided by 9, as does $1 + 0 + 2 + 0 + 8 = 11$.
(c) $10{,}034 + 3004 + 400 + 20 = 13{,}458$; $8 + 7 + 4 + 2 = 21$ has a remainder 3 when divided by 9, as does $1 + 3 + 4 + 5 + 8$. **(d)** Answers vary.
(e) $1003 - 46 = 957$; $4 - 1 = 3$ has a remainder of 3 when divided by 9, as does $9 + 5 + 7 = 21$.

(f) $345 \cdot 56 = 19,320$. 345 has a remainder of 3 when divided by 9; 56 has a remainder of 2 when divided by 9; $3 \cdot 2 = 6$ and $345 \cdot 56 = 19,320$ when divided by 9.
(g) Answers vary.
18. (a) 1, 3, and 7 divide n. 1 divides every number. Also, because $n = 21 \cdot d, d \in I$, then $n = (3 \cdot 7)d = 3(7d) = 7(3d)$, which implies that n is divisible by 3 and by 7. **(b)** 1, 2, 4, and 8 divide n. 1 divides every number. Also, because $16|n$, then $n = 16 \cdot d, d \in I$. Therefore, $n = (2 \cdot 8)d = 2(8d) = 8(2d) = 4(4d)$. Hence n is divisible by 2, 4, and 8.
19. (a) All of the numbers are divisible by 11. **(b)** Yes, by definition all four-digit palindromes are in the form *abba* for integers a and b. (a might equal b.) The divisibility test for 11 states that the number is divisible by 11 if $11|(a + b) - (b + a)$ or $11|0$. Because $11|0$, then 11 divides the four-digit palindrome. **(c)** No, for example, consider 12,321 which is a five-digit palindrome and it is not divisible by 11.
(d) Yes, a six-digit palindrome is in the form *abccba* for integers $a, b,$ and c where $a, b,$ and c do not have to be distinct. Therefore 11 divides the palindrome if $11|(a + c + b) - (b + c + a)$ or $11|0$. Because $11|0$, then 11 divides the six-digit palindrome.
20. In a palindromic pair, the sum of the digits in one number is the same as the sum of the digits in the other number. Therefore if 3 divides one number, then 3 must divide the other number.
21. (a) Yes, if $5|x$ and $5|y$, then $5|(x + y)$. **(b)** Yes, if $5|y$, then $5|(^-y)$. If $5|x$ and $5|(^-y)$, then $5|(x + (^-y))$ or $5|x - y$.
(c) Yes, if $5|x$, then 5 divides all the multiples of x and in particular $5|xy$. **(d)** No, $5|5$ and $5|10$, but $5\nmid(10/5)$.
22. 6,868,395 is divisible by 15 because it is divisible by both 3 and 5. The last digit is 5 and the sum of the digits is 45, which is divisible by 3.
23. (a) False; $2|4$, but $2\nmid1$ and $2\nmid3$ **(b)** False (same example as in 23 (a)) **(c)** False; $12|72$ but $12\nmid8$ and $12\nmid9$
(d) True **(e)** False; if $a = 5$ and $b = ^-5$, then $a|b$ and $b|a$, but $a \neq b$. **(f)** True **(g)** False; $2\nmid3$ and $2\nmid9$ but $2|(3 + 9)$ **(h)** False; $50|10^2$, but $50\nmid10$
(i) False; $50\nmid10$, but $50|100$
24. Suppose that $d|a, d\nmid b,$ and $d|(a + b)$. $d|a$ implies that there exists an integer c such that $cd = a$. $d|(a + b)$ implies that there exists an integer e such that $ed = a + b$. Using substitution: $ed = cd + b$
$$ed - cd = b$$
$$(e - c)d = b$$
which implies $d|b$. This contradicts the assumption that $d\nmid b$. Therefore $d\nmid(a + b)$.
25. Let $n = a \cdot 10^4 + b \cdot 10^3 + c \cdot 10^2 + d \cdot 10 + e$.
$$a \cdot 10^4 = a \cdot (10,000) = a \cdot (9999 + 1) = a \cdot 9999 + a$$
$$b \cdot 10^3 = b \cdot (1000) = b \cdot (999 + 1) = b \cdot 999 + b$$
$$c \cdot 10^2 = c \cdot (100) = c \cdot (99 + 1) = c \cdot 99 + c$$
$$d \cdot 10 = d \cdot (10) = d \cdot (9 + 1) = d \cdot 9 + d$$
Thus, $n = (a \cdot 9999 + b \cdot 999 + c \cdot 99 + d \cdot 9) + (a + b + c + d + e)$. Because $9|9, 9|99, 9|999, 9|9999$, it follows that if

$9|a + b + c + d + e$ then $9|[(a \cdot 9999 + b \cdot 999 + c \cdot 99 + d \cdot 9) + (a + b + c + d + e)]$; that is, $9|n$. If, on the other hand, $9\nmid(a + b + c + d + e)$, it follows that $9\nmid n$.
26. (a) The result is always 9. **(b)** The result is always 18.
(c) Let the number be $a \cdot 10 + b$. The number with the digits reversed is $b \cdot 10 + a$.
$$\text{Now, } a \cdot 10 + b - (b \cdot 10 + a) = a \cdot 10 + b - b \cdot 10 - a$$
$$= a \cdot 10 - a + b - b \cdot 10$$
$$= 9a - 9b$$
$$= 9(a - b)$$
Thus, the difference is a multiple of 9.
(d) The result is a multiple of 9.

Communication

27. No, both 6 and 9 are multiples of 3 and 1895 is not divisible by 3, so 1895 is not divisible by either 6 or 9.
28. (a) Yes, $d|n$ because a display of 32 implies that $n = 32 \cdot d$ and this implies that $d|n$. **(b)** No, $d\nmid n$ because the display implies that n is not a multiple of d. If the display was 16, then $d|n$.
29. (a) Yes, $4|52,832$, so 4 divides any integer times 52,832. Therefore 4 divides $52,832 \cdot 324,518$, which is the area.
(b) Yes, 2 is a factor of 52,834 and 2 is a factor of 324,514, so $2 \cdot 2$ or 4 is a factor of $52,834 \cdot 324,514$ which is the area.
30. No, the multiples of 3 occur every third number in the natural numbers, that is, 1, 2, **3**, 4, 5, **6**, 7, 8, **9**, 10, 11, **12**, ... Therefore if a natural number is chosen at random it will either be a multiple of 3 or one less or one more than a multiple of 3. In no case can you find three consecutive natural numbers none of which is a multiple of 3.
31. (a) No. If $5\nmid d$ for any integer d, then there is no integer m such that $5m = d$. If we assume $10|d$, this means there exists n such that $10n = d$ or $5(2n) = d$. This contradicts the original assumption that d is not divisible by 5. **(b)** Yes. All odd multiples of 5 are not divisible by 10 but are divisible by 5.
32. Suppose a number n has the digits $a, b, c, \ldots, n, n \in I$, repeated exactly 3 times. Then the sum of the digits is $3a + 3b + 3c + \ldots + 3n$ or $3(a + b + c + \ldots + n)$. By the divisibility test for 3, this implies that $3|n$.
33. 243; Yes; Consider any number n of the form *abcabc*. Then we have the following:
$$n = (a \cdot 10^5) + (b \cdot 10^4) + (c \cdot 10^3) + (a \cdot 10^2) + (b \cdot 10^1) + c$$
$$= a(10^5 + 10^2) + b(10^4 + 10^1) + c(10^3 + 1)$$
$$= a(100,000 + 100) + b(10,000 + 10) + c(1001)$$
$$= a(1001 \cdot 100) + b(1001 \cdot 10) + c(1001)$$
$$= (1001)[(a \cdot 100) + b(10) + c(1)]$$
$$= (7 \cdot 11 \cdot 13)[(a \cdot 100) + b(10) + c(1)]$$
Therefore, $7|n, 11|n,$ and $13|n$.
34. $abcd = a \cdot 10^3 + b \cdot 10^2 + c \cdot 10 + d$
$$= a \cdot (91 \cdot 11 - 1) + b(9 \cdot 11 + 1) + c(11 - 1) + d$$
$$= [(a \cdot 91 + b \cdot 9 + c) \cdot 11] + [^-a + b - c + d].$$

The integer in the first set of brackets is a multiple of 11 and hence divisible by 11. The integer in the second set of brackets is $d - c + b - a$. If that integer is divisible by 11 then the sum of the brackets is divisible by 11 and if it is not divisible by 11 the sum is not divisible by 11.

Open-Ended

35. **(a)** Answers vary; for example, upon inspection of the given numbers we notice that all the numbers are multiples of 3. Since 3 divides each number, then 3 divides the sum of any of the numbers. Because 100 is not divisible by 3, there is no winning combination of the given numbers that will sum to 100.
(b) Answers vary; for example, since many of these multiples of 3 sum to 99 ($33 + 66, 45 + 51 + 3$, etc.), the company could place at most 1000 cards with the number 1 on the card. This would ensure that there are at most 1000 winners. Other numbers could also be used.

Cooperative Learning

36. Answers vary.

Review Problems

37. **(a)** $^-2$ **(b)** No such integers exist **(c)** No such integers exist **(d)** All integers **(e)** No such integers exist **(f)** All positive integers
38. **(a)** $5x - 1$ **(b)** x^2 **(c)** $x - y$ **(d)** 1
39. **(a)** $f(^-5) = 10 - 3 = 7$ **(b)** $^-10$
(c) No. If $^-2x - 3 = 2$, then $^-2x = 5$, which has no solution in integers. **(d)** The set of all odd integers.
40. **(a)** Profit of $\$^-400$, that is, a loss of $400.
(b) $P(x) = 2x - 1800$ **(c)** 900

Ongoing Assessment 4-4

1. 30
2. (a) Prime **(b)** Not prime **(c)** Not prime
(d) Prime **(e)** Prime **(f)** Prime
3. (a)
```
            504
           /\
          2  252
            /\
           2  126
             /\
            2  63
              /\
             3  21
               /\
              3  7
```
$504 = 2^3 \cdot 3^2 \cdot 7$
(b)
```
      2475
     /\
    3  825
      /\
     3  275
       /\
      5  55
        /\
       5  11
```
$2475 = 3^2 \cdot 5^2 \cdot 11$

(c)
```
      11250
     /\
    2  5625
      /\
     3  1875
       /\
      3  625
        /\
       5  125
         /\
        5  25
          /\
         5  5
```
$11250 = 2 \cdot 3^2 \cdot 5^4$
4. (a)
```
          210
         /  \
        2   105
           /  \
          21   5
         /  \
        3    7
```
(b) You could multiply the $2 \cdot 3 \cdot 7 \cdot 5$.
5. 73
6. (a) $1 \times 48, 2 \times 24, 3 \times 16, 4 \times 12$
(b) Only one, 1×47.
7. Yes; 177 flotillas of one ship each, one flotilla of 177 ships; 59 flotillas of three ships each; three flotillas of 59 ships.
8. **(a)** 3, 5, 15, 29 people **(b)** 145 committees of 3; 87 committees of 5; 29 committees of 15; 15 committees of 29.
9. (a) 1, 2, 3, 4, 6, 9, 12, 18, or 36 **(b)** 1, 2, 4, 7, 14, or 28
(c) 1 or 17 **(d)** 1, 2, 3, 4, 6, 8, 9, 12, 16, 18, 24, 36, 48, 72, or 144
10. 27,720
11. 90
12. (a) The Fundamental Theorem of Arithmetic says that n can be written as a product of primes in one and only one way. Since $2|n$ and $3|n$ and 2 and 3 are both prime, they must be included in the unique factorization.
That is, $2 \cdot 3 \cdot p_1 \cdot p_2 \cdot \ldots \cdot p_m = n$.
Therefore, $(2 \cdot 3)(p_1 \cdot p_2 \cdot \ldots \cdot p_m) = n$.
Thus, $6|n$.
(b) Yes. If $a|n$, there exists an integer c such that $ca = n$. If $b|n$, there exists an integer d such that $db = n$.
Therefore, $(ca)(db) = n^2$
$(cd)(ab) = n^2$.
Hence, $ab|n^2$.
13. $97^2 = 9409$
14. 101, 103, 107, 109, 113, 127, 131, 137, 139, 149, 151, 157, 163, 167, 173, 179, 181, 191, 193, 197, 199
15. 3, 5; 5, 7; 11, 13; 17, 19; 29, 31; 41, 43; 59, 61; 71, 73; 101, 103; 107, 109; 137, 139; 149, 151; 179, 181; 191, 193; 197, 199
16. Every number would have its "usual" factorization $1(p_1 \cdot p_2 \cdot p_3 \cdot \ldots \cdot p_n)$, along with infinitely many other such factorizations because $1^n = 1$; n may be any natural number.
17. 1, 2, 3, 6, 7, 14, 21
18. No, because 5^z has no factors of either 2 or 3.

19. There are infinitely many composites of the form 1, 11, 111, 1111, 11111, 111111 . . . since every third member of this sequence will be divisible by 3.

20. The numbers 9, 21, 33, 45, . . . , which are in arithmetic sequence with the difference 12, belong to the original sequence and are divisible by 3.

21. If $2N = 2^6 \cdot 3^5 \cdot 5^4 \cdot 7^3 \cdot 11^7$, then $N = 2^5 \cdot 3^5 \cdot 5^4 \cdot 7^3 \cdot 11^7 = (2 \cdot 3 \cdot 5 \cdot 7 \cdot 11)$ $(2^4 \cdot 3^4 \cdot 5^3 \cdot 7^2 \cdot 11^6)$, which implies that $(2 \cdot 3 \cdot 5 \cdot 7 \cdot 11)$ is a factor of N.

22. Yes, because $(3^2 \cdot 2^4) \cdot (3^2 \cdot 2^3) = 3^4 \cdot 2^7$.

23. (a) $3 \cdot 5 \cdot 7 \cdot 11 \cdot 13$ is composite because it is divisible by 3, 5, 7, 11, and 13. **(b)** $(3 \cdot 4 \cdot 5 \cdot 6 \cdot 7 \cdot 8) + 2 = 2((3 \cdot 2 \cdot 5 \cdot 6 \cdot 7 \cdot 8) + 1)$ and so it is composite. **(c)** $(3 \cdot 5 \cdot 7 \cdot 11 \cdot 13) + 5 = 5((3 \cdot 7 \cdot 11 \cdot 13) + 1)$ and so it is composite. **(d)** $10! + 7 = 7((10 \cdot 9 \cdot 8 \cdot 6 \cdot 5 \cdot 4 \cdot 3 \cdot 2 \cdot 1) + 1)$ and so it is composite. **(e)** $10! + k$ can be factored as in part (d) for the given values of k and so it is composite.

24. $2^3 \cdot 3^2 \cdot 25^3$ is not a prime factorization because 25 is not prime. The prime factorization is $2^3 \cdot 3^2 \cdot 5^6$.

25. (a) 4, 6, 8, 0, or 5 **(b)** 1 and 9 **(c)** 23, 29, 31, 37, 53, 59, 71, 73, 79 **(d)** Answers vary. For example, 233 or 373.

26. No. $4 | 6 \cdot 10$ but $4 \nmid 6$ and $4 \nmid 10$.

27. (a) $2^{35} \cdot 3^{35} \cdot 7^{40}$ **(b)** $2^{200} \cdot 3^{40} \cdot 5^{200}$ **(c)** $2 \cdot 3^6 \cdot 5^{110}$ **(d)** 2311

28. If $p | ab$ then $ab = kp$ where k is some whole number. Thus p is in the prime factorization of ab. If p were not in the prime factorization of a nor of b, we could factor ab into a product of primes that does not include p. By the Fundamental Theorem of Arithmetic each integer greater than 1 has only one prime factorization so ab cannot be factored in one way to include p and in another not to include p.

Communication

29. In any set of three consecutive numbers, there is one number that is divisible by 3 and at least one of the other two numbers is divisible by 2. Therefore the product will be divisible by 2 and by 3 and so it is divisible by 6.

30. In any set of four consecutive numbers, there are one or two numbers divisible by 3, a number divisible by 4, and a number divisible by 2 but not 4. Therefore the product of the four consecutive numbers will have 2, 4, and 3 as distinct factors and so the product is divisible by $2 \cdot 3 \cdot 4 = 24$.

31. No, they are not both correct. Using 3 and 4 is correct because they have no common divisors. But 2 and 6 have a common divisor of 2. Using this test will ensure only that the number is divisible by 6.

32. The multiples of 4, 8, and 10 were crossed out with the multiples of 2. The multiples of 6 were crossed out when the multiples of 2 and 3 were crossed out. The multiples of 9 were crossed out when the multiples of 3 were crossed out. All

composite numbers less than 100 must have a factor less than or equal to 10 and these are all accounted for. Therefore the remaining numbers that have not been crossed out are prime.

33. Let $a = 2 \cdot 3 \cdot 5 \cdot 7$ and $b = 11 \cdot 13 \cdot 17 \cdot 19$. Then each prime p less than or equal to 19 appears in the prime factorization of a or of b but not in both. If p is in the prime factorization of a, then $p | a$ but $p \nmid b$ and hence $p \nmid a + b$. A similar argument holds if p is in prime factorization of b.

34. 91 eggs. Let n be the number of eggs in the basket, then $n - 1$ is a multiple of 3 and of 5. Hence $n - 1 = 3 \cdot 5k$ for some integer k. Thus, $n = 15k + 1$. We know that $n \leq 100$ and that $7 | n$. We substitute $k = 1, 2, 3, . . .$ to obtain the following values for n that are less than or equal to 100:

$$16, 31, 46, 61, 76, 91$$

Among these values, only 91 is divisible by 7. Hence, $n = 91$.

35. Suppose n is composite and d its least positive divisor other than 1. We need to show that d is prime. Suppose that some prime p less than d will divide d and hence will divide n, which contradicts the fact that d is the smallest divisor of n greater than 1.

36. (a) No, only perfect squares have an odd number of divisors. **(b)** The perfect squares less than 1000 are $1^2, 2^2, 3^2, . . . 31^2$. Therefore there are 31 perfect squares between 1 and 1000, and hence 31 numbers with an odd number of divisors. Consequently $1000 - 31$, or 969, numbers between 1 and 1000 have an even number of divisors. Clearly the student is wrong.

37. (a) Each prime in the list divides $2 \cdot 3 \cdot 5 \cdot 7 \cdot . . . \cdot p$ but does not divide the sum $2 \cdot 3 \cdot 5 \cdot 7 \cdot . . . \cdot p + 1$. **(b)** Since $N > 1$, some prime appears in the prime factorization of N and hence it divides N. If N is prime then because $N | N$, some prime still divides N. **(c)** Make p the discovered prime. The argument assures us that there is a prime greater than p. **(d)** Yes. The argument assures us that for each prime we can find a greater prime. **(e)** Apply the argument for $p = 19$.

Open-Ended

38. (a) Answers vary. **(i)** 25 **(ii)** 21 **(iii)** 16 **(iv)** 16 **(b)** 13, in the interval 100–199 **(c)** **(i)** 8 **(ii)** 7 **(iii)** 4 **(iv)** 6 **(d)** Answers vary.

39. Answers vary depending on the size of the print. If the number was typed, then there are about 10 numbers per inch. Therefore, there are 65,050/10 in., or 542.08 ft, of numbers. Using standard 8 1/2 in. paper, it would take about 765.3 sheets of paper to print the number in a single line or 12.75 sheets if printed 60 lines per page.

40. (a) (i) $1 + 2 + 3 + 4 + 6 = 16$, so 12 is abundant. **(ii)** $1 + 2 + 4 + 7 + 14 = 28$, so 28 is perfect. **(iii)** $1 + 5 + 7 = 13$, so 35 is deficient. **(b)** Answers vary; for example, 10 and 14 are deficient, 18 is abundant, and 496 and 8128 are perfect.

Cooperative Learning

41. The students must have had the first 23 prime numbers for the number of tiles; that is, 2, 3, 5, 7, 11, 13, 17, 19, 23, 29, 31, 37, 41, 43, 47, 53, 59, 61, 67, 71, 73, 79, 83 tiles. Therefore the number of tiles is the sum of the first 23 prime numbers, which is 874 tiles.

Review Problems

42. (a) False **(b)** True **(c)** True **(d)** True
43. (a) 2, 3, 6 **(b)** 2, 3, 5, 6, 9, 10
44. If $12|n$, there exists an integer a such that $12a = n$.
$(3 \cdot 4)\, a = n$
$\quad 3(4a) = n$
Thus, $3|n$.
45. Yes, among 8 people. Each would get \$422.

Ongoing Assessment 4-5

1. (a) $D_{18} = \{1, 2, 3, 6, 9, 18\}$
$D_{10} = \{1, 2, 5, 10\}$
$\text{GCD}(18, 10) = 2$
$M_{18} = \{18, 36, 54, 72, 90, \ldots\}$
$M_{10} = \{10, 20, 30, 40, 50, 60, 70, 80, 90, \ldots\}$
$\text{LCM}(18, 10) = 90$
(b) $D_{24} = \{1, 2, 3, 4, 6, 8, 12, 24\}$
$D_{36} = \{1, 2, 3, 4, 6, 9, 12, 18, 36\}$
$\text{GCD}(24, 36) = 12$
$M_{24} = \{24, 48, 72, 96, 120, 144, 168, \ldots\}$
$M_{36} = \{36, 72, 108, 144, 180, \ldots\}$
$\text{LCM}(24, 36) = 72$
(c) $D_8 = \{1, 2, 4, 8\}$
$D_{24} = \{1, 2, 3, 4, 6, 8, 12, 24\}$
$D_{52} = \{1, 2, 4, 13, 26, 52\}$
$\text{GCD}(8, 24, 52) = 4$
$M_8 = \{8, 16, 24, 32, 40, 48, 56, 64, 72, 80, 88, 96, \ldots\}$
$M_{24} = (24, 48, 72, 96, 120, 144, 168, 192, 216, 240, 264, 288, 312, \ldots)$
$M_{52} = \{52, 104, 156, 208, 260, 312, \ldots\}$
$\text{LCM}(8, 24, 52) = 312$
(d) $\text{GCD}(7, 9) = 1$
$\text{LCM}(7, 9) = 7 \cdot 9 = 63$
2. (a) $132 = 2^2 \cdot 3 \cdot 11$
$504 = 2^3 \cdot 3^2 \cdot 7$
$\text{GCD}(132, 504) = 2^2 \cdot 3 = 12$
$\text{LCM}(132, 504) = 2^3 \cdot 3^2 \cdot 7 \cdot 11 = 5544$
(b) $65 = 5 \cdot 13$
$1690 = 2 \cdot 5 \cdot 13^2$
$\text{GCD}(65, 1690) = 5 \cdot 13 = 65$
$\text{LCM}(65, 1690) = 2 \cdot 5 \cdot 13^2 = 1690$
(c) $96 = 2^5 \cdot 3$
$900 = 2^2 \cdot 3^2 \cdot 5^2$
$630 = 2 \cdot 3^2 \cdot 5 \cdot 7$
$\text{GCD}(96, 900, 630) = 2 \cdot 3 = 6$
$\text{LCM}(96, 900, 630) = 2^5 \cdot 3^2 \cdot 5^2 \cdot 7 = 50{,}400$

(d) $108 = 2^2 \cdot 3^3$
$360 = 2^3 \cdot 3^2 \cdot 5$
$\text{GCD}(108, 360) = 2^2 \cdot 3^2 = 36$
$\text{LCM}(108, 360) = 2^3 \cdot 3^3 \cdot 5 = 1080$
(e) GCD is 1, LCM is $11 \cdot 19$
3. (a) $\text{GCD}(2924, 220) = \text{GCD}(220, 64) = \text{GCD}(64, 28) = \text{GCD}(28, 8) = \text{GCD}(8, 4) = \text{GCD}(4, 0) = 4$
(b) $\text{GCD}(14{,}595, 10{,}856) = \text{GCD}(10{,}856, 3739) = \text{GCD}(3739, 3378) = \text{GCD}(3378, 361) = \text{GCD}(361, 129) = \text{GCD}(129, 103) = \text{GCD}(103, 26) = \text{GCD}(26, 25) = \text{GCD}(25, 1) = 1$ **(c)** $\text{GCD}(123{,}152, 122{,}368) = \text{GCD}(122{,}368, 784) = \text{GCD}(784, 64) = \text{GCD}(64, 16) = \text{GCD}(16, 0) = 16$
4. (a) 72 **(b)** 1440 **(c)** 630 **(d)** $9^{100} \cdot 25^{100}$
5. (a) $220 \cdot 2924/4$, or 160,820 **(b)** $14{,}595 \cdot 10{,}856/1$, or 158,443,320 **(c)** $123{,}152 \cdot 122{,}368/16$, or 941,866,496
6. $\text{GCD}(6, 10) = 2$, $\text{LCM}(6, 10) = 30$
7. (a) $\text{LCM}(15, 40, 60) = 120$ minutes = 2 hours. So the clocks alarm again together at 8:00 A.M. **(b)** No
8. 24
9. 24 nights
10. 15 cookies
11. After 7 1/2 hours, or 2:30 A.M.
12. 36 minutes
13. (a) ab **(b)** $\text{GCD}(a, a) = a$; $\text{LCM}(a, a) = a$
(c) $\text{GCD}(a^2, a) = a$; $\text{LCM}(a^2, a) = a^2$ **(d)** $\text{GCD}(a, b) = a$; $\text{LCM}(a, b) = b$ **(e)** $\text{GCD}(a, b) = 1$; $\text{LCM}(a, b) = ab$
(f) $a|b$ **(g)** $b|a$
14. (a) True. If a and b are even, then $\text{GCD}(a, b) \geq 2$.
(b) True. $\text{GCD}(a, b) = 2$ implies that a and b are even. **(c)** False. The GCD could be a multiple of 2; for example, $\text{GCD}(8, 12) = 4$. **(d)** False. For $a \neq b$, $\text{LCM} > \text{GCD}$.
(e) True, by Theorem 4-8 **(f)** True. If the $\text{GCD}(a, b) > a$, then the GCD could not divide a. **(g)** True. If $\text{LCM}(a, b) < a$, then the LCM could not be a multiple of a.
15. (a) 15 **(b)** 1
16. (a) $4 = 2^2$. Since 97,219,988,751 is odd, it has no prime factors of two. Consequently, 1 is their only common divisor and they are relatively prime. **(b)** 11 only has prime factor 11. 181,345,913 is not divisible by 11. Therefore 1 is the only common divisor and they're relatively prime.
17. 20th caller
18. \$48
19. 120 days
20. Two packages of plates, four packages of cups, and three packages of napkins
21. 12 revolutions
22. 3 for gear 1, 5 for gear 2, and 2 for gear 3
23. (a)

Prime factors of 10   Prime factors of 15
Prime factors of 8
Prime factors of 60

(b) Prime factors of 8   Prime factors of 16

Prime factors of 24

24. $1, 2, 2^2, 2^3, \ldots, 2^{20}$

25. $\{1, 2, 3, 4, 6, 7, 8, 9, 11, 12, 13, 14, 16, 17, 18, 19, 21, 22, 23, 24\}$

Communication

26. No, the set of common multiples is infinite and therefore there could be no greatest common multiple.

27. Answers vary; most teachers will use an example such as 6. The divisors are $\{1, 2, 3, 6\}$ whereas the multiples of 6 are $\{6, 12, 18, 24, 30, 36, \ldots\}$.

28. No; for example, consider $GCD(2, 4, 10) = 2$, $LCM(2, 4, 10) = 20$, and the $GCD \cdot LCM = (2 \cdot 20) = 40$ while $abc = 2 \cdot 4 \cdot 10 = 80$.

29. The length of a side of each square is 6 meters and there will be 18,786 such squares. One way to approach the problem is as follows: Let n be the length (in meters) of a side of each square. Suppose there are x such squares laying on the longer side of the plot and y on the shorter side. Then $nx = 1212$ and $ny = 558$. Because we are looking for the largest possible square we need to find the largest possible n, that is, the $GCD(1212, 558)$. Using the Euclidean algorithm we find the GCD to be 6. Hence $x = \dfrac{1212}{6} = 202$ and $y = \dfrac{558}{6} = 93$. Thus, the number of squares is $202 \cdot 93$, or 18,786.

30. No. Let $a = 2 \cdot 3$, $b = 3 \cdot 5$, $c = 5 \cdot 7$. Then $GCD(a, b, c) = 1$ but $GCD(a, b) = 3$ and $GCD(b, c) = 5$.

31. Yes. The hypothesis implies that 2 is a common divisor of a, b, and c. If a number greater than 2 divided a, b, and c, then in particular that number would have to divide a and b, which is impossible because $GCD(a, b) = 2$. Thus, $GCD(a, b, c) = 2$.

32. The LCM equals the product of the numbers if and only if the numbers have no prime factors in common. Because $GCD(a, b) \cdot LCM(a, b) = ab$, $LCM(a, b) = ab$ if and only if $GCD(a, b) = 1$; that is, a and b have no prime factors in common.

33. No. Answers vary; one way is to notice that $LCM(a, b) = \dfrac{ab}{GCD(a, b)}$. Because $GCD(a, b) \geq 1$, it follows that $LCM(a, b) \leq ab$.

Open-Ended

34. Answers vary.

35. Answers vary.

36. Answers vary. From the answer to problem 33 it follows that $LCM(a, b) < ab$ if and only if $GCD(a, b) > 1$; that is, if and only if a and b have at least one prime in common.

37. Answers vary. If a and b are relatively prime, then **(a)** $GCD(2a, 2b) = 2$. **(b)** $GCD(6a, 6b) = 6$. **(c)** $GCD(91a, 91b) = 91$.

Cooperative Learning

38. Answers vary.

Review Problems

39. $x = 15,625$; $y = 64$

40. **(a)** 83,151; 83,451, 83,751 **(b)** 86,691 **(c)** 10,396

41. No, 3 divides the sum of the digits and therefore 3 divides 3111.

42. Answers may vary. $30,030 = 2 \cdot 3 \cdot 5 \cdot 7 \cdot 11 \cdot 13$

43. 27,720

44. 43

Ongoing Assessment 4-6

1. 2:00 P.M.

2. **(a)** 3 **(b)** 2 **(c)** 6 **(d)** 8 **(e)** 3 **(f)** 4 **(g)** Does not exist **(h)** 10

3. **(a)** 2 **(b)** 1 **(c)** 2 **(d)** 4 **(e)** 1 **(f)** 1 **(g)** 2 **(h)** 4

4. **(a)**

$\oplus$	1	2	3	4	5	6	7
1	2	3	4	5	6	7	1
2	3	4	5	6	7	1	2
3	4	5	6	7	1	2	3
4	5	6	7	1	2	3	4
5	6	7	1	2	3	4	5
6	7	1	2	3	4	5	6
7	1	2	3	4	5	6	7

(b) $6 = 5 \ominus 6$; $4 = 2 \ominus 5$ **(c)** Every subtraction problem can be written as an addition problem, which can always be performed.

5. **(a)**

$\otimes$	1	2	3	4	5	6	7
1	1	2	3	4	5	6	7
2	2	4	6	1	3	5	7
3	3	6	2	5	1	4	7
4	4	1	5	2	6	3	7
5	5	3	1	6	4	2	7
6	6	5	4	3	2	1	7
7	7	7	7	7	7	7	7

(b) $3 \div 5 = 2$; $4 \div 6 = 3$ **(c)** Yes. Division by numbers other than 7 is possible since each row and column in the table contains every element 1 through 6.

6. **(a)** 10 **(b)** 9 **(c)** 7 **(d)** 7 **(e)** 1 **(f)** 6

7. **(a)** 2, 9, 16, 30 **(b)** 3, 10, 17, 24, 31 **(c)** $366 \equiv 2 (\bmod\ 7)$; Wednesday

8. **(a)** 4 **(b)** 0 **(c)** 0 **(d)** 7

9. **(a)** $x = 2k$, k is an integer **(b)** $x - 1 = 2k$ implies $x = 2k + 1$ where k is an integer. **(c)** $x - 3 = 5k$ implies $x = 3 + 5k$ where k is an integer.

Communication

10. Each wheel (or place) uses mod 10; that is, on the first wheel 25 tenths of a mile is congruent to 5 tenths of a mile. Most cars have four wheels, and so the odometer when considered as a whole is a mod 100,000 system.

Open-Ended

11. On a 12-hour clock, 12 is the additive identity, while for integers 0 is the additive identity. We define $^-3$ as the solution of the equation $x + 3 = 12$. Because $9 + 3 = 12$ we have $^-3 = 9$. In general if a is a whole number on the 12-hour clock, then $^-a = 12 - a$ and $^-12 = 12$. The last statement is analogous to $^-0 = 0$ in integers. Properties of additive inverse such as $^-(a + b) = {}^-a + {}^-b$ hold on the clock.

Cooperative Learning

12. **(b)** Only on the 11-hour clock **(c)** The rows and columns in each contain all the elements except the identity.

Chapter Review

1. **(a)** $^-3$ **(b)** a **(c)** 0 **(d)** $^-x - y$
(e) $x - y$ **(f)** $x + y$ **(g)** $^-32$ **(h)** $^-32$
2. **(a)** $^-7$ **(b)** 8 **(c)** 8 **(d)** 0 **(e)** 8 **(f)** 15
3. **(a)** 3 **(b)** $^-5$ **(c)** Any integer except 0
(d) No integer will work **(e)** $^-41$ **(f)** Any integer
4. $2(^-3) = {}^-6; 1(^-3) = {}^-3; 0(^-3) = 0$; if the pattern continued, then $^-1(^-3) = 3; {}^-2(^-3) = 6$.
5. **(a)** $10 - 5 = 5$ **(b)** $1 - (^-2) = 3$
6. **(a)** ^-x **(b)** $y - x$ **(c)** $3x - 1$
(d) $2x^2$ **(e)** 0 **(f)** $^-x^2 - 6x - 9$ **(g)** $4 - x^2$
7. **(a)** ^-2x **(b)** $x(x + 1)$ **(c)** $(x - 6)(x + 6)$
(d) $(9y^3 + 4x^2)(9y^3 - 4x^2)$ **(e)** $5(1 + x)$ **(f)** $(x - y)x$
8. **(a)** False; it is not positive for $x = 0$.
(b) False, if one value is positive and one is negative.
(c) False, if $b < 0$. **(d)** True
9. **(a)** $2/1 \neq 1/2$ **(b)** $3 - (4 - 5) \neq (3 - 4) - 5$
(c) 1/2 is not an integer **(d)** $8/(4 - 2) \neq 8/4 - 8/2$
10. **(a)** False **(b)** False **(c)** True **(d)** False; 12, for example **(e)** False; 9, for example
11. **(a)** False; 7|7 and 7∤3 yet 7|3 · 7
(b) False; 3∤(3 + 4) but 3|3 and 3∤4 **(c)** True
(d) True **(e)** True **(f)** False; 4∤2 and 4∤22 but 4|44
12. **(a)** Divisible by 2, 3, 4, 5, 6, 8, 9, 11 **(b)** Divisible by 3, 11
13. If 10,007 is prime, 17∤10,007. We know 17|17, so 17∤(10,007 + 17) by Theorem 4-2(b).
14. **(a)** 87<u>2</u>4; 87<u>5</u>4; 87<u>8</u>4 **(b)** 41,856; 44,856; 47,856 **(c)** 87,<u>1</u>74; 87,<u>4</u>64; 87,<u>7</u>54
15. **(a)** The student's claim is true. Examples vary.
(b) Let n be an integer. Then $n + (n + 1) + (n + 2) + (n + 3) + (n + 4) = 5n + 10 = 5(n + 2)$. Thus, the sum is divisible by 5.
16. **(a)** Composite **(b)** Prime

17. Check for divisibility by 3 and 8, 24|4152.
18. **(a)** 4 **(b)** 73
19. **(a)** $2^4 \cdot 5^3 \cdot 7^4 \cdot 13 \cdot 29$ **(b)** 77,562
20. Answers vary; for example, 16. To obtain 5 divisors, we raise a prime (2) to the $(5 - 1)$ power.
21. 1, 2, 3, 4, 6, 8, 9, 12, 16, 18, 24, 36, 48, 72, 144
22. **(a)** $2^2 \cdot 43$ **(b)** $2^5 \cdot 3^2$ **(c)** $2^2 \cdot 5 \cdot 13$
(d) $3 \cdot 37$
23. The LCM of all positive integers less than or equal to 10 is $2^3 \cdot 3^2 \cdot 5 \cdot 7$, or 2520.
24. $0.31
25. 9:30 A.M.
26. We know that the GCD$(a, b) \cdot$ LCM$(a, b) = ab$. Because GCD$(a, b) = 1$, then LCM$(a, b) = ab$.
27. 5 packages
28. 15 minutes
29. 71 lattes. Because $9869 = 71 \cdot 139$ and 71 as well as 139 are prime, she sold 71 lattes at $1.39 each.
30. We first show that among any three consecutive odd integers, there is always one that is divisible by 3. For that purpose, suppose that the first integer in the triplet is not divisible by 3. Then by the division algorithm that integer can be written in the form $3n + 1$ or $3n + 2$ for some integer n. Then the three consecutive odd integers are $3n + 1, 3n + 3, 3n + 5$ or $3n + 2, 3n + 4, 3n + 6$. In the first triplet $3n + 3$ is divisible by 3, and in the second $3n + 6$ is divisible by 3. This implies that if the first odd integer is greater than 3 and not divisible by 3, then the second or the third must be divisible by 3, and hence cannot be prime.
31. $n = a \cdot 10^2 + b \cdot 10 + c$
$n = a(99 + 1) + b(9 + 1) + c$
$n = 99a + 9b + c + b + a$
Since $9|99a$ and $9|9b$, $9|[99a + 9b + (a + b + c)]$ if, and only if, $9|(a + b + c)$
32. Friday
33. mod 360. It would cover all the area encircling the lighthouse.

Chapter 5

Ongoing Assessment 5-1

1. **(a)** The solution to $8x = 7$ is 7/8. **(b)** Jane ate seven of her eight pieces of candy. **(c)** The ratio of boys to girls is seven to eight.
2. **(a)** 1/6 **(b)** 1/4 **(c)** 2/6 or 1/3 **(d)** 7/12
(e) 5/16 **(f)** 2/16 = 1/8
3. **(a)** 2/3 **(b)** 4/6 or 2/3 **(c)** 6/9 or 2/3
(d) 8/12 or 2/3. The diagram illustrates the Fundamental Law of Fractions.
4. **(a)**

$$0 \quad \frac{1}{5} \quad \frac{2}{5} \quad \frac{3}{5} \quad \frac{4}{5} \quad 1$$

(b) ●●●○○

(c)

(d)

(e)

(f)

5. (a) No, not equal parts   **(b)** Yes   **(c)** Yes
6. (a) 9/24 or 3/8   **(b)** 12/24 or 1/2   **(c)** 4/24 or 1/6
(d) 8/24 or 1/3
7. (a) 4/18, 6/27, 8/36   **(b)** $^-$4/10, 2/$^-$5, $^-$10/25
(c) 0/1, 0/2, 0/4   **(d)** 2a/4, 3a/6, 4a/8
8. (a) 52/31   **(b)** 3/5   **(c)** $^-$5/7   **(d)** 0/1
(e) 144/169   **(f)** It is simplified.
9. Impossible to determine. Because 20/25 = 24/30 = 4/5, the same fraction of students passed in each class, but the actual scores in one class could have been higher than in the other.
10. (a) undefined   **(b)** undefined   **(c)** 0   **(d)** cannot be simplified   **(e)** cannot be simplified   **(f)** 2/3   **(g)** 5/3
11. (a) $\dfrac{a-b}{3}$ **(b)** 2x/9y **(c)** a/1   **(d)** 1/(3 + b)
12. (a) equal   **(b)** equal   **(c)** equal   **(d)** not equal
13. (a) not equal   **(b)** not equal   **(c)** equal   **(d)** not equal
14. Yes, 1/32 in.
15.

 $\rightarrow$

16. 36/48
17. A. 3 minutes
18.

19. (a) $2\dfrac{7}{8}$ in.   **(b)** $2\dfrac{3}{8}$ in.   **(c)** $1\dfrac{3}{8}$ in.   **(d)** $\dfrac{7}{8}$ in.

20. (a) False, $\dfrac{ab+c}{b} = \dfrac{ab}{b} + \dfrac{c}{b} = a + \dfrac{c}{b}$
(b) False; because we have additions, the Fundamental Law of Fractions does not hold.
(c) True, $\dfrac{ab+ac}{ac} = \dfrac{a(b+c)}{ac} = \dfrac{b+c}{c}$

21. (a) 32/3   **(b)** $^-$36   **(c)** x is any rational number except 0
22. (a) $a = b, c \neq 0$ **(b)** $b = c \neq 0$ or $a = 0$, but $b \neq 0$ and $c \neq 0$.
23. (a) $N \subseteq W \subseteq I \subseteq Q$
(b)

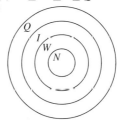

24. Bren's class
25. (a) >   **(b)** >   **(c)** <   **(d)** <   **(e)** =   **(f)** =
26. (a) $\dfrac{11}{13}, \dfrac{11}{16}, \dfrac{11}{22}$ **(b)** $\dfrac{^-1}{5}, \dfrac{^-19}{36}, \dfrac{^-17}{30}$
27. $\dfrac{a}{b} < 1$ and $\dfrac{c}{d} > 0$ imply $\dfrac{a}{b} \cdot \dfrac{c}{d} < 1 \cdot \dfrac{c}{d}$ or $\dfrac{a}{b} \cdot \dfrac{c}{d} < \dfrac{c}{d}$.
28. We need to show that $\dfrac{n}{n+1} < \dfrac{n+1}{n+2}$. This inequality is equivalent to $n^2 + 2n < n^2 + 2n + 1$, or $0 < 1$.

29. Answers may vary. The following are possible answers.
(a) $\dfrac{10}{21}, \dfrac{11}{21}$ **(b)** $\dfrac{^-22}{27}, \dfrac{^-23}{27}$ **(c)** $\dfrac{997}{1200}, \dfrac{998}{1200}$ **(d)** $0, \dfrac{1}{2}$
30. (a) 1   **(b)** 1   **(c)** The ratios are the same. To show this, let x equal the top circled number. Then the sum of the circled numbers is $x + (x + 12) + (x + 19) + (x + 31) = 4x + 62$. The sum of the four interior numbers is $(x + 10) + (x + 11) + (x + 20) + (x + 21) = 4x + 62$. Here the ratio is always 1.
31. 456 mi
32. (a) 6/16, or 3/8 of a pound; 6/32,000, or 3/16,000 of a ton
(b) $\dfrac{10}{100}$, or $\dfrac{1}{10}$ **(c)** $\dfrac{15}{60}$, or $\dfrac{1}{4}$ **(d)** $\dfrac{8}{24}$, or $\dfrac{1}{3}$

Communication

33. Because there are 24 hours in a day, there must be 24 time zones on the earth.
34. Each class does not have to have the same number of females. One class could have 8 females in a class of 24 and another could have 12 females in a class of 36.
35. The new fraction is equal to $\dfrac{1}{2}$. The principle can be generalized as follows:

$$\frac{a}{b} = \frac{ar_1}{br_1} = \frac{ar_2}{br_2} = \frac{ar_3}{br_3} = \ldots = \frac{ar_n}{br_n} =$$
$$\frac{a(r_1 + r_2 + r_3 + \ldots + r_n)}{b(r_1 + r_2 + r_3 + \ldots + r_n)} = \frac{a}{b}.$$

36. No; depends on the context of problem. Answers vary.
37. (a) Suppose the rational numbers are $\dfrac{2}{16}$ and $\dfrac{1}{4} \cdot \dfrac{1}{4} > \dfrac{2}{16}$. Iris is incorrect.   **(b)** Suppose the rational numbers are $\dfrac{5}{1}$ and $\dfrac{1}{2} \cdot \dfrac{5}{1} > \dfrac{1}{2}$. Shirley is incorrect.

38. The points determined by the coordinates lie along a line. Students will not realize this yet, but essentially they are graphing points along the line with slope $\frac{1}{3}$.

39. Because 36 in. = 1 yd, then to convert x in. to yards, we could consider how to write equivalent fractions 36/1 and $x/1$ unknown yards. By seeing how many 36's are in x, we could determine the unknown number of yards. Because 1 in. = 1/36 yd, the process to convert yards to inches could be accomplished using similar methods.

Open-Ended

40. Frequently in recipes, measurements are found in fractional parts of cups, teaspoons, tablespoons. For example, a recipe might call for 1/2 teaspoon of salt and 2/3 cup of flour.

41. Answers will certainly vary. Some mathematics educators argue that positive and negative integers are easier for students to comprehend than are rational numbers. Such educators also argue that the operations on integers are easier than are operations on rational numbers.

Cooperative Learning

42. (a) Answers vary, students must work together to determine the heights and to order the people according to height. For example, if the heights are 60″, 52″, 56″, and 58″, the fractions could be $\frac{60}{60}, \frac{52}{60}, \frac{56}{60},$ and $\frac{58}{60}.$
(b) Answers vary depending on part (a).

Ongoing Assessment 5-2

1. (a)

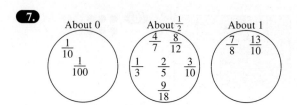

$$\frac{1}{2} + \frac{2}{3} = \frac{14}{12}, \text{ or } \frac{7}{6}$$

$$\frac{1}{2} = \frac{6}{12} \qquad \frac{2}{3} = \frac{8}{12}$$

(b) $\frac{-4}{12}$ or $\frac{-1}{3}$ **(c)** $\frac{5y - 3x}{xy}$ **(d)** $\frac{-3y + 5x + 14y^2}{2x^2y^2}$

(e) $\frac{71}{24}$ or $2\frac{23}{24}$ **(f)** $\frac{-23}{3}$ or $-7\frac{2}{3}$

2. (a) $18\frac{2}{3}$ **(b)** $2\frac{4}{5}$ **(c)** $-2\frac{93}{100}$ **(d)** $-5\frac{7}{8}$

3. (a) $\frac{27}{4}$ **(b)** $\frac{15}{2}$ **(c)** $\frac{-29}{8}$ **(d)** $\frac{-14}{3}$

4. $\frac{2}{6} + \frac{5}{8}$

5. (a) 1/3, high **(b)** 1/6, low **(c)** 3/4, low
(d) 1/2, high
6. (a) Beavers **(b)** Ducks **(c)** Bears **(d)** Tigers
(e) Lions **(f)** Wildcats, Badgers

7.

About 0	About $\frac{1}{2}$	About 1
$\frac{1}{10}$ $\frac{1}{100}$	$\frac{4}{7}$ $\frac{8}{12}$ $\frac{1}{3}$ $\frac{2}{5}$ $\frac{3}{10}$ $\frac{9}{18}$	$\frac{7}{8}$ $\frac{13}{10}$

8. (a) 1/2, high **(b)** 0, low **(c)** 3/4, high **(d)** 1, high
(e) 1, low **(f)** 0, high **(g)** 3/4, low **(h)** 1/2, high
9. (a) 2 **(b)** 3/4 **(c)** 0 **(d)** 0
10. (a) 1/4 **(b)** $5\frac{1}{8}$ **(c)** 0 **(d)** 10
11. (a) A **(b)** H **(c)** T **(d)** H
12. Approximately $4 \cdot 3 = 12.$
13. $\frac{1}{4}$

14. (a) $\frac{1}{30}$ **(b)** $\frac{2}{20}$ or $\frac{1}{10}$ **(c)** $\frac{1}{60}$ **(d)** No, the total number of dollars might have been greater in 1990 than in 2000, but the fraction of the total dollars might still be greater in 2000.

15. $6\frac{7}{12}$ yards

16. $1\frac{3}{4}$ cups

17. $2\frac{5}{6}$ yards

18. $22\frac{1}{8}$ inches

19. (a) Team 4, $76\frac{11}{16}$ pounds **(b)** $3\frac{11}{16}$ pounds

20. (a) $\frac{1}{2} + \frac{3}{4} \in Q$ **(b)** $\frac{1}{2} + \frac{3}{4} = \frac{3}{4} + \frac{1}{2}$
(c) $\left(\frac{1}{2} + \frac{1}{3}\right) + \frac{1}{4} = \frac{1}{2} + \left(\frac{1}{3} + \frac{1}{4}\right)$

21. (a) $\frac{3}{2}, \frac{7}{4}, 2$; arithmetic; $\frac{1}{2} - \frac{1}{4} = \frac{3}{4} - \frac{1}{2} = 1 - \frac{3}{4} = \frac{5}{4} - 1$
(b) $\frac{6}{7}, \frac{7}{8}, \frac{8}{9}$; not arithmetic; $\frac{2}{3} - \frac{1}{2} \neq \frac{3}{4} - \frac{2}{3}$ **(c)** $\frac{17}{3}, \frac{20}{3}, \frac{23}{3}$; arithmetic; $\frac{5}{3} - \frac{2}{3} = \frac{8}{3} - \frac{5}{3} = \frac{11}{3} - \frac{8}{3} = \frac{14}{3} - \frac{11}{3}$
(d) $\frac{-5}{4}, \frac{-7}{4}, \frac{-9}{4}$; arithmetic;
$\frac{3}{4} - \frac{5}{4} = \frac{1}{4} - \frac{3}{4} = \frac{-1}{4} - \frac{1}{4} = \frac{-3}{4} - \left(\frac{-1}{4}\right)$

22. (a) $\frac{1}{4}n$ **(b)** $\frac{n}{n+1}$ **(c)** $\frac{3n-1}{3}$ or $n - \frac{1}{3}$
(d) $\frac{-2n+7}{4}$ or $\frac{7}{4} - \frac{1}{2}n$

23. $1, \frac{7}{6}, \frac{8}{6}, \frac{9}{6}, \frac{10}{6}, \frac{11}{6}, 2$

24. (a) (i) $\frac{3}{4}$ **(ii)** $\frac{25}{12}$, or $2\frac{1}{12}$ **(iii)** 0
(b) (i) $\frac{1}{4}$ **(ii)** $\frac{-7}{4}$ **(iii)** $\frac{-1}{4}$

25. (a) $f(0) = {}^-2$ **(b)** $f({}^-2) = 0$ **(c)** $f({}^-5) = \dfrac{1}{2}$
(d) $f(5) = \dfrac{7}{4}$

26. (a) (i) $\dfrac{1}{4} + \dfrac{1}{3 \cdot 4} = \dfrac{1}{4} + \dfrac{1}{12} = \dfrac{16}{48} = \dfrac{1}{3}$
(ii) $\dfrac{1}{5} + \dfrac{1}{4 \cdot 5} = \dfrac{1}{5} + \dfrac{1}{20} = \dfrac{25}{100} = \dfrac{1}{4}$
(iii) $\dfrac{1}{6} + \dfrac{1}{5 \cdot 6} = \dfrac{1}{6} + \dfrac{1}{30} = \dfrac{36}{180} = \dfrac{1}{5}$
(h) $\dfrac{1}{n} = \dfrac{1}{n + 1} + \dfrac{1}{n(n + 1)}$

Communication

27. It might be easier but she would be incorrect. Think of the numerator as the number of pieces of pie cut into the denominator's value of slices. Then to add the pieces of pie, we would add the numerators and have that number of pieces.
28. (a) Yes. If *a, b, c,* and *d* are integers, $b \neq 0$, $d \neq 0$, then $\dfrac{a}{b} - \dfrac{c}{d} = \dfrac{ad - bc}{bd}$ is a rational number.
(b) No. For example,
$\dfrac{1}{2} - \dfrac{1}{4} \neq \dfrac{1}{4} - \dfrac{1}{2}$ **(c)** No. For example,
$\dfrac{1}{2} - \left(\dfrac{1}{4} - \dfrac{1}{8}\right) \neq \left(\dfrac{1}{2} - \dfrac{1}{4}\right) - \dfrac{1}{8}.$ **(d)** No. If there is an identity for subtraction it must be 0, since only for 0 does $\dfrac{a}{b} - 0 = \dfrac{a}{b}.$ However, in general $0 - \dfrac{a}{b} \neq \dfrac{a}{b} - 0$, and hence there is no identity. **(e)** No. Since there is no identity, an inverse cannot be defined.
29. (a) Like digits are being canceled. **(b)** Numerators and denominators are both being added. **(c)** Numerators and denominators of fractional portions are both being subtracted. **(d)** Multiplication is by *a/a* rather than by *a*/1.

Open-Ended

30. (a) (i) $\dfrac{1}{3} = \dfrac{1}{4} + \dfrac{1}{12}$; $\dfrac{1}{3} = \dfrac{1}{6} + \dfrac{1}{6}$
(ii) $\dfrac{1}{7} = \dfrac{1}{8} + \dfrac{1}{56}$; $\dfrac{1}{7} = \dfrac{1}{14} + \dfrac{1}{14}$
(b) $\dfrac{1}{n} - \dfrac{1}{n + 1} = \dfrac{(n + 1) - n}{n(n + 1)} = \dfrac{1}{n(n + 1)}$
(c) Based on part (b), $\dfrac{1}{n} = \dfrac{1}{n + 1} + \dfrac{1}{n(n + 1)}.$ Therefore,
$\dfrac{1}{17} = \dfrac{1}{18} + \dfrac{1}{17(18)} = \dfrac{1}{18} + \dfrac{1}{306}.$ Also, $\dfrac{1}{17} = \dfrac{1}{34} + \dfrac{1}{34}.$

Cooperative Learning

31. Depending on the people interviewed, students may hear an answer like the following from a teacher: I use fractions in determining total grades for my classes. For example, if a paper is 1/2 of the grade and a test is another 1/3 of the grade, I need to know what fractional part of the grade is yet to be determined.

Review Problems

32. (a) $\dfrac{2}{3}$ **(b)** $\dfrac{13}{17}$ **(c)** $\dfrac{25}{49}$ **(d)** $\dfrac{a}{1}$, or *a* **(e)** simplified
33. (a) equal **(b)** not equal **(c)** equal **(d)** not equal
34. (a) February **(b)** The answer depends upon whether the year is a leap year. If it is a leap year, the answer is 185/366; if not, the answer is 184/365. **(c)** Most people consider there to be 365 1/4 days in a year. As an improper fraction, this number is 1461/4.
35. Greater than, consider $\dfrac{a}{b}$ and $\dfrac{a + x}{b + x}$ when $a < b$ $\dfrac{a}{b} < \dfrac{a + x}{b + x}$ because $ab + ax < ab + bx$. This is true because $a < b$ and $x > 0$ imply $ax < bx$.

Ongoing Assessment 5-3

1. (a) $\dfrac{1}{4} \cdot \dfrac{1}{3} = \dfrac{1}{12}$ **(b)** $\dfrac{2}{4} \cdot \dfrac{3}{5} = \dfrac{6}{20}$
2. (a) **(b)**

(c)

3. (a) $\dfrac{1}{5}$ **(b)** $\dfrac{b}{a}$ **(c)** $\dfrac{za}{x^2 y}$ **(d)** $\dfrac{35}{4}$, or $8\dfrac{3}{4}$
(e) $\dfrac{44}{3}$, or $14\dfrac{2}{3}$ **(f)** $\dfrac{-25}{4}$, or $-6\dfrac{1}{4}$
4. (a) $10\dfrac{1}{2}$ **(b)** $8\dfrac{1}{3}$ **(c)** $24{,}871\dfrac{1}{20}$
5. (a) $^-3$ **(b)** $\dfrac{3}{10}$ **(c)** $\dfrac{y}{x}$ **(d)** $\dfrac{-1}{7}$
6. (a) 26 **(b)** 29 **(c)** 92 **(d)** 18 **(e)** 6 **(f)** 7
(g) 9 **(h)** $2\dfrac{1}{4}$
7. (a) 20 **(b)** 16 **(c)** 2 **(d)** 1
8. (a) 18 **(b)** 25 **(c)** 7 **(d)** 6
9. (a) Less than 1 **(b)** Less than 1 **(c)** Greater than 2
(d) Less than 4 **(e)** Greater than 4
10. (c)
11. $\dfrac{29}{36}$
12. 9600 students
13. 400 students
14. $\dfrac{1}{6}$
15. (a) 39 uniforms **(b)** $\dfrac{1}{4}$ yd
16. \$240

17. (a) $121,000 **(b)** $90,000 **(c)** $300,000
18. 246 pages
19. $225
20. (a) Peter, 30 min.; Paul, 25 min.; Mary, 20 min.
(b) Peter, 10; Paul, 12; Mary, 15
21. (a) $89\frac{3}{5}°$F **(b)** $^-40°$C
22. $2253\frac{1}{8}$
23. 32 marbles
24. 120 1/4 lb
25. (a) $1/3^{13}$ **(b)** 3^{13} **(c)** 5^{11} **(d)** 5^{19} **(e)** $1/(^-5)^2$, or $1/5^2$ **(f)** a^5 **(g)** a^2 **(h)** $1/a$
26. (a) $(1/2)^{10}$ **(b)** $(1/2)^{15}$ **(c)** $(2/3)^9$ **(d)** 1
(e) $(3/5)^{11}$ **(f)** $(5/6)^{21}$
27. (a) False. $2^3 \cdot 2^4 \neq (2 \cdot 2)^{3+4}$ **(b)** False.
$2^3 \cdot 2^2 \neq (2 \cdot 2)^{3 \cdot 4}$ **(c)** False. $2^3 \cdot 2^3 \neq (2 \cdot 2)^{2 \cdot 3}$
(d) False. $a^0 = 1$ if $a \neq 0$ **(e)** False. $(2 + 3)^2 \neq 2^2 + 3^2$
(f) False. $(2 + 3)^{-2} \neq \frac{1}{2^2} + \frac{1}{3^2}$ **(g)** False. $2^{2 \cdot 3} \neq 2^2 \cdot 2^3$
(h) True. $\left(\frac{a}{b}\right)^{-1} = \frac{1}{a/b} = \frac{b}{a}$
28. (a) 5 **(b)** 6 or $^-6$ **(c)** $^-2$ **(d)** $^-4$ **(e)** 0
(f) 15
29. (a) $2 \cdot 10^{11}$ **(b)** $2 \cdot 10^5$
30. (a) $x \leq 4$ **(b)** $x \leq 1$ **(c)** $x \geq 2$ **(d)** $x \geq 1$
31. (a) $\left(\frac{1}{2}\right)^3$ **(b)** $\left(\frac{3}{4}\right)^8$ **(c)** $\left(\frac{4}{3}\right)^{10}$ **(d)** $\left(\frac{4}{5}\right)^{10}$
(e) $\left(\frac{4}{3}\right)^{10}$ **(f)** $\left(\frac{3}{4}\right)^{100}$
32. (a) 10^{10} **(b)** $10^{10} \cdot \left(\frac{6}{5}\right)^2 = 1.44 \cdot 10^{10} = 14.4$ billion
33. (a) $2S = 2\left(\frac{1}{2} + \frac{1}{2^2} + \ldots + \frac{1}{2^{64}}\right) = 1 + \frac{1}{2} + \frac{1}{2^2} + \ldots + \frac{1}{2^{63}}$
(b) Note that $2S = 1 + S - \frac{1}{2^{64}}$. Hence,
$2S - S = 1 + S - \frac{1}{2^{64}} - S = 1 - \frac{1}{2^{64}}$. **(c)** $1 - \frac{1}{2^n}$
34. (a) $1\frac{49}{99}$ **(b)** $25 \cdot \left(2\frac{49}{99}\right) = 62\frac{37}{99}$
35. (a) $\frac{3}{4}$ **(b)** 24 **(c)** $\frac{3}{128}$ **(d)** $^-9$
36. (a) $\frac{3}{2}, \frac{3}{4}, \frac{3}{8}, \frac{3}{16}, \frac{3}{32}$ **(b)** Each of the four ratios is $\frac{1}{2}$.
(c) $\frac{3}{1024}$
37. (a) 32^{50}, since $32^{50} = (2^5)^{50} = 2^{250}$ and $4^{100} = (2^2)^{100} = 2^{200}$
(b) $(^-3)^{-75}$, since $(^-27)^{-15} = (^-3)^{-45} = \frac{^-1}{3^{45}} < \frac{^-1}{3^{75}}$
38. (a) $n(n + 1) + \left(\frac{1}{2}\right)^2$ **(b)** $\left(n + \frac{1}{2}\right)^2 = n^2 + 2n \cdot \frac{1}{2} + \left(\frac{1}{2}\right)^2 = n^2 + n + \left(\frac{1}{2}\right)^2 = n(n + 1) + \left(\frac{1}{2}\right)^2$

39. (a) First 3, second 4, third 5. Guess 6. The guess is correct
since $\left(1 + \frac{1}{1}\right)\left(1 + \frac{1}{2}\right)\left(1 + \frac{1}{3}\right)\left(1 + \frac{1}{4}\right)\left(1 + \frac{1}{5}\right) =$
$5\left(1 + \frac{1}{5}\right) = 6$ **(b)** 102 **(c)** $n + 2$
40. $0 < \frac{a}{b} < \frac{c}{d}$ so that $0 < \frac{1}{2} \cdot \frac{a}{b} < \frac{1}{2} \cdot \frac{c}{d}$.
Also $0 < \frac{a}{b} = \frac{1}{2} \cdot \frac{a}{b} + \frac{1}{2} \cdot \frac{a}{b} < \frac{1}{2} \cdot \frac{a}{b} + \frac{1}{2} \cdot \frac{c}{d} = \frac{1}{2}\left(\frac{a}{b} + \frac{c}{d}\right)$.
Similarly, $\frac{1}{2}\left(\frac{a}{b} + \frac{c}{d}\right) < \frac{c}{d}$, and therefore $0 < \frac{a}{b} <$
$\frac{1}{2}\left(\frac{a}{b} + \frac{c}{d}\right) < \frac{c}{d}$.

Communication

41. Never less than n. $0 < \frac{a}{b} < 1$ implies $0 < 1 < \frac{b}{a}$. The last
inequality implies $0 < n < n \cdot \left(\frac{b}{a}\right)$. Also $n \div \left(\frac{a}{b}\right) = n \cdot \frac{b}{a} > n$.
42. B is the closest. Because both C and D are less than 1, their product should be less than either.
43. The second number must be the reciprocal of the first and must be less than 1.
44. (a) $2 \div 1 \neq 1 \div 2$ **(b)** $(1 \div 2) \div 3 \neq 1 \div (2 \div 3)$
(c) There is no rational number a such that
$2 \div a = a \div 2 = 2$. **(d)** Because there is no identity, there can be no inverse.

Open-Ended

45. Answers will vary about class use. 7 ounces

Cooperative Learning

46. The answers depend on the size of the bricks and the size of the joints. In all likelihood, the measurements will be made in fractions of inches for the size of the joints. The size of the bricks may be done in inches. An alternative is to measure in centimeters. Thus, all measurement is approximate and some rounding or estimation may occur.

Review Problems

47. (a) $\frac{25}{16}$, or $1\frac{9}{16}$ **(b)** $\frac{25}{18}$, or $1\frac{7}{18}$ **(c)** $\frac{5}{216}$
(d) $\frac{259}{30}$, or $8\frac{19}{30}$ **(e)** $\frac{37}{24}$, or $1\frac{13}{24}$ **(f)** $\frac{^-39}{4}$, or $^-9\frac{3}{4}$
48. 120 students

Ongoing Assessment 5-4

1. (a) $5:21$ **(b)** $21:5$ **(c)** $21:26$ **(d)** Answers vary. For example, minor.
2. (a) 30 **(b)** $^-3\frac{1}{3}$ **(c)** $23\frac{1}{3}$ **(d)** $10\frac{1}{2}$

3. 36 lb

4. 2469 teenage drivers

5. $1.19

6. 270 mi

7. 64 pages

8. 72 min for 30 in.

9. **(a)** 42, 56 **(b)** 24 and 32 (or $^-$24 and $^-$32)

10. 500 ft $\times$ 900 ft

11. $14,909.09; $29,818.18; $37,272.73

12. $77 and $99

13. 135

14. **(a)** 1:6 **(b)** 1:1 **(c)** 7:12

15. Answers vary; for example,

$\dfrac{1¢}{3 \text{ oz}} = \dfrac{3¢}{9 \text{ oz}}; \quad \dfrac{3¢}{9 \text{ oz}} = \dfrac{2¢}{6 \text{ oz}}; \quad \dfrac{1¢}{3 \text{ oz}} = \dfrac{12¢}{36 \text{ oz}}$

16. **(a)** 5/7 **(b)** 6 ft

17. 120 ft

18. 8 days

19. **(a)** 27 **(b)** 20

20. Approximately 34 cm

21. 312 lb

22. **(a)** 2:5. Because the ratio is 2:3, there are $2x$ boys and $3x$ girls; hence, the ratio of boys to all students is $2x/(2x + 3x) = 2/5.$ **(b)** $m:(m + n)$

23. **(a)** 2/3 tsp mustard seeds, 1 c scallions, $2\dfrac{1}{6}$ c beans

(b) 2/3 tsp mustard seeds, 2 c tomato sauce, $2\dfrac{1}{6}$ c beans

(c) 7/13 tsp mustard seeds, $1\dfrac{8}{13}$ c tomato sauce, $\dfrac{21}{26}$ c scallions

24. 15.12 Ω

25. 20 additional teachers

26. 35 ft

27. 74.6 cm

28. The ratio between the mass of the gold in the ring and the mass of the ring is 18/24. If x is the number of ounces of pure gold in the ring that weighs 0.4 oz we have $18/24 = x/0.4.$ Hence $x = (18 \cdot 0.4)/24,$ or 0.3 oz. Consequently, the price of the gold in the ring is $0.3 \cdot \$300,$ or $90.

29. **(a)**

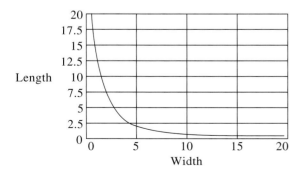

(b) $WL = 10$ **(c)** $W = 10/L$ **(d)** $L = 10/W$

30. **(a)** 1:2 **(b)** Let $\dfrac{a}{b} = \dfrac{c}{d} = \dfrac{e}{f} = r.$

Then $a = br$
$\quad c = dr$
$\quad e = fr.$

So, $a + c + e = br + dr + fr$
$\quad a + c + e = r(b + d + f)$
$\quad \dfrac{a + c + e}{b + d + f} = r.$

31. **(a)** $\dfrac{a}{b} = \dfrac{c}{d}$ implies $\dfrac{a}{b} + 1 = \dfrac{c}{d} + 1,$ which implies

$\dfrac{a + b}{b} = \dfrac{c + d}{d}.$ **(b)** By inverting $\dfrac{b}{a} = \dfrac{d}{c}$ and by part (a),

$\dfrac{b + a}{a} = \dfrac{d + c}{c}.$ Then inverting again gives $\dfrac{a}{a + b} = \dfrac{c}{d + c}.$

(c) $\dfrac{a}{b} = \dfrac{c}{d}$ implies $\dfrac{a}{b} - 1 = \dfrac{c}{d} - 1,$ which implies

$\dfrac{a - b}{b} = \dfrac{c - d}{d}.$ From part (a) and this last result, we have

$\dfrac{a + b}{b} + \dfrac{a - b}{b} = \dfrac{c + d}{d} + \dfrac{c - d}{d},$ which implies

$\dfrac{a + b}{a - b} = \dfrac{c + d}{c - d},$ which implies $\dfrac{a - b}{a + b} = \dfrac{c - d}{c + d}.$

Communication

32. **(a)** 40/700, or 4/70, or 2/35 **(b)** 525 cm
(c) For the first set, $\dfrac{\text{footprint length}}{\text{thighbone length}} = \dfrac{40}{100} = \dfrac{20}{50};$ i.e., a 50-cm thighbone would correspond to a 20-cm footprint. Thus it is not likely that the 50-cm thighbone is from the animal which left the 30 cm footprint. (Notice that $\dfrac{20}{50} \neq \dfrac{30}{50}.$)

33. No, the ratio of the prices is proportional to the ratio of the areas and not to the ratio of the diameters.

34. Answers vary. For example, you might tell Amy that the ration 5:6 means that there are 5 girls for every 6 boys but we don't know the total number of students. There could be 10 girls and 12 boys or there could be 15 girls and 18 boys and still have a ratio of 5:6.

35. Answer vary but the discussion should include the fact that two equal ratios form a proportion.

Open-Ended

36. Answers vary. For example, ratios and proportions are seen in census reports, economic data about joblessness, and baseball statistics.

37. **(a)** 57.6 lb per sq in. **(b)** Answers vary. For example, the wavelength of light times the frequency equals the speed of light (about $3 \cdot 10^8$ m/sec).

Cooperative Learning

38. Answers will vary depending on the texts chosen. Dimensional analysis is used to help keep ratios and proportions straight.

39. Just as financial analysts disagree on how to rate stocks, students will as well.

Review Problems

40. (a) 0 **(b)** 5 **(c)** 588/13, or 45 3/13

(d) $x \leq 588/13$, or $45\dfrac{3}{13}$.

41. All rational numbers except 0 have a multiplicative inverse.

42. 2, 2 1/4, 2 1/2, 2 3/4, 3

43. 256/9, or 28 4/9

44. (a) $\dfrac{3+3}{3} \neq \dfrac{3}{3} + 3$ **(b)** $\dfrac{4}{2+2} \neq \dfrac{4}{2} + \dfrac{4}{2}$

(c) $\dfrac{ab+c}{a} \neq \dfrac{ab+c}{a}$ **(d)** $\dfrac{a \cdot a - b \cdot b}{a-b} \neq \dfrac{a \cdot a - b \cdot b}{a-b}$

(e) $\dfrac{a+c}{b+c} \neq \dfrac{a+c}{b+c}$

Chapter Review

1. (a)   **(b)**

(c)

2. Answers may vary; for example, $\dfrac{10}{12}, \dfrac{15}{18}, \dfrac{20}{24}$

3. (a) $\dfrac{6}{7}$ **(b)** $\dfrac{ax}{b}$ **(c)** $\dfrac{0}{1}$ **(d)** $\dfrac{5}{9}$ **(e)** $\dfrac{b}{1}$ **(f)** $\dfrac{2}{27}$

4. (a) = **(b)** > **(c)** > **(d)** <

5. (a) $^{-}3, \dfrac{1}{3}$ **(b)** $^{-}3\dfrac{1}{7}, \dfrac{7}{22}$ **(c)** $\dfrac{^{-}5}{6}, \dfrac{6}{5}$ **(d)** $\dfrac{3}{4}, \dfrac{^{-}4}{3}$

6. $^{-}2\dfrac{1}{3}, -1\dfrac{7}{8}, 0, \left(\dfrac{71}{140}\right)^{300}, \dfrac{69}{140}, \dfrac{1}{2}, \dfrac{71}{140}, \left(\dfrac{74}{73}\right)^{300}$

7. Yes. By the definition of multiplication and the commutative and associative laws of addition, we can do the following:

$$\frac{4}{5} \cdot \frac{7}{8} \cdot \frac{5}{14} = \frac{4 \cdot 7 \cdot 5}{5 \cdot 8 \cdot 14}$$
$$= \frac{4 \cdot 7 \cdot 5}{8 \cdot 14 \cdot 5}$$
$$= \frac{4}{8} \cdot \frac{7}{14} \cdot \frac{5}{5}.$$

8. (a) 24; because $\dfrac{1}{3}(8 \cdot 9)$ is equal to $\left(\dfrac{1}{3} \cdot 9\right) \cdot 8 = 3 \cdot 8 = 24$.

(b) 66; because $36 \cdot 1\dfrac{5}{6}$ is equal to $36 \cdot \dfrac{11}{6} = 6 \cdot 11 = 66$.

9. 17 pieces, $\dfrac{11}{6}$ yd

10. (a) 15 **(b)** 15 **(c)** 4

11. $\dfrac{a}{b} \div \dfrac{c}{d} = x$ if and only if $\dfrac{a}{b} = \dfrac{c}{d} \cdot x$. $x = \dfrac{d}{c} \cdot \dfrac{a}{b}$ is the solution of the equation because $\dfrac{c}{d} \cdot \left(\dfrac{d}{c} \cdot \dfrac{a}{b}\right) = \dfrac{a}{b}$.

12. 9

13. 76/100, 78/100, but answers may vary.

14. $\boxed{5}\,\boxed{0}\,\boxed{4}\,\boxed{7}\,\boxed{9}\,\boxed{2}\,\boxed{\times}\,\boxed{2}\,\boxed{3}\,\boxed{\frac{1}{x}}\,\boxed{=}$

15. $333\dfrac{1}{3}$ calories

16. 752 times

17. 240/1000 = 6/25

18. It is not reasonable to say that the university won $3/4 + 5/8$, or $\dfrac{11}{8}$, of its basketball games.

19. The numerators of the rational numbers are integers and follow the properties of integers; the same is true of the denominators. Thus both the numerator and denominator of the answer are integers, and we can apply another property of integers to determine the sign of the answer.

20. You should show him that the given fraction could be written as an integer over an integer. In this case, the result is 8/9.

21. 112 bags

22. 4/15

23. $^{-}12/10$ is greater than $^{-}11/9$ because $^{-}12/10 - (^{-}11/9)$ is a positive number.

24. (a) 3 **(b)** 3

25. The ratio of hydrogen to the total is 1:9. Therefore $\dfrac{1}{9} = \dfrac{x}{16}$ implies $x = 1\dfrac{7}{9}$ oz.

26. 560 fish

27. No. The ratio depends on how many chips came from each plant.

28. $1 : r^2$

Chapter 6

Ongoing Assessment 6-1

1. (a) $0 \cdot 10^0 + 0 \cdot 10^{-1} + 2 \cdot 10^{-2} + 3 \cdot 10^{-3}$

(b) $2 \cdot 10^2 + 0 \cdot 10^1 + 6 \cdot 10^0 + 0 \cdot 10^{-1} + 6 \cdot 10^{-2}$

(c) $3 \cdot 10^2 + 1 \cdot 10^1 + 2 \cdot 10^0 + 0 \cdot 10^{-1} + 1 \cdot 10^{-2} + 0 \cdot 10^{-3} + 3 \cdot 10^{-4}$ **(d)** $0 \cdot 10^0 + 0 \cdot 10^{-1} + 0 \cdot 10^{-2} + 0 \cdot 10^{-3} + 1 \cdot 10^{-4} + 3 \cdot 10^{-5} + 2 \cdot 10^{-6}$

2. (a) 4356.78 **(b)** 4000.608 **(c)** 40,000.03

(d) 0.2004007

3. (a) 536.0076 **(b)** 3.008 **(c)** 0.000436

(d) 5,000,000.2

4. (a) $\dfrac{436}{1000} = \dfrac{109}{250}$ **(b)** $\dfrac{2516}{100} = \dfrac{629}{25}$ **(c)** $\dfrac{^{-}316,027}{1000}$

(d) $\dfrac{281902}{10000} = \dfrac{140951}{5000}$ **(e)** $\dfrac{^{-}43}{10}$ **(f)** $\dfrac{^{-}6201}{100}$

5. (a) yes (b) yes (c) yes (d) yes (e) yes
(f) yes (g) no (h) yes (i) no (j) yes
6. (a) 0.8 (b) 3.05 (c) 0.5 (d) 0.03125
(e) 0.01152 (f) 0.2128 (h) 0.08 (i) 0.4
7. (a) 13.492, 13.49199, 13.4919, 13.49183
(b) ⁻1.4053, ⁻1.45, ⁻1.453, ⁻1.493
8. (a) 0.014 ln.
(b) 365.24 da
9.

There are 32 of 100 squares shaded representing $\frac{32}{100}$ of the whole grid, or 0.32 of the grid.

10. 0.84
11. For example, 8.3401
12. The number of digits in the terminating decimal is the greater of *m* or *n*.
13. $100{,}000^3 = 1000^5$ and these are the greatest.
14. Three-twenty-two could be interpreted as three hundred twenty-two, but the batting average is 0.322. A batting average cannot be greater than 1.000.
15. (a) A meaning could be as follows:
$3 \cdot 6^0 + 1 \cdot 6^{-1} + 4 \cdot 6^{-2} + 5 \cdot 6^{-3}$
(b) A meaning could be as follows:
$0 \cdot 7^0 + 0 \cdot 7^{-1} + 0 \cdot 7^{-2} + 3 \cdot 7^{-3} + 3 \cdot 7^{-4} + 4 \cdot 7^{-5}$
16. Rhonda, Martha, Kathy, Molly, Emily

Communication

17. Answers vary; for example, you would use 2 blocks to represent the units, 3 flats to represent the tenths, 4 longs to represent the hundredths, and 5 cubes to represent the thousandths. In this way each base-ten block represents 1/10 of the base-ten block to its left and there are enough base-ten blocks for all the numbers used.

18. Answers vary; for example, a fraction can be written as a terminating decimal if it can be written as a fraction with a denominator that is a power of 10. The denominator can be written as a power of 10 if it contains only factors of 2 and 5. Other factors may appear in the denominator if the fraction is not in simplest form. For example, in 28/35 the denominator of 35 has a factor of 7, but in its simplest form, 4/5, there is no factor of 7.

19. Answers vary; for example, a decimal point is a marker that tells how many units there are and how many parts of a unit there are. It is placed between the ones column and the tenths column to show where the whole number portion of the number ends and where the fractional part begins.

Open-Ended

20. Answers vary, but most countries will be similar to ours.
21. Answers vary depending on the textbooks chosen.

Cooperative Learning

22. Answers vary depending on the objects chosen.
For example, if a 5 × 5 flat is used to represent 1, then a 1 × 5 long would represent $\frac{1}{5}$, and a 1 × 1 unit would represent $\frac{1}{25}$.

Ongoing Assessment 6-2

1. $231.24
2. 35.83
3.

8.2	1.9	6.4
3.7	5.5	7.3
4.6	9.1	2.8

4. $8.00/lb
5. (a) It costs $3.21 to heat the house for one day.
(b) The light bulb would have to stay on 358.9 hr (rounded).
6. (a) Approx. 6391 cm³ (rounded to nearest cm³)
(b) Approx. 183 in.³ (rounded to nearest in.³)
7. 21.3 mi/hr (rounded to nearest tenth mile)
8. (a) 5.4, 6.3, 7.2 (b) 1.3, 1.5, 1.7 (c) 0.0625, 0.03125, 0.015625 (d) 6.7, 8.0, 9.3
9. No, the bank is over $7.74
10. (a) 0.0000000032
(b) 3,200,000,000
(c) 0.42
(d) 620,000
11. (a) $1.27 \cdot 10^7$
(b) $4.486 \cdot 10^9$
(c) $5 \cdot 10^7$
12. (a) 0.0000044
(b) 19,900
(c) 3,000,000,000
13. (a) $4.8 \cdot 10^{28}$
(b) $4 \cdot 10^7$
(c) $2 \cdot 10^2$
14. (a) 200 (b) 200 (c) 204
(d) 203.7 (e) 203.65
15. 19
16. 55 + 5 + 18 = 78 dollars.
17. Estimates may vary. Exact answers are the following:
(a) 122.06 (b) 57.31 (c) 25.40 (d) 136.15
18. Profit of $2098 (rounded to nearest dollar)
19. (a) 373.65 (b) $464 (c) 4 hundreds, 2 twenties because she needs $429.84
20. (a) 2.3 · 1 = 2.3; 8.7 · 9 = 78.3
(b) 1.3 · 2.4 = 3.12; 8.7 · 9.6 = 83.52
21. (a) 49,736.5281 (b) 41,235.6789

22. Answers vary; for example, $40 \cdot 6 = \$240$ plus

$\$40\left(\dfrac{1}{4}\right) = \$10$, so her salary is $250.

23. **(a)** 12 **(b)** 0.6 **(c)** 2b **(d)** (2b)

24. (a), (b), and (d) have equal quotients.

25. (a) 181.56 **(b)** 148.551

26. (a) Yes **(b)** No

27. Answers vary, for example, 10.3 because $9 \cdot 10 = 90$ and $9 \cdot 0.3$ is about 3.

28. (a) $1.5^2, 2.5^2$; $3 \cdot 4 + 0.25 = 3.5^2$; $4 \cdot 5 + 0.25 = 4.5^2$

(b) The above equations are correct.

(c) $n \cdot (n + 1) + 0.25 = (n + 0.5)^2$

Communication

29. Answers vary; for example, the multiplication of decimals is exactly like the multiplication of whole numbers if the decimal points are ignored. The difference occurs when the decimal point is placed to obtain the final answer.

30. Answers vary; for example, many of the estimation techniques that work for whole-number division also work for decimal division. The long division algorithm is more efficient when good estimates are used. Also, estimates are important to determine whether an answer obtained by long division is reasonable. Estimation techniques can also be used to place the decimal point in the quotient when decimals are divided.

31. Answers vary; for example, which form is easier depends on the numbers to be multiplied or divided. In most cases, it is probably easier to work with decimals because the algorithms work just as they do for whole numbers except for the placement of the final decimal point, which in turn is very easy. However, when infinite repeating decimals are involved it is much easier to work with fractions, for example, $\dfrac{2}{3} \cdot \dfrac{3}{4} = \dfrac{6}{12} = \dfrac{1}{2}$, or 0.5 versus $0.\overline{6} \cdot 0.75$.

32. Answers vary; for example, lining up the decimal points acts like using place value.

Open-Ended

33. Answers vary depending on the articles chosen.

34. Answers vary; for example, the calculator could be used to explore the result of placing the decimal point when multiplying by a power of 10 or of placing the decimal point when multiplying two decimals.

Cooperative Learning

35. Answers vary depending on groups. For example, students need to understand place value, expanded form, basic addition facts, and whole-number algorithms for addition. They also need to understand what a decimal point does and how place value is used with decimals.

36. Follow the flowchart and play the game.

Review Problems

37. $14.0479 = 1 \cdot 10^1 + 4 \cdot 10^0 + 0 \cdot 10^{-1} + 4 \cdot 10^{-2} + 7 \cdot 10^{-3} + 9 \cdot 10^{-4}$

38. $\dfrac{35}{56}$ is a terminating decimal.

39. Yes. For example, $\dfrac{13}{26} = \dfrac{1}{2} = 0.5$.

40. 0.625. The decimal terminates because $\dfrac{35}{56} = \dfrac{7}{8}$ in simplest form and $8 = 2^3$.

Ongoing Assessment 6-3

1. (a) $0.\overline{4}$ **(b)** $0.\overline{285714}$ **(c)** $0.\overline{27}$ **(d)** $0.0\overline{6}$
(e) $0.02\overline{6}$ **(f)** $0.0\overline{1}$ **(g)** $0.8\overline{3}$ **(h)** $0.0\overline{76923}$
(i) $0.0\overline{47619}$ **(j)** $0.\overline{157894736842105263}$

2. (a) $\dfrac{4}{9}$ **(b)** $\dfrac{61}{99}$ **(c)** $\dfrac{7}{5}$ **(d)** $\dfrac{5}{9}$ **(e)** $\dfrac{-211}{90}$ **(f)** $\dfrac{-2}{90}$

3. $^-1.454 > ^-1.45\overline{4} > ^-1.4\overline{54} > ^-1.4\overline{54} = ^-1.4\overline{5}$

4. (a) $1.\overline{6}, 2, 2.\overline{3}$ **(b)** $\dfrac{6}{7}, \dfrac{7}{8}, \dfrac{8}{9}$ or $0.\overline{857142}, 0.875, 0.\overline{8}$

5. (a) 6 digits **(b)** The answer is a rational number and there are 4 digits in the repetend.

6. Yes. Zeros can be repeated.

7. (a) Answers vary; for example, 3.221, 3.2211, 3.22111.
(b) Answers vary; for example, 462.2425, 462.2426, 462.2427

8. (a) $0.47\overline{2}$ **(b)** 1.05

9. (a) Answers vary; for example, 0.751, 0.752, 0.753.
(b) Answers vary; for example, 0.334, 0.335, 0.336.

10. (a) 8 **(b)** 7

11. (a) $\dfrac{1}{9}, \dfrac{1}{99}, \dfrac{1}{999}$ **(b)** $\dfrac{1}{9999}$ **(c)** $0.0\overline{1}$

12. (a) $\dfrac{2}{9}$ **(b)** $\dfrac{3}{9}$ or $\dfrac{1}{3}$ **(c)** $\dfrac{5}{9}$ **(d)** $\dfrac{25}{9}$ **(e)** 10

13. (a) $\dfrac{5}{99}$ **(b)** $\dfrac{3}{999}$ or $\dfrac{1}{333}$ **(c)** $\dfrac{322}{99}$ **(d)** $\dfrac{3122}{999}$

Communication

14. Yes. Zeros can be appended to any finite decimal to make it an infinite decimal.

15. Answers vary; for example, it is easier to compute addition of fractions when there is a common denominator, as in $\dfrac{1}{7} + \dfrac{5}{7}$. When nonrepeating decimals are involved it becomes hard to do additions because of lining up the place value. When denominators are different and terminating decimals are obtained, it is easier to use decimals, as in $\dfrac{2}{5} + \dfrac{1}{4} = 0.40 + 0.25 = 0.65$.

Open-Ended

16. (a) They each have six-digit repetends using each of the digits 1, 2, 4, 5, 7, 8 exactly once.   **(b)** Answers vary; for example, the patterns of the digits are cyclic; that is, they repeat in the same order. You also need to compute what the first digit is.   **(c)** For example, $\frac{n}{14}$ **(d)** If $\frac{k}{14}$ cannot be reduced, knowing $\frac{1}{14} = 0.0\overline{714285}$, we can start dividing k by 14 until two consecutive digits from the repetend appear. We then continue until we find the cyclic pattern. For example, because $\frac{9}{14} = 0.642\ldots$, we know the digits that follow 42 are 8571.

Cooperative Learning

17. Answers vary.

Review Problems

18. $22,761.95
19. $2.35 \cdot 10^{13}$ miles
20. 0.077. The rule says that the placement should be four places or 0.0770. Because 0.077 and 0.0770 are equivalent, the rule still works.
21. Answers may vary. **(a)** 3.024 **(b)** ⁻3.024 **(c)** 134.8 **(d)** 0.00713

Ongoing Assessment 6-4

1. (a) 789% **(b)** 3.2% **(c)** 19,310% **(d)** 20%
(e) $83\frac{1}{3}\%$ **(f)** 15% **(g)** 12.5% **(h)** 37.5%
(i) 62.5% **(j)** $16\frac{2}{3}\%$ **(k)** 80% **(l)** 2.5%
2. (a) $0.1\overline{6}$ **(b)** 0.045 **(c)** $0.00\overline{2}$ **(d)** $0.00\overline{285714}$
(e) $0.13\overline{6}$ **(f)** 1.25 **(g)** $0.00\overline{3}$ **(h)** 0.0025
3. (a) 4 **(b)** 2 **(c)** 25 **(d)** 200 **(e)** 12.5
4. It depends on the calculator.
5. (a) 2.04 **(b)** 50% **(c)** 60 **(d)** 3.43
(e) 300% **(f)** 40
6. (a) $\frac{5x}{100}$
(b) $10a$
7. 63 boxes
8. $16,960
9. $25,500
10. (a) Bill sold 221. **(b)** Joe sold 90%. **(c)** Ron started with 265.
11. 20%
12. Approximately 17.65%
13. Approximately 18.4%
14. Approximately 61% increase

15. 100%
16. $22.40
17. $5.10
18. 50 cups
19. $336
20. 35%
21. $3200
22. 1200 employees
23. $\frac{325}{500}$; $\frac{325}{500} = \frac{650}{1000} = \frac{65}{100} = 65\%$, while $\frac{600}{1000} = \frac{60}{100} = 60\%$.
24. (a) Answers vary; for example, you can find 10% of the number and then multiply this amount by 3. Next add $\frac{1}{2}$ of 10% of the number, and you have 35% of the number.
(b) $2.80
25. It is less than 30; 30 is the number plus 50% of the number.
26. 40% of 50% = 20%
27. $16.\overline{6}\%$
28. (a) $76; $76 **(b)** 8 or 10 items would cost the same under this plan, but it is a better buy in terms of cost per item to purchase 10.
29. 11.1% (approximately)
30. $440
31. $33\frac{1}{3}\%$
32. Approximately $9207.58
33. (a) $3.30 **(b)** $24.00 **(c)** $1.90 **(d)** $24.50
34. (a) 4% **(b)** 32% **(c)** 64%
35. (a) Answers vary. **(b) (i)** About 0.366 sec. between beats **(ii)** About 0.0061 min between beats
36. Apprentice makes $700. Journeyman makes $1400. Master makes $2100.
37. (a) 4% **(b) (i)** 44 **(ii)** 8.8%
38. $82,644.63

Communication

39. Yes. 40% of $30 - \left(\frac{40}{100}\right)\left(\frac{30}{1}\right) = \frac{40 \cdot 30}{100} = \frac{30 \cdot 40}{100}$
$= \left(\frac{30}{100}\right)\left(\frac{40}{1}\right) = 30\%$ of 40.
40. Answers vary; for example, a price can go up 150%. If an item is bought for $100, it can be sold for $150. The price can't go down 150%, because 100% is all there is and it can't go lower. A price cannot be less than 0.
41. Answers vary; for example, percent means per hundred, and if we don't know exactly how many there are per hundred, we can use a proportion to find out. In this case, we solve $\frac{90}{100} = \frac{x}{20}$ to find $x = 18$. Therefore, the student would have to score $\frac{18}{20}$ in order to score 90%.

42. Let x be the amount invested. The first stock option will yield $(1.15x) \cdot 0.85$ after two years. The second stock will yield $(0.85x) \cdot 1.15$. Because each yield equals $(1.15 \cdot 0.85)x$, the investments are equally good.

Open-Ended

43. Answers vary.
44. Answers vary.
45. Answers may vary.   **(a)** 115 is 37% of what number?
(b) a is $P\%$ of what number?

Cooperative Learning

46. Answers vary.

Review Problems

47. (a) 2.5   **(b)** 2.5
48. $\dfrac{6544}{900} = \dfrac{1636}{225}$
49. Answers vary; for example, $0.2\overline{1}$.
50. $\dfrac{5}{3}, 2.0\overline{5}, 2.\overline{15}, \dfrac{7}{3}, 2.5$

51. Answers vary; for example, $\dfrac{2}{3} = 0.\overline{6}$ and $\dfrac{1}{3} = 0.\overline{3}$ so

$0.\overline{9} = 0.\overline{6} + 0.\overline{3} = \dfrac{2}{3} + \dfrac{1}{3} = 1$; $n = 0.\overline{9}$, so $10n = 9.\overline{9}$;

$10n - n = 9.\overline{9} - 0.\overline{9}$, so $9n = 9$ and $n = 1$; $0.\overline{4} = \dfrac{4}{9}$, $0.\overline{5} = \dfrac{5}{9}$,

$0.\overline{6} = \dfrac{6}{9}, 0.\overline{7} = \dfrac{7}{9}, 0.\overline{8} = \dfrac{8}{9}$ so $0.9 = \dfrac{9}{9}$ or 1.

Ongoing Assessment 6-5

1.	Int. Rate per Period	No. of Periods	Amt. of Int. Paid
(a)	3%	4	$125.51
(b)	2%	12	$268.24
(c)	$\dfrac{10}{12}\%$	60	$645.31
(d)	$\dfrac{12}{365}\%$	1460	$615.95

2. $5,460.00
3. $24.45
4. 3.5%
5. Invest $32,040.82
6. $64,800
7. $23,720.58
8. $1944
9. (c) at 13.2%
10. Approximately $2.53
11. Approximately $23,673.64
12. Approximately $3592.89
13. Approximately 12.79%
14. Approximately $7.026762 \cdot 10^8$ or $7.03 \cdot 10^8$
15. $4416.35

16. $81,628.81
17. The Pay More Bank offers a better rate.
18. $10,935

Communication

19. Let a be the original value of the house. Because it depreciates 10% each year for the first 3 years, using compound depreciation the price after 3 years will be $a(1 - 0.10)^3$ or $a \cdot 0.9^3$. Because of compound appreciation, after another 3 years the value of the house will be $a(0.9^3) \cdot 1.1^3$ or $a(0.9^3 \cdot 1.1^3)$, which equals approximately $a \cdot 0.9703$. Because $a \cdot 0.9703 < a$, the value of the house decreased after 6 years. The value of the house decreases by approximately 3%.
20. If we want our money doubled, then $2 = 1(1 + 0.10)^n$, or $2 = 1.1^n$, and we are looking for n. By trial and error, we can find that $1.1^{7.3} = 2.005$, so it would take about 7.3 years to double an investment at 10% compounded annually.
21. No. The percentages cannot be added because each time the percent is of a different quantity. The 15% is a savings of the original price of the fuel. The second savings of 35% is of the new price after the first savings. We could find the percentage of savings as follows. For each $100 of the cost of fuel, the new cost after a 15% savings will be $85. When the second device is installed, an additional 35% is saved, and the new cost is $(65/100) \cdot 85$. After the third device is installed, an additional 50% is saved, and the new cost is $(50/100) \cdot (65/100) \cdot 85$. The savings on a $100 initial cost is $100 - (50/100) \cdot (65/100) \cdot 85$, or $72.375. Because the savings were based on a $100 initial cost, the percentage of total savings with all three devices is 72.375%.
22. No. The percentages cannot be added because each time the percent is of a different quantity. After 5 years, the car would have depreciated 67.232%.

Open-Ended

23. **(a)** Answers vary.   **(b)** Let a be an initial cost of an item that depreciates at a rate of $p\%$ each period of time. If n is the number of periods and $C(n)$ is the cost (as a function of n) after n periods, then $C(n) = a(1 - p/100)^n$.
24. Answers vary.
25. Answers vary.

Cooperative Learning

26. **(a)** Answers vary.   **(b)** When a person takes a loan of a at an annual rate of $p\%$, a lending institution often adds other costs to the loan (processing and other fees). Suppose all the additional costs for the loan are b. Then the customer would have to pay interest and fees in the amount $ap/100 + b$. The percent of the original amount that equals this total is the

APR. If the APR is $x\%$, then $\dfrac{ax}{100} = \dfrac{ap}{100} + b$. Hence

$ax = ap + 100b$, and $x = \dfrac{(ap + 100b)}{a}$.

Ongoing Assessment 6-6

1. Answers vary. One answer is 0.232233222333 . . . .
2. (a) $\sqrt{6}$ **(b)** 2 **(c)** 3
3. $0.\overline{9}$, 0.998, $\sqrt{0.98}$, 0.98, 0.988, 0.9, $0.\overline{898}$
4. (a) Yes **(b)** No **(c)** No **(d)** Yes **(e)** Yes
(f) Yes
5. (a) 15 **(b)** 13 **(c)** Impossible **(d)** 25
6. (a) 2.65 **(b)** 0.11 **(c)** 4.51 **(d)** 1.28
7. (a) False; $\sqrt{2} + 0$ **(b)** False; $^{-}\sqrt{2} + \sqrt{2}$
(c) False; $\sqrt{2} \cdot \sqrt{2}$ **(d)** False; $\sqrt{2} - \sqrt{2}$
8. Answers vary. For example, $\sqrt{2}$, $\sqrt{3}$, and $\sqrt{5}$.
9. Answers vary. For example, assume the following pattern continues: 0.54544544454444 . . .
10. (a) R **(b)** ∅ **(c)** Q **(d)** ∅ **(e)** R **(f)** R
11. (a) Q, R **(b)** N, I, Q, R **(c)** R, S **(d)** I, Q, R
(e) Q, R
12. (a) N, I, Q, R **(b)** Q, R **(c)** R, S
(d) N, I, Q, R **(e)** None **(f)** Q, R
13. (a) 64 **(b)** None **(c)** $^{-}$64 **(d)** None
(e) All real numbers greater than zero. **(f)** None
14. 6.4 ft
15. (a) $\sqrt{180} = 6\sqrt{5}$ **(b)** $\sqrt{363} = 11\sqrt{3}$.
(c) $\sqrt{252} = 6\sqrt{7}$
16. (a) $^{-}3\sqrt[3]{2}$ **(b)** $2\sqrt[5]{3}$ **(c)** $5\sqrt[3]{2}$ **(d)** $^{-}3$
17. (a) $5, 5\sqrt[3]{2}, 5\sqrt[3]{4}, 10$ **(b)** Answers may vary.
$2, 2\sqrt[4]{1/2}, 2\sqrt[4]{1/4}, 2\sqrt[4]{1/8}, 1$
18. (a) 2^{10} **(b)** 2^{11} **(c)** 2^{12}
19. (a) 4 **(b)** 3/2 **(c)** $^{-}4/7$ **(d)** 5/6
20. (a) Rational **(b)** Rational **(c)** Irrational
(d) Irrational

Communication

21. Answers vary; for example, to be rational $\sqrt{2}$ must be able to be written in the form $\frac{a}{b}$, where a and b are integers. When $\sqrt{2}$ is written as $\frac{\sqrt{2}}{1}$, it still fails to have a numerator that is an integer.
22. The value of $\sqrt{3}$ on a calculator is approximate because $\sqrt{3}$ is an irrational number. Because $\sqrt{3}$ is irrational when written as a decimal, it is nonterminating and nonrepeating.
23. False: $\sqrt{64 + 36} \neq \sqrt{64} + \sqrt{36}$.
24. No; 22/7 is a rational number that can be represented by the repeating decimal $3.\overline{142857}$.
25. No; $\sqrt{13}$ is an irrational number. So when it is expressed as a decimal, it is nonterminating and nonrepeating.
26. No; $\sqrt{9 + 16} = 5$ but $3 + 4 = 7$.
27. Notice that $(4/25)^{-1/3} = (25/4)^{1/3}$ and $(4/25)^{-1/4} = (25/4)^{1/4}$. Because $(25/4)^{1/4} < (25/4)^{1/3}$, we have $(4/25)^{-1/4} < (4/25)^{-1/3} = (25/4)^{1/3}$.

Open-Ended

28. Answers vary. For example:
(a) $1, 2, 3, 4, 5, \ldots$ **(b)** , $\sqrt{2}, \sqrt{3}, \sqrt{5}, \sqrt{7}, \ldots$ or π, $\pi^2, \pi^3, \pi^4, \ldots$

29. Answers vary. For example:
(a) $\sqrt{1/2}$, $\pi/6$, $\sqrt[3]{2/5}$, 0.505005000500005 . . . , $\sqrt{3/10}$
(b) 0.505005000500005 . . . , 0.505105000500005 . . . , 0.505105100500005 . . . , 0.505105100510005 . . .
30. (a) When a number between 0 and 1 is raised to larger and larger exponents, the results approach 0. **(b)** Answers vary. **(c)** Answers vary.
31. $3.7^{2.4} = 3.7^{\frac{24}{10}} = 3.7^{\frac{12}{5}} = \sqrt[5]{3.7^{12}}$

Review Problems

32. (a) 21.6 lb **(b)** 48 lb
33. (a) 418/25 **(b)** 3/1000 **(c)** $^{-}$507/100
(d) 123/1000
34. (a) $4.\overline{9}$ **(b)** $5.0\overline{9}$ **(c)** $0.4\overline{9}$
35. 3/12,500
36. 8/33
37. (a) 208,000 **(b)** 0.00038

Chapter Review

1. (a) $A = 0.02$, $B = 0.05$, $C = 0.11$.
(b)

2. (a) $\dfrac{32012}{100}$ **(b)** $\dfrac{103}{100,000}$
3. A fraction in simplest form, $\frac{a}{b}$, can be written as a terminating decimal if, and only if, the prime factorization of the denominator contains no primes other than 2 or 5.
4. 8 shelves
5. (a) $0.\overline{571428}$ **(b)** 0.125 **(c)** $0.\overline{6}$ **(d)** 0.625
6. (a) 7/25 **(b)** $^{-}$507/100 **(c)** 1/3 **(d)** 94/45
7. (a) 307.63 **(b)** 307.6 **(c)** 308 **(d)** 300
8. (a) $4.26 \cdot 10^5$ **(b)** $3.24 \cdot 10^{-4}$ **(c)** $2.37 \cdot 10^{-6}$
(d) $3.25 \cdot 10^{-1}$
9. $1.451\overline{9}$, $1.45\overline{19}$, $1.45\overline{19}$, 1.4519, $0.13\overline{401}$, $^{-}0.134$, $^{-}0.13401$,
10. (a) $5\sqrt{2}$ **(b)** $1/\sqrt[4]{4}$, $1/\sqrt[4]{16}$, $1/\sqrt[4]{64}$
11. (a) $1.78341156 \cdot 10^6$ **(b)** $3.47 \cdot 10^{-6}$ **(c)** $4.93 \cdot 10^9$
(d) $2.94 \cdot 10^{17}$ **(e)** $4.7 \cdot 10^{35}$ **(f)** $1.536 \cdot 10^{-6}$
12. Answers vary. For example: **(a)** 0.105, 0.104, 0.103, 0.102, 0.101 **(b)** 0.0005, 0.001, 0.002, 0.004 **(c)** 0.15, 0.175, 0.1875, 0.19375
13. (a) 25% **(b)** 192 **(c)** $56.\overline{6}$ **(d)** 20%
14. (a) 12.5% **(b)** 7.5% **(c)** 627% **(d)** 1.23%
(e) 150%
15. (a) 0.60 **(b)** $0.00\overline{6}$ **(c)** 1
16. $9280
17. $3.\overline{3}$%
18. 88.6%
19. $5750
20. It makes no difference.
21. $80

22. $15,000

23. $15,110.69

24. (a) Irrational **(b)** Irrational (c) Rational **(d)** Rational (e) Irrational

25. (a) $11\sqrt{2}$ **(b)** $12\sqrt{2}$ (c) $6\sqrt{10}$ **(d)** $3\sqrt[3]{6}$

26. (a) No; $\sqrt{2} + (^-\sqrt{2})$ is rational. **(b)** No; see (a). (c) No; $\sqrt{2} \cdot \sqrt{2}$ is rational. **(d)** No; $\sqrt{2}/\sqrt{2}$ is rational.

27. 4.796

Chapter 7

Ongoing Assessment 7-1

1. **(a)** $\dfrac{56}{80}$ or $\dfrac{7}{10}$ **(b)** $\dfrac{24}{80}$ or $\dfrac{3}{10}$

(c) Probably not. In an experiment with only a relatively small number of tosses, the outcome will probably not be identical. Experimental probability is based only on the number of times the experiment is repeated, not on what will happen in the long run. **(d)** You would probably obtain approximately the same results, but experimental probability does not guarantee the exact results.

2. (a) No **(b)** Yes (c) Yes **(d)** No

3. (a) {0, 1, 2, 3, 4, 5, 6, 7, 8, 9} **(b)** {0, 1, 2, 3, 4} (c) {1, 3, 5, 7, 9} **(d)** {0, 1, 3, 4, 5, 6, 7, 8, 9} (e) $\dfrac{5}{10}$, or $\dfrac{1}{2}$ (f) $\dfrac{5}{10}$, or $\dfrac{1}{2}$ (g) $\dfrac{9}{10}$

4. (a) $\dfrac{5}{26}$ **(b)** $\dfrac{21}{26}$ (c) $\dfrac{11}{26}$

5. (a) $\dfrac{3}{8}$ **(b)** $\dfrac{2}{8}$ or $\dfrac{1}{4}$ (c) $\dfrac{4}{8}$ or $\dfrac{1}{2}$ **(d)** $\dfrac{2}{8}$ or $\dfrac{1}{4}$ (e) 0

(f) $\dfrac{3}{8}$ (g) $\dfrac{1}{8}$

6. (a) $\dfrac{26}{52}$ or $\dfrac{1}{2}$ **(b)** $\dfrac{12}{52}$ or $\dfrac{3}{13}$ (c) $\dfrac{28}{52}$ or $\dfrac{7}{13}$

(d) $\dfrac{4}{52}$ or $\dfrac{1}{13}$ (e) $\dfrac{48}{52}$ or $\dfrac{12}{13}$ **(f)** $\dfrac{22}{52}$ or $\dfrac{11}{26}$

(g) $\dfrac{3}{52}$ **(h)** $\dfrac{30}{52}$ or $\dfrac{15}{26}$

7. (a) $\dfrac{4}{12}$ or $\dfrac{1}{3}$ **(b)** $\dfrac{8}{12}$ or $\dfrac{2}{3}$ (c) 0 **(d)** $\dfrac{6}{12}$ or $\dfrac{1}{2}$

8. (a) 1 **(b)** 30 will guarantee at least one pair of each color for the following reason: the socks cannot be all of the same color since the largest number of socks of the same color is 16 (blue socks). The socks cannot all be of two colors because the largest number of socks of only two colors is 12 black and 16 blue socks, that is, 28 socks. Note that 30 is the smallest number, since pulling 28 socks could result in two colors only, namely 12 black and 16 blue. (c) $\dfrac{28}{34}$ or $\dfrac{14}{17}$

9. **(a)** $\dfrac{1}{6}$ **(b)** $\dfrac{4}{6}$ or $\dfrac{2}{3}$

10. (a) $\dfrac{8}{36}$ or $\dfrac{2}{9}$ **(b)** $\dfrac{4}{36}$ or $\dfrac{1}{9}$ (c) $\dfrac{24}{36}$ or $\dfrac{2}{3}$

(d) 6 and 8 both have $\dfrac{5}{36}$ probability. **(e)** 0 **(f)** 1

(g) 10 times

11. 70%, P (No Rain) $= 1 - P$ (Rain) $= 1 - 0.30 = 0.70$

12. (a) $\dfrac{18}{38}$ or $\dfrac{9}{19}$ **(b)** $\dfrac{2}{38}$ or $\dfrac{1}{19}$ (c) $\dfrac{26}{38}$ or $\dfrac{13}{19}$

(d) $\dfrac{20}{38}$ or $\dfrac{10}{19}$

13. 10 times

14. (a) No **(b)** Yes (c) Yes **(d)** Yes (e) No **(f)** Yes (g) No **(h)** No

15. (a) $\dfrac{2}{4}$ or $\dfrac{1}{2}$ **(b)** $\dfrac{3}{4}$ (c) $\dfrac{3}{4}$

16. $\dfrac{350}{1380}$ or $\dfrac{35}{138}$

17. **(a)** **(b)**

18. Assuming the dealt cards are not put back into the deck, the answers are: (a) $\dfrac{20}{50}$ or $\dfrac{2}{5}$ **(b)** $\dfrac{40}{50}$ or $\dfrac{4}{5}$ (c) 0

19. The answers may vary depending on how the 6, 7, and 9 are formed. The following answers are based on a Casio digital watch. (a) $\dfrac{8}{10}$ **(b)** $\dfrac{8}{10}$ (c) $\dfrac{7}{10}$ **(d)** $\dfrac{10}{10}$ or 1

20. (a) The probability of students taking algebra or chemistry **(b)** The probability of students taking algebra and chemistry (c) This represents 1 minus the probability of a student taking chemistry or the probability of a student not taking chemistry.

21. 0.7

22. (a) $\dfrac{45}{80}$ or $\dfrac{9}{16}$ **(b)** $\dfrac{10}{80}$ or $\dfrac{1}{8}$ (c) $\dfrac{60}{80}$ or $\dfrac{3}{4}$ **(d)** $\dfrac{30}{80}$ or $\dfrac{3}{8}$

23. 0.4

24. (a) 22 **(b)** 10

25. **(a)** Not possible. Suppose x white, x black, and x red balls are added to the box. Then the probability of drawing a black ball is $\dfrac{3+x}{(5+x)+(3+x)+(2+x)}$ or $\dfrac{3+x}{10+3x}$. There is no x for which this ratio is $\dfrac{1}{3}$, because $\dfrac{3+x}{10+3x} = \dfrac{1}{3}$ is equivalent to $9 + 3x = 10 + 3x$, which has no solution. **(b)** Yes, add 5 balls of each color. Reason: the solution of the equation $\dfrac{3+x}{10+3x} = 0.32$ is $x = 5$.

Communication

26. All probabilities are less than or equal to 1 and greater than or equal to 0. If events are mutually exclusive, then $P(A \cup B) = P(A) + P(B)$. Therefore, if A and B are mutually exclusive, $P(A \cup B) = P(A) + P(B) = 0.8 + 0.9 = 1.7$, which is impossible. Therefore, events A and B are not mutually exclusive.

27. Bobbie's reasoning is not correct unless her theoretical probability of making a basket is really $\frac{1}{2}$. The outcomes of making a basket or missing it are probably not equally likely, so this definition does not apply. To calculate her experimental probability of making a free throw, divide the number of shots made by the number attempted.

28. Joe's conjecture is incorrect. Each of the numbers 1 through 4 has probability $\frac{1}{4}$ of occurring because each angle where the arrow is located measures 90 degrees and the spinner has the same chance of landing in any of the regions.

29. We could ask José to draw a tree diagram for this experiment. He will then see the sample space is $\{BB, BG, GB, GG\}$ with each outcome having probability $\frac{1}{4}$. Therefore the probability of having two boys is $\frac{1}{4}$, not $\frac{1}{3}$.

Open-Ended

30. Answers vary depending on the book selected.

31. Answers vary; for example, batting averages are really probabilities that a hitter will get a hit, or a free-throw shooting percentage is really a probability that a basketball player will make a free throw. Insurance companies use probabilities to determine rates.

32. Answers vary; for example, event A is an impossible event such as rolling a 10 on a single roll of a standard die. Event B has low probability such as the chance of rain being 20%. Event C is around 0.5, so this might be something like obtaining a head when tossing a fair coin. Event D has a high probability of happening, but it is not certain (for example, tossing a number less than 6 on a toss of a standard die). Event E has probability 1, so it has to happen (for example, tossing either a head or a tail on the toss of a fair coin). Event F has probability greater than 1, but this cannot happen, so no event is possible.

Cooperative Learning

33. (a) Most often, 1 and 2 and then 0 and 3; least often, 6 and then 5.   **(b)** Answers vary.
(c) The theoretical probabilities for the differences are
$P(0) = \frac{6}{36}$, $P(1) = \frac{10}{36}$, $P(2) = \frac{8}{36}$, $P(3) = \frac{6}{36}$, $P(4) = \frac{4}{36}$, $P(5) = \frac{2}{36}$, $P(6) = \frac{0}{36}$.   **(d)** Using the probabilities from part (c), the 18 markers should be distributed from left to right as 3, 5, 4, 3, 2, 1, and 0.

34. (b) The person who receives four times the value of the number on the die wins when 1, 2, and 3 are tossed. The person who receives the square of the number showing wins when a 5 or a 6 is tossed. When a 4 is tossed, the game is a draw. The person who receives four times the value of the die has a greater chance of winning, and therefore the game is not fair.

Ongoing Assessment 7-2

1. (a)

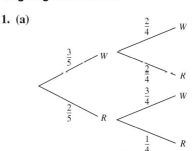

The probability that two balls are of different colors is
$\frac{3}{5} \cdot \frac{2}{4} + \frac{2}{5} \cdot \frac{3}{4} = \frac{3}{5}$ **(b)** $\frac{12}{25}$

2. (a) $\{(1, 1), (1, 2), (1, 3), (2, 1), (2, 2), (2, 3)\}$
(b) $\{(2, 2)\}$ **(c)** $\{(1, 2), (2, 1), (2, 2), (2, 3)\}$
(d) $\{(1, 2), (2, 1), (2, 3)\}$

3. (a) $\frac{1}{216}$ **(b)** $\frac{1}{120}$

4. (a) $\frac{1}{24}$ **(b)** $\frac{1}{64}$ **(c)** $\frac{1}{84}$ **(d)** $\frac{7}{36}$

5. $\frac{1}{30}$

6. (a) Box 1, with probability $\frac{1}{3}$ (Box 2 has probability $\frac{1}{5}$.)
(b) Either, with probability $\frac{4}{27}$

7. (a) $\frac{64}{75}$ **(b)** $\frac{11}{75}$

8. 0.0005

9. (a) $\frac{1}{5}$ **(b)** $\frac{4}{5}$ **(c)** $\frac{11}{15}$ **(d)** $\frac{8}{15}$

10. $\frac{5}{16}$

11. $\frac{1}{16}$

12. (a) $\frac{1}{4}$ **(b)** $\frac{5}{8}$ **(c)** $\frac{1}{8}$

13. (a) $\frac{4}{10}$ or $\frac{2}{5}$ **(b)** Yes, now $P(\text{Even}) = \frac{9}{10}$

14. $\frac{2}{16}$ or $\frac{1}{8}$

15. (a) $\frac{1}{320}$ **(b)** $\frac{63}{4000}$ **(c)** 0   **(d)** $\frac{171}{320}$

16. (a) The first spinner. If you choose the first spinner, you win if and only if the spinning combinations are as follows:

Outcome on spinner A	Outcome on spinner B
4	3
6	3 or 5
8	3 or 5

The probability of this happening is
$$\frac{1}{3}\cdot\frac{1}{3}+\frac{1}{3}\cdot\frac{2}{3}+\frac{1}{3}\cdot\frac{2}{3}=\frac{5}{9}.$$

If you choose spinner *B*, the probability of winning is only $\frac{4}{9}$.

(b) Answers vary. One choice is given below.

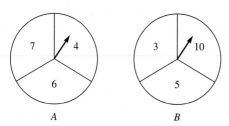

If you choose *A*, the probability of winning is $\frac{5}{9}$. If you choose *B*, the probability of winning is only $\frac{4}{9}$.

17. (a) $\frac{5}{8}$ **(b)** $\frac{3}{8}$

18. $\frac{1}{32}$

19. **(a)** $\frac{16}{81}$ **(b)** $\frac{8}{27}$

20. $\frac{1}{256}$

21. $\frac{1}{34,650}$

22. (a) $\frac{1}{25}$ **(b)** $\frac{8}{25}$ (c) $\frac{16}{25}$

23. (a) 100 square units

(b) $P(\text{Region A}) = \frac{4}{100}$, or $\frac{1}{25}$

$P(\text{Region B}) = \frac{12}{100}$, or $\frac{3}{25}$

$P(\text{Region C}) = \frac{20}{100}$, or $\frac{1}{5}$

$P(\text{Region D}) = \frac{28}{100}$, or $\frac{7}{25}$

$P(\text{Region E}) = \frac{36}{100}$, or $\frac{9}{25}$

(c) $\frac{1}{625}$ **(d)** $\frac{36}{100}$, or $\frac{9}{25}$

24. 0.7

25. $\frac{1}{12}$

26. $\frac{271}{1000}$

27. $\frac{2}{5}$

28. $\frac{25}{30}$ or $\frac{5}{6}$

29. $\frac{2}{28}$ or $\frac{1}{14}$

30. $\frac{69}{3000}$ or $\frac{23}{1000}$

31. **(a)**

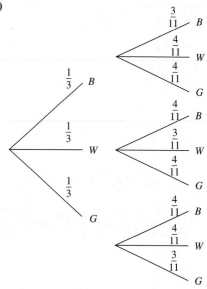

(b) $\frac{1}{3}\cdot\frac{3}{11}+\frac{1}{3}\cdot\frac{3}{11}+\frac{1}{3}\cdot\frac{3}{11}$ or $\frac{3}{11}$ (c) $\frac{1}{3}\cdot\frac{3}{11}=\frac{1}{11}$

(d) 1

32. Each room has probability $\frac{1}{2}$ of being chosen. Hence it does not matter where the car is placed.

33. Billie-Bobby-Billie because the probability of winning two in a row is greater this way. Note, it does not say win two out of three.

34. She should serve the first one hard and then it does not matter what she does on the second serve.

Communication

35. If the die is fair, the probability that Jim will roll a 3 on the next roll is $\frac{1}{6}$, which is the same probability of rolling any one of the other numbers. The results of the first three rolls should have no effect on the next roll.

36. Finding a witness with blond hair and blue eyes has a greater probability. The probability of a red car introduces another number that is less than 1 to the product. When you multiply *a*, the probability that you have for blond hair and blue eyes, by a number less than 1 and greater than 0, the probability becomes smaller.

37. The red ball in one of the boxes and the three white balls in the other box. In this case the probability of getting the red ball is $\frac{1}{2}\cdot1+\frac{1}{2}\cdot0$ or $\frac{1}{2}$. In the three other arrangements, the probability of getting the red ball is smaller.

38. Answers vary depending on how complex the game is. The game could be as simple as player *A* wins if the sum of the digits is even and player *B* wins if the sum of the digits is odd.

39. One possibility is that one die has the numbers 0, 0, 0, 3, 3, 3, and the other die has the numbers 1, 2, 3, 7, 8, 9. The probability of each outcome is $\frac{3}{36}$ or $\frac{1}{12}$.

40. Answers vary; but $\frac{3}{5}$ of the area of the board must be labeled in a certain way.

Cooperative Learning

41. If the first player chooses *TT* and the second *HT*, then the first player wins the game if and only if tails appears on the first and second flips. The probability of this happening is $\frac{1}{4}$. The probabilities of winning the game for other choices are summarized below:

| | | \multicolumn{4}{c}{**First Player's Choice**} |
		HH	**HT**	**TH**	**TT**
Second	**HH**	—	0.50	0.75	0.50
Player's	**HT**	0.50	—	0.50	0.25
Choice	**TH**	0.25	0.50	—	0.50
	TT	0.50	0.75	0.50	—

Of the 12 possible games, only eight result in choices with equally likely probabilities. Therefore, the game is not fair.
42. (a) The game is not fair. You should choose spinner *A*.
(b) The game is not fair. You should choose spinner *C*. It has a winning probability of $\frac{35}{99}$.

Review Problems

43. (a) v **(b)** iii **(c)** ii **(d)** i **(e)** iv
44. (a) $\frac{1}{30}$ **(b)** 0 **(c)** $\frac{19}{30}$

Ongoing Assessment 7-3

1. Answers vary; for example, a black card might represent the birth of a boy and a red card might represent the birth of a girl. Choose a card to represent a birth.
2. (a) Answers vary; for example, you could use a random-digit table. The numbers 1 through 9 could represent rain, and 0 could represent no rain. **(b)** Answers vary but should be close to 0.48. **(c)** Approximately 0.52.
3. (a) Let 1, 2, 3, 4, 5, and 6 represent the numbers on the die and ignore the numbers 0, 7, 8, 9. **(b)** Number the persons 01, 02, 03, . . . , 18, 19, 20. Go to the random-digit table and mark off groups of two. The three persons chosen are the first three whose numbers appear. **(c)** Represent red by the numbers 0, 1, 2, 3, 4; green by the numbers 5, 6, 7; yellow by the number 8; and white by the number 9.

4. Mark off 30 blocks of three digits in a random-digit table. Disregard 000 or any numbers that are greater than 500. These are the numbers of the 30 students who will be chosen for the trip.
5. To simulate Monday, let the digits 1 through 8 represent rain and 0 and 9 represent no rain. If rain occurred on Monday, repeat the same process for Tuesday. If it did not rain on Monday, let the digits 1 through 7 represent rain and 0, 8, and 9 represent dry. Repeat a similar process for the rest of the week.
6. Answers vary; for example, mark off blocks of two digits and let the digits 00, 01, 02, . . . , 13, 14 represent contracting the disease and 15 to 99 represent no disease. Mark off blocks of six digits to represent the three children. If at least one of the numbers is in the range 00 to 14, then this represents a child in the three-child family having strep.

7. $\frac{3}{10}$

8. 1200 fish
9. (a) 7 **(b)** Answers vary; for example, let the digits 0, 1, 2, 3, 4 represent a victory by team A and the digits 5, 6, 7, 8, 9 represent a victory by team B. Then go to the random-digit table, pick a starting place, and count the number of digits (games) it takes for one of the teams to win. Repeat this experiment a number of times for four games and for seven games and use the definition of probability to compute the experimental probability.
10. One way to simulate the problem is to use a random-digit table. Because Carmen's probability of making any basket is 80%, we could use the occurrence of a 0, 1, 2, 3, 4, 5, 6, or 7 to simulate making the basket and the occurrence of an 8 or a 9 to simulate missing the basket. Another way to simulate the problem is to construct a spinner with 80% of the spinner devoted to making a basket and 20% of the spinner devoted to missing the basket. This could be done by constructing the spinner with 80% of the 360 degrees (that is, 288 degrees) devoted to making the basket and 72 degrees devoted to missing the basket.

We can compute the theoretical probability for this experiment by using a *tree diagram*, as shown below. Thus theoretical probabilities for the number of points scored in 25 attempts can be computed. These theoretical estimates are given in the table below. Compare these results with the experimental probability obtained by simulation.

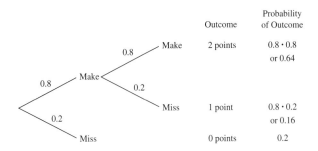

	Outcome	Probability of Outcome
Make – 2 points	2 points	0.8 · 0.8 or 0.64
Miss – 1 point	1 point	0.8 · 0.2 or 0.16
Miss – 0 points	0 points	0.2

Number of Points	Expected Number of Times Points Are Scored in 25 Attempts
0	5
1	4
2	16

Communication

11. See Kanold, C. "Teaching Probability Theory Modeling Real Problems." *Mathematics Teacher* 85 (April 1994): 232–235.
12. Answers vary; one way is to turn left when an even number comes up, turn right when the number 1 comes up, and move straight when 3 or 5 come up.

Open-Ended

13. Answers vary; one could use a random-digit table with blocks of two digits, or a spinner could be designed with 12 sections representing the different months. The spinner could be spun five times to represent the birthdays of five people. We could then keep track of how many times at least two people have the same birthday.
14. Answers vary; for example, use a random-digit table. Let the digits 1–8 represent a win and the digits 0 and 9 represent losses. Mark off blocks of three. If only the digits 1–8 appear, then this represents three wins in a row.
15. Let the 10 ducks be represented by the digits 0, 1, 2, 3, . . . , 8, 9. Then pick a starting point in the table and mark off 10 digits to simulate which ducks the hunters shoot at. Count how many of the digits 0 through 9 are not in the 10 digits and this represents the ducks that escaped. Do this experiment many times and take the average to determine an answer. See how close your simulation comes to 3.49 ducks.

Cooperative Learning

16. (d) The probability of two boys and two girls is $\frac{6}{16}$ or $\frac{3}{8}$.
17. (d) $\left(\frac{1}{2}\right)^{10} = \frac{1}{1024}$
18. Answers depend on the simulation.
19. Pick a starting spot in the table and count the number of digits it takes before all the numbers 1 through 9 are obtained. Repeat this experiment many times and find the average number of boxes.

Review Problems

20. No, you will win about $\frac{6}{16}$ or $\frac{3}{8}$ of the games.
21. (a) $\frac{1}{4}$ **(b)** $\frac{1}{52}$ **(c)** $\frac{48}{52}$ or $\frac{12}{13}$ **(d)** $\frac{3}{4}$
(e) $\frac{1}{2}$ **(f)** $\frac{1}{52}$ **(g)** $\frac{16}{52}$ or $\frac{4}{13}$ **(h)** 1

22. (a) $\frac{15}{19}$ **(b)** $\frac{56}{361}$ **(c)** $\frac{28}{171}$

Ongoing Assessment 7-4

1. (a) 12 to 40 or 3 to 10 **(b)** 40 to 12 or 10 to 3
2. 30 to 6 or 5 to 1
3. 15 to 1
4. (a) $\frac{1}{2}$ **(b)** $\left(\frac{1}{2}\right)^{10}$ or $\frac{1}{1024}$ **(c)** 1023 to 1
5. $\frac{5}{8}$
6. 1 to 1
7. 4 to 6 or 2 to 3
8. 20 to 18 or 10 to 9
9. $\frac{1}{27}$
10. (a) $\frac{1}{2}$ **(b)** $\frac{1}{4}$
11. (a) 0 **(b)** 0 **(c)** $\frac{1}{5}$ **(d)** $\frac{1}{3}$
12. $\frac{4}{9}$
13. $E = \frac{1}{6}(10) + \frac{5}{6}(^-2) = \frac{10}{6} + \left(\frac{^-10}{6}\right) = 0$.
Therefore, you should come out about even if you play a long time.
14. (a) $\frac{1}{38}$ **(b)** 37 to 1 **(c)** $^-\frac{2}{38}$ or $\frac{^-1}{19}$ dollars
15. Approximately 8¢
16. $10,000
17. (a) 20 ¢, and the expected loss is 17 ¢. **(b)** 20 ¢
18. (a) $7 **(b)** No

Communication

19. Odds are determined from probabilities. The *odds in favor* of an event, E, are determined by $\frac{P(E)}{P(\overline{E})}$. The *odds against* an event are determined by $\frac{P(\overline{E})}{P(E)}$.
20. Don't believe it. If the odds of getting AIDS are 68,000 to 1, then the probability of getting AIDS is $\frac{68,000}{68,001}$. Therefore the probability of getting AIDS is almost certain. The article should have talked about the odds against getting AIDS.
21. 25¢, because $P(HH) = \frac{1}{4}$ so $E = \frac{1}{4}($1) = $.25$.

Open-Ended

22. Answers vary. The premium would have to cost at least $\left(\frac{47}{100,000}\right)($50,000) = 23.50. Then the cost of overhead would have to be taken into account along with the desired amount of profit.

23. Answers vary. One possibility is a game involving a spinner with five sectors of equal area numbered 1 through 5. You pay $2 for playing the game. If the spinner lands on regions 1 or 2, you win $5. The expected winnings in this game are $5 \cdot \frac{2}{5} - 2$ or 0.

Cooperative Learning

24. Games and rules will vary, as will the odds and expected values of the game.

Review Problems

25. (a) {1, 2, 3, 4}   **(b)** {Red, Blue}   **(c)** {(1, Red), (1, Blue), (2, Red), (2, Blue), (3, Red), (3, Blue), (4, Red), (4, Blue)}
(d) {(Blue, 1), (Blue, 2), (Blue, 3), (Blue, 4), (Blue, 5), (Blue, 6), (Red, 1), (Red, 2), (Red, 3), (Red, 4), (Red, 5), (Red, 6)}
(e) {(1, 1), (1, 2), (1, 3), (1, 4), (2, 1), (2, 2), (2, 3), (2, 4), (3, 1), (3, 2), (3, 3), (3, 4), (4, 1), (4, 2), (4, 3), (4, 4)}   **(f)** {(Red, Red), (Red, Blue), (Blue, Red), (Blue, Blue)}
26. The blue section must have 300°; the red has 60°.
27. $\frac{25}{676}$

Ongoing Assessment 7-5

1. 224
2. 32
3. 10,000
4. 1352 with three-letter call letters; 35,152 with four-letter call letters
5. 180
6. (a) True   **(b)** False   **(c)** False   **(d)** False
(e) True   **(f)** True   **(g)** True
7. 40,320
8. 15
9. (a) 12   **(b)** 210   **(c)** 3360   **(d)** 34,650   **(e)** 3780
10. 13,860
11. (a) 24,360   **(b)** 4060
12. 792
13. $\frac{1}{120}$
14. 45
15. 1260
16. (a) 6   **(b)** 36
17. eight people
18. (a) $\frac{1}{13}$ **(b)** $\frac{8}{65}$
19. 2,598,960 different five-card hands (Order within the hand is not important.)
20. 11,232,000
21. $\frac{1}{25,827,165}$
22. 10^9 or 1,000,000,000
23. $\frac{13440}{59049}$ or approx. 0.228

24. (a) $\frac{1}{6^8}$ **(b)** $\left(\frac{1}{6}\right)^2 \cdot \left(\frac{5}{6}\right)^6 \cdot {}_8C_2 \approx 0.260476$
(c) $1 - \left(\frac{5}{6}\right)^8 \approx 0.767$
25. (a) $\left(\frac{6}{36}\right)^8$ or $\frac{1}{6^5} \approx 0.00013$ **(b)** $\left(\frac{1}{6}\right)^2 \times \left(\frac{5}{6}\right)^3 \times$
${}_5C_2 = \frac{1250}{7776} \approx 0.161$
26. (a) $\frac{{}_{12}C_4}{{}_{22}C_4} = \frac{9}{133}$ **(b)** $1 - \frac{{}_{10}C_4}{{}_{22}C_4}$ or $\frac{203}{209}$ **(c)** $\frac{{}_{10}C_4}{{}_{22}C_4}$ or $\frac{6}{209}$
27. (a) $({}_{20}C_2 \cdot {}_{21}C_4 \cdot {}_4C_2) \div {}_{45}C_8 \approx 0.032$
(b) $\frac{{}_{25}C_8}{{}_{45}C_8} \approx 0.005$ **(c)** $1 - \frac{{}_{25}C_8}{{}_{45}C_8} \approx 0.995$
(d) $\frac{{}_{20}C_8}{{}_{45}C_8} \approx 5.84 \cdot 10^{-4}$
28. 2,598,956 : 4 or 649,739 : 1
29. ${}_{24}C_{12} = 2,704,156$

Communication

30. Answers vary. For example, the Fundamental Counting Principle (FCP) says that to find the number of ways of making several decisions in a row, multiply the number of choices that can be made for each decision. The FCP can be used to find the number of permutations. A permutation is an arrangement of things in a definite order. A combination is a selection of things in which the order is not important. We could find the number of combinations by using the FCP and then divide by the number of ways in which the things can be arranged.
31. Answers vary. For example, for the formula
$_nP_r = n!/(n - r)!$ to work for $_nP_n$, then $_nP_n = n!/(n - n)! = \frac{n!}{0!}$.
To make this equation true we must define 0! to be 1.
32. (a) There are 10 choices for the number on the first reel, 10 choices for the number on the second reel, and 10 choices for the number on the third reel. By the Fundamental Counting Principle, there are $10 \cdot 10 \cdot 10$, or 1000, choices for the combination of the lock.   **(b)** The correct name should probably be "permutation" locks, since the order in which the three numbers are entered makes a difference, and so this is a permutation rather than a combination.
33. (a) $8! \cdot 3!$. If the family is considered a unit and each of the remaining people also a unit, we have 8 units. There are 8! ways to arrange the 8 units. For each of the 8! ways the family unit can be arranged in 3! ways and hence the number of seating arrangements is $8! \cdot 3!$.   **(b)** $10! - 8! \cdot 3!$. We need to subtract the answer in part (a) from the number of all possible seating arrangements.
34. 3840. Consider each couple as a unit. The five units can be arranged in 5! ways. For each of the 5! arrangements, each of the five couples can be arranged in 2 ways. Consequently there are $5! \cdot 2^5$ arrangements.

Open-Ended

35. (a) 10^6 or 1,000,000 **(b)** Yes, Montana, Wyoming, Alaska, Delaware, North Dakota, South Dakota, Vermont **(c)** Answers vary. For example, you would first find the population of California and then experiment with using letters in the license plates. This would help because the choice is for 26 letters in a slot rather than 10 numbers.

36. The game is not fair. The expected payoff is $\frac{1}{38} \cdot \$36$, or approximately 95¢. Therefore, you can expect to lose on the average about 5¢ a game if you play it a large number of times.

Cooperative Learning

37. (a) Answers vary. The first and last numbers in every row are ones. Every other number is obtained by adding the numbers immediately above. The next two rows are 1, 7, 21, 35, 35, 21, 7, 1 and 1, 8, 28, 56, 70, 56, 28, 8, 1. **(b)** Answers vary. For example, the diagonal 1, 3, 6, 10, 15 are triangular numbers.   **(c)** The sums of the numbers in the rows are 1, 2, 4, 8, 16, 32, 64. The sum in the 10th row is $2^{10} = 1024$.   **(d)** Yes, a similar relationship holds in all the rows for the entries in Pascal's triangle.   **(e)** The entries in the nth row are given by $_nC_r$ where n is the number of the row and $r = 0$ to n. For example, the first three entries in the sixth row are $_6C_0, _6C_1, _6C_2$.

Review Problems

38. (a) $\frac{396}{2652}$, or $\frac{33}{221}$ **(b)** $\frac{1352}{2652}$, or $\frac{26}{51}$

39. $\frac{3}{36}$, or $\frac{1}{12}$

40. $E = \$0$ so the game is fair.

Chapter Review

1. (a) {*HHH, HHT, HTH, HTT, TTT, TTH, THH, THT*}
(b) {*HHH, HHT, HTH, THH*}   **(c)** $\frac{4}{8}$ or $\frac{1}{2}$

2. (a) {Monday, Tuesday, Wednesday, Thursday, Friday, Saturday, Sunday}   **(b)** {Tuesday, Thursday}   **(c)** $\frac{2}{7}$

3. There are 800 blue ones, 125 red ones, and 75 that are neither blue nor red.

4. (a) Approximately 0.501   **(b)** Approximately 0.499 **(c)** 34,226,731 to 34,108,157 $\doteq 1.003 : 1$

5. (a) $\frac{5}{12}$ **(b)** $\frac{9}{12}$ or $\frac{3}{4}$ **(c)** $\frac{5}{12}$ **(d)** $\frac{9}{12}$ or $\frac{3}{4}$ **(e)** 0
(f) 1

6. (a) $\frac{13}{52}$ or $\frac{1}{4}$ **(b)** $\frac{1}{52}$ **(c)** $\frac{22}{52}$ or $\frac{11}{26}$
(d) $\frac{48}{52}$ or $\frac{12}{13}$

7. (a) $\frac{64}{729}$ **(b)** $\frac{24}{504}$ or $\frac{1}{21}$

8. $\frac{6}{25}$

9. $\frac{14}{80}$ or $\frac{7}{40}$

10. $\frac{7}{45}$

11. 4 to 48 or 1 to 12
12. 3 to 3 or 1 to 1

13. $\frac{3}{8}$

14. $0.30

15. $33\frac{1}{3}$¢ or 34¢

16. The expected value is $1.50. The expected average earnings are $^-\$0.50$.
17. 900
18. 120
19. 5040

20. $\frac{2}{20}$, or $\frac{1}{10}$

21. (a) $5 \cdot 4 \cdot 3$ or 60   **(b)** $\frac{3}{60}$ or $\frac{1}{20}$ **(c)** $\frac{1}{60}$

22. $\frac{15}{36} = \frac{5}{12}$

23. $\frac{2}{5}$

24. $7! = 5040$

25.   Yes, $_nC_r = \dfrac{n!}{r!(n-r)!}$.

Also, $_nC_{n-r} = \dfrac{n!}{(n-r)!([n-(n-r)])!}$

$= \dfrac{n!}{(n-r)!r!}$.

Therefore, $_nC_r = {}_nC_{n-r}$.

26. 0.027

27. $\frac{63}{80}$

28. Answers vary.

29. (a) $\frac{1}{8}$ **(b)** $\frac{1}{4}$ **(c)** $\frac{1}{16}$

30. $\frac{8}{20}$ or $\frac{2}{5}$

Chapter 8

Ongoing Assessment 8-1

1.

	Glasses of Lemonade Sold
Monday	
Tuesday	
Wednesday	
Thursday	
Friday	

represents 10 glasses

2. (a) 225 million   **(b)** 375 million   **(c)** 550 million

3.
Student Ages at Washington School

4. (a) 72, 74, 81, 81, 82, 85, 87, 88, 92, 94, 97, 98, 103, 123, 125   **(b)** 72 lbs   **(c)** 125 lbs

5.

Weights of Students in East Junior
High Algebra I Class

6. Answers will vary. For example,
(a) A line plot will have two columns of x's, one for heads and one for tails.
(b) A histogram will have two bars, one for Heads and one for Tails. The vertical axis will be partitioned to show frequencies of each.

7. (a) November, 30 cm   **(b)** 50 cm

8. (a)

Ages of HKM Employees

```
1 | 889
2 | 01113333334566679
3 | 224447
4 | 1115568          3 | 4 represents
5 | 2248                34 years old
6 | 233
```

(b) There are more employees in their 40s.   **(c)** 20
(d) 17.5%

9. (a) Approximately 3800 km   **(b)** Approximately 1900 km

10.

Distances from the Sun

11.

Coin Toss

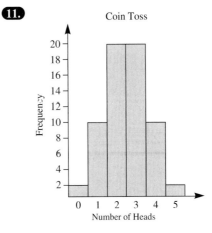

12.

Course Grades for Elementary Teachers

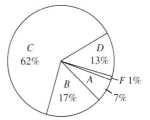

Percentages are rounded. Part F rounds to 2%.

13. About 9%

14. Measures are approximate. Savings 0.8 cm; rent 2.4 cm; food 0.9 cm; auto payment 2.2 cm; tuition 1.7 cm

15. (a)

Fall Textbook Costs

```
1 | 6
2 | 33
3 | 0357799
4 | 0122589
5 | 00138
6 | 022        2 | 3 represents $23
```

(b)

Fall Textbook Costs

Classes	Tally	Frequency
$15–19	I	1
$20–24	II	2
$25–29		0
$30–34	II	2
$35–39	⌇⌇⌇	5
$40–44	IIII	4
$45–49	III	3
$50–54	IIII	4
$55–59	I	1
$60–64	III	3
		25

(c)

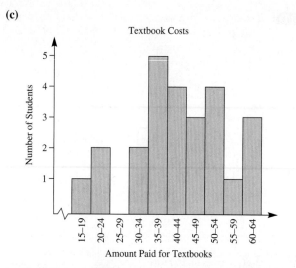

Textbook Costs

16. **(a)** Chicken **(b)** 10 mph **(c)** Cheetah **(d)** Yes
17. **(a)** Women **(b)** Approximately one year
(c) About 5.5 years
18. **(a)** Approximately $8400 **(b)** $14,000
(c) Approximately $7000 **(d)** Right after two years
19. **(a)** Asia **(b)** Africa **(c)** It is about 2/3 as large.
(d) Asia and Africa **(e)** 5:16 **(f)** Approximately 58.6
million square miles
20. **(a)**

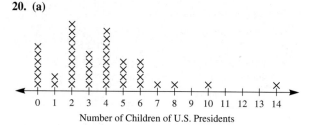

Number of Children of U.S. Presidents

(b)

Number of Children	Tally	Frequency
0	JHT I	6
1	II	2
2	JHT IIII	9
3	IIII	4
4	JHT III	8
5	IIII	4
6	IIII	4
7	I	1
8	I	1
9		0
10	I	1
11		0
12		0
13		0
14	I	1
		$\overline{42}$

(c) 2
21. **(a)**

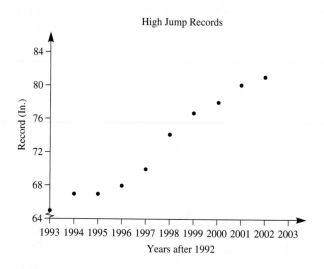

High Jump Records

(b) Positive
22. **(a)** Negative **(b)** Approximately 10 **(c)** About 22
yr old
23. **(a)** Answers vary; for example, a line graph is given
below.

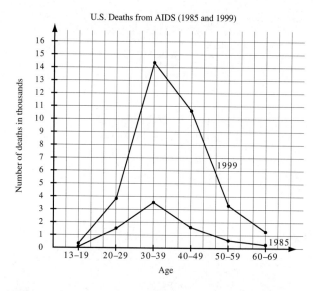

U.S. Deaths from AIDS (1985 and 1999)

(b) Answers vary; for example, the number of deaths from
AIDS dramatically increased in 1999 over 1985. The 30–39
age group was the hardest hit during both periods. The
increase in deaths from ages 20–29 to 30–39 was greater in
1999 than 1985. There was a more dramatic decrease in
deaths in 1999 than in 1985 in the 40–49 to 50–59 age
groups.

Communication

24. **(a)** Answers vary; for example, in a pictograph, we can observe change over time and make comparisons between similar situations. In a circle graph it is hard to make these observations.
(b) Answers vary; for example, circle graphs are used when comparing parts to a whole. Circle graphs allow for visual comparisons of fractional parts. Bar graphs and line graphs can't handle these comparisons as well.
(c) Answers vary; for example, in a stem-and-leaf plot, we can see the same shape and information as in a histogram but no data points are lost in the display as they may be in a histogram, especially when intervals are used.
25. Answers vary; for example, if only percentages are shown on the circle graph then the circle graph would not change. If data are shown, the numbers in the graph change but not the shape of the graph.
26. Answers vary; for example, the percents are of a whole and the circle represents the complete whole or 100%. Because of rounding, it may happen that the sum of the percents is close to 100% but not exactly 100%.
27. Answers vary; for example, the budget for 1 yr is usually represented with a circle graph because the circle graph looks somewhat like a dollar and a circle graph allows for a visual comparison of the relative sizes of fractional parts which is what the graph of the federal budget is attempting to show.
28. **(a)** Answers vary; for example, a line graph is more appropriate since we have continuous data changing over time.

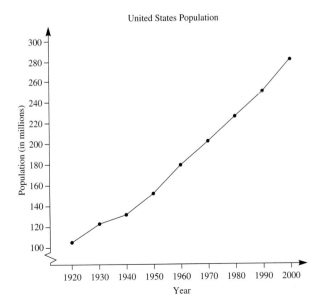

United States Population

(b) The data fall into distinct categories and are not continuous, so we use a histogram or bar graph.

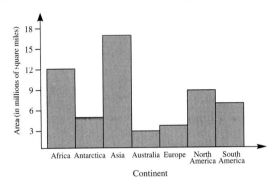

29. Answers vary; for example, the percentage of small cars sold has decreased by 11% over the time period while the sales of midsize cars has increased by 8% and the sales of luxury cars increased 7%. The sales of large cars decreased 4%.
30. Answers vary; for example, the line graph is more useful because we can approximate the point midway between 8:00 A.M. and 12:00 noon and then draw a vertical line upward until it hits the line graph. An approximation for the 10:00 A.M. temperature can be obtained from the vertical line.

Open-Ended

31. Answers vary; a good source of graphs is in *U.S.A. Today*.
32. Answers vary.
33. **(a)**

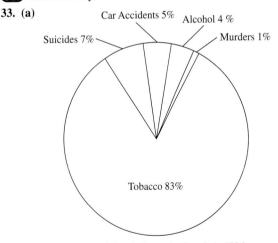

Estimated Death Causes in Canada in 1996

(b) Answers may vary.
(c) Answers may vary.
34. Answers vary depending on data chosen.
35. Answers vary; for example, death rates have been decreasing from cardiovascular diseases since around 1965. Deaths from cancer have been on the rise since 1900. Deaths from influenza and pneumonia have been decreasing since

1900 except for a very serious outbreak in the years around 1918. Tuberculosis deaths continued to drop from 1900 to about 1960 and since then there have been few or no deaths.

Cooperative Learning

36. Answers vary; for example, students may not be able to make definitive decisions other than for their class. You may want to check in department stores to see if they can determine the desired size.

Ongoing Assessment 8-2

1. (a) Mean = 6.625, median = 7.5, mode = 8.
(b) Mean = 13.4̄, median = 12, mode = 12.
(c) Mean ≐ 19.9, median = 18, modes = 18 and 22.
(d) Mean = 81.4̄, median = 80, mode = 80.
(e) Mean = 5.83̄, median = 5, mode = 5.
2. (a) The mean, median, and mode are all 80.
(b) Answers may vary. One set is {70, 80, 80, 80, 90}.
3. 1500
4. 150 pounds
5. 78.3̄
6. (a) $\bar{x}$ = 18.4 years **(b)** 23.4 years **(c)** 28.4 years
(d) The mean in (b) is equal to the mean in (a) plus five years. The mean in (c) is equal to the mean in (a) plus 10 years or the mean in (b) plus five years.
7. Mode, answers vary.
8. Approximately 2.59
9. Approximately 215.5 lb
10. $1880
11. (a) $41,275 **(b)** $38,000 **(c)** $38,000
12. (a) Balance beam—Olga (9.575); Uneven Bars—Lisa (9.85); Floor—Lisa (9.925) **(b)** Lisa (29.20)
13. $19\frac{2}{3}$ mpg
14. 58 years old
15. (a) A **(b)** B and C **(c)** C **(d)** D
16. 91
17. 96, 90, and 90
18. 2
19. (a) (i) $\bar{x}$ = 5, median = 5 (ii) $\bar{x}$ = 100, median = 100 (iii) $\bar{x}$ = 307, median = 307.
(b) The mean and median of an arithmetic sequence are the same.
20.

21. (a) A—$25, B—$50 **(b)** B **(c)** $80 at B
(d) Answers vary. There is more variation at Theater B; also there are higher prices at Theater B.

22.

23. (a)

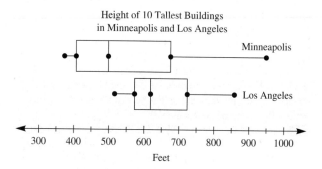

Height of 10 Tallest Buildings in Minneapolis and Los Angeles

(b) There are no outliers.
(c) Answers vary; for example, Minneapolis has more spread in its 10 tallest buildings and has higher buildings than Los Angeles. However, all of the tallest buildings in Los Angeles are higher than more than 50% of the tallest buildings in Minneapolis. All of the tallest buildings in Los Angeles are between 516 ft and 858 ft. The highest building in the two groups is located in Minneapolis and is 950 ft tall.
24. Answers vary; for example, they both practice on the average about 8 hours per week, but Dick's practice time is more spread out, ranging from 5 to 11 hours per week, whereas Tom stays between 6 and 10 hours per week.
25. s ≐ 7.3 cm
26. (a) s = 0 **(b)** Yes
27. (a) Approximately 76.8 **(b)** 76 **(c)** 71
(d) 14 **(e)** Approximately 156.8
(f) Approximately 12.5
28. (a) (i) Increase by $1000 (ii) Increase by $1000 (iii) Increase by $1000 (iv) Increase by $1000 (v) Stays the same (vi) Stays the same
(b) (i) Increase by 5% (ii) Increase by 5%.
29. (a) 1020 **(b)** 1425 **(c)** 1.5, so 1 or 2 people
30. 97.5%
31. 0.68
32. 16%
33. They are equal.
34. (a) 47.5% **(b)** 16%
35. 0.84
36. 90
37. Between 60.5 in and 70.5 in.
38. 50
39. 1600 students

40.
$$v = \frac{(x_1 - \bar{x})^2 + (x_2 - \bar{x})^2 + \cdots + (x_n - \bar{x})^2}{n}$$

$$= \frac{\begin{array}{c}(x_1^2 - 2\bar{x}x_1 + \bar{x}^2) + (x_2^2 - 2\bar{x}x_2 + \bar{x}^2) \\ + \cdots + (x_n^2 - 2\bar{x}x_n + \bar{x}^2)\end{array}}{n}$$

$$= \frac{(x_1^2 + x_2^2 + \cdots x_n^2) - 2\bar{x}(x_1 + x_2 + \cdots + x_n) + n\bar{x}^2}{n}$$

$$= \frac{(x_1^2 + x_2^2 + \cdots + x_n^2)}{n} - \frac{2\bar{x}(x_1 + x_2 + \cdots + x_n)}{n} + \frac{n\bar{x}^2}{n}$$

$$= \frac{(x_1^2 + x_2^2 + \cdots + x_n^2)}{n} - 2\bar{x}^2 + \bar{x}^2$$

$$= \frac{(x_1^2 + x_2^2 + \cdots + x_n^2)}{n} - \bar{x}^2$$

Communication

41. One might use the mode. If you collect the data of all states and consider the most common age at which one could get a license, that would be the mode. Both the mean and median might be decimals, and no state would worry about a decimal age for a driver's license.

42. The answers must be the mode. One cannot compute the mean and median on non-numerical data without a numerical coding.

43. The government probably uses the mean of data collected over a period of time.

44. (a) Mean = 90, median = 90, mode = 90.
(b) Median or mode **(c)** Mean

45. (a) For example, 10, 30, 70, and 90. **(b)** Choose four numbers whose mean is 50. **(c)** The mean of the new numbers is 50.

46. No. To find the average speed we divide the distance traveled by the time it takes to drive it. The first part of the trip took $\frac{5}{30}$, or $\frac{1}{6}$, of an hour. The second part of the trip took $\frac{5}{50}$, or $\frac{1}{10}$, of an hour. Therefore, to find the average speed we compute $\dfrac{10}{\frac{1}{6} + \frac{1}{10}}$ to obtain 37.5 mph.

Open-Ended

47. (a) Answers vary; for example, the more time spent in school, the better the math scores will be.
(b)

1991 Math Scores on International
Assessment of Educational Progress

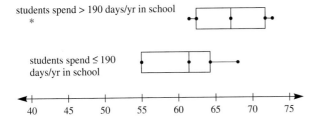

(c) Answers vary; for example, the graph shows that overall the more time that is spent in school, the better the math scores. It also shows that the score of 40 for countries that spend more than 190 days is an outlier. It appears that almost 50% of the countries that spent more than 190 days outscored all of the countries that spent 190 days or fewer.
(d)

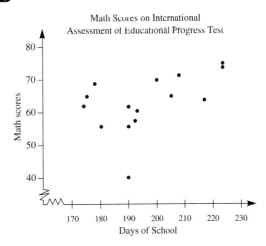

Math Scores on International
Assessment of Educational Progress Test

48. Answers will vary depending on student choice. Probably a good choice might be a box plot with two sets of data depicted so that comparisons could be seen easily.

Cooperative Learning

49. Answers will vary. To do this problem, the class will have to be divided in such a way that the choice of newspapers does not overlap. A teacher may want to discuss how one might do a random sample of newspapers.

Review Problems

50. Answers vary; for example, the number of men in the work force has increased by a factor of about 4 over the last hundred years, while the number of women in the work force has increased by about a factor of 17. As late as 1960, there were more than 200% more men in the work force than there were women. In 1970, this was no longer true, and now in 2000 there are only about 15% more men.

51. Approximately, midsize—173°, large—25°, luxury—61°, small—101°

52. (a) Everest, approximately 8500 m **(b)** Aconcagua, Everest, McKinley

53. (a)

History Test Scores

5	5
6	48
7	2334679
8	0255567889
9	00346

7 | 2 represents
a score of 72

(b)

History Test Scores

Classes	Tally	Frequency
55–59	I	1
60–64	I	1
65–69	I	1
70–74	IIII	4
75–79	III	3
80–84	II	2
85–89	⊮ III	8
90–94	IIII	4
95–99	I	1

(c)

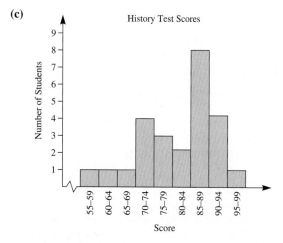

History Test Scores

(d) Approximately 115°

Ongoing Assessment 8-3

1. Answers may vary in all parts of this question.
(a) A question to ask is whether the car is running. If it is not running, then there is no sound and the car would be quieter.
(b) One question is how many motorcycles were sold in what years. **(c)** 11% more fruit solids than 10% is very little.
(d) Any time there is a percentage involved, one should ask "percentage of what?" **(e)** "Up to" is very indefinite, as are the conditions under which the 30 was obtained. 6 mpg is "up to" 30 mpg. **(f)** "Brighter" than what? **(g)** How many dentists responded? **(h)** Most accidents occur in the home because a majority of time is spent in the home. The argument is specious. **(i)** A question to ask is whether another airline flies to the city.
2. Answers may vary. One possibility is that the temperature is always 25°C.
3. She could have taken a different number of quizzes during the first part of the quarter than the second part.
4. When the radius of a circle is doubled, the area is quadrupled, which is misleading since the population has only doubled.
5. The horizontal axis does not have uniformly sized intervals and both the horizontal axis and the graph are not labeled.

6. There were more scores above the mean than below, but the mean was affected more by low scores.
7. It could very well be that most of the pickups sold in the last 10 years were actually sold during the last two years. In such a case, most of the pickups have been on the road for only two years, and therefore the given information might imply, but would not substantiate, that the average life of a pickup is around 10 years.
8. Answers vary; however, he is assuming that there are no deep holes in the river where he crosses.
9. The three-dimensional drawing distorts the graph. The result of doubling the radius and the height of the can is to increase the volume by a factor of 8.
10. No labels for vertical axis, so we cannot compare actual sales. Also, there is no scale on the vertical axis.
11. One would need more information; for example, is the graph in percentages or actual numbers?
12. (a) False, prices vary only by $30.   **(b)** False, the bar has four times the area but this is not true of prices.   **(c)** True
13. (a) This bar graph could have perhaps 20 accidents at the point where the scale starts. Then 38 in 2003 would appear to be almost double the 24 of 1999, when in fact it is only 58% higher.   **(b)** This bar graph would have 0 accidents at the point where the scale starts.
14. Answers may vary, but one such would be 5, 5, 5, 5, 5, 5, 100, 100. The mean would be 28.75 and the median 5. Neither are representative.
15. You could not automatically conclude correctly that the population of the West Coast has increased since 1790. However, based on the westward movement of the mean center of population, there would be strong suspicion that that was the case.
16. Answers will vary. The mean moved approximately 4 cm during the first 100 years and 3.5 cm during the next 100 years. One could expect it to move 5.5 cm during the next 200 years (3 cm in the first 100 and 2.5 cm in the next 100). If this pattern continued, then at the end of 400 years, the mean would have moved yet another 3.5 cm.
17. The homeowner may be looking at a scatterplot of years versus interest rates. The rates have dropped in the 1990s and early 2000s. Whether the pattern continues depends on the economy.
18. A student would need to know the highest possible score that a person could make. Also the scores of other students would be important.
19. You would need to know the standard deviation of the number of students in the classes. You could not answer the overcrowding condition on the one number alone.
20. You could report the mode of a selected number of spots if enough spots were chosen at random. It is also possible that the mode would not exist. A median might be misleading, depending on the number of data points given. Also the mean

would not be sufficient. A report of the mean, median, and standard deviation would be the most helpful of all "averages" studied.

21. It is possible. Such a country might be the Netherlands. The country has dikes to help keep out the sea.

22. Answers may vary. A sample size is needed. Then, one way to pick a random sample of adults in the town is to use the telephone book or a voter registration list. These methods will not list all adults in the town, but these are probably the most accessible sets of data. To pick the sample, one might roll a die and consider the number n that appears on it. Then starting at some point in the adult list, choose every nth person after the start on the list.

23. One of the primary reasons that this statement could be true is that the cost of replacing defective chips is less expensive than attempting to correct the problems that caused the disks to be defective in the first place. The claim seems impossible, but it is true.

Review Problems

24. (a) About 74.17 (b) 75 (c) 65
(d) About 237.97 (e) About 15.43
25. About 27.74
26. $76.\overline{6}$
27.

```
        Men's Olympic
        100-m Run Times
          1896–2000

   9 | 7899
  10 | 00011233334568888
  11 | 00              10 | 0 represents
  12 | 0                  10.0 seconds
```

28.

From examining the box plot, we can see that the times on the 100-m butterfly are much greater (relatively speaking) than the times on the 100-m freestyle.

Chapter Review

1. If the average is 2.41 children, then the mean is being used. If the average is 2.5, then the mean or the median might have been used.
2. 23
3. (a) Mean = 30, median = 30, mode = 10.
  (b) Mean = 5, median = 5, modes = 3, 5, 6.

4. (a) Range = 50, variance $\doteq$ 371.4, standard deviation $\doteq$ 19.3. (b) Range = 8, variance = 5.2, standard deviation $\doteq$ 2.28.

5. (a)

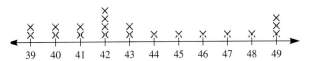

(b)

```
        Miss Rider's Class
        Masses in Kilograms

   3 | 99
   4 | 001122223345678999   4 | 0 represents
                                 40 kg
```

(c)

Mass	Tally	Frequency
39	II	2
40	II	2
41	II	2
42	IIII	4
43	II	2
44	I	1
45	I	1
46	I	1
47	I	1
48	I	1
49	III	3
		20

Miss Rider's Class
Masses in Kilograms

(d)

6. (a)

Test Grades

Classes	Tally	Frequency
61–70	JHT I	6
71–80	JHT JHT I	11
81–90	JHT II	7
91–100	JHT I	6
		30

(b)

Grade Distribution

7.

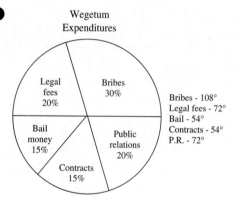

Wegetum Expenditures

Bribes - 108°
Legal fees - 72°
Bail - 54°
Contracts - 54°
P.R. - 72°

8. The widths of the bars are not uniform.

9. $2840

10.

Running Speeds

11. (a)

Life Expectancies
of Males and Females

Females		Males
	67	1446
	68	28
	69	156
	70	0049
	71	02235578
	72	01145
	73	1689
7	74	
9310	75	
86	76	
88532	77	
9999854332211	78	
54210	79	

7 | 74 | represents
74.7 years old

| 67 | 1 represents
67.1 years old

(b)

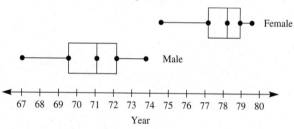

Life Expectancies

12. Larry was correct because his average was $3.2\overline{6}$, while Marc's was 2.73.

13. (a) 360 **(b)** None **(c)** 350 **(d)** $s \doteq 108.2$

14. (a) 67 **(b)** UQ = 74, LQ = 64

(c)

Car Speeds

(d) Approximately 50% **(e)** 30% **(f)** No, there are fewer speeds close to 67 in the third quartile than in the second quartile.

15. (a) Positive **(b)** 170 lb **(c)** 67 in. **(d)** 64 in. **(e)** 50 lb

16. Answers may vary. **(a)** One way would be to leave the television on, even if no one is watching. **(b)** They show very popular shows during "ratings sweeps" periods.

17. Answers may vary. For example, graphs may show area or volume instead of relative size; another is to select a horizontal baseline that will support the point trying to be made.

18. The advertisement is not reasonable. One would expect the snow to be okay, but with reports like those given, there is little information about the snow in the middle of the mountain. If it is cold enough to have 23 in. at the bottom of a hill, one would expect there to be snow all the way to the top. However, if the bottom and the top are shaded, then there could be much variation if a part of the hill were sunny.

19. (a) Answers vary, for example, **5.**1.
(b) Between 83–84 and 84–85.
(c) A line graph is more appropriate because the data is continuous over time.
(d) Answers vary; for example, you could change the scale on the *y*-axis to go up by 5s or 10s rather than by 20s.
20. (a)

U.S. Infant Mortality Rates 1980–99
(rates are per 1000 live births)

Females		Males
86554	6	
8642	7	78
9981	8	0038
631	9	34
720	10	038
2	11	02599
	12	38
	13	19

6 | 6 | represents 6.6 | 13 | 1 represents 13.1

(b) Answers vary; for example, the number of male deaths is consistently higher than female deaths and the difference has stayed about the same. The mortality rates for both males and females is decreasing, and is decreasing at about the same rate.
(c) Answers vary; for example, a double-bar graph showing male and female deaths for each year or a box plot showing male and female deaths would be appropriate.
21. (a) 25   **(b)** 475   **(c)** 16%
22. 475

Chapter 9

Ongoing Assessment 9-1

1. (a) In 12 ways, if different order implies different name.
(b) 60 ways, if different order implies different name.
2. (a) For example: $\overleftrightarrow{BC}$ and $\overleftrightarrow{DH}$ or $\overleftrightarrow{AE}$ and $\overleftrightarrow{BD}$
(b) Parallel   **(c)** No   **(d)** Empty set (since $\overleftrightarrow{BD}$ and plane *EFG* have no points in common)   **(e)** Point *H*
(f) Planes *BFC* and *EFG*, or planes *BFD* and *EFG*
(g) For example: $\overleftrightarrow{BF}$ and $\overleftrightarrow{DH}$
3. (a) $\angle EFB$ **(b)** 90°   **(c)** Two planes are perpendicular if the measure of any of the four dihedral angles created by the planes is 90°.   **(d)** $\overleftrightarrow{FH}$ is the line of intersection of the two planes. Line *DH* is perpendicular to plane *FGH* because it is

perpendicular to lines *HG* and *EH* in that plane. Thus line *DH* is perpendicular to any line through *H* in the plane *FGH*. Consequently, $\overleftrightarrow{DH} \perp \overleftrightarrow{FH}$. If we construct a line ℓ through *H* in the plane *FGH* and perpendicular to line ℓ, line *DH* will be perpendicular to line ℓ. Thus one of the dihedral angles created by the two planes in question measures 90°.
4. (a) ∅   **(b)** {C}   **(c)** {A}   **(d)** Answers vary; for example, $\overleftrightarrow{AC}$ and $\overleftrightarrow{BE}$ **(e)** $\overleftrightarrow{AC}$ and $\overleftrightarrow{DE}$ or $\overleftrightarrow{AD}$ and $\overleftrightarrow{CE}$
(f) Plane *BCD* or plane *BEA*
5. 14
6. Answers vary. For example: **(a)** intersecting crossroads   **(b)** angle on a yield sign   **(c)** the top of a coat hanger
7. (a) 110°   **(b)** 40°   **(c)** 20°   **(d)** 130°
8. (a) Approximately 36°   **(b)** Approximately 120°
9. (a) (i) 41°31'10"   **(ii)** 79°48'47"   **(b) (i)** 54'
   (ii) 15°7'48"
10. (a) (i) 90°   **(ii)** 12°30'   **(iii)** 205°   **(b)** 52°30'
(c) Approximately 32 min and 43. 6 sec after 12 noon
11. 2:27
12. (a) 6   **(b)** 8   **(c)** $2(n - 1)$
13. (a)

Number of Intersection Points

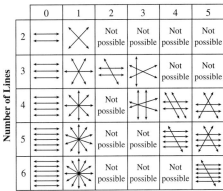

	0	1	2	3	4	5

Number of Lines: 2, 3, 4, 5, 6

(b) $n(n - 1)/2$
14. Answers vary.
15. Answers may vary.
16. (a) No   **(b)** Yes   **(c)** Yes
17. (a) 1   **(b)** 4   **(c)** $_nC_3$, or $\dfrac{n(n - 1)(n - 2)}{3 \cdot 2 \cdot 1}$, or $\dfrac{n(n - 1)(n - 2)}{6}$

Communication

18. (a) Answers vary.   **(b)** The fire is located near the intersection of the two bearing lines.   **(c)** Answers vary.
19. No; if all 4 points are collinear, then one line is determined; if only 3 are collinear, then 4 lines are determined; if no 3 are collinear, then 6 lines are determined.
20. $2 + 2 + 3 + 4 + \ldots + n$, or $1 + \dfrac{n(n + 1)}{2}$.

Cooperative Learning

21. (a) An angle of 20° can be drawn by tracing a 50° angle and a 30° angle, as shown in the following figure. Another 20° angle adjacent to the first 20° angle can be drawn in a similar way, thus creating a 40° angle.

(b) Yes; answers vary. **(c)** All multiples of 10°.

Open-Ended

22. Answers depend on the classroom.
23. Answers depend on students.

Ongoing Assessment 9-2

1. (a) 1, 4, 6, 7, 8 **(b)** 1, 6, 7, 8 **(c)** 6, 7 **(d)** 1, 8
2. 8
3. A concave polygon
4. (a) and (c) are convex, since no matter which two points in the interior of the figure are chosen, the entire segment connecting the points lies within the figure; (b) and (d) are concave since two points within the figure can be chosen such that the segment formed by the two points does not lie entirely within the figure.
5. (d) and (e) are impossible because each angle of an equilateral triangle has measure 60°.
6. (a) 35 **(b)** 170 **(c)** 4850 **(d)** $\dfrac{n(n-3)}{2}$
7. (a) Isosceles and equilateral **(b)** Isosceles **(c)** Scalene
8. (a) and (b) represent rhombuses and rectangles.
9. (a) *T, Q, R, H, G, I, F, J* **(b)** *Y, Z, E*
(c) *W, D, A, Z, U, E* **(d)** *Q, J, F, G, H* **(e)** *Y*

Communication

10. Answers vary. An 8 1/2 × 11 in. piece of rectangular paper requires only one fold.

Open-Ended

11. Answers vary.

Cooperative Learning

12. Answers vary.
13. (a) The trapezoid definition is different.

(b)

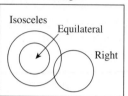

14. (a) Reuleaux triangles aren't truly triangles. They are curves of constant width. **(b)** Reuleaux triangles have equal-sized arcs while equilateral triangles have sides of the same length.
15. (a) Answers will vary. Typically the "sides" of a triangle on a globe are arcs of great circles. **(b)** A square cannot exist.

Review Problems

16. (a) 45 **(b)** $n(n-1)/2$
17. ∅, 1 point, 2 points, ray
18. (a) False. A ray has only one endpoint. **(b)** True
(c) False. Skew lines cannot be contained in the single plane.
(d) False. $\overrightarrow{MN}$ has endpoint *M* and extends in the direction of point *N*; $\overrightarrow{NM}$ has endpoint *N* and extends in the direction of point *M*. **(e)** True **(f)** False. Their intersection is a line.

Ongoing Assessment 9-3

1. 6
2. (a) 60° **(b)** 45° **(c)** 60° **(d)** 60°
3. (a) Yes. A pair of corresponding angles are 50° each.
(b) Yes. A pair of corresponding angles are 70° each.
(c) Yes. A pair of alternate interior angles are 40° each.
(d) Yes. A pair of corresponding angles are 90° each.
4. 70° and 20°
5. (a) 20 **(b)** 150°
6. (a) 70° **(b)** 70° **(c)** 65° **(d)** 45°
7. $m(\angle 1) = 40°, m(\angle 2) = 140°, m(\angle 3) = 115°, m(\angle 4) = 140°, m(\angle 5) = 40°, m(\angle 6) = 65°$
8. (a) 50° **(b)** 85° **(c)** 40° **(d)** 55°
9. (a) $x = 40°$ and $y = 50°$ **(b)** $x = 18°$
(c) $x = 50°$ and $y = 60°$ **(d)** $x = 83°$
10. (a) 60° **(b)** 90°
11. (a) 360° **(b)** 360° **(c)** 360°
12. 60°, 84°, 108°, 132°, 156°
13. 90°
14. 111°
15. $m(\angle 1) = 60°, m(\angle 2) = 30°, m(\angle 3) = 110°$
16. 135°
17. (a) 100° **(b)** The measure of the exterior angle equals the sum of the remote interior angles. Since ∠1 and ∠ACB are supplementary, then $m(\angle 1) + m(\angle ACB) = 180°$. We also know that the sum of the measures of the angles of a triangle equals 180°; that is, $m(\angle A) + m(\angle B) + m(\angle C) = 180°$. So $m(\angle 1) = m(\angle A) + m(\angle B)$.

18. (a) $m(\angle ACB) = 40°, m(\angle ABD) = 40°, m(\angle DBC) = 50°$
(b) $m(\angle ACB) = 90 - \alpha, m(\angle ABD) = 90 - \alpha, m(\angle DBC) = \alpha.$
19. $60°, 120°, 60°.$
20. $76°30', 103°30', 103°30'$

Communication

21. Place a long ruler or board so that it touches all the stairs and the ground. The angle α that the board makes with the ground measures the steepness of the stairs.

22. (a) No. Two or more obtuse angles will produce a sum of more than 180°. **(b)** Yes. For example, each angle may have measure 60°. **(c)** No. The sum of the measures of the three angles would be more than 180°. **(d)** No. It may have an obtuse or right angle as well.
23. No, it is not possible. The sum of all the measures of the angles in $\triangle ABC$ must equal 180°, but $m(\angle ABC) + m(\angle ACB) + m(\angle BAC) = 90° + 90° + m(\angle BAC) > 180°$. Hence, the situation shown in the diagram is not possible.
24. (a) Five triangles will be constructed in which the sum of the angles of each triangle is 180°. The sum of the measures of the angles of all the triangles equals 5(180°), from which we subtract 360° (the sum of all the measures of the angles of triangles with vertex P). Thus $5(180°) - 360° = 540°$.
(b) Here, n triangles are constructed, so we have $n(180°)$ from which we subtract 360° (the sum of all the measures of the angles of the triangles with vertex P). Thus we obtain $n(180°) - 360°$, which is the same answer stated in Section 9-3.
25. $x = 30°$. Possible explanation: The ladder makes an isosceles triangle with base angles of 60° (since the angle supplementary to 120° is 60°, as shown in the following figure). The bar across the ladder is parallel to the ground and hence creates corresponding angles formed by the bar, the ground, and the side of the ladder. Consequently, the angle formed by the bar and the side of the ladder is 60°. Since the line from the apple is perpendicular to the bar crossing the ladder, we have $x = 90° - 60° = 30°$. Hence $x = 30°$.

26. (a) Fold the isosceles triangle so the congruent sides match up. The two angles will fall on top of each other. **(b)** Fold

the triangle so the two congruent angles fall on top of each other. The two sides will match up. **(c)** Choose a vertex and fold the triangle at that vertex so that the other two vertices fall on top of each other. Two angles of the triangle should fall on top of each other. Repeat at a second vertex. **(d)** Fold the trapezoid so that its congruent sides fall on top of each other and check that the base angles fall on top of each other as well.
27. (a) Divide the quadrilateral into two triangles: $\triangle ABC$ and $\triangle ACD$. The sum of the measures of the interior angles of each triangle is 180°, so the sum of the measures of the interior angles of the quadrilateral is 2(180°), or 360°. **(b)** This is also true for nonconvex polygons. **(c)** Any concave pentagon can be divided into three triangles and a concave hexagon can be divided into four triangles. In general, it seems that any concave n-gon can be divided into $n - 2$ triangles so that the sum of the measures of the angles of the triangles is the sum of the measures of the interior angles of the n-gon.
28. No. Regular hexagons fit because the measure of each vertex angle is 120°, three hexagons fit to form 360°, and the plane can be filled. For a regular pentagon, the measure of each vertex angle is 108°, so pentagons cannot be placed together to form 360° (360 is not divisible by 108) and the plane cannot be filled.
29. Yes. From the hypothesis, we see that $\angle 1$ is supplementary to $\angle 2$. Because $\angle 3$ is also supplementary to $\angle 2$, we have $\angle 1 \cong \angle 3$. Thus corresponding angles created by lines a and b and the transversal c are congruent. Consequently, a and b are parallel.
30. Extend $\overline{BO}$ to intersect line a at C. $m(\angle BOA) = 360° - 250° = 110°, m(\angle AOC) = 180° - 110° = 70°$. In $\triangle AOC$: $m(\angle C) = 180° - (60° + 70°) = 50°$. Thus the alternate interior angles DBC and ACB created by the lines a and b and the transversal BC are congruent, which implies that a and b are parallel.

31.
$$\begin{aligned}
m(\angle DCB) + m(\angle ABC) &= 180° - (m(\angle 3) + m(\angle 4)) \\
&\quad + 180° - (m(\angle 2) + m(\angle 1)) \\
&= 360° - (2m(\angle 3) + 2m(\angle 2)) \\
&= 360° - 2(m(\angle 3) + m(\angle 2)) \\
&= 360° - 2 \cdot 90° \\
&= 180°.
\end{aligned}$$
Thus by the result in problem 29, the lines CD and AB are parallel.
32. $ABCD$ is a parallelogram. Let the measures of the congruent angles at A and C be x degrees, and the measures of the congruent angles at B and D be y degrees. Then:

$$\begin{aligned}
x + y + x + y &= 360 \\
2x + 2y &= 360 \\
x + y &= 180.
\end{aligned}$$

Consequently $m(\angle A) + m(\angle B) = x + y = 180$, and by problem 29, lines AD and BC are parallel. Similarly $m(\angle A) + m(\angle D) = x + y = 180°$, and hence lines AB and DC are parallel. Thus $ABCD$ is a parallelogram.

Open-Ended

33. Answers vary. You should get a multiple of $360°$.
34. Answers vary. The following are some properties of figures in a plane and corresponding properties on a sphere:

Property in a Plane	Property on a Sphere
Two lines in a plane may intersect in one point or may be parallel.	Two great circles (lines on a sphere) always intersect in two points.
Two points determine a unique line.	Two points do not always determine a unique great circle.
A line has no length, and any point on the line separates it into two parts.	A great circle has a finite length ($2\pi r$ where r is the radius of the sphere) and is not separated into two parts by a point on the circle.

Cooperative Learning

35. (a) If $m(\angle A) = \alpha$ and $m(\angle B) = \beta$, then $m(\angle D) = 180 - \left(\dfrac{\alpha}{2} + \dfrac{\beta}{2}\right)$. **(b)** If $m(\angle C)$ is always the same, no matter what the measures of $\angle A$ and $\angle B$ are, then $m(\angle D)$ is always the same. **(c)** Answers vary. The following is a possible solution. From (a):

$$m(\angle D) = 180 - \left(\frac{\alpha + \beta}{2}\right) = \frac{360 - (\alpha + \beta)}{2}.$$ Because

$\alpha + \beta = 180 - m(\angle C)$, we get the following:

$$m(\angle D) = \frac{360 - (180 - m(\angle C))}{2}$$
$$= \frac{360 - 180 + m(\angle C)}{2}$$
$$= 90 + \frac{1}{2}m(\angle C).$$

Because the answer for $m(\angle D)$ depends only on $m(\angle C)$, the conjecture is justified.
36. (a) Because congruent supplementary angles are formed **(b)** The theorem concerning the sum of the measures of the angles of a triangle **(c)** When A and C are folded, congruent supplementary angles are formed and hence, each is a right angle. When B is folded along $\overline{BB'}$, the crease $\overline{DE}$ formed is perpendicular to $\overline{BB'}$ (again because congruent supplementary angles are formed), consequently, $\overline{DE} \parallel \overline{GF}$. Thus D and E are

also right angles. **(d)** $GF = GB' + B'F = 1/2\,AB' + (1/2)\,B'C = 1/2\,(AB' + B'C) = 1/2\,AC$. Hence $GF = 1/2\,AC$.

Review Problems

37. (a) All angles must be right angles, and all diagonals are the same length. **(b)** All sides are the same length, and all angles are right angles. **(c)** This is impossible because all squares are parallelograms.
38. (a) Two sets of parallel sides—A, B, C, D, E, F, G; one set of parallel sides—I and J (exactly one); No parallel lines: H
(b) Four right angles—D, F, G; exactly two right angles—I No right angles: A, B, C, E, H, J
(c) 4 congruent sides—B, C, F, G; Two pairs of congruent sides only—E, H, A, D; One pair of congruent sides only—J; No sides congruent—I
(d) D, F, G, J
39. Answers will vary but should include the following:
- Congruent opposite sides describe a parallelogram.
- All sides congruent describe a rhombus (and square).
- Four right angles describe a rectangle (and square).
- Two pairs of consecutive sides congruent describe a kite.

Ongoing Assessment 9-4

1. (a) Quadrilateral pyramid **(b)** Quadrilateral prism; possibly a trapezoidal prism **(c)** Pentagonal pyramid
2. (a) A, D, R, W **(b)** $\overline{AR}, \overline{RD}, \overline{AD}, \overline{AW}, \overline{WR}, \overline{WD}$
(c) $\triangle ARD, \triangle AWD, \triangle AWR, \triangle WDR$ **(d)** $\{R\}$ **(e)** $\overline{DW}$
3. Answers vary; for example, rectangular prism, cylinder, pyramid, and sphere.
4. (a) 5 **(b)** 4 **(c)** 4
5. (a) True **(b)** False **(c)** True **(d)** False
(e) False **(f)** False **(g)** False **(h)** True
6. All are possible.
7. Answers vary.
8. Answers may vary.
(a) **(b)**

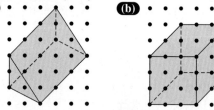

9. (a) 7 cubes; 10 faces. **(b)** 40 cubes; 74 faces.
10. (a) Hexagonal pyramid **(b)** Quadrilateral (square) pyramid **(c)** Cube **(d)** Rectangular prism
(e) Hexagonal prism
11. (a) Triangular right prism **(b)** A right pyramid with a square base
12. Answers vary.
13. (a) iv **(b)** ii
14. (a) i, ii, and iii **(b)** ii, iii, and iv

15.

Vertices per Base	Diagonals per Vertex	Total Number of Diagonals
4	1	4
5	2	10
6	3	18
7	4	28
8	5	40
.	.	.
.	.	.
.	.	.
n	$(n - 3)$	$n(n - 3)$

16. (a) **(b)**

17. (a) (2) **(b)** (4)

18. (a)
Triangle

(b)
Rectangle

(c)
Circle

(d)
Pentagon

(e)
Circle

(f)
Ellipse or oval

19. (a) Parallelogram, rectangle, square, triangle
(b) Rectangle, parallelogram, circle, ellipse
20. (a) $10 + 7 - 15 = 2$ **(b)** $9 + 9 - 16 = 2$
21. (a) 6 **(b)** 48 **(c)** 11
The suggested relationship is $V + F - E = 2$.
22.

	Pyramid	Prism
(a)	$n + 1$	$n + 2$
(b)	$n + 1$	$2n$
(c)	$2n$	$3n$
(d)	$(n + 1) + (n + 1) - 2n = 2$	$(n + 2) + 2n - 3n = 2$

Communication

23. 3. Each pair of parallel faces could be considered bases.
24. Answers vary; for example, a cone is a many-sided pyramid and a cylinder is a many-sided prism.
25. Both could be drawings of a quadrilateral pyramid. In (**a**), we are directly above the pyramid, and in (**b**), we are directly below the pyramid.

Open-Ended

26. Answers vary. A sphere has infinitely many planes of symmetry.

Cooperative Learning

27. Answers vary.
28. Answers vary.
29. (a) Parallelogram, rectangle, square, scalene triangle, isosceles triangle, equilateral triangle **(b)** Triangle, quadrilateral

Review Problems

30. Yes because the sum of the angles of a triangle is 180°.
31. $m(\angle BCD) = 60°$.
32. 140°
33. (a) True **(b)** True **(c)** False (e.g., equilateral triangle)
34. Lines in the same plane and perpendicular to the same line are parallel. This is because corresponding angles are right angles and hence are congruent.

Ongoing Assessment 9-5

1. All except (d), (f), and (i) are traversable; (a), (b), and (j) are Euler circuits (starting and stopping points are the same)
(a)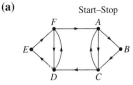

Path:
ABCACDEFDFA;
any point can be a
starting point.

(b)

Path:
DACDCBABC;
only points *C* and *D*
can be starting points.

(c)

Start Stop

Path:
ABCFAEDCEFB;
only points *A* and *B*
can be starting points.

(d) Not traversable; has more than two odd vertices.

(e)

Start

Path:
ABCBDCAD;
only points *A* and *D*
can be starting points.

(f) Not traversable; has more than two odd vertices.

(g)

Start Stop

Path:
FADABCBGFEDCHEHG;
only points *F* and *G*
can be starting points.

(h)

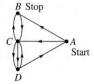

Path:
ACBCDCDAB;
only points *A* and *B*
can be starting points.

(i) Not traversable; has more than two odd vertices.

(j)

Path:
EFHKLNABDFGHLMNBCDE;
any point can be a
starting point.

2. All of them

3.

Path: *CEBABCADEDC*; any point can be a starting point.

4. (a)

(i)

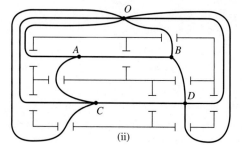

(ii)

(b) Network (i) is not traversable because it has four odd vertices. Network (ii) has two odd vertices, so it is traversable, as shown in the following figure:

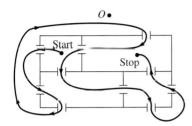

5. Yes. See the following figure:

6. It is not possible.

7.

Network	R	V	A	R + V − A
(a)	6	6	10	2
(b)	6	4	8	2
(c)	6	6	10	2
(d)	4	4	6	2
(e)	5	4	7	2
(f)	8	8	14	2
(g)	9	8	15	2
(h)	6	4	8	2
(i)	7	7	12	2
(j)	8	12	18	2

8.

All vertices are even, so the trip is possible. It makes no difference where she starts.

Communication

9. Answers vary. Possibilities are as follows:
(a)   **(b)**

(c) Answers vary.

10. The bridge could be built anywhere and we would have two odd vertices. Thus the network would be traversable.

11. There is one-to-one correspondence between the faces of the polyhedron and the plane regions of the network, provided that the pentagonal upper face of the polyhedron corresponds to the infinite region outside the larger pentagon of the network. There is also a one-to-one correspondence between the edges of the polyhedron and the edges of the network. Similarly, there is one-to-one correspondence between the vertices of the polyhedron and the vertices of the network.

Open-Ended

12. (a) A postal worker would have to travel each route twice (both sides). A traveling salesperson would only be interested in vertices (cities or stores). A highway inspector would travel each arc only once.   **(b)** Answers vary.

13. Answers vary; for example:

14. Answers vary.
15. Answers vary.

Cooperative Learning

16. Answers vary.

Chapter Review

1. (a) $\overleftrightarrow{AB}$, $\overleftrightarrow{BC}$, and $\overleftrightarrow{AC}$ **(b)** $\overrightarrow{BA}$ and $\overrightarrow{BC}$ **(c)** $\overline{AB}$ **(d)** AB
2. (a) Answers may vary.   **(b)** Planes APQ and BPQ
(c) $\overleftrightarrow{AQ}$ **(d)** No. $\overleftrightarrow{PQ}$ and $\overleftrightarrow{AB}$ are skew lines, so no single plane contains them.
3. Answers vary.
4. (a) No. The sum of the measures of two obtuse angles is greater than 180°, which is the sum of the measures of the angles of any triangle.   **(b)** No. The sum of the measures of the four angles in a parallelogram must be 360°. If all the angles are acute, the sum would be less than 360°.
5. 18°, 36°, 126°

6. (a) Given any convex *n*-gon, pick any vertex and draw all possible diagonals from this vertex. This will determine $n - 2$ triangles. Because the sum of the measures of the angles in each triangle is 180°, the sum of the measures of the angles in the *n*-gon is $(n - 2)180°$. **(b)** 90 sides

7. Answers vary.

8. Answers vary, but the possibilities are a point, a segment, a triangle, a quadrilateral, or an empty set.

9. $m(\angle 3) = m(\angle 4) = 45°$.

10. 35°8′35″

11. (a) 60° **(b)** 120° **(c)** 120°

12. (a) Alternate interior angles are congruent.
(b) Corresponding angles are congruent. **(c)** $m(\angle B) + m(\angle C) + m(\angle BAC) = m(\angle BAD) + m(\angle DAE) + m(\angle BAC) = 180°$.

13. (a) $5 \cdot 180° - 360°$, or $3 \cdot 180°$. **(b)** From the sum of the measures of all the interior angles of the *n* triangles we need to subtract the measures of the angles with vertex at *P*, that is, 360°. We get $n \cdot 180° - 360°$ or $(n - 2) \cdot 180°$.
(c) Answer vary. One way is to connect *B* with *E* and *A* with *F*. We get two quadrilaterals and a triangle. Thus the sum of all the measures of the interior angles of the polygon is $2 \cdot 360° + 180°$ or 900°.

14. $m(\angle 1) = m(\angle 2) = 65°, m(\angle 3) = m(\angle 4) = 115°, m(\angle 5) = 70°$.

15. 55°

16. (a) $\angle 3$ and $\angle 4$ are supplements of congruent angles.
(b) $m(\angle 3) > m(\angle 4)$. Reason: $m(\angle 3) = 180° - m(\angle 1)$ and $m(\angle 4) = 180° - m(\angle 2)$. Because $m(\angle 1) < m(\angle 2)$, $^-m(\angle 1) > ^-m(\angle 2)$. After adding 180° to both sides of the last inequality, the result follows.

17. (a) The measure of one of the dihedral angles formed by planes α and γ is $m(\angle APS) = 90°$. The measure of one of the dihedral angles formed by planes β and γ is $m(\angle BPQ) = 90°$ because line *PQ* is perpendicular to line *AB* (given).
(b) *AB* is perpendicular to the lines *PQ* and *PS* in plane γ.

18. Sketches may vary, but the possibilities are the empty set, a single point, a segment, a quadrilateral, a triangle, a pentagon, and a hexagon. Various types of quadrilaterals are possible.

19. 8

20. 48°

21. Answers may vary.

(a) **(b)** **(c)**

(d) **(e)** **(f)**

22. $_nC_3$, or $\dfrac{n(n - 1)(n - 2)}{3 \cdot 2 \cdot 1} = \dfrac{n(n - 1)(n - 2)}{6}$.

23. Yes if the model is scaled down; no if the model is large. In the latter case, perspective will make the segments appear nonparallel.

24. No; see definition.

25. Answers vary; for example,

26. (a) (i), (ii), and (iv)
(b) (i)

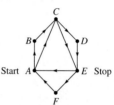

Path: *ABCDEFACEA*; any point can be used as a starting point.

(ii)

Path: *ABCDAEDBE*; points *A* and *E* are possible starting points.

(iv)

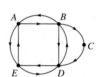

Path: *BDEABAEDBCD*; points *B* and *D* are possible starting points.

Chapter 10

Ongoing Assessment 10-1

1. Otherwise the definition applies to three-dimensional space and thus a sphere.

2. On a plane perpendicular to $\overline{AB}$

3. (a) $m(\angle A) > m(\angle B)$
(b) The side of greater length is opposite the angle of greater measure.

4. (a) Construction **(b)** Construction
(c) A scalene right triangle **(d)** Not possible
(e) Construction **(f)** Construction
(g) Construction **(h)** Construction
(i) Construction

5. (b) Yes
(c) Yes
(d) There is no triangle.
(e) Yes

(f) Yes

(g) The triangle is not unique.

(h) Yes

(i) Yes

6. 22

7. **(a)** Yes; (SAS)

(b) Yes; (SSS)

(c) No

8. The diagonals form triangles, which are rigid structures and thus make the gate stronger. The diagonals ensure that the gate is and stays rectangular (assuming the diagonals are the same length).

9. The lengths must be the same because they are corresponding parts of congruent triangles.

10. The construction makes $\triangle ABC \cong \triangle DBC$ by SAS, so $AB = DB$; by measuring DB, AB is known.

11. **(a)** Construction

(b) Construction

(c) Construction

12. **(a)** Construction   **(b)** Construction

13. **(a)** The three sides are congruent in any order; i.e.,

$$\triangle ABC \cong \triangle ABC$$
$$\triangle ABC \cong \triangle BAC$$
$$\triangle ABC \cong \triangle CAB$$
$$\triangle ABC \cong \triangle ACB$$
$$\triangle ABC \cong \triangle BCA$$
$$\triangle ABC \cong \triangle CBA$$

(b) $\triangle ABC \cong \triangle BCA$, so $\angle A \cong \angle B$ and $\angle B \cong \angle C$ implying $\angle A \cong \angle B \cong \angle C$.

14. **(a)** One method is to start at any point on the circle and with a compass opened to the length of the radius of the circle mark off equally spaced points; there will be six equal arcs.

(b) Construction

(c) Congruent by SSS

(d) The length of each side of the hexagon constructed in part (a) is equal to r, the radius of the circle.

Consider one of the six congruent triangles in the hexagon; let A and B be the two vertices of the triangle which are on the circle and the third vertex be O, at the center of the circle.

$OA = OB = r$, implying the triangle is isosceles; the measure of the angle at O equals $\dfrac{360°}{6} = 60°$.

The base angles in an isosceles triangle are congruent and the sum of their measures is $180° - 60° = 120°$, implying each must measure $\dfrac{120°}{2} = 60°$.

Since all the angles of $\triangle AOB$ are congruent ($60°$) and the triangle is equilateral, $AB = r$.

(e) Anywhere on the circle construct a chord $\overline{AB}$ congruent to the radius of the circle, then construct BC, CD, DE, and EF all congruent to the radius of the circle; the hexagon $ABCDEF$ is a regular hexagon.

(f) From part (e), $\triangle ACE$ is an equilateral triangle inscribed in the circle.

(g) Construction

15. **(a)** F is the midpoint of both diagonals ($\triangle ABC \cong \triangle ADC$ SSS and $\angle CAB \cong \angle CAD$ by CPCTC and $\triangle BAF \cong \triangle DAF$ by SAS $\Rightarrow \overline{BF} = \overline{DF}$, so F is a midpoint; a similar argument will show $\overline{AF} \cong \overline{CF}$.

(b) $90°$. They are congruent and supplementary.

16. Congruent arcs are arcs of circles with equal radii whose central angles have the same measure.

17. The side of one cube is congruent to a side of the other cube.

18. Two parts (e.g., the length of a side of the base and the height)

19. **(a)** 6

(b) 24

(c) $n(n-1)(n-2) \cdots 3 \cdot 2 \cdot 1$ or $n!$

20. Congruent by SAS

21. Perimeters are equal. If sides are congruent the sums of their lengths must be the same.

22. The center of the circle is the intersection of the perpendicular bisectors of any two sides of the triangle. Because the triangle is obtuse, its center is exterior to the triangle. The radius of the circle is the distance from the center to any of the vertices of the triangle.

23. (a), (b); Constructions

24. **(a)** Only six points are determined.

(b) The figure is a regular hexagon. All sides are congruent. By a process similar to that used in problem 14, the angles can be proved congruent. The hexagon is regular.

25. A circle can be circumscribed about the sign.

26. **(a)** A square is formed.

(b) In the figure below, triangles ABO, BCO, CDO, and DAO are isosceles right triangles. They are congruent by SAS, so $\overline{AB} \cong \overline{BC} \cong \overline{CD} \cong \overline{DA}$. We can argue that each base angle of the isosceles triangles have measure $45°$, so $m(\angle ABC) = m(\angle BCD) = m(\angle CDA) = m(\angle DAB) = 90°$. Thus, $ABCD$ is a square.

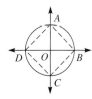

27. **(a)** The perpendicular bisector of $\overline{MN}$ contains O.

(b) By Theorem 10-2a, O is on the perpendicular bisector of $\overline{MN}$.

Communication

28. P is not on the circle because it doesn't fit the definition.

29. The arguments might be as follows: **(a)** By the definition of an isosceles triangle, $\overline{AB} \cong \overline{AC}$. Since congruence is an equivalence relation, we have the symmetric statement

$\overline{AC} \cong \overline{AB}$. Also $\overline{BC} \cong \overline{CB}$. Hence by SSS, $\triangle BAC \cong \triangle CAB$ and by CPCTC, $\angle ABC \cong \angle ACB$.

(b) The two triangles formed by the altitude are congruent by SAS. Then use corresponding parts of congruent triangles are congruent.

Theorem 10-2 may be proved by forming two triangles and proving them congruent using SAS. Then use corresponding parts of congruent triangles are congruent.

30. (a) $\triangle ABC \cong \triangle ADC$ by SSS. Hence $\angle BAC \cong \angle DAC$ and $\angle BCM \cong \angle DCM$ by CPCTC. Therefore $\overleftrightarrow{AC}$ bisects $\angle A$ and $\angle C$. **(b)** The angles formed are right angles. By part (a), $\angle BAM \cong \angle DAM$. Hence $\triangle ABM \cong \triangle ADM$ by SAS. $\angle BMA \cong \angle DMA$ by CPCTC. Since $\angle BMA$ and $\angle DMA$ are adjacent congruent angles, each must be a right angle. Since vertical angles formed are congruent, all four angles formed by the diagonals are right angles. **(c)** By part (b) $\overline{BM} \cong \overline{MD}$; CPCTC.

Open-Ended

31. (a) Answers may vary. Some objects are tins of food and floor tiles. **(b)** Answers may vary. Photographs and their enlargements, an original and its projected image in an overhead projector, and a slide and its image are examples.
32. Answers may vary. One possible pattern is the stamp-block quilt that is a quilt constructed entirely of squares.
33. (a) $\triangle AFB \cong \triangle CED$ by SAS because $\overline{AF} \cong \overline{CE}$, $\overline{FB} \cong \overline{ED}$ and $\angle F \cong \angle E$ (each is a right angle). Hence $\overline{AB} \cong \overline{CD}$ (corresponding parts in congruent triangles).
(b) Because $\triangle AFB$ is a right triangle we have $m(\angle A) + m(\angle B) = 90°$. The congruence of triangles in part (a) implies that $\angle A \cong \angle C$. Hence $m(\angle C) + m(\angle B) = 90°$. This implies that $\angle G$ in $\triangle BCG$ is a right angle and hence that $\overline{AB}$ and $\overline{CD}$ are perpendicular.

Cooperative Learning

34. Answers may vary.

Ongoing Assessment 10-2

1. (a)–(c) Constructions
(d) Infinitely many are possible.
2. (a) No; by ASA, the triangle is unique.
(b) No; by AAS, the triangle is unique.
(c) No; by ASA, the triangle is unique.
(d) Yes; AAA determines a unique shape, but not size.
3. The third angles of the triangles must also be congruent (the sum of the measures of the three angles of a triangle must be 180°; with two angles given the third is determined)
4. (a) (i) ASA: If one leg and an acute angle of one right triangle are congruent, respectively, to a leg and an acute angle of another right triangle, the triangles are congruent.
(ii) AAS: If the hypotenuse and an acute angle of one right triangle are congruent, respectively, to the hypotenuse and an acute angle of another right triangle, the triangles are congruent.

(b) (i) If one leg and an acute angle of one right triangle are congruent, respectively, to a leg and an acute angle of another right triangle, the triangles are congruent by ASA.
(ii) If the hypotenuse and an acute angle of a right triangle are congruent, respectively, to the hypotenuse and an acute angle of another right triangle, the triangles are congruent by AAS.
5. (a) Yes; ASA
(b) Yes; AAS
(c) No; SSA does not assure congruence.
(d) No; AAA does not assure congruence.
6. When the parallel ruler is open at any setting, the distance $BC = BC$; it is given that $AB = DC$ and $AC = BD$, so $\triangle ABC \cong \triangle DCB$ by SSS. Hence $\angle ABC \cong \angle DCB$ by CPCTC. Because these are alternate interior angles formed by lines $\overleftrightarrow{AB}$ and $\overleftrightarrow{CD}$ with transversal line $\overleftrightarrow{BC}$, then $\overline{AB} \parallel \overline{DC}$.
7. (a) Parallelogram **(b)** None **(c)** None
(d) Rectangle **(e)** Rhombus **(f)** Square
(g) Parallelogram
8. An isosceles trapezoid is formed and the angles formed with one base as a side are congruent, as are the angles formed on the other base. The congruent angles are sometimes referred to as the base angles of the isosceles trapezoid.
9. (a) True
(b) True
(c) True
(d) True
(e) True
(f) False. A trapezoid may have two consecutive right angles with the other two not right angles.
(g) True
(h) False. A square is both a rectangle and a rhombus.
(i) False. A square satisfies all conditions of a trapezoid, so some trapezoids must be squares.
(j) True
10. (a) Answers may vary.
(b) No. If the quadrilateral has three right angles, then the fourth must also be a right angle.
(c) No; any parallelogram with a pair of right angles must have right angles as its other pair and hence it must also be a rectangle.
11. The sides fit the definition. Also, $\triangle ABD \cong \triangle CBD$ by SSS. So $\angle BDA \cong \angle BDC$ by CPCTC. This implies $\angle ADE \cong \angle CDE$ because they are supplements of congruent angles. Now $\triangle ADE \cong \triangle CDE$ by SAS. Hence $\angle DEA \cong \angle DEC$. Because these congruent angles are supplementary, they have measure 90° each. Therefore, $\overline{BE} \perp \overline{AC}$, so the diagonals of the chevron are congruent. Thus $ABCD$ is a kite.

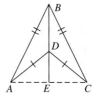

12. (a) Rectangle

(b) Trapezoid

13. It appears to be a parallelogram whose opposite sides are congruent. Because the opposite sides are congruent, it is a parallelogram.

14. (a) 5

(b) Yes; they are congruent rectangles.

15. There are four possibilities: one parallelogram and three kites. (There are four kites but two are congruent.)

16 A rhombus, because all the sides are congruent.

17. Either the arcs or the central angles must have the same measure (radii are the same since the sectors are part of the same circle).

18. Make one of the quadrilaterals a square and the other a rectangle.

19. (a) The sides which are not bases in an isosceles trapezoid are congruent.

(b) The diagonals are congruent.

(c) Let $ABCD$ (below) be an isosceles trapezoid with $\angle A \cong \angle D$ and $\overline{BC} \parallel \overline{AD}$; The opposite sides of a rectangle are congruent, so $\overline{BX} \cong \overline{CY}$. $\triangle BAX \cong \triangle CDY$ by AAS. Thus, $\overline{AB} \cong \overline{DC}$ by CPCTC. $\triangle ABD \cong \triangle DCA$ by SAS, so $\overline{AC} \cong \overline{DB}$ by CPCTC.

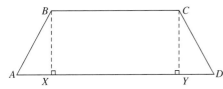

20. $h = \dfrac{a-b}{2}$

21. Construct the first kite by constructing a segment to become a diagonal and then construct two isosceles triangles with the segment as a common base.

Construct the second kite starting with a segment not congruent to the first and construct two isosceles triangles with that segment as their common base but the sides congruent to the corresponding sides of the isosceles triangles in the first construction.

22. (a) Rhombus; use SAS to prove that $\triangle ECF \cong \triangle GBF \cong \triangle EDH \cong \triangle GAH$.

(b) Parallelogram

(c) Suppose $ADCB$ in part (a) is a parallelogram; by SAS $\triangle EDH \cong \triangle GBF$, so $\overline{EH} \cong \overline{GF}$.

Similarly, $\triangle ECF \cong \triangle GAH$ so $\overline{EF} \cong \overline{GH}$; by SSS $\triangle EFG \cong \triangle GHE$. Now $\angle GEH \cong \angle EGF$ and $\overline{FG} \parallel \overline{EH}$.

Similarly, $\overline{EF} \parallel \overline{HG}$.

23. (a) The lengths of one side of each square must be equal.

(b) The lengths of the sides of two perpendicular sides of the rectangles must be equal.

(c) Answers may vary; one solution is that two adjacent sides must have equal lengths and the included angle of one must be congruent to the other.

24. Answers may vary; e.g., the polygons must have the same number of sides with one pair congruent (all regular polygons with the same number of sides are similar, so if they have the same number of sides with one pair congruent, they are congruent).

25. (a) Use the definition of a parallelogram and ASA to prove that $\triangle ABD \cong \triangle CDB$ and $\triangle ADC \cong \triangle CBA$.

(b) Use a pair of triangles from (a).

(c) *Hint:* Prove that $\triangle ABF \cong \triangle CDF$.

(d) *Hint:* Extend $\overline{AB}$ and look for corresponding angles.

Communication

26. The triangle formed by Stan's head, Stan's feet, and the opposite bank is congruent to the triangle formed by Stan's head, Stan's feet, and the spot just obscured by the bill of his cap. These triangles are congruent by ASA since the angle at Stan's feet is 90° in both triangles, Stan's height is the same in both triangles, and the angle formed by the bill of his cap is the same in both triangles. The distance across the river is approximately equal to the distance he paced off, since these distances are corresponding parts of congruent triangles.

27. One way is to make both legs of the ironing board the same length and fasten them together with a hinge at their centers. If one of these legs is attached to the board at a fixed spot and the other leg can be attached at various spots, then the height of the ironing board can be adjusted. Since the legs form the diagonals of a rectangle, the board will always be parallel to the floor. (It can be shown that a quadrilateral whose diagonals are the same length and bisect each other is a rectangle.) In most commercially available ironing boards, the legs are designed to form the diagonals of a trapezoid. The fact that the surface is always parallel to the floor follows from properties of similar triangles discussed in Section 10-4.

Open-Ended

28. (a) All rolls of wallpaper are not congruent. They come in different widths and lengths. Typically with the same pattern, they are congruent. **(b)** Answers may vary. Wallpaper books give the exact drop length. Drop length is the length before a pattern repeats. **(c)** If rolls were congruent and there were a zero drop length in the pattern, then there would be less waste in cutting and matching patterns.

Cooperative Learning

29. (a) In many secondary school and middle school geometry books, kites are not defined. For many of these books, a trapezoid is a quadrilateral with exactly one set of parallel sides. **(c)** The definition used in this text allows a structure among the quadrilaterals that does not exist with the definition in part (a), namely, the subset relationships among the quadrilaterals. The one in this text does cause some difficulty in the definition of an isosceles trapezoid. It must be defined in terms of its base angles, not its sides.

Review Problems

30. The triangles that are congruent to triangle *ABC* are triangles *AED, CDE, ABE,* and *BCD*. They are all congruent by SAS. Students may need to cut these triangles out and compare shapes.

31. and **32.** Constructions

33. (a) Yes; SAS (b) Yes; SSS (c) No

Ongoing Assessment 10-3

1. Construction

2. Constructions. Paper folding is a tactile approach to the problem. The Mira is easy to use when the paper on which the constructions are to be performed may not be altered. Using a compass and straightedge is the classical way to do constructions. The Geometer's Sketchpad demands that exact measurements be used on the screen.

3. (a) A right triangle

(b) The altitude is the extension of the cable from vertex *A* to the ground.

4. (a) The perpendicular bisectors of the sides of an acute triangle meet inside the triangle.

(b) The perpendicular bisectors of the sides of a right triangle meet at the midpoint of the hypotenuse.

(c) The perpendicular bisectors of the sides of an obtuse triangle meet outside the triangle.

(d) Construction

5. (a) This point is equidistant from all vertices because it is on all three perpendicular bisectors. Being at the intersection of two of the perpendicular bisectors forces the point to be equidistant from all three vertices.

(b) Same as part (a)

6. Construction

7. (a) If the rectangle is not a square, it is impossible to construct an inscribed circle. The angle bisectors of a rectangle do not intersect in a single point.

(b) Possible. The center of the circle is the intersection of the diagonals (which are also the angle bisectors of the vertices) and the radius of the circle is the distance from the center of any of the sides.

(c) Possible. The angle bisectors intersect at a single point.

(d) Possible. The intersection of the three longest diagonals is the center of the circle.

8. Construction

9. Answers may vary; for example

(i) Draw a line segment (10¢).

(ii) Draw two intersecting arcs (20¢) to construct a perpendicular segment (10¢).

(iii) With compass point at the intersection of the two segments, sweep a wide arc (10¢) intersecting both segments.

(iv) Maintain the same compass setting and measure an arc from each of these points to determine the fourth point (20¢).

(v) Draw the two segments to complete the square (20¢). The total cost is 90¢.

10. Construction

11. (a) $\overrightarrow{PQ}$ is the perpendicular bisector of $\overline{AB}$.

(b) *Q* is on the perpendicular bisector of $\overline{AB}$ because $AQ \cong QB$; similarly, *P* is on the perpendicular bisector of $\overline{AB}$. A unique line contains two points so the perpendicular bisector contains $\overrightarrow{PQ}$.

(c) $\overrightarrow{PQ}$ is the angle bisector of $\angle APB$; $\overrightarrow{QC}$ is the angle bisector of $\angle AQB$.

(d) Show that $\triangle APQ \cong \triangle BPQ$ by SSS; then $\angle APQ \cong \angle BPQ$ by CPCTC. Show that $\triangle AQC \cong \triangle BQC$ by SAS so that $\angle AQC \cong \angle BQC$.

12. As close to 26 in. as the jack can open.

13. Trapezoid because $\overline{XT} \parallel \overline{IO}$.

14. Rhombus; see problem 23.

15. (a) Possible (see problem 8)

(b) Possible. Construct two perpendicular segments bisecting each other and congruent to the given diagonal.

(c) There is no unique rectangle. The endpoints of two segments bisecting each other and congruent to the given diagonal determine a rectangle, but since the segments may intersect at any angle there are infinitely many such rectangles.

(d) There is no unique parallelogram. Without the angle between the sides, there are infinitely many parallelograms which could be constructed from the two given sides.

(e) Possible. Construct two perpendicular segments bisecting each other and congruent to the given diagonals.

(f) Not possible because the sum of the measurements of the angles would be greater than 180°.

(g) There is no unique parallelogram because the fourth angle must also be a right angle.

16. (a) Construct an equilateral triangle and bisect one of its angles.

(b) Bisect a 30° angle.

(c) Add 30° and 15° angles or bisect a right angle.

(d) Add 60° and 15° angles or 45° and 30° angles.

(e) Add 60°, 30°, and 15° angles.

17. Construction

18. (a) Because the triangles are congruent, the acute angles formed by the hypotenuse and the line are congruent; the corresponding angles are congruent so the hypotenuses are parallel (the line formed by the top of the ruler is the transversal).

(b) Construction

19. Make the edge of the ruler coincide with ℓ; let one of the legs of the right triangle slide along the edge of the ruler until the other leg goes through *P*. The line along the edge containing *P* is the required perpendicular.

20. **(a)** The point is determined by the intersection of the angle bisector of ∠A and the perpendicular bisector of $\overline{BC}$. Because the point is on the angle bisector of ∠BAD, it is equidistant from its sides. Because it is on the perpendicular bisector of $\overline{BC}$, it is equidistant from B and C.
(b) The point is determined by the intersection of the angle bisector of ∠A and ∠B.
(c) The point is determined by the intersection of the perpendicular bisectors of $\overline{AB}$ and $\overline{BC}$.
(d) Not possible. If such a point existed it would have to be on the perpendicular bisector of all the sides, but because the perpendicular bisectors of the four sides of a quadrilateral do not necessarily intersect in a single point (this is the case for the given quadrilateral), such a point does not exist.
21. Construct two perpendicular diameters. Their endpoints will determine a square.
22. *Hint:* Bisect the angles formed by the diagonals of the square.

Communication

23. Given ∠BAC, put one strip of tape so that an edge of the tape is along $\overline{AB}$ and another strip of the tape so that one of its edges is on $\overline{AC}$ as shown. Two edges of the strips of tape intersect in the interior of the angle at D. Connect A with D. $\overline{AD}$ is the angle bisector. Because the diagonals of a rhombus bisect its angles, this construction can be justified by showing that AEDF is a rhombus. (E and F are the points of intersection of the tops of the tape pieces and the opposite sides.) AEDF is a parallelogram. (Why?) It remains to be shown that $\overline{AF} \cong \overline{AE}$. For that purpose, we show that △FAG ≅ △EAH. We have $\overline{FG} \cong \overline{HE}$ because the two strips of tape have the same width. ∠A ≅ ∠A, and the angles at H and G are right angles. Thus the triangles are congruent by AAS.

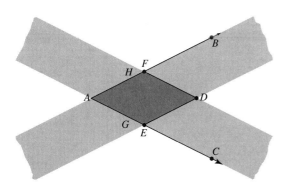

24. Answers may vary. Most students will probably lobby to have other tools included as construction tools.

Open-Ended

25. Most students will probably say that there are more perpendiculars from a point to a line using the North Pole as a point and the equator as a line. All lines of longitude intersect at the North Pole and all are perpendicular to the equator.
26. There are no parallels on a sphere. All great circles (that represent lines) intersect in two points.
27. This depends totally on the geometry utility.
28. **(a)** A possible explanation is as follows: Form a second crease so that A folds onto B. When we unfold the paper, we get two creases $\overline{AB}$ and $\overline{PQ}$, each of which is a perpendicular bisector of the other. This is so because M is the midpoint of each segment and all the angles formed at M are right angles (two congruent angles are formed at M whose measures add up to 180°, and hence each must be 90°). Every point on the perpendicular bisector of $\overline{PQ}$ is equidistant from the endpoints P and Q (Theorem 10-2). **(b)** From part (a) it follows that $AP = AQ$ and $BQ = BP$. Because $\overleftrightarrow{PQ}$ is also the perpendicular bisector of $\overline{AB}$ we have $AP = BP$. Consequently all the sides of the quadrilateral APBQ are congruent. This implies that the quadrilateral is a parallelogram and because all the sides are congruent, it is a rhombus.

Review Problems

29. △ABC ≅ △DEC by ASA ($\overline{BC} \cong \overline{CE}$; ∠ACB ≅ ∠ECD as vertical angles, and ∠B ≅ ∠E as alternate interior angles formed by the parallels $\overline{AB}$ and $\overline{ED}$ and the transversal $\overleftrightarrow{EB}$. $\overline{AB} \cong \overline{DE}$ by CPCTC.
30. Construction
31. $\overline{AB}$ in the trapezoid below equals $\overline{CD}$:

(a) Draw a line through C parallel to $\overline{AB}$; let E be the point where the line intersects $\overline{AD}$. ABCE is a parallelogram ($\overline{BC} \parallel \overline{AE}$ and $\overline{AB} \parallel \overline{EC}$); in a parallelogram opposite sides are congruent (properties of a parallelogram). $\overline{AB} \cong \overline{CE}$ then along with the hypothesis $\overline{AB} \cong \overline{CD}$, $\overline{CE} \cong \overline{CD}$. Thus △ECD is an isosceles triangle. ∠E ≅ ∠D; ∠E and ∠A are corresponding angles formed by the parallel segments $\overline{AB}$ and $\overline{CE}$ and the transversal $\overline{AD}$. Thus ∠A ≅ ∠E, so ∠A ≅ ∠D.
(b) △ABD ≅ △DCA by SAS since $\overline{AB} \cong \overline{DC}$, $\overline{AD} \cong \overline{DA}$, and ∠BAD ≅ ∠CDA, so $\overline{BD} \cong \overline{CA}$ by CPCTC.
32. If ∠A is not the right angle, the triangles are congruent. If ∠A is the right angle, the triangles are not necessarily congruent.

Ongoing Assessment 10-4

 83/70

2. (a) Yes; AAA

(b) Yes; sides are proportional and angles are congruent.

(c) No

(d) No

(e) Yes; radii are proportional.

(f) No

(g) Yes; sides are proportional and angles are congruent.

3. Make all dimensions three times as long; that is, in part (c) each side would be three diagonal units long. One possible solution set is shown below:

(a)

(b)

(c)

(d)
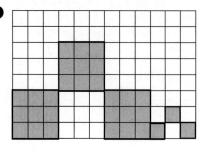

4. (a) and **(b)** Construct triangles as specified.
(c) The triangles are similar when their corresponding sides are proportional.

5. (a) and **(b)** Construct triangles as specified.
(c) The triangles are similar if in $\triangle ABC$ and $\triangle DEF$,
$\dfrac{AB}{DE} = \dfrac{AC}{DF}$ and $\angle A \cong \angle D$.

6. Answers may vary.
(a) Two rectangles, one of which is a square and the other is not

(b) Two rhombuses with the same length sides but with different angles

7. The ratio of the perimeters is the same as the ratio of the sides.

8. (a) (i) $\triangle ABC \sim \triangle DEF$ (by AA)
(ii) $\triangle ABC \sim \triangle EDA$ (by AA)
(iii) $\triangle ACD \sim \triangle ABE$ (by AA)
(iv) $\triangle ABE \sim \triangle DBC$ (by AA)

(b) (i) $\dfrac{2}{3}$

(ii) $\dfrac{1}{2}$

(iii) $\dfrac{3}{4}$

(iv) $\dfrac{3}{4}$

9. (a) 7

(b) $\dfrac{24}{7}$

(c) 3

(d) $\dfrac{96}{13}$

10. Construction

11. (a) (i) $\triangle ABC \sim \triangle ACD$ by AA because $\angle ADC$ and $\angle ACB$ are right angles and $\angle A$ is common to both.
(ii) $\triangle ABC \sim \triangle CBD$ by AA because $\angle CDB$ and $\angle ACB$ are right angles and $\angle B$ is common to both.
(iii) Using (1) and (2), $\triangle ACD \sim \triangle CBD$ by the transitive property.

(b) (i) $\dfrac{AC}{AB} = \dfrac{CD}{CB} = \dfrac{AD}{AC}$

(ii) $\dfrac{CB}{AB} = \dfrac{CD}{AC} = \dfrac{DB}{CB}$

(iii) $\dfrac{AC}{CB} = \dfrac{AD}{CD} = \dfrac{CD}{DB}$

(c) From part (b): $\dfrac{a}{x} = \dfrac{c}{a}$, then $a^2 = cx$. Similarly $\dfrac{b}{y} = \dfrac{c}{b}$, then $b^2 = cy$.

(d) From part (c): $a^2 + b^2 = cx + cy$
$= c(x + y)$
$= c \cdot c$
$a^2 + b^2 = c^2$.

In a right triangle, the square of the hypotenuse is equal to the sum of the squares of the legs.

12. No. The maps are similar and even though the scales may change, the actual distances do not.

13. 15 m

14. 9 m

15. **(a)** In $\triangle ABC$ below, let $m(\angle B) = 90°$:

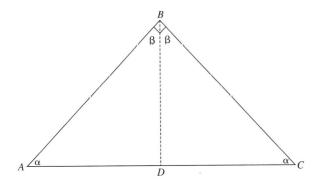

Let $AB = BC$ and let $\overline{BD}$ be the angle bisector of $\angle B$. Then $\overline{BD} \perp AC$ and $\alpha + \beta = 90°$. Consequently, the angles of $\triangle ABC$ are 45°, 45°, and 90°.

Now suppose in $\triangle ABC$ below, the angle bisector is one of the base angles:

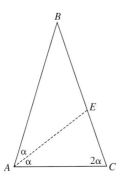

The measure of each of the base angles is 2α; $\triangle AEC$ is isosceles if, and only if, $m(\angle AEC) = 2\alpha$.

Then in $\triangle AEC$, $\alpha + 2\alpha + 2\alpha = 180°$, so $\alpha = 36°$, $2\alpha = 72°$ and $m(\angle B) = 180° - 2 \cdot 72° = 36°$; the angles of $\triangle ABC$ are 72°, 72°, and 36°.

(b) The angle bisector of the right angle partitions the original triangle into two congruent isosceles right triangles with base angles measuring 45°; the new triangles are similar to the original triangle. The angle bisector of one of the 72° base angles partitions the original triangle into two isosceles triangles, which are neither congruent nor similar to each other; but one of the new triangles is similar to the original triangle.

16. About 232.6 in. or 19.4 feet

17. **(a)** (i) Connect B with D and then apply Theorem 10-8 to triangles ABD and BCD. Let P be the midpoint of $\overline{MN}$.

(ii) Theorems 10-7 and 10-8 imply that $MP = \frac{1}{2}a$ and $PN = \frac{1}{2}b$.

Thus, $MN = MP + PN = \frac{1}{2}a + \frac{1}{2}b = \frac{1}{2}(a + b)$.

(b) From part (a), $c = \frac{1}{2}(a + b)$ or $2c = a + b$.

$$c + c = a + b$$
$$c + c - b = a$$
$$c - b = a - c$$

This shows that b, c, and a form an arithmetic sequence having difference $= c - b$, which is equal to $a - c$.

(c) Part (b) proved that the lengths of any three consecutive segments form an arithmetic sequence, so the lengths of all ten segments form an arithmetic sequence. Denote the lengths of the consecutive parallel segments by $b_1, b_2, b_3, \ldots, b_{10}$, where $b_1 = b$ and $b_{10} = a$; because b_1, b_2, b_3 form an arithmetic sequence $\Rightarrow b_2 - b_1 = b_3 - b_2 = d$ (where d is the common difference). But b_2, b_3, and b_4 are also lengths of three consecutive segments, and $b_3 - b_2 = b_4 - b_3 = d$; proceed in the same way to show that $b_4 - b_3 = d$ and so on.

Use the formula for the sum of an arithmetic sequence,

$$S_{10} = \frac{10}{2}(b_1 + b_{10}) = 5(a + b).$$

18. **(a)** Rectangle

(b) Rectangle

(c) Rhombus

(d) Rectangle

19. All sides in each regular octagon are congruent and all interior angles are congruent.

20. $\frac{1}{k}$; their sum (i.e., the perimeter) must be in the same proportion.

21. They have exactly the same shape but not necessarily the same diameter; i.e., they are similar.

22. No; cross sections would be circular (and so similar) if cut parallel to the bases, but could also be rectangular or elliptical if cut perpendicularly or at an angle, respectively, to the bases.

23. 37.785′ or about 37.8′

Communication

24. Any two cubes are similar because they have the same shape.

25. In theory the real product is similar to the model. In reality, this is rarely the case because of changes in the building once the building has been started.

26. Lay the licorice diagonally on the paper so it spans a number of spaces equal to the number of children. (See the figure.) Cut on the lines. Equidistant parallel lines will divide any transversal into congruent segments.

Open-Ended

27. **(a)** The answers may vary depending upon the construction **(b)** The perimeters of the bases should be in the same ratio as the heights in part (a).

Cooperative Learning

28. (b) The following are two different size triangles with the given data (the given angle measures are approximate). The triangles are approximately similar but not congruent. (The ratio of the corresponding sides is $\frac{80}{100}, \frac{4}{5}$.) Hence, the surveyor and the architect could both have been correct in their conclusions.

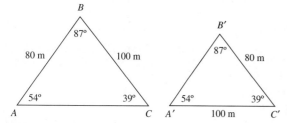

(c) One way for them to avoid their confusion is to specify which sides are opposite which angles.

Review Problems

29. No; the image is two-dimensional while the original person is three-dimensional.
30. Construction
31. Start with the given base and construct the perpendicular bisector of the base. The vertex of the required triangle must be on that perpendicular bisector. Starting at the point where the perpendicular bisector intersects the base, mark on the perpendicular bisector a segment congruent to the given altitude. The endpoint of the segment not on the base is the vertex of the required isosceles triangle.
32. Construct an equilateral triangle with the given side, then construct the perpendicular from any vertex to the opposite side.
33. Answers may vary. Students may suggest that angles of measure 45° be constructed with the endpoints of the hypotenuse as vertices of the 45° angles and the hypotenuse as one of the sides of the angles. Both angles need to be constructed on the same side of the hypotenuse.
34. SASAA or SASSS

Ongoing Assessment 10-5

1. (a) About 13.1 m
(b) About 43.6 m
(c) About 9.5 m
(d) About 11.9 m
2. About 5.1′
3. sin 45° ≐ 0.707
   cos 45° ≐ 0.707
   tan 45° = 1

4. About 8.3 m
5. Horizontal: about 11.0 lb; vertical: about 8.6 lb
6. **(a)** About 35.7°
(b) About 99.3′
7. About 63.9′
8. **(a)** About 561.9′
(b) About 1390.8′
9. A 42′ ladder is needed.
10. About 8.4 mi
11. **(a)** Decimals are rounded to four places:

Angle Measure	sine	cosine	sin^2	cos^2	sin^2 + cos^2
10°	0.1736	0.9848	0.0302	0.9690	1
20°	0.3420	0.9397	0.1170	0.8830	1
30°	0.5000	0.8660	0.2500	0.7500	1
40°	0.6428	0.7660	0.4132	0.5868	1
50°	0.7660	0.6428	0.5868	0.4132	1
60°	0.8660	0.5000	0.7500	0.2500	1
70°	0.9397	0.3420	0.8830	0.1170	1
80°	0.9848	0.1736	0.9698	0.0302	1

(b) The sum of the squares of the sine and cosine is 1 for any angle.
12. About 297′
13. Tangent; we measure the ratio of the opposite side (vertical rise) to the adjacent side (horizontal distance).
14. Tangent; we measure the ratio of rise (change along the y-axis) to run (change along the x-axis).
15. About 63.6 mi horizontally; about 101.8 mi vertically.
16. **(a)** About 121.8°
(b) About 42.9°
(c) About 1.7 m

Ongoing Assessment 10-6

1. The graph of $y = mx + 3$ contains the point (0, 3) and is parallel to the line $y = mx$. Similarly the graph of $y = mx - 3$ contains the point (0, $^-3$) and is parallel to $y = mx$.

2. **(a)**

$y = -\frac{3}{4}x + 3$

(b)

$y = -3$

(c)

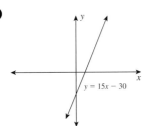

$y = 15x - 30$

(d)

$x = -2$

(e)

$3x - y = 1$

(f)

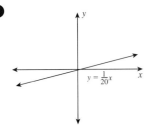

$y = \frac{1}{20}x$

3.

	x-intercept	y-intercept
(a)	4	3
(b)	None	-3
(c)	2	-30
(d)	-2	None
(e)	1/3	-1
(f)	0	0

4. **(a)** Using (0, 32) and (100, 212), the slope is $(212 - 32)/(100 - 0) - 9/5$. So $F - (9/5)C + b$. Plug in the point (0, 32). Thus $b = 32$, and the equation is $F = (9/5)C + 32$.
(b) $C = 5/9(F - 32)$

5. (a) $y = (1/3)x$ **(b)** $y = -x + 3$ (c) $y = -4x/3 + 4$
(d) $y = (3/4)x + 7/4$ (e) $y = (1/3)x$ **(f)** $y = x$

6. (a) $y = -x - 1$ **(b)** $y = (1/2)x$ (c) $y = 1$
(d) $x = 2$ (e) $y = x - 1/2$ **(f)** $y = 0$

7. Answers vary.

8. **(a)** $x = -2$; y is any real number. **(b)** x is any real number; $y = 1$. **(c)** $x > 0$ and $y < 0$; x and y are real numbers.

9. Perimeter = 12 units; area = 8 sq units

10. (a) $x = 3$ **(b)** $y = -2$ (c) $y = 5$ **(d)** $x = -4$

11. (a) 1/3 **(b)** 1/9 (c) 0 **(d)** No slope (e) 20,000
(f) 1 if $a \neq b$

12. **(a)** $y = \frac{1}{3}x + \frac{5}{3}$

(b) $y = \frac{1}{9}x + \frac{13}{9}$

(c) $y = 2$

(d) $x = -3$

(e) $y = 20,000x - 19,990$

(f) $y = x$

13. Answers may vary, depending on estimates from the fitted line; for example:
(a) From the fitted line, estimate point coordinates of (50, 8) and (60, 18); the slope is $\frac{10}{10} = 1$.
Use the point (50, 8) and substitute $T = 50$ and $C = 8$ into $C = 1T + b$ (i.e., an equation of the form $y = mx + b$), so $8 = 1(50) + b \Rightarrow b = -42$; the equation is then $C = T - 42$.
(b) 48 chirps in 15 seconds
(c) $N - 4T - 168$

14. **(a)** (i) The plotted points are shown below:

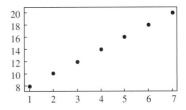

(ii) Answers may vary. One possible answer is $y = 2x + 6$.
(b) 26

15. (a) Unique solution of (2, 5)
(b) No solution
(c) Unique solution of (1, -5)

(d) Infinite number of solutions; x may be any real number $\Rightarrow$ $y = \dfrac{4x - 1}{6}$.

16. $y = 8x - 40$; $y = \dfrac{-4}{7}x + \dfrac{40}{7}$; $y = \dfrac{1}{2}x$; $\left(\dfrac{16}{3}, \dfrac{8}{3}\right)$.

17. 4000 gallons of gasoline and 1000 gallons of kerosene

18. (a) \$2000

(b) 6% annually, or 0.5% per month

19. 17 quarters, 10 dimes

20. (a) all solutions are $(^-1, 2)$

(b) Answers may vary; e.g., $10x + 11y = 12$ and $13x + 14y = 15$ have the solution $(^-1, 2)$.

(c) (i) These equations are of the form $nx + (n + 1)y = (n + 2)$ and $(n + 3)x + (n + 4)y = (n + 5)$.

(ii) All solutions will be $(^-1, 2)$.

21. Answers vary; (50, 106)

22. No; it is curved.

23. (a) 1

(b) -1

24. It is negative.

Communication

25. The intersection point gives the solution of the system

$\left. \begin{array}{l} C° = F° \\ C° = 5/9(F° - 32°) \end{array} \right\}$ The solution of this system tells when

$C° = F°$, that is, when the temperature measured in degrees Celsius equals the temperature measured in degrees Fahrenheit.

26. Answers will vary.
Explanation 1: If two distinct lines have the same slope m, then the equations are $y = mx + b$ and $y = mx + c$ for some real numbers b and c (with $b \neq c$). To show that the lines are parallel, it is sufficient to show that the lines do not intersect; that is, that the system of equations has no solution. Indeed, if we try to solve the equations we get $mx + b = mx + c$. Because $b \neq c$, this equation has no solution. Explanation 2: With $y = mx + b$ and $y = mx + c$, each is a vertical shift of the same line, $y = mx$.

27. Tell Jonah that $5 - 5x$ is not equal to 0 (his order of operations is incorrect). We have $5 - 5x = 5 \cdot 1 - 5x = 5(1 - x)$, which is not 0.

28. Lines with undefined slopes are vertical lines and hence parallel.

Open-Ended

29. Answers vary.

30. Answers vary.

Cooperative Learning

31. Answers vary.

Review Problems

32. 10

33. Yes. Parallel segments are created. Use the midsegments theorem.

34. $\dfrac{12}{7}$

35. 8.2

Chapter Review

1. (a) $\triangle ADB \cong \triangle CDB$ by SAS

(b) $\triangle GAC \cong \triangle EDB$ by SAS

(c) $\triangle ABC \cong \triangle EDC$ by AAS

(d) $\triangle BAD \cong \triangle EAC$ by ASA

(e) $\triangle ABD \cong \triangle CBD$ by ASA or SAS

(f) $\triangle ABD \cong \triangle CBD$ by SAS

(g) $\triangle ABD \cong \triangle CBE$ by SSS

(h) $\triangle ABC \cong \triangle ADC$ by SSS; $\triangle ABE \cong \triangle ADE$ by SSS or SAS; $\triangle EBC \cong \triangle EDC$ by SSS or SAS

2. Parallelogram; $\triangle ADE \cong \triangle CBF$ by SAS, so $\angle DEA \cong \angle CFB$; $\angle DEA \cong \angle EAF$ (alternate interior angles between the parallels $\overleftrightarrow{DC}$ and $\overleftrightarrow{AB}$ and the transversal $\overleftrightarrow{AE}$): and $\angle EAF \cong \angle CFB$; and therefore $\overline{AE} \parallel \overline{FC}$.
$\overline{EC} \parallel \overline{AF}$ (parallel sides of the square); two pairs of parallel opposite sides implies a parallelogram.

3. Construction

4. (a) (i) $x = 8$ cm   (ii) $y = 5$ cm

(b) $x = 6$ m

5. Construction

6. $\dfrac{a}{b} = \dfrac{c}{d}$ (by the transitive property)

7. *Hint:* Find the intersection of the perpendicular bisector of $\overline{AB}$ and line ℓ.

8. (a) (i) $\triangle ACB \sim \triangle DEB$ by AA   (ii) $x = \dfrac{24}{5}$ in.

(b) (i) $\triangle AED \sim \triangle ACB$ by AA   (ii) $y = \dfrac{4'}{3}$
(iii) $x = \dfrac{55'}{6}$

9. (a) False: A chord has its endpoints on the circle.

(b) True

10. 12 m

11. (a) Polygons (ii) and (iii)

(b) Any convex regular polygon can be inscribed in a circle.

12. $h = 6$ m

13. $d = \dfrac{256}{5}$ m

14. True in some cases and false in others.
If the diagonals bisect each other, then the quadrilateral is a square. If not, it is not a square.

15. (a) $y = \dfrac{-4}{3}x - \dfrac{1}{3}$ **(b)** $y = \dfrac{1}{3}x + 1$

16. No; if a line connects all three points, the slope between any two must be the same.

Slope between $(4, 2)$ and $(0, {}^{-}1) = \dfrac{{}^{-}1 - 2}{0 - 4} = \dfrac{3}{4}$; slope

between $(0, {}^{-}1)$ and $(7, {}^{-}5) = \dfrac{{}^{-}5 - {}^{-}1}{7 - 0} = \dfrac{{}^{-}4}{7}$.

Slopes are unequal, so there is no line through the points.

17. **(a)** Unique solution of $\left(4\dfrac{1}{5}, \dfrac{{}^{-}3}{5}\right)$

(b) Unique solution of $\left(\dfrac{10}{9}, \dfrac{4}{3}\right)$

(c) No solution; parallel lines

18. Congruent triangles have two corresponding angles that are congruent. This makes them similar by AA.

19. $\sin 60$ is about 0.87; $2 \sin 30$ is about 1.087 is approximately equal to 1.

20. **(a)** $x \doteq 68.7$ m   **(b)** $x = 30°$

21. **(a)** $\dfrac{\sin 30}{\cos 30} = \dfrac{\dfrac{\text{side opposite } 30°}{\text{hypotenuse}}}{\dfrac{\text{side adjacent to } 30°}{\text{hypotenuse}}}$

$= \dfrac{\text{side opposite } 30°}{\text{side adjacent to } 30°} = \tan 30°$

(b) $\dfrac{\sin A}{\cos A} = \dfrac{\dfrac{\text{side opposite } A}{\text{hypotenuse}}}{\dfrac{\text{side adjacent to } A}{\text{hypotenuse}}}$

$= \dfrac{\text{side opposite } A}{\text{side adjacent to } A} = \tan A$

Chapter 11

Ongoing Assessment 11-1

1. **(a)** 0.9 cm   **(b)** 0.9 cm   **(c)** 8 cm   **(d)** 0.5 cm
(e) 0.7 cm   **(f)** 4.9 cm   **(g)** 7.3 cm   **(h)** 5.2 cm
2. Answers vary
3. **(a)** 960 farthings   **(b)** 1.5 pounds   **(c)** 2880 pence
4. **(a)** 2 7/9   **(b)** 14,400   **(c)** 100   **(d)** 31
5. Answers vary.
6. **(a)** 72   **(b)** 7.2
7. **(a)** Centimeters   **(b)** Millimeters
(c) Centimeters or meters   **(d)** Centimeters or millimeters   **(e)** Centimeters   **(f)** Meters or centimeters
8. **(a)** Inches   **(b)** Inches   **(c)** Feet   **(d)** Inches
(e) Inches   **(f)** Feet
9. **(a)** 0.35, 350   **(b)** 163, 1630   **(c)** 0.035, 3.5
(d) 0.1, 10   **(e)** 200, 2000
10. **(a)** 10.00   **(b)** 0.770   **(c)** 10.0
(d) 15.5   **(e)** 195.0   **(f)** 8.100   **(g)** 40.0
11. 6 m, 5218 mm, 245 cm, 700 mm, 91 mm, 8 cm

12. Answers vary.
13. **(a)** 8 cm   **(b)** 12 cm   **(c)** 9 cm   **(d)** 20 cm
14. **(a)** 1 cm   **(b)** 0.262 km   **(c)** 3000 m   **(d)** 0.03 m
(e) 3500 cm   **(f)** 0.359 m   **(g)** 64.7 cm   **(h)** 1 mm
15. **(a)** $AB + BC > AC$ **(b)** $BC + CA > AB$
(c) $AB + CA > BC$
16. **(a)** Can be   **(b)** Cannot be   **(c)** Cannot be. In (b) and (c) the numbers cannot be the lengths of the sides of a triangle because in (b) $10 + 40 - 50$ and in (c) $260 + 14 < 410$, each of which contradicts the triangle inequality.
17. **(a)** The ratios of the perimeters are the same as the ratio of the sides.
(b) Yes
18. **(a)** The minimum perimeter is attained when the second longest side is not part of the perimeter.   **(b)** The maximum perimeter is attained when the longer sides are part of the perimeter; for example,

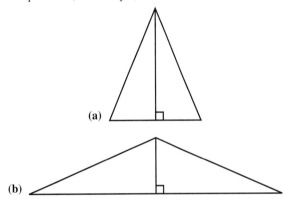

(a)

(b)

19. **(a)** Answers vary; for example, add 4 squares to the end of row one.   **(b)** 8 squares   **(c)** 20 squares.
20. **(a)** 6 cm   **(b)** $3/\pi$ m   **(c)** $0.335/\pi$ m   **(d)** 46 cm
21. **(a)** 6π cm   **(b)** 6π cm   **(c)** 4 cm   **(d)** $6\pi^2$ cm
22. The circumference will double.
23. πr
24. **(a)** About $9.5 \cdot 10^{12}$ km   **(b)** About $4.1 \cdot 10^{13}$ km
(c) About $6.8 \cdot 10^{8}$ hr or about 78,000 years   **(d)** 2495 hr, or about 104 days
25. **(a)** 3096 km/hr   **(b)** 1032 m/sec
(c) Approximately Mach 4.04
26. $(50 + 6\pi)$ ft
27. 49 cm
28. **(a)** 0.5 m   **(b)** 0.05 cm   **(c)** 0.005 m or 5 mm
29. No, speed is distance divided by time, so the base of the inside horse is traveling at $3(6\pi)$, or 18π m/min, while the base of the outside horse is traveling at $3(12\pi)$, or 36π m/min.

Communication

30. **(a)** Answers vary; for example, the metric system is a base ten system and works "almost like" our money system. Conversions are much easier because of the decimal relationship between certain units of measure.

(b) Metric relationships are easier to remember. Also, because it is a base 10 system, conversions are easier. **(c)** Answers vary; for example, things like property descriptions and building materials will probably not change.
31. The height is $3d$, where d is the diameter of a tennis ball. The perimeter is πd or about $3.14d$, which is greater than $3d$.
32. The outer curve has a greater radius and a correspondingly greater distance (i.e., arc length) to run. To compensate for the extra distance, the runner in the outer lane is given an apparent head start.

Open-Ended

33. (a) Answers vary. For example: 1-1-1 and 2-2-1 work, 2-3-6 and 1-2-3 do not. **(b)** A triangle can be constructed if, and only if, $a + b > c$ and $a + c > b$ and $b + c > a$ where a, b, and c are the lengths of the three sides.

Cooperative Learning

34. (a) Answers vary. **(b)** Answers vary. **(c)** Answers vary. Students should conjecture that the length of the outstretched arms is about the same as a person's height. **(d)** Answers vary. They should all agree with the conjecture in part (c).
35. (a) Answers vary. **(b)** If the circles are the same size, then regardless of the radius of each circle the amount of wire needed is the same. **(c)** Let the radius of each circle be r cm. Then the number of circles needed for each chain is $\dfrac{60}{2r}$ (why?). The circumference of each circle is $2\pi r$ and hence the amount of wire, which is the total circumference of all the circles, is $\dfrac{60}{2r} \cdot 2\pi r$, or 60π cm. Because this number does not depend on the value of r, the amount of wire needed for the chain is the same regardless of the radius of each circle.

Ongoing Assessment 11-2

1. Answers vary.
2. (a) cm², in.² **(b)** cm², in.² **(c)** m² or cm², yd² or in.²
(d) m², yd² **(e)** m², yd² **(f)** km², mi²
3. Answers vary, for example, **(a)** 1.5 m²
(b) 1400 cm² **(c)** 2500 cm² **(d)** 3 m²
4. (a) 0.0588 m², 58,800 mm² **(b)** 0.000192 m², 1.92 cm²
(c) 15,000 cm², 1,500,000 mm² **(d)** 0.01 m², 10,000 mm²
(e) 0.0005 m², 500 mm²
5. (a) 444 4/9 yd² **(b)** approx. 0.32 mi² **(c)** 6400 acres
(d) 130,680 ft²
6. (a) 4900 m² **(b)** 98a **(c)** 0.98 ha
7. (a) 3 sq. units **(b)** 3 sq. units **(c)** 2 sq. units
(d) 5 sq. units **(e)** 6 sq. units **(f)** 4 1/2 sq. units

8. They all check; i.e., $I + (1/2)B - 1 = A$.
9. (a) 20 cm² **(b)** 900 cm², or 0.09 m² **(c)** 7.5 m²
(d) 39 cm²
10. (a) 9 cm² **(b)** 96 cm² **(c)** 20 cm² **(d)** 84 cm²
(e) 105 cm²
11. (a) (i) 1.95 km² (ii) 195 ha **(b)** (i) 0.63 mi²
approx. (ii) 402.89 acres approx. **(c)** Answers vary; for example, the metric system is easier because you only have to move the decimal point to convert units within the system.
12. (a) True **(b)** Don't know. It could be. **(c)** It could be 60 cm², so false. **(d)** Don't know. It could be 60 cm².
13. $(1/2)ab$
14. (a) $405.11 **(b)** $550
15. (a) 25π cm² **(b)** $(8/3)\pi$ cm² **(c)** $(9/2)\pi$ cm²
(d) 100 cm²
16. 1200 tiles
17. 8 bags of seed
18. (a) $24\sqrt{3}$ cm² **(b)** $9\sqrt{3}$ cm²
19. In the first picture the wasted space is $\pi r^2 - 2r^2$ or about $1.14\, r^2$. The wasted space for the circle in the square is $4r^2 - \pi r^2$ or about $0.86\, r^2$. Therefore the circle in the square has less wasted space.
20. (a) 16π cm² **(b)** $r = s/\sqrt{\pi}$
21. (a) 2π cm² **(b)** $(\pi/2 + 2)$ cm² **(c)** 2π cm²
(d) $(50\pi - 100)$ cm² **(e)** $(1/4)\pi r^2$ **(f)** $(1/8)\pi r^2$
(g) $(1/16)\pi r^2$
22. 7π m²
23. (a) 48 cm **(b)** 64 cm²
24. (a) The area is quadrupled. **(b)** 1:25
25. (a) The area is quadrupled. **(b)** The area is 1.1^2, or 1.21, times as great. **(c)** The area is increased by a factor of 9.
26. 40 m
27. The first is a better buy at 10 ft² per dollar versus 9.375 ft² per dollar.
28. $(320 + 64\pi)$ m²
29. 1 in.
30. P should be connected to the point that is 2 units above P and 1 1/2 units to the right of P. Area of each is $2\frac{1}{2}$ square units.
31. (a)

Width / Length graph with values 1–6 on both axes.

(b)

32. The area of the outside shaded portion is the same as the area of the inside shaded region, 9π in.^{2}.

33. $MA = 32$ units and $AT = 33$ units

34. (a)

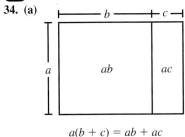

$a(b + c) = ab + ac$

(b)

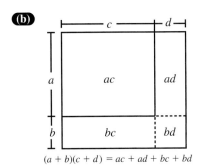

$(a + b)(c + d) = ac + ad + bc + bd$

35. Answers vary; for example, rectangles that are 3×4 and 2×5.

36. (a) The shape of the rectangle becomes less like a square; that is, it become elongated.
(b) The shape of the rectangle becomes more like a square. The maximum area for minimum perimeters for a rectangle is when you have a square.

37. The area of each triangle is 10 cm^2 because the base of each triangle is $\overline{AB}$ and the height of each triangle is the perpendicular distance between the two lines. Because each triangle has the same base and height, the areas of the triangles are the same.

38. (a) 6 cm^2 **(b)** 30 cm^2

39. $\triangle BDE$ is $\frac{1}{9}$ the area of $\triangle BAC$.

40. Draw altitudes $\overline{BE}$ and $\overline{DF}$ of triangles BCP and DCP, respectively. $\triangle ABE \cong \triangle CDF$ by AAS. Thus $\overline{BE} \cong \overline{DF}$. Because $\overline{CP}$ is a base of $\triangle BCP$ and $\triangle DCP$, and because the heights are the same, the areas must be equal.

Communication

41. Answers vary; for example, you could show her that with a given length of string you could enclose many different areas. For example, with a 16 in. string you could have a 4 in. $\times$ 4 in. square with area 16 in.^{2} But you could also have the same for a 1 in. $\times$ 7 in. rectangle with area 7 in.^{2} If you formed a circle, you would have area over 20 in.^{2}

42. John is correct if they were thinking about area. John's garden has area 900 ft^2 and Al's garden has area 450 ft^2, so John has twice the area that Al has for a graden.

43. (a) The area of the 10-in. pizza is 25π in.^{2} The area of the 20-in. pizza is 100π in.^{2}. Because the area of the 20-in. pizza is four times as great, this pizza might cost four times as much, or $40. However, this is not the case because other factors are considered rather than just the area of the pizza. **(b)** If the price is based only on the area of pizza, then the ratio between prices should be $1 : k^2$.

44. (a) Rotate the shaded region 180° about point E. The area of the triangle is the same as the area of the parallelogram that is formed. The area of the parallelogram is $(h/2)\, b$.
(b) Use paper cutting and try it.

45. After the rotations, a rectangle is formed. The area of the rectangle is length times width which in the case of the parallelogram is the same as the base times the height.

Open-Ended

46. (a) Answers vary depending on the size of the hand.
(b) Answers vary; for example, many people will trace their hands on square-centimeter paper and then count the number of squares that are entirely contained in the outline. Next, they count the number of squares that are partially contained in the hand outline and multiply this number by 1/2. The final estimate is the sum of the two numbers.

47. (a) Answers vary; for example, a square 4 cm on a side and a rectangle that is 7 cm $\times$ 1 cm.
(b) Answers vary; for example, a square that is 4 cm on a side and a rectangle that is 8 cm $\times$ 2 cm.

Cooperative Learning

48. (a) 5 square units **(b)** 12 units **(c)** (i) 3 (ii) 15 (iii) 20 **(d)** Answers vary depending on chosen shape. **(e)** Answers vary depending on chosen shape.

Ongoing Assessment 11-3

1. (a) $\sqrt{20} \doteq 4.5$
(b) $\sqrt{17} \doteq 4.1$
2. (a) 6 **(b)** $5a$ **(c)** 12 **(d)** $s\sqrt{3}/2$ **(e)** 9
(f) 13 **(g)** $2\sqrt{2}$ **(h)** $3\sqrt{5}$ **(i)** $3\sqrt{3}$ **(j)** $5/3$

3. (a) Make a right triangle with sides 2 and 3, and then $h = \sqrt{13}$. **(b)** Make a right triangle with sides 1 and 2, and then $h = \sqrt{5}$. **(c)** Make a right triangle with sides 1 and 3, and then $h = \sqrt{10}$.

4. $6\sqrt{5}$, $12\sqrt{5}$

5. (a) No **(b)** Yes **(c)** Yes **(d)** Yes

6. $\sqrt{450}$ or $15\sqrt{2}$

7. About 2622 km

8. $\sqrt{125}$ mi, or about 11.2 mi

9. (a) No, in order for it to be a square the sides must be the same length and the angles must be right angles. The sides are of different lengths. **(b)** The diagonal is $\sqrt{45}$ units long which is about 6.7 units. **(c)** The length of the diagonal is doubled. **(d)** No, the diagonal should measure about 6.7.

10. $6\sqrt{6}$ or about 14.7 ft

11. 9.8 m approx.

12. (a) $(s^2\sqrt{3})/4$ **(b)** $s^2/2$

13. (a) $x = 8$, $y = 2\sqrt{3}$ **(b)** $x = 4$, $y = 2$

14. 1.5 m approx.

15. (a) $4\sqrt{21}$ cm^2 **(b)** $2\sqrt{24}$ cm^2 or $4\sqrt{6}$ cm^2

16. 12.5 cm; 15 cm

17. 8 cm

18. We are not clear how she will saw it. If she saws straight across, we get $8 - \sqrt{34}$, or about 2.17 ft.

19. $90\sqrt{2}$, or about 127.28 ft

20. The longest piece of straight spaghetti will be $\sqrt{116}$ in., or approximately 10.77 in.

21. (a) **(b)** Not possible

(c)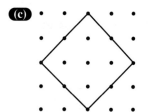

(d) Not possible **(e)** Not possible

22. $\triangle ACD \sim \triangle ABC$; $AC/AB = AD/AC$ implies $b/c = x/b$ which implies $b^2 = cx$; $\triangle CBD \sim \triangle ABC$; $AB/CB = CB/DB$ implies $c/a = a/y$ which implies $a^2 = cy$; $a^2 + b^2 = cx + cy = c(x + y) = cc = c^2$

23. $\sqrt{10}$, or approximately 3.16 m

24. Approximately 16.97 in. so 17.0 in.

25. Approximately 99.5 ft.

26. Approximately 10.6 mi.

27. The area of the trapezoid is equal to the sum of the areas of the three triangles. Thus,

$$1/2(a + b)(a + b) = (1/2)ab + (1/2)ab + (1/2)c^2$$
$$1/2(a^2 + 2ab + b^2) = ab + (1/2)c^2$$
$$a^2/2 + ab + b^2/2 = ab + c^2/2$$

Subtracting ab from both sides and multiplying both sides by 2, we have $a^2 + b^2 = c^2$. The reader should also verify that the angle formed by the two sides of the length c has measure 90°.

28. The area of the large square is equal to the sum of the areas of the small square and the four right triangles. Therefore, $(a + b)^2 = c^2 + 4(ab/2)$. Thus, $a^2 + 2ab + b^2 = c^2 + 2ab$ which in turn implies that $c^2 = a^2 + b^2$. It must also be shown that the inside quadrilateral is really a square.

29. It can be shown that the outside quadrilateral is a square of area c^2. The inside quadrilateral is a square with area $(b - a)^2$ or $b^2 - 2ab + a^2$. Each of the four right triangles has area $\dfrac{ab}{2}$. Therefore,

$$c^2 = (b^2 - 2ab + a^2) + 4\left(\frac{ab}{2}\right)$$
$$= b^2 - 2ab + a^2 + 2ab$$
$$= b^2 + a^2$$

Therefore $c^2 = a^2 + b^2$.

30. Yes

31. Yes

32. (a) 4 **(b)** 5 **(c)** $2\sqrt{13}$ **(d)** $\dfrac{\sqrt{365}}{4}$, or approx. 4.78

33. $10 + \sqrt{10}$

34. The sides have lengths $\sqrt{45}$, $\sqrt{180}$, and $\sqrt{225}$. Because $(\sqrt{45})^2 + (\sqrt{180})^2 = (\sqrt{225})^2$, the triangle is a right triangle.

35. The side lengths are 5, $7\sqrt{2}$, and 5 and so the triangle is isosceles.

36. $x = 9$ or $^-7$

37. $c\sqrt{3}/4$

Communication

38. (a) Let the length of the side of the square be s. Draw the diagonal of the square and make the new square have side lengths equal to the diagonal. Then the area is $(\sqrt{2}\,s)^2 = 2s^2$. **(b)** Make the lengths of the new square 1/2 the length of the diagonal, or $(\sqrt{2}s/2)$; then the area of the new square is $(\sqrt{2}s/2)^2 = s^2/2$.

39. Yes, because they are right triangles the third legs must be equal and these legs could be found using the Pythagorean theorem. Then the two triangles must be congruent by SSS (or SAS).

40. Yes, she had a right triangle because the converse of the Pythagorean Theorem implies that if $13^2 = 12^2 + 5^2$, then the triangle is a right triangle. Because this is true, she has a right triangle and therefore a right angle.

Open-Ended

41. Areas vary depending on the triangles drawn, but the Pythagorean Theorem works only for the right triangles.

42. Answers vary; for example, many students will discuss applications involving designing or building a construction project.

43 **(a)** Answers vary, for example, 6-8-10, and 12-16-20.
(b) Yes, we know that if *a-b-c* is a Pythagorean triple, then $a^2 + b^2 = c^2$. This implies that $4(a^2 + b^2) = 4c^2$, and that $(2a)^2 + (2b)^2 = (2c)^2$. **(c)** No; for example, consider adding 2 to 3 4-5 which results in 5-6-7 which is not a Pythagorean triple.
(d) $a^2 + b^2 = (2uv)^2 + (u^2 - v^2)^2$
$= 4u^2v^2 + u^4 - 2u^2v^2 + v^4$
$= u^4 + 2u^2v^2 + v^4$
$= (u^2 + v^2)^2$
$= c^2$

Cooperative Learning

44. Answers vary depending on the triangles that are formed.

Review Problems

45. 0.032 km, 322 cm, 3.2 m, 3.020 mm.
46. (a) 33.25 cm^2 **(b)** 30 cm^2 **(c)** 32 m^2
47. (a) 10 cm, 10π cm, 25π cm^2 **(b)** 12 cm, 24π cm, 144π cm^2 **(c)** $\sqrt{17}$ m, $2\sqrt{17}$ m, $2\pi\sqrt{17}$ m **(d)** 10 cm, 20 cm, 100π cm^2
48. $25/\pi$ m^2

Ongoing Assessment 11-4

1. (a) 96 cm^2 **(b)** 216π cm^2 **(c)** 236 cm^2
(d) $25 + 10\sqrt{31.25}$ cm^2 or $25 + 25\sqrt{5}$ **(e)** 24π cm^2
(f) 90 cm^2 **(g)** 1500π ft^2 **(h)** $(32\pi + 16\pi\sqrt{5})$ cm^2
2. 2.5 L so buy 3 L
3. 2688π mm^2
4. $162,307,600\pi$ km^2
5. 4:9
6. (a) They have equal lateral surface areas. **(b)** The one with radius 6
7. $(108\sqrt{21} + 216\sqrt{3})$ m^2
8. Approx. 32.99 in.^{2}
9. $\left(100 + \dfrac{50}{\pi}\right)$, or 115.92 cm^2 approx.
10. Approx. 91.86 ft^2
11. $\ell = 11$ cm, $w = 8$ cm, $h = 4$ cm
12. (a) The surface area is multiplied by 4. **(b)** The surface area is multiplied by 9. **(c)** The surface area is multiplied by k^2.
13. (a) The lateral area is multiplied by 3. **(b)** The lateral area is tripled. **(c)** The lateral area is multiplied by 9.
14. (a) The surface area is multiplied by 4. **(b)** The surface area is multiplied by 9.
15. $(100 + 100\sqrt{17})$ cm^2
16. (a) 44 **(b)** 38 (add the cube to the center hole)
(c) Yes, for example, place five cubes in the shape of a C. Then adding a cube to the center of the *C* would add no surface area.

17. (a) 1.5π m^2 **(b)** 2.5π m^2
18. (a) $100\pi (1 + \sqrt{5})$ cm^2 **(b)** 1350π cm^2
(c) 2250π cm^2
19. (a) Approx. 42 cm **(b)** Approx. 73 cm
20. (a) S.A. $= 100 + 20\sqrt{125} = 100 + 100\sqrt{5}$ in. or about 323.6 in.^{2}
(b) S.A. $- 25\pi + 5\sqrt{125}\pi = 25\pi + 25\sqrt{5}\pi$ in.^{2} or about 254 in.^{2}
21. $(6400\pi\sqrt{2} + 13,600\pi)$ cm^2
22. 375π cm^2

Communication

23. The ice cubes would melt faster because they have a greater surface area that is exposed to the air.
24. She would need four times as much cardboard. If each measurement is doubled, then the area of each face is increased by a factor of 4; that is, $A_1 = \ell w$ and $A_2 = (2\ell)(2w) = 4\ell w = 4A_1$. Because this is true for all faces, the surface area is multiplied by 4.
25. (a) Estimates vary. **(b)** The height of the can is $3d$ or $6r$, where d is the diameter of the ball. The circumference of the can is $2\pi r$. Therefore, the *L.S.A.* is $(2\pi r)6r = 12\pi r^2$. The surface area of three balls is $3(4\pi r^2) = 12\pi r^2$. Therefore the surface area of the three balls is the same as the lateral surface area of the can.

Open-Ended

26. (a) 2% **(b)** Estimates vary. **(c)** Estimates vary depending on the size of the person. **(d)** Answers vary depending on the size of the person and the desk.
27. Answers vary; for example, a regular square pyramid with square side 2 cm and slant height 1.5 cm has area 10 cm^2.

Cooperative Learning

28.

(a)

Number of Sides Painted	Number of Pieces
6	0
5	0
4	0
3	8
2	12
1	6
0	1

(b)

Number of Sides Painted	Number of Pieces
6	0
5	0
4	0
3	8
2	24
1	24
0	8

(c) There could never be more than three sides painted. The number of pieces with three sides painted is always 8. The number of pieces with two sides painted is always a multiple of 12. The number of pieces with two sides painted is $12(n - 2)$. The number of pieces with one side painted is the number of pieces in the center square of each side. The length of the square is $(n - 2)$ so there are $(n - 2)^2$ pieces on each of the six sides. Therefore there are $6(n - 2)^2$ pieces. The number of pieces with no sides painted is the number of the interior cubes, which is two units less than the dimensions of the original cube, or $(n - 2)^3$.

29. Answers vary.

Review Problems

30. (a) 100,000   **(b)** 1.3680   **(c)** 500   **(d)** 2,000,000
(e) 1   **(f)** 1,000,000
31. $10\sqrt{5}$ cm
32. $20\sqrt{5}$ cm
33. (a) 240 cm; 2400 cm^2 **(b)** $(10\sqrt{2} + 30)$ cm, 75 cm^2
34. Length of side is 25 cm. Diagonal $\overline{BD}$ is 30 cm.

Ongoing Assessment 11-5

1. (a) 8000   **(b)** 0.0005   **(c)** 0.000675
(d) 3,000,000   **(e)** 7   **(f)** 2000   **(g)** 0.00857 approx.
(h) 675   **(i)** 345.6   **(j)** $0.69\overline{4}$
2. 32.4 L
3. 5.6 L
4. 2000 ft^2
5. (a) $\left(\dfrac{256}{3}\right)\pi$ cm^3 **(b)** 120 cm^3 **(c)** 216 cm^3
(d) $\dfrac{125}{3}$ cm^2 or 41 2/3 cm^2 **(e)** 15π cm^3 **(f)** 432π cm^3
(g) $(4000/3)\pi$ cm^3 **(h)** 22,800 ft^3 **(i)** $(20,000/3)\pi$ ft^3
(j) 76,200 ft^3
6. (a) 2000, 2, 2000   **(b)** 0.5, 0.5, 500   **(c)** 1500, 1.5, 1500
(d) 5000, 5, 5   **(e)** 0.75, 0.75, 750   **(f)** 4.8, 4.8, 4800
7. (a) 200.0   **(b)** 0.320   **(c)** 1.0   **(d)** 5.00
8. 1680π mm^3
9. 8/27
10. It is multiplied by 8.
11. (a) 2000, 2, 2   **(b)** 6000, 6, 6   **(c)** 2 dm, 4000, 4
(d) 2.5 dm, 7500, 7.5
12. $253,500\pi$ L
13. 64 to 1
14. 2,500,000 L
15. π mL
16. (a) It is multiplied by 8.   **(b)** It is multiplied by 27.
(c) It is multiplied by n^3.
17. The Great Pyramid has the greater volume. It is approx. 25.12 times greater.

18. Approx. 16363.62, or 16,363 apartments
19. 600 m^3
20. No, approx. 7.33 cm^3 of steel would still be needed.
21. 33.3 cm
22. 1/8 of the cone is filled.
23. It is multiplied by 2.197.
24. The $2 \times 2 \times 4$ ft freezer is a better buy at $25/ft^3.
25. 66 2/3% occupied by balls, so 33 1/3% occupied by air.
26. About 21.5%
27. They are equal.
28. Approx. 2.2 cm
29. No, it is only 1/3 of the volume for 1/2 the price.
30. The volume of the 5-cm grapefruit is approx. 523.6 cm^3 which gives a cost of 0.042 cents/cm^3. The cost for the larger grapefruit is approx. 0.034 cents/cm^3, so the larger grapefruit is the better buy.
31. The larger is the better buy. The volume of the larger melon is 1.728 times the volume of the smaller but is only 1.5 times as expensive.
32. (a) Answers vary; for example, a square base with sides 5 m and a height of 12 m.   **(b)** Infinitely many. Because $V = 100 = (1/3)a^2h$, where a is a side of the square base, then $300 = a^2h$. This equation has infinitely many solutions.
33. 512,000 cm^3
34. (a) It won't hold the cream at 10 cm tall; it would have to be 20 cm tall.   **(b)** Approx. 6.7 cm
35. It is approx. 0.8 times the original radius.
36. (a) Kilograms or metric tons   **(b)** Kilograms
(c) Grams   **(d)** Metric tons   **(e)** Grams   **(f)** Grams
(g) Metric tons   **(h)** Kilograms or grams
37. (a) Milligrams   **(b)** Kilograms   **(c)** Milligrams
(d) Grams   **(e)** Grams   **(f)** Milligrams
38. (a) 15   **(b)** 8   **(c)** 36   **(d)** 0.072   **(e)** 4.320
(f) 5750   **(g)** 30   **(h)** 41.6   **(i)** 1.5625   **(j)** 60.8
39. (a) No   **(b)** Possibly   **(c)** Yes   **(d)** Yes   **(e)** Yes
40. 16 kg
41. (a) $^-$12°C   **(b)** $^-$18°C   **(c)** $^-$1°C   **(d)** 38°C
(e) 100°C   **(f)** $^-$40°C
42. (a) No   **(b)** No   **(c)** Yes   **(d)** No   **(e)** Yes
(f) Chilly   **(g)** Hot
43. (a) 200,000 L   **(b)** 200,000 kg, or 200 t

Communication

44. (a) Doubling the height will only double the volume. Doubling the radius will multiply the volume by 4. This happens because the value of the radius is squared after it is doubled.   **(b)** Yes
45. Answers vary.
46. Answers vary; for example, fill the shape with sand and dump the sand into a container that can be used to measure the sand.

47. **(i)** The volume is approx. 144.7 ft³, the capacity is approx. 1082.45 gal, and the weight of the water is approx. 9043.75 lb. **(ii)** The volume is 8 m³, the capacity is 8000 L, and the mass is 8000 kg. The metric problem is much easier to work because the conversions are much easier. They just involve moving the decimal point. The relationships among length, volume, capacity, and mass are much easier than in the English system.

Open-Ended

48. Answers vary but should have volumes close to 24π or 75.4 in.³, for example, a rectangular prism that is 6 in. long, 4 in. wide, and 3.14 in. high.

49. If the cookies are stood up so the 6-cm diameter is toward the front of the box, then the minimum surface area is obtained by having two cookies across (12 cm), two cookies high (12 cm), and 12 cookies deep (12 cm).

50. Answers vary, but the volume must be 1000 cm³. Some students will worry about shelf space while others will worry about what shape is easiest to hold.

Cooperative Learning

51. Answers vary depending on the cans selected.

Review Problems

52. **(a)** $(20 + 6\pi)$ cm; $(48 + 18\pi)$ cm²   **(b)** 40π cm; 100π cm²
53. **(a)** 35   **(b)** 0.16   **(c)** 400,000   **(d)** 0.00052
54. **(a)** Yes   **(b)** No
55. **(a)** 2400π cm²   **(b)** $(6065 + 40\sqrt{5314})$ cm²

Chapter Review

1. **(a)** $16\frac{2}{3}$ yd   **(b)** Approx. 0.538 mi   **(c)** 3960 ft
(d) Approx. 9.694 yd   **(e)** 5000 m   **(f)** 1.65 m
(g) 520 mm   **(h)** 0.125 km
2. **(a)** Not possible, $p > q + r$ **(b)** Not possible, $p = q + r$
3. **(a)** 8 1/2 cm²   **(b)** 6 1/2 cm²   **(c)** 7 cm²
4. The pieces of the trapezoid are rearranged to form a rectangle with width $h/2$ and length $(b_2 + b_1)$. The area is $A = h/2(b_2 + b_1)$ which is the area of the initial trapezoid.
5. $\triangle ABC$, $\triangle ABD$, and $\triangle ABE$ (same) and $\triangle ABF$. All the triangles have the same base, so the ordering is just by height and $\triangle ABD$ and $\triangle ABE$ have the same height.
6. **(a)** $54\sqrt{3}$ cm²   **(b)** 36π cm²
7. **(a)** 12π cm²   **(b)** $(12 + 4.5\pi)$ cm²   **(c)** 24 cm²
(d) 4π cm²   **(e)** 64.5 cm²   **(f)** 178.5 m²

8. 5400 cm²
9. $\sqrt{16,200} \doteq 127.3$ ft
10. 3
11. **(a)** Yes   **(b)** No
12. **(a)** $S.A. = 32(2 + \sqrt{13})$ cm²; $V = 128$ cm³
(b) $S.A. = 96\pi$ cm²; $V = 96\pi$ cm³   **(c)** $S.A. = 100\pi$ m²; $V = (500\pi)/3$ m³   **(d)** $S.A. = 54\pi$ cm²; $V = 54\pi$ cm³
(e) $S.A. = 304$ m²; $V = 320$ m³
13. 65π m²
14. The graph on the right has 8 times the volume of the figure on the left, rather than double as it should be.
15. 252 cm²
16. **(a)** 340 cm   **(b)** 6000 cm²
17. $2\sqrt{2}$ m²
18. 62 cm
19. 30 cm
20. **(a)** Metric tons   **(b)** 1 cm³   **(c)** 1 g   **(d)** Same volume   **(e)** 25   **(f)** 2000   **(g)** 51,800
(h) 10,000,000   **(i)** 50,000   **(j)** 5.830   **(k)** 25,000
(l) 75,000   **(m)** 52.813   **(n)** 4.8
21. $h_1^3/h_2^3 = V_1/V_2$
22. **(a)** 6000 kg   **(b)** Approx. 1.5565 m
23. **(a)** L   **(b)** kg   **(c)** g   **(d)** g   **(e)** kg
(f) t   **(g)** mL
24. **(a)** Unlikely   **(b)** Likely   **(c)** Unlikely
(d) Unlikely   **(e)** Unlikely
25. **(a)** 2000   **(b)** 1000   **(c)** 3   **(d)** 0.0042
(e) 0.0002

Chapter 12

Ongoing Assessment 12-1

1. **(a)**   **(b)**

2. Reverse the translation so that the image completes a slide from X' to X (to its preimage). Then check by carrying out the given motion in the "forward" direction; that is, see if $\overline{AB}$ goes to $\overline{A'B'}$.

(a)   **(b)**

3. **(a)** Construct as suggested by the following: Trace $\overline{BC}$ and the line containing the slide arrow on the tracing paper and label the trace of B as B' and the trace of C as C'. Mark on the original paper and on the tracing paper the initial point of the arrow by P and the head of the arrow by Q. Slide the tracing paper along the line $\overleftrightarrow{PQ}$ so that P will fall on Q. Trace $\overline{BC}$. The segment $\overline{B'C'}$ is the image of $\overline{BC}$ under the translation.

(b) Construct a parallelogram with $\overline{BC}$ and $\overline{B'C'}$ as opposite sides similar to that of Figure 12-4.

4. **(a)** $(3, {}^-4)$ **(b)** $(0, 0)$ **(c)** $({}^-3, {}^-13)$
(d) $(10, 10)$ **(e)** $(h + 3, k - 4)$

5. **(a)** $(3, {}^-4)$ **(b)** $(0, 0)$ **(c)** $({}^-3, {}^-13)$
(d) $(10, 10)$ **(e)** $(h + 3, k - 4)$

6. (a)

(b)

(c)

(d)

7. (a)

(b)

8.

9. (a) $y = 2x - 3$
(b) $y = 2x - 7$
(c) $y = 2x + 7$
10. $y = {}^-2x - 1$
11. P', P, and O are collinear because the measure of angle POP' must be $180°$.

12.

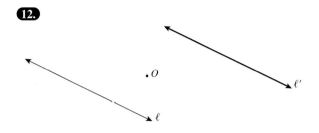

13. Reverse the rotation (to the counterclockwise direction) to locate $\overline{AB}$; that is, the preimage.

(a)

(b)

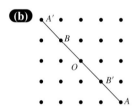

14. Answers may vary, but *H, I, N, O, S, X,* or *Z* could appear in such rotational words. Examples include *SOS.* Variations could use *M* and *W* in rotational images; for example, MOW.

15. **(a)** When the figure is creased and folded along the perpendicular to $\overline{PP'}$, the point *P* falls on *P'*. This shows that the perpendicular also bisects $\overline{PP'}$. Alternatively, by the definition of rotation $\overline{PO} = \overline{PO'}$. This implies that *O* is equidistant from *P* and *P'*, and hence, it is on the perpendicular bisector of $\overline{PP'}$. **(b)** From (a), *O* is on the perpendicular bisector of $\overline{AA'}$ and $\overline{BB'}$ as well as $\overline{CC'}$. Consequently, *O* can be found by finding the point at which any two of the perpendicular bisectors intersect. $\angle AOA'$ is the angle of rotation. **(c)** The perpendicular bisectors of the corresponding sides are not concurrent.

16. *Hints:* An angle whose measure is 45° can be constructed by bisecting a right angle. An angle whose measure is 60° can be constructed by first constructing an equilateral triangle.

17. **(a)** $(^-4, 0)$ **(b)** $(0, ^-3)$ **(c)** $(^-2, ^-4)$ **(d)** $(2, ^-5)$ **(e)** $(2, 4)$ **(f)** $(^-a, ^-b)$ **(g)** (a, b)

18. *Hint:* Find the images of the vertices.

19. **(a)** $\ell' = \ell$ **(b)** $\ell' \parallel \ell$ **(c)** $\ell' \perp \ell$ **(d)** ℓ' and ℓ intersect at a 60° angle.

20. **(a)** First rotate $\triangle ABC$ by angle α to obtain $\triangle A'B'C'$ and then rotate $\triangle A'B'C'$ by angle β to obtain $\triangle A'B'C'$. **(b)** No. **(c)** Yes, by rotation about *O* by angle $|\alpha - \beta|$ in the direction of the larger of α and β.

21. **(a)** A circle **(b)** The vertices *A* and *B* trace an identical path if, and only if, $OA = OB$, that is, if and only if, *O* is on the perpendicular bisector of $\overline{AB}$. Thus all points *O* for which two vertices trace an identical path are the points on the perpendicular bisectors of the sides of the triangle. **(c)** Yes. The intersection of the perpendicular bisector (center of the circumscribed circle)

22. **(a)** A translation from *A* to *C* **(b)** A translation from *A* to *C* **(c)** No; it is the same.

Communication

23. Yes. If the congruent segments are $\overline{AB}$ and $\overline{CD}$, connect *A* with *C* and *B* with *D*, as shown. The perpendicular bisectors of $\overline{AC}$ and $\overline{BD}$ intersect at *O*. (If they do not intersect, connect *A* with *D* and *B* with *C*.) The point *O* is the center of the required rotation. The angle of rotation is $\angle AOC$ in a clockwise direction. The image of *A* will be *C* because the rotation is by $\angle AOC$. To show that under this rotation the image of $\overline{AB}$ is $\overline{CD}$, we need only show that $\angle AOC \cong \angle BOD$. This can be checked experimentally by performing the rotation or by measuring $\angle AOC$ and $\angle BOD$.

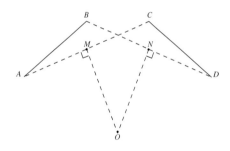

24. **(a)** The image is the same. The result in each case is a half-turn. **(b)** The image is the same. The result is a complete turn.

25. **(a)** A parallelogram. Under a half-turn, the image of a line is parallel to the line. Thus $\overline{AB} \parallel \overline{CD}$ and $\overline{AC} \parallel \overline{DB}$; therefore *ABCD* is a parallelogram.

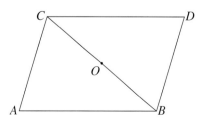

(b) A parallelogram. The image of $\overline{AB}$ is $\overline{FE}$ and thus $\overline{AB} \parallel \overline{EF}$. Consequently, $\overline{BF} \parallel \overline{AE}$ and *ABFE* is a parallelogram.

(c) A square. Because the image of *A* is *C* and the image of *B* is *D*, the image of *ABCD* is *CDAB*.
26. The original and the image lie along perpendicular lines.

Open-Ended

27. Answers vary.
28. Answers vary.
29. Answers vary. If rotation is by 30°, there will be 360/30, or 12, images.

Cooperative Learning

30. (a) The path will look like the one shown in the following figure. Such a path traced by *P* on the circle is called a *cycloid*.

(b) The path is not an arc of a circle. The perpendicular bisectors of all the chords (segments connecting two points on the arc) do not intersect in a single point. **(c)** The length of $\overline{AB}$ is the circumference of the circle.

Ongoing Assessment 12-2

1. Locate the image of vertices directly across (perpendicular to) ℓ on the geoboard.
(a)

(b)

2.

3. Find the image of the center of the circle and one point on the circumference of the circle to determine the image of the circle.
4. Reflecting lines are described for each. **(a)** All diameters (infinitely many) **(b)** Perpendicular bisector of the segment **(c)** The line containing the ray **(d)** Any line perpendicular to the given line **(e)** Perpendicular bisectors of the sides and lines containing the diagonals **(f)** Perpendicular bisectors of pairs of parallel sides **(g)** None **(h)** Perpendicular bisector of the side that is not congruent to the other two **(i)** Perpendicular bisectors of each side **(j)** None **(k)** Perpendicular bisector of parallel sides **(l)** Perpendicular bisector of the chord connecting the endpoints of the arc **(m)** The line containing the diagonal determined by vertices of the noncongruent angles **(n)** The lines containing the diagonals **(o)** Perpendicular bisectors of parallel sides and three diameters determined by vertices on the circumscribed circle **(p)** There will be *n* reflecting lines in all. If *n* is even, the lines are determined as in part (n). If *n* is odd, the lines are the perpendicular bisectors of the sides.
5. The original figure
6. (a) The final images are congruent but in different locations, and hence not the same. **(b)** A translation determined by a slide arrow from *P* to *R* is determined as follows: Let *P* be any point on ℓ and *Q* on *m* such that $\overline{PQ} \perp \ell$. Point *R* is on $\overrightarrow{PQ}$ such that $PQ = QR$.
7. (a)

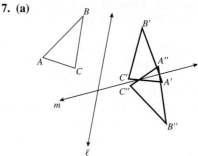

(b) A rotation about *O* by 2α from ℓ to *m* as shown
(c) A half-turn about *O*
8. Construction
9. The line of reflection is the perpendicular bisector of $\overline{BB'}$.
10. (a) Examples include MOM, WOW, TOOT, and HAH.
(b) Examples include BOX, HIKE, CODE, etc. B, C, D, E, H, I, K (depending on construction), O, and X may be used.
(c) 1, 8, 11, 88, 101, 181, 808, 818, 888, 1001, 1111, 1881
11. (a) The images are the same. **(b)** Yes
12. None of the images has a reverse orientation, so there are no reflections or glide reflections involved. Thus

    1 to 2 is a counterclockwise rotation.

    1 to 3 is a clockwise rotation.

1 to 4 is a translation down.

1 to 5 is a rotation (with an exterior point as the center of rotation).

1 to 6 is a translation (sides are parallel to 1).

1 to 7 is a translation (sides are parallel).

13. (a) $A'(3, {}^{-}4)$, $B'(2, 6)$, $C'({}^{-}2, {}^{-}5)$ **(b)** $A'({}^{-}3, 4)$, $B'({}^{-}2, {}^{-}6)$, $C'(2, 5)$ **(c)** $A'(4, 3)$, $B'({}^{-}6, 2)$, $C'(5, {}^{-}2)$ **(d)** $A'({}^{-}4, {}^{-}3)$, $B'(6, {}^{-}2)$, $C'({}^{-}5, 2)$

14. (a) (i) $(x, {}^{-}y)$ **(ii)** $({}^{-}x, y)$ **(iii)** (y, x) **(iv)** $({}^{-}y, {}^{-}x)$ **(b)** $({}^{-}x, {}^{-}y)$ From (a), the reason can be seen in the following figure:

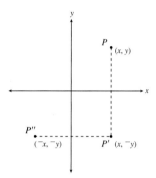

15. If *H* represents the house, *P* the pole, and *T* the other house, then the shortest path connecting *H* and *T'* (the reflection of *T* in *r*) is a segment. The intersection of $\overline{HT'}$ and *r* determines the point on the road at which the pole should be placed, as in (a).

(a)

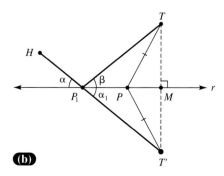

(b)

To prove that the path from *H* to P_1 to *T* is the shortest possible, we need to prove that $HP_1 + P_1T < HP + PT$, where *P* is any point on *r* different from P_1, as in (b). Because $HP_1 + P_1T = HP_1 + P_1T' = HT'$ (why?) and $HP + PT = HP + PT'$ (why?), the inequality that we need to prove is equivalent to $HT' < HP + PT'$. This last inequality follows from the Triangle Inequality.

16. (a) All the points on ℓ. **(b)** The point *O* **(c)** None **(d)** None

Communication

17. The minimum number of sides is two, as shown.

18. Find *A'* the image of *A* under reflection in $\overline{EH}$ and *B'*, the image of *B* under reflection in $\overline{GH}$. Mark the intersections of $\overline{A'B'}$ with $\overline{EH}$ and $\overline{GH}$, respectively, by *C* and *D*. The player should aim the ball at *A* toward the point *C*. The ball will hit *D*, bounce off, and hit *B*. To justify the answer, we need to show that the path $A-C-D-B$ is such that $\angle 1 \cong \angle 3$ and $\angle 4 \cong \angle 6$. Notice that $\angle 1 \cong \angle 2$ and $\angle 6 \cong \angle 5$ because the image of an angle under reflection is congruent to the original angle. Also $\angle 2 \cong \angle 3$ and $\angle 4 \cong \angle 5$ as each pair constitutes a vertical angle. Consequently, $\angle 1 \cong \angle 3$ and $\angle 4 \cong \angle 6$.

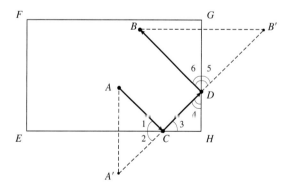

19. (a) If $\overline{AB} \cong \overline{BC}$, then the perpendicular bisector of $\overline{AC}$ is the required line. The image of *B* is *B*, the image of *A* is *C*, and the image of *C* is *A*. Hence, the image of $\triangle ABC$ is $\triangle CBA$. **(b)** Equilateral triangles. Each side could be considered a base. **(c)** No. Since no sides (or angles) are congruent, bisecting any side or angle will leave noncongruent portions of the triangle on opposite sides of the bisector. **(d)** All lines containing diameters will satisfy this situation. Diameters divide a circle into two congruent semicircles.

20. The angle of incidence is the same as the angle of reflection. With the mirrors tilted 45°, the object's image reflects to 90° down the tube and then 90° to the eyepiece. The two reflections "counteract" each other, leaving the image upright.

Open-Ended

21. (a) Reflect the location P of the ball in $\overline{AB}$. The intersection of $\overline{P'Q}$ with $\overline{AB}$ is the point at which the ball should be aimed. The justification is similar to the one given in problem 18.

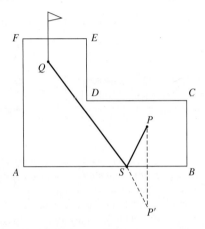

(b) Reflect P in $\overline{CB}$ and Q in $\overline{AB}$. Connect the images P' and Q' by a straight line. The intersection of $\overline{P'Q'}$ with $\overline{BC}$ is the point at which the ball should be aimed. The justification is similar to the one given in problem 18.

22. Answers vary.

23. Answers vary.

24. Answers vary. The following are some examples:
(a) When a scalene $\triangle ABC$ is reflected in $\overline{AB}$, its image is $\triangle AC'B$. Because a reflection preserves distance, $AC'BC$ is a kite. By definition of a reflection, $\overline{AB}$ is the perpendicular bisector of $\overline{CC'}$. Hence, in a kite the diagonals are perpendicular. One of the diagonals bisects the other and bisects a pair of opposite angles.

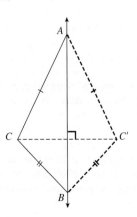

(b) If a trapezoid with a right angle is reflected in one of its legs as shown in the following figure, an isosceles trapezoid is obtained. It follows from the fact that a reflection preserves angle measure that the base angles in an isosceles trapezoid are congruent.   **(c)** Answers vary.

Cooperative Learning

25. (a) Constructions will vary.   **(b)** The experiment will work for rectangular tables in which the length is twice the width and for any position of B.

Review Problems

26. Depending on how they are drawn: 0, 1, and 8.

27. $(^-a, ^-b)$

28. (a) A rotation by any angle about the center of the circle will result in the same circle.   **(b)** Reflections about lines containing diameters

29. Construct $\overline{BE}$ perpendicular to $\overline{AD}$, as shown. Next translate $\triangle ABE$ by the slide arrow from B to C. The image of $\triangle ABE$ is $\triangle DCE'$. The rectangle $BCE'E$ is the required rectangle.

Ongoing Assessment 12-3

1. (a) Slide the smaller triangle down three units (translation). Then complete a size transformation with scale factor 2 using the top-right vertex as the center.   **(b)** Slide the smaller triangle right 5, and up 1. Then complete the size transformation as in (a).   **(c)** Rotate 90° counterclockwise with the lower-right vertex of the smaller triangle as the center of rotation. Then complete a size transformation with scale factor 2 using the same point as center.

2.

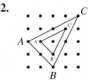

3. (a) Translation taking B to B' followed by a size transformation with center B' (and scale factor 2) **(b)** Rotate 90° counterclockwise using center B, translate to take B to B', and then complete a size translation with a scale factor 1/2. **(c)** Size transformation with scale factor 1/2 and center A followed by a half-turn with the midpoint of $\overline{AA'}$ as center. **(d)** Half-turn about C followed by a size transformation with center C and scale factor 3/2.

4. (a) $x = 6$, $y = 5.2$. Scale factor 2/5. **(b)** $x = 98/15$, $y = 90/7$. Scale factor 7/15.

5. 12 cm

6. (a) Scale factor 3, $x = 12$, $y = 10$ **(b)** Scale factor 2, $x = 5$, $y = 4$

7. (a) $(12, 18)$, $(^-12, 18)$ **(b)** Same as in (a). **(c)** $(5, 6)$, $(^-3, 9)$ **(d)** $(6, 12)$, $(^-2, 12)$ **(e)** Answers depend on the order.

8. The size transformation with center O and scale factor $1/r$

Communication

9. (a) It does change. For example, consider the segment whose endpoints are $(0, 0)$ and $(1, 1)$ and has length $\sqrt{2}$. Under the size transformation with center at $(0, 0)$ and scale factor 2, the image of the segment is a segment whose endpoints are $(0, 0)$ and $(2, 2)$. That segment has length $2\sqrt{2}$. **(b)** It does not change. Under a size transformation, the image of a triangle is a similar triangle and the angles of corresponding angles of two similar triangles are congruent. **(c)** It does not change. Given two parallel lines, draw a transversal that intersects each line. Because the lines are parallel, the corresponding angles are congruent. From (b), the images of the angles will also be congruent and hence the image lines will be parallel.

10. Suppose $\triangle ABC \sim \triangle A'B'C'$. If $\overline{AA'}$, $\overline{BB'}$, and $\overline{CC'}$ intersect at the same point, the required size transformation exists. The intersection point will be the center of the size transformation and $A'B'/AB$ will be the scale factor.

11. (a) A single size transformation with center O and scale factor $\frac{1}{2} \cdot \frac{1}{3}$ or $\frac{1}{6}$. Let P be any point and P' its image under the first size transformation and P'' the image of P' under the second size transformation. Then $\frac{OP'}{OP} = \frac{1}{2}$ and $\frac{OP''}{OP'} = \frac{1}{3}$. Consequently, $\left(\frac{OP'}{OP}\right) \cdot \left(\frac{OP''}{OP'}\right) = \frac{1}{2} \cdot \frac{1}{3}$, or $\frac{OP''}{OP} = \frac{1}{2} \cdot \frac{1}{3}$. Thus P' can be obtained from P by a size transformation with center O and scale factor $\frac{1}{2} \cdot \frac{1}{3}$. **(b)** The size transformation with center O and scale factor $r_1 r_2$.

12. The scale factor $= \frac{A'B'}{AB} = \frac{3}{4}$. The center must be the intersection of $\overrightarrow{BB'}$ and $\overrightarrow{CC'}$.

13. (a) Yes. Suppose the size transformation with center O has a scale factor r. The image of any point P on the circle with radius d is P' such that $\frac{OP'}{OP} = r$. Thus $OP' = r(OP)$ or $OP' = rd$. This means that the image of every point on the circle is at the same distance rd from O and hence on a circle with radius rd. **(b)** Let C be the center of the circle with radius d and let P be any point on the circle. Let C' and P' be the respective images of C and P under a size transformation with center O and scale factor r. Because the image of $\overline{CP}$ is $\overline{C'P'}$, it follows that $C'P' = rCP = rd$. This means that all the images of points on the circle are at the same distance rd from the point C'. Hence the image of the circle is a circle with center C' and radius rd.

Open-Ended

14. Answers vary; for example, a 50% reduction in size when making a photocopy.

15. The result is equivalent to a half-turn through the origin.

Cooperative Learning

16. (a) If p is the perimeter of the figure and p' the perimeter of the image, then $p' = 3p$. **(b)** If A is the area of the figure and A' the area of the image, then $A' = 9A$. **(c)** $p' = rp$ **(d)** $A' = r^2 A$ **(e)** Answers vary.

Review Problems

17. (a) The translation given by slide arrow from N to M **(b)** A counterclockwise rotation of 75° about O **(c)** A clockwise rotation of 45° about A **(d)** A reflection in m and translation from B to A **(e)** A second reflection in n

18. (a) $(4, 3)$ reflects about m to $(4, 1)$; $(4, 1)$ reflects about n to $(2, 1)$. **(b)** $(0, 1) \to (0, 3) \to (6, 3)$ **(c)** $(^-1, 0) \to (^-1, 4) \to (7, 4)$ **(d)** $(0, 0) \to (0, 4) \to (6, 4)$

Ongoing Assessment 12-4

1. The symbol can be read the same backward, forward, and upside down.

2. (a) (i) Yes. A line may be drawn through the center of the circle, either horizontally or vertically. A line may also be drawn through any of the sets of arrows. (ii) Yes. The figure will match the original figure after rotations of 90°, 180°, or 270° about the center of the circle. (iii) Yes. Any figure having 180° rotational symmetry has point symmetry about the turn center. **(b)** (i) Yes. A vertical line through the middle of the bulb is a line of symmetry. (ii) No. The figure will not match the original under rotation of less than 360°. (iii) No. The figure does not have 180° rotational symmetry. **(c)** (i) Yes. A vertical line through the stem is a line of symmetry. (ii) No (iii) No **(d)** (i) Yes. A horizontal line through the middle of the plane is a line of symmetry. (ii) No (iii) No

3. Answers may vary, but some possibilities are the following: **(a)** The Yellow Pages symbol   **(b)** A regular pentagon (Chrysler symbol)   **(c)** The letter *N*

4. Reflect the given portions about ℓ.

(a)

(b)

5. (a) (i) Four lines of symmetry; the diagonals and horizontal or vertical lines through the center (ii) No lines of symmetry (iii) Two lines of symmetry; horizontally and vertically through the center (iv) One line of symmetry; vertically through the center

(b) (i)

Switzerland

(ii)

South Korea-NONE

(iii)

Israel

(iv)

Barbados

6. (a) 6   **(b)** Yes. The figure has 60° rotational symmetry.

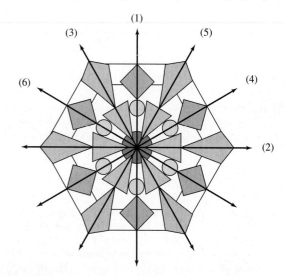

7. (a) One; vertically through the center   **(b)** One; vertically through the center   **(c)** None   **(d)** Five; one through each vertex and its opposite face

8. (a)

(b)

9. (a) Seven; three through the "peaks," three through the "valleys," and one perpendicular to the others through the width of the figure   **(b)** Two; one through the middle "peak" and one through the width   **(c)** Seven; three through the vertices, three through the faces, and one perpendicular to the others through the width of the figure   **(d)** 17; 8 through the peaks, 8 through the valleys, and one through the width

10. (a) Point symmetry   **(b)** Rotational symmetry about the center by 36°   **(c)** Point symmetry   **(d)** Rotational symmetry by 36° and five line symmetries.

Communication

11. (a) Yes. The definition of point symmetry is that it is rotational symmetry of 180°. **(b)** No. It may have rotational symmetry of other than 180°; an equilateral triangle is an example. **(c)** Yes. A circle is an example, as is the figure in problem 1. **(d)** No. Consider the letter Z. (Nor is the converse true.) **(e)** Yes. Point symmetry implies 180° rotational symmetry.

Open-Ended

12. (a) A scalene triangle **(b)** An isosceles triangle that is not equilateral **(c)** Not possible **(d)** An equilateral triangle

13. Answers may vary, but examples include the letter *S* and the Chevrolet logo.

14. (a) All figures will have two line symmetries. Some will have other symmetries. **(b)** All figures will consist of a union of disjoint curves and hence will have only two line symmetries.

15. Answers vary.

Cooperative Learning

16. Answers vary.

17. Answers vary; for example, consider a rectangle. You would report that your figure has two lines of symmetry and a rotational symmetry of 180°.

18. Answers vary.

Review Problems

19. One method is to trace the figure. Then fold at ℓ and trace along the figure as seen through the paper.

20. Find the images of the vertices.

Ongoing Assessment 12-5

1. (a)

(b)

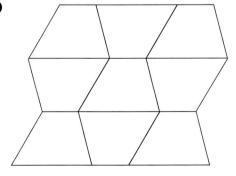

2. (a) Perform half-turns about the midpoints of all sides. **(b)** Yes. If a polygon tessellates the plane, the sum of the angles around every vertex must be 360°. Successive 180° turns of a quadrilateral about the midpoints of its sides will produce four congruent quadrilaterals around a common vertex, with each of the quadrilateral's angles being represented at each vertex. These angles must add up to 360°, as angles of any quadrilateral do.

3. Experimentation by cutting out shapes and moving them about is one way to learn about these types of problems.

(a)

(b) Cannot be tessellated.

(c)

(d) Tessellate as in (a).

4. *Hint:* Consider figures like a pentagon formed by combining a square and an equilateral triangle, or the figure in problem 7 of this Ongoing Assessment.

5. (a) Construction **(b)** It combines a translation and a reflection. **(c)** It will tessellate the plane.

6. (a) The dual is another tessellation of squares. (congruent to those given). **(b)** A tessellation of equilateral triangles **(c)** The tessellation of equilateral triangles; it is illustrated in the statement of the problem.

7.

8. (a) is not semiregular; the rest are semiregular

Communication

9. (a) The image *ABCD* under a half-turn in *M* (the midpoint of *CD*) is the trapezoid *FEDC*. Because the trapezoids are congruent, *ABFE* is a parallelogram. The area of the parallelogram is $AE \cdot h$ or $(a + b) \cdot h$. The parallelogram is the union of two nonoverlapping congruent trapezoids. The area of each trapezoid is $(a + b)(h/2)$.

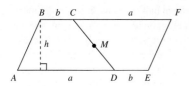

(b) To tessellate the plane with $\triangle ABC$, we find $\triangle A'BC$ the image of $\triangle ABC$ under a half-turn about M the midpoint of $\overline{BC}$. If N is the midpoint of $\overline{AB}$ then the image of N is N'. It can be shown, that N, M, and N' are collinear and hence that $ANN'C$, is a parallelogram. Because the image of $\overline{NM}$ is $\overline{MN'}$ it follows that $NM = MN'$. Hence $NM = \frac{1}{2}NN' = \frac{1}{2}AC$. Thus $NM = \frac{1}{2}AC$. Also $\overline{NM} \parallel \overline{AC}$.

10. See the explanation in Section 12-5.

Open-Ended

11. Answers vary. In the given design, the tessellation can be obtained by half-turns followed by reflections.

12. Answers vary.

13. Answers vary. For example, a right rectangular prism, as well as a tetrahedron, will tile the space, but a cylinder or a square pyramid will not.

Cooperative Learning

14. Answers vary.

15. (a) Two such figures can be put together to form a parallelogram. Because parallelograms tessellate the plane, the original figure tessellates the plane. **(b)** There are 17 such figures. Two figures are different if they are not congruent and not similar. **(c)** Answers vary. For example the following figure is a rep-tile.

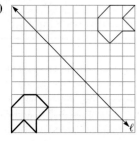

16. All will tessellate. Arguments vary.

Chapter Review

1. (a)

(b)

(c)

2. In each part find the images of the vertices.

3. (a) 4 **(b)** 1 **(c)** 1 **(d)** None **(e)** 2 **(f)** 2

4. (a) Line and rotational **(b)** Line, rotational, and point **(c)** Line

5. (a) Infinitely many **(b)** Infinitely many **(c)** 3 **(d)** 9

6. This answer depends totally upon how the letters are made, but generally we have the following: C has line symmetry; I and M have line symmetry; O has line, rotational, and point symmetry; S has rotational and point symmetry; T has line symmetry; V has line symmetry; W has line symmetry; X has line, rotational, and point symmetry; Z has rotational and point symmetry.

7. $A = A'$, B is the midpoint of $\overline{A'B'}$, and C is the midpoint of $\overline{A'C'}$.

8. In each case, half-turn about X.

9. (a) Rotation by 120° about the center of the hexagon **(b)** A reflection in the perpendicular bisector of $\overline{BY}$

10. Reflection in $\overleftrightarrow{SO}$

11. Let $\triangle H'O'R'$ be the image of $\triangle HOR$ under a half-turn about R. Then $\triangle SER$ is the image of $\triangle H'O'R'$ under a size transformation with center R and scale factor $\frac{2}{3}$. Thus $\triangle SER$ is the image of $\triangle HOR$ under the half-turn about R followed by the size transformation described above.

12. Rotate $\triangle PIG$ 180° (half-turn) about the midpoint of $\overline{PT}$, then perform a size transformation with scale factor 2 and center $P'(= T)$.

13. (a) $A(^-3, 12.91)$, $B(^-8, 0.07)$, $C(1.83, 5)$ **(b)** Under the translation $(x, y) \rightarrow (x - 3, y + 5)$

14. $(x, y) \rightarrow (x, y)$. It is an "identity" transformation with every point its own image.

15. (a) $A(^-3, ^-2)$, $B(^-2, 3)$, $C(^-5, 5)$ **(b)** $(x, y) \rightarrow (x + 3, y + 2)$

16. (a) (i) A translation from *A* to *C*
(ii) Same as (i)
(b) A rotation about *O* by 60° counterclockwise.
(c) (i) A size transformation with center *O* and scale factor 6
(ii) Same as (i)
17. (a) Square. A square has four lines of symmetry, a 90° rotational symmetry about its center, which implies that it has a 180° rotational symmetry (i.e., point symmetry) as well as 270° rotational symmetry. A rhombus has only two lines of symmetry and a 180° rotational symmetry (point symmetry).
(b) Equally symmetrical. An isosceles trapezoid has one line of symmetry (the line through the midpoints of the bases). A parallelogram has one point symmetry (a 180° rotational symmetry about the point formed by the intersection of the diagonals).
(c) A cube. All the symmetries of a rectangular right box are also symmetries of a cube but not vice versa. For example, a cube has a plane symmetry determined by the diagonals of opposite faces (there are two such planes) but a rectangular box that is not a cube does not have such planes of symmetries.
18. The measure of each exterior angle of a regular octagon is $\frac{360°}{8}$, or 45°. Hence the measure of each interior angle is 180° − 45° or 135°. Because 135 $\nmid$ 360, a regular octagon does not tessellate the plane.
19. No.
20. Yes, but unless the shape fits exactly into the object being measured, it may be difficult.

Appendix I

Ongoing Assessment A-I

1. Answers will vary. An example follows:
(a) 5, 9, 13, 17, 21, . . . **(b)** Column A should contain the numbers 1, 2, 3, 4, 5, 6, . . . **(c)** The formula = A1 + 1 should be used to find A2 and then to fill down the rest of the column. **(d)** Column B for this example will start with 5, and each successive term is 4 more than the previous one.
(e) The formula = B1 + 4 could be used here. **(f)** The Σ key should be used when the cell where the sum is wanted is highlighted. **(g)** In an arithmetic sequence, no matter which one was used the data should lie along a line.
2. Answers will vary. An example follows:
(a) 3, 6, 12, 24, 48, . . . **(b)** Column A should contain the numbers 1, 2, 3, 4, 5, 6, . . . **(c)** Column B for this example will start with 3, and each successive term is 2 times the previous one. **(d)** The formula = B1*2 could be used here. **(e)** The Σ key should be used when the cell where the sum is wanted is highlighted. **(f)** In a geometric

sequence, no matter which particular sequence is used the data should lie along an exponential curve. For example, the graph crosses the *y*-axis at (0, 1) and curves up sharply if the common ratio is greater than 1. It will approach the *x*-axis if the common ratio is less than 1 but greater than 0.
3. If all the data is listed in the first 14 cells of column A, the Σ key can be used to find the sum of all the data, and the sum can be placed in cell A15. The formula = A15/14 can be used to place the mean in cell A16.
4. Column B can be used to find the individual data items minus the mean using the formula = A1 − $A$16 with the Fill Down feature. Column C can be filled with the square of the items in column B using the formula = B1^2 and filling down appropriately. Cell C15 might be used to find the sum of the first 14 cells of column C. The standard deviation might then be found using the formula = sqrt(C15/14), or approximately 25.60, and placed in cell C16. The spreadsheet then might appear as follows:

	A	**B**	**C**
1	23	⁻39.285714	1543.36735
2	45	⁻17.285714	298.795918
3	67	4.71428571	22.2244898
4	78	15.7142857	246.938776
5	98	35.7142857	1275.5102
6	54	⁻8.2857143	68.6530612
7	36	⁻26.285714	690.938776
8	76	13.7142857	188.081633
9	75	12.7142857	161.653061
10	24	⁻38.285714	1465.79592
11	43	⁻19.285714	371.938776
12	54	⁻8.2857143	68.6530612
13	100	37.7142857	1422.36735
14	99	36.7142857	1347.93878
15	872		9172.85714
16			25.59695

5. A sample spreadsheet follows. All decimals have been truncated to two places. In reality, the lending agency would probably not truncate the decimals. The value in C1 was created as 1000+0.015*1000−40. For all cells in Column C after C1, the formula = C1−0.015*C1+40 was used.

	A	B	C
1	1	40	$975.00
2	2	40	$949.63
3	3	40	$923.87
4	4	40	$897.73
5	5	40	$871.19
6	6	40	$844.26
7	7	40	$816.93
8	8	40	$789.18
9	9	40	$761.02
10	10	40	$732.43
11	11	40	$703.42
12	12	40	$673.97
13	13	40	$644.08
14	14	40	$613.74
15	15	40	$582.95
16	16	40	$551.69
17	17	40	$519.97
18	18	40	$487.77
19	19	40	$455.08
20	20	40	$421.91
21	21	40	$388.24
22	22	40	$354.06
23	23	40	$319.37
24	24	40	$284.16
25	25	40	$248.42
26	26	40	$212.15
27	27	40	$175.33
28	28	40	$137.96
29	29	40	$100.03
30	30	40	$ 61.53
31	31	40	$ 22.79

Note that the last payment was for only $22.79 and not $40. The payments took 31 months.

6. The first step is to create a column A that is the number of the term by placing 1 in cell A1 and using the formula $= A1 + 1$ to fill down for a total of 100 cells in column A. Next we could use the formula $= 13*A:A$ and fill down for a total of 100 cells in column B.

7. Answers may vary depending upon the method used for computing grade points at your college. In general, you may use 4 quality points for each hour of A, 3 quality points for each hour of B, 2 for each hour of C, 1 for each hour of D, and 0 for each hour of F. After multiplying each hour by the respective number of quality points, find the total of all quality points, then divide by the total number of hours.

8. **(a)** A sample spreadsheet follows where the A column is created by entering 1 in cell A1 and using the formula $= A1 + 1$ and Fill Down to create a total of 25 cells. The B column is found by entering 1 in cell B1 and 1 in cell B2. The remainder of the cells are created using the formula $= B1 + B2$. Column C is created using the formula $= B1{\wedge}2$. Column D is created by filling cell D1 with $= C1$, and using the formula $= D1 + C2$ to create the remainder of the cells.

	A	B	C	D
1	1	1	1	1
2	2	1	1	2
3	3	2	4	6
4	4	3	9	15
5	5	5	25	40
6	6	8	64	104
7	7	13	169	273
8	8	21	441	714
9	9	34	1156	1870
10	10	55	3025	4895
11	11	89	7921	12816
12	12	144	20736	33552
13	13	233	54289	87841
14	14	377	142129	229970
15	15	610	372100	602070
16	16	987	974169	1576239
17	17	1597	2550409	4126648

18	18	2584	6677056	10803704
19	19	4181	17480761	28284465
20	20	6765	45765225	74049690
21	21	10946	119814916	193864606
22	22	17711	313679521	507544127
23	23	28657	821223649	1328767776
24	24	46368	2149991424	3478759200
25	25	75025	5628750625	9107509825

(b) The sum of the squares of the first *n* terms of the Fibonacci sequence is $a_n a_{n+1}$. **(c)** The same conjecture is not true.

9. The A column can be created by entering 1 in cell A1 and using the formula = A1 + 1 and Fill Down to fill as many cells as wanted. The B column can be created by entering = A1 in cell B1 and = B1*A2 with the Fill Down feature to complete the wanted cells.

Appendix II

Ongoing Assessment A-II

1. Approximately 11.896, or 11.9 years.
2. 96
3. ($^-$10, 257) and (10, 357)
4. **(a)** The graphs all pass through the point (0, 3) and all are linear. **(b)** They differ in steepness **(c)** As the slope becomes greater, the graph becomes steeper. The lines have slopes of 1, 2, 3, and 4, respectively.
5. **(a)** The graphs are all linear and are parallel. They all have the same slope. **(b)** They cross the *y*-axis at different points. **(c)** The point where each graph crosses the *y*-axis is the *y*-intercept and it is the point at the end of each of these equations. In general, in the equation $y = mx + b$, the point *b* tells where the graph crosses the *y*-axis.
6. Approximately (1.22, $^-$0.55)
7. **(a)** She needs to find the intersection points of Y_1, Y_2, and Y_3 with Y_4. **(b)** two hours
8. **(a)** Sign changes occur at $x = 1$ and $x = 4$.
(b) Graph on calculator. **(c)** The graph crosses at $x = 1$ and $x = 4$.
9. 18 dimes and 15 quarters

Appendix III

Ongoing Assessment A-III

1. **(a)** – **(h)** are constructions, so answers will vary. The final construction in part (h) should look something like the one below.

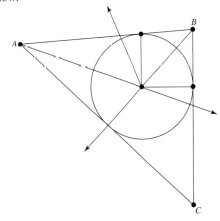

2. **(a)** – **(e)** are constructions, so answers will vary.
(f) The measure of the inscribed angle should be one-half that of the central angle.
3. **(a)** – **(f)** are constructions, so answers will vary.
(g) Slope $= \dfrac{PX}{OX}$
4. **(a)** – **(e)** are constructions, so answers will vary.
5. **(a)** – **(g)** Drawings may vary. A sample answer using a regular pentagon follows. The entire pentagon is labeled polygon 3. The triangle with the white oval is labeled polygon 2. The height of the triangle is 1.15 in. The area of each triangle is approximately 0.96 in². The area of the pentagon is approximately 4.79 in². The perimeter of the pentagon is approximately 8.34 in. The ratio of the area to the perimeter is 8.34/4.79, or approximately 0.57. The ratio 0.57 is approximately one-half of 1.15. This approximation tends to support the formula for the area of a regular polygon as $(1/2)ap$, where *a* is the apothem and *p* is the perimeter.

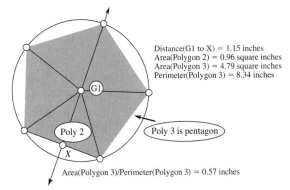

Distance(G1 to X) = 1.15 inches
Area(Polygon 2) = 0.96 square inches
Area(Polygon 3) = 4.79 square inches
Perimeter(Polygon 3) = 8.34 inches

Poly 2
Poly 3 is pentagon

Area(Polygon 3)/Perimeter(Polygon 3) = 0.57 inches

6. **(a)**–**(c)** A pentagon is given as a demonstration. The ratio of the perimeter to the length of the longest diagonal is approximately 3.10 in.

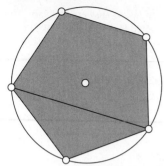

Length(Segment t1) = 1.83 inches
Perimeter(Polygon 4) = 5.66 inches
Perimeter(Polygon 4)/Length(Segment t1) = 3.10 inches

(d)–**(e)** Continuing the process should approximate π because the regular polygons inscribed in the circle approach the circle. The longest diameter is a diameter and the perimeter approaches the circumference of the circle.

7. **(a)** The percent of area in the square not covered by the circle is approximately 21%. **(b)** The percent of area in the circle not covered by the square is approximately 36%. **(c)** The answers in parts (a) and (b) suggest that the circular peg will fit better in the square hole than vice versa.

8. **(a)** Approximately 21% **(b)** Approximately 21% **(c)** The answer doesn't change.

9. This exercise can be used to practice fair division. GSP allows the moving of the line and the finding of areas with relative ease.

10. This exercise can be used to practice estimation of areas and the estimation of percentages.

—Index—

Solutions to back cover puzzles

If two squares side by side is a "domino" then five squares joined side by side is a "pentomino." There are twelve distinct pentominoes, as seen on the front cover. Pentominoes have some very interesting mathematical properties providing an endless array of challenging puzzles. Problems with pentominoes commonly involve arranging the shapes to fill some region, without gaps or overlaps, subject to some constraints.

The solutions to the puzzles on the back cover are explained below. For more information on pentominoes type in the keyword "pentomino" on any Web search engine.

Shape 1

Shape 2

Shape 3

Shape 5

Shape 4

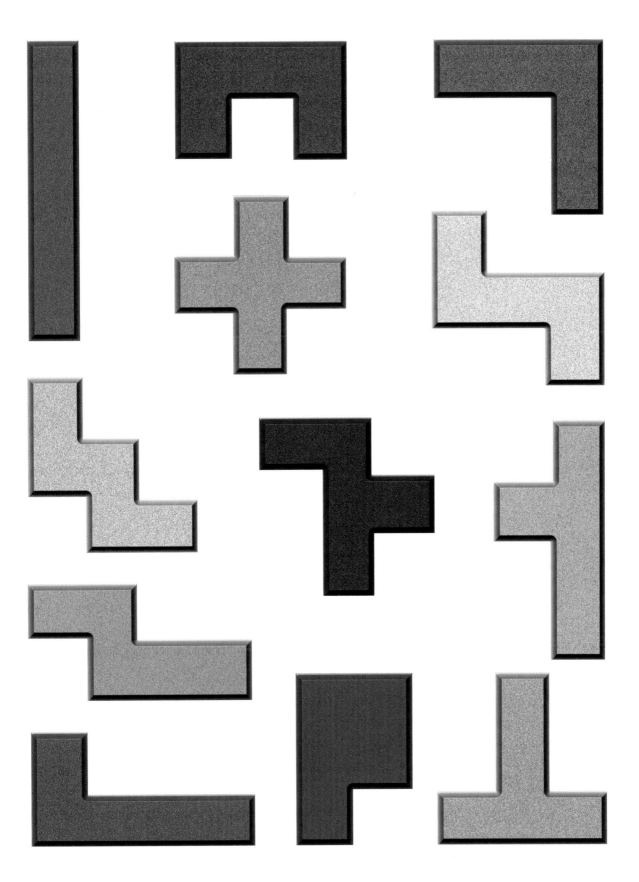

Apply transformations and use symmetry to analyze mathematical situations and should—
- Predict and describe the results of sliding, flipping, and turning two-dimensional shapes;
- Describe a motion or a series of motions that will show that two shapes are congruent;
- Identify and describe line and rotational symmetry in two- and three-dimensional shapes and designs

Use visualization, spatial reasoning, and geometric modeling to solve problems and should—
- Build and draw geometric objects;
- Create and describe mental images of objects, patterns, and paths;
- Identify and build a three-dimensional object from a two-dimensional representation of that object;
- Identify and build a two-dimensional representation of a three-dimensional object;
- Use geometric models to solve problems in other areas of mathematics, such as number and measurement;
- Recognize geometric ideas and relationships and apply them to other disciplines and to problems that arise in the classroom or in everyday life

MEASUREMENT
In grades 3–5 all students should—

Understand measurable attributes of objects and the units, systems, and processes of measurement and should—
- Understand such attributes as length, area, weight, volume, and size of angle and select the appropriate type of unit for measuring each attribute;
- Understand the need for measuring with standard units and become familiar with standard units in the customary and metric systems;
- Carry out simple unit conversions, such as from centimeters to meters, within a system of measurement;
- Understand that measurements are approximations and understand how differences in units affect precision;
- Explore what happens to measurements of a two-dimensional shape such as its perimeter and area when the shape is changed in some way

Apply appropriate techniques, tools, and formulas to determine measurements and should—
- Develop strategies for estimating the perimeters, areas, and volumes of irregular shapes;
- Select and apply appropriate standard units and tools to measure length, area, volume, weight, time, temperature, and the size of angles;
- Select and use benchmarks to estimate measurements;
- Develop, understand, and use formulas to find the area of rectangles and related triangles and parallelograms;
- Develop strategies to determine the surface areas and volumes of rectangular solids

Formulate questions that can be addressed with data and collect, organize, and display relevant data to answer them and should—
- Design investigations to address a question and consider how data-collection methods affect the nature of the data set;
- Collect data using observations, surveys, and experiments;
- Represent data using tables and graphs such as line plots, bar graphs, and line graphs;
- Recognize the difference in representing categorical and numerical data

Select and use appropriate statistical methods to analyze data and should—
- Describe the shape and important features of a set of data and compare related data sets, with an emphasis on how the data are distributed;
- Use measures of center, focusing on the median, and understand what each does and does not indicate about the data set;
- Compare different representations of the same data and evaluate how well each representation shows important aspects of the data

Develop and evaluate inferences and predictions that are based on data and should—
- Propose and justify conclusions and predictions that are based on data and design studies to further investigate the conclusions or predictions

Understand and apply basic concepts of probability and should—
- Describe events as likely or unlikely and discuss the degree of likelihood using such words as certain, equally likely, and impossible;
- Predict the probability of outcomes of simple experiments and test the predictions;
- Understand that the measure of the likelihood of an event can be represented by a number from 0 to 1

Understand numbers, ways of representing numbers, relationships among numbers, and number systems and should—
- Work flexibly with fractions, decimals, and percents to solve problems;
- Compare and order fractions, decimals, and percents efficiently and find their approximate locations on a number line;
- Develop meaning for percents greater than 100 and less than 1;
- Understand and use ratios and proportions to represent quantitative relationships;
- Develop an understanding of large numbers and recognize and appropriately use exponential, scientific, and calculator notation;
- Use factors, multiples, prime factorization, and relatively prime numbers to solve problems;
- Develop meaning for integers and represent and compare quantities with them

Grades 6–8
NUMBER AND OPERATIONS (continued)

Understand meanings of operations and how they relate to one another and should—
- Understand the meaning and effects of arithmetic operations with fractions, decimals, and integers;
- Use the associative and commutative properties of addition and multiplication and the distributive property of multiplication over addition to simplify computations with integers, fractions, and decimals;
- Understand and use the inverse relationships of addition and subtraction, multiplication and division, and squaring and find square roots to simplify computations and solve problems

Compute fluently and make reasonable estimates and should—
- Select appropriate methods and tools for computing with fractions and decimals from among mental computation, estimation, calculators or computers, and paper and pencil, depending on the situation, and apply the selected methods;
- Develop and analyze algorithms for computing with fractions, decimals, and integers and develop fluency in their use;
- Develop and use strategies to estimate the results of rational-number computations and judge the reasonableness of the results;
- Develop, analyze, and explain methods for solving problems involving proportions, such as scaling and finding equivalent ratios

ALGEBRA
In grades 6–8 all students should—

Understand patterns, relations, and functions and should—
- Represent, analyze, and generalize a variety of patterns with tables, graphs, words, and, when possible, symbolic rules;
- Relate and compare different forms of a representation for a relationship;
- Identify functions as linear or nonlinear and contrast their properties from tables, graphs, or equations

Represent and analyze mathematical situations and structures using algebraic symbols and should—
- Develop an initial conceptual understanding of different uses of variables;
- Explore relationships between symbolic expressions and graphs of lines, paying particular attention to the meaning of intercept and slope;
- Use symbolic algebra to represent situations and to solve problems, especially those that involve linear relationships;
- Recognize and generate equivalent forms for simple algebraic expressions and solve linear equations

Use mathematical models to represent and understand quantitative relationships and should—
- Model and solve contextualized problems using various representations, such as graphs, tables, and equations

Analyze change in various contexts and should—
- Use graphs to analyze the nature of changes in quantities in linear relationships

Grades 6–8
GEOMETRY
In grades 6–8 all students should—

Analyze characteristics and properties of two- and three-dimensional geometric shapes and develop mathematical arguments about geometric relationships and should—
- Precisely describe, classify, and understand relationships among types of two- and three-dimensional objects using their defining properties;
- Understand relationships among the angles, side lengths, perimeters, areas, and volumes of similar objects;
- Create and critique inductive and deductive arguments concerning geometric ideas and relationships, such as congruence, similarity, and the Pythagorean relationship

Specify locations and describe spatial relationships using coordinate geometry and other representational systems and should—
- Use coordinate geometry to represent and examine the properties of geometric shapes;
- Use coordinate geometry to examine special geometric shapes, such as regular polygons or those with pairs of parallel or perpendicular sides

Apply transformations and use symmetry to analyze mathematical situations and should—
- Describe sizes, positions, and orientations of shapes under informal transformations such as flips, turns, slides, and scaling;
- Examine the congruence, similarity, and line or rotational symmetry of objects using transformations

Use visualization, spatial reasoning, and geometric modeling to solve problems and should—
- Draw geometric objects with specified properties, such as side lengths or angle measures;
- Use two-dimensional representations of three-dimensional objects to visualize and solve problems such as those involving surface area and volume;
- Use visual tools such as networks to represent and solve problems;
- Use geometric models to represent and explain numerical and algebraic relationships;
- Recognize and apply geometric ideas and relationships in areas outside the mathematics classroom, such as art, science, and everyday life